Engineering Calculus

Carl V. Lutzer • H.T. Goodwill

D1415809

Engineering Calculus / MTH 285/295/515

Wiley Custom Learning Solutions

Copyright © 2014 by John Wiley & Sons, Inc.

All rights reserved.

Cover Image © leminuit/iStockphoto

No part of this publication may be reproduced, stored in a retrieval system or transmitted in any
form or by any means, electronic, mechanical, photocopying, recording, scanning or otherwise,
except as permitted under Sections 107 or 108 of the 1976 United States Copyright Act, without
either the prior written permission of the Publisher, or authorization through payment of the
appropriate per-copy fee to the Copyright Clearance Center, Inc., 222 Rosewood Drive, Danvers,
MA 01923, website www.copyright.com. Requests to the Publisher for permission should be
addressed to the Permissions Department, John Wiley & Sons, Inc., 111 River Street, Hoboken,
NJ 07030-5774, (201)748-6011, fax (201)748-6008, website http://www.wiley.com/go/permissions.

To order books or for customer service, please call 1(800)-CALL-WILEY (225-5945).

Printed in the United States of America.

ISBN 978-1-118-95072-2
Printed and bound by Courier Digital Solutions.

10 9 8 7 6 5 4 3 2

Contents

Appendices 1316

End Matter

Chapter 11 Vectors

The first ten chapters were principally devoted to the calculus of real-valued functions of a single variable. Now we turn our attention to situations that require more information than a single number can provide. For instance, in order to predict the landfall of a hurricane, the National Oceanic and Atmospheric Administration uses information about not only its speed but also its direction of travel. In this chapter we develop mathematical tools that allow us to deal with situations in which both magnitude and direction play important roles.

11.1 Introduction to Vectors

Previous chapters focused primarily on quantities that can be described by a single number, such as time, mass and temperature. These are called *scalar* quantities. In this chapter we extend our discussion to quantities that are described by both magnitude *and* direction, such as velocity and force. This kind of quantity is called a ***vector***. In the following paragraphs we introduce notation for vectors, discuss magnitude, and introduce vocabulary that is helpful when talking about direction.

Key Idea(s): *A vector has both magnitude and direction, so vectors are drawn as arrows in diagrams.*

Displacement,   velocity and force are all examples of vectors.

When writing, we typically indicate a vector by decorating a variable with an arrow or writing it in bold, so $\vec{v}$ and $\mathbf{v}$ denote vectors while v is a scalar. When communicating graphically, we depict vectors as directed line segments (arrows), which naturally communicate direction and magnitude (see Figure 1.1). The tip of the arrow is often called its ***head***, and the other end its ***tail***. For example, a ***displacement vector*** is one that indicates a change in position; its *tail* is at the initial position, and its *head* is at the terminal position. Closely related to this is a ***position vector***, often denoted by $\mathbf{r}$, which has its tail at the origin and its head at a specified location.

The word *position* tells you how the vector is being used, rather than telling you something about the vector itself.

The magnitude of a vector $\mathbf{v}$ (also called the ***norm*** of the vector) is typically written as $\|\mathbf{v}\|$, and when $\|\mathbf{v}\| = 1$ we say that $\mathbf{v}$ is a ***unit vector***. The magnitude of a force vector is its "strength," and could be measured in newtons; the magnitude of a velocity vector means "speed," so its units could be meters per second; the magnitude of a displacement vector is "distance," which could be measured in kilometers. The units associated with magnitude depend on what's being described and how it's measured, but no matter what it means, *magnitude is a quantity that is never negative*.

When drawing vectors, we communicate magnitude by adjusting the length of their arrow representations. Longer arrows correspond to larger distances, or greater speeds, or stronger forces depending on context.

Figure 1.1: The direction and strength (magnitude) of gravitational force depends on where you are relative to the planet.

The word orthogonal is pronounced "or-THOG-ō-null," and means the same thing as "perpendicular" in spirit.

Vectors in the plane are said to be ***parallel*** when their arrow representations lie on parallel lines. Similarly, we say they are ***perpendicular*** or ***orthogonal*** when their arrow representations lie on perpendicular lines. Intuitively speaking, two vectors are parallel when one is a stretched version of the other (although the definition allows for them to point in exactly opposite directions), and they are orthogonal when the angle between them is right.

Modeling with vector addition

Example 1.1. Suppose an aircraft is slowing down and descending as it flies due west. Draw vectors representing the thrust, drag, lift and weight of the aircraft.

Solution: Because the aircraft's engines are pushing it due west, we will represent their combined force on the plane with an arrow that's pointed left; the drag force points in the opposite direction. Because the aircraft is slowing, the drag force must have a greater magnitude, so we represent it with a longer arrow. Similarly, the lift force points up and the weight the plane is a vector that points down; the latter of these is longer because the plane is descending (so the magnitude of the weight force must exceed that of the lift). These have been drawn in Figure 1.2. ■

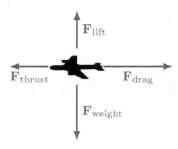

Figure 1.2: The vectors in Example 1.1.

✛ The Algebra of Vectors

Scaling, adding, and subtracting vectors is slightly more involved than working with numbers, but detecting when two vectors are equal is pretty easy since vectors carry only two pieces of information: direction, and magnitude. We say that two vectors are **equal** when they have the *same magnitude* and the *same direction*. Geometrically, two vectors are equal when their depictions as directed line segments are translations of one another.

Vector equality

Example 1.2. Which vectors in Figure 1.1 are equal?

Solution: None of them. The vectors with tails are on the inner circle all have the same magnitude but different directions, so none of them are equal. When we compare each vector on the inner circle to its counterpart on the outer circle, we see that they point in the same direction but have different magnitudes, so they're not equal. ■

Vector equality

Example 1.3. Suppose the vectors in Figure 1.3 depict the displacement of musicians in a marching band. Which displacement vectors are equal?

Solution: All of them. The musicians have different initial and terminal positions, but they all have the same displacement (i.e., *change* in position). ■

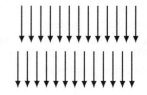

Figure 1.3: Vectors for Example 1.3.

▷ Scaling vectors

Changing the magnitude of a vector but not its direction is called **scaling** the vector, and is often indicated by a coefficient. For example, the notation $2\mathbf{v}$ means "the vector that points in the direction of $\mathbf{v}$, with twice its magnitude." That is

$$\|2\mathbf{v}\| \;\; = \;\; 2\|\mathbf{v}\|. \tag{1.1}$$

$\underbrace{\qquad}$ $\underbrace{\qquad}$
The magnitude of $2\mathbf{v}$ is   twice the magnitude of $\mathbf{v}$.

Similarly, when $k > 0$, the notation $k\mathbf{v}$ is what we write when we mean "the vector with magnitude $k\|\mathbf{v}\|$ points in the direction of $\mathbf{v}$." Stated as an equation,

$$\|k\mathbf{v}\| = k\|\mathbf{v}\| \text{ when } k > 0. \tag{1.2}$$

Practice with positive scalars (algebraic)

Example 1.4. Suppose $\mathbf{v}$ is a unit vector, and $\|\mathbf{u}\| = 3$. What are the magnitudes of (a) $7\mathbf{v}$, and (b) $0.5\mathbf{u}$?

Solution: (a) Since $\mathbf{v}$ is a unit vector we know that $\|\mathbf{v}\| = 1$, so $\|7\mathbf{v}\| = 7\|\mathbf{v}\| = (7)(1) = 7$. (b) The magnitude of $0.5\mathbf{u}$ is $\|0.5\mathbf{u}\| = 0.5\|\mathbf{u}\| = (0.5)(3) = 1.5$. ∎

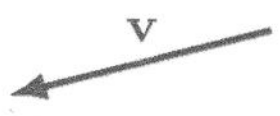

Figure 1.4: For Example 1.5

Practice with positive scalars (geometric)

Example 1.5. The vector $\mathbf{v}$ is shown in Figure 1.4. Draw the vectors $2\mathbf{v}$ and $\frac{2}{3}\mathbf{v}$.

Solution: The vectors $2\mathbf{v}$ and $\frac{2}{3}\mathbf{v}$ are shown below.

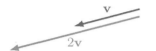

The vectors have been offset in order to avoid overlapping, but remember that vectors are defined only by magnitude and direction. ∎

Now let's turn our attention to negative scale factors. The vector that has the same magnitude as $\mathbf{v}$ but points in the opposite direction is denoted by $-\mathbf{v}$. In essence, we swap the head and tail of $\mathbf{v}$ to find $-\mathbf{v}$. The vector $-k\mathbf{v}$ is the opposite of $k\mathbf{v}$ in the same sense. Note that $\pm k\mathbf{v}$ have the same magnitude (but opposite directions), so we can generalize equation (1.2) by writing

$$\|k\mathbf{v}\| = |k|\,\|\mathbf{v}\|.$$

Scaling by a negative

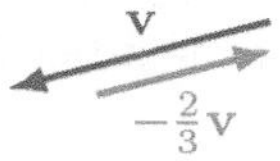

Example 1.6. Suppose $\mathbf{v}$ is the vector drawn in Figure 1.4. Draw $-\frac{2}{3}\mathbf{v}$.

Solution: We already drew the vector $\frac{2}{3}\mathbf{v}$ in Example 1.5. Now we need only reverse its direction. This has been done in Figure 1.5. ∎

Figure 1.5: Vectors for Example 1.6

Lastly, we complete our discussion of scaling by addressing the case when $k = 0$. Based on what we've done so far, $0\mathbf{v}$ should mean the vector with magnitude

$$0\|\mathbf{v}\| = 0. \tag{1.3}$$

This leads us to define the ***zero vector***, denoted by $\mathbf{0}$, to be the unique vector with a magnitude of 0. With this notation we can write

$$0\mathbf{v} = \mathbf{0}. \tag{1.4}$$

The zero on the left-hand side of this equation is a number. The zero on the right-hand side is a vector.

The zero vector is the only vector without a well-defined direction. If we treat it as a displacement vector, the zero vector amounts to facing in any direction you want but staying where you are.

Note: Equation (1.3) is a statement about scalars, while equation (1.4) is a statement about vectors.

▷ Adding vectors

Imagine that you're hiking. Starting at a reference point, you (1) walk 100 paces due north, and then (2) walk 200 paces due east. You changed position in each leg of the trip, and that change in position is characterized by a displacement vector. Your *net* displacement is also characterized by a vector. If we denote "100 paces due north" by $\mathbf{u}$, and "200 paces due east" by $\mathbf{v}$, the vector for the *net* displacement is called the ***resultant*** and is denoted by $\mathbf{u} + \mathbf{v}$ (see Figure 1.6).

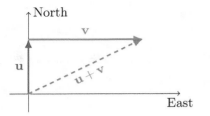
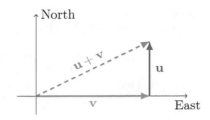

Figure 1.6: The vectors $\mathbf{u} + \mathbf{v}$ and $\mathbf{v} + \mathbf{u}$ have the same direction and magnitude, so $\mathbf{u} + \mathbf{v} = \mathbf{v} + \mathbf{u}$

Of course, your net displacement is the same if you perform steps (1) and (2) in the opposite order. So as with real numbers, ***vector addition is commutative***:

$$\mathbf{u} + \mathbf{v} = \mathbf{v} + \mathbf{u}.$$

In Figure 1.6 you see that adding vectors is accomplished by a ***head-to-tail*** method of addition, in which we put the tail of one vector at the head of the other.

Practice with scaling and adding

Example 1.7. Figure 1.7 shows $\mathbf{u}$ and $\mathbf{v}$. Draw the vector $4\mathbf{v} + 2\mathbf{u}$.

Figure 1.7: For Example 1.7

Solution: We find $4\mathbf{v} + 2\mathbf{u}$ in two steps. First draw the vectors $4\mathbf{v}$ and $2\mathbf{u}$. Then we use the head-to-tail method of addition.

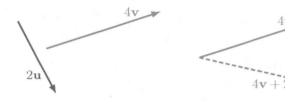

■

Practice with scaling and adding

Example 1.8. Suppose $\mathbf{v}$ is the vector from Example 1.5. (a) Use head-to-tail addition to determine $\mathbf{v} + (-\mathbf{v})$, and (b) interpret what you see.

Solution: (a) The vector $-\mathbf{v}$ is drawn by swapping the head and tail of $\mathbf{v}$. Then using head-to-tail addition, we see the following:

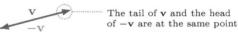

The tail of $\mathbf{v}$ and the head of $-\mathbf{v}$ are at the same point.

(b) If $\mathbf{v}$ and $-\mathbf{v}$ are displacement vectors, the resultant $\mathbf{v} + (-\mathbf{v})$ describes a trip that starts and ends at the same point, so the net displacement is zero. Said with vector addition, $\mathbf{v} + (-\mathbf{v}) = \mathbf{0}$ (the zero vector). ■

The notation $\mathbf{v} + (-\mathbf{v})$ is cumbersome, so we typically write $\mathbf{v} - \mathbf{v}$ instead. More generally, we write $\mathbf{v} - \mathbf{u}$ when we mean $\mathbf{v} + (-\mathbf{u})$.

Scaling vectors graphically

Example 1.9. With $\mathbf{u}$ and $\mathbf{v}$ as shown in Figure 1.8, draw the vector $\mathbf{v} - \mathbf{u}$.

Solution: Since $\mathbf{v} - \mathbf{u}$ is the same as $\mathbf{v} + (-\mathbf{u})$, we begin by drawing $-\mathbf{u}$. Then we use head-to-tail addition. Since vector addition is commutative, it doesn't matter whether we put the head of $\mathbf{v}$ at the tail of $-\mathbf{u}$ or vice versa (see Figure 1.9). ■

Figure 1.8: For Example 1.9

Figure 1.9: (left) The first step in drawing $\mathbf{v} - \mathbf{u}$ is drawing $-\mathbf{u}$; (middle) using head-to-tail addition; (right) a depiction of the fact that $\mathbf{u} + (\mathbf{v} - \mathbf{u}) = \mathbf{v}$

In the right-hand image of Figure 1.9 you see that adding $\mathbf{v} - \mathbf{u}$ to the vector $\mathbf{u}$ yields $\mathbf{v}$. Intuitively, that makes sense when you think about walking along those displacement vectors. And from an algebraic point of view, you'd hope that it happens because

$$\mathbf{u} + (\mathbf{v} - \mathbf{u}) = (\mathbf{u} - \mathbf{u}) + \mathbf{v} = \mathbf{0} + \mathbf{v},$$

but that leads us to ask, "Does the order of vector addition matter?" No, and you'll explain why in the exercise set. In technical language, we say that **vector addition is associative**:

$$(\mathbf{u} + \mathbf{v}) + \mathbf{w} = \mathbf{u} + (\mathbf{v} + \mathbf{w}).$$

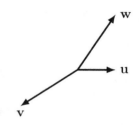

Figure 1.10: Vectors for Example 1.10

Graphical arithmetic of vectors

Example 1.10. Using the vectors $\mathbf{u}$, $\mathbf{v}$ and $\mathbf{w}$ shown in Figure 1.10, draw (a) $\mathbf{u}+\mathbf{w}$, (b) $\mathbf{v} + \mathbf{w}$, (c) $\mathbf{u} - \mathbf{v}$, and (d) $\mathbf{u} - \mathbf{w}$.

Answer: See the on-line solution. ■

In the box below we summarize basic facts about vectors.

Solution
On-line

Vector Operations: Suppose $\mathbf{u}, \mathbf{v}$ and $\mathbf{w}$ are vectors, and c and k are real numbers. Then

1. $\mathbf{u} + \mathbf{v} = \mathbf{v} + \mathbf{u}$
2. $(\mathbf{u} + \mathbf{v}) + \mathbf{w} = \mathbf{u} + (\mathbf{v} + \mathbf{w})$
3. $\mathbf{u} + (-\mathbf{u}) = \mathbf{0}$
4. $\mathbf{u} + \mathbf{0} = \mathbf{u}$
5. $0\mathbf{u} = \mathbf{0}$

6. $-1\mathbf{u} = -\mathbf{u}$
7. $(ck)\,\mathbf{u} = c(k\mathbf{u})$
8. $k(\mathbf{u} + \mathbf{v}) = k\mathbf{u} + k\mathbf{v}$
9. $(c + k)\mathbf{u} = c\mathbf{u} + k\mathbf{u}$
10. $\|k\mathbf{u}\| = |k|\,\|\mathbf{u}\|.$

✛ Life in 3-D

The figures so far have depicted vectors in a plane, but everything we've discussed about vectors is independent of dimension. Ideas of scaling, head-to-tail addition, the zero vector, and the algebraic properties listed above all extend seamlessly to vectors in three dimensions. Most importantly, as in two dimensions, vectors in three dimensions are defined entirely by direction and magnitude. For example, suppose you're walking with a friend through a neighborhood when you see a tree house in a stand of trees. In order to show your friend, you point in the direction of the tree house and tell him that it's not in the first tree, but the second—in essence, specifying the location of the tree house by communicating the direction and magnitude of the displacement vector between you and it.

Vectors such as displacement, force and velocity are useful in both two-dimensional and three-dimensional characterizations of problems. We close our introduction to the topic of vectors by introducing one that is "native" to the three-dimensional setting. The **angular velocity vector**, often denoted by ω, arises when describing the rotation of a spinning object (see Figure 1.11). The magnitude of ω is the speed of the object's rotation in radians per second, and ω points along the object's axis of rotation. More specifically, the direction of ω is determined by a *right-hand rule*, meaning that if you were to grab the axis of rotation so that your fingers curled around it in the direction of the spin, your extended thumb would point in the direction of ω.

> The angular velocity vector is sometimes characterized as something called a *pseudovector*, a brief introduction to which can be found in the End Notes for this chapter.

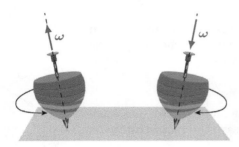

Figure 1.11: The direction of ω tells us both the axis and direction of rotation (according to a right-hand rule), and the vector's magnitude tells us the rate of spin.

✧ In Closing

In closing, we should mention that the science and engineering communities often need to be more specific, and so often use the word *parallel* in a slightly different way: two vectors are said to be *parallel* when they point in the same direction, and *antiparallel* when their directions are exactly opposite.

You should know

- the terms *vector, scalar, head, tail, position vector, magnitude, norm, unit vector, parallel, perpendicular, orthogonal, equal* (as applied to vectors), *scaling, resultant,* and *zero vector,* and the notation $\|\mathbf{u}\|$;
- that vectors have direction and magnitude;
- scaling a vector by a positive constant changes its magnitude but not its direction;
- that vector addition is associative and commutative.

You should be able to

- scale vectors graphically (with positive and negative scalars, as well as zero);
- add and subtract vectors graphically using the head-to-tail method;
- determine when two vectors are equal.

❖ 11.1 Skill Exercises

1. Consider the vectors shown in Figure 1.12 (labeled at their heads) and answer the following questions.

   (a) Which of the vectors are equal?

   (b) Which of the vectors are parallel but not equal?

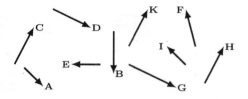

Figure 1.12: Vectors for #1

Figure 1.13: Vectors for #2.

2. The vectors **v** and **u** are shown in Figure 1.13. Use them to draw (a) **3u**, (b) **u + v**, and (c) **2u − v**.

3. With vectors **A, B**, and **C** from #1, use head-to-tail addition to show that **A + (B + C) = (A + B) + C**.

4. With the vectors from #2, use head-to-tail addition to show that **u+v = v+u**.

Use Figure 1.14 to draw the vectors specified in #5–12.

Figure 1.14: For #5–12.

5. **3u**	7. **u + v**	9. **2u − 1.5v**	11. **2u + 2v + w**
6. **−2v**	8. **u − v**	10. **3.5u − 2.5w**	12. **0.5u − 2v + 3w**

13. Figure 1.15 shows a regular hexagon with the point O at its center. The vector $\overrightarrow{OA}$ reaches from O to A, and $\overrightarrow{OB}$ reaches from O to B. Scale and/or add $\overrightarrow{OA}$ and $\overrightarrow{OB}$ to make each of the following:

   (a) $\overrightarrow{OC}$ (c) $\overrightarrow{CF}$ (e) $\overrightarrow{EF}$

   (b) $\overrightarrow{OE}$ (d) $\overrightarrow{AB}$ (f) $\overrightarrow{FA}$

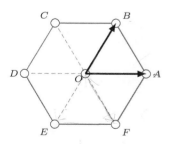

Figure 1.15: Hexagon for #13.

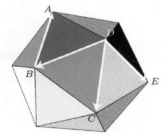

Figure 1.16: Icosahedron for #14.

14. Figure 1.16 depicts an ***icosahedron*** and the vectors $\overrightarrow{DB}$, $\overrightarrow{DC}$, $\overrightarrow{DE}$, and $\overrightarrow{BA}$. Scale and/or add these vectors to make each of the following:

(a) $\overrightarrow{CA}$ (c) $\overrightarrow{BC}$ (e) $\overrightarrow{EC}$

(b) $\overrightarrow{AE}$ (d) $\overrightarrow{DA}$ (f) $\overrightarrow{CE}$

❖ 11.1 Concept and Application Exercises

15. Suppose that $\mathbf{T}$ is the thrust of a rocket, and $\mathbf{D}$ is the drag due to air resistance. Write a single equation that says, "The thrust of the rocket is 4023 times stronger than the drag, and the two forces act in opposite directions."

       | Quantitative Literacy |

16. Suppose $k < 0$, and $\mathbf{v}$ is a vector in the plane with $\|\mathbf{v}\| = 1$.

       | Quantitative Literacy |

  (a) In full English sentences, explain why $\|k\mathbf{v}\| = k\|\mathbf{v}\|$ cannot be true.

  (b) Adjust the equation so that it's correct, regardless of whether k is positive, negative, or zero.

Exercises # 17 and 18 are about regular n-gons (polygons with n sides of equal length). We'll label the vertices of such a polygon as $1, 2, 3, \ldots, n$, and denote by $\mathbf{r}_j$ the position vector that reaches from the center of polygon to vertex j.

       | Geometry |

17. Suppose a regular n-gon has an even number of vertices, $\mathbf{r}_j$. Show that $\mathbf{r}_1 + \mathbf{r}_2 + \cdots + \mathbf{r}_n = \mathbf{0}$. *(Hint: start by drawing a square and a regular hexagon.)*

18. Suppose a regular n-gon has an odd number of vertices, v_j. Show that $\mathbf{r}_1 + \mathbf{r}_2 + \cdots + \mathbf{r}_n = \mathbf{0}$. *(Hint: if the vector sum were <u>not</u> zero, it would have to rotate when you rotate the n-gon. Can you think of a good way to rotate an n-gon?)*

An aircraft is flying due east in each of the scenarios described by exercises #19–22. Draw vectors representing the forces due to thrust, drag, lift, and gravity. (What matters is the relative magnitudes of these forces.)

       | Aviation |

19. The aircraft is speeding up but descending.

20. The aircraft is slowing down, but ascending.

21. The aircraft is speeding up and ascending.

22. The aircraft is speeding up but maintaining altitude.

23. Suppose you drop several ping-pong balls into a *vortex* (i.e., a whirlpool with a downdraft) centered at the origin. The ping-pong balls are carried around and slightly toward the center, in a clockwise direction, picking up speed as they move toward the center. Sketch vectors for ping-pong balls at various distances from the origin that indicate the balls' direction of travel and speed (adjust the length accordingly).

       | Vortices |

24. Suppose that $\mathbf{u}, \mathbf{v}$, and $\mathbf{w}$ are vectors in the plane. In full English sentences, use the "hiking" story to explain why $(\mathbf{u} + \mathbf{v}) + \mathbf{w} = \mathbf{u} + (\mathbf{v} + \mathbf{w})$.

       | Quantitative Literacy |

25. Suppose $\boldsymbol{\omega}$ is Earth's angular velocity vector. If the tail of $\boldsymbol{\omega}$ is at the center of the planet, does the vector point toward the north pole or the south pole?

26. Suppose $\boldsymbol{\omega}$ is Earth's angular velocity vector. What is $\|\boldsymbol{\omega}\|$?

27. Suppose $\boldsymbol{\omega}_1, \boldsymbol{\omega}_2, \boldsymbol{\omega}_3, \ldots$ are the angular velocity vectors for the planets in our solar system, in order: 1 indicates the spin of Mercury about its axis, 2 for Venus, 3 for Earth, etc. Most but not all of these point in roughly the same direction. Which do (does) not, and why?

28. If we were to associate an angular velocity vector with a hurricane off the atlantic coast of the United States, would it point toward the sea or the sky?

11.2   Component Descriptions of Vectors

In this section, our primary goal is to develop a quantitative algebra for vectors in the plane. We'll do it by choosing vectors to serve as "building blocks," and describing all other vectors in terms of them. As seen in Figure 2.1,

> **i** will denote the unit vector that points in the direction of increasing x, and
> **j** will denote the unit vector that points in the direction of increasing y.

Since any displacement in the plane can be accomplished by traveling horizontally and then vertically, any vector in the plane can be described by $x\mathbf{i} + y\mathbf{j}$ for some numbers x and y (see Figure 2.1); the numbers x and y are called the vector's **components**. Since each vector **v** in the plane is described by two components, we call them **2-vectors**, or **two-dimensional vectors**.

Once we've agreed to always use **i** and **j** as the "building blocks," there's no need to write them over and over again. Instead, it's common practice to use a shorthand notation called a **component representation**. Both

$$\begin{bmatrix} x \\ y \end{bmatrix} \quad \text{and} \quad \langle x, y \rangle \quad \text{are commonly used to mean} \quad x\mathbf{i} + y\mathbf{j}. \tag{2.1}$$

Using this notation, we have

$$\mathbf{i} = 1\mathbf{i} + 0\mathbf{j} = \langle 1, 0 \rangle = \begin{bmatrix} 1 \\ 0 \end{bmatrix} \quad \text{and} \quad \mathbf{j} = 0\mathbf{i} + 1\mathbf{j} = \langle 0, 1 \rangle = \begin{bmatrix} 0 \\ 1 \end{bmatrix}.$$

Finding component representations

Example 2.1. Determine the component representations of the vectors (a) $\mathbf{u} = 4\mathbf{i} + 2\mathbf{j}$, and (b) $\mathbf{v} = 8\mathbf{i} - 5\mathbf{j}$.

Solution: (a) According to (2.1) we can write $\mathbf{u} = \langle 4, 2 \rangle$ and $\mathbf{v} = \langle 8, -5 \rangle$, or equivalently,

$$\mathbf{u} = \begin{bmatrix} 4 \\ 2 \end{bmatrix} \quad \text{and} \quad \mathbf{v} = \begin{bmatrix} 8 \\ -5 \end{bmatrix}. \qquad \blacksquare$$

Figure 2.2 shows the close relationship between the coordinate notation we use to reference points and the component representation of vectors. If the point P lies at the head of the position vector $\langle x, y \rangle$, we give P the coordinate name (x, y).

❖ Magnitude

Perhaps the simplest example of magnitude is that of a position vector. In this case magnitude means "distance," and is calculated by finding the distance between the origin and the specified location.

Calculating magnitude

Example 2.2. Determine the magnitude of the position vector $\mathbf{r} = \langle 1, 2 \rangle$.

Solution: The vector $\mathbf{r}$ extends from the origin to the point $(1, 2)$. The magnitude of $\mathbf{r}$ is the distance between those points, which we calculate using the Pythagorean Theorem, $\|\mathbf{r}\| = \sqrt{(1-0)^2 + (2-0)^2} = \sqrt{5}$. $\qquad \blacksquare$

Key Idea(s): *The components of a vector describe how it's constructed from basic elements.*

Adding and scaling vectors is straightforward when using component notation.

It's often useful to "divide out" the magnitude of a vector so that we isolate its directional information.

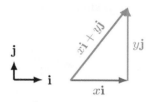

Figure 2.1: The vectors **i** and **j** can be used to build all other in the plane.

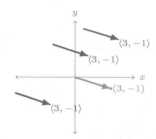

Figure 2.2: The vector $\langle 3, -1 \rangle$ and the point $(3, 1)$. The point $(3, -1)$ lies at the head of the vector $\langle 3, -1 \rangle$ when its tail is at the origin (i.e., when it's treated as a position vector).

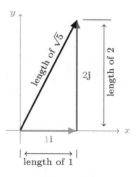

Figure 2.3: For Example 2.2

Calculating magnitude

Example 2.3. During play, the quarterback of a football team takes the ball to a point that's six yards directly behind its starting location, and then passes the ball forward to a receiver who is 12 yards to the left, and 3 yards forward of the ball's initial position (see Figure 2.4). Determine the displacement vector that describes the forward pass, and calculate its magnitude.

Solution: Taking the ball's initial position to be the origin, the quarterback throws the ball from the point $(0, -6)$ to the point $(-12, 3)$. This displacement is described by the vector $\mathbf{u} = -12\mathbf{i} + 9\mathbf{j}$. Using the Pythagorean Theorem we calculate the magnitude of $\mathbf{u}$ to be $\|\mathbf{u}\| = \sqrt{(-12)^2 + 9^2} = 15$ yards (note that this is the distance between the points at the tail and head of the displacement vector). ∎

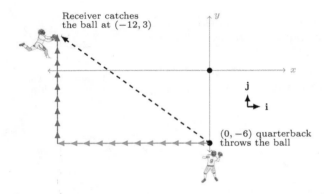

Figure 2.4: Diagram of the forward pass in Example 2.3. Distance is measured in yards.

As you've seen in the previous examples, we can use the Pythagorean Theorem to calculate the magnitude of $\langle x, y \rangle = x\mathbf{i} + y\mathbf{j}$ because $\mathbf{i}$ and $\mathbf{j}$ are orthogonal.

Magnitude: The magnitude of the vector $\langle x, y \rangle$ is denoted by $\| \langle x, y \rangle \|$, and is defined to be

$$\| \langle x, y \rangle \| = \sqrt{x^2 + y^2}. \tag{2.2}$$

Magnitude of displacement vectors

Example 2.4. Suppose the sun is at the origin and Earth's position vector is $\mathbf{r} = \langle 119.68, 89.76 \rangle$, where x and y represent *millions* of kilometers. Find $\|\mathbf{r}\|$.

Answer: 149.6 (measured in millions of km). ∎

Solution On-line

❖ Scaling

Recall that $2\mathbf{v}$ is the vector that points in the direction of $\mathbf{v}$ but is twice as long. Figure 2.5 shows that $2x\mathbf{i} + 2y\mathbf{j}$ points in the same direction as $x\mathbf{i} + y\mathbf{j}$, and it's easy to check that its magnitude is twice as large using equation (2.2):

$$\| \langle 2x, 2y \rangle \| = \sqrt{(2x)^2 + (2y)^2} = \sqrt{4(x^2 + y^2)} = 2\sqrt{x^2 + y^2} = 2\| \langle x, y \rangle \|.$$

Written in component notation, we've found that $2\langle x, y \rangle = \langle 2x, 2y \rangle$. More generally, the same basic reasoning leads us to the following result.

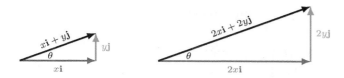

Figure 2.5: We can double the size of a vector by doubling the size of its constituent parts.

Scaling: Suppose $\mathbf{u} = \langle x, y \rangle$ and c is a real number. Then the component representation of $c\mathbf{u}$ is $\langle cx, cy \rangle$. That is,

$$c \begin{bmatrix} x \\ y \end{bmatrix} = \begin{bmatrix} cx \\ cy \end{bmatrix}. \tag{2.3}$$

The vectors $\mathbf{u}$ and $c\mathbf{u}$ point in the same direction when $c > 0$ (provided that $\mathbf{u} \neq \mathbf{0}$), and point in opposite directions when $c < 0$.

Scaling with component representations

Example 2.5. Use equation (2.3) to verify that the vector $\mathbf{v}$ from Example 2.4 can be written as $149.6\mathbf{u}$ where $\mathbf{u}$ is the unit vector $\langle 0.8, 0.6 \rangle$.

Solution: $149.6\mathbf{u} = 149.6\langle 0.8, 0.6 \rangle = \langle 149.6(0.8), 149.6(0.6) \rangle = \langle 119.68, 89.76 \rangle$. ∎

In Example 2.4 we calculated $\|\mathbf{v}\| = 149.6$, so Example 2.5 shows that

$$\|\mathbf{v}\|\mathbf{u} = \mathbf{v}, \quad \text{which is the same as saying} \quad \mathbf{u} = \frac{1}{\|\mathbf{v}\|}\mathbf{v}.$$

That is, the act of scaling a nonzero vector $\mathbf{v}$ by $1/\|\mathbf{v}\|$ (which we call ***normalizing***) results in a unit vector, which is useful because it isolates the vector's directional information. We typically denote this normalized vector with a "hat," as seen below.

> Recall that $\|\mathbf{v}\|$ is sometimes called the *norm* of $\mathbf{v}$.

Normalizing: When $\mathbf{v}$ is a vector with $\|\mathbf{v}\| \neq 0$, the vector

$$\hat{\mathbf{v}} = \frac{1}{\|\mathbf{v}\|}\mathbf{v} \tag{2.4}$$

is a unit vector that points in the same direction as $\mathbf{v}$.

Normalizing and rescaling vectors

Example 2.6. Suppose $\mathbf{v} = \langle 5, 12 \rangle$. Determine (a) the vector $\hat{\mathbf{v}}$, and (b) the vector $\mathbf{u}$ that points in the direction of $\mathbf{v}$ but has a magnitude of 17.

Solution: (a) Using equation (2.3) we calculate $\|\mathbf{v}\| = 13$, so $\hat{\mathbf{v}} = \frac{1}{13}\langle 5, 12 \rangle = \langle 5/13, 12/13 \rangle$. (b) The vectors $\mathbf{v}$ and $\hat{\mathbf{v}}$ point in the same direction, and $\|\hat{\mathbf{v}}\| = 1$, so we can achieve our goal by stretching $\hat{\mathbf{v}}$ to have a length of 17. That is,

$$\mathbf{u} = 17\hat{\mathbf{v}} = 17 \begin{bmatrix} 5/13 \\ 12/13 \end{bmatrix} = \begin{bmatrix} 85/13 \\ 204/13 \end{bmatrix}. \quad ∎$$

Don't just read it! Check that $\hat{\mathbf{v}}$ is a unit vector by calculating its magnitude for yourself.

Normalizing a vector to extract its directional information

Example 2.7. If the forward pass in Example 2.3 takes 1.2 seconds, and the ball travels along a straight line at a constant speed, determine the ball's velocity vector.

Solution: The ball's velocity vector points in the direction of its motion, and the vector's length is the speed of the ball. To get the direction, we can use the ball's displacement vector $\mathbf{u} = \langle -12, 9 \rangle$, which has a magnitude of 15 yards (from Example 2.3). Normalizing this vector gives us

$$\hat{\mathbf{u}} = \frac{1}{15} \begin{bmatrix} -12 \\ 9 \end{bmatrix} = \begin{bmatrix} -12/15 \\ 9/15 \end{bmatrix} = \begin{bmatrix} -4/5 \\ 3/5 \end{bmatrix},$$

which points in the direction of the ball's motion, but has unit length. To get the length of the vector, we need to know the speed at which the ball travels. Since the ball travels 15 yards in 1.2 seconds, its speed is $15/1.2 = 12.5$ yards per second. Scaling the unit vector $\hat{\mathbf{u}}$ by this number gives us a vector that points in the direction of the ball's velocity, and has the correct magnitude. That is, the ball's velocity vector is

$$\mathbf{v} = 12.5\hat{\mathbf{u}} = 12.5 \begin{bmatrix} -4/5 \\ 3/5 \end{bmatrix} = \begin{bmatrix} -10 \\ 7.5 \end{bmatrix}. \qquad \blacksquare$$

Scaling with component representations

Example 2.8. A tiger shark is observed making a strike on a piece of bait put out by a researcher. The shark begins 5 meters in front the researcher and 3 meters to the right. The bait is 2 meters to the researcher's left and 2 meters in front, and at the same depth as the shark. The strike lasts a mere 0.85 seconds! If the researcher is facing north, and the shark travels at constant speed along a straight line during the observation, find the shark's velocity vector.

Solution On-line

Answer: $\mathbf{v} = \langle -100/17, -60/17 \rangle$ $\blacksquare$

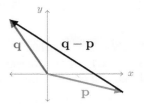

❖ Addition and Subtraction

Adding vectors using component representations is as straightforward as scaling. For example, consider

$$\begin{bmatrix} 3 \\ 7 \end{bmatrix} + \begin{bmatrix} 6 \\ -11 \end{bmatrix} = (3\mathbf{i} + 7\mathbf{j}) + (6\mathbf{i} + (-11)\mathbf{j}). \qquad (2.5)$$

Because vector addition is commutative and associative, we can collect the $\mathbf{i}$ and $\mathbf{j}$ terms respectively, and this becomes

$$\begin{bmatrix} 3 \\ 7 \end{bmatrix} + \begin{bmatrix} 6 \\ -11 \end{bmatrix} = (3+6)\mathbf{i} + (7 + (-11))\mathbf{j} = \begin{bmatrix} 9 \\ -4 \end{bmatrix}. \qquad (2.6)$$

That is, when vectors are written in component representation, their addition is done component by component. Similarly for their difference.

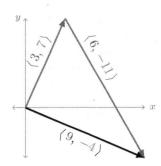

Figure 2.6: Addition of vectors is done component by component.

> **Addition and Subtraction of Two-Dimensional Vectors:** Suppose $\mathbf{u} = \langle x_1, y_1 \rangle$ and $\mathbf{v} = \langle x_2, y_2 \rangle$. Then
>
> $$\mathbf{u} \pm \mathbf{v} = \begin{bmatrix} x_1 \\ y_1 \end{bmatrix} \pm \begin{bmatrix} x_2 \\ y_2 \end{bmatrix} = \begin{bmatrix} x_1 \pm x_2 \\ y_1 \pm y_2 \end{bmatrix}.$$

Subtraction with component representations

Example 2.9. Suppose P is the point at $(4, -1)$ and Q is the point at $(-2, 3)$. Determine (a) the component representation of the displacement vector from P to Q, and (b) the distance between P and Q.

Solution: (a) The points P and Q are at the heads of the position vectors $\mathbf{p} = \langle 4, -1 \rangle$ and $\mathbf{q} = \langle -2, 3 \rangle$, respectively. So the displacement vector that reaches from P to Q is $\mathbf{q} - \mathbf{p}$ (because $\mathbf{p} + (\mathbf{q} - \mathbf{p}) = \mathbf{q}$).

Figure 2.7: The vectors for Example 2.9.

$$\mathbf{q} - \mathbf{p} = \begin{bmatrix} -2 \\ 3 \end{bmatrix} - \begin{bmatrix} 4 \\ -1 \end{bmatrix} = \begin{bmatrix} -2 - 4 \\ 3 - (-1) \end{bmatrix} = \begin{bmatrix} -6 \\ 4 \end{bmatrix}.$$

(b) The distance between P and Q is the magnitude of the displacement vector that extends between them, $\|\langle -6, 4 \rangle\| = \sqrt{36 + 16} = \sqrt{52}$ units. ∎

Vector arithmetic with component representations

Example 2.10. Suppose $\mathbf{u} = \langle 3, -1 \rangle$ and $\mathbf{v} = \langle 2, 7 \rangle$. Determine a component representation of the unit vector that points in the direction of $\mathbf{u} + \mathbf{v}$.

Answer: $\langle 5/\sqrt{61}, \, 6/\sqrt{61} \rangle$. ∎

Solution On-line

Using vector addition to solve a hanging weight problem

Example 2.11. Suppose a 300 pound crate is held aloft by a pair of cables, as in Figure 2.8. Determine the tension (i.e., the magnitude of the force vector) associated with each cable.

Solution: The force vector associated with each cable points along it. We'll call these forces $\mathbf{F}_1$ and $\mathbf{F}_2$, as shown in Figure 2.9 with the force due to gravity, $\mathbf{F}_g$.

Since the crate weighs 300 pounds, the force due to gravity is $\mathbf{F}_g = 0\mathbf{i} - 300\mathbf{j}$. The vector $\mathbf{F}_2$ makes an angle of $30°$ with the horizontal, so it must be a scaled version of the unit vector $\cos(30°)\mathbf{i} + \sin(30°)\mathbf{j}$. Similarly, $\mathbf{F}_1$ must be a scaled version of the unit vector $-\cos(45°)\mathbf{i} + \sin(45°)\mathbf{j}$, so we write

$$\mathbf{F}_1 = T_1 \begin{bmatrix} -\sqrt{2}/2 \\ \sqrt{2}/2 \end{bmatrix} \qquad \text{and} \qquad \mathbf{F}_2 = T_2 \begin{bmatrix} \sqrt{3}/2 \\ 1/2 \end{bmatrix},$$

where T_1 and T_2 are nonzero real numbers. In fact, because we've written $\mathbf{F}_1$ and $\mathbf{F}_2$ as scaled unit vectors, the tension in cable 1 is $\|\mathbf{F}_1\| = |T_1|$, and the tension in cable 2 is $\|\mathbf{F}_2\| = |T_2|$.

Because the box is at equilibrium, it must be that $\mathbf{F}_1 + \mathbf{F}_2 + \mathbf{F}_g = \mathbf{0}$. That is,

$$T_1 \begin{bmatrix} -\sqrt{2}/2 \\ \sqrt{2}/2 \end{bmatrix} + T_2 \begin{bmatrix} \sqrt{3}/2 \\ 1/2 \end{bmatrix} + \begin{bmatrix} 0 \\ -300 \end{bmatrix} = \begin{bmatrix} 0 \\ 0 \end{bmatrix}.$$

In order for the first component of the resultant to be 0, we must have

$$-\frac{\sqrt{2}}{2}T_1 + \frac{\sqrt{3}}{2}T_2 = 0 \tag{2.7}$$

Similarly, the second component of the resultant can only be 0 if

$$\frac{\sqrt{2}}{2}T_1 + \frac{1}{2}T_2 = 300 \tag{2.8}$$

Equation (2.7) tells us that $T_2 = \sqrt{2/3}\,T_1$, which reduces equation (2.8) to

$$\frac{\sqrt{2}}{2}T_1 + \frac{1}{\sqrt{6}}T_1 = 300 \qquad \Rightarrow \qquad T_1 = \frac{300\sqrt{6}}{1 + \sqrt{3}} \text{ pounds.}$$

Then because $T_2 = \sqrt{2/3}\,T_1$, we conclude that $T_2 = 600/(1+\sqrt{3})$ pounds. ∎

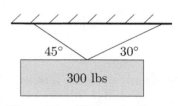

Figure 2.8: Diagram for Example 2.11. Note the angle of elevation for each wire.

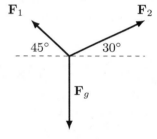

Figure 2.9: Diagram of forces in Example 2.11.

❖ Life in 3-D

Throughout this section the unit vectors $\mathbf{i}$ and $\mathbf{j}$ have served as the basis for our component representation of vectors in the xy-plane. In order to use the same kind of notation for vectors in three-dimensional space we need a third unit vector, which we denote by $\mathbf{k}$. If you lay your right hand along the vector $\mathbf{i}$ so that your fingers curl toward $\mathbf{j}$, the vector $\mathbf{k}$ points in the direction of your extended thumb (see Figure 2.10). Now extending our notation is relatively straightforward: when we write either

$$\begin{bmatrix} x \\ y \\ z \end{bmatrix} \quad \text{or} \quad \langle x, y, z \rangle \quad \text{we mean} \quad x\mathbf{i} + y\mathbf{j} + z\mathbf{k}.$$

Since such vectors are described by 3 components, we call them **3-vectors**, or **three-dimensional vectors**. Using this notation, we can write

$$\mathbf{i} = \langle 1, 0, 0 \rangle = \begin{bmatrix} 1 \\ 0 \\ 0 \end{bmatrix}, \quad \mathbf{j} = \langle 0, 1, 0 \rangle = \begin{bmatrix} 0 \\ 1 \\ 0 \end{bmatrix}, \quad \text{and} \quad \mathbf{k} = \langle 0, 0, 1 \rangle = \begin{bmatrix} 0 \\ 0 \\ 1 \end{bmatrix}.$$

For the same reasons that we add 2-vectors by adding their components (see equations (2.5) and (2.6)), the addition of three-dimensional vectors is done in a component-by-component fashion. Similarly for subtraction, so

$$\langle x_1, y_1, z_1 \rangle \pm \langle x_2, y_2, z_2 \rangle = \langle x_1 \pm x_2, \ y_1 \pm y_2, \ z_1 \pm z_2 \rangle. \tag{2.9}$$

In the exercise set you'll show that scaling is also done in a component-by-component way,

$$c\langle x, y, z \rangle = \langle cx, \ cy, \ cz \rangle, \tag{2.10}$$

and that the magnitude of a 3-vector is

$$\| \langle x, y, z \rangle \| = \sqrt{x^2 + y^2 + z^2}. \tag{2.11}$$

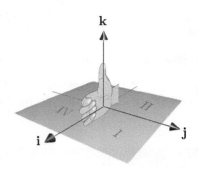

Figure 2.10: The direction of the unit vector $\mathbf{k}$ is determined from $\mathbf{i}$ and $\mathbf{j}$ using a right-hand rule. The xy-plane appears in blue, and its quadrants are labeled.

Vectors in three-dimensional space

Example 2.12. Suppose a soccer player kicks the ball from the corner toward a spot that's 6 yards directly in front of the near goalpost (see Figure 2.11). The ball is 32 yards from the goal post (along the goal line) at the moment it's kicked. It leaves the ground at a 30° angle of elevation, and has an initial speed of 25 yards per second. Determine the ball's initial velocity vector.

Solution: Let's start by finding a vector $\mathbf{u}$ that points in the direction of the ball's initial velocity. Then we'll scale $\mathbf{u}$ so that its magnitude is the ball's speed. As indicated in Figure 2.11, the lines of the field provide a natural frame of reference. Using $\mathbf{i}$ and $\mathbf{j}$ as shown, the displacement between the ball's initial position and the target point is $6\mathbf{i} + 32\mathbf{j}$, which has a magnitude of $\sqrt{6^2 + 32^2} = \sqrt{1060}$ yards. We know that the ball is kicked with a 30° angle of elevation (see Figure 2.12), so at least initially, it rises $1/\sqrt{3}$ yard for every yard it travels along the ground. If the ball were to continue along its initial direction of travel, it would rise

$$\sqrt{1060} \times \tfrac{1}{\sqrt{3}} = \sqrt{\tfrac{1060}{3}} \ \text{yards}$$

by the time it was over the target (the red spot in Figure 2.11). That is, the ball is kicked in the direction of $\mathbf{u} = 6\mathbf{i} + 32\mathbf{j} + \sqrt{1060/3}\,\mathbf{k}$. This is not the ball's initial velocity vector because

$$\|\mathbf{u}\| = \sqrt{6^2 + 32^2 + \left(\sqrt{\tfrac{1060}{3}}\right)^2} = \frac{4\sqrt{795}}{3}$$

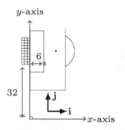

Figure 2.11: Diagram of the soccer field for Example 2.12, not to scale. Here you see $\mathbf{i}$ and $\mathbf{j}$ drawn away from the origin, but remember that vectors are defined by magnitude and direction, not position.

Figure 2.12: The initial velocity vector has a 30° angle of elevation.

and we want a vector with a magnitude of 25. So we normalize $\mathbf{u}$ and scale it by 25 to arrive at

$$\mathbf{v} = 25\hat{\mathbf{u}} = 25\,\frac{1}{\|\mathbf{u}\|}\,\mathbf{u} = \frac{15\sqrt{795}}{636}\,\mathbf{u} = \tfrac{15\sqrt{795}}{106}\,\mathbf{i} + \tfrac{40\sqrt{795}}{53}\,\mathbf{j} + \tfrac{25}{2}\,\mathbf{k}. \qquad \blacksquare$$

▷ Points in 3-D

When $\mathbf{r} = x\mathbf{i} + y\mathbf{j}$ is a two-dimensional position vector, we denote the point at its head by (x, y). Similarly, as shown in Figure 2.13, we say that a point in 3-space has coordinates (x, y, z) when it sits at the head of the position vector $x\mathbf{i} + y\mathbf{j} + z\mathbf{k}$. This convention naturally partitions space into 8 regions as follows: there are 4 quadrants in the Cartesian xy-plane, and you can either be "above" ($z > 0$) or "below" ($z < 0$) any of them. Each region is called an **octant,** and the octant above the first quadrant (where x, y, and z are all positive, which is the vantage point used in Figure 2.13) is called the **first octant**.

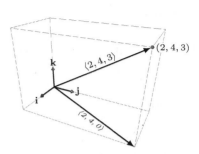

Figure 2.13: The point $(2, 4, 3)$ is so named because it sits at the head of the position vector $\mathbf{r} = \langle 2, 4, 3 \rangle$.

Distance in 3-D

Example 2.13. Determine the distance between the points $P = (4, 7, 2)$ and $Q = (7, 1, -3)$.

Solution: As in two dimensions, we determine the distance between points in 3-space by calculating the magnitude of the displacement vector between them. The points P and Q sits at the heads of the position vectors $\mathbf{p} = \langle 4, 7, 2 \rangle$ and $\mathbf{q} = \langle 7, 1, -3 \rangle$, respectively. The displacement vector between P and Q is the difference $\mathbf{p} - \mathbf{q} = \langle -3, 6, 5 \rangle$, which has a magnitude of

$$\|\mathbf{p} - \mathbf{q}\| = \sqrt{(-3)^2 + (6)^2 + (5)^2} = \sqrt{70} \text{ units}$$

according to equation (2.11). $\qquad \blacksquare$

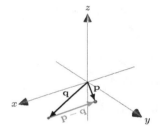

Figure 2.14: The distance between points P and Q is the magnitude of the displacement vector that extends between them.

You should know

- the terms 2-*vector*, 3-*vector*, *component representation*, *component*, *normalize*, and *octant*.

You should be able to

- write $\langle x, y \rangle$ in terms of $\mathbf{i}$, and $\mathbf{j}$, and write $\langle x, y, z \rangle$ in terms of $\mathbf{i}$, $\mathbf{j}$ and $\mathbf{k}$ (and vice versa);
- find the component representation of $\mathbf{u} \pm \mathbf{v}$ when you already know the component representations of $\mathbf{u}$ and $\mathbf{v}$;
- find the component representation of $b\mathbf{u}$ when you already know the component representation of $\mathbf{u}$;
- determine $\|\mathbf{u}\|$ when you know the component representation of $\mathbf{u}$;
- normalize a vector;
- find a vector that points in the direction of (or opposite direction of) a given $\mathbf{u}$ with a specified magnitude.

❖ 11.2 Skill Exercises

1. Suppose the tail of $\mathbf{u}$ is at $(4, 6)$ and the head is at $(13, 7)$. (a) Write the vector $\mathbf{u}$ in terms of $\mathbf{i}$ and $\mathbf{j}$. Then (b) write its component representation.

2. Suppose the tail of **u** is at $(5, -7)$ and the head is at $(3, 1)$. (a) Write the vector **u** in terms of **i** and **j**. Then (b) write its component representation.

Find component representations for each of the vectors in #3–6. Then draw **i**, **j** and **u** on the same Cartesian plane.

3. $\mathbf{u} = 5\mathbf{i} + 3\mathbf{j}$ 4. $\mathbf{u} = -4\mathbf{i} + 2\mathbf{j}$ 5. $\mathbf{u} = 2\mathbf{i} - 3\mathbf{j}$ 6. $\mathbf{u} = -3\mathbf{i} - 9\mathbf{j}$

In #7–12 write the given vector in terms of **i** and **j** (and **k** if appropriate).

7. $\langle 2, 4 \rangle$ 9. $\langle -7, 4 \rangle$ 11. $\langle -2, 7, 8 \rangle$

8. $\langle 3, 1 \rangle$ 10. $\langle 3, -5 \rangle$ 12. $\langle 20, -1, 10 \rangle$

In exercises #15–16 (a) find a component representation for **w**, and (b) draw **u**, **v**, and **w** on the same plane.

13. $\mathbf{u} = \langle 1, 1 \rangle, \mathbf{v} = \langle -2, 3 \rangle, \mathbf{w} = \mathbf{u} - \mathbf{v}$ 15. $\mathbf{u} = \langle 1, 1 \rangle, \mathbf{v} = \langle 2, 2 \rangle, \mathbf{w} = \mathbf{u} + \mathbf{v}$

14. $\mathbf{u} = \langle 3, -1 \rangle, \mathbf{v} = \langle -3, 4 \rangle, \mathbf{w} = \mathbf{u} + 4\mathbf{v}$ 16. $\mathbf{u} = \langle 1, 1 \rangle, \mathbf{v} = \langle -3, 3 \rangle, \mathbf{w} = 3\mathbf{u} + \mathbf{v}$

In #17–24 determine $\|\mathbf{u}\|$.

17. $\mathbf{u} = 2\mathbf{i} + 8\mathbf{j}$ 21. $\mathbf{u} = 9\mathbf{i} - \mathbf{j} + 4\mathbf{k}$

18. $\mathbf{u} = 3\mathbf{i} - 5\mathbf{j}$ 22. $\mathbf{u} = \mathbf{i} + 3\mathbf{j} - 5\mathbf{k}$

19. $\mathbf{u} = \langle 7, 1 \rangle$ 23. $\mathbf{u} = \langle 1, 1, 2 \rangle$

20. $\mathbf{u} = \langle 4, -1 \rangle$ 24. $\mathbf{u} = \langle 7, 3, 1 \rangle$

In #25–28 determine the distance between the points P and Q.

25. $P = (1, 4, 3)$ and $Q = (-2, 1, 7)$ 27. $P = (1, 1, 1)$ and $Q = (2, 2, 2)$

26. $P = (-3, 1, 7)$ and $Q = (8, 0, -1)$ 28. $P = (5, 1, -7)$ and $Q = (-5, -1, 7)$

In exercises #29–32 normalize the given vector.

29. $\mathbf{u} = \langle -3, 4 \rangle$ 30. $\mathbf{u} = \langle 2, \sqrt{7} \rangle$ 31. $\mathbf{v} = \langle 1, 4, 3 \rangle$ 32. $\mathbf{v} = \langle -1, 12, \sqrt{2} \rangle$

In exercises #33–36 the vector **v** points in the direction of **u** but has the specified magnitude. (a) Write the vector **v** in terms of **i** and **j** (and **k** when **v** is a 3-vector), and then (b) write its component representation.

33. $\mathbf{u} = \langle 3, 7 \rangle$, and $\|\mathbf{v}\| = 10$ 35. $\mathbf{u} = \langle 1, 2, 3 \rangle$, and $\|\mathbf{v}\| = \sqrt{7}$

34. $\mathbf{u} = \langle 4, 3 \rangle$, and $\|\mathbf{v}\| = 8$ 36. $\mathbf{u} = \langle 4, 1, -2 \rangle$, with $\|\mathbf{v}\| = 5$

In exercises #37–40 the vector **v** points in the opposite direction of **u**. (a) Write the vector **v** in terms of **i** and **j** (and **k** when **v** is a 3-vector), and then (b) write its component representation.

37. $\mathbf{u} = \langle 1, 2 \rangle$, and $\|\mathbf{v}\| = \sqrt{3}$ 39. $\mathbf{u} = \langle 3, -2, -7 \rangle$, and $\|\mathbf{v}\| = 6$

38. $\mathbf{u} = \langle 4, -5 \rangle$, and $\|\mathbf{v}\| = \sqrt{5}$ 40. $\mathbf{u} = \langle 3, 7, 6 \rangle$, and $\|\mathbf{v}\| = 10$

In exercises #15–44 (a) determine what vector can be added to **u** in order to make **v**, and (b) if the vectors are two-dimensional, draw all three of them in the plane to demonstrate that you're right.

41. $\mathbf{u} = \langle 1, -2 \rangle$ and $\mathbf{v} = \langle -2, -1 \rangle$ 43. $\mathbf{u} = \langle 8, 2, 4 \rangle$ and $\mathbf{v} = \langle 0, 3, -1 \rangle$

42. $\mathbf{u} = \langle -3, -7 \rangle$ and $\mathbf{v} = \langle 11, 9 \rangle$ 44. $\mathbf{u} = \langle 2, 1, 0 \rangle$ and $\mathbf{v} = \langle 81, 15, -4 \rangle$

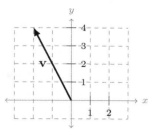

45. The vector $\mathbf{v}$ is shown in Figure 2.15. For what value of k is $k\mathbf{v}$ a unit vector?

46. Find component representations for the displacement vectors below, and answer the following questions. (a) Which of the vectors are equal? (b) Which of the vectors are parallel but not equal? (c) Which of the vectors point in opposite directions?

Figure 2.15: For #45

a extends from $(-1, 1)$ to $(-0.5, 3.5)$ **g** extends from $(-9, -1)$ to $(-2, -2)$
b extends from $(-6, -6)$ to $(-4, -5)$ **h** extends from $(1, -4)$ to $(3, -3)$
c extends from $(7, 2)$ to $(9, 5)$ **i** extends from $(-2, 6)$ to $(-6, 0)$
d extends from $(8, 15)$ to $(6, 11)$ **j** extends from $(-3, -5)$ to $(-1, -2)$
e extends from $(3, -8)$ to $(4, -3)$ **k** extends from $(-12, -9)$ to $(-8, -1)$
f extends from $(0, 0)$ to $(2, 3)$ **l** extends from $(1, 5)$ to $(4, 1)$

❖ 11.2 Concept and Application Exercises

47. The points $(-4, 3, 4), (3, 4, -1)$ and $(5, 0, 1)$ are three corners of a rectangle. Determine the location of the fourth corner.

48. The points $(-3, 2, 6), (5, 0, 12)$ and $(2, -1, 7)$ are corners of a parallelogram with equal-length sides. Determine the location of the fourth corner.

49. Suppose an object is moving east at 10 meters per second and, simultaneously, north at 2 meters per second. Draw the object's velocity as a 2-vector, and determine the speed of the object.

50. Suppose an object experiences a force of $8\mathbf{i}$ and, simultaneously, a force of $7\mathbf{j}$. Draw the net force acting on the object as a single vector.

51. Suppose a force is described by $\mathbf{F} = 3\mathbf{i} + 18\mathbf{j}$, measured in newtons. Explain what the numbers 3 and 18 mean to us physically.

52. A vector is defined by only *two* pieces of information (direction and magnitude), so why does a vector in 3-space require *three* components? Answer with full English sentences (try to avoid using pronouns).

| Quantitative Literacy |

In #15–56 a 2-kg object is traveling in the xy-plane with a velocity of $\mathbf{v} = \langle 1, 0 \rangle$ meters per second. The momentum of this object is defined to be $\mathbf{p} = 2\mathbf{v}$, and Newton's Second Law of Motion tells us that it will change by $\Delta\mathbf{p} = t\mathbf{F}$ when a constant force of $\mathbf{F}$ newtons is applied for t seconds. Draw the object's initial velocity vector, and then on the same diagram, draw the velocity vector after the object experiences the given force for (a) 1 second, (b) 2 seconds, and (c) 3 seconds.

| Physics |

53. $\mathbf{F} = \mathbf{j}$ 54. $\mathbf{F} = -\mathbf{i}$ 55. $\mathbf{F} = -\mathbf{i} + \mathbf{j}$ 56. $\mathbf{F} = \mathbf{i} - \mathbf{j}$

57. Suppose $\mathbf{r}$ is a two-dimensional position vector.

| Quantitative Literacy |

   (a) If $\mathbf{r} = \langle x, y \rangle$, show that $\|\mathbf{r} - \langle 1, 2 \rangle\| = 5$ is equivalent to

$$(x - 1)^2 + (y - 2)^2 = 25.$$

   (b) Draw the position vector $\langle 1, 2 \rangle$ and the circle described in part (a).

   (c) Draw the region described by $\|\mathbf{r} - \langle 1, 2 \rangle\| \leq 5$.

(d) Draw the region described by $2 \leq \|\mathbf{r} - \langle 1, 2 \rangle\| \leq 5$.

58. Suppose that $\mathbf{r}$ is a three-dimensional position vector.   Quantitative Literacy

   (a) Based on what you saw in #57 what shape is described by the equation $\|\mathbf{r} - \langle x_0, y_0, z_0 \rangle\| = 5$?

   (b) If $\mathbf{r} = \langle x, y \rangle$, show that $\|\mathbf{r} - \langle x_0, y_0, z_0 \rangle\| = 5$ is equivalent to

$$(x - x_0)^2 + (y - y_0)^2 + (z - z_0)^2 = 25.$$

   (c) What region is described by $2 \leq \|\mathbf{r} - \langle x_0, y_0, z_0 \rangle\| \leq 5$?

59. A person is walking due east on the deck of a ship at a rate of 4 km/hr. The ship is traveling due north at a rate of 10 km/hr in still water.

   (a) Draw the person's velocity vector (relative to the water).

   (b) Calculate the person's speed (relative to the water).

60. Suppose you're riding a skateboard in the Cartesian plane, and your velocity vector is $\langle 0.2, 0.3 \rangle$.   Physics

   (a) Draw your initial velocity vector with its tail at the origin.

   (b) Suppose a friend pushes you from behind with a force of 8 newtons. Write the force vector from the push in component form, and draw it on your diagram.

   (c) Suppose air resistance slows you down with a force of 1 newton. Write the force due to air resistance in component form, and draw it on your diagram.

   (d) Write the net force you experience in component form, and add it to your diagram.

61. Suppose that you point your canoe in the direction of $\langle 2, 7 \rangle$ and start paddling the canoe forward at 2 miles per hour.   Recreation

   (a) If you're in still water, what's your displacement vector after 15 minutes?

   (b) If you're in water that's moving with a velocity of $\langle 1, -1 \rangle$ miles per hour. What's your canoe's resulting velocity vector?

62. Suppose that you want to move your canoe in the direction of $\mathbf{i}$, and you can paddle at 2 miles per hour. If the water is moving with a velocity of $\langle 1, -1 \rangle$, in what direction do you have to point your canoe?   Recreation

63. Suppose a 100 lb object is suspended from the ceiling by two cables that make angles of 30° and 20° with the ceiling, as seen in Figure 2.16. Determine the tension in each cable.   Physics

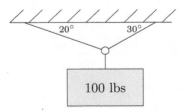

20°   30°

100 lbs

60° θ

40 lbs

100 lbs

Figure 2.16: For exercise #15.   Figure 2.17: For exercise #64

64. Suppose a 100 lb object is suspended from the ceiling by two cables, one of which provides a force of 40 lbs and makes an angle of 60° with the ceiling, as seen in Figure 2.17. Determine the tension in the other cable, and the angle it makes with the ceiling.

        | Physics |

65. Suppose a biologist is observing a flying squirrel. The squirrel is 50 feet directly in front of the biologist, on a branch that's 35 feet above the ground. It jumps from the tree, and lands on another branch that's 20 feet above the ground, 75 feet in front of the biologist, and 10 feet to her left. What was the squirrel's displacement vector? (Use **i** as the direction the biologist is facing initially, and let **k** point directly upwards.)

        | Biology |

66. Suppose the bait in Example 2.8 is on the surface of the water, and the tiger shark is initially at a depth of 2 meters. If the shark travels along a straight line when it makes its strike, determine its velocity vector.

        | Biology |

67. Suppose a baseball comes off a bat at 80 feet per second, and travels from home plate toward a fielder who is positioned 100 feet from the first-base foul line, and 75 feet from the third-base foul line (both perpendicular distances). Determine a component representation of the ball's initial velocity vector, given that is has a 15° angle of elevation. (Use the direction from home plate to first base as **i**, and let **k** point directly upward.)

        | Sports |

68. During Bucky's first test of his homemade radar station, he detects a meteor 40 miles east of his position, and 15 miles north, at an altitude of 5 miles. It's headed directly at him at a speed of 200 miles per hour. If Bucky's equipment is functioning properly, (a) what is the meteor's velocity vector? And (b) if it continues in a straight line, how long does Bucky have before the meteor hits his house? (Use **j** as pointing due north, and let **k** point directly upwards.)

        | Meteorology |

69. Suppose a metal sphere with a net charge of $q_1 < 0$ is hung from an insulated line. If the mass of the sphere is m, the magnitude of the force due to gravity is $\|\mathbf{F}_g\| = mg$ where g has a numerical value of 9.8.

        | Physics |

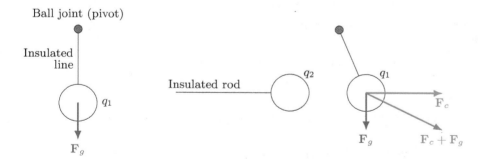

When a second metal sphere is introduced that carries a net charge of $q_2 < 0$, the electrostatic force experienced by the hanging sphere has a magnitude of

$$\|\mathbf{F}_c\| = \frac{|q_1 q_2|}{4\pi\varepsilon r^2} \quad \left(\begin{array}{l}\text{This is known as } \textbf{\textit{Coulomb's Law}}. \text{ No-}\\ \text{tice that, like the force due to gravity,}\\ \text{Coulomb's Law is an inverse square law.}\end{array}\right),$$

where r is the distance between the spheres' centers (in meters) and ε is a number called the *permittivity*. The permittivity of air has a numerical value of 8.85×10^{-12}.

> The value of ε depends on the medium (air, in this case) and is determined by the medium's ability to polarize in response to the presence of charge. Notice that larger permittivities correspond to weaker electrostatic force since ε occurs in the denominator.

   (a) Write a component representation for the force due to gravity, $\mathbf{F}_g$.

(b) If the second sphere is held at the same altitude as the first, write a component representation for the electrostatic force experienced by the hanging sphere, $\mathbf{F}_c$.

(c) Calculate the sum of these forces: $\mathbf{F}_g + \mathbf{F}_c$

(d) When the sphere comes to rest at equilibrium, the insulated line from which it hangs will align with the vector that you calculated in part (c). What angle does the line make with the vertical? (Your answer will be in terms of the parameters, q_1, q_2, r, ε, and m.)

(e) If the two spheres are held at a fixed distance apart, the hanging sphere will remain at its equilibrium position. This can only happen if some force balances $\mathbf{F}_g + \mathbf{F}_c$. Identify the source of this force and find a component representation for it.

70. Suppose P is a regular hexagon centered at the origin (see Figure 2.18).

(a) Find component representations for the position vectors that locate each of the 6 vertices of P. (*Hint: suppose that one vertex is at* $(1,0)$. *Then you just need to know the angle between consecutive vertices.*)

(b) Without using a calculator, show that the sum of these vectors is zero by adding them in the component-by-component fashion that we established in this section.

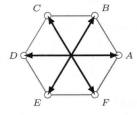

Figure 2.18: For #70.

Checking the details

71. We can discuss the direction of $\langle x, y, z \rangle$ by calculating the "rise-to-run" ratios z/x and z/y. Show that $\langle x, y, z \rangle$ and $\langle bx, by, bz \rangle$ have the same rise-to-run ratios.

72. To quantify the magnitude of $\langle x, y, z \rangle$, we apply the Pythagorean Theorem to the triangle whose legs are the vectors $\langle x, y, 0 \rangle$ and $\langle 0, 0, z \rangle$.

(a) Verify that $\langle x, y, z \rangle = \langle x, y, 0 \rangle + \langle 0, 0, z \rangle$.

(b) The leg $\langle 0, 0, z \rangle$ points in the direction of $\mathbf{k}$. What is its length?

(c) The leg $\langle x, y, 0 \rangle$ lies in the Cartesian plane, so we can think of it as the vector $\langle x, y \rangle$. What is the length of this vector?

(d) Use the Pythagorean Theorem with parts (b) and (c) to complete the equation

$$\| \langle x, y, z \rangle \|^2 = \underline{\hspace{2cm}} + \underline{\hspace{2cm}}. \qquad (2.12)$$

(e) Verify that taking the square-root of both sides of equation (2.12) yields equation (2.11).

(f) Now that you've verified equation (2.11), use it to show that

$$\| \langle bx, by, bz \rangle \| = |b| \, \| \langle x, y, z \rangle \|.$$

11.3   The Dot Product

In this section we develop a vector operation called the *dot product* that enables us to determine the angle between vectors, and "how much" of one vector is in the direction of another. We'll begin our discussion with a simple real-world scenario in which the dot product arises naturally from simple trigonometry. Then based on the resulting geometric characterization of the dot product, we'll establish some elementary algebraic facts about it, and these will lead us to a simple formula for making calculations.

> **Key Idea(s):** *The dot product is a way of calculating the angle between vectors, and "how much" of one is in the direction of another.*
>
> *The dot product of vectors* $\mathbf{u}$ *and* $\mathbf{v}$ *is the number* $\|\mathbf{u}\|\,\|\mathbf{v}\|\cos\theta$ *where* θ *is the angle between them.*
>
> *The dot product of* $\langle u_1, u_2, u_3 \rangle$ *and* $\langle v_1, v_2, v_3 \rangle$ *is the number* $u_1 v_1 + u_2 v_2 + u_3 v_3$.

�֎ Introduction to the Dot Product

The *dot product* is a quantity that arises naturally when force and displacement vectors point in different directions. For example, imagine that in order to move a box up a ramp, you apply a constant horizontal force of $\mathbf{F}$ over a displacement of $\mathbf{d}$, which has a 30° angle of elevation (see Figure 3.1). In scenarios like this, when a constant force is applied over a distance, the *work* you do is simply the product of distance and force—*but only the part of the force that's parallel to the direction of motion.* Figure 3.1 shows that $\mathbf{F} = \mathbf{u} + \mathbf{v}$, where $\mathbf{u}$ is the part $\mathbf{F}$ that's parallel to the motion, and $\mathbf{v}$ is orthogonal to it. So the work done by pushing the box is (distance) × (force) = $\|\mathbf{d}\|\,\|\mathbf{u}\|$ joules. Notice that $\|\mathbf{u}\| = \|\mathbf{F}\|\cos 30°$, so we can write this calculation of work as

$$\|\mathbf{d}\|\,\|\mathbf{u}\| = \|\mathbf{d}\|\,\|\mathbf{F}\|\cos 30°.$$

> The technical definition of the word *work* was introduced in Chapter 7.

> Because $\mathbf{u}, \mathbf{v}$ and $\mathbf{F}$ form a 30-60-90 triangle in this scenario,
> $$\cos 30° = \frac{\|\mathbf{u}\|}{\|\mathbf{F}\|}.$$

This number is often called the *dot product* or the *scalar product* of the vectors $\mathbf{F}$ and $\mathbf{d}$, and denoted by $\mathbf{F} \cdot \mathbf{d}$. The definition below generalizes this idea.

Definition: Suppose the angle between the nonzero vectors $\mathbf{u}$ and $\mathbf{v}$ is $\theta \in [0, \pi]$. Then the **dot product** of $\mathbf{u}$ and $\mathbf{v}$ (also called the **scalar product**) is the number $\|\mathbf{u}\|\,\|\mathbf{v}\|\cos\theta$. The dot product is often denoted by $\mathbf{u} \cdot \mathbf{v}$, so we write

$$\mathbf{u} \cdot \mathbf{v} = \|\mathbf{u}\|\,\|\mathbf{v}\|\cos\theta. \tag{3.1}$$

Additionally, since $\|\mathbf{0}\| = 0$ we define $\mathbf{u} \cdot \mathbf{0} = 0$ for every $\mathbf{u}$.

> The direction of $\mathbf{0}$ is not well defined, which is why we've treated it separately.

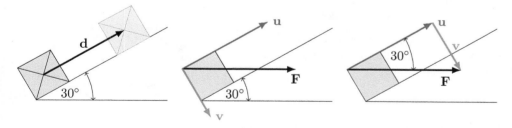

Figure 3.1: (left) An object is moved up an inclined plane; (middle) vector $\mathbf{v}$ pushes into the inclined plane, and $\mathbf{u}$ pushes up it; (right) $\mathbf{F}$ is the sum of effective and ineffective forces.

Dot products with i, j and k

Example 3.1. Determine the products (a) $\mathbf{i} \cdot \mathbf{j}$, and (b) $\mathbf{j} \cdot \mathbf{j}$.

Solution: (a) Since $\mathbf{i}$ and $\mathbf{j}$ are orthogonal unit vectors, equation (3.1) tells us that $\mathbf{i} \cdot \mathbf{j} = \|\mathbf{i}\|\,\|\mathbf{j}\|\cos \pi/2 = (1)(1)(0) = 0$. (b) Since the angle between $\mathbf{j}$ and itself is 0, equation (3.1) tells us that $\mathbf{j} \cdot \mathbf{j} = \|\mathbf{j}\|\,\|\mathbf{j}\|\cos 0 = (1)(1)(1) = 1$. ∎

Dot products and vector components

Example 3.2. Suppose $\mathbf{u} = \langle 3, 2 \rangle$ and $\mathbf{v} = \langle -1, 1.8 \rangle$. Calculate the dot products (a) $\mathbf{u} \cdot \mathbf{i}$, and (b) $\mathbf{v} \cdot \mathbf{j}$.

Solution: The vector $\mathbf{u}$ is shown with $\mathbf{i}$ and $\mathbf{j}$ in Figure 3.2. (a) When θ is the angle between $\mathbf{u}$ and $\mathbf{i}$, we have $\cos\theta = 3/\|\mathbf{u}\|$ so that

$$\mathbf{u} \cdot \mathbf{i} = \|\mathbf{u}\| \ \|\mathbf{i}\| \ \cos\theta = \|\mathbf{u}\| \ (1) \ \frac{3}{\|\mathbf{u}\|} = 3.$$

(b) Similarly, when θ is the angle between $\mathbf{v}$ and $\mathbf{j}$ we see that $\cos\theta = 1.8/\|\mathbf{v}\|$, so

$$\mathbf{v} \cdot \mathbf{j} = \|\mathbf{v}\| \ \|\mathbf{j}\| \ \cos\theta = \|\mathbf{v}\| \ (1) \ \frac{1.8}{\|\mathbf{v}\|} = 1.8. \qquad \blacksquare$$

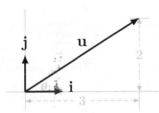
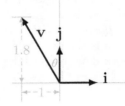

Figure 3.2: (left) When calculating $\mathbf{u} \cdot \mathbf{i}$ we take θ to be the angle between them; (right) calculating $\mathbf{v} \cdot \mathbf{j}$.

▷ Scalar and Vector Projections

Equation 3.1 defines the dot product in terms of two lengths and an angle, and is the geometric characterization to which we alluded in the opening paragraph of this section. Our next task is to further develop the geometric interpretation by making precise the idea of "how much" of one vector is in the direction of another.

Suppose light rays are speeding across the plane, and $\mathbf{u}$ points along a line that's perpendicular to their direction of travel. If $\mathbf{v}$ blocks the light from reaching that line, how long is the shadow? When the angle between $\mathbf{u}$ and $\mathbf{v}$ is acute, as in Figure 3.3, the answer is $\|\mathbf{v}\|\cos\theta$. This leads us to make the following definitions.

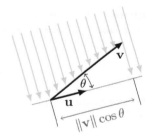

Figure 3.3: The shadow of $\mathbf{v}$ on the line through $\mathbf{u}$ has a length of $\|\mathbf{v}\|\cos\theta$ when θ is acute.

Projections: Suppose the angle between the nonzero vectors $\mathbf{u}$ and $\mathbf{v}$ is θ. Then the ***component*** of $\mathbf{v}$ in the direction of $\mathbf{u}$ (also called the the ***scalar projection***) is denoted by $\text{comp}_{\mathbf{u}}\mathbf{v}$, and is defined to be the number

$$\text{comp}_{\mathbf{u}}\mathbf{v} = \|\mathbf{v}\|\cos\theta = \mathbf{v} \cdot \hat{\mathbf{u}}. \qquad (3.2)$$

When $\theta \in [0, \pi/2]$, the vector with length $\text{comp}_{\mathbf{u}}\mathbf{v}$ that points in the direction of $\mathbf{u}$ is called the ***projection*** (or ***vector projection***) of $\mathbf{v}$ onto $\mathbf{u}$, and is denoted by $\text{proj}_{\mathbf{u}}\mathbf{v}$. That is,

$$\text{proj}_{\mathbf{u}}\mathbf{v} = (\text{comp}_{\mathbf{u}}\mathbf{v})\hat{\mathbf{u}}. \qquad (3.3)$$

Equation (3.3) defines the vector projection of $\mathbf{v}$ onto $\mathbf{u}$ even when the angle between $\mathbf{v}$ and $\mathbf{u}$ is obtuse; in this case the number $\text{comp}_{\mathbf{v}}\mathbf{u} < 0$, so $\text{proj}_{\mathbf{v}}\mathbf{u}$ points in the direction of $-\mathbf{u}$ (see Figure 3.4).

Recall that $\mathbf{u}$ points in the same direction as $\mathbf{u}$, so the angle between $\mathbf{v}$ and $\hat{\mathbf{u}}$ is also θ.

When $\theta \in [0, \pi/2]$ the number $\text{comp}_{\mathbf{u}}\mathbf{v} \geq 0$ so we can think of it as a length. When $\theta \in (\pi/2, \pi]$ the number $\text{comp}_{\mathbf{u}}\mathbf{v} < 0$, so it's not a length. Rather, the length of $\text{proj}_{\mathbf{u}}\mathbf{v}$ is $|\text{comp}_{\mathbf{u}}\mathbf{v}|$ in that case.

Note: In some books, $\text{comp}_{\mathbf{v}}\mathbf{u}$ is called a *scalar component* and $\text{proj}_{\mathbf{v}}\mathbf{u}$ is called a *vector component*. In this book, the word "component" will always mean a number.

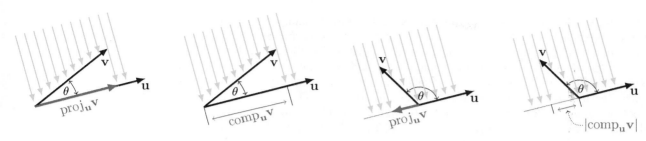

Figure 3.4: (left pair) The scalar and vector projections of $\mathbf{v}$ onto $\mathbf{u}$ when $\theta \in [0, \pi/2)$; (right pair) the scalar and vector projections of $\mathbf{v}$ onto $\mathbf{u}$ when $\theta \in (\pi/2, \pi]$. In this case $\text{comp}_{\mathbf{u}}\mathbf{v} < 0$, and the magnitude of vector projection is $|\text{comp}_{\mathbf{u}}\mathbf{v}|$.

Scalar and vector projections

Example 3.3. The angle between $\mathbf{u} = \langle 9\sqrt{3}, 9 \rangle$ and $\mathbf{v} = \langle 0, 4 \rangle$ is $\theta = \pi/3$ radians. Determine (a) $\text{comp}_{\mathbf{u}}\mathbf{v}$, and (b) $\text{proj}_{\mathbf{u}}\mathbf{v}$.

Solution: (a) The angle between $\mathbf{u}$ and $\mathbf{v}$ is acute, so

$$\text{comp}_{\mathbf{u}}\mathbf{v} = \|\mathbf{v}\| \cos\tfrac{\pi}{3} = (4)\left(\frac{1}{2}\right) = 2$$

is the length of the "shadow" that $\mathbf{v}$ casts onto a line that extends in the direction of $\mathbf{u}$, as in Figure 3.3.

(b) The vector $\text{proj}_{\mathbf{u}}\mathbf{v}$ has a magnitude of $\text{comp}_{\mathbf{u}}\mathbf{v} = 2$ and points in the direction of $\hat{\mathbf{u}}$, which we find by normalizing $\mathbf{u}$. The magnitude of $\mathbf{u}$ is $\sqrt{(9\sqrt{3})^2 + 9^2} = 18$, so

$$\text{proj}_{\mathbf{u}}\mathbf{v} = 2\,\hat{\mathbf{u}} = 2\left(\frac{1}{18}\mathbf{u}\right) = \frac{1}{9}\mathbf{u} = \langle \sqrt{3}, 1 \rangle. \qquad \blacksquare$$

Scalar and vector projections

Example 3.4. Suppose $\mathbf{u}$ and $\mathbf{v}$ are the vectors in Example 3.3. Determine (a) $\text{comp}_{\mathbf{v}}\mathbf{u}$, and (b) $\text{proj}_{\mathbf{v}}\mathbf{u}$.

Answer: (a) 9, (b) $9\mathbf{j}$. $\blacksquare$

Solution
On-line

▷ Properties of the Dot Product

The dot product exhibits many properties reminiscent of the multiplication that you learned in elementary school, and these lead to a simple formula for calculating $\mathbf{u} \cdot \mathbf{v}$ when we know the components of $\mathbf{u}$ and $\mathbf{v}$.

Properties of the Dot Product: Suppose $\mathbf{u}, \mathbf{v}, \mathbf{w}$ are vectors, and a, b are scalars. Then

$$\mathbf{u} \cdot \mathbf{u} = \|\mathbf{u}\|^2 \qquad (3.4)$$

$$|\mathbf{u} \cdot \mathbf{v}| \leq \|\mathbf{u}\|\,\|\mathbf{v}\| \qquad (3.5)$$

$$\mathbf{0} \cdot \mathbf{u} = 0 \qquad (3.6)$$

$$\mathbf{u} \cdot \mathbf{v} = \mathbf{v} \cdot \mathbf{u} \qquad (3.7)$$

$$(a\mathbf{u}) \cdot (b\mathbf{v}) = ab(\mathbf{u} \cdot \mathbf{v}) \qquad (3.8)$$

$$\mathbf{u} \cdot (\mathbf{v} + \mathbf{w}) = \mathbf{u} \cdot \mathbf{v} + \mathbf{u} \cdot \mathbf{w} = (\mathbf{v} + \mathbf{w}) \cdot \mathbf{u} \qquad (3.9)$$

Further, nonzero vectors $\mathbf{u}$ and $\mathbf{v}$ are orthogonal if and only if

$$\mathbf{u} \cdot \mathbf{v} = 0 \qquad (3.10)$$

The last statement in this box is *unlike* the multiplication that you learned in elementary school. Here we see that the dot product of two vectors can be 0 even when neither of the vectors is $\mathbf{0}$.

Proof. Equation (3.4) follows directly from equation (3.1), since the angle between the vector $\mathbf{u}$ and itself is 0. So does (3.5), which is known as the ***Cauchy-Schwarz inequality***, because $|\cos\theta|$ never exceeds 1. Equation (3.10) follows from the fact that $\|\mathbf{u}\|\,\|\mathbf{v}\|\cos\theta$ can only be 0 if one of its factors is, and equation (3.6) is true because $\|\mathbf{0}\| = 0$. Equation (3.7) is a consequence of the commutativity of real-number multiplication: $\mathbf{u}\cdot\mathbf{v} = \|\mathbf{u}\|\,\|\mathbf{v}\|\,\cos\theta = \|\mathbf{v}\|\,\|\mathbf{u}\|\,\cos\theta = \mathbf{v}\cdot\mathbf{u}$.

The proof of equation (3.8) is a little more technical, but also comes directly from the definition. When $a > 0$ is a scalar, equation (3.1) tells us that

$$(a\mathbf{u})\cdot\mathbf{v} = \|a\mathbf{u}\|\,\|\mathbf{v}\|\cos\theta = \underbrace{|a|\,\|\mathbf{u}\|\,\|\mathbf{v}\|\cos\theta}_{|a|=a\ \text{because}\ a>0} = a(\mathbf{u}\cdot\mathbf{v}).$$

When $a < 0$ the vectors $\mathbf{u}$ and $a\mathbf{u}$ point in opposite directions, so $a\mathbf{u}$ is separated from $\mathbf{v}$ by an angle of $\pi - \theta$. In this case

$$(a\mathbf{u})\cdot\mathbf{v} = \underbrace{|a|\,\|\mathbf{u}\|\,\|\mathbf{v}\|\cos(\pi-\theta) = -a\,\|\mathbf{u}\|\,\|\mathbf{v}\|\big(-\cos\theta\big)}_{|a|=-a\ \text{because}\ a<0} = a\|\mathbf{u}\|\,\|\mathbf{v}\|\cos\theta = a(\mathbf{u}\cdot\mathbf{v}).$$

Scaling $\mathbf{v}$ results in a similar result (which you can show algebraically using the commutativity property), so that $(a\mathbf{u})\cdot(b\mathbf{v}) = a\big(\mathbf{u}\cdot(b\mathbf{v})\big) = ab(\mathbf{u}\cdot\mathbf{v})$.

Lastly, we prove that the dot product is distributive. Note that equation (3.9) is trivial when $\mathbf{u} = \mathbf{0}$, so here we address the case when $\mathbf{u} \neq \mathbf{0}$ by using the connection between the dot product and the scalar projection. In Figure 3.5 you see a geometric proof that the scalar projection is additive when $\mathbf{u}, \mathbf{v}$ and $\mathbf{w}$ are vectors in the plane. That is,

$$\mathrm{comp}_{\mathbf{u}}(\mathbf{v}+\mathbf{w}) = \mathrm{comp}_{\mathbf{u}}\mathbf{v} + \mathrm{comp}_{\mathbf{u}}\mathbf{w}. \tag{3.11}$$

Later in this section we'll use a variation of Figure 3.5 to show that equation (3.11) is also true when $\mathbf{u}, \mathbf{v}$ and $\mathbf{w}$ are 3-vectors. Now using equation (3.2) to rewrite (3.11) in terms of dot products,

$$\hat{\mathbf{u}}\cdot(\mathbf{v}+\mathbf{w}) = \hat{\mathbf{u}}\cdot\mathbf{v} + \hat{\mathbf{u}}\cdot\mathbf{w}. \tag{3.12}$$

> In equation (3.2) we wrote $\mathrm{comp}_{\mathbf{v}}\mathbf{u}$ as $\mathbf{v}\cdot\hat{\mathbf{u}}$, but recall that the dot product is commutative, so this is the same number as $\hat{\mathbf{u}}\cdot\mathbf{v}$

Since $\mathbf{u} = \|\mathbf{u}\|\hat{\mathbf{u}}$, multiplying equation (3.12) by $\|\mathbf{u}\|$ yields

$$\mathbf{u}\cdot(\mathbf{v}+\mathbf{w}) = \mathbf{u}\cdot\mathbf{v} + \mathbf{u}\cdot\mathbf{w}.$$

And because the dot product is commutative, this is the same as saying that $(\mathbf{v}+\mathbf{w})\cdot\mathbf{u} = \mathbf{v}\cdot\mathbf{u} + \mathbf{w}\cdot\mathbf{u}$. ∎

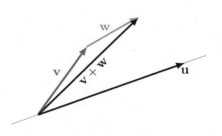
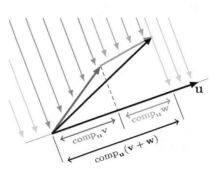

Figure 3.5: (left) The vectors $\mathbf{u}, \mathbf{v}, \mathbf{w}$ and $\mathbf{v}+\mathbf{w}$; (right) the scalar projection is additive. (both) The angle between $\mathbf{u}$ and $\mathbf{v}$ is acute, as is the angle between $\mathbf{u}$ and $\mathbf{w}$. Similar diagrams show the fact when one or both angles are obtuse.

Now having established property (3.8), we can write $\text{proj}_\mathbf{u}\mathbf{v}$ in a way that often makes calculation easier (although the formula is less intuitive)

$$\text{proj}_\mathbf{u}\mathbf{v} = (\mathbf{v} \cdot \hat{\mathbf{u}})\hat{\mathbf{u}} = \left(\mathbf{v} \cdot \frac{\mathbf{u}}{\|\mathbf{u}\|}\right)\frac{1}{\|\mathbf{u}\|}\mathbf{u} = \left(\frac{\mathbf{v} \cdot \mathbf{u}}{\|\mathbf{u}\|^2}\right)\mathbf{u} = \left(\frac{\mathbf{v} \cdot \mathbf{u}}{\mathbf{u} \cdot \mathbf{u}}\right)\mathbf{u}.$$

❖ Component Formula for Calculating the Dot Product

The distributive property is the key to deriving a simple formula for calculating the dot product of vectors when we know their component representations.

> **Calculating the Dot Product of Two-Dimensional Vectors:** Suppose $\mathbf{u} = \langle u_1, u_2 \rangle$ and $\mathbf{v} = \langle v_1, v_2 \rangle$. Then
>
> $$\mathbf{u} \cdot \mathbf{v} = u_1 v_1 + u_2 v_2. \tag{3.13}$$

> Not only is equation (3.13) easy to use, but it allows us to calculate the dot product of two vectors without knowing the angle between them!

Proof. When we write $\mathbf{u} = u_1\mathbf{i} + u_2\mathbf{j}$ and use both the distributive and scaling properties of the dot product, we see that

$$\mathbf{u} \cdot \mathbf{v} = (u_1\mathbf{i} + u_2\mathbf{j}) \cdot \mathbf{v} = (u_1\mathbf{i}) \cdot \mathbf{v} + (u_2\mathbf{j}) \cdot \mathbf{v}$$
$$= u_1(\mathbf{i} \cdot \mathbf{v}) + u_2(\mathbf{j} \cdot \mathbf{v}) = u_1 v_1 + u_2 v_2. \qquad \blacksquare$$

In the next examples we'll combine equations (3.2) and (3.13) to calculate scalar projections.

Using the dot product to calculate projections

Example 3.5. Figure 3.6 shows $\mathbf{v} = \langle 4, 2 \rangle$ and $\mathbf{u} = \langle 3, 5 \rangle$. Determine (a) the number $\text{comp}_\mathbf{u}\mathbf{v}$, and (b) the vector $\text{proj}_\mathbf{u}\mathbf{v}$.

Solution: (a) Since $\|\mathbf{u}\| = \sqrt{34}$, the component of $\mathbf{v}$ in the direction of $\mathbf{u}$ is

$$\text{comp}_\mathbf{u}\mathbf{v} = \mathbf{v} \cdot \hat{\mathbf{u}} = \frac{\mathbf{v} \cdot \mathbf{u}}{\|\mathbf{u}\|} = \frac{\langle 4, 2 \rangle \cdot \langle 3, 5 \rangle}{\sqrt{34}} = \frac{(4)(3) + (2)(5)}{\sqrt{34}} = \frac{22}{\sqrt{34}}.$$

(b) The vector projection of $\mathbf{v}$ in the direction of $\mathbf{u}$ is just a scaled version of $\hat{\mathbf{u}} = \frac{1}{\sqrt{34}}\mathbf{u}$. Specifically, the scale factor is the number we found in part (a). So

$$\text{proj}_\mathbf{u}\mathbf{v} = (\text{comp}_\mathbf{u}\mathbf{v})\,\hat{\mathbf{u}} = \frac{22}{\sqrt{34}}\left(\frac{1}{\sqrt{34}}\mathbf{u}\right) = \frac{11}{17}\langle 3, 5 \rangle = \langle \tfrac{33}{17}, \tfrac{55}{17} \rangle. \qquad \blacksquare$$

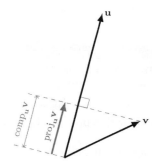

Figure 3.6: The vectors $\mathbf{u}$, $\mathbf{v}$ and $\text{proj}_\mathbf{u}\mathbf{v}$ from Example 3.5. The number $\text{comp}_\mathbf{u}\mathbf{v}$ is the length of $\text{proj}_\mathbf{u}\mathbf{v}$ because the angle between $\mathbf{u}$ and $\mathbf{v}$ is acute.

Vector and scalar projections with an obtuse angle

Example 3.6. The right-hand image in Figure 3.7 depicts $\mathbf{u} = \langle 2, -1 \rangle$ and $\mathbf{v} = \langle -3, -1 \rangle$. Find (a) the scalar projection and (b) the vector projection of $\mathbf{u}$ onto $\mathbf{v}$.

Solution: (a) Since $\mathbf{u} \cdot \mathbf{v} = \langle 2, -1 \rangle \cdot \langle -3, -1 \rangle = (2)(-3) + (-1)(-1) = -5$, and $\|\mathbf{v}\| = \sqrt{10}$, the scalar projection of $\mathbf{u}$ onto $\mathbf{v}$ is

$$\text{comp}_\mathbf{v}\mathbf{u} = \mathbf{u} \cdot \hat{\mathbf{v}} = \frac{\mathbf{u} \cdot \mathbf{v}}{\|\mathbf{v}\|} = \frac{-5}{\sqrt{10}}.$$

(b) The vector projection of $\mathbf{u}$ onto $\mathbf{v}$ is

$$\text{proj}_\mathbf{v}\mathbf{u} = (\text{comp}_\mathbf{v}\mathbf{u})\,\hat{\mathbf{v}} = \left(\frac{\mathbf{u} \cdot \mathbf{v}}{\|\mathbf{v}\|}\right)\frac{\mathbf{v}}{\|\mathbf{v}\|} = \frac{-5}{10}\begin{bmatrix} -3 \\ -1 \end{bmatrix} = \begin{bmatrix} 1.5 \\ 0.5 \end{bmatrix}.$$

Unlike the previous example, the number $\text{comp}_\mathbf{v}\mathbf{u}$ is *negative* here. This happens whenever $\theta > \pi/2$ because $\cos\theta < 0$. Consequently, the vectors $\mathbf{v}$ and $\text{proj}_\mathbf{v}\mathbf{u}$ point

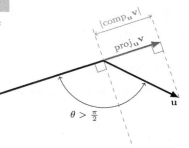

Figure 3.7: The vectors $\mathbf{v}, \mathbf{u}$ and $\text{proj}_\mathbf{v}\mathbf{u}$ from Example 3.6. In this case, the length of $\text{proj}_\mathbf{v}\mathbf{u}$ is $|\text{comp}_\mathbf{v}\mathbf{u}|$ because the angle between $\mathbf{u}$ and $\mathbf{v}$ is obtuse (so the scalar projection is negative).

in opposite directions.   ∎

Using the dot product to calculate scalar and vector projections

Example 3.7. Suppose $\mathbf{u} = \langle 1, 5 \rangle$, $\mathbf{v} = \langle -8, -2 \rangle$, and $\mathbf{w} = \langle 0, -3 \rangle$. Determine (a) $\text{comp}_\mathbf{v}\mathbf{u}$, and (b) $\text{proj}_\mathbf{v}\mathbf{w}$.

Answer: $\text{comp}_\mathbf{v}\mathbf{u} = -18/\sqrt{68}$ and $\text{proj}_\mathbf{v}\mathbf{w} = \langle -12/17, -3/17 \rangle$.   ∎

Solution On-line

▷ The Angle Between Vectors

Equation (3.13) gives us with a quick way to determine the angle between vectors.

> **Angle Between Vectors:** The angle between the nonzero vectors $\mathbf{u}$ and $\mathbf{v}$ is
>
> $$\theta = \cos^{-1}\left(\frac{\mathbf{u} \cdot \mathbf{v}}{\|\mathbf{u}\|\,\|\mathbf{v}\|} \right). \qquad (3.14)$$

Recall that the range of the arccosine is $[0, \pi]$.

Calculating angles

Example 3.8. Determine the angle between $\mathbf{u} = \langle 1, \sqrt{3} \rangle$, and $\mathbf{v} = \langle -1, \sqrt{3} \rangle$.

Solution: The magnitude of both vectors is 2, so equation (3.14) tells us that the angle between them is

$$\theta = \cos^{-1}\left(\frac{(1)(-1) + (\sqrt{3})(\sqrt{3})}{(2)(2)} \right) = \cos^{-1}\left(\frac{1}{2} \right) = \frac{\pi}{3}.$$
     ∎

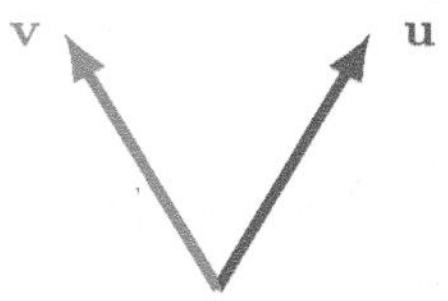

Figure 3.8: The vectors $\mathbf{u}$ and $\mathbf{v}$ in Example 3.8.

Using angles to better understand dot products

Example 3.9. Suppose $\mathbf{u}$ and $\mathbf{v}$ are nonzero vectors. What do you know about $\mathbf{u} \cdot \mathbf{v}$ when the vectors are (a) orthogonal, and (b) point in the same direction?

Solution: (a) When the vectors $\mathbf{u}$ and $\mathbf{v}$ are orthogonal, the angle between them is $\pi/2$, so their dot product is $\mathbf{u} \cdot \mathbf{v} = \|\mathbf{u}\|\,\|\mathbf{v}\| \cos \pi/2 = 0$.

This example is an extension of the facts that you saw in Example 3.1.

(b) When $\theta = 0$ we have $\mathbf{u} \cdot \mathbf{v} = \|\mathbf{u}\|\,\|\mathbf{v}\| \cos 0 = \|\mathbf{u}\|\,\|\mathbf{v}\|$.   ∎

✤ Applications of the Dot Product

We started this section with a discussion of *work,* so let's begin our discussion of applications with that topic.

Calculating work

Example 3.10. Suppose you slide an object up an incline by applying a force of $\mathbf{F} = \langle 200, 40 \rangle$ newtons. If the displacement of the object is $\mathbf{d} = \langle 3, 1 \rangle$ meters, how much work have you done?

Solution: Based on our earlier discussion, we know that the work done is $W = \|\mathbf{F}\|\,\|\mathbf{d}\| \cos \theta$, where θ is the angle between $\mathbf{F}$ and $\mathbf{d}$, which we don't know. We could find it, but it's easier to recognize that $W = \mathbf{F} \cdot \mathbf{d}$ and make the needed calculation with equation (3.13).

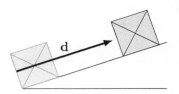

Figure 3.9: For Example 3.11.

$$W = \mathbf{F} \cdot \mathbf{d} = \langle 200, 40 \rangle \cdot \langle 3, 1 \rangle = (200)(3) + (40)(1) = 640 \text{ joules.}$$
     ∎

Calculating work

Example 3.11. Suppose a 25-kg box is placed two meters up a roller conveyer that's inclined in the direction of $\langle 4, 1 \rangle$, as shown in Figure 3.9. Use the dot product to calculate the work done by gravity in pulling the box back to the ground.

Answer: $W = 490/\sqrt{17}$ joules.   ■

Solution
On-line

▷ Changing the Frame of Reference

We've been using **i** and **j** as the basis of our component representation of two-dimensional vectors, but there are situations (see Example 3.14 for instance) when we can simplify a problem conceptually or computationally by describing it in terms of other unit vectors instead. In the discussion below we develop the general tools and concepts for making such a change.

Consider the orthogonal vectors $\hat{\mathbf{v}}$ and $\hat{\mathbf{w}}$ shown in the left-hand image of Figure 3.10. Because $\hat{\mathbf{v}}$ and $\hat{\mathbf{w}}$ are orthogonal, we can build any vector in the plane by scaling and adding them: $\mathbf{u} = a\hat{\mathbf{v}} + b\hat{\mathbf{w}}$. The numbers a and b are easily calculated with the dot product:

> The orthogonal relationship between $\hat{\mathbf{v}}$ and $\hat{\mathbf{w}}$ is convenient because it makes some dot products 0, but it's not strictly necessary. We can build any vector in the plane with $\hat{\mathbf{v}}$ and $\hat{\mathbf{w}}$ as long as they are not multiples of each other.

$$\mathbf{u} \cdot \hat{\mathbf{v}} = (a\hat{\mathbf{v}} + b\hat{\mathbf{w}}) \cdot \hat{\mathbf{v}} = a(\hat{\mathbf{v}} \cdot \hat{\mathbf{v}}) + b(\hat{\mathbf{w}} \cdot \hat{\mathbf{v}}). \qquad (3.15)$$

The number $\hat{\mathbf{v}} \cdot \hat{\mathbf{v}} = \|\hat{\mathbf{v}}\|^2 = 1$ because $\hat{\mathbf{v}}$ is a unit vector, and $\hat{\mathbf{v}} \cdot \hat{\mathbf{w}} = 0$ because $\hat{\mathbf{v}}$ and $\hat{\mathbf{w}}$ are orthogonal, so equation (3.15) reduces to $a = \mathbf{u} \cdot \hat{\mathbf{v}}$. Similarly, $b = \mathbf{u} \cdot \hat{\mathbf{w}}$. That is,

$$a = \text{comp}_{\mathbf{v}}\mathbf{u} \quad \text{and} \quad b = \text{comp}_{\mathbf{w}}\mathbf{u},$$

so we get

$$\mathbf{u} = (\text{comp}_{\mathbf{v}}\mathbf{u})\hat{\mathbf{v}} + (\text{comp}_{\mathbf{w}}\mathbf{u})\hat{\mathbf{w}} = \text{proj}_{\mathbf{v}}\mathbf{u} + \text{proj}_{\mathbf{w}}\mathbf{u}.$$

Figure 3.10: (left) The vectors $\hat{\mathbf{v}}$ and $\hat{\mathbf{w}}$ can be used to "build" all other vectors; (right) a vector $\mathbf{u}$ for which $a > 0$ and $b > 0$.

Changing the frame of reference

Example 3.12. Write $\mathbf{u} = \langle 3, 8 \rangle$ in terms of $\mathbf{v} = \langle 1, 7 \rangle$ and $\mathbf{w} = \langle -14, 2 \rangle$.

Solution: First, note that $\mathbf{v} \cdot \mathbf{w} = 0$, so the vectors $\mathbf{v}$ and $\mathbf{w}$ are orthogonal. The vector projection of $\mathbf{u}$ onto $\mathbf{v}$ is

$$\text{proj}_{\mathbf{v}}\mathbf{u} = (\mathbf{u} \cdot \hat{\mathbf{v}})\hat{\mathbf{v}} = \left(\frac{\mathbf{u} \cdot \mathbf{v}}{\|\mathbf{v}\|} \right) \frac{\mathbf{v}}{\|\mathbf{v}\|} = \left(\frac{\mathbf{u} \cdot \mathbf{v}}{\|\mathbf{v}\|^2} \right) \mathbf{v}.$$

Equation (3.13) tells us that $\mathbf{u} \cdot \mathbf{v} = 59$, and $\|\mathbf{v}\|^2 = 50$, so $\text{proj}_{\mathbf{v}}\mathbf{u} = \frac{59}{50}\mathbf{v}$. Similarly, $\text{proj}_{\mathbf{w}}\mathbf{u} = \left(\frac{\mathbf{u} \cdot \mathbf{w}}{\|\mathbf{w}\|^2} \right)\mathbf{w} = -\frac{13}{100}\mathbf{w}$ so $\mathbf{u} = \frac{59}{50}\mathbf{v} - \frac{13}{100}\mathbf{w}$.   ■

Changing the frame of reference

Example 3.13. Write $\mathbf{u} = \langle 1, -3 \rangle$ in terms of $\mathbf{v} = \langle 4, 2 \rangle$ and $\mathbf{w} = \langle -1, 2 \rangle$.

Answer: $\mathbf{u} = -\frac{1}{10}\mathbf{v} - \frac{7}{5}\mathbf{w}$ ■

Solution
On-line

Changing the frame of reference

Example 3.14. Suppose a plane is at $\mathbf{r} = \langle -240, 10 \rangle$, where distance is measured in miles, and it's traveling in a straight-line path with velocity vector $\mathbf{v} = \langle 400, 90 \rangle$ miles per hour. A control tower is at the origin, and its radar range is 100 miles (see Figure 3.11). How long will the plane stay in radar range of the tower?

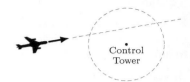

Figure 3.11: Diagram of a plane approaching the radar range of a control tower.

Solution: As you can see in Figure 3.12, our solution strategy is to change our frame of reference to one that naturally reflects the motion in this problem. We'll let the plane's velocity, $\mathbf{v}$, determine one of our "building block" directions, and we'll let $\mathbf{u} = \langle -90, 400 \rangle$ determine the other since it's orthogonal to $\mathbf{v}$ (note that $\mathbf{u} \cdot \mathbf{v} = 0$).

If we use the vectors $\hat{\mathbf{v}}$ and $\hat{\mathbf{u}}$ to define a coordinate system at the control tower, as seen in Figure 3.12, the circular boundary of the tower's radar range is described by $v^2 + u^2 = 100^2$, and in this frame of reference the u-coordinate of the plane is constant. Specifically, the plane's u-coordinate is just the scalar projection of $\mathbf{r}$ onto the direction of $\mathbf{u}$ (see Figure 3.12):

$$\mathbf{r} \cdot \hat{\mathbf{u}} = \langle -240, 10 \rangle \cdot \frac{\langle -90, 400 \rangle}{410} = \frac{2560}{41}.$$

Since the plane's route has a constant $u = {}^{2560}/_{41}$ we can easily determine where it enters and leaves the circle by solving the equation $v^2 + u^2 = 100^2$ for

$$v = \pm\sqrt{10000 - \left(\frac{2560}{41}\right)^2} = \pm\sqrt{\frac{10{,}256{,}400}{1681}} \approx \pm 78.111$$

So the distance traveled by the plane as it passes through the tower's radar range is approximately $2 \times 78.111 = 156.222$ miles. Since the speed of the plane is $\|\mathbf{v}\| = 410$ miles per hour, the plane crosses through the radar range in

$$\underbrace{2\sqrt{\frac{10{,}256{,}400}{1681}}}_{\text{miles}} \underbrace{\frac{1}{410}}_{\text{hours per mile}} = \frac{\sqrt{10{,}256{,}400}}{8405} \text{ hours} \approx 22.862 \text{ minutes.} \quad \blacksquare$$

> A coordinate system is a way of locating points. By using $\hat{\mathbf{v}}$ and $\hat{\mathbf{u}}$ instead of $\mathbf{i}$ and $\mathbf{j}$, we've changed our frame of reference. Now we're thinking of a position vector as $v\hat{\mathbf{v}} + u\hat{\mathbf{u}}$. The point at the head of such a vector is denoted by (v, u). This is what we mean by using "the vectors $\hat{\mathbf{v}}$ and $\hat{\mathbf{u}}$ to define a coordinate system."

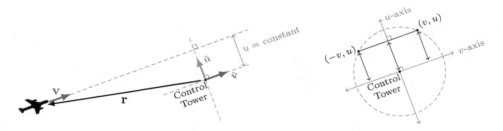

Figure 3.12: Diagrams (not to scale) for Example 3.14. (left) The airplane's closest approach to the tower is the scalar projection of $\mathbf{r}$ onto $\mathbf{u}$; (right) once we know the distance of closest approach, u, we can determine the length of the chord across which the plane will travel.

❖ Life in 3-D

We first introduced the dot product as $\mathbf{u} \cdot \mathbf{v} = \|\mathbf{u}\| \|\mathbf{v}\| \cos\theta$, where $\theta \in [0, \pi]$ is the angle between $\mathbf{u}$ and $\mathbf{v}$. Though we have focused on 2-vectors, the dot product of 3-vectors is also important, so here we establish a natural analog of equation (3.13) that allows for quick calculation of the dot product.

> **Calculating the Dot Product of Three-Dimensional Vectors:** Suppose
> $\mathbf{u} = \langle u_1, u_2, u_3 \rangle$ and $\mathbf{v} = \langle v_1, v_2, v_3 \rangle$. Then
>
> $$\mathbf{u} \cdot \mathbf{v} = u_1 v_1 + u_2 v_2 + u_3 v_3 \qquad (3.16)$$

Proof. This proof relies on two facts. The first is that the dot product of $\mathbf{u}$ with $\mathbf{i}$ is u_1, with $\mathbf{j}$ is u_2, and with $\mathbf{k}$ is u_3. (You can show this by using the technique presented in Example 3.2.) The second fact at the heart of our proof is that the dot product of 3-vectors is distributive. We stated this in property (3.9) but have only proved it for 2-vectors. In 3-dimensional space, the vectors $\mathbf{u}, \mathbf{v}$ and $\mathbf{w}$ might not all lie in the same plane, which makes the fact more difficult to see, but consider Figure 3.13, which shows why $\hat{\mathbf{u}} \cdot (\mathbf{v} + \mathbf{w}) = \hat{\mathbf{u}} \cdot \mathbf{v} + \hat{\mathbf{u}} \cdot \mathbf{w}$. Since $\mathbf{u} = \|\mathbf{u}\| \hat{\mathbf{u}}$, multiplying this equation by $\|\mathbf{u}\|$ yields the desired result:

$$\mathbf{u} \cdot (\mathbf{v} + \mathbf{w}) = \mathbf{u} \cdot \mathbf{v} + \mathbf{u} \cdot \mathbf{w}.$$

And due to the commutativity, $(\mathbf{v} + \mathbf{w}) \cdot \mathbf{u} = \mathbf{v} \cdot \mathbf{u} + \mathbf{w} \cdot \mathbf{u}$. Equation (3.16) now follows in exactly the same manner as the proof of equation (3.13). ∎

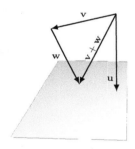 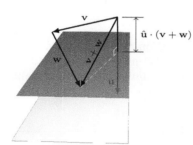 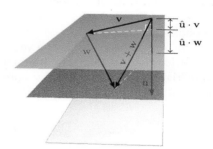

Figure 3.13: (left) The vectors $\mathbf{v}, \mathbf{w}, \mathbf{v} + \mathbf{w}$ and $\mathbf{u}$, with a white plane that has been included to help communicate the 3-dimensional nature of the setting; (middle) a plane perpendicular to $\mathbf{u}$ to shows the projection of $\mathbf{v} + \mathbf{w}$ onto the direction of $\mathbf{u}$; (right) planes perpendicular to $\mathbf{u}$ show the projections of $\mathbf{v}$ and $\mathbf{w}$ onto the direction of $\mathbf{u}$.

Vector projection in 3-dimensions

Example 3.15. Suppose an airplane is traveling in the direction of $\mathbf{v} = \langle 1, 1, 1/4 \rangle$, and the wind exerts a force of $\mathbf{F} = \langle 2, -3, -1 \rangle$ newtons. (a) Determine the component representation of $\text{proj}_{\mathbf{v}} \mathbf{F}$, and (b) interpret your results.

Solution: (a) As with two-dimensional vectors, the vector projection of $\mathbf{F}$ onto $\mathbf{v}$ is

$$\text{proj}_{\mathbf{v}} \mathbf{F} = \underbrace{(\mathbf{F} \cdot \hat{\mathbf{v}})}_{\text{Scale factor}} \underbrace{\hat{\mathbf{v}}}_{\text{Direction}} = \left(\mathbf{F} \cdot \frac{1}{\|\mathbf{v}\|} \mathbf{v} \right) \frac{1}{\|\mathbf{v}\|} \mathbf{v} = \frac{\mathbf{F} \cdot \mathbf{v}}{\|\mathbf{v}\|^2} \mathbf{v}.$$

Since $\|\mathbf{v}\|^2 = \mathbf{v} \cdot \mathbf{v} = (1)(1) + (1)(1) + (1/4)(1/4) = 33/16$, and

$$\mathbf{F} \cdot \mathbf{v} = (2)(1) + (-3)(1) + (-1)\left(\tfrac{1}{4}\right) = -\tfrac{5}{4},$$

we have $\text{proj}_{\mathbf{v}} \mathbf{F} = -\frac{5/4}{33/16} \langle 1, 1, 1/4 \rangle = -\frac{20}{33} \langle 1, 1, 1/4 \rangle$.

(b) Note that $\text{proj}_{\mathbf{v}} \mathbf{F}$ and $\mathbf{v}$ point in opposite directions (which happens because $\mathbf{F} \cdot \mathbf{v} < 0$). This means the aircraft is facing a headwind, and $\text{proj}_{\mathbf{v}} \mathbf{F}$ is the part of the wind's force that is directly opposed to the flight of the aircraft. ∎

Work in three-space

Example 3.16. Suppose distance is measured in meters, and a particle is moved from the point $(1, 0, 0)$ to the point $(2, 3, 10)$ under a constant force of $\mathbf{F} = \langle 1, 2, 7 \rangle$ newtons. How much work was done by the force?

Solution: The particle starts with a position vector of $\langle 1, 0, 0 \rangle$ and ends with a position vector of $\langle 2, 3, 10 \rangle$. The displacement due to the force is their difference: $\mathbf{d} = \langle 2, 3, 10 \rangle - \langle 1, 0, 0 \rangle = \langle 1, 3, 10 \rangle$, so the work done by the force is

$$\mathbf{F} \cdot \mathbf{d} = (1)(1) + (2)(3) + (7)(10) = 77 \text{ joules.} \qquad \blacksquare$$

Dot products with vectors in three dimensions

Example 3.17. Suppose $\mathbf{u} = \langle -1, 2, -5 \rangle$, $\mathbf{v} = \langle 3, 1, 4 \rangle$, and $\mathbf{w} = \langle 37, 73, -46 \rangle$. (a) Show that $\mathbf{v}$ and $\mathbf{w}$ are orthogonal, and (b) calculate $\mathrm{comp}_\mathbf{w} \mathbf{u}$.

Answer: (a) $\mathbf{v} \cdot \mathbf{w} = 0$, (b) $339/\sqrt{8814}$. $\blacksquare$

Solution
On-line

❖ Common Difficulties with Projections

Students often find it difficult to remember whether $\mathrm{proj}_\mathbf{u} \mathbf{v}$ means to project $\mathbf{v}$ onto $\mathbf{u}$, or $\mathbf{u}$ onto $\mathbf{v}$ (it means the former). You might find it helpful to think about the notation without the subscript: $\mathrm{proj}\,\mathbf{v}$ means the projection of $\mathbf{v}$, but the projection *onto what?* The subscript tells us the direction onto which we're projecting. The same convention holds for $\mathrm{comp}_\mathbf{u} \mathbf{v}$.

A common mistake when calculating the vector projection of $\mathbf{v}$ onto $\mathbf{u}$ is forgetting to normalize $\mathbf{u}$ (so that we take only its direction). You may find it helpful to always talk about "the vector projection of $\mathbf{v}$ onto the *direction of* $\mathbf{u}$" in order help yourself remember to use $\hat{\mathbf{u}}$ in the calculation.

You should know

- the terms *dot product, vector projection,* and *scalar projection;*
- the notation $\mathrm{proj}_\mathbf{v} \mathbf{u}$ and $\mathrm{comp}_\mathbf{v} \mathbf{u}$;
- that $\mathbf{u} \cdot \mathbf{v}$ is a number (not a vector);
- that $\mathbf{u} \cdot \hat{\mathbf{v}}$ tells us the "amount" of $\mathbf{u}$ in the direction of $\hat{\mathbf{v}}$;
- the properties of the dot product.

You should be able to

- determine the angle between vectors using the dot product;
- find the scalar and vector projections of $\mathbf{u}$ onto $\mathbf{v}$;
- use projections to calculate quantities like *work*

❖ 11.3 Skill Exercises

In exercises #1–12 calculate $\mathbf{u} \cdot \mathbf{v}$.

$\|\mathbf{u}\| = 4$

$30°$

$\|\mathbf{v}\| = 8$

1.

$\|\mathbf{u}\| = 8$

$45°$

$\|\mathbf{v}\| = 6$

2.

3.

4.

5. $\mathbf{u} = \langle 8, 3 \rangle$, $\mathbf{v} = \langle -4, 7 \rangle$

6. $\mathbf{u} = \langle 2, 7 \rangle$, $\mathbf{v} = \langle 3, 5 \rangle$

7. $\mathbf{u} = 8\mathbf{i} + 2\mathbf{j}$, $\mathbf{v} = 9\mathbf{i} - 2\mathbf{j}$

8. $\mathbf{u} = 13\mathbf{j}$, $\mathbf{v} = 12\mathbf{i} - 7\mathbf{j}$

9. $\mathbf{u} = \langle 11, -1, 5 \rangle$, $\mathbf{v} = \langle 1, -7, -3 \rangle$

10. $\mathbf{u} = \langle -1, 2, 3 \rangle$, $\mathbf{v} = \langle -4, 7, 2 \rangle$

11. $\mathbf{u} = \mathbf{i} + 3\mathbf{j} - 2\mathbf{k}$, $\mathbf{v} = 19\mathbf{i} - \mathbf{j} - 3\mathbf{k}$

12. $\mathbf{u} = 18\mathbf{j}$, $\mathbf{v} = 14\mathbf{i} + 9\mathbf{k}$

In exercises #13–20 determine the angle between $\mathbf{u}$ and $\mathbf{v}$.

13. $\mathbf{u} = \langle 1, 10 \rangle$, $\mathbf{v} = \langle -40, 4 \rangle$

14. $\mathbf{u} = \langle 18, 3 \rangle$, $\mathbf{v} = \langle -1, 6 \rangle$

15. $\mathbf{u} = \mathbf{i} + \mathbf{j}$, $\mathbf{v} = 3\mathbf{i} + 8\mathbf{j}$

16. $\mathbf{u} = 4\mathbf{i} - 7\mathbf{j}$, $\mathbf{v} = 13\mathbf{i} + 81\mathbf{j}$

17. $\mathbf{u} = \langle 2, 3, 1 \rangle$, $\mathbf{v} = \langle 1, -2, -3 \rangle$

18. $\mathbf{u} = \langle 1, 4, 10 \rangle$, $\mathbf{v} = \langle -2, -2, 1 \rangle$

19. $\mathbf{u} = 2\mathbf{i} + 3\mathbf{j} + 9\mathbf{k}$, $\mathbf{v} = 3\mathbf{j} - \mathbf{k}$

20. $\mathbf{u} = 12\mathbf{i} + \mathbf{j} - \mathbf{k}$, $\mathbf{v} = 4\mathbf{i} + \mathbf{j} + 9\mathbf{k}$

In exercises #21–26 use the dot product to determine the magnitude of $\mathbf{u}$.

21. $\mathbf{u} = \langle 2, 7 \rangle$

22. $\mathbf{u} = \langle -1, 3 \rangle$

23. $\mathbf{u} = \langle 3, -1, 4 \rangle$

24. $\mathbf{u} = \langle 1, 7, -2 \rangle$

25. $\mathbf{u} = 8\mathbf{i} + 9\mathbf{j}$

26. $\mathbf{u} = 2\mathbf{i} - \mathbf{j} + 3\mathbf{k}$

In exercises #27–32 determine which pairs of vectors (if any) among $\mathbf{u}, \mathbf{v}$ and $\mathbf{w}$ are orthogonal.

27. $\mathbf{u} = \langle 1, -5 \rangle$, $\mathbf{v} = \langle 2, -3 \rangle$, $\mathbf{w} = \langle 6, 4 \rangle$

28. $\mathbf{u} = \langle 10, 2 \rangle$, $\mathbf{v} = \langle -60, -12 \rangle$, $\mathbf{w} = \langle 1, -5 \rangle$

29. $\mathbf{u} = \langle 5, 2, 1 \rangle$, $\mathbf{v} = \langle 7, -13, -9 \rangle$, $\mathbf{w} = \langle -1, 3, -1 \rangle$

30. $\mathbf{u} = \langle 2, 2, 3 \rangle$, $\mathbf{v} = \langle 17, 1, -10 \rangle$, $\mathbf{w} = \langle -1, -5, 11 \rangle$

31. $\mathbf{u} = 14\mathbf{i} + 35\mathbf{j}$, $\mathbf{v} = 6\mathbf{i} - 5\mathbf{j}$, $\mathbf{w} = -10\mathbf{i} + 25\mathbf{j}$

32. $\mathbf{u} = 10\mathbf{i} - 8\mathbf{j} + \mathbf{k}$, $\mathbf{v} = 4\mathbf{i} + 5\mathbf{j} + 0\mathbf{k}$, $\mathbf{w} = -2\mathbf{i} + \mathbf{j} + 3\mathbf{k}$

In exercises #33–40 determine (a) $\text{comp}_\mathbf{v}\mathbf{u}$, and (b) $\text{proj}_\mathbf{v}\mathbf{u}$ for the given 2-vectors.

33. $\mathbf{u} = \langle 3, 5 \rangle$, $\mathbf{v} = \mathbf{i}$

34. $\mathbf{u} = \langle 2, 7 \rangle$, $\mathbf{v} = \mathbf{j}$

35. $\mathbf{u} = \langle 1, 7 \rangle$, $\mathbf{v} = \langle 5, 1 \rangle$

36. $\mathbf{u} = \langle 3, 8 \rangle$, $\mathbf{v} = \langle -2, 10 \rangle$

37. $\mathbf{u} = 8\mathbf{i} + \mathbf{j}$, $\mathbf{v} = -\mathbf{i} - 17\mathbf{j}$

38. $\mathbf{u} = 2\mathbf{i} + 3\mathbf{j}$, $\mathbf{v} = 6\mathbf{i} - 4\mathbf{j}$

In exercises #39–44 determine (a) $\text{comp}_\mathbf{v}\mathbf{u}$, and (b) $\text{proj}_\mathbf{v}\mathbf{u}$ for the given 3-vectors.

39. $\mathbf{u} = \langle 2, 8, -4 \rangle$, $\mathbf{v} = \mathbf{k}$

40. $\mathbf{u} = \langle 10, -1, 11 \rangle$, $\mathbf{v} = \mathbf{j}$

41. $\mathbf{u} = \langle 10, -1, 11 \rangle$, $\mathbf{v} = \langle 1, 2, 3 \rangle$

42. $\mathbf{u} = \langle -1, -2, 4 \rangle$, $\mathbf{v} = \langle 4, 5, -2 \rangle$

43. $\mathbf{u} = 3\mathbf{i} + 8\mathbf{j} - \mathbf{k}$, $\mathbf{v} = \mathbf{i} + 7\mathbf{j} + 2\mathbf{k}$

44. $\mathbf{u} = \mathbf{i} + \mathbf{j} + \mathbf{k}$, $\mathbf{v} = 3\mathbf{i} + 7\mathbf{j} - 10\mathbf{k}$

In exercises #45–50 determine a nonzero vector orthogonal to each 2-vector, and a pair of nonzero vectors (not multiples of each other) that are orthogonal to each 3-vector. Assume that a, b and c are nonzero constants.

45. $\mathbf{u} = \langle 3, 4 \rangle$ 47. $\mathbf{u} = \langle a, b \rangle$ 49. $\mathbf{u} = \langle 2, -1, 3 \rangle$

46. $\mathbf{u} = \langle -1, 7 \rangle$ 48. $\mathbf{u} = \langle -4, 1, -9 \rangle$ 50. $\mathbf{u} = \langle a, b, c \rangle$

In exercises #51-54, (a) determine a nonzero vector $\mathbf{w}$ that is orthogonal to the given vector $\mathbf{v}$, then (b) use the dot product to determine values of a and b so that $\mathbf{u} = a\mathbf{v} + b\mathbf{w}$.

51. $\mathbf{u} = \langle 2, 3 \rangle$, $\mathbf{v} = \langle 1, 1 \rangle$ 53. $\mathbf{u} = \langle -1/2, -3/4 \rangle$, $\mathbf{v} = \langle 4, -1 \rangle$

52. $\mathbf{u} = \langle -5, 6 \rangle$, $\mathbf{v} = \langle 0.9, -2.3 \rangle$ 54. $\mathbf{u} = \langle 0, 1 \rangle$, $\mathbf{v} = \langle -6, -9 \rangle$

❖ 11.3 Concept and Application Exercises

55. Use the dot product to write an equation that says, "The angle between $\hat{\mathbf{u}}$ and $\hat{\mathbf{v}}$ is $\pi/6$."

56. Use the dot product to write an equation that says, "The angle between $\mathbf{u}$ and $\mathbf{v}$ is the same as the angle between $\mathbf{u}$ and $\mathbf{w}$."

57. What does the equation $\hat{\mathbf{u}} \cdot \hat{\mathbf{v}} = -0.78$ tell us about the vectors, geometrically, and why?

58. Suppose $\text{comp}_{\mathbf{v}}\mathbf{u} = \text{comp}_{\mathbf{u}}\mathbf{v}$, and neither $\mathbf{u}$ nor $\mathbf{v}$ is the zero vector. Then one of two things must be true. What are those two things? *(Hint: compare the formulas for $\text{comp}_{\mathbf{u}}\mathbf{v}$ and $\text{comp}_{\mathbf{v}}\mathbf{u}$.)*

59. In this exercise we connect dot products to lines in the plane. | Geometry |

    (a) Draw several position vectors for which $\mathbf{r} \cdot \mathbf{i} = 3$. What do you notice about the heads of these vectors?

    (b) Draw several position vectors for which $\mathbf{r} \cdot \mathbf{i} = 6$. What do you notice about the heads of these vectors?

    (c) How does c change the collection of vectors for which $\mathbf{r} \cdot \mathbf{i} = c$?

60. Suppose $\hat{\mathbf{v}} = \langle 0.5\sqrt{2}, 0.5\sqrt{2} \rangle$. | Geometry |

    (a) Draw several position vectors for which $\mathbf{r} \cdot \mathbf{v} = 3$. What do you notice about the heads of these vectors?

    (b) Draw several position vectors for which $\mathbf{r} \cdot \mathbf{v} = 6$. What do you notice about the heads of these vectors?

    (c) How does c change the collection of vectors for which $\mathbf{r} \cdot \mathbf{v} = c$?

61. Suppose $\hat{\mathbf{v}} = \langle 0.6, 0.8 \rangle$. | Geometry |

    (a) Verify that $\|\hat{\mathbf{v}}\| = 1$.

    (b) Draw the vector $\hat{\mathbf{v}}$ with its tail at the origin.

    (c) Draw the position vector $\mathbf{r} = \langle 2, 5 \rangle$.

    (d) Determine the scalar projection of $\mathbf{r}$ onto $\hat{\mathbf{v}}$.

    (e) Draw 5 other vectors that have the same scalar projection onto $\hat{\mathbf{v}}$.

    (f) How does the drawing change if we look for vectors whose scalar projection onto $\hat{\mathbf{v}}$ is 6, or 7, or 8 instead?

62. The vectors $\hat{\mathbf{u}}$ and $\hat{\mathbf{v}}$ are depicted in the Figure 3.14.

    (a) Draw the set of vectors, $\mathbf{w}$, that satisfy $\mathbf{w} \cdot \hat{\mathbf{u}} = \mathbf{w} \cdot \hat{\mathbf{v}}$.

Figure 3.14: For #62

(b) How does your picture change if $\|\mathbf{u}\| \neq \|\mathbf{v}\|$?

63. Draw vectors $\mathbf{u}, \mathbf{v}$ so that $\text{comp}_\mathbf{v}\mathbf{u} < 0$.

64. Draw nonzero vectors $\mathbf{u}, \mathbf{v}$ so that $\text{comp}_\mathbf{v}\mathbf{u} = 0$.

65. Determine the value(s) of k for which $\langle 2, -4, 1 \rangle$ and $\langle -4, k, k^2 \rangle$ are orthogonal.

66. Suppose $\mathbf{u} = \langle 1, k, k^2 \rangle$. Find scalars $a, b,$ and c so that $\mathbf{u}$ is ...

   (a) never orthogonal to $\langle a, b, c \rangle$, no matter the value of k.

   (b) orthogonal to $\langle a, b, c \rangle$ for exactly one value of k.

   (c) orthogonal to $\langle a, b, c \rangle$ for exactly two values of k.

67. Use the dot product to show that the zero vector is orthogonal to every vector.

68. Use the dot product to show that the zero vector is the *only* vector that is orthogonal to every vector.

69. You know that slopes of perpendicular lines are negative reciprocals. This exercise shows you why. Suppose x_1 and y_1 are nonzero numbers, and ℓ_1 is the line that passes through the origin and $P = (x_1, y_1)$.   Geometry

   (a) Find the slope of ℓ_1.

   (b) Find the component representation of the position vector that points to P, which we'll call $\mathbf{r}$.

   (c) Find numbers v_1 and v_2 so that $\langle v_1, v_2 \rangle \cdot \mathbf{r} = 0$.

   (d) Suppose ℓ_2 is the line that passes through the origin and the point (v_1, v_2). Find the slope of the line ℓ_2.

   (e) How are the components of $\mathbf{r}$ and $\mathbf{v}$ related?

   (f) What does that tell you about the slopes of ℓ_1 and ℓ_2?

70. Suppose $\mathbf{u} = \langle 2, 3 \rangle$, and $\mathbf{v}$ is a nonzero vector for which $\mathbf{u} \cdot \mathbf{v} = 0$.   Geometry

   (a) Draw $\mathbf{u}$ with its tail at the origin of the xy-plane .

   (b) Draw a candidate for the vector $\mathbf{v}$ (also with its tail at the origin).

   (c) Draw a line through the origin that extends in the direction of $\mathbf{v}$.

   (d) The line you drew in part (c) should have a negative slope. What can you say about the number $\mathbf{u} \cdot \mathbf{r}$ when the head of the position vector $\mathbf{r}$ lies "above" this line?

   (e) What can you say about the number $\mathbf{u} \cdot \mathbf{r}$ when the head of $\mathbf{r}$ lies below the line?

71. Suppose $P_1 = (x_1, y_1)$ is on the circle of radius r that's centered at the origin, and A is some other point in the plane. The displacement vector that reaches between them will be denoted by $\overrightarrow{AP_1}$.   Geometry

   (a) Suppose $\mathbf{r}_1 = \langle x_1, y_1 \rangle$. Explain why $\|\mathbf{r}_1\| = r$.

   (b) Suppose P_2 is diametrically opposed to P_1 on the circle (so P_1 and P_2 are connected by a diameter of the circle), and $\mathbf{r}_2$ is the position vector that points to it. Find a component representation for $\mathbf{r}_2$.

   (c) Show that $\mathbf{r}_1 \cdot \mathbf{r}_2 = -r^2$.

   (d) Show that $(\overrightarrow{AP_1}) \cdot (\overrightarrow{AP_2}) = 0$ when A is on the circle.

   (e) Show that $(\overrightarrow{AP_1}) \cdot (\overrightarrow{AP_2}) < 0$ when A is inside the circle.

(f) Show that $(\overrightarrow{AP_1}) \cdot (\overrightarrow{AP_2}) > 0$ when A is outside the circle.

72. Suppose A is a point on the positive x-axis, B is a point on the positive z-axis, and C is a point on the positive y-axis.

Geometry

    (a) Show that the angle $\angle ABC$ is acute.

    (b) Do we really need to restrict ourselves to the *positive* x-axis in order for this result to be true? If so, explain why. If not, provide an example.

Exercises #73 and #74 are intended to show you why we say that $\mathbf{v} \cdot \hat{\mathbf{u}}$ is called the *component* of $\mathbf{v}$ in the direction of $\mathbf{u}$.

73. Suppose $\mathbf{v} = 2\mathbf{i} + 3\mathbf{j}$. (a) Calculate $\text{comp}_{\mathbf{i}}\mathbf{v}$ and $\text{comp}_{\mathbf{j}}\mathbf{v}$. (b) Show that $\mathbf{v}$ can be written as $(\text{comp}_{\mathbf{i}}\mathbf{v})\mathbf{i} + (\text{comp}_{\mathbf{j}}\mathbf{v})\mathbf{j}$.

Geometry

74. Suppose $\mathbf{v} = \langle -2, 3 \rangle$, $\mathbf{u} = \langle 6, 4 \rangle$, and $\mathbf{w} = \langle 1, 7 \rangle$.

Geometry

    (a) Use the dot product to verify that $\mathbf{u}$ and $\mathbf{v}$ are orthogonal.

    (b) Calculate $\text{comp}_{\mathbf{u}}\mathbf{w}$ and $\text{proj}_{\mathbf{u}}\mathbf{w}$.

    (c) Calculate $\text{comp}_{\mathbf{v}}\mathbf{w}$ and $\text{proj}_{\mathbf{v}}\mathbf{w}$.

    (d) Draw the position vectors $\mathbf{u}, \mathbf{v}, \mathbf{w}, \text{proj}_{\mathbf{u}}\mathbf{w}$ and $\text{proj}_{\mathbf{v}}\mathbf{w}$.

    (e) Verify numerically that $\mathbf{w} = (\text{comp}_{\mathbf{u}}\mathbf{w})\hat{\mathbf{u}} + (\text{comp}_{\mathbf{v}}\mathbf{w})\hat{\mathbf{v}}$.

    (f) Show graphically that $\mathbf{w} = (\text{comp}_{\mathbf{u}}\mathbf{w})\hat{\mathbf{u}} + (\text{comp}_{\mathbf{v}}\mathbf{w})\hat{\mathbf{v}}$.

    (g) If we based the component representation of a vector on $\hat{\mathbf{u}}$ and $\hat{\mathbf{v}}$ instead of $\mathbf{i}$ and $\mathbf{j}$, what would the component representation of $\mathbf{w}$ be?

75. Suppose $\mathbf{v} = \langle a, b, c \rangle$ is a nonzero vector that makes angles of α, β and γ with $\mathbf{i}, \mathbf{j}$ and $\mathbf{k}$, respectively. These are called the **direction angles** of $\mathbf{v}$. The **direction cosines** of $\mathbf{v}$ are the cosines of the direction angles. Show that

$$\cos \alpha = \frac{a}{\|\mathbf{v}\|}, \quad \cos \beta = \frac{b}{\|\mathbf{v}\|}, \quad \text{and} \quad \cos \gamma = \frac{c}{\|\mathbf{v}\|}.$$

76. Suppose α, β and γ are the direction cosines of a nonzero 3-vector $\mathbf{v}$ (see #75). Show that $\cos^2 \alpha + \cos^2 \beta + \cos^2 \gamma = 1$.

77. In this exercise you'll see how the **Pythagorean Theorem** is related to the dot product.

Geometry

    (a) Draw the vectors $\mathbf{u}, \mathbf{v}$, and $\mathbf{u} - \mathbf{v}$, so that $\mathbf{u} \cdot \mathbf{v} = 0$.

    (b) Use the fact that $\|\mathbf{w}\|^2 = \mathbf{w} \cdot \mathbf{w}$ to show algebraically that $\|\mathbf{u} - \mathbf{v}\|^2 = \|\mathbf{u}\|^2 + \|\mathbf{v}\|^2$. (You shouldn't see any components in your equation, such as u_1 or v_2. You should only see $\mathbf{u}, \mathbf{v}$, and dot products of them.)

78. The **triangle inequality** says that $\|\mathbf{u} + \mathbf{v}\| \le \|\mathbf{u}\| + \|\mathbf{v}\|$. In this exercise, you'll use the dot product to establish this fact algebraically.

Geometry

    (a) Use the dot product to show that $\|\mathbf{u} + \mathbf{v}\|^2 = \|\mathbf{u}\|^2 + 2(\mathbf{u} \cdot \mathbf{v}) + \|\mathbf{v}\|^2$. *(You'll need to use the fact that the dot product is distributive).*

    (b) Explain why $\mathbf{u} \cdot \mathbf{v} \le \|\mathbf{u}\| \, \|\mathbf{v}\|$.

    (c) Make the value of your expression from part (a) *larger* by replacing $\mathbf{u} \cdot \mathbf{v}$ with $\|\mathbf{u}\| \, \|\mathbf{v}\|$. *(This will force you to write $\|\mathbf{u} + \mathbf{v}\|^2 \le \cdots$ instead of $\|\mathbf{u} + \mathbf{v}\|^2 = \cdots$.)*

    (d) Recognize the right-hand side of your inequality as a perfect square, and apply the square root to both sides.

(e) Draw vectors **u** and **v**, and use head-to-tail addition to draw **u** + **v**. Interpret the triangle inequality geometrically, based on your drawing.

79. A major electronics retailer sells TVs for $1500, Blu-ray players for $300, and video game systems for $250. If a particular store sells 30 TVs, 64 Blu-ray players and 400 game systems in one month, its data can be organized into the vectors $\mathbf{q} = \langle 30, 64, 400 \rangle$ and $\mathbf{p} = \langle 1500, 300, 250 \rangle$.

   (a) Calculate $\mathbf{q} \cdot \langle 1, 1, 1 \rangle$ and explain what it tells us.

   (b) Calculate $\mathbf{p} \cdot \langle 1, 1, 1 \rangle$ and explain what it tells us.

   (c) Calculate $\mathbf{q} \cdot \mathbf{p}$ and explain what it tells us.

80. Suppose a river is 50 yards wide and flows in the direction of $\mathbf{v} = \langle -3, -1 \rangle$ at 2 feet per second. You're on the northwestern side of the river and want to paddle your canoe to the other shore as quickly as possible but without being pushed downstream by the current. If you can paddle through still water at 6 feet per second, (a) what direction should you point your canoe, and (b) how long will it take to cross the river?

Starting point

Figure 3.15: A canoe crossing the current in a river (for #80).

81. Suppose an aircraft is at $\mathbf{r} = \langle 150, 50 \rangle$ and is traveling at 500 miles per hour in the direction of $\mathbf{v} = \langle -4, -1 \rangle$. How long will it stay within the 50-mile radar range of the control tower at the origin?

Aviation

82. In Example 3.14 the plane stayed in the radar range of the control tower for about 23 minutes. That control tower was at the origin. Determine all other possible locations of the control tower for which the plane's time inside the radar range is 23 minutes.

Aviation

83. Suppose aircraft are at $\mathbf{r}_1 = \langle -700, 300 \rangle$ and $\mathbf{r}_2 = \langle -400, -200 \rangle$, where distance is measured in miles, and are traveling with velocities of $\mathbf{v}_1 = \langle 500, 100 \rangle$ and $\mathbf{v}_2 = \langle 10, 600 \rangle$ miles per hour, respectively. If the aircraft can communicate when they are within 60 miles of each other, how long will they stay in contact? *(Hint: consider this problem from the point of view of the pilots in one of the aircraft. At constant velocity, they feel still, much like the operators in a control tower.)*

Aviation

84. Two planes were in contact for at least 10 minutes. The initial position of the first plane was $\mathbf{r}_1 = \langle 500, 200 \rangle$ (length measured in miles) and it traveled with a constant velocity of $\mathbf{v}_1 = \langle -200, 400 \rangle$ miles per hour. The second airplane traveled at a constant velocity of $\mathbf{v}_2 = \langle 500, 200 \rangle$ miles per hour. If the transceivers on both aircraft have a range of 70 miles, what initial positions are possible for the second plane?

Aviation

In exercises #85–88 suppose you apply a force of **F** newtons to a block on a ramp that inclines in the direction of the vector **u**. (a) Determine the component of **F** (in newtons) that is effective in moving the block up the ramp; (b) calculate the amount of work required to move the block 1.5 meters up the ramp; (c) compute the vector $\mathbf{F} - \text{proj}_{\mathbf{u}}\mathbf{F}$ and draw it with **u** and $\text{proj}_{\mathbf{u}}\mathbf{F}$, with all the vectors' tails at the same spot; and (d) explain the effect of $\mathbf{F} - \text{proj}_{\mathbf{u}}\mathbf{F}$ on the block.

Work

85. $\mathbf{F} = \langle 80, 110 \rangle$; $\mathbf{u} = \langle 5, 3 \rangle$.   86. $\mathbf{F} = \langle 840, 41 \rangle$; $\mathbf{u} = \langle 16, 1 \rangle$.

87. $\|\mathbf{F}\|$ is 100 newtons and **F** is inclined 25° from **i**; **u** is inclined 30° from **i**.

88. $\|\mathbf{F}\|$ is 640 newtons and **F** is inclined 8° from **i**; **u** is inclined 20° from **i**.

89. Determine the work done by a force of $\mathbf{F} = \langle 40, 20, 60 \rangle$ newtons that moves an object from the origin to the point $(1, 2, 5)$, when distance is measured in meters.

    ___| Work |

90. Determine the work done by a force $\mathbf{F} = \langle 60, 40, 140 \rangle$ newtons that moves an object from $(1, 4, 7)$ to $(-3, -4, -2)$, when distance is measured in meters.

    ___| Work |

91. When the Erie canal first opened, cargo barges were pulled by mules walking along towpaths parallel to the canal. Suppose a mule is exerting a 1000 newtons of force on a tow rope. The rope is long enough that the mule is 9 meters to the right and 15.25 meters ahead of the barge. Determine the work the mule does in hauling the barge 100 meters.

    ___| Work |

92. Suppose a barge is being hauled up a canal by two mules (one on each side) harnessed to towropes 18 meters long. Because of differences in topography, one mule is 10 meters to the left and 1 meter above the barge. The other mule is 8 meters to the right and 2 meters above the barge. If each mule exerts 1000 newtons of force on its tow rope, determine (a) the component of each mule's force that is effective in towing the barge, and (b) the amount of work done by each mule in hauling the barge 100 meters.

    ___| Work |

93. Suppose an object of m kilograms sits on an inclined plane that makes an angle of θ radians with the horizontal (see Figure 3.16).

    ___| Physics |

    (a) Determine a component representation for $\hat{\mathbf{v}}$ (in terms of θ).

    (b) The force on the mass due to gravity is $\mathbf{F}_g = \langle 0, -mg \rangle$, where g is the acceleration due to gravity. Calculate the scalar projection of $\mathbf{F}_g$ onto $\hat{\mathbf{v}}$.

    (c) Experimentally, we find that the friction force between the mass and the plane is proportional to the number that you calculated in part (b). Explain why this makes sense. *(Hint: consider $\theta = 0$.)*

    (d) If the constant of proportionality from part (c) is $k > 0$, the magnitude of the friction force is $kmg \cos \theta$. What's the direction of the friction force? *(Hint: which way will the block tend to slide? Does friction help or hinder the sliding?)*

    (e) Calculate the scalar projection of $\mathbf{F}_g$ onto $-\mathbf{u}$ and explain its practical significance.

    (f) The mass will slip when magnitude of force you calculated in part (e) is larger than $kmg \cos \theta$. Explain why this makes sense.

    (g) Show that the angle at which the block will slip does not depend on the mass of the block, or the planet on which we carry out the experiment.

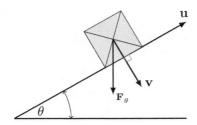

Figure 3.16: For #93.   Figure 3.17: Diagram for #94.

94. Molecules in which a central atom bonds with four atoms of the same type, such as CH_4 (methane) and XeO_4 (xenon tetroxide), have a tetrahedral shape.

    ___| Chemistry |

Consider a central atom at $\mathbf{c} = \langle 1/2, 1/2, 1/2 \rangle$, bonded to atoms with position vectors $\mathbf{i}, \mathbf{j}, \mathbf{k}$ and $\mathbf{r} = \langle 1, 1, 1 \rangle$. The vectors $\mathbf{c} - \mathbf{i}$ and $\mathbf{c} - \mathbf{j}$ represent bonds. Use the dot product to determine the angle between them.

95. Suppose the width and length of a soccer field are defined by $\mathbf{w} = \langle -69, 23 \rangle$ and $\mathbf{u} = \langle 36, 108 \rangle$, where distance is measured in yards, $\mathbf{i}$ points due east, and $\mathbf{j}$ points due north (see Figure 3.18).

Sports

   (a) Use the dot product to verify that $\mathbf{w}$ and $\mathbf{u}$ are orthogonal.

   (b) If the ball is passed with a velocity of $\mathbf{v} = \langle 14, 2 \rangle$ yards per second, how quickly is it moving up the field, toward goal?

96. A ski slope is 200 feet wide in the direction of $\mathbf{w} = \langle 1, 2, 0 \rangle$, and extends 1000 feet in the direction of $\mathbf{u} = \langle -1, 1, 1.3 \rangle$. Bucky is skiing across the slope with a velocity vector of $\mathbf{v} = \langle -2.5, -27.5, -9.75 \rangle$ ft/sec (see Figure 3.19).

   (a) What is Bucky's speed?

   (b) Bucky has learned how to maintain his speed by angling his skis, but unwisely got onto the slope before sufficiently developing the skill of turning. If he maintains his speed of travel on the slope, but does not turn, how long will it take him to cross from one side to the other?

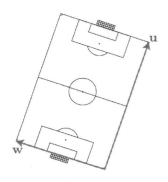

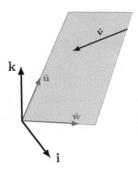

Figure 3.18: For #95.   Figure 3.19: For #96.

Checking the details

97. Suppose $\mathbf{u}$ and $\mathbf{v}$ are 2-vectors. Use the definition of the dot product to show that (a) $\mathbf{u} \cdot \mathbf{v} = \mathbf{v} \cdot \mathbf{u}$; (b) $(b\mathbf{u}) \cdot \mathbf{v} = b(\mathbf{u} \cdot \mathbf{v}) = \mathbf{u} \cdot (b\mathbf{v})$ when b is any real number; (c) $\mathbf{u} \cdot (\mathbf{v} + \mathbf{w}) = \mathbf{u} \cdot \mathbf{v} + \mathbf{u} \cdot \mathbf{w}$.

98. Discuss how your calculations in #97 change when $\mathbf{u}$ and $\mathbf{v}$ are 3-vectors.

11.4 The Cross Product

In Section 11.3 we used the dot product to determine the angle between a pair of nonzero vectors, say **u** and **v**. Now in 3-space we develop a method of finding a third vector, denoted by **u** × **v** and called the *cross product*, that's orthogonal to both of them. As we did in the previous section, we'll begin with a simple real-world situation in which the cross product naturally arises. This will lead us to a geometric characterization of it, and after using that geometric characterization to establish some algebraic facts about the cross product, we'll derive a formula for making calculations.

> **Key Idea(s):** *The cross product* **u** × **v** *is a vector that's orthogonal to* **u** *and* **v**.
>
> *The direction of the cross product is determined by the so-called "right hand rule."*
>
> *The magnitude of the cross product is often interpreted as the area of a parallelogram, as a speed, or as the strength of a rotational force (torque).*

✥ Introduction to the Cross Product

The *cross product* arises naturally when talking about a spinning object, such as an ice skater, a baseball or a planet. More specifically, it arises when calculating the velocity of a point on the object, say P. That velocity depends on both the location of P (relative to the axis of revolution) and the rate at which the object is spinning. Let's suppose that the object is centered at the origin, that **r** is the position vector of the point P, and that the object's angular velocity vector is $\boldsymbol{\omega}$ (see Section 11.1).

Figure 4.1 shows this scenario when P is a point on the surface of a spinning sphere (e.g., your position on the surface of the earth). If the angle between **r** and $\boldsymbol{\omega}$ is θ radians, the rotation of the sphere carries P around a circle of radius of $\|\mathbf{r}\| \sin\theta$, and circumference $2\pi\|\mathbf{r}\| \sin\theta$, so it's linear speed is

> The vector $\boldsymbol{\omega}$ points along the axis of rotation, and $\|\boldsymbol{\omega}\|$ is the rate at which the object is spinning in radians per second.

$$\underbrace{\frac{\|\boldsymbol{\omega}\|}{2\pi}}_{\text{Rotations per second}} \underbrace{2\pi\|\mathbf{r}\| \sin\theta}_{\text{Distance per rotation}} = \|\boldsymbol{\omega}\| \, \|\mathbf{r}\| \sin\theta. \tag{4.1}$$

Also note that the direction of motion is orthogonal to both $\boldsymbol{\omega}$ and **r** at any given instant. More specifically, if you lay your right hand along the vector $\boldsymbol{\omega}$ so that your fingers curl toward **r**, your extended thumb points in the direction of travel (we call this the *right-hand rule*).

Now that we know the speed and direction of travel in terms of $\boldsymbol{\omega}$ and **r**, we can characterize the linear velocity of P at any instant: the velocity vector is orthogonal to $\boldsymbol{\omega}$ and **r** (its direction is determined by the right-hand rule), and its magnitude is $\|\boldsymbol{\omega}\| \, \|\mathbf{r}\| \sin\theta$. This vector is called the *cross product* of $\boldsymbol{\omega}$ and **r**, and is often denoted by $\boldsymbol{\omega} \times \mathbf{r}$. The cross product is useful in many other situations, so we generalize it below.

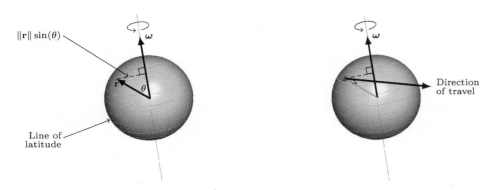

Figure 4.1: (left) The vectors **r** and $\boldsymbol{\omega}$ are separated by an angle of θ radians; (right) the direction of travel is orthogonal to both **r** and $\boldsymbol{\omega}$.

Cross Product: Suppose **u** and **v** are nonzero vectors that are separated by an angle of $\theta \in [0, \pi]$. The ***cross product*** (also called the ***vector product*** of **u** and **v** is denoted by $\mathbf{u} \times \mathbf{v}$ and defined as

$$\mathbf{u} \times \mathbf{v} = \|\mathbf{u}\| \, \|\mathbf{v}\| \sin(\theta) \, \mathbf{n}, \qquad (4.2)$$

where **n** is a unit vector that is orthogonal to **u** and **v**, and points in the direction determined by the ***right-hand rule*** —meaning that when you lay your right hand along the vector **u** so that your fingers curl toward **v**, your extended thumb points in the direction of **n**.

In the opening paragraph of this section, we said that the *cross product* would help us to find a vector that's orthogonal to two others. There are typically two such directions (e.g., $\pm\mathbf{k}$ are both orthogonal to **i** and **j**). The right-hand rule provides a consistent way to make a choice, so there's no ambiguity.

Elementary cross products

Example 4.1. Determine the cross products (a) $\mathbf{i} \times \mathbf{j}$, (b) $\mathbf{j} \times \mathbf{k}$, and (c) $\mathbf{k} \times \mathbf{i}$.

Solution: (a) The right-hand rule tells us that $\mathbf{i} \times \mathbf{j}$ points in the direction of **k** (see Figure 4.3), and the angle between **i** and **j** is $\pi/2$ radians, so $\|\mathbf{i} \times \mathbf{j}\| = \|\mathbf{i}\| \, \|\mathbf{j}\| \sin(\pi/2) = 1 \cdot 1 \cdot 1 = 1$. Therefore, $\mathbf{i} \times \mathbf{j} = \mathbf{k}$.

(b) The right hand rule tells us that $\mathbf{j} \times \mathbf{k}$ points in the direction of **i**. And the magnitude of $\mathbf{i} \times \mathbf{j}$ is 1 because **j** and **k** are orthogonal unit vectors, so $\mathbf{j} \times \mathbf{k} = \mathbf{i}$.

(c) The right-hand rule tells us that $\mathbf{k} \times \mathbf{i}$ points in the direction of **j**. As in parts (a) and (b), the vector $\mathbf{k} \times \mathbf{i}$ has a magnitude of 1, so $\mathbf{k} \times \mathbf{i} = \mathbf{j}$.

These results are communicated succinctly by Figure 4.2.　　■

Figure 4.2: The cross-product relationship among **i**, **j** and **k**.

Elementary cross products

Example 4.2. Determine the cross products (a) $\mathbf{j} \times \mathbf{i}$, (b) $\mathbf{k} \times \mathbf{j}$, and (c) $\mathbf{i} \times \mathbf{k}$.

Answer: (a) $-\mathbf{k}$, (b) $-\mathbf{i}$, (c) $-\mathbf{j}$.　　■

Solution On-line

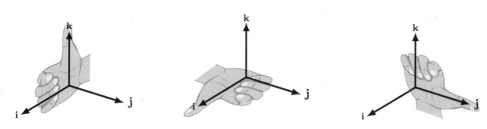

Figure 4.3: Using the right hand rule to determine the direction of a cross product; (left) $\mathbf{i} \times \mathbf{j}$ points in the direction of **k**, (middle) $\mathbf{j} \times \mathbf{k}$ points in the direction of **i**; (right) $\mathbf{k} \times \mathbf{i}$ points in the direction of **j**.

▷ Properties of the Cross Product

The cross product exhibits some properties reminiscent of the multiplication that you learned in elementary school, but there are also some very important differences. For instance, in equation (4.6) you see that switching the order of **u** and **v** negates the result (we say that the cross product is ***anticommutative***).

Properties of the Cross Product: Suppose $\mathbf{u}, \mathbf{v}$ and $\mathbf{w}$ are 3-vectors, a and b are scalars, and θ is the angle between $\mathbf{u}$ and $\mathbf{v}$. Then the direction of $\mathbf{u} \times \mathbf{v}$ is determined by the right hand rule, and

$$\|\mathbf{u} \times \mathbf{v}\| = \|\mathbf{u}\| \, \|\mathbf{v}\| \sin\theta \tag{4.3}$$

$$\mathbf{u} \cdot (\mathbf{u} \times \mathbf{v}) = 0 \tag{4.4}$$

$$\mathbf{v} \cdot (\mathbf{u} \times \mathbf{v}) = 0 \tag{4.5}$$

$$\mathbf{u} \times \mathbf{v} = -(\mathbf{v} \times \mathbf{u}) \tag{4.6}$$

$$\mathbf{u} \times (b\mathbf{u}) = \mathbf{0} \tag{4.7}$$

$$ab(\mathbf{u} \times \mathbf{v}) = (a\mathbf{u}) \times (b\mathbf{v}) \tag{4.8}$$

$$\mathbf{u} \times (\mathbf{v} + \mathbf{w}) = \mathbf{u} \times \mathbf{v} + \mathbf{u} \times \mathbf{w} \tag{4.9}$$

$$(\mathbf{v} + \mathbf{w}) \times \mathbf{u} = \mathbf{v} \times \mathbf{u} + \mathbf{w} \times \mathbf{u} \tag{4.10}$$

$$\mathbf{u} \cdot (\mathbf{v} \times \mathbf{w}) = \mathbf{w} \cdot (\mathbf{u} \times \mathbf{v}) = \mathbf{v} \cdot (\mathbf{w} \times \mathbf{u}) \tag{4.11}$$

> In order to remember (4.11) correctly, notice that the *order* of the vectors is always the same: when you start at $\mathbf{u}$ and read from left to right (looping around to the beginning when you reach the end), it's always $\mathbf{u}, \mathbf{v}, \mathbf{w}$. Swapping the order of the symbols results in a negative sign.

Proof. Equation (4.3) is a consequence of equation (4.2), since $\|\mathbf{n}\| = 1$, and equations (4.4) and (4.5) are true because $\mathbf{n}$ is orthogonal to both $\mathbf{u}$ and $\mathbf{v}$.

To understand why equation (4.6) is true, consider the vectors in Figure 4.4. The right-hand rule tells you that the vector $\mathbf{u} \times \mathbf{v}$ points out of the page, but when you lay your right hand along the vector $\mathbf{v}$ and curl your fingers toward $\mathbf{u}$, you see that $\mathbf{v} \times \mathbf{u}$ points *into* the page. The vectors $\mathbf{u} \times \mathbf{v}$ and $\mathbf{v} \times \mathbf{u}$ have opposite directions but the same magnitude, $\|\mathbf{u}\| \, \|\mathbf{v}\| \sin\theta$, so they're opposites.

Note that in the case when $\mathbf{v} = \mathbf{u}$, equation (4.6) becomes $\mathbf{u} \times \mathbf{u} = -(\mathbf{u} \times \mathbf{u})$. Only the zero vector is its own opposite, so we conclude that $\mathbf{u} \times \mathbf{u} = \mathbf{0}$. More generally, when the angle between the vectors $\mathbf{u}$ and $\mathbf{v}$ is either 0 or π radians we see that $\|\mathbf{u} \times \mathbf{v}\| = \|\mathbf{u}\| \, \|\mathbf{v}\| \sin\theta = 0$. For this reason, $\mathbf{u} \times \mathbf{v} = \mathbf{0}$ whenever $\mathbf{v}$ is a scaled version of $\mathbf{u}$, which is equation (4.7).

> This is very different than the arithmetic of scalars, where $u \times u = 0$ only when $u = 0$.

Toward establishing equation (4.8), note that $\mathbf{u}$ and $a\mathbf{u}$ point in the same direction when $a > 0$, so the right-hand rule tells us that $\mathbf{u} \times \mathbf{v}$ and $(a\mathbf{u}) \times \mathbf{v}$ have the same direction. Further,

$$\|(a\mathbf{u}) \times \mathbf{v}\| = \|a\mathbf{u}\| \, \|\mathbf{v}\| \sin\theta = a\|\mathbf{u}\| \, \|\mathbf{v}\| \sin\theta = a\|\mathbf{u} \times \mathbf{v}\| = \|a(\mathbf{u} \times \mathbf{v})\|.$$

Figure 4.4: The vector $\mathbf{u} \times \mathbf{v}$ points out of the page (toward you), but the vector $\mathbf{v} \times \mathbf{u}$ points into the page.

Since $(a\mathbf{u}) \times \mathbf{v}$ has the same direction and magnitude as $a(\mathbf{u} \times \mathbf{v})$, they are equal. In the exercise set you'll show that they are also equal when $a \leq 0$. Similarly, the vectors $\mathbf{u} \times (b\mathbf{v})$ and $b(\mathbf{u} \times \mathbf{v})$ are the same. Equation (4.8) combines these facts.

Equations (4.9) and (4.10) are reminiscent of real-number arithmetic, but because the cross product is anticommutative, the order in which we write the vectors is important—note that $\mathbf{u}$ is either *always* on the left or *always* on the right in an equation. The proof that the cross product is distributive is not difficult, but it requires an elementary understanding of planes in 3-space (which we'll discuss in Section 11.5), so we've placed it in the End Notes for this chapter. Also, we postpone the proof of equation (4.11) until Example 4.12.   ∎

❖ Component Formula for Calculating the Cross Product

The properties discussed above lead to a quick method of calculating cross products. Suppose $\mathbf{u} = \langle u_1, u_2, u_3 \rangle$ and $\mathbf{v} = \langle v_1, v_2, v_3 \rangle$. Then

$$\mathbf{u} \times \mathbf{v} = \mathbf{u} \times (v_1\mathbf{i} + v_2\mathbf{j} + v_3\mathbf{k}) = (\mathbf{u} \times v_1\mathbf{i}) + (\mathbf{u} \times v_2\mathbf{j}) + (\mathbf{u} \times v_3\mathbf{k})$$

$$= (u_1\mathbf{i} + u_2\mathbf{j} + u_3\mathbf{k}) \times v_1\mathbf{i} + (u_1\mathbf{i} + u_2\mathbf{j} + u_3\mathbf{k}) \times v_2\mathbf{j} + (u_1\mathbf{i} + u_2\mathbf{j} + u_3\mathbf{k}) \times v_3\mathbf{k}.$$

Equation (4.10) allows us to distribute from the right, so when we use equation (4.8) to move the scalars in front of the vector products, we see

$$(u_1\mathbf{i} + u_2\mathbf{j} + u_3\mathbf{k}) \times v_1\mathbf{i} = u_1v_1(\mathbf{i} \times \mathbf{i}) + u_2v_1(\mathbf{j} \times \mathbf{i}) + u_3v_1(\mathbf{k} \times \mathbf{i})$$
$$= u_1v_1\mathbf{0} - u_2v_1\mathbf{k} + u_3v_1\mathbf{j}.$$

Similarly,

$$(u_1\mathbf{i} + u_2\mathbf{j} + u_3\mathbf{k}) \times v_2\mathbf{j} = u_1v_2\mathbf{k} - u_3v_2\mathbf{i}, \text{ and}$$
$$(u_1\mathbf{i} + u_2\mathbf{j} + u_3\mathbf{k}) \times v_3\mathbf{k} = u_2v_3\mathbf{i} - u_1v_3\mathbf{j}.$$

Adding these together, we have

$$\mathbf{u} \times \mathbf{v} = (u_2v_3 - u_3v_2)\mathbf{i} + (u_3v_1 - u_1v_3)\mathbf{j} + (u_1v_2 - u_2v_1)\mathbf{k} \qquad (4.12)$$

▷ Determinant formula for the cross product

Many people find the formula in equation (4.12) difficult to remember, but a mnemonic has been developed using a 3×3 matrix. When $\mathbf{u} = \langle u_1, u_2, u_3 \rangle$ and $\mathbf{v} = \langle v_1, v_2, v_3 \rangle$, the cross product of $\mathbf{u}$ and $\mathbf{v}$ is

$$\mathbf{u} \times \mathbf{v} = \begin{vmatrix} \mathbf{i} & \mathbf{j} & \mathbf{k} \\ u_1 & u_2 & u_3 \\ v_1 & v_2 & v_3 \end{vmatrix} \overset{\text{def}}{=} \begin{vmatrix} u_2 & u_3 \\ v_2 & v_3 \end{vmatrix} \mathbf{i} - \begin{vmatrix} u_1 & u_3 \\ v_1 & v_3 \end{vmatrix} \mathbf{j} + \begin{vmatrix} u_1 & u_2 \\ v_1 & v_2 \end{vmatrix} \mathbf{k} \quad (4.13)$$

where the notation

$$\begin{vmatrix} a & b \\ c & d \end{vmatrix} \text{ means } ad - bc,$$

which is called the ***determinant*** of the matrix $\begin{bmatrix} a & b \\ c & d \end{bmatrix}$.

> Note that each term on the right-hand side of equation (4.13) includes all three colors.
>
> The matrix
> $$\begin{bmatrix} u_2 & u_3 \\ v_2 & v_3 \end{bmatrix}$$
> comes from omitting the column and row of the 3×3 matrix that contains $\mathbf{i}$. Similarly, the matrix
> $$\begin{bmatrix} u_1 & u_3 \\ v_1 & v_3 \end{bmatrix}$$
> comes from omitting the column and row of the 3×3 matrix that contains $\mathbf{j}$, and the matrix
> $$\begin{bmatrix} u_1 & u_2 \\ v_1 & v_2 \end{bmatrix}$$
> comes from omitting the column and row of the 3×3 matrix that contains $\mathbf{k}$.

Use the determinant to find the cross product

Example 4.3. Suppose $\mathbf{u} = \langle 4, 8, 5 \rangle$ and $\mathbf{v} = \langle 3, 1, 2 \rangle$. (a) Calculate $\mathbf{u} \times \mathbf{v}$, and (b) verify that your answer from part (a) is orthogonal to both $\mathbf{u}$ and $\mathbf{v}$.

Solution: (a) Equation (4.13) tells us that

$$\mathbf{u} \times \mathbf{v} = \begin{vmatrix} \mathbf{i} & \mathbf{j} & \mathbf{k} \\ 4 & 8 & 5 \\ 3 & 1 & 2 \end{vmatrix} = \begin{vmatrix} 8 & 5 \\ 1 & 2 \end{vmatrix} \mathbf{i} - \begin{vmatrix} 4 & 5 \\ 3 & 2 \end{vmatrix} \mathbf{j} + \begin{vmatrix} 4 & 8 \\ 3 & 1 \end{vmatrix} \mathbf{k}. \qquad (4.14)$$

The first of these 2×2 determinants is $\begin{vmatrix} 8 & 5 \\ 1 & 2 \end{vmatrix} = (8)(2) - (5)(1) = 11$. Similarly,

$$\begin{vmatrix} 4 & 5 \\ 3 & 2 \end{vmatrix} = -7 \text{ and } \begin{vmatrix} 4 & 8 \\ 3 & 1 \end{vmatrix} = -20.$$

Substituting those numbers into equation (4.14) gives us

$$\mathbf{u} \times \mathbf{v} = (11)\mathbf{i} - (-7)\mathbf{j} + (-20)\mathbf{k} = \langle 11, 7, -20 \rangle.$$

(b) To verify that $\mathbf{u} \times \mathbf{v}$ is orthogonal to both $\mathbf{u}$ and $\mathbf{v}$ we calculate the dot products: $\langle 11, 7, -20 \rangle \cdot \langle 4, 8, 5 \rangle = 0$ and $\langle 11, 7, -20 \rangle \cdot \langle 3, 1, 2 \rangle = 0$. ∎

Use the determinant to find the cross product

Example 4.4. Suppose $\mathbf{u} = \langle 2, 1, 4 \rangle$ and $\mathbf{v} = \langle 3, -2, -5 \rangle$. (a) Use the determinant to find $\mathbf{u} \times \mathbf{v}$, and (b) verify that your answer from part (a) is orthogonal to both $\mathbf{u}$ and $\mathbf{v}$.

Answer: (a) $\mathbf{u} \times \mathbf{v} = \langle 3, 22, -7 \rangle$, (b) see on-line solution. ∎

Solution On-line

▷ An alternative method for calculating the cross product

Another method for calculating the cross product involves the action of a matrix on a vector, which is discussed in Appendix F. Specifically, when $\mathbf{u} = \langle x, y, z \rangle$ and $\mathbf{v} = \langle a, b, c \rangle$,

$$\mathbf{u} \times \mathbf{v} = \begin{bmatrix} 0 & -z & y \\ z & 0 & -x \\ -y & x & 0 \end{bmatrix} \begin{bmatrix} a \\ b \\ c \end{bmatrix}. \tag{4.15}$$

Notice that the numbers in the matrix "reflect to their opposites" across the diagonal of zeros. Such a matrix is said to be **skew symmetric.**

Using matrix action to find the cross product

Example 4.5. Suppose $\mathbf{u} = \langle 4, 8, 5 \rangle$ and $\mathbf{v} = \langle 3, 1, 2 \rangle$. Use equation (4.15) to calculate $\mathbf{u} \times \mathbf{v}$.

Solution: The first step is to build a skew-symmetric matrix from $\mathbf{u} = \langle 4, 8, 5 \rangle$. According to equation (4.15) this matrix is

$$U = \begin{bmatrix} 0 & -5 & 8 \\ 5 & 0 & -4 \\ -8 & 4 & 0 \end{bmatrix}.$$

Then using the technique discussed in Appendix F, we calculate $\mathbf{u} \times \mathbf{v}$ to be

$$U\mathbf{v} \overset{\text{def}}{=} \begin{bmatrix} \langle 0, -5, 8 \rangle \cdot \mathbf{v} \\ \langle 5, 0, -4 \rangle \cdot \mathbf{v} \\ \langle -8, 4, 0 \rangle \cdot \mathbf{v} \end{bmatrix} = \begin{bmatrix} 11 \\ 7 \\ -20 \end{bmatrix},$$

which is exactly the vector we calculated in Example 4.3.   ∎

Using the matrix-action method to find the cross product

Example 4.6. Suppose $\mathbf{u} = \langle 2, 1, 4 \rangle$ and $\mathbf{v} = \langle 3, -2, -5 \rangle$. Use equation (4.15) to calculate $\mathbf{u} \times \mathbf{v}$.

Answer: $\mathbf{u} \times \mathbf{v} = \langle 3, 2, -7 \rangle$.   ∎

Solution On-line

✤ Geometric Facts About the Cross Product

Suppose $\mathbf{u}$ and $\mathbf{v}$ are displacement vectors, and length is measured in meters. Then $\|\mathbf{u}\|$ and $\|\mathbf{v}\|$ have units of meters, so $\|\mathbf{u} \times \mathbf{v}\| = \|\mathbf{u}\| \, \|\mathbf{v}\| \sin\theta$ has units of m², which leads us to think that $\|\mathbf{u} \times \mathbf{v}\|$ is an area. That's correct, and it's easy to see when you draw the vectors $\mathbf{u}$ and $\mathbf{v}$ with their tails at the same point (see Figure 4.5). The parallelogram they define has a length of $\ell = \|\mathbf{v}\|$ and a width of $w = \|\mathbf{u}\| \sin\theta$, so its area is $\ell w = \|\mathbf{v}\| \, \|\mathbf{u}\| \sin\theta = \|\mathbf{u} \times \mathbf{v}\|$. Note that the area of the parallelogram is 0 when $\mathbf{u}$ is a multiple of $\mathbf{v}$, because the shape has no height. This agrees with the formula since $\sin 0$ and $\sin \pi$ are both 0.

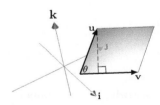

Figure 4.5: The area of a parallelogram defined by two vectors is the product of "width" and "length."

> **Cross Product and Area:** The parallelogram determined by $\mathbf{u}$ and $\mathbf{v}$ has an area of $\|\mathbf{u} \times \mathbf{v}\|$.

Area of a parallelogram

Example 4.7. Calculate the area of the parallelogram determined by $\mathbf{u} = \langle 4, 8, 5 \rangle$ and $\mathbf{v} = \langle 3, 1, 2 \rangle$.

Solution: In Example 4.3 (and 4.5) we showed that $\mathbf{u} \times \mathbf{v} = \langle 11, 7, -20 \rangle$, which has a magnitude of $\sqrt{570}$, so the area of the parallelogram is $\sqrt{570}$ square units.   ∎

Area of a triangle

Example 4.8. Suppose length is measured in cm. Sketch the triangle defined by the origin and the points at the heads of the position vectors $\mathbf{u} = \langle 1, 1, 0 \rangle$ and $\mathbf{v} = \langle 2, -3, 0 \rangle$, and use the cross product to determine its area.

Answer: Area $= 2.5$ cm^2.   ∎

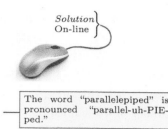

Just as a parallelogram is determined by two vectors, its three-dimensional analog, called a **parallelepiped**, is determined by three vectors (see Figure 4.6). Suppose these vectors are $\mathbf{u}, \mathbf{v}$ and $\mathbf{w}$. If we think of $\mathbf{u}$ and $\mathbf{v}$ as defining a parallelogram-shaped base, we can write the volume of the parallelepiped as

Volume = (area of the parallelogram base) (height) = $\|\mathbf{u} \times \mathbf{v}\|$(height).

The word "parallelepiped" is pronounced "parallel-uh-PIE-ped."

The height of a parallelepiped is measured in the direction orthogonal to its base (see Figure 4.6), which is the direction of $\mathbf{u} \times \mathbf{v}$. So to finish our formula we need only calculate how far $\mathbf{w}$ extends in the direction of $\mathbf{u} \times \mathbf{v}$. We do that with the scalar projection of $\mathbf{w}$ onto $\mathbf{u} \times \mathbf{v}$. That is, the height of the parallelepiped is

$$\text{height} = \left| \mathbf{w} \cdot \frac{\mathbf{u} \times \mathbf{v}}{\|\mathbf{u} \times \mathbf{v}\|} \right|.$$

In general, we'll need to use the absolute value of the scalar projection, as in equation (4.16), since the number might be negative.

Substituting this into our formula for volume, we see

$$\text{Volume} = \underbrace{\|\mathbf{u} \times \mathbf{v}\|}_{\text{Area of the base}} \underbrace{\left| \mathbf{w} \cdot \frac{\mathbf{u} \times \mathbf{v}}{\|\mathbf{u} \times \mathbf{v}\|} \right|}_{\text{Height}} = |\mathbf{w} \cdot (\mathbf{u} \times \mathbf{v})|. \tag{4.16}$$

The number $\mathbf{w} \cdot (\mathbf{u} \times \mathbf{v})$, which appears on the right-hand side of equation (4.16), is called the **scalar triple product** of the vectors $\mathbf{u}, \mathbf{v}$, and $\mathbf{w}$, and its magnitude is the volume of the parallelepiped they define. Using this language, we can state our result as follows:

> **Cross Product and Volume:** The volume of the parallelepiped determined by $\mathbf{u}, \mathbf{v}$ and $\mathbf{w}$ is the magnitude of their scalar triple product: $V = |\mathbf{w} \cdot (\mathbf{u} \times \mathbf{v})|$.

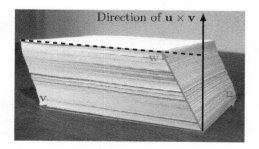
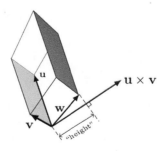

Figure 4.6: (left) A parallelepiped with a rectangular base; (right) a parallelepiped with a parallelogram as its base; (both) the height of a parallelepiped is measured in the direction orthogonal to the base

Volume of a parallelepiped

Example 4.9. Suppose length is measured in cm. Calculate the volume of the parallelepiped defined by $\mathbf{u} = \langle 7, 0, 2 \rangle$, $\mathbf{v} = \langle 1, 2, 1 \rangle$, and $\mathbf{w} = \langle 1, 1, 3 \rangle$.

Solution: In order to use the scalar triple product, we begin by calculating $\mathbf{u} \times \mathbf{v} = \langle -4, -5, 14 \rangle$. Then according to (4.16), the volume of this parallelepiped is

$$|\mathbf{w} \cdot (\mathbf{u} \times \mathbf{v})| = |\langle 1, 1, 3 \rangle \cdot \langle -4, -5, 14 \rangle| = |-4 - 5 + 42| = 33 \text{ cm}^3. \quad \blacksquare$$

Volume of a parallelepiped

Example 4.10. Suppose length is measured in inches. Calculate the volume of the parallelepiped defined by $\langle 2, 1, 5 \rangle$, $\langle -2, 3, 3 \rangle$, and $\langle 1, -1, -2 \rangle$ using (a) $\mathbf{w} = \langle 2, 1, 5 \rangle$, (b) $\mathbf{w} = \langle -2, 3, 3, \rangle$, and (c) $\mathbf{w} = \langle 1, -1, -2 \rangle$.

Answer: (a) 12 in^3, (b) 12 in^3, (c) 12 in^3. $\quad \blacksquare$

Solution On-line

Volume of a parallelepiped

Example 4.11. Determine the volume of the parallelepiped defined by $\mathbf{u} = \langle 7, 0, 2 \rangle$, $\mathbf{v} = \langle 1, 2, 1 \rangle$, and $\mathbf{w} = \langle 8, 2, 3 \rangle$.

Solution: The vectors $\mathbf{u}$ and $\mathbf{v}$ are the same as in Example 4.9, so when we use the scalar triple product to calculate the volume of the parallelepiped, we see $|\mathbf{w} \cdot (\mathbf{u} \times \mathbf{v})| = |\langle 8, 2, 3 \rangle \cdot \langle -4, -5, 14 \rangle| = |-32 - 10 + 42| = 0. \quad \blacksquare$

The parallelepiped in Example 4.11 has a volume of 0 because $\mathbf{u}, \mathbf{v}$ and $\mathbf{w}$ all lie in the same plane (we say they are ***coplanar***), so the height of their "parallelepiped" is zero.

Establishing equation (4.11) in the list of Properties of the Cross Product

Example 4.12. Use the connection between the scalar triple product and volume to establish equation (4.11).

Solution: Equation (4.11) is a statement about the scalar triple product of $\mathbf{u}$, $\mathbf{v}$ and $\mathbf{w}$, which define a parallelepiped. Fundamentally, the equation is true because the volume of that parallelepiped is the same, regardless of which side we choose to call its base—i.e., whether we say that the base of the parallelepiped is the parallelogram defined by $\mathbf{u}$ and $\mathbf{v}$, or by $\mathbf{u}$ and $\mathbf{w}$, or by $\mathbf{v}$ and $\mathbf{w}$. By virtue of the right-hand rule, if the scalar projection of $\mathbf{v} \times \mathbf{w}$ onto $\mathbf{u}$ is positive, so is that of $\mathbf{w} \times \mathbf{u}$ onto $\mathbf{v}$, and that of $\mathbf{u} \times \mathbf{v}$ onto $\mathbf{w}$, so they are all equal. The other scalar triple products have the same magnitude, but the opposite sign. $\quad \blacksquare$

> The numbers
> $$\mathbf{u} \cdot (\mathbf{v} \times \mathbf{w})$$
> $$\mathbf{v} \cdot (\mathbf{w} \times \mathbf{u})$$
> $$\mathbf{w} \cdot (\mathbf{u} \times \mathbf{v})$$
> all have the same sign, as do
> $$\mathbf{v} \cdot (\mathbf{u} \times \mathbf{w})$$
> $$\mathbf{u} \cdot (\mathbf{w} \times \mathbf{v})$$
> $$\mathbf{w} \cdot (\mathbf{v} \times \mathbf{u}).$$

▷ Determinants and the scalar triple product

When $\mathbf{u} = \langle u_1, u_2, u_3 \rangle$ and $\mathbf{v} = \langle v_1, v_2, v_3 \rangle$, we calculate $\mathbf{u} \times \mathbf{v}$ as

$$\begin{vmatrix} \mathbf{i} & \mathbf{j} & \mathbf{k} \\ u_1 & u_2 & u_3 \\ v_1 & v_2 & v_3 \end{vmatrix} \overset{\text{def}}{=} \begin{vmatrix} u_2 & u_3 \\ v_2 & v_3 \end{vmatrix} \mathbf{i} - \begin{vmatrix} u_1 & u_3 \\ v_1 & v_3 \end{vmatrix} \mathbf{j} + \begin{vmatrix} u_1 & u_2 \\ v_1 & v_2 \end{vmatrix} \mathbf{k}. \quad (4.17)$$

So the scalar triple product of $\mathbf{u}, \mathbf{v}$ and $\mathbf{w} = \langle w_1, w_2, w_3 \rangle$ is

$$\mathbf{w} \cdot (\mathbf{u} \times \mathbf{v}) = \begin{vmatrix} u_2 & u_3 \\ v_2 & v_3 \end{vmatrix} \mathbf{w} \cdot \mathbf{i} - \begin{vmatrix} u_1 & u_3 \\ v_1 & v_3 \end{vmatrix} \mathbf{w} \cdot \mathbf{j} + \begin{vmatrix} u_1 & u_2 \\ v_1 & v_2 \end{vmatrix} \mathbf{w} \cdot \mathbf{k}$$

$$= \begin{vmatrix} u_2 & u_3 \\ v_2 & v_3 \end{vmatrix} w_1 - \begin{vmatrix} u_1 & u_3 \\ v_1 & v_3 \end{vmatrix} w_2 + \begin{vmatrix} u_1 & u_2 \\ v_1 & v_2 \end{vmatrix} w_3. \quad (4.18)$$

Based on the similarity between the right-hand side of equations (4.18) and (4.17), we define

$$\begin{vmatrix} w_1 & w_2 & w_3 \\ u_1 & u_2 & u_3 \\ v_1 & v_2 & v_3 \end{vmatrix} \stackrel{\text{def}}{=} \begin{vmatrix} u_2 & u_3 \\ v_2 & v_3 \end{vmatrix} w_1 - \begin{vmatrix} u_1 & u_3 \\ v_1 & v_3 \end{vmatrix} w_2 + \begin{vmatrix} u_1 & u_2 \\ v_1 & v_2 \end{vmatrix} w_3.$$

> The numbers w_1, w_2 and w_3 are often written on the left of the 2×2 determinants instead of the right.

We have referred to this number as the scalar triple product of the vectors $\mathbf{u}, \mathbf{v}$ and $\mathbf{w}$. It is also called the ***determinant*** of the 3×3 matrix they constitute.

Using the determinant to calculate the scalar triple product

Example 4.13. Use the determinant to calculate the volume of the parallelepiped defined by $\mathbf{u} = \langle 4, 8, 5 \rangle$, $\mathbf{v} = \langle 3, 1, 2 \rangle$, and $\mathbf{w} = \langle 2, 1, 4 \rangle$.

Solution: In this case, we have

$$\mathbf{w} \cdot (\mathbf{u} \times \mathbf{v}) = \begin{vmatrix} 2 & 1 & 4 \\ 4 & 8 & 5 \\ 3 & 1 & 2 \end{vmatrix} = 2 \underbrace{\begin{vmatrix} 8 & 1 \\ 5 & 2 \end{vmatrix}}_{=11} - 4 \underbrace{\begin{vmatrix} 1 & 1 \\ 4 & 2 \end{vmatrix}}_{=-2} + 3 \underbrace{\begin{vmatrix} 1 & 8 \\ 4 & 5 \end{vmatrix}}_{=-27} = -51,$$

so the volume is $|\mathbf{w} \cdot (\mathbf{u} \times \mathbf{v})| = 51$ cubic units. ∎

Calculating the scalar triple product

Example 4.14. Use the determinant to calculate the volume of the parallelepiped defined by $\langle -1, 2, 4 \rangle$, $\langle 3, 2, 1 \rangle$, and $\langle 1, 3, 2 \rangle$.

Answer: 17 cubic units. ∎

Solution On-line

✣ Applications of the Cross Product

We close this section with some applications in which the cross product is used.

▷ Computer graphics

Modern computer games are often called upon to draw objects in a virtual 3-D environment. That's a computationally intensive task, but we can accelerate the process by drawing only the parts of a surface that the user can see, as suggested by Figure 4.7.

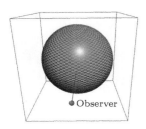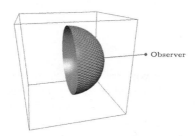

Figure 4.7: (both) The bounding box has been included to add perspective; (left) a sphere drawn by a computer, as seen by a user (observer); (right) the same scenario as seen from the virtual "side." The user cannot tell that only half of the sphere was drawn by the computer.

Computers often draw surfaces as a collection of many small, triangular facets, and the program that's rendering the surface has to decide whether each facet in a given scene is observable by the user. One method for making that decision

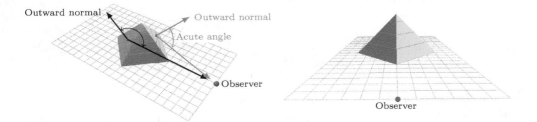

Figure 4.8: (left) The computer knows that the observer can see the yellow face of the pyramid because its normal vector makes an acute angle with the displacement vector that points from the yellow face toward the observer; the red face is not visible (and so should not be rendered) because its normal vector makes an obtuse angle with the displacement vector that points from the red face toward the observer; (right) the pyramid as seen on screen by the observer.

employs the cross product. Specifically, suppose $\mathbf{u}$ and $\mathbf{v}$ extend between vertices of a triangle, and $\mathbf{u} \times \mathbf{v}$ points out of the object (in this context we refer to $\mathbf{u} \times \mathbf{v}$ as an **outward normal vector** vector). If the outward normal vector points toward the observer, the facet is visible and should be drawn by the computer (see Figure 4.8). This means that after calculating $\mathbf{u} \times \mathbf{v}$ we have to detect its orientation, and as you'll see in Example 4.15, that's done by calculating the dot product of $\mathbf{u} \times \mathbf{v}$ with a displacement vector that extends from the facet to the observer's vantage point.

> The word *normal* means "orthogonal to a surface" when used in this way. It does not imply anything about the length of the vector (except that the vector is not $\mathbf{0}$).

Computer graphics: efficient rendering of surfaces in virtual 3-space

Example 4.15. Suppose a triangular facet on the surface of an object has one corner at the point $(-30, 0, 2)$. The vectors $\mathbf{u} = \langle 0, -1, 0.5 \rangle$ and $\mathbf{v} = \langle 1, 0, -0.8 \rangle$ lie along the edges of the facet, and $\mathbf{u} \times \mathbf{v}$ points out of the object. Determine whether an observer at the origin can see the facet.

Solution: Because the corner of the triangle has a position vector of $\mathbf{r} = \langle -30, 0, 2 \rangle$, the displacement vector that reaches from the corner to the observer is $\mathbf{w} = -\mathbf{r} = \langle 30, 0, -2 \rangle$. The outward direction of this facet is give by

$$\mathbf{u} \times \mathbf{v} = \begin{vmatrix} -1 & 0.5 \\ 0 & -0.8 \end{vmatrix} \mathbf{i} - \begin{vmatrix} 0 & 0.5 \\ 1 & -0.8 \end{vmatrix} \mathbf{j} + \begin{vmatrix} 0 & -1 \\ 1 & 0 \end{vmatrix} \mathbf{k} = \langle 0.8, 0.5, 1 \rangle.$$

Since the dot product of these vectors is $\mathbf{w} \cdot (\mathbf{u} \times \mathbf{v}) = 22 > 0$, the angle between them is acute. That means the facet can be seen by the observer at the origin, and should be drawn by the computer. ∎

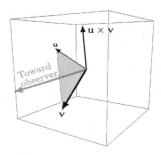

Figure 4.9: The cross product calculates a vector orthogonal to a facet. The dot product determines whether the facet is viewable by or hidden from the observer.

▷ Torque

Think about closing a laptop computer. The farther you grab the screen from the hinges, the easier it is to close the machine. in action: when trying to rotate an object about an axis (e.g., rotating the screen about the axis where it connects to the keyboard) the effectiveness of a given force is proportional to both (1) the magnitude of the force, and (2) the distance between the axis of rotation and the point at which the force is applied.

Another example of the lever principle is the application of a wrench to a bolt. As in Figure 4.10, we'll denote by $\mathbf{r}$ the displacement vector that extends from the center of the bolt to the portion of the wrench that you're grasping, and $\mathbf{F}$ will denote the force that you apply. Only some of $\mathbf{F}$ is responsible for turning the bolt. To be more specific, let's write $\mathbf{F} = \mathbf{F}_r + \mathbf{F}_t$, where $\mathbf{F}_r$ is a multiple of $\mathbf{r}$ and $\mathbf{F}_t$ is tangent to the circle of radius $\|\mathbf{r}\|$ about the bolt. Then the portion of your

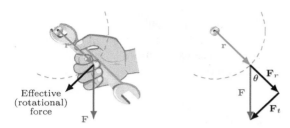

Figure 4.10: When applying a wrench to a bolt, only some of the force affects a turn

force that actually turns the bolt is $\mathbf{F}_t$. The strength of that force is $\|\mathbf{F}_t\|$, and it's applied $\|\mathbf{r}\|$ units away from the axis of rotation, so the lever principle tells us that the magnitude of the rotational force is

$$\|\mathbf{r}\|\,\|\mathbf{F}_t\| = \|\mathbf{r}\|\,\|\mathbf{F}\| \sin\theta = \|\mathbf{r} \times \mathbf{F}\|.$$

We call $\mathbf{r} \times \mathbf{F}$ the **torque vector** or **vector moment**. Its direction tells us the axis about which the bolt is turning, and its magnitude—often called **torque**, or the **scalar moment**—measures the effective force that turns the bolt. The units of torque reflect the fact that it depends on both the strength of the force and the distance at which that force is applied.

> You can think of torque as a direct analog of the *force* that you know from Newton's Second Law of Motion. Just as force causes a change in momentum, torque causes a change in something called *angular momentum*, which is discussed in the End Notes.

$$\|\mathbf{r} \times \mathbf{F}\| = \underbrace{\|\mathbf{r}\|}_{\text{meters}}\ \underbrace{\overbrace{\|\mathbf{F}\|}^{\text{newtons}}\ \sin\theta}_{\text{dimensionless}}$$

We say that torque has units of "newton-meters."

Calculating torque

Example 4.16. A rigid lever stretches from the origin to the point $(0.1, 0.1, 0.2)$, at which a force of $\mathbf{F} = \langle -1, 1, 7 \rangle$ newtons is applied. If distance is measure in meters, find the scalar moment, and the axis about which $\mathbf{F}$ induces rotation.

Solution: This force induces rotation about the axis whose direction is $\mathbf{r} \times \mathbf{F} = \langle 0.5, -0.9, 0.2 \rangle$, and the scalar moment is $\|\mathbf{r} \times \mathbf{F}\| \approx 1.0489$ newton-meters.   ∎

Calculating torque

Example 4.17. Suppose distance is measure in meters. A rigid lever stretches from the origin to the point $(0.1, 0.2, 0.4)$, at which a force of $\mathbf{F} = \langle 2, 3, 2 \rangle$ newtons is applied. Find (a) the scalar moment of torque, and (b) the axis about which that force induces rotation.

Answer: (a) $\approx \sqrt{1.005}$ N-m, and (b) the line through the origin that extends in the direction of $\langle -8, 6, -1 \rangle$.   ∎

Solution
On-line

▷ Magnetic fields, charge, and force

Suppose $\mathbf{B}$ is a vector that points in the direction of a magnetic field, and $\|\mathbf{B}\|$ is the strength of the magnetic field. When a particle with a charge of q coulombs and a velocity of $\mathbf{v}$ meters per second passes through the magnetic field, it experiences a force called the *Lorentz force*, which is

$$\mathbf{F} = q(\mathbf{v} \times \mathbf{B}). \tag{4.19}$$

> The strength of a magnetic field is measured in *teslas*.
>
> Equation (4.19) includes both the direction *and* magnitude of the force that's experienced by the ion due to the magnetic field.

Calculating the force on an ion due to a magnetic field

Example 4.18. Suppose a proton with velocity is $\mathbf{v} = \langle 1, -2, 4 \rangle$ travels through a magnetic field described by $\mathbf{B} = \langle 1, 2, 7 \rangle$. Determine the Lorentz force experienced by the proton. (The electric charge on a proton is 1.6×10^{-19} coulombs.)

Solution: According to equation (4.19) the Lorentz force is

$$\mathbf{F} = (1.6 \times 10^{-19})(\mathbf{v} \times \mathbf{B}) = (1.6 \times 10^{-19})\langle -22, -3, 4 \rangle,$$

which has a magnitude of $\|\mathbf{F}\| = (1.6 \times 10^{-19})\sqrt{509} \approx 3.6 \times 10^{-18}$ newtons.　■

You should know

- the terms *cross product, vector product, right-hand rule, anticommutative, determinant of a matrix, skew symmetric matrix, parallelepiped, coplanar, scalar triple product, torque vector, vector moment, scalar moment,* and *torque;*
- that $\mathbf{u} \times \mathbf{v}$ is orthogonal to both $\mathbf{u}$ and $\mathbf{v}$, and its direction is determined by the right hand rule;
- the algebraic properties of the cross product.

You should be able to

- find the cross product of two vectors;
- use the cross product to calculate the area of the parallelogram defined by two vectors, and the volume of the parallelepiped defined by three;
- use the scalar triple product to determine when three vectors are coplanar;
- calculate torque, and the force experienced by a charge in a magnetic field.

❖ 11.4 Skill Exercises

In #1–4 calculate $\|\mathbf{u} \times \mathbf{v}\|$ and determine the direction of $\mathbf{u} \times \mathbf{v}$.

1.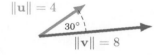

2.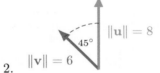

3.

4.

In #5–10 calculate the cross product.

5. $\langle 3, 0, 2 \rangle \times \langle 2, 1, 4 \rangle$

6. $\langle 1, 1, 0 \rangle \times \langle 4, -1, -2 \rangle$

7. $\langle 4, 8, 10 \rangle \times \langle 6, 12, 15 \rangle$

8. $\langle 81, -9, -27 \rangle \times \langle -54, 6, 18 \rangle$

9. $\langle 2, 7, 1 \rangle \times \langle -3, 1, 1 \rangle$

10. $\langle 3, 1, 1 \rangle \times \langle 0, 0, 0 \rangle$

In #11–14 calculate the scalar triple product $\mathbf{w} \cdot (\mathbf{u} \times \mathbf{v})$.

11. $\mathbf{u} = \mathbf{i}, \mathbf{v} = \mathbf{j}, \mathbf{w} = \mathbf{k}$

12. $\mathbf{u} = \mathbf{j}, \mathbf{v} = \mathbf{i}, \mathbf{w} = \mathbf{k}$

13. $\mathbf{u} = \langle 1, 3, 1 \rangle, \mathbf{v} = \langle 2, 2, 1 \rangle, \mathbf{w} = \langle -1, -3, 4 \rangle$

14. $\mathbf{u} = \langle -2, 1, 0 \rangle, \mathbf{v} = \langle 2, 1, 0 \rangle, \mathbf{w} = \langle 0, -3, -1 \rangle$

15. Determine which of the following equations are correct, and change the others so that they are correct: (a) $\mathbf{i} \times \mathbf{j} = \mathbf{k}$, (b) $\mathbf{i} \times \mathbf{k} = \mathbf{j}$, (c) $\mathbf{j} \times \mathbf{i} = \mathbf{k}$.

16. Determine which of the following equations are correct, and change the others so that they are correct: (a) $\mathbf{j} \times \mathbf{k} = \mathbf{i}$, (b) $\mathbf{k} \times \mathbf{i} = \mathbf{j}$ (c) $\mathbf{k} \times \mathbf{j} = \mathbf{i}$.

17. Find all vectors of the form $\mathbf{u} = \langle x, y, 0 \rangle$ so that $\mathbf{i} \times \mathbf{u} = \mathbf{k}$.

18. Find all vectors of the form $\mathbf{u} = \langle x, y, 0 \rangle$ so that $\mathbf{u} \times \mathbf{j} = 10\mathbf{k}$.

❖ 11.4 Concept and Application Exercises

19. Use the cross product to write an equation that implies the nonzero vectors $\mathbf{u}$ and $\mathbf{v}$ are parallel.

20. Use the cross product to write an equation that says $\mathbf{u}, \mathbf{v}$, and $\mathbf{w}$ are coplanar.

21. Suppose $\mathbf{u}, \mathbf{v}$ and $\mathbf{w}$ are not coplanar. Then only one of $\mathbf{u} \cdot (\mathbf{v} \times \mathbf{w})$ and $\mathbf{u} \cdot (\mathbf{w} \times \mathbf{v})$ is a volume. Why? (Include a discussion of the geometry of the situation in your answer.)

22. Suppose a friend writes $\mathbf{u} \times \mathbf{v} = \mathbf{w} \;\Rightarrow\; \mathbf{v} = \dfrac{\mathbf{w}}{\mathbf{u}}$. In complete sentences, explain to your friend what's wrong.

23. Consider the statement, "If the sum of $|\mathbf{u} \cdot \mathbf{v}|$ and $\|\mathbf{u} \times \mathbf{v}\|$ is 0, at least one of $\mathbf{u}$ and $\mathbf{v}$ must be the zero vector." Is the statement certainly true? Is it certainly false? Explain your answer in complete sentences.

24. Consider the statement about nonzero vectors $\mathbf{u}$ and $\mathbf{v}$, "The vector $(\mathbf{u} \times \mathbf{v}) \times \mathbf{u}$ is parallel to $\mathbf{v}$." In complete sentences, explain the conditions (if any) in which the statement true.

25. Suppose $\mathbf{v} \neq \mathbf{0}$. If $\mathbf{u} \cdot \hat{\mathbf{v}} = -2$ and $\|\mathbf{u} \times \hat{\mathbf{v}}\| = 5$, determine $\|\mathbf{u}\|$.

26. Suppose all the components of the three-dimensional position vectors $\mathbf{u}$ and $\mathbf{v}$ are positive. Denote by $\mathbf{u}_{\text{ref}}$ the vector obtained by reflecting $\mathbf{u}$ over the xy-plane (so the first two components of $\mathbf{u}$ and $\mathbf{u}_{\text{refl}}$ are the same, but the third components are opposites). If we define $\mathbf{v}_{\text{ref}}$ and $(\mathbf{u} \times \mathbf{v})_{\text{ref}}$ in the same way, is it true that $\mathbf{u}_{\text{ref}} \times \mathbf{v}_{\text{ref}} = (\mathbf{u} \times \mathbf{v})_{\text{ref}}$? If so, how can you tell? If not, how are they different?

In #27–30, find the area of the parallelogram defined by the given pair of vectors.

27. $\langle 4, 0, -2 \rangle$, $\langle 1, 0, -3 \rangle$

28. $\langle -3, -5, -6 \rangle$, $\langle 1, 4, 1 \rangle$

29. $\langle 2, -2, 1 \rangle$, $\langle -1, 1, -0.5 \rangle$

30. $\left\langle \frac{1}{2}, -1, 3 \right\rangle$, $\langle 2, -4, 12 \rangle$

31. $\langle 5, 1, -2 \rangle$, $\langle 0, 4, 3 \rangle$

32. $\langle 4, 0, -5 \rangle$, $\langle -1, 3, 5 \rangle$

In #33–36, find the volume of the parallelepiped defined by the given vectors.

33. $\langle 2, 1, 1 \rangle$, $\langle 1, 1, 3 \rangle$, $\langle 4, 1, 4 \rangle$

34. $\left\langle 5/3, -2, \frac{5}{3} \right\rangle$, $\langle 1, 1, 1 \rangle$, $\langle -3, 5, 8 \rangle$

35. $\langle 5, -2, 4 \rangle$, $\langle 4, -1, 0 \rangle$, $\langle -1, 2, -3 \rangle$

36. $\langle -3, -5, 1 \rangle$, $\langle -3, 1, -4 \rangle$, $\langle 2, 4, 4 \rangle$

37. $\langle 3, 0.5, 0.3 \rangle$, $\langle 1, 5, -6 \rangle$, $\langle 3.5, 3, -2.7 \rangle$

38. $\langle 1, -2, -5 \rangle$, $\langle 2, 5, -1 \rangle$, $\langle -4, -19, -7 \rangle$

In #39–42 find the surface area of the parallelepiped defined by the given vectors.

39. $\langle 2, 1, 1 \rangle$, $\langle 1, 1, 3 \rangle$, $\langle 4, 1, 4 \rangle$

40. $\langle 5/3, -2, 5/3 \rangle$, $\langle 1, 1, 1 \rangle$, $\langle -3, 5, 8 \rangle$

41. $\langle 1, -1, 1 \rangle$, $\langle 2, -1, 1 \rangle$, $\langle 2, 0, 2 \rangle$

42. $\langle 3, 4, 0 \rangle$, $\langle -0.5, 1, 6 \rangle$, $\langle 5, 4, 2 \rangle$

In #43–46 use the scalar triple product to determine whether the given vectors are coplanar.

43. $\langle 2, 4, 8 \rangle$, $\langle -1, 3, 4 \rangle$, $\langle 4, 13, 24 \rangle$

44. $\langle -2, 1, 13 \rangle$, $\langle 4, 5, -2 \rangle$, $\langle 6, 11, 9 \rangle$

45. $\langle -1, 0, 5 \rangle$, $\langle 14, 1, -3 \rangle$, $\langle 3, 1, -6 \rangle$

46. $\langle -3, 2, 4 \rangle$, $\langle 1, 41, -2 \rangle$, $\langle 5, -8, -7 \rangle$

47. Suppose the vertices of a triangular facet on a virtual surface are $A = (22, 15, 13)$, $B = (22.1, 15.2, 12.9)$ and $C = (22.2, 14.9, 13.3)$, labeled so that $\overrightarrow{AB} \times \overrightarrow{BC}$ points outward. If the observer is at the origin, should the computer render this facet? | Game Design |

48. Suppose you throw a ball with spin. The smoke filaments in Figure 4.11 show that the spin of the ball disrupts air flow on the side that's rotating into the on-coming air. The flow is deflected on that side, and this change in momentum results in a force on the ball called the *Magnus force*, which is orthogonal to both the ball's velocity and the axis about which it's spinning. In 1987, R. Watts and R. Ferrer reported experimental evidence that the magnitude of the Magnus force is jointly proportional to the ball's rate of spin and its speed through the air, so let's write it as $\mathbf{F} = c(\boldsymbol{\omega} \times \mathbf{v})$ where c is a positive constant, $\boldsymbol{\omega}$ is the ball's angular velocity vector, and $\mathbf{v}$ is the ball's translational velocity. As a pitcher who throws the ball in the direction of $\mathbf{j}$, how would you spin the ball so that the Magnus force is in the direction of $\mathbf{k}$ (i.e., opposing gravity)? (Answer in terms of $\boldsymbol{\omega}$.)

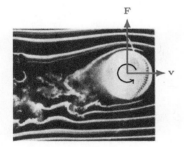

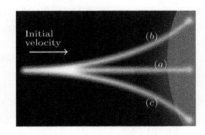

Figure 4.11: For #48. The vector $\boldsymbol{\omega}$ points out of the page, and the ball's velocity is $\mathbf{v}$.

Figure 4.12: Image for #49. An electron beam is deflected by the presence of a magnetic field.

49. Figure 4.12 shows a triple exposure of an electron beam that has been directed into a cathode ray tube (the electrons are headed to the right as they enter the tube). No magnetic field is present in exposure (a). In exposure (b), the Lorentz force experienced by the electrons points "upward" (i.e. toward the top of the page), so the beam is deflected in that direction. Similarly, the Lorentz force experienced by the electrons points "downward" in exposure (c). Use the right hand rule to determine the direction of the magnetic field in exposures (b) and (c). | Physics |

50. Suppose a charged particle is traveling through a magnetic field. Based on (4.19) and what you know of the cross product, explain why the particle will | Physics |

experience no Lorentz force if it travels in the direction of, or directly against the field ($\theta = 0$ or $\theta = \pi$).

51. An ionized particle with a charge of $q = 4.80 \times 10^{-19}$ coulombs travels in the direction of $\langle 3, 4, 0 \rangle$ at 12 meters/second. What force does it experience when it passes through the magnetic field $\mathbf{B} = \langle 2, 1, 6 \rangle$?   <u> </u> Physics

52. An ionized particle with a charge of $q = -25.6 \times 10^{-19}$ coulombs travels in the direction of $\langle -2, 1, 2 \rangle$ at 200 meters per second. What force does it experience when it passes through the magnetic field $\mathbf{B} = \langle -1, 2, -8 \rangle$?   <u> </u> Physics

53. When current passes through a wire, it produces a magnetic field that's oriented according to the right hand rule; if you were to grab the wire so that your thumb pointed in the direction of the current, your fingers would wrap around the wire in the direction of the magnetic field. For example, the vectors in Figure 4.13 point in the direction of the magnetic field that's induced by current flowing through the origin, upward, out of the page. (They are not directly related this exercise.) For the purposes of this exercise, suppose that current is coursing through a power cable from south to north.   <u> </u> Physics

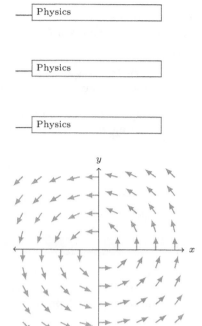

Figure 4.13: The direction of a magnetic field induced by current flowing through the origin, upward, out of the page.

    (a) If the cable is suspended *above* you, what direction is the magnetic field pointed where you are?

    (b) If the cable is buried *below* you, what direction is the magnetic field pointed where you are?

54. Figure 4.13 shows the magnetic field induced by current that's flowing through the origin, upward, out of the page. If there is another wire that carries positive charge up through the page at the point $(0.5, 0)$, use the Lorentz force law to determine the direction of the force experienced by those charges. Does the force change if the positive charges in the second wire are headed *into* the page? If so, how?

55. Suppose you want to remove the front wheel of your motorcycle. While using a wrench to remove the lug nuts, you apply a force of $\mathbf{F} = \langle 0, 0, -10 \rangle$ newtons.   <u> </u> Torque

    (a) If the displacement vector (along the length of the wrench) that connects the bolt to your hand is $\langle 0.04, 0.005, 0 \rangle$, where distance is measured in meters, what is the scalar moment of torque experienced by the bolt?

    (b) If the displacement vector (along the length of the wrench) that connects the bolt to your hand is parallel to $\langle 40, 5, 0 \rangle$, where distance is measured in meters, how far away from the bolt do you have to hold the wrench in order to exert a torque of 5.8 newton-meters.

56. A construction worker needs to loosen a bolt, so he grabs a wrench.   <u> </u> Torque

    (a) The displacement vector from the center of the bolt to the place where the worker holds the wrench is $\langle 0.05, 0.05, -0.13 \rangle$, where distance is measured in meters, and there he applies the force vector $\mathbf{F} = \langle 5.7, 4.6, 6.8 \rangle$. What is the magnitude of the force the worker applies to the wrench, and what is the scalar moment of torque experienced by the bolt?

    (b) Suppose the bolt turns about an axis parallel to $\mathbf{u} = \langle 1, -1, 0 \rangle$, and holding the wrench at the same place as in part (a), the worker imparts a force of 160 newtons to the wrench. Determine the force vector, $\mathbf{F}$, that maximizes the scalar moment of torque.

In the introductory discussion of this section, you saw that the velocity of a point on a rotating body is $\mathbf{v} = \boldsymbol{\omega} \times \mathbf{r}$, where $\boldsymbol{\omega}$ is the body's angular velocity vector and $\mathbf{r}$ is the point's position vector (taking the body's center of mass as the origin). If an object of mass m is at this point, its *angular momentum* is the vector $\mathbf{L} = \mathbf{r} \times m\mathbf{v}$. In #57 and 58 you will investigate $\mathbf{L}$.

57. Suppose an object of mass 2 kg is at the point $\mathbf{r} = \langle 2, 1, -3 \rangle$ on a body that's rotating with an angular velocity vector of $\boldsymbol{\omega} = \langle 5, 0, 4 \rangle$. Determine the object's angular momentum.

Physics

58. Suppose an object of mass m is at the point $\mathbf{r} = \langle a, b, c \rangle$ on a body that's rotating with an angular velocity vector of $\boldsymbol{\omega}$. Show that the object's angular momentum is $\mathbf{L} = I\boldsymbol{\omega}$ where I is the matrix

Physics

$$ I = \begin{bmatrix} m(b^2 + c^2) & -mab & -mac \\ -mab & m(a^2 + c^2) & -mbc \\ -mac & -mab & m(a^2 + b^2) \end{bmatrix}. $$

Physicists use the letter I for *inertia*. Mathematicians reserve the letter I for the *identity* matrix. You can learn about the action of a matrix on a vector in Appendix F.

Checking the details

59. Suppose $\mathbf{u} = \langle u_1, u_2, u_3 \rangle$ and $\mathbf{v} = \langle v_1, v_2, v_3 \rangle$. Find an expression for the vector $\mathbf{u} \times \mathbf{v}$, and then show that it's orthogonal to both $\mathbf{u}$ and $\mathbf{v}$ by calculating the appropriate dot products.

11.5   Lines and Planes in 3-Space

When you pick a direction in 3-space, say $\mathbf{v}$, the collection of position vectors that are multiples of $\mathbf{v}$ define a line, and those that are orthogonal to $\mathbf{v}$ define a plane. In the following discussion we use these ideas to develop equations describing lines and planes in three dimensions.

Key Idea(s):   *Suppose* $\mathbf{v}$ *points along a line. If P and Q are points on that line, the displacement vector between them is a multiple of* $\mathbf{v}$.

The equation $\mathbf{u} \cdot \mathbf{n} = 0$ *says that* $\mathbf{u}$ *is orthogonal to* $\mathbf{n}$. *The collection of all such position vectors is a plane.*

✤ Lines in 3-Space

Imagine that you shine a laser pointer in the direction of $\mathbf{v} = \langle a, b, c \rangle$. The laser light travels along a line, and if we treat the tip of the laser pointer as the origin, the position vector of any point on that line is a multiple of $\mathbf{v}$, say $\mathbf{r} = k\mathbf{v} = \langle ka, kb, kc \rangle$, so its coordinates have the form $x = ka$, $y = kb$ and $z = kc$. By solving these equations for their common term, k, we see

$$k = \frac{x}{a}, \qquad k = \frac{y}{b}, \quad \text{and} \quad k = \frac{z}{c}.$$

Since these ratios are all equal to k, they are equal to each other. That is, a point (x, y, z) is on the line when

$$\frac{x}{a} = \frac{y}{b} = \frac{z}{c} \qquad\qquad (5.1)$$

More generally, suppose ℓ is the line through the point (x_0, y_0, z_0) that extends in the direction of $\mathbf{v} = \langle a, b, c \rangle$. If (x, y, z) is any other point on ℓ, the displacement vector between it and (x_0, y_0, z_0) lies along the line, so that vector is a multiple of $\mathbf{v}$. That is, there is some scalar k for which $\langle x - x_0, y - y_0, z - z_0 \rangle = k\langle a, b, c \rangle$. So

$$x - x_0 = ka, \quad y - y_0 = kb, \quad \text{and} \quad z - z_0 = kc.$$

Solving these equations for k brings us to the generalized form of (5.1), which is displayed as equation (5.2) below.

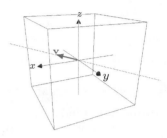

Figure 5.1: A line through the origin that extends in the direction of $\mathbf{v}$. The edges of a cube have been added to help establish the visual perspective.

Suppose ℓ is the line through the point (x_0, y_0, z_0) that extends in the direction of $\mathbf{v} = \langle a, b, c \rangle$, where neither a nor b nor c is 0. Then (x, y, z) is a point on ℓ if and only if

$$\frac{x - x_0}{a} = \frac{y - y_0}{b} = \frac{z - z_0}{c}. \qquad\qquad (5.2)$$

We refer to (5.2) as the ***symmetric equations*** for the line ℓ.

Note: If a component of $\mathbf{v}$ is zero, all points on the line have the same x, or y, or z coordinate (depending on which component of $\mathbf{v}$ is zero). We state that fact separately, and write the remaining ratios as equal. See Example 5.4.

Using symmetric equations

Example 5.1. Suppose ℓ is the line described by the symmetric equations $\frac{x-3}{8} = \frac{y-2}{1} = \frac{z+4}{-5}$. Find the point on ℓ that has an x-coordinate of 11.

Solution: When $x = 11$ we have $(x-3)/8 = (11-3)/8 = 1$. Equation (5.2) means that all three of those numbers are the same, so $1 = (y-2)/1$ and $1 = (z+4)/-5$. Solving these equations for y and z, we find that the point is $(11, 3, -9)$. ∎

Understanding symmetric equations in terms of the point-slope formula

Example 5.2. Imagine that the line described by $\frac{x-2}{5} = \frac{y-4}{-3} = \frac{z-11}{1}$ is a solid wire. When sunlight streams down from above, traveling in the direction of $-\mathbf{k}$, the wire makes a shadow on the xy-plane. Write a Cartesian equation describing that shadow.

Figure 5.2: Sunlight hits a wire and makes a "shadow" in the xy-plane.

Solution: Each point (x, y, z) on the wire corresponds to a point $(x, y, 0)$ on the shadow. Although the z-coordinates of these points are different, their x- and y-coordinates are the same, so

$$\frac{x-2}{5} = \frac{y-4}{-3}$$

When we rewrite this in point-slope form, we see that it's a line with slope $m = -3/5$ that passes through the point $(2, 4)$. ∎

In this example you see that the constants b and a in equation (5.2) tell us a slope in the xy-plane. Similarly, the fractions a/c and b/c are rise-to-run ratios that apply to the xz- and the yz-planes, respectively.

Using symmetric equations

Example 5.3. Suppose ℓ is the line described by the symmetric equations $\frac{x-4}{11} = \frac{y-3}{23} = \frac{z+7}{-12}$. (a) Find the point on ℓ that has a z-coordinate of 5. (b) As in Example 5.2, this line makes shadow on the xz-plane when light travels through space in the direction of $-\mathbf{j}$. Write a Cartesian equation describing that line.

Answer: (a) $(-7, -20, 5)$; (b) $\frac{x-4}{11} = \frac{z+7}{-12}$. ∎

Solution On-line

Finding symmetric equations of lines

Example 5.4. Find symmetric equations for (a) the line through $(1, -2, 4)$ heading in the direction of $\mathbf{v} = \langle 3, 1, 5 \rangle$, and then (b) the line that passes through $(-2, 1, 41)$ and heads in the direction of $\mathbf{v} = \langle -7, 11, 0 \rangle$.

Solution: Using equation (5.2), we set up the symmetric equations

$$\frac{x-1}{3} = \frac{y+2}{1} = \frac{z-4}{-5}.$$

(b) Since $\mathbf{v}$ indicates no "vertical" change in position, we can assert that $z = 41$ for all points on our line. We finish our description by using equation (5.2) to relate x and y, and so write

$$z = 41 \quad \text{and} \quad \frac{x+2}{-7} = \frac{y-1}{11}.$$ ∎

This line is just like one in the xy-plane, except that we've "lifted" it 41 units "upward."

Non-parallel, non-intersecting lines

Example 5.5. Use the equations below to show that (a) lines ℓ_1 and ℓ_2 are parallel, and (b) lines ℓ_2 and ℓ_3 are neither parallel nor intersecting.

$$\ell_1 : \frac{x-1}{2} = \frac{y-2}{3} = \frac{z-4}{7}$$
$$\ell_2 : \frac{x-7}{4} = \frac{y-3}{6} = \frac{z-2}{14}$$
$$\ell_3 : \frac{x-6}{1} = \frac{y-13}{5} = \frac{z-20}{2}$$

Solution: Lines ℓ_1 and ℓ_2 are parallel because $\langle 4, 6, 14 \rangle$ is a nonzero multiple of $\langle 2, 3, 7 \rangle$. To verify that they are distinct lines (not two versions of the same line) we note that $(7, 3, 2)$ is on ℓ_2 but does not satisfy the symmetric equations for ℓ_1.

(b) Lines ℓ_2 and ℓ_3 are not parallel because $\langle 4, 6, 14 \rangle$ is not a nonzero multiple of $\langle 1, 5, 2 \rangle$. To show that they don't intersect, let's imagine what would happen if they did. If a point (x, y, z) were to sit on both lines, it would be true that

$$\underbrace{\frac{x-7}{4} = \frac{y-3}{6}}_{\text{From the symmetric equations for } \ell_2} \quad \text{and} \quad \underbrace{\frac{x-6}{1} = \frac{y-13}{5}}_{\text{From the symmetric equations for } \ell_3}.$$

These equations are solved by $x = 19/7$ and $y = -24/7$, in which case the symmetric equations for ℓ_3 require that $z = 94/7$ but the symmetric equations for ℓ_2 tell us that $z = -13$. These can't be true simultaneously, so the lines don't intersect. ∎

In Example 5.5 you saw a pair of lines that were not parallel but did not intersect. Such pairs of lines are said to be **skew**.

Non-parallel, non-skew lines

Example 5.6. Are lines ℓ_1 and ℓ_3 from Example 5.5 parallel? Are they skew?

Answer: Neither.   ∎

Solution On-line

▷ Parameterization of a Line

Now we turn from the description of lines to a characterization of simple motion along them. In the next examples an object moves along a linear path, so its position vector changes with time and we write it as $\mathbf{r}(t)$. We'll start with examples in the plane, and then extend the techniques we develop to address motion in 3-space.

Motion along a line

Example 5.7. Suppose distance is measured in meters and time in seconds. Describe your position vector as a function of time if you start at the point $(4, 2)$ and jog toward $(6, 7)$ at 1.5 meters per second.

Solution: The statement of this scenario includes information about (1) initial position and (2) velocity. We can use these two pieces of information to construct a position function of the form

$$\mathbf{r}(t) = \left(\begin{array}{c}\text{initial}\\\text{position}\end{array}\right) + \left(\begin{array}{c}\text{displacement from ini-}\\\text{tial to current position}\end{array}\right),$$

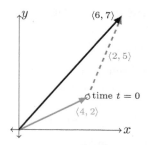

Figure 5.3: Starting at $(4, 2)$ and heading toward $(6, 7)$.

where the second term (displacement) depends on time. Since you start at the head of the position vector $\mathbf{r}_0 = \langle 4, 2 \rangle$ and travel toward the point at $(6, 7)$, you move in the direction of the vector $\mathbf{u} = \langle 6, 7 \rangle - \langle 4, 2 \rangle = \langle 2, 5 \rangle$, as shown Figure 5.3. To construct the proper velocity vector, we scale $\hat{\mathbf{u}}$ to have the correct magnitude. In this case, the specified speed is 1.5 m/sec, so

$$\mathbf{v} = 1.5\hat{\mathbf{u}} = \frac{1.5}{\|\mathbf{u}\|}\mathbf{u} = \frac{1.5}{\sqrt{29}}\begin{bmatrix}2\\5\end{bmatrix} = \begin{bmatrix}\frac{3}{\sqrt{29}}\\\frac{7.5}{\sqrt{29}}\end{bmatrix}.$$

Now because this motion happens at a constant speed, we can write your displacement over t seconds as $\mathbf{v}t$, and your position after t seconds as

$$\mathbf{r}(t) = \mathbf{r}_0 + \mathbf{v}t = \begin{bmatrix}4\\2\end{bmatrix} + \begin{bmatrix}\frac{3}{\sqrt{29}}\\\frac{7.5}{\sqrt{29}}\end{bmatrix}t = \begin{bmatrix}4 + \frac{3t}{\sqrt{29}}\\2 + \frac{7.5t}{\sqrt{29}}\end{bmatrix}.$$ ∎

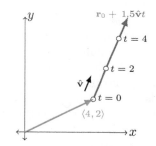

Figure 5.4: Walking along a linear path at a specified speed.

We've been talking about linear motion in the plane, but the parameterization technique works just as well in three dimensions.

Practice with a line in 3-space

Example 5.8. Suppose length is measured in meters, and a particle travels linearly at 10 meters per second through the point $(2, 3, 7)$, in the direction $\langle 1, -8, 2 \rangle$. Determine this particle's position as a function of time.

Answer: $\mathbf{r}(t) = \left(2 + \frac{10t}{\sqrt{69}}\right)\mathbf{i} + \left(3 - \frac{80t}{\sqrt{69}}\right)\mathbf{j} + \left(7 + \frac{20t}{\sqrt{69}}\right)\mathbf{k}$ ∎

Solution On-line

The results of Examples 5.7 and 5.8 are generalized in the box below.

> **Motion Along a Line (Constant Velocity):** In general, linear motion with constant velocity is described by
>
> $$\mathbf{r}(t) = \mathbf{r}_0 + \mathbf{v}\,t = \mathbf{r}_0 + \|\mathbf{v}\|\hat{\mathbf{v}}\,t,$$
>
> Initial position ⟶   Speed ⟶   ⟶ Direction
>
> where $\mathbf{r}_0$ indicates the initial position, and $\mathbf{v}$ is the (constant) velocity vector of the motion.

If we extract the components of $\mathbf{r}(t)$, you see parametric equations that describe the line, just as in Chapter 9. For example, our work in Example 5.7 yields

$$x(t) = 4 + \frac{3t}{\sqrt{29}} \quad \text{and} \quad y(t) = 2 + \frac{7.5t}{\sqrt{29}}.$$

For this reason, we extend the language of Chapter 9 and say that $\mathbf{r}(t)$ is a ***parameterization*** of, or that it ***parameterizes*** a line.

❖ Planes in 3-Space

In the discussion below you'll see that the equation describing a plane can be understood as a statement about the orthogonality of vectors.

▷ Planes through the origin

The most familiar plane is the xy-plane, so let's talk about it first. All of its points have position vectors that are orthogonal to $\langle 0, 0, 1 \rangle$. That is, (x, y, z) is a point on the plane exactly when the position vector $\langle x, y, z \rangle$ satisfies the equation

$$\langle 0, 0, 1 \rangle \cdot \langle x, y, z \rangle = 0, \tag{5.3}$$

which is the same as saying that $z = 0$. Fundamentally, all planes in 3-space that pass through the origin are described by equations like (5.3), with only minor differences. To understand why, imagine that the tail of $\langle 0, 0, 1 \rangle$ is physically, rigidly connected to the xy-plane at the origin. When we grab the vector $\langle 0, 0, 1 \rangle$ as if it's a handle, and pivot it to the side (leaving its tail at the origin, as in Figure 5.5), the plane to which it's rigidly attached also pivots. Now the "handle" of our plane doesn't point in the direction $\langle 0, 0, 1 \rangle$ any more, but it's still orthogonal to every vector that lies in the plane. In general, we call the "handle" the ***normal vector*** of the plane and denote it by $\mathbf{n}$ so the generalized version of equation (5.3) is just

$$\underbrace{\mathbf{n} \cdot \langle x, y, z \rangle = 0.}_{} \tag{5.4}$$

This says the vector $\mathbf{n}$ is orthogonal to the position vector $\langle x, y, z \rangle$.

> Earlier in this chapter we talked about *normalizing* a vector (which means to scale it so that it becomes a unit vector). The word "normal" in this context is unrelated to our previous usage. Here, it means "the special direction that's orthogonal to a plane."

Practice with normal vectors

Example 5.9. Write the equation of the plane through the origin that has a normal vector of (a) $\mathbf{n} = \langle 9, -7, -5 \rangle$, and (b) $\mathbf{n} = \langle 18, -14, -10 \rangle$.

Solution: Equation (5.4) tells us that these planes are described by

     (a) $9x - 7y - 5z = 0$ (b) $18x - 14y - 10z = 0$

Note that whenever (x, y, z) solves the first equation it also satisfies the second (i.e., these equations describe the same plane). This happens because the normal vector in part (b) is just a scaled version of the one in part (a).   ∎

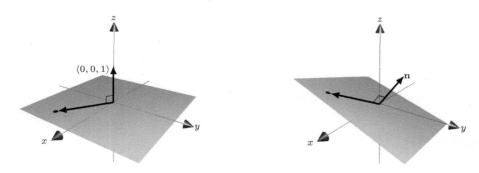

Figure 5.5: (left) The plane described by equation (5.3); (right) a tilted plane that passes through the origin.

Normal vectors and planar equations

Example 5.10. (a) Write the equation of the plane through the origin that has a normal vector of $\mathbf{n} = \langle 2, -7, -1 \rangle$, and (b) determine a normal vector for the plane $-3x + y + 4z = 0$.

Answer: (a) $2x - 7y - 1z = 0$; (b) $\langle -3, 1, 4 \rangle$ (other answers are possible). ■

Solution On-line

Practice with normal vectors

Example 5.11. Suppose $\mathbf{u} = \langle 1, 2, 3 \rangle$ and $\mathbf{v} = \langle 4, -1, 5 \rangle$ are in a plane that passes through the origin. Find the equation of that plane.

Solution: In order to use equation (5.4) we need to know a normal vector to the plane. As indicated in Example 5.9 any nonzero vector perpendicular to the plane will do (we don't have to worry about magnitude), so let's set $\mathbf{n} = \mathbf{u} \times \mathbf{v} = \langle 13, 7, -9 \rangle$. Thus, the equation of our plane is $13x + 7y - 9z = 0$. ■

▷ Planes *not* through the origin

A plane that does *not* pass through the origin is described by an equation that's very similar to (5.4). In fact, the only difference is that the right-hand side of the equation is not zero. To understand why, imagine that the normal vector $\mathbf{n}$ is rigidly attached to the plane described by equation (5.4). Suppose we grab $\mathbf{n}$, and without changing its direction, we pull its tail over to the point P_0, which is located at the head of the position vector $\mathbf{r}_0 = \langle x_0, y_0, z_0 \rangle$. The plane that's rigidly attached moves too, but its orientation in space does not change because the direction of $\mathbf{n}$ remains the same. If the position vector $\mathbf{r} = \langle x, y, z \rangle$ locates another point on the now-translated plane, say P, the vector $\mathbf{r} - \mathbf{r}_0$ lies in the plane, so it's orthogonal to the normal vector, $\mathbf{n}$. That is,

$$\mathbf{n} \cdot \big(\underbrace{\langle x, y, z \rangle - \langle x_0, y_0, z_0 \rangle}_{\text{This displacement vector extends from } P_0 \text{ to } P.} \big) = 0.$$

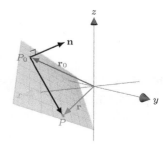

Figure 5.6: A plane not through the origin. Vectors that lie in the plane are orthogonal to $\mathbf{n}$.

Since dot products distribute over sums, we can rewrite this as

$$\begin{aligned} \mathbf{n} \cdot \langle x, y, z \rangle - \mathbf{n} \cdot \langle x_0, y_0, z_0 \rangle &= 0 \\ \mathbf{n} \cdot \langle x, y, z \rangle &= \mathbf{n} \cdot \langle x_0, y_0, z_0 \rangle. \end{aligned} \tag{5.5}$$

If we denote the number on the right-hand side of equation (5.5) by d, we can write the equation simply as

$$\mathbf{n} \cdot \langle x, y, z \rangle = d, \tag{5.6}$$

which is a generalization of equation (5.4).

> **Equations of Planes:** Suppose $a, b, c, d \in \mathbb{R}$, and at least one of a, b, c is nonzero. Then the equation
>
> $$a\,x + b\,y + c\,z = d$$
>
> describes a plane in 3-space with a normal vector of $\mathbf{n} = \langle a, b, c \rangle$. The plane passes through the origin if and only if $d = 0$.

Finding the equation for a plane not through the origin

Example 5.12. Find an equation for the plane that passes through the point $(4, -2, -9)$ and has a normal vector $\mathbf{n} = \langle -2, 2, 5 \rangle$.

Solution: Looking back to equation (5.5), we see that the right-hand side of the equation should be $\mathbf{n} \cdot \langle x_0, y_0, z_0 \rangle = \langle -2, 2, 5 \rangle \cdot \langle 4, -2, -9 \rangle = -57$. So our equation is $-2x + 2y + 5z = -57$. ∎

Finding the equation for a plane not through the origin

Example 5.13. Find an equation that describes the plane through the point $(2, 5, -3)$ and has a normal vector $\mathbf{n} = \langle 8, -1, -2 \rangle$.

Answer: $8x - y - 2z = 17$. ∎

Solution On-line

Using coplanar points to generate a normal vector

Example 5.14. Determine the equation of the plane that passes through the points $(2, 1, 3)$, $(4, -1, -1)$, and $(3, 0, 4)$.

Solution: Since both $(4, -1, -1)$, and $(3, 0, 4)$ lie in the plane, the displacement vector between them does too. That vector is $\mathbf{u} = \langle 4, -1, -1 \rangle - \langle 3, 0, 4 \rangle = \langle 1, -1, -5 \rangle$. Similarly, the vector $\mathbf{v} = \langle 4, -1, -1 \rangle - \langle 2, 1, 3 \rangle = \langle 2, -2, -4 \rangle$ also lies in the plane. Since $\mathbf{u}$ and $\mathbf{v}$ lie in the plane, their cross product points in a normal direction. So we calculate $\mathbf{n} = \mathbf{u} \times \mathbf{v} = \langle 2, 2, 0 \rangle$. Now with a point and a normal vector, we can write the equation of the plane as

$$\underbrace{2x + 2y + 0z}_{\mathbf{n}\cdot\langle x,y,z\rangle} \;=\; \underbrace{6}_{\mathbf{n}\cdot\langle 2,1,3\rangle} \; .$$

∎

> The equation of a plane is determined by a point and a normal vector. In this example we're given *three* points but *no* vectors.

Using coplanar points to generate a normal vector

Example 5.15. Determine the equation of the plane that passes through the points $(1, 4, 1)$, $(0, 2, -5)$, and $(7, 0, -1)$.

Answer: $20x + 38y - 16z = 156$. ∎

▷ Planes and scalar projections

Figure 5.7 depicts a plane as seen edge-on. Notice that in order to move from the origin to any point on the plane, we have to travel the same distance in the direction of the plane's normal vector, $\mathbf{n}$ (which has been drawn at the origin in Figure 5.7, pointing toward the plane). In order to make this idea useful, we need to know the position vector of some point on the plane, say $\mathbf{r}_0 = \langle x_0, y_0, z_0 \rangle$. With that information in hand, we know that the position vector for any other point on the plane, say $\mathbf{r} = \langle x, y, z \rangle$, satisfies the equation

$$\underbrace{\hat{\mathbf{n}} \cdot \mathbf{r}}_{\text{The "amount" of } \mathbf{r} \text{ in the direction of } \mathbf{n}} \;=\; \underbrace{\hat{\mathbf{n}} \cdot \mathbf{r}_0}_{\text{The "amount" of } \mathbf{r}_0 \text{ in the direction of } \mathbf{n}} .$$

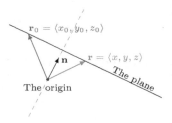

Solution On-line

Figure 5.7: A plane with normal vector $\mathbf{n}$ seen edge-on.

Multiplying this equation by $\|\mathbf{n}\|$ yields $\mathbf{n} \cdot \langle x, y, z \rangle = \mathbf{n} \cdot \langle x_0, y_0, z_0 \rangle$, which is exactly equation (5.5). So intuitively speaking, you can understand equation (5.5) to mean that when you travel from the origin to the plane, regardless of where you arrive you have to travel the same distance in the $\hat{\mathbf{n}}$-direction; we use a known point on the plane to determine that distance.

Using the scalar projection to determine the distance between a point and a plane

Example 5.16. Determine the perpendicular distance between the point $P = (5, 9, 8)$ and the plane $x + 2y + 5z = 6$.

Solution: Figure 5.8 (compare to Figure 5.7) hints at our strategy for solving this problem. Suppose $\mathbf{r}$ is the position vector for P, $\mathbf{n}$ is a normal vector for the plane, and $\mathbf{r}_0$ is the position vector for a point on the plane. Then the perpendicular distance between P and the plane is $D = \text{comp}_{\mathbf{n}}\mathbf{r} - \text{comp}_{\mathbf{n}}\mathbf{r}_0$. In this particular example, $\mathbf{n} = \langle 1, 2, 5 \rangle$, $\mathbf{r} = \langle 5, 9, 8 \rangle$, and the position vector $\mathbf{r}_0 = \langle 5, -2, 1 \rangle$ locates a point on the plane ($\mathbf{r}_0$ was chosen arbitrarily), so

$$\text{distance} = |\text{comp}_{\mathbf{n}}\mathbf{r} - \text{comp}_{\mathbf{n}}\mathbf{r}_0)| = \left| \frac{(\mathbf{r} - \mathbf{r}_0) \cdot \mathbf{n}}{\|\mathbf{n}\|} \right| = \frac{57}{\sqrt{30}}. \qquad \blacksquare$$

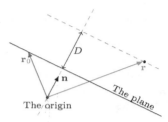

Figure 5.8: A schematic of the solution to Example 5.16. The plane is shown edge-on.

Distance between a point and a plane

Example 5.17. Determine the perpendicular distance between the point $(2, 7, 1)$ and the plane $9x + y + 8z = 10$.

Answer: $23/\sqrt{146}$ $\blacksquare$

Solution On-line

The method demonstrated in Examples 5.16 and 5.17 is generalized below.

Distance Between a Point and a Plane: Suppose $\mathbf{r}$ is the position vector for the point P. Then the distance between the point P and the plane described by $\mathbf{n} \cdot \langle x, y, z \rangle = d$ is

$$\text{distance} = \left| \frac{\mathbf{r} \cdot \mathbf{n} - d}{\|\mathbf{n}\|} \right|.$$

❖ Examples of Planar Equations From Other Disciplines

Said colloquially, planes are useful in mathematics because they are flat, which makes them easy to work with. They also allow us to visualize and understand relationships between quantities in other disciplines.

Planes and production constraints

Example 5.18. Suppose a business uses silk to make three kinds of products: ties, skirts, and shirts. The silk is cut from bolts of fabric, so the amount of raw material needed to create a product is measured in yards (i.e., rolled off the bolt). Data regarding the production are shown in Table 1 (in the margin). If the company has 3000 yards of fabric to use in a given month, write an equation that describes the production constraint for the company.

Product	Yards
Tie	0.1
Skirt	1.6
Shirt	3.3

Table 1: Production data for Example 5.18.

Solution: Suppose the number of ties made by the company in a given month is x. Then the fabric used for these ties is $0.1x$ yards. Similarly, producing y skirts requires $1.6y$ yards of fabric, and $3.3z$ yards is needed to make z shirts. If we were to use all the silk fabric in a given month, the point (x, y, z) would sit on the plane $0.1x + 1.6y + 3.3z = 3000$. Only points in the first octant that are on or below this plane represent feasible levels of production.   ■

Planes and chemical equilibrium

Example 5.19. Suppose a molecule of type Z is formed by combining two molecules of type X and three of type Y. It often happens that molecules of type Z spontaneously disassociate, and revert to molecules of type X and Y, so we write $2X + 3Y \rightleftharpoons Z$. The reaction comes to equilibrium when neither creating nor disassociating molecules of Z can reduce the potential energy of the chemical solution. Write an equation that describes this condition.

> More specifically, chemical reactions come to equilibrium when neither making nor breaking a molecule of Z reduces a quantity called the *Gibbs free energy* of the solution.

Solution: Let's denote by z the increase in potential energy due to the creation of a single molecule of type Z. Similarly the increase due to an additional molecule of X is x, and the increase due to an additional molecule of Y is y. When the chemical reaction produces a molecule of Z by consuming two molecules of X and three of Y, the change in energy is

> The numbers x, y and z are called *chemical potentials*.

$$\underbrace{z}_{\substack{\text{Energy increase from in-}\\\text{creased numbers of } Z}} \quad - \quad \underbrace{(2x + 3y)}_{\substack{\text{Energy decrease due to fewer}\\\text{molecules of } X \text{ and } Y}}. \qquad (5.7)$$

> When a molecule of Z is created, two molecules of X and three of Y are consumed, so the number of type Z goes up while the numbers of type X and Y go down.

Similarly, when a molecule of Z disassociates into two of X and three of Y, the change in the solution's energy is

$$\underbrace{2x + 3y}_{\substack{\text{Energy increase from greater}\\\text{numbers of } X \text{ and } Y}} \quad - \quad \underbrace{z}_{\substack{\text{Energy decrease from de-}\\\text{creased numbers of } Z}}. \qquad (5.8)$$

Since the quantities that you see in (5.8) and (5.7) are opposites, the only way for neither to offer a reduction in energy is for $2x + 3y - z = 0$. This equation describes a plane through the origin with a normal vector of $\mathbf{n} = \langle 2, 3, -1 \rangle$.   ■

Note: When we have more than three variables representing production numbers, or more than three chemicals involved in a reaction, we continue to think about the associated equations as planes, but residing in a higher-dimensional space.

You should know

- the terms *symmetric equations, parameterize, normal vector,* and *plane;*
- the plane described by $\mathbf{n} \cdot \langle x, y, z \rangle = d$ passes through the origin if and only if $d = 0$.

You should be able to

- determine the symmetric equations for a line;
- parameterize a line as $\mathbf{r}(t) = \mathbf{u} + t\mathbf{v}$;
- parameterize motion along a line with constant velocity;
- determine the equation of a plane from relevant data (e.g., a point and a normal vector, or three points in the plane);
- determine the distance between a point and a plane.

✢ 11.5 Skill Exercises

In #1–6 find symmetric equations for the line through P in the direction of $\mathbf{v}$.

1. $P = (14, 0, -9)$, $\mathbf{v} = \langle 3, 3, -8 \rangle$ 4. $P = (2, -4, -5)$, $\mathbf{v} = \langle 1, -3, 5 \rangle$

2. $P = (0, 5, 12)$, $\mathbf{v} = \langle 1, -3, 5 \rangle$ 5. $P = (1, -11, 3)$, $\mathbf{v} = \langle -4, 0, 5 \rangle$

3. $P = (1, 1, -2)$, $\mathbf{v} = \langle 4, 7, -5 \rangle$ 6. $P = (3, 7, 17)$, $\mathbf{v} = \langle 9, 2, 0 \rangle$

In #7–10 determine the symmetric equations for the line through the given points.

7. $P_1 = (14, 0, -9)$, $P_2 = (14, -3, -11)$ 9. $P_1 = (4, 13, -1)$, $P_2 = (5, 9, 1)$

8. $P_1 = (1, 10, 2)$, $P_2 = (4, -13, -8)$ 10. $P_1 = (2, 2, -7)$, $P_2 = (2, -3, -3)$

In #11–14 determine whether the lines ℓ_1 and ℓ_2 intersect, are parallel, or are skew.

11. $\ell_1 : \frac{(x-2)}{3} = \frac{(y-7)}{2} = \frac{(z-1)}{5}$, and $\ell_2 : \frac{(x+4)}{3} = \frac{(y+1)}{2} = \frac{(z+10)}{5}$

12. $\ell_1 : \frac{(x-2)}{3} = \frac{(y-7)}{2} = \frac{(z-1)}{5}$, and $\ell_2 : \frac{(x+1)}{6} = \frac{(y-3)}{4} = \frac{(z-1)}{5}$

13. $\ell_1 : \frac{(x-2)}{3} = \frac{(y-7)}{2} = \frac{(z-1)}{5}$, and $\ell_2 : \frac{(x+10)}{6} = \frac{(y+1)}{4} = \frac{(z+9)}{5}$

14. $\ell_1 : \frac{(x-2)}{6} = \frac{(y-7)}{1} = \frac{(z-1)}{7}$, and $\ell_2 : \frac{(x+10)}{6} = \frac{(y+1)}{3} = \frac{(z+24)}{8}$

In #15–18 parameterize linear motion that passes through P in the direction of $\mathbf{w}$ at the constant speed v. Distance is measured in meters, and time in seconds.

15. $P = (1, 6)$; $\mathbf{w} = \langle -2, 5 \rangle$; $v = 2$ m/sec   17. $P = (3, -1, 10)$; $\mathbf{w} = \langle 7, -2, 15 \rangle$; $v = 4$ m/sec

16. $P = (4, -5)$; $\mathbf{w} = \langle 7, 8 \rangle$; $v = 3$ m/sec   18. $P = (5, 13, -4)$; $\mathbf{w} = \langle 3, 1, 2 \rangle$; $v = 5$ m/sec

In #19–26 parameterize the linear motion of an object that travels with constant velocity from P to Q in the allotted time, or at the specified speed. Distance is measured in meters and time in seconds.

19. $P = (0, 8, 13)$, $Q = (1, 12, -4)$; 1 second   23. $P = (1, -2)$, $Q = (5, -5)$; $v = 5$ m/sec

20. $P = (1, 2, -5)$, $Q = (4, 6, 7)$; 1 second   24. $P = (-8, 7)$, $Q = (-21, 8)$; $v = 6$ m/sec

21. $P = (2, -3, 1)$, $Q = (4, -2, -4)$; 2 seconds   25. $P = (4, -2, 9)$, $Q = (5, 11, 20)$; $v = \pi$ m/sec

22. $P = (10, 4, 5)$, $Q = (0, -1, -2)$; 3 seconds   26. $P = (8, 12, -5)$, $Q = (18, 11, -1)$; $v = e$ m/sec

In exercises #27–32 Find an equation for the plane that passes through the given point and has the specified normal vector.

27. $P = (0, 0, 0)$, $\mathbf{n} = \langle 12, 22, 70 \rangle$ 30. $P = (1, 0, 5)$, $\mathbf{n} = \langle -1, 3, 9 \rangle$

28. $P = (0, 0, 0)$, $\mathbf{n} = \langle -13, 43, 59 \rangle$ 31. $P = (2, -4, 18)$, $\mathbf{n} = (-2, 1, 8)$

29. $P = (2, -4, 3)$, $\mathbf{n} = \langle 2, 2, 7 \rangle$ 32. $P = (3, -14, 32)$, $\mathbf{n} = \langle 5, 2, -1 \rangle$

In exercises #33–36 find an equation for the plane that passes through the given point and contains the displacement vectors $\mathbf{u}$ and $\mathbf{v}$.

33. $P = (2, -4, 3)$, $\mathbf{u} = \langle 2, 2, 7 \rangle$, $\mathbf{v} = \langle 3, 2, 2 \rangle$ 35. $P = (2, -4, 18)$, $\mathbf{u} = \langle -2, 1, 8 \rangle$, $\mathbf{v} = \langle -2, -4, 5 \rangle$

34. $P = (1, 0, 5)$, $\mathbf{u} = \langle -1, 3, 9 \rangle$, $\mathbf{v} = \langle 1, 2, -2 \rangle$ 36. $P = (3, -14, 32)$, $\mathbf{u} = \langle 5, 2, -1 \rangle$, $\mathbf{v} = \langle 2, 12, -5 \rangle$

In #37–40 find an equation for the plane passing through the given points.

37. $P_1 = (2, 1, 4)$, $P_2 = (2, -1, -3)$, $P_3 = (0, 10, 0)$ 39. $P_1 = (1, 0, 1)$, $P_2 = (2, -3, -1)$, $P_3 = (-1, 1, 2)$

38. $P_1 = (0, -1, 1)$, $P_2 = (0, -1, 4)$, $P_3 = (0, 0, 2)$ 40. $P_1 = (2, 1, 4)$, $P_2 = (2, -1, -3)$, $P_3 = (4, 5, 17)$

In #41–44 determine the distance between the point and the plane.

41. $P = (2, 7, 1); \; 3x - 4y + z = 0$ 43. $P = (3, 2, 1); \; -x + 2y + 3z = 10$

42. $P = (-3, 1, -1); \; x + y - z = 0$ 44. $P = (1, -1, 5); \; 5x + y + 2z = 9$

45. Use the scalar projection to determine the distance between the point $(3, 4, 5)$ and the line described by the symmetric equations $\frac{x-3}{5} = \frac{y+1}{2} = \frac{z+3}{4}$.

46. Use the scalar projection to determine the distance between the point $(1, 5, -6)$ and the line described by the symmetric equations $\frac{x+3}{2} = \frac{y-1}{3} = \frac{z-5}{7}$.

In #47–52 determine the equation of the plane that's described.

47. Passing through the point $(1, 4, -2)$ and containing the line described by the symmetric equations $\frac{x-11}{2} = \frac{y-1}{3} = \frac{z-8}{5}$

48. Passing through the point $(-3, -5, 1)$ and containing the line parameterized by $\mathbf{r}(t) = \langle 1 + t, 2 - 3t, 4 + 5t \rangle$

49. Containing the lines parameterized by $\mathbf{r}_1(t) = (3 + 2t)\mathbf{i} + (-1 + 7t)\mathbf{j} + (9 - 5t)\mathbf{k}$ and $\mathbf{r}_2(t) = (4t - 1)\mathbf{i} + (8t - 15)\mathbf{j} + 19\mathbf{k}$.

50. Containing the lines parameterized by $\mathbf{r}_1(t) = \langle 1 + 2t, -1 + t, 3 + 4t \rangle$ and $\mathbf{r}_2(t) = \langle 3 - 9t, 10t, 7 + 3t \rangle$.

51. Containing the line described by $\frac{x+9}{1} = \frac{y-2}{4} = \frac{z-7}{3}$, with a normal vector that's parallel to the line parameterized by $\mathbf{r}(t) = 2t\mathbf{i} - 5t\mathbf{j} + 6t\mathbf{k}$

52. Containing the line parameterized by $\mathbf{r}(t) = \langle 2 - 3t, 5 + 2t, 1 + t \rangle$, with a normal vector that's parallel to the line described by $\frac{x-17}{2} = \frac{y-19}{6} = \frac{z-1}{7}$

53. All points on the plane are equidistant from the points $(1, 2, 3)$ and $(4, 5, 6)$.

54. Intersects the x-axis at $x = 5$, the y-axis at $y = 6$, and the z-axis at $z = -1$.

❖ 11.5 Concept and Application Exercises

55. Suppose a particle's position is described by $\mathbf{r}(t) = \langle 2 + 3t, 4 + 7t \rangle$, where time is measure in seconds and distance in meters.

    Linear motion

   (a) Explain what the numbers 2 and 4 mean physically in this context.

   (b) The numbers 3 and 7 tell us two things in this context. What are they?

56. Suppose you walk down a long, straight sidewalk and your position is $\mathbf{r}(t) = \langle -1 + t, 3 + 0.5t \rangle$, where distance is measured in meters and time in seconds.

    Linear Motion

   (a) Plot your position in the xy-plane at times $t = 0, 1, 2$.

   (b) If you're walking with a friend who stays one meter to your right, parameterize the path of your friend.

   (c) Suppose you spot someone else you know when $t = 0$, 40 meters directly in front of you and walking toward you at 1 meter per second. Parameterize the path of this acquaintance.

57. Suppose you start from the point $(4, 5)$ and jog in the direction of $\langle -4, 2 \rangle$ at 5 meters per second. Parameterize your motion.

    Linear motion

58. Suppose a particle moves at a constant rate along a line, and moves from $(12, -3, 4)$ and $(5, 6, 1)$ in 1 second, where distance is measured in meters. Determine a parameterization of the motion.

    Linear motion

59. Consider the line described by the symmetric equations $\frac{x-3}{2} = \frac{y-4}{9} = \frac{z-1}{b}$ where $b > 0$. Explain how increasing the value of b affects the line.

60. Consider the line described by the symmetric equations $\frac{x-3}{2} = \frac{y-4}{9} = \frac{z-k}{5}$ where $k > 0$. Explain how increasing the value of k affects the line.

61. Consider plane described by $7x + 2y + 3z = d$.

    (a) What can you say about the plane when $d = 0$?

    (b) What happens to the plane if we let the parameter d increase from zero? (You should address both its orientation and its location.)

62. Consider plane described by $7x + 2y + kz = 17$.

    (a) What can you say about the plane when $k = 0$? (Address both its orientation and location.)

    (b) Suppose $k \neq 0$. Divide both sides of the equation by k, and describe what happens to the plane as the parameter k becomes very large. (Address both its orientation and its location.)

63. In complete sentences, explain how the number θ affects the location and orientation of the plane $\cos(\theta)x + \sin(\theta)y = 1$.

64. Both of the equations $6x + 7y + 8z = 12$ and $6x + 7y + 8z = 2$ describe planes. Explain why we cannot solve both of them simultaneously from (a) an algebraic point of view, and (b) a geometric point of view.

65. Suppose P_1 is the plane described by $\mathbf{n}_1 \cdot \langle x, y, z \rangle = d_1$, and P_2 is the plane described by $\mathbf{n}_2 \cdot \langle x, y, z \rangle = d_2$. Then the angle between the planes is the same as the angle between their normal vectors, $\mathbf{n}_1$ and $\mathbf{n}_2$ (see Figure 5.9). Use this fact to find the angle between the planes $4x + 2y - 8z = 10$ and $3x - 4y - 9z = 0$.

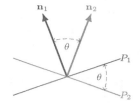

Figure 5.9: Looking at planes P_1 and P_2 "edge on."

In exercises #66–68 find the angle between the planes, as you did in exercise #65.

66. $7x - 3y + 4z = 2$ and $5x - 2y + 3z = -44$

67. $x + y = 3$ and $y - z = 7$

68. $2x + 2y - 3z = 0$ and $3z + 3y + 4z = 10$

69. Suppose that you and a friend each write the equation of a plane. If each of those planes makes an angle of $35°$ with the plane $4x + y - 7z = 2$, and the point $(1, 1, 1)$ is on both of them, do your equations both describe the same plane? If so, why? If not, explain how the planes could differ.

70. This exercise is about the relationship between the area of a rectangular patch on a tilted plane, and the area of its "shadow" in the xy-plane.

    (a) Suppose R is the rectangle in the plane $z = -10$ for which $x \in [1, 3]$ and $y \in [2, 7]$. What is the area of R?

    (b) Suppose we pivot the plane in which R lies, so that its normal vector points in the direction of $\mathbf{n} = \langle \sin\theta, 0, -\cos\theta \rangle$. What angle does the newly-pivoted plane make with the xy-plane?

    (c) Imagine that light rays travel vertically through 3-space, parallel to $\mathbf{k}$, and the newly-pivoted rectangle R casts a shadow on the xy-plane. What is the area of that shadow? (Answer in terms of θ.)

    (d) If the shadow in part (c) has an area of 6 square units, what is θ?

(e) Consider a new rectangle R in a plane that makes an angle of θ radians with the xy-plane. If the rectangular shadow of R on the xy-plane has an area of A, what is the area of R? (Answer in terms of A and θ.)

Consider Figure 5.10, which shows the point $P_1 = (-3, 2, 4)$ above the xy-plane. The shortest path from P_1 to the xy-plane is the one that drops straight down to the point $P_2 = (-3, 2, 0)$. Any other point P is farther away (since $\overrightarrow{PP_1}$ is the hypotenuse of a right-triangle for which $\overrightarrow{P_1P_2}$ is a leg). In #71–74 you will generalize this basic idea to find the point on a plane that's closest to specified location.

71. Suppose $P = (-3, 2, 4)$, and we want to find the point on the plane $2x + 2y + 7z = 10$ that's closest to P.

   (a) Write the symmetric equations for the line through P that extends in the direction of the plane's normal vector.

   (b) The equations from part (a) express a particular relationship between x, y, and z that must happen when a point is on that line. Use them to write y and z in terms of x.

   (c) The point on the plane that's closest to P will be on that line, so your equations for y and z (in terms of x) will hold true there. Use this fact to reduce the equation for the plane to an equation involving only x, and then solve it.

   (d) Use your solution from part (c) and the equation for the line that you wrote in part (a) to determine the values of y and z.

   (e) Now that you know the exact location of the point on the plane that's closest to P, calculate the distance between them.

72. Repeat #71 with $P = (3, 12, -7)$ and the plane $-2x - 6y + 4z = 8$.

73. Suppose P is the point at $(-3, 2, 4)$, and we want to find the point on the plane $2x + 2y + 7z = 10$ that's closest to it.

   (a) Write a parameterization of the line through P in the direction of the plane's normal vector, $\mathbf{r}(t) = \ldots$, so that $\mathbf{r}(0) = \langle -3, 2, 4 \rangle$.

   (b) Determine the value of t for which $\mathbf{r}(t)$ satisfies the equation of the plane.

   (c) Use your answer from part (b) to determine the point on the plane that's closest to P.

74. Suppose P_1 and P_2 are distinct, parallel planes, and Q is a point that's on neither of them.

   (a) Explain why, when using the technique of #73 to find the point on each plane that's closest to Q, we can use the same $\mathbf{r}(t)$.

   (b) Suppose we use $\mathbf{r}(t)$ to locate the points on P_1 and P_2 that are closest to Q. How do we tell whether Q is between the planes without any further computation?

75. Any two non-parallel planes in 3-space intersect in a line (e.g., see Figure 5.11). To find the equation of that line we need to know (a) a point on it, and (b) the direction in which it extends.

   (a) When two planes are non-parallel, there will always by *some* variable that you can set to zero, reducing the problem to 2 equations and 2 variables.

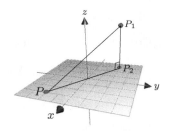

Figure 5.10: The fastest way to reach a plane is by traveling in the direction of its normal vector

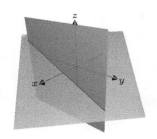

Figure 5.11: The intersection of two planes is a line

Show that you can set any one of $x, y,$ or z to zero in the following pair of planar equations, and successfully solve for the other two.

$$6x + 7y + 8z \;=\; 13 \qquad\qquad (5.9)$$
$$2x + 1y + 9z \;=\; 11 \qquad\qquad (5.10)$$

(b) Sometimes, however, you have to be more careful. For example, show that you cannot set $z = 0$ and successfully solve for x and y when the planes are described by the equations

$$6x + 7y + 8z \;=\; 12$$
$$6x + 7y + 10z \;=\; 0$$

(c) Based on what you found in part (b), you know that there is *no* point on the xy-plane (i.e., when $z = 0$) that's on the line of intersection. What does that tell you about the orientation of the line in space?

(d) If you haven't already, find a point on the intersection of the planes P_1 and P_2, described by (5.9) and (5.10) respectively, by setting $z = 0$.

(e) The line where P_1 and P_2 intersect must always stay on P_1, so its direction must be orthogonal to $\mathbf{n}_1 = \langle 6, 7, 8 \rangle$. Similarly, the line must stay on P_2, so its direction must be orthogonal to $\mathbf{n}_2 = \langle 2, 1, 9 \rangle$. Use the cross product to find a direction that is orthogonal to both $\mathbf{n}_1$ and $\mathbf{n}_2$.

(f) Now that you know a point on the line and a direction, write the symmetric equations for the line.

(g) Repeat part (d), but this time set $y = 0$ and use the pair of equations to determine the associated values of x and z. Using the directional information from part (e), write symmetric equations for the line through this new point. Is it the same as what you found in part (f)? *Should* it be?

In exercises #76–78, use the technique of #75 to determine symmetric equations for the line where the given planes intersect.

76. $4x - 7y + 3z = 0$ and $5x + 2y - 12z = 8$

77. $14x + 4y - 3z = 0$ and $14x + 4y - 10z = 6$

78. $-x + y + z = 12$ and $3x + 10y - z = 0$

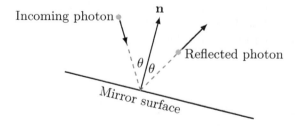

Figure 5.12: For #79, a photon reflecting off of a mirrored surface.

79. When a photon of light reflects off of a surface, the angle of incidence, θ, equals the angle of reflection. The angle θ is the angle between the linear path of the photon and the normal vector to the surface, $\mathbf{n}$, as seen in Figure 5.12. Suppose that a photon of light is traveling in the direction $\mathbf{v} = \langle 1, -7 \rangle$ when it encounters a flat mirror described by $x + 3y = 0$.

Optics

(a) Write a normal vector for the mirror, **n**.

(b) Find a vector **m** that is orthogonal to **n**.

(c) Determine the following numbers: $\hat{\mathbf{n}} \cdot \hat{\mathbf{n}}$, $\hat{\mathbf{m}} \cdot \hat{\mathbf{m}}$, and $\hat{\mathbf{n}} \cdot \hat{\mathbf{m}}$.

(d) Use the dot product to determine numbers a and b for which $\mathbf{v} = a\hat{\mathbf{n}} + b\hat{\mathbf{m}}$.

(e) Draw the vectors $a\hat{\mathbf{n}}$, $b\hat{\mathbf{m}}$ and $a\hat{\mathbf{n}} + b\hat{\mathbf{m}}$.

(f) When the photon reflects off of the mirror, the component of its velocity in the direction of **n** changes sign. Draw the vector $\tilde{\mathbf{v}} = -a\hat{\mathbf{n}} + b\hat{\mathbf{m}}$ on your diagram from part (e).

(g) Express $\tilde{\mathbf{v}}$ in terms of **i** and **j**.

80. Suppose a photon of light is traveling in the direction $\mathbf{v} = \langle 3, -2 \rangle$ when it encounters a flat mirror described by $2x - y = 0$. Determine the direction in which the photon will travel after it's reflected off of the mirror.

Optics

81. Suppose a photon of light is traveling in the direction $\mathbf{v} = \langle 1, -2, -4 \rangle$ when it encounters a flat mirror described by $x + y + 7z = 0$. Determine the direction in which the reflected photon will travel after it's reflected off of the mirror.

Optics

82. Suppose a photon of light is traveling in the direction $\mathbf{v} = \langle 1, -1, 4 \rangle$ when it encounters a flat mirror described by $x - y + 6z = 0$. Determine the direction in which the reflected photon will travel after it's reflected off of the mirror.

Optics

83. Suppose the extension ladder of a ladder truck is elevated 39° with respect to the horizontal road, and is positioned directly over the truck. The ladder is initially retracted, and its last rung is 45 feet from the base of the ladder. Design a position function $\mathbf{r}(t)$ that describes the position of the last rung on the ladder as it extends at a constant rate for 180 seconds, after which the final rung is 121 feet from the base of the ladder. Use the base of the ladder as the origin (see Figure 5.13), let **i** denote the direction in which the truck is facing, and let **k** denote the vertical direction.

84. Suppose the extension ladder of the truck in #83 is not initially positioned directly over the truck, but rather is swung 30° to the left of the truck. Using the vectors **i** and **k** as described in #83, and the additional vector **j**, design a position function $\mathbf{r}(t)$ that describes the position of the last rung on the ladder as it extends at a constant rate over the course of 180 seconds, after which the final rung is 121 feet from the base of the ladder.

Figure 5.13: A ladder truck.

85. Suppose that, while doing some internet research, you find the recommended daily allowance of Vitamin A is 3000 IU (International Units), the RDA of Vitamin C is 90 mg, and the RDA of Vitamin E is 15 mg. Additionally, you find the vitamin content of certain foods, listed in the table below:

Nutrition Science

1 serving \ Vitamin	A (IU)	C (mg)	E (mg)
Broccoli	103	89	0.78
Bell pepper	500	174	0.65
Apple	98	8.4	0.33

where 1 serving of broccoli or bell pepper means 100 g, and of apple means a medium sized apple. Using x, y and z to represent servings of broccoli, apple, and bell pepper respectively, write inequalities saying that your recommended daily allowance of vitamins A, B and C is satisfied by your consumption of these foods each day.

86. Excess vitamin intake can result in health problems. Suppose that your internet research indicates that you should not have more than 10,000 IU of Vitamin A per day, nor more than 2000 mg of Vitamin C, nor more than 1000 mg of Vitamin E. (a) Using the data from the table in #85, express the daily constraints of vitamin consumption in terms of x, y and z, (b) explain how these surfaces differ from those in #85, and (c) determine the volume of 3-space in which (x, y, z) safely satisfies your nutritional requirements.

                | Nutrition Science |

87. Suppose you have three plants that supply a specific commodity to various markets around the world. A specific market requires a total of 10000 units of your commodity. Let x, y and z denote the units shipped to this market from plants X, Y and Z respectively. (a) Write an equation saying that your company meets the demand in this market. (b) Describe the surface defined by your equation in part (a). (c) Explain what happens to this surface when the demand in this market changes.

                | Business |

88. Suppose your company supplies a specific commodity to various markets around the world. Let x, y and z denote the units shipped to markets X, Y and Z respectively. The production capacity of your company's plant is 3500 units per month. (a) Write an inequality saying that the total number of items shipped does not exceed the plant's capacity, and (b) in complete sentences describe the surface determined by the equation in part (a), including a discussion of how increasing the plant's capacity affects the surface.

                | Business |

89. Suppose molecules of type X and Y combine to make Z according to $X + 3Y \rightleftharpoons 2Z$, and x, y, z are the respective changes in free energy. Write an equation that says the chemical reaction is at equilibrium.

                | Chemistry |

90. Suppose molecules of type X and Y combine to make Z according to $3X + 5Y \rightleftharpoons Z$, and x, y, z are the respective changes in free energy. If $3x + 5y - z = -2$, will molecules of type Z tend to be created, tend to disassociate, or is the chemical reaction at equilibrium?

                | Chemistry |

Chapter 11 Review

❖ True or False?

1. Vectors are determined by position, direction, and magnitude.

2. If the vectors $\mathbf{u}$ and $\mathbf{v}$ point in opposite directions, they are parallel.

3. Suppose $\mathbf{u}$ and $\mathbf{v}$ are nonzero vectors for which $|\mathbf{u} \cdot \mathbf{v}| = \|\mathbf{u}\|\,\|\mathbf{v}\|$. Then $\mathbf{u}$ is a multiple of $\mathbf{v}$.

4. Suppose $\mathbf{u}$ is a unit vector in the plane, and $\mathbf{v}$ and $\mathbf{w}$ are nonzero 2-vectors for which $\mathbf{v} \cdot \mathbf{u} = 0$ and $\mathbf{w} \cdot \mathbf{u} = 0$. Then $\mathbf{v}$ is a multiple of $\mathbf{w}$.

5. Suppose $\mathbf{u}$ is a two-dimensional unit vector, and $\mathbf{v}$ and $\mathbf{w}$ are 2-vectors for which $\mathbf{v} \cdot \mathbf{u} = 0$ and $\mathbf{w} \cdot \mathbf{u} = 0$. Then $\mathbf{v}$ is a multiple of $\mathbf{w}$.

6. $\operatorname{proj}_{\mathbf{v}} \mathbf{u} = (\operatorname{comp}_{\mathbf{v}} \mathbf{u})\,\hat{\mathbf{v}}$

7. $\operatorname{proj}_{\mathbf{v}} \mathbf{v} = \mathbf{v}$

8. $\operatorname{comp}_{\mathbf{u}} \mathbf{u} = \|\mathbf{u}\|$

9. When $\mathbf{u} \cdot \mathbf{v} = 0$ we know that either $\mathbf{u} = 0$ or $\mathbf{v} = 0$.

10. When $\mathbf{u} \times \mathbf{v} = 0$ we know that either $\mathbf{u} = 0$ or $\mathbf{v} = 0$.

11. *Normal* vectors and *normalized* vectors are the same thing.

12. Suppose $\mathbf{u}, \mathbf{v}$ and $\mathbf{w}$ are 3-vectors. Then $(\mathbf{u} \times \mathbf{v}) \cdot \mathbf{w} = -(\mathbf{u} \times \mathbf{w}) \cdot \mathbf{v}$.

13. Suppose $b \in \mathbb{R}$. Then $\|b\mathbf{u}\| = b\|\mathbf{u}\|$.

14. Suppose $b \in \mathbb{R}$. Then $\mathbf{u}$ and $b\mathbf{u}$ point in the same direction.

15. When $\mathbf{u} \cdot \mathbf{v} < 0$, the angle between $\mathbf{u}$ and $\mathbf{v}$ is obtuse.

16. $\operatorname{proj}_{\mathbf{u}} \mathbf{v} = \operatorname{proj}_{\mathbf{u}}(\operatorname{proj}_{\mathbf{u}} \mathbf{v})$

17. The cross product $\mathbf{u} \times \mathbf{v}$ is parallel to $\langle 5, 9, 12 \rangle$ when $\mathbf{u} = \langle 4, 2, 3 \rangle$ and $\mathbf{v} = \langle 1, 7, 9 \rangle$.

18. The vectors $\mathbf{u} \times \mathbf{v}$ and $\mathbf{v} \times \mathbf{u}$ are the same.

19. The vector $\mathbf{u} \times \mathbf{v}$ is orthogonal to $\mathbf{u}$.

20. The planes $2x + 4y + z = 10$ and $2x + 4y + z = 14$ are parallel.

21. The plane described by $3x - 7y + 6z = 0$ passes through the origin.

22. The origin is 10 units away from the plane $x + 4y - 2z = 10$.

❖ Multiple Choice

23. Which of the following quantities (if any) are vectors?

    (a) profit
    (b) temperature
    (c) momentum

    (d) speed
    (e) price

24. A unit vector is ...

    (a) a vector whose magnitude is 1   (d) a vector whose components multiply to 1

    (b) a vector whose components are all ones   (e) none of the above

    (c) a vector whose components sum to 1

25. The notation $\mathbf{u} \cdot (\mathbf{v} \cdot \mathbf{w})$ ...

    (a) denotes a scalar   (d) doesn't make sense

    (b) denotes a vector   (e) none of the above

    (c) is always zero

26. The term $\text{proj}_{\mathbf{v}}\mathbf{u}$ means ...

    (a) the vector projection of $\mathbf{u}$ onto $\mathbf{v}$ (d) the scalar projection of $\mathbf{v}$ onto $\mathbf{u}$

    (b) the scalar projection of $\mathbf{u}$ onto $\mathbf{v}$ (e) none of the above

    (c) the vector projection of $\mathbf{v}$ onto $\mathbf{u}$

27. The term $\text{comp}_{\mathbf{v}}\mathbf{u}$ is ...

    (a) a vector   (d) a scalar

    (b) a *unit* vector   (e) none of the above

    (c) a function

28. Suppose $\mathbf{u}$ is a nonzero 2-vector, and $f(\mathbf{v})$ is the component of $\mathbf{u}$ in the direction of $\mathbf{v}$. Then $f(\mathbf{v})$ ...

    (a) is largest when $\mathbf{v}$ points in the direction of $\mathbf{u}$ (d) is always between -1 and 1

    (b) is largest when $\mathbf{v}$ is orthogonal to $\mathbf{u}$ (e) none of the above

    (c) is zero exactly one time

29. Suppose that $\mathbf{u} \cdot \mathbf{v} = 1$. Then ...

    (a) $\mathbf{u} = 1/\mathbf{v}$ (d) either $\mathbf{u} = 1$ or $\mathbf{v} = 1$

    (b) $\|\mathbf{u}\| = \|\mathbf{v}\|^{-1}$ (e) none of the above

    (c) $\mathbf{u} = \mathbf{v}$

30. The number $\|\mathbf{u} \times \mathbf{v}\|$ is ...

    (a) $\|\mathbf{u}\|\,\|\mathbf{v}\| \cos\theta$, where θ is the angle between $\mathbf{u}$ and $\mathbf{v}$

    (b) $(\|\mathbf{u}\|+\|\mathbf{v}\|)/2$

    (c) the area of a parallelogram

    (d) orthogonal to both $\mathbf{u}$ and $\mathbf{v}$

    (e) none of the above

31. The scalar triple product is ...

    (a) zero if the vectors are coplanar   (d) the volume of a parallelepiped

    (b) the area of a parallelogram   (e) none of the above

    (c) the average length of the vectors

32. Suppose that $\mathbf{u} \times \mathbf{v} = \mathbf{u} \times \mathbf{w}$. Then ...

    (a) $\mathbf{v} = \mathbf{w}$ (d) $\mathbf{v}$ and $\mathbf{w}$ are parallel

    (b) $\mathbf{u} \times \mathbf{v} = 0$ (e) none of the above

    (c) $\mathbf{v}$ and $\mathbf{w}$ are coplanar

33. Determine whether any three of the following vectors are coplanar.

$$\mathbf{u} = \langle 2.3, 10.4, 7.5 \rangle, \qquad \mathbf{v} = \langle -1.5, -2.1, 3.4 \rangle,$$

$$\mathbf{w} = \langle 7.7, 39.5, 33.4 \rangle, \qquad \mathbf{z} = \langle -2.87, -17.66, -17.65 \rangle$$

    (a) $\mathbf{u}, \mathbf{v}$ and $\mathbf{w}$ are coplanar   (d) All of the vectors are coplanar

    (b) $\mathbf{u}, \mathbf{v}$ and $\mathbf{z}$ are coplanar   (e) No three are coplanar

    (c) $\mathbf{u}, \mathbf{w}$ and $\mathbf{z}$ are coplanar

34. Which of the following lines (if any) are the same?

    i $(x-2)/6 = (y+4)/6 = (z-5)/3$ iii $(x-2)/2 = (y+4)/2 = (z-5)/1$

    ii $(x-5)/1 = (y+2)/4 = (z+8)/9$ iv $(x-3)/1 = (y-5)/4 = (z-7)/9$

    (a) only (i) and (iii)   (d) all are different lines

    (b) only (ii) and (iv)   (e) all are the same line

    (c) only (i) and (iv)

❖ Exercises

35. Explain what's wrong with the notation in (a) $\|\mathbf{u} \cdot \mathbf{v}\| = 7$ and (b) $|\mathbf{u}| = 2$.

36. Suppose a friend needs to determine $\text{proj}_\mathbf{u}\mathbf{v}$, and so calculates $\left(\mathbf{v} \cdot \frac{\mathbf{u}}{\|\mathbf{u}\|} \right) \frac{\mathbf{v}}{\|\mathbf{v}\|}$. Explain what's wrong with his calculation.

37. Suppose $\mathbf{v} = \langle 2, 1, 7 \rangle$ and $\mathbf{u} = \langle 4, 2, 14 \rangle$. Explain why $\text{proj}_\mathbf{v}\mathbf{w} = \text{proj}_\mathbf{u}\mathbf{w}$ for every 3-vector $\mathbf{w}$.

38. What do you know about the nonzero vectors $\mathbf{u}$ and $\mathbf{v}$ if $\text{proj}_\mathbf{v}\mathbf{u} = \mathbf{0}$?

39. Suppose $\mathbf{v}$ is a 2-vector and $\|\mathbf{v}\| = 4$. What is described by (a) $\hat{\mathbf{u}} \cdot \mathbf{v} = 2$, and (b) $\hat{\mathbf{u}} \cdot \mathbf{v} \le 2$?

40. Suppose $\mathbf{v}$ is a 3-vector and $\|\mathbf{v}\| = 4$. What is described by (a) $\hat{\mathbf{u}} \cdot \mathbf{v} = 2$, and (b) $\hat{\mathbf{u}} \cdot \mathbf{v} \le 2$?

41. Find a vector with a magnitude of 5 that points in the opposite direction of $\langle 13, -1 \rangle$.

42. Find $\mathbf{u}$ if it points in the direction of $\langle 2, 5, -3 \rangle$, and $\|\mathbf{u}\| = 7$.

43. Suppose $\mathbf{u} = \langle 2, 3 \rangle$, $\mathbf{v} = \langle 1, 4 \rangle$, and $\mathbf{w} = \langle 1, -1/4 \rangle$. (a) Verify that $\mathbf{v}$ and $\mathbf{w}$ are orthogonal, and (b) use the dot product to determine values for a and b so that $\mathbf{u} = a\mathbf{v} + b\mathbf{w}$.

44. Suppose $\mathbf{u} = \langle 5, 2, -6 \rangle$, $\mathbf{v} = \langle 3, -1, -4 \rangle$, $\mathbf{w} = \langle 0, 4, -1 \rangle$, and $\mathbf{n} = \langle 17, 3, 12 \rangle$. (a) Verify that each of $\mathbf{v}$, $\mathbf{w}$, and $\mathbf{n}$ is orthogonal to the other two vectors, (b) then use the dot product to determine numbers a, b, and c so that $\mathbf{u} = a\mathbf{v} + b\mathbf{w} + c\mathbf{n}$.

45. Find a vector that's orthogonal to $\langle 3, 8 \rangle$.

46. Find two vectors that are orthogonal to $\langle 3, -2, 8 \rangle$.

47. Determine the area of the parallelogram defined by $\mathbf{v} = \langle 1, 9, 0 \rangle$ and $\mathbf{u} = \langle -2, 1, 0 \rangle$.

48. Suppose $\mathbf{u} = \langle 1, 1, 7 \rangle$ and $\mathbf{v} = \langle 1, -2, -4 \rangle$. A student makes the calculation $\mathbf{u} \times \mathbf{v} = \langle 10, 14, -3 \rangle$. She checks her work and finds that $\mathbf{u} \cdot \langle 10, 14, -3 \rangle = 3$. Explain how she knows that there must be an error in her work.

49. Show that the plane through the origin defined by $\langle 3, 1, 2 \rangle$ and $\langle -1, -4, 5 \rangle$ is the same as the plane through the origin defined by $\langle 11.4, 32.4, -36.6 \rangle$ and $\langle -25.8, -15.2, -7 \rangle$.

50. Find the equation of the plane that passes through the points $(5, 4, 6)$, $(2, 1, 3)$ and $(-2, -7, 8)$.

51. Find the equation of the plane that passes through the point $(5, 4, 6)$ and contains the directions $\langle 2, 1, 3 \rangle$ and $\langle -2, -7, 8 \rangle$.

52. Calculate the volume of the parallelepiped defined by $\mathbf{u} = \langle 1, 2, 3 \rangle$, $\mathbf{v} = \langle 3, 2, 1 \rangle$, and $\mathbf{w} = \langle -1, -1, 1 \rangle$.

53. Suppose a photon of light is traveling in the direction $\mathbf{v} = \langle 2, 5 \rangle$ when it encounters a flat mirror described by $x - 2y = 0$. Determine the direction in which the photon will travel after it's reflected off of the mirror.

54. Suppose a photon of light is traveling in the direction $\mathbf{v} = \langle 1, -3, 1 \rangle$ when it encounters a flat mirror described by $2x + y - z = 0$. Determine the direction in which the photon will travel after it's reflected off of the mirror.

55. Suppose that points A, B, C lie on the circle of radius r that's centered at the origin. These points define a triangle $\triangle ABC$. Denote by D the point at which the altitudes extending from vertices A and C intersect (see Figure 6.1), and O will denote the origin.

(a) Explain why $\overrightarrow{AD} \cdot \overrightarrow{BC} = 0$.

(b) Use head-to-tail addition to show that $\overrightarrow{AD} = \overrightarrow{OD} - \overrightarrow{OA}$.

(c) Use head-to-tail addition to show that $\overrightarrow{BC} = \overrightarrow{OC} - \overrightarrow{OB}$.

(d) Explain why $\overrightarrow{CD} \cdot \overrightarrow{BA} = 0$.

(e) Use head-to-tail addition to show that $\overrightarrow{CD} = \overrightarrow{OD} - \overrightarrow{OC}$.

(f) Use head-to-tail addition to show that $\overrightarrow{BA} = \overrightarrow{OA} - \overrightarrow{OB}$.

(g) Explain why the following equation is true: *(Hint: angles)*

$$\left(\overrightarrow{OD} - \overrightarrow{OC} \right) \cdot \left(\overrightarrow{OA} - \overrightarrow{OB} \right) = \left(\overrightarrow{OD} - \overrightarrow{OA} \right) \cdot \left(\overrightarrow{OC} - \overrightarrow{OB} \right). \tag{6.1}$$

(h) Distribute the dot products in equation (6.1) and verify that it can be rewritten as

$$\left(\overrightarrow{OD} - \overrightarrow{OB} \right) \cdot \left(\overrightarrow{OA} - \overrightarrow{OC} \right) = 0. \tag{6.2}$$

(i) Explain how (6.2) tells us that D also lies on the altitude of $\triangle ABC$ that proceeds from vertex B.

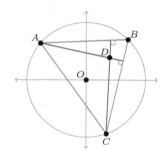
Figure 6.1: For #55

56. Suppose the sun is at the origin of the Cartesian plane, and Earth is at the point $(10.94, 5.47)$, where x and y are measured in *millions* of kilometers. Find the force experienced by the sun due to the earth's gravity.

Astronomy

57. Suppose an object with a mass of m kilograms is 17,000 km from the center of the Earth, at the point (x, y, z), where we have taken the origin to be at the center of the earth.

Physics

    (a) Show that the force experienced by the mass is

$$\mathbf{F} = -\frac{3.98199 \times 10^{14} m}{(17,000)^3} \begin{bmatrix} x \\ y \\ z \end{bmatrix}.$$

    (b) Back in Chapter 1, we said that the gravitational force was an inverse-*square* law, so why is the exponent in the denominator a 3?

58. An ionized particle with a charge of $q = 8.0108823 \times 10^{-19}$ coulombs is traveling in the direction of $\langle 3, -1, 8 \rangle$ at 50 meters per second. What force does it experience as it passes through a magnetic field of $\mathbf{B} = \langle 4, 5, -2 \rangle$, measured in teslas?

Physics

59. Use the fact that $\|\mathbf{w}\|^2 = \mathbf{w} \cdot \mathbf{w}$ to verify the *parallelogram law*, which says that $\|\mathbf{u} + \mathbf{v}\|^2 + \|\mathbf{u} - \mathbf{v}\|^2 = 2\|\mathbf{u}\|^2 + 2\|\mathbf{v}\|^2$.

Geometry

60. The *polarization identity* says $\mathbf{u} \cdot \mathbf{v} = \frac{1}{4}\left(\|\mathbf{u} + \mathbf{v}\|^2 - \|\mathbf{u} - \mathbf{v}\|^2\right)$.

Geometry

    (a) Use the fact that $\|\mathbf{w}\|^2 = \mathbf{w} \cdot \mathbf{w}$ to verify the polarization identity.

    (b) Draw nonzero 2-vectors $\mathbf{u}$ and $\mathbf{v}$ with their tails together.

    (c) Add the vectors $\mathbf{u} + \mathbf{v}$ and $\mathbf{u} - \mathbf{v}$ onto the drawing from part (b) as the diagonals of the parallelogram defined by $\mathbf{u}$ and $\mathbf{v}$.

    (d) What does the polarization identity say about these diagonals when $\mathbf{u}$ and $\mathbf{v}$ are orthogonal?

    (e) What does the polarization identity say about these diagonals when the angle between $\mathbf{u}$ and $\mathbf{v}$ is acute? obtuse?

61. Suppose the vectors shown in Figure 6.2 are $\mathbf{u} = \langle \cos\theta, \sin\theta \rangle$ and $\mathbf{v} = \langle \cos\phi, \sin\phi \rangle$.

    (a) Verify that $\|\mathbf{u}\| = 1$ and $\|\mathbf{v}\| = 1$.

    (b) The angle between these unit vectors is $\phi - \theta$, so we know that their dot product is
$$\mathbf{u} \cdot \mathbf{v} = \|\mathbf{u}\| \, \|\mathbf{v}\| \, \cos(\phi - \theta) = \cos(\phi - \theta).$$

    However, we could also use the component formula for calculating the dot product to make the same calculation. This leads us to write (you should complete the equation)

$$\cos(\phi - \theta) = \mathbf{u} \cdot \mathbf{v} = \underline{\hspace{3cm}}.$$

    (c) Compare your answer from part (b) to the difference formula for the cosine.

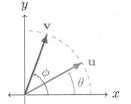

Figure 6.2: Vectors for #61 and #62.

62. Suppose the vectors shown in Figure 6.2 are $\mathbf{u} = \langle \cos\theta, \sin\theta, 0 \rangle$ and $\mathbf{v} = \langle \cos\phi, \sin\phi, 0 \rangle$.

    (a) Verify that $\|\mathbf{u}\| = 1$ and $\|\mathbf{v}\| = 1$.

(b) The angle between these unit vectors is $\phi - \theta$, so the magnitude of their cross product is

$$\|\mathbf{u} \times \mathbf{v}\| = \|\mathbf{u}\| \|\mathbf{v}\| \sin(\phi - \theta) = \sin(\phi - \theta).$$

We also know that, due to the right-hand rule, the vector $\mathbf{u} \times \mathbf{v}$ points out of the page (toward you) in the direction of $\mathbf{k}$. So the first two components of $\mathbf{u} \times \mathbf{v}$ are 0, and the last is positive. Determine a formula for the last component of $\mathbf{u} \times \mathbf{v}$ and use that information to complete the following equation:

$$\sin(\phi - \theta) = \|\mathbf{u} \times \mathbf{v}\| = \underline{\hspace{3cm}}.$$

(c) Compare your answer from part (b) to the difference formula for the sine.

63. Determine the symmetric equations for the line that passes through the points $(3, 4, -10)$ and $(-4, 1, 2)$.

64. Suppose ℓ is the line described by $\frac{x-4}{3} = \frac{y-1}{2} = \frac{z-5}{9}$. Write the symmetric equations for a line through the point $(9, 1, -6)$ that's parallel to ℓ.

65. The point $(9, 2, 1)$ is on the plane P. If you stay on the plane but move one unit in the direction of $\mathbf{i}$, the value of z increases by 3. If you move one unit in the direction of $\mathbf{j}$ while staying on the plane, the value of z increases by 5. Determine an equation that describes P.

66. The point $(2, 3, -1)$ is on the plane P. If you stay on the plane but move one unit in the direction of $\mathbf{i}$, the value of z decreases by 7. If you move one unit in the direction of $\mathbf{j}$ while staying on the plane, the value of z increases by 12. Determine an equation that describes P.

67. When hydrogen gas is mixed with oxygen gas, they synthesize to make water: | Chemistry |

$$2H_2 + O_2 \rightleftharpoons 2H_2O.$$

Write the equation for the plane that describes the equilibrium condition for this reaction.

Chapter 11 Projects and Applications

❖ Rings

Imagine that in the planning stages for an unmanned mission to Jupiter, the science team decides to have the probe investigate the Jovian rings. Part of that investigation will involve locating objects in a particular ring, and transmitting their coordinates back to Earth. The science team will use a computer to detect and remove errors in the data received from the probe, and then determine the size of the ring from the cleaned data.

In this project, your job is to design and implement a simple, preliminary version of the computer algorithm. It must (1) detect whether specified points are coplanar, and if so (2) determine whether the points lie on a circle, and if so (3) determine the center and radius of the circle. Your algorithm will have to tolerate the finite precision of the data you receive, in which coordinates will be measured in kilometers.

Data sets for testing your algorithm are provided below.

	POINT 1	POINT 2	POINT 3	POINT 4	POINT 5	POINT 6	POINT 7	POINT 8	POINT 9
x	−28.0393	74.1882	−5.6971	−29.8231	14.8866	29.0794	34.0089	6.1058	−1.9667
y	75.3177	121.393	108.456	81.6755	115.889	119.027	119.826	113.220	110.137
z	16.6877	99.5737	83.7228	30.4291	96.5008	101.098	102.076	92.1137	86.7474

	POINT 1	POINT 2	POINT 3	POINT 4	POINT 5	POINT 6	POINT 7	POINT 8	POINT 9
x	42.1031	42.0108	42.1706	39.6732	42.8543	42.6131	42.4412	42.5359	41.2444
y	60.7645	61.5128	60.0761	61.8664	59.4701	60.2325	59.6329	59.7659	62.2911
z	79.6893	80.1919	79.3054	79.3395	79.4047	79.7734	79.2062	79.3507	80.05913

	POINT 1	POINT 2	POINT 3	POINT 4	POINT 5	POINT 6	POINT 7	POINT 8	POINT 9
x	53.8561	62.6378	−2.8748	63.4142	37.7435	−5.1248	8.8819	30.5510	68.2079
y	1.3763	−6.7552	34.0217	−7.5675	13.2413	34.8827	29.0539	17.7233	−13.1223
z	47.8327	48.3958	26.9741	48.3647	44.1542	25.7710	32.8534	41.8068	47.7055

After designing and testing your algorithm, you should write a report in which you analyze these data and explain the mathematical ideas and techniques that you use.

❖ Remote Sensing, Vectors and Statistics

When search planes or spy satellites photograph an area, they're typically looking for a target of some kind—be it a small brush fire, a lost hiker, or an enemy tank. The photos that are produced by these fly-overs can contain huge amounts of data, which leads us to develop algorithms that automatically alert analysts to potential targets. This project is intended to begin a discussion of such algorithms by introducing a method based on *standard deviation*, which is calculated using a dot product.

▷ Development of basic statistical tools

For the sake of simplicity while we develop the relevant ideas, we're going to deal with only *three* data: x_1, x_2 and x_3.

> We're going to discuss data sets with only three samples because we can visualize them as 3-vectors, but data sets are typically much larger. Luckily, the ideas that we develop for small data sets extend to any number of data. (You'll see this formally in a course called *Linear Algebra*.)

Broadly speaking, one of the most important things to understand about data is the extent to which it varies from its average. In this case, the word *average* refers to the *arithmetic mean* of the data:

$$\mu = \frac{x_1 + x_2 + x_3}{3} \ ,$$

or equivalently,

$$3\mu = x_1 + x_2 + x_3. \tag{7.1}$$

If our data didn't vary from the mean at all, the vector $\mathbf{x} = \langle x_1, x_2, x_3 \rangle$ would be $\langle \mu, \mu, \mu \rangle = \mu\mathbf{1}$ (where $\mathbf{1} = \langle 1, 1, 1 \rangle$).

1. The vector $\mathbf{x} - \mu\mathbf{1}$ is the difference between our data set and what it *would* be if it *were* constant (with the same mean). Use the dot product to show that $\mathbf{x} - \mu\mathbf{1}$ is orthogonal to $\mu\mathbf{1}$, as suggested by Figure 7.1.

2. Based on #1, we can quantify the extent to which the components of $\mathbf{x}$ are not constant by

$$\|\mathbf{x} - \mu\mathbf{1}\| = \sqrt{(x_1 - \mu)^2 + (x_2 - \mu)^2 + (x_3 - \mu)^2}. \tag{7.2}$$

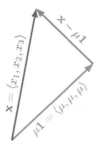

Figure 7.1: Constant, and nonconstant data sets.

The terms under the radical are not negative, so their average will also be non-negative; that average is called the **variance** of the data and is denoted σ^2, so the analog of equation (7.1) is

$$3\sigma^2 = (x_1 - \mu)^2 + (x_2 - \mu)^2 + (x_3 - \mu)^2.$$

This allows us to simplify equation (7.2) by rewriting it as

$$\|\mathbf{x} - \mu\mathbf{1}\| = \sqrt{3\sigma^2} = \sigma\sqrt{3} \ . \tag{7.3}$$

The number σ is called the **standard deviation** of the data. If x_1, x_2 and x_3 are measured in meters, what are the units associated with the mean, variance, and standard deviation of the data?

3. How do the formulas for variance and standard deviation change if we have n data instead of just 3?

> When dealing with a random sample of a population, which we are not doing here, the *sample variance* of n data is commonly found by adding the squared-difference-from-the-means and then dividing by $n - 1$ instead of n (so we would use the number 2 instead of 3 in this example). This accounts for something called *bias*, which you'll see in an introductory statistics course. We don't face it here because we are including the entire "population" of pixels.

▷ Application to photo analysis

Each pixel in a photo defines a 3-vector according to the amount of red, green, and blue required to render it. That is, pixel j corresponds to the vector $\langle r_j, g_j, b_j \rangle$. When the image has n pixels, the "average pixel" is

$$\boldsymbol{\mu} = \frac{1}{n} \sum_{j=1}^{n} \langle r_j, g_j, b_j \rangle.$$

> Real data sets are often treated with *hyper-spectral imaging* techniques in which the light spectrum is divided into k bands, where k is much larger than 3, so each pixel corresponds to vector in k-space. You can learn to work with such vectors in a course called *Linear Algebra*.

The vector $\boldsymbol{\mu}$ serves to estimate the image *background*, and our target-detection method is to look for pixels that a stray "far enough" from it. The key to implementing such an algorithm is quantifying "far enough." In this case, we're going to focus on direction. The angle that separates pixel-vector j from the "average" direction is

$$\theta_j = \cos^{-1}\left(\frac{\langle r_j, g_j, b_j \rangle \cdot \boldsymbol{\mu}}{\|\langle r_j, g_j, b_j \rangle\| \, \|\boldsymbol{\mu}\|} \right).$$

With these angles in hand, we can calculate the mean and standard deviation of θ_j, denoted by μ_θ and σ_θ respectively. For our purposes, let's say that a pixel will be "too far" from the background if it's "more than one standard deviation beyond the mean separation from $\boldsymbol{\mu}$." For example, the blue dots in Figure 7.2 lie at the heads of pixel-vectors that are too far away from $\boldsymbol{\mu}$, and so warrant closer scrutiny.

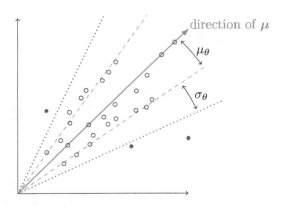

Figure 7.2: A diagram depicting the relationship among $\boldsymbol{\mu}$, μ_θ and σ_θ. The white circles are placed at the heads of $\langle r, g, b \rangle$ vectors from an image. The blue circles correspond to pixels that require attention because they vary "too far" from the background.

Even a small image has far too many pixels to print in a book, but here's a data set that you can work with more easily. Try using the method described above to locate the outlier(s).

Pixel	1	2	3	4	5	6	7	8	9	10
r	103	116	35	123	122	18	101	104	86	50
g	115	80	69	20	61	53	122	108	96	83
b	16	12	122	123	102	116	83	119	94	21

▷ Vectors and correlation

In various contexts, we often want to know the extent to which two sets of data vary together. Sometimes the relationship is linear, or *almost* linear, in which case we talk about the **correlation** of the data sets. The exercises below will examine this idea through the lens of vector algebra.

1. Suppose we have a $\mathbf{x} = \langle x_1, x_2, x_3 \rangle$ with mean μ_x and standard deviation σ_x, and $\mathbf{y} = \langle y_1, y_2, y_3 \rangle$ with a mean of μ_y and standard deviation of σ_y. Show that

$$\frac{1}{\sqrt{3}\,\sigma_x}(\mathbf{x} - \mu_x \mathbf{1}) \quad \text{and} \quad \frac{1}{\sqrt{3}\,\sigma_y}(\mathbf{y} - \mu_y \mathbf{1})$$

are unit vectors, so

$$\frac{(\mathbf{y} - \mu_y \mathbf{1}) \cdot (\mathbf{x} - \mu_x \mathbf{1})}{3\sigma_y \sigma_x} = \cos\theta, \tag{7.4}$$

where θ is the angle between $(\mathbf{x} - \mu_x \mathbf{1})$ and $(\mathbf{y} - \mu_y \mathbf{1})$.

> We are restricting the scope of this discussion to sets of only 3 data because we know what it means to find the dot product of vectors in 3-space, and we understand how it relates to angles between 3-vectors. However, equation (7.4) can be extended to sets of n data once you understand the relationship between angles and dot products in n-dimensional space. This topic is covered in a course called *Linear Algebra*.

2. The value of $\cos\theta$ calculated in (7.4) is called the **correlation** of the data sets, and here we'll denote it by $\rho(x, y)$. When $\rho(x, y) = 1$, what do you know about the vectors $(\mathbf{x} - \mu_x \mathbf{1})$ and $(\mathbf{y} - \mu_y \mathbf{1})$?

3. Suppose $\mathbf{x} = \langle 2, 7, 3 \rangle$, and $\mathbf{y}$ is another data set with $\mu_y = 2$ and $\sigma_y = 1.2$, for which $\rho(x, y) = 1$. Determine y_1, y_2, and y_3.

4. Suppose $\rho(x, y) = 0$. What do you know about $(\mathbf{x} - \mu_x \mathbf{1})$ and $(\mathbf{y} - \mu_y \mathbf{1})$?

✧ Physical Fields

The following exercises will introduce you to the modern ideas of vector fields in the physical sciences. We begin with the gravitational field because of our general familiarity with gravity, and then move to electric fields, which are important to modern technology.

▷ Gravitational fields

The arrows drawn in Figure 7.3 serve to conclude the sentence, "If a mass of m kilograms were *here,* it would experience a force of . . . ." Such force vectors have a magnitude of $\|\mathbf{F}\| = (GM)(m)/r^2$, where G is the gravitational constant, M is the mass of the earth, and r is the distance between the earth and our hypothetical object (in meters). Now that you understand the component representation of vectors, you know that when the center of the earth is taken as the origin . . .

Figure 7.3:   Arrows representing gravitational force vectors.

a mass of	2 kg	3 kg	4 kg
at the point (x,y,z) would experience a force of	$(2)\frac{GM}{r^3}\begin{bmatrix} -x \\ -y \\ -z \end{bmatrix}$	$(3)\frac{GM}{r^3}\begin{bmatrix} -x \\ -y \\ -z \end{bmatrix}$	$(4)\frac{GM}{r^3}\begin{bmatrix} -x \\ -y \\ -z \end{bmatrix}$

$$(7.5)$$

where r is the distance (in meters) between the origin and the point (x, y, z). The part of the force vector that's always the same is

$$\mathbf{F}_e = -\frac{Gm_e}{r^3}\,\langle x, y, z\rangle, \qquad (7.6)$$

The "e" in $\mathbf{F}_e$ is for "Earth."

which we call the *gravitational field* due to the earth. We often use it to write the force calculation from equation (7.5) as $m\mathbf{F}_e$. If the earth is *not* at the origin, the component representation of the vector looks a little different, but the idea is the same.

1. In the paragraph above, we said that $m\mathbf{F}_e$ is a force, where m is the mass (measured in kilograms). What are the units associated with $\mathbf{F}_e$?

Now assume that distance is measured in meters.

2. Suppose the sun is at the origin, and Earth is at the point $(10.94 \times 10^9, 5.47 \times 10^9, 0)$. Find a component representation for the gravitational field due to the Earth, $\mathbf{F}_e$.

The formula will be slightly different than what you see in (7.6) because the Earth isn't at the origin, but all of the ideas are the same. The vectors will point at the center of the Earth.

3. Suppose that Jupiter, which has a mass of $M_j = 1.8987 \times 10^{27}$ kilograms, is at the point $(2 \times 10^{11}, 7.5216 \times 10^{11}, 0)$. Find a formula describing the gravitational field due to Jupiter, $\mathbf{F}_j$.

4. The sun (at the origin) has a mass of 1.98892×10^{30} kg. Find the gravitational field due to the sun, $\mathbf{F}_s$.

5. Find a formula for the net gravitational field of the sun, Earth and Jupiter by adding $\mathbf{F}_s + \mathbf{F}_e + \mathbf{F}_j$.

6. If we consider only the sun, Earth and Jupiter, determine the net gravitational *force* experienced by a mass of 100,000 kg at the point $(200 \times 10^9, 150 \times 10^9, 0)$.

▷ Electric fields

Just as matter experiences a force due to other matter (gravitational force), electric charges experience force due to other charges. However, while there is only one kind of matter from the standpoint of gravitational force, there are *two* kinds of charge, which we call positive and negative. The interaction we see depends on what charges are present: opposite charges attract (positive-negative), and like charges repel (positive-positive or negative-negative). The force that one stationary charge feels in the presence of another is called *electrostatic* force. Specifically, suppose an electron is at the origin. Then a particle at the point (x, y, z) with a charge of q coulombs will experience a force of

$$\mathbf{F} = -\frac{eq}{4\pi\varepsilon r^3} \langle x, y, z \rangle, \tag{7.7}$$

Notice that the force points *toward* the origin when $q > 0$ (e.g., when our particle is a proton) and points *away* from the origin when $q < 0$ (e.g., when our particle is an electron).

where $e = 1.60217646 \times 10^{-19}$ coulombs, r is the distance between charges (in meters), and ε is a number called the *permittivity*. (The permittivity of a vacuum is $\varepsilon = 8.8541878176 \times 10^{-12}$.) The part of this force that's always the same, regardless of the charge on the second particle, is

$$\mathbf{E} = -\frac{e}{4\pi\varepsilon r^3} \langle x, y, z \rangle. \tag{7.8}$$

which we call the *electric field* due to the electron at the origin. We often use it to write the force calculation from equation (7.7) as $q\mathbf{E}$. Of course, if the electron is *not* at the origin, the component representation of the vector looks a little different, but the idea is the same.

7. In the paragraph above we said that $q\mathbf{E}$ is a force, where q is a charge (measured in coulombs). What are the units associated with $\mathbf{E}$?

Now suppose that distance is measured in meters.

The formula in #8 will be slightly different than what you see in equation (7.8). The vectors in #8 are directed toward $(5, 0, 7)$.

8. Find the electric field due to an electron at $(5, 0, 7)$.

9. Find the electric field due to an electron at $(-1, 0, 4)$.

10. Now suppose there's a proton at $(2, 0, -1)$. Where would we need to place an electron in order to hold the proton in place (i.e., to balance the forces from the electrons in #8 and #9)?

▷ Electrostatic vs. gravitational

Since $r = \sqrt{x^2 + y^2 + z^2} = \|\langle x, y, z \rangle\|$ in equation 7.8, we see that $\|\mathbf{E}\|$ is governed by an inverse square law, just like gravity. This fact was initially discovered by Charles Augustin de Coulomb (June 14, 1736–August 23, 1806), so we call it the *coulombic force law,* or just *Coulomb's Lomb* and write

$$\|\mathbf{F}_c\| = \frac{|q_1 q_2|}{4\pi\varepsilon r^2} \tag{7.9}$$

where q_1 and q_2 are signed quantities that measure the two charges in units of coulombs, r is the distance between them in meters.

11. An electron has a charge of $-1.60217646 \times 10^{-19}$ coulombs. Suppose that one electron sits at the origin, and another is two meters away. Find the magnitude of the electrostatic force on these electrons, $\|\mathbf{F}_c\|$.

12. An electron has a mass of $9.10938188 \times 10^{-31}$ kilograms. Find the magnitude of the gravitational force on the same two electrons, $\|\mathbf{F}_g\|$.

13. Use your answers from #11 and #12 to compare the magnitude of gravitational and electrostatic forces (e.g., calculate $\|\mathbf{F}_c\|/\|\mathbf{F}_g\|$).

▷ An application of fields to chemistry & physics

A technique called *mass spectroscopy* is used to find the molecular weight of substance, or to determine the purity of sample or the distribution of isotopes in it. Said simply, we ionize particles of the sample and hurl them into a magnetic field. If they're all going at the same speed, and all have the same induced charge, they'll all experience the same force, but that force will have a greater effect on the lighter particles and a lesser effect on the heavier ones—i.e., the particles are naturally sorted according to their masses. This leads to the questions, (1) how do we guarantee that they all have the same charge, and (2) how do we guarantee that they're all going the same speed? Here we address the latter of these questions.

Using a magnetic envelope, the charged particles are directed into a tube (called a *velocity selector*) that is penetrated by a uniform electric field, and a uniform magnetic field (see Section 11.4).

> The word "uniform" means that all the field vectors are equal.

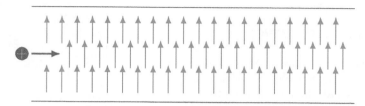

Figure 7.4: The electric field, **E**, points in the direction of force experienced by a positively charged particle

Figure 7.4 depicts a scenario in which a particle with charge $q > 0$ experiences a force of $q\|\mathbf{E}\|\langle 0, 1, 0\rangle$ due to the electric field.

14. A moving charge experiences a force of $\mathbf{F} = q\mathbf{v} \times \mathbf{B}$ due to a magnetic field. Use the right-hand rule to determine what direction the uniform magnetic field, **B**, should point in order to provide a force in the direction $\langle 0, -1, 0\rangle$.

15. Because the force due to the magnetic field is proportional to a particle's velocity, particles that move too slow will be deflected "up" (the force from the electric field is greater than the force from the magnetic field) and particles that move too fast will be deflected down. Only those at the "correct" speed will travel through the tube in a straight line. What is the "correct" speed? *(Your answer will be in terms of q, $\|\mathbf{E}\|$ and $\|\mathbf{B}\|$.)* |seecross product|

Chapter 12
Vector-Valued Functions

In this chapter we investigate vector quantities that depend on an independent variable. We will see how they are related to curves and space, and will discuss the geometric and physical meaning of their derivatives and integrals.

Key Idea(s): *Some vector quantities change over time (direction and/or magnitude).*

We can often use vector addition to write complicated vector-valued functions as the sum of simpler ones.

We'll focus on linear and circular motion, and their combination.

12.1 Vector-Valued Functions and Space Curves

The chapter opener referred to vector quantities that depend on an independent variable. One of the most familiar examples is a moving object's position vector, which depends on time. You saw examples of this at the end of Chapter 11 when we described motion along a line by writing an object's position vector as $\mathbf{r}(t)$. In that discussion we addressed motion with constant speed, but as you'll see in the next example, we can use similar techniques to characterize linear motion in which speed is not constant.

Linear motion with non-constant speed

Example 1.1. Suppose distance is measured in meters and time in seconds. An object is at the point $(4, 2, 1)$ when $t = 0$, and moves in the direction of $\mathbf{w} = \langle 1, -1, 4 \rangle$. If the object's speed after t seconds is $7t$ m/sec, describe the object's position as a vector-valued function of time.

Solution: Because this object is always moving in the direction of $\mathbf{w}$, it travels along a linear path. So much as we did in Chapter 11, our strategy will be to write its position vector as

$$\mathbf{r} = (\text{initial position vector}) + \left(\begin{array}{c} \text{displacement from} \\ \text{initial position} \end{array} \right). \qquad (1.1)$$

We know that the object starts at the point $(4, 2, 1)$, so the initial position vector is $\langle 4, 2, 1 \rangle$. Now let's describe the displacement from that initial position. The object's speed is $7t$, so the distance it travels in t seconds is

$$\int_0^t 7\tau \, d\tau = 3.5t^2 \text{ meters.}$$

Since the object is traveling in the direction of $\mathbf{w} = \langle 1, -1, 4 \rangle$, its displacement after t seconds is

$$3.5t^2 \hat{\mathbf{w}} = 3.5t^2 \, \frac{1}{\|\mathbf{w}\|} \mathbf{w} = \frac{3.5t^2}{\sqrt{18}} \langle 1, -1, 4 \rangle.$$

Distance ⎯⏋ ⎿⎯ Direction

Inserting this into equation (1.1) yields

$$\mathbf{r}(t) = \langle 4, 2, 1 \rangle + \frac{3.5t^2}{\sqrt{18}} \langle 1, -1, 4 \rangle. \qquad \blacksquare$$

Linear motion with non-constant speed

Example 1.2. Suppose distance is measured in feet and time in minutes. An object is at the point $(-2, -1, 8)$ when $t = 0$, and moves in the direction of $\mathbf{w} = \langle 3, 5, -1 \rangle$. If the object's speed after t seconds is $e^{-t/2}$ ft/min, describe the object's position as a vector-valued function of time.

Answer: $\mathbf{r}(t) = \langle -2, -1, 8 \rangle + \frac{2\sqrt{35}(1 - e^{-t/2})}{35} \langle 3, 5, -1 \rangle$. ∎

Solution On-line

Wind velocity as a function of time

Example 1.3. Suppose you're standing in a park, and the force of the wind at time t seconds is $\mathbf{F}(t) = x(t)\mathbf{i} + y(t)\mathbf{j}$, which is shown below for several values of t. (a) Describe the function $y(t)$. Then (b) sketch a graph of $\|\mathbf{F}(t)\|$, and (c) describe your experience of the wind.

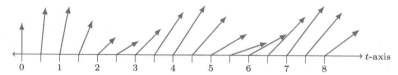

Solution: (a) The "height" of the arrow head above the t-axis at time t is $y(t)$. We see that it initially grows as t increases, and that it has a local maximum near $t = 1$. Then $y(t)$ decreases and achieves a local minimum near $t = 2.5$, and the cycle repeats. The heights of the arrows alternately rise and fall, much like we see in the graph of a trigonometric function. A graph of y is provided below, along with part (b), the graph of $\|\mathbf{F}(t)\|$:

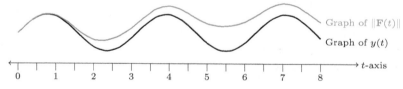

Graph of $\|F(t)\|$

Graph of $y(t)$

Note that $\|\mathbf{F}(t)\| \geq y(t)$, which happens because

$$\|\mathbf{F}(t)\| = \sqrt{\left(x(t)\right)^2 + \left(y(t)\right)^2} \geq \sqrt{0 + \left(y(t)\right)^2} = |y(t)|.$$

The graphs meet at $t = 0$ because $x(0) = 0$, and there is a large separation near $t = 5.5$ because $x(t)$ is relatively large there. (c) Each of the force vectors shown above occurs at the same point in the park (at your location). Let's suppose that you're facing in the direction of $\mathbf{F}(0)$, which is due north. The graph indicates that there is a northerly gust that lasts for about 1.5 seconds. Then the wind dies down and you feel a gentle, northeasterly breeze for about a second. When $t \approx 2.5$, the wind picks up again, and there is a gust in a north-easterly direction. The wind remains relatively strong while $t \in [4, 8]$ but changes direction, becoming more-easterly near $t = 6$, and then returning to its northeasterly direction. ∎

Angular velocity as a function of time

Example 1.4. Imagine a child's spinning top (see Figure 1.1). Explain how the top's angular velocity vector, $\boldsymbol{\omega}$, changes with time.

Solution: In Section 11.1 we said that $\|\boldsymbol{\omega}\|$ is the rate at which the top is spinning, which decreases over time due to friction on the floor. And $\boldsymbol{\omega}$ points along the axis of rotation, which changes as the top's axis of rotation precesses. ∎

Figure 1.1: If you could grab the axis of rotation with your right hand so that your fingers curl around it in the direction that the top is spinning, your thumb would point in the direction of $\boldsymbol{\omega}$.

Examples 1.1–1.4 introduced different kinds of vector quantitates that change over time. Regardless of its practical meaning, when a vector quantity depends on an independent variable, such as

$$\mathbf{u}(t) = f(t)\mathbf{i} + g(t)\mathbf{j} + h(t)\mathbf{k} = \langle f(t), g(t), h(t) \rangle,$$

we say that it's a ***vector function*** or a ***vector-valued function***, and refer to the functions f, g and h as its ***component functions***. In the remainder of this section we combine ideas of linear and circular motion to describe some more-complicated vector functions and the curves they parameterize.

❖ Circular and Cycloid Motion

We first introduced the ***cycloid*** in Section 9.1 by supposing that your car comes to a stop on a spot of wet paint. As you roll forward again, the spot of paint on your tire follows the path of a cycloid (see Figure 1.2). With vector addition at our disposal, we can describe this complicated motion as the sum of simple displacements.

> You may find it helpful to review the cycloid discussion in Section 9.1 before reading on.

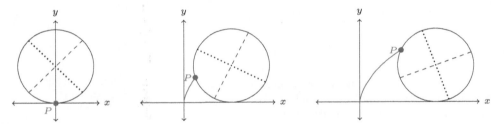

Figure 1.2: As the wheel rolls without slipping, the point P moves along a cycloid.

In the following sequence of examples, we'll characterize the tire as a circle of radius R meters that sits on the x-axis, with its center at $(0, R)$ at time $t = 0$. The spot of paint will be at the point P, which begins at the bottom of the circle (i.e., at the origin).

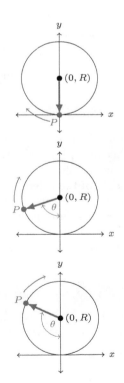

Figure 1.3: When the wheel slips, the point P travels along a circular path.

Circular motion

Example 1.5. Suppose that the center of the circle remains at $(0, R)$ as the wheel turns clockwise (perhaps because the tire slips when you touch the accelerator). Use a vector-valued function to describe the path of the point P.

Solution: We're going to write this vector-valued function as $\mathbf{r} = \mathbf{u} + \mathbf{w}$, where $\mathbf{u}$ is the position vector for the wheel's center, and $\mathbf{w}$ is the displacement from there to the point P, which lies on the circle's edge.

Step 1 (finding $\mathbf{u}$): Because the center remains in place in this scenario, the vector $\mathbf{u} = \langle 0, R \rangle$ is constant.

Step 2 (finding $\mathbf{w}$): Since the point P is traveling around a circle of radius R, the components of $\mathbf{w}$ will be $R\cos\theta$ and $R\sin\theta$, or their opposites, where θ is the radian angle through which the wheel has turned. More specifically, since the point P is directly below the center when $\theta = 0$, initially the vector $\mathbf{w}$ should be $\langle 0, -R \rangle$. This tells us that the first component of $\mathbf{w}$ depends on $\sin\theta$ (which is 0 when $\theta = 0$), so $\mathbf{w}$ has the form $\langle \pm R\sin\theta, -R\cos\theta \rangle$. In order to determine which of $\pm$ to use, note that the point P is initially moving toward the left, so the first component of $\mathbf{w}$ is decreasing. This leads us write $\mathbf{w} = \langle -R\sin\theta, -R\cos\theta \rangle$. So

$$\mathbf{r}(\theta) = \begin{bmatrix} 0 \\ R \end{bmatrix} + \begin{bmatrix} -R\sin\theta \\ -R\cos\theta \end{bmatrix} = \begin{bmatrix} 0 \\ R \end{bmatrix} - \begin{bmatrix} R\sin\theta \\ R\cos\theta \end{bmatrix} = \begin{bmatrix} -R\sin\theta \\ R - R\cos\theta \end{bmatrix}. \qquad \blacksquare$$

Cycloid motion

Example 1.6. Suppose that the tire does *not* slip when you touch the accelerator, so that the center of the circle moves to the right (as in Figure 1.2). Use a vector-valued function to describe the path of the point P.

Solution: We need only adapt our answer from Example 1.5 by allowing the vector **u** (which locates the center of the wheel) to depend on θ. Recall that an angle of θ radians corresponds to an arc of length $R\theta$. Since the wheel is not slipping, this is exactly the horizontal distance traveled by the center as the wheel rolls. So $\mathbf{u} = \langle R\theta, R \rangle$ and

$$\mathbf{r}(\theta) = \begin{bmatrix} R\theta \\ R \end{bmatrix} - \begin{bmatrix} R\sin\theta \\ R\cos\theta \end{bmatrix} = \begin{bmatrix} R\theta - R\sin\theta \\ R - R\cos\theta \end{bmatrix}. \qquad \blacksquare$$

Cycloid motion

Example 1.7. Suppose a circle of radius 2 is initially centered at $(2,2)$, and P is the point that's initially at $(0,2)$. Parameterize the path followed by P as the circle rolls vertically, up the y-axis. As in Example 1.6, assume that the wheel does not slip, and use θ as the parameter.

Answer: $\mathbf{r} = (2 - 2\cos\theta)\mathbf{i} + (2 + 2\theta - 2\sin\theta)\mathbf{j}$. $\qquad \blacksquare$

Solution
On-line

In Example 1.6 we described the path followed by P in terms of θ, the angle through which the wheel has rolled, but we're more accustomed to thinking in terms of time than radians, so let's adjust our answer.

Parameterizing the cycloid in time

Example 1.8. Suppose the circle in Example 1.6 moves to the right at 5 meters per second. Parameterize the path of P in time instead of radians.

Solution: After t seconds, the center of the circle will have traveled $5t$ meters to the right, so its x-coordinate will be $5t = R\theta \;\Rightarrow\; \theta = 5t/R$. By substituting this into our formula from Example 1.6 we can parameterize the path of P as $\mathbf{r}(t) = \left(5t - R\sin\frac{5t}{R}\right)\mathbf{i} + \left(R - R\cos\frac{5t}{R}\right)\mathbf{j}$. $\qquad \blacksquare$

Parameterizing the cycloid in time

Example 1.9. Suppose the circle in Example 1.7 completes 3.7 revolutions per second. Parameterize the path of P in seconds instead of radians.

Answer: $\mathbf{r}(t) = \left(2 - 2\cos(7.4\pi t)\right)\mathbf{i} + \left(2 + 14.8\pi t - 2\sin(7.4\pi t)\right)\mathbf{j}$. $\qquad \blacksquare$

Solution
On-line

❖ Helices and Spirals

A cycloid is produced when linear and circular motion occur in the same plane. When linear motion happens in a direction that's orthogonal to the circular motion, we get a helix.

Helices

Example 1.10. Explain the qualitative differences between the helices parameterized by the vector functions $\mathbf{r}(t) = \langle \cos t, \sin t, 3t \rangle$ and $\mathbf{h}(t) = \langle 2\sin t, 2\cos t, t \rangle$.

Solution: If the third components of these vector functions were held at 0, the function $\mathbf{r}(t)$ would parameterize a circle of radius $\sqrt{\cos^2 t + \sin^2 t} = 1$ in the xy-plane, starting at the point $(1, 0, 0)$ and moving in the counterclockwise direction. By contrast, the function $\mathbf{h}(t)$ would parameterize a circle of radius 2 in the xy-plane, starting at the point $(0, 2, 0)$ and moving in the clockwise direction. However, the third components of these vector functions increase with t, so the points with position vectors $\mathbf{r}(t)$ and $\mathbf{h}(t)$ rise off of the xy-plane, and circle the z-axis as they ascend. We say that the helix parameterized by $\mathbf{r}(t)$ is *right-handed* because, if you grab the central axis with your right hand, the helix wraps around the axis in the direction of your fingers as it proceeds along the axis in the direction of your extended thumb. The helix parameterized by $\mathbf{h}(t)$ is said to be *left-handed* for the same reason (see Figure 1.4).

Both helices complete one turn around the z-axis when $t = 2\pi$, but by that time $\mathbf{r}(t)$ has risen 6π units off of the xy-plane while $\mathbf{h}(t)$ has risen only 2π units. Since each turn of $\mathbf{h}(t)$ corresponds to a smaller vertical change, the helix parameterized by $\mathbf{h}(t)$ appears more tightly coiled than the helix parameterized by $\mathbf{r}(t)$. ∎

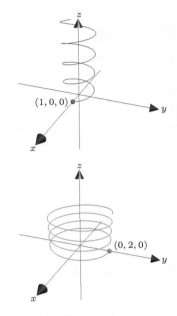

Figure 1.4: The helices parameterized by $\mathbf{r}$ (top) and $\mathbf{h}$ (bottom).

Helices in Biology: DNA

Example 1.11. In 1953 James Watson and Francis Crick suggested the double helix structure for DNA. Specifically, they proposed that each strand follows a right-handed helix of radius 10 angstroms, and that the helix completes one revolution about its central axis every 34 angstroms. Parameterize the path followed by a strand of DNA.

Solution: We're going to measure distance in angstroms. We'll orient our coordinate system so that the central axis of the DNA helix is the z-axis, and so that one strand of the DNA passes through the point $(10, 0, 0)$.

The function $\mathbf{r}(\theta) = \langle 10\cos\theta, 10\sin\theta, 0 \rangle$ parameterizes the circle of radius 10 in the xy-plane that's centered at the origin. And if you grab the z-axis with your right hand so that your extended thumb points is the $\mathbf{k}$-direction, the point at the head of $\mathbf{r}(\theta)$ moves in the direction of your fingers. We can make this circle into a helix by allowing the third component to increase with θ. Specifically, when $\theta = 2\pi$ we complete one loop around the circle, at which point we want $z = 34$, so let's set $z = 34(\theta/2\pi) \Rightarrow \theta = 2\pi z/34$. This leads us to write

$$\mathbf{r}(z) = 10\cos\left(\frac{2\pi z}{34}\right)\mathbf{i} + 10\sin\left(\frac{2\pi z}{34}\right)\mathbf{j} + z\mathbf{k}.$$ ∎

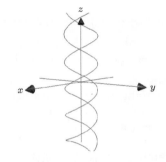

Figure 1.5: A model of DNA.

A Spiral

Example 1.12. Suppose $\mathcal{C}$ is a spiral that starts at the origin, and is centered on the z-axis. If $\mathcal{C}$ completes one revolution every 7 units along the z-axis, and its radius grows like $5\sqrt{z}$, parameterize $\mathcal{C}$.

Solution: This spiral is essentially a modified helix in which the radius changes as we move down the central axis, so using the same reasoning as in Example 1.11 we begin by writing $\mathbf{r}(z) = R\cos\left(\frac{2\pi z}{7}\right)\mathbf{i} + R\sin\left(\frac{2\pi z}{7}\right)\mathbf{j} + z\mathbf{k}$. Lastly, we allow the radius R to depend on z as specified. This brings us to

$$\mathbf{r}(z) = 5\sqrt{z}\cos\left(\frac{2\pi z}{7}\right)\mathbf{i} + 5\sqrt{z}\sin\left(\frac{2\pi z}{7}\right)\mathbf{j} + z\mathbf{k}$$ ∎

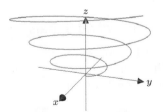

Figure 1.6: The spiral from Example 1.12.

You should know

- the terms *angular velocity*, *vector-valued function*, *parametric form (of a line)*, and *cycloid*.

You should be able to

- parameterize a line (without information about speed);
- parameterize linear motion through a given point, at a given speed;
- parameterize a circular motion about a moving center.

❖ 12.1 Skill Exercises

In #1–6 parameterize linear motion that starts at the point P, and moves in the direction of $\mathbf{w}$ with a speed of $s(t)$.

1. $P = (0,0,0)$; $\mathbf{w} = \langle 2,2,1 \rangle$; $s(t) = t^2$
2. $P = (0,0,0)$; $\mathbf{w} = \langle 4,2,4 \rangle$; $s(t) = 1 + t^4$
3. $P = (3,1,4)$; $\mathbf{w} = \sqrt{24}\,\mathbf{i} + \mathbf{k}$; $s(t) = e^{5t}$

4. $P = (2,0,7)$; $\mathbf{w} = 3\mathbf{j} + \sqrt{7}\,\mathbf{k}$; $s(t) = 2 + \cos t$
5. $P = (-1,10,3)$; $\mathbf{w} = 5\mathbf{j} - 2\mathbf{k}$; $s(t) = 1/(1+t^2)$
6. $P = (7,-6,-1)$; $\mathbf{w} = \langle 2,-1,5 \rangle$; $s(t) = \cosh(t)$

In #7–10 parameterize the helix that winds around the stated axis at the given rate, and with the specified radius. The terms *right-handed* and *left-handed* were defined in Example 1.10.

7. about the z-axis; right-handed; 1 revolution per 12 units along the axis; $R = 8$

8. about the x-axis; right-handed; 5 revolutions per 3 units along the axis; $R = 7$

9. about the y-axis; left-handed; 3 revolutions per unit along the axis; $R = 16$

10. about the z-axis; left-handed; 3 revolutions per 4 units along the axis; $R = 21$

In #11–14 parameterize the spiral that winds around the stated axis at the given rate, and with the specified radius. The terms *right-handed* and *left-handed* were defined in Example 1.10.

11. about z-axis; right-handed; 2 revolutions per 7 units along the axis; $R = 1$ when $z = 0$, and grows linearly so that $R = 8$ when $z = 3$

12. about z-axis; left-handed; 5 revolutions per 8 units along the axis; R is proportional to z^2 such that $R = 5$ when $z = 2$

13. about x-axis; left-handed; 5 revolutions per 6 units along the axis; R is proportional to e^x such that $R = 3$ when $x = 0$

14. about y-axis; right-handed; 11 revolutions per 2 units along the axis; R is inversely proportional to y^3 such that $R = 4$ when $y = 10$

❖ 12.1 Concept and Application Exercises

15. Suppose the extension ladder of a fire truck has been elevated to an angle of 39° with respect to the horizontal road, but is retracted to its minimum length (see Figure 1.7). Design a vector-valued function $\mathbf{r}(t)$ that describes the position of the ladder's top rung (45 feet from the base) as the ladder rotates left so that it's aligned with the vector $\mathbf{j}$. Use the base of the ladder as the origin, and assume that the rotation happens at a constant rate over 60 seconds.

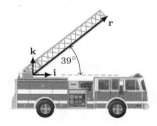

Figure 1.7: The truck in #15 and #17.

16. Suppose the extension ladder of a fire truck is retracted and pointing in the direction of $\mathbf{i}$ (see Figure 1.8). Without extending, the ladder swings up to a 60° angle of elevation with respect to the horizontal road, and rotates left so that it's aligned with $\mathbf{j}$. Assume that the rotations happen together at constant rates, and take 100 seconds to complete. Design a vector-valued function $\mathbf{r}(t)$ that describes the position of the top rung on the ladder, which is 45 feet from the base. Use the base of the ladder as the origin.

Figure 1.8: The truck in #17.

17. Suppose the extension ladder of a ladder truck is elevated 39° with respect to the horizontal road, and is positioned directly over the truck (see Figure 1.7). The ladder is initially retracted, and its last rung is 45 feet from the base of the ladder. In order to avoid sudden jerks that could unbalance firefighters, the ladder extends according to the acceleration curve shown in Figure 1.9. Determine (a) the time T at which the ladder should begin slowing in order for its final length to be 120 feet (from the last rung to the base of the ladder). Then (b) design a position function $\mathbf{r}(t)$ that describes the position of the last rung on the ladder during the interval $t \in [0, T+5]$. Use the base of the ladder as the origin, let $\mathbf{i}$ denote the direction in which the truck is facing, and let $\mathbf{k}$ denote the vertical direction.

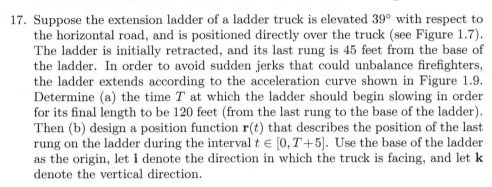

Figure 1.9: The ladder's acceleration curve for #17.

18. Suppose the Ferris wheel at a local carnival sits on a platform three meters tall. The wheel has a diameter of 50 meters, and completes one revolution every 6 minutes when it spins without interruption. You're standing 35 meters from the middle of the platform, watching your friend, who is in a car at the base of the Ferris wheel at time $t = 0$. We'll call your position the origin (see Figure 1.10).

(a) Parameterize the path followed by your friend with respect to time, $\mathbf{r}_c(t)$, assuming the car travels around the 50-m diameter circle.

(b) Suppose you wait w seconds and then toss a 1-kg ball toward your friend as his car comes around; you release the ball 2 meters above the ground at 20 meters per second, with a 60° radian angle of elevation. If the only force acting on the ball is gravity, parameterize the position of the ball, $\mathbf{r}_b(t)$.

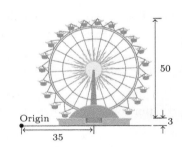

Figure 1.10: Diagram for exercise #18.

(c) In complete sentences explain what $\mathbf{r}(t) = \mathbf{r}_b(t) - \mathbf{r}_c(t)$ tells us.

(d) Suppose your friend can catch the ball if it comes within one meter of him. How long should you wait so that he can catch the ball, or is it impossible? (Consider using a graphing utility.)

19. Suppose you're riding a bicycle, and you're headed east at 5 meters per second. Because of the gear you're in, you maintain your velocity by pedaling at 0.5 revolutions per second. The right pedal is in the down position at time $t = 0$,

which is 12 cm from the ground and 18 cm from the center of the gear (see Figure 1.11). If the origin is the point on the ground that's directly below the pedal's center at time $t = 0$, parameterize the path of the pedal's center as a function of time.

20. A cheerleader is hurled into the air by her team, and she swings her legs up into a split during her 1-second ascent. Parameterize the path of her feet during the ascent, assuming that she is in a standing position at the moment she is tossed, her legs are 1.34 meters long, and her hips travel according to $\mathbf{u}(t) = \langle 0, -4.9t^2 + 9.8t + 1.5 \rangle$ after she's released.

Figure 1.11: For #19.

Sports

21. In a pike dive from the 10 meter platform, a diver jumps backwards and bends at the waist. He spins as he drops, all the while keeping his legs straight. For the sake of simplicity, suppose that the diver rotates about his hips, and that they follow the path parameterized by $\mathbf{u}(t) = \langle 1.2 + t/3, -4.9t^2 + t/3 + 10 \rangle$. Assuming that his legs are 1.2 meters long, and that his ankles complete 2.5 rotations about his hips in 1.4 seconds, circling at a constant rate, parameterize the path followed by his ankles.

22. The equatorial radius of the earth is 6,378.137 km. For this exercise, let's treat the Earth as a sphere of that radius. New York City sits at 40.783 north latitude, so if the origin is at the center of the sphere, the city's position vector makes an angle of 40.783° with the plane through the equator (see Figure 1.12). Find a parameterization for the path that New York City travels in one day, using the equatorial plane as the xy-plane.

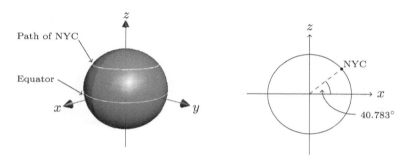

Figure 1.12: The position of New York, NY, for #22.

23. Suppose a circle of radius R passes through the origin and is centered in the first quadrant of the Cartesian plane (see Figure 1.13). We'll denote by P the point of the circle that's initially touching the line $y = -x$. When the circle rolls to the right along the line $y = -x$, the point P revolves about the center of the circle, and in this exercise you'll parameterize the path of P.

(a) Supposing that the circle rolls along the line $y = -x$ without slipping, use a vector-valued function to describe the position of the point P in terms of the angle through which the wheel has rolled, θ.

(b) Suppose that the wheel rolls at a constant rate of 5 revolutions per second. Describe the position of the point P as a function of time.

24. Suppose the point P begins at $(R, 0)$, and that it "rolls" along the inside of the circle of radius R like a point on a "wheel" of radius r (see Figure 1.14). The point P traces out a curve called a **hypocycloid.**

(a) How far is it from the origin to the center of the wheel?

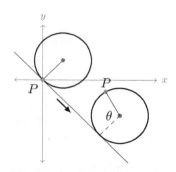

Figure 1.13: For #23 (not to scale).

(b) Determine the coordinate representation of the displacement vector from the origin to the center of the wheel when it makes an angle of ϕ radians with $\mathbf{i}$. (Your answer will be in terms of R and r.)

(c) What length of arc along the larger circle has been traversed when the angle is ϕ radians? (Your answer will be in terms of R.)

(d) Assuming that the wheel hasn't slipped, how many radians has it turned through?

(e) What's the displacement vector from the center of the wheel to P?

(f) Add your answers from parts (b) and (e) to determine the position vector for the point P.

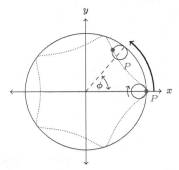

Figure 1.14: Creating a hypocycloid, as in #24.

25. Suppose a wheel is spinning in the xy-plane (counter-clockwise when we look from a vantage point where $z > 0$).

(a) If the wheel has a radius of 1 meter and completes 4 cycles per second, parameterize the motion of the point that starts at $(1, 0, 0)$.

(b) Parameterize the path of the circle's center as we lift it upward along the z-axis at 1.2 meters per second.

(c) Put these two motions together to parameterize the path of the point $(1, 0, 0)$ as the wheel spins and we lift it upward. What shape does your parameterization describe?

26. Suppose a wheel of radius 0.2 meters is "upright" in the yz-plane (i.e., $x = 0$), and spins counter-clockwise at 2.3 cycles per second (when seen from a vantage point on the positive-x axis).

(a) Parameterize the path followed by the point that starts at $(0, 0, 1)$, assuming that the wheel is held in place.

(b) Parameterize the motion of the center, assuming that we move it in the direction of $\mathbf{k}$ at 3 meters per second.

(c) Put these two motions together to parameterize the path of the point $(0, 0, 1)$ as the wheel spins and we walk it forward. What shape does your parameterization describe?

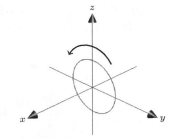

Figure 1.15: Spinning wheel for #26, centered at the origin.

27. Figure 1.16 depicts 22 different snap-shots of the wind's velocity at a particular location, $\mathbf{v}(t) = \langle x(t), y(t) \rangle$. (a) Sketch the graphs of $x(t)$ and $y(t)$ as functions of time, and (b) sketch a graph of $\|\mathbf{v}(t)\|$.

Figure 1.16: 22 different snap-shots of the wind's velocity at a particular location for #27.

28. Suppose you're facing due north and holding a compass. Then you walk counterclockwise around a circle of radius 10 meters at a constant rate of 0.25 m/sec. At each point along your path, we denote by $\hat{\mathbf{f}}$ your forward-pointing unit vector, and by $\hat{\mathbf{r}}$ the unit vector that points to your right side (see Figure 1.17). In this frame of reference (which you experience as being constant—forward is always forward), the needle on your compass initially points in the direction $1\hat{\mathbf{f}} + 0\hat{\mathbf{r}}$, and one-quarter of the way around the circle it points in the direction $0\hat{\mathbf{f}} + 1\hat{\mathbf{r}}$. Denote by $\mathbf{N}$ the north-pointing needle of the compass, which is 2 cm long. Determine functions $a(t)$ and $b(t)$ for which $\mathbf{N} = a(t)\hat{\mathbf{f}} + b(t)\hat{\mathbf{r}}$.

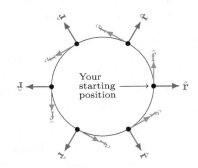

Figure 1.17: For #28, your frame of reference as you walk in a circle.

12.2   Calculus of Vector-Valued Functions

As with scalar-valued functions, the calculus of vector-valued functions rests on the concept of limits. So this section begins with a discussion of limits in the vector-valued setting, and then moves on to the ideas of continuity, differentiation and integration.

❖ Limits and Continuity

In Chapter 2 you learned what it means to write $\lim_{t \to c} y(t) = y_0$. Said colloquially, the difference between $y(t)$ and y_0 vanishes in the limit, and this is what the following definition says in the context of vectors.

Definition: Suppose the vector-valued function $\mathbf{r}(t)$ is defined on some open interval containing $t = c$, except perhaps at c. We say that the vector $\mathbf{L}$ is the *limit* of $\mathbf{r}(t)$ as t approaches c, and write

$$\lim_{t \to c} \mathbf{r}(t) = \mathbf{L}, \quad \text{when} \quad \lim_{t \to c} \|\mathbf{r}(t) - \mathbf{L}\| = 0. \tag{2.1}$$

Note: This definition extends seamlessly to the case of $\lim_{t \to \infty} \mathbf{r}(t)$, provided that $\mathbf{r}$ is defined on some interval (a, ∞).

Although the equation $\lim_{t \to c} \mathbf{r}(t) = \mathbf{L}$ is a statement about vectors, it's defined in terms of $\|\mathbf{r}(t) - \mathbf{L}\|$ and the number 0, which are scalars. The following theorem makes the connection between the limits of vector functions and scalar-valued functions even more explicit.

Theorem: Suppose $\mathbf{r}(t) = \langle x(t), y(t), z(t) \rangle$. Then

$$\lim_{t \to c} \mathbf{r}(t) = \begin{bmatrix} x_0 \\ y_0 \\ z_0 \end{bmatrix} \quad \text{if and only if} \quad \begin{cases} \lim_{t \to c} x(t) = x_0 \\ \lim_{t \to c} y(t) = y_0 \\ \lim_{t \to c} z(t) = z_0 \end{cases}. \tag{2.2}$$

Proof. Let's set $\mathbf{L} = \langle x_0, y_0, z_0 \rangle$. Since

$$\|\mathbf{r}(t) - \mathbf{L}\| = \sqrt{\left(x(t) - x_0\right)^2 + \left(y(t) - y_0\right)^2 + \left(z(t) - z_0\right)^2} \geq |x(t) - x_0| \geq 0,$$

the Squeeze Theorem guarantees that $x(t) \to x_0$ whenever $\|\mathbf{r}(t) - \mathbf{L}\| \to 0$; similarly, we conclude that $y(t) \to y_0$ and $z(t) \to z_0$. On the other hand, if we know that

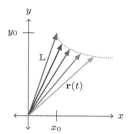 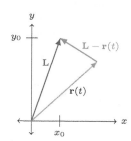 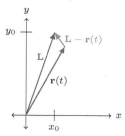

Figure 2.1: (left) A depiction of $\mathbf{r}(t) \to \mathbf{L}$ as $t \to c$; (middle and right) the vector difference $\mathbf{L} - \mathbf{r}(t)$ tends to $\mathbf{0}$ as $t \to c$.

Key Idea(s): *The limit of* $\mathbf{r}(t)$ *can be found by calculating the limits of its component functions.*

The derivative (or integral) of $\mathbf{r}(t)$ *can be found by differentiating (or integrating) its component functions.*

We use the same techniques to differentiate and integrate vector-valued functions as in the scalar-valued setting.

When $\mathbf{r}(t)$ *tells us an object's position, the functions* $\mathbf{r}'(t)$ *and* $\mathbf{r}''(t)$ *tell us its instantaneous velocity and acceleration, respectively.*

The definite integral of $\mathbf{r}'(t)$ *tells us an object's net change in position.*

You can make this theorem a statement about 2-vectors by omitting all mention of the third component.

In the first part of the proof we show that $|x(t) - x_0| \to 0$ when $\|\mathbf{r}(t) - \mathbf{L}\| \to 0$ (similarly for y and z). In the second part we show that $\|\mathbf{r}(t) - \mathbf{L}\| \to 0$ when the three individual limits are known:

$$|x(t) - x_0| \to 0$$
$$|y(t) - y_0| \to 0$$
$$|z(t) - z_0| \to 0.$$

$|x(t) - x_0|$, $|y(t) - y_0|$ and $|z(t) - z_0|$ are all limiting to 0, so is their maximum, which we will denote by $M(t)$. It follows that

$$0 \leq \|\mathbf{r}(t) - \mathbf{L}\| = \sqrt{|x(t) - x_0|^2 + |y(t) - y_0|^2 + |z(t) - z_0|^2} \leq \sqrt{3M(t)}.$$

Since $M(t) \to 0$, the Squeeze Theorem guarantees that $\|\mathbf{r}(t) - \mathbf{L}\|$ does too. ∎

End behavior of vector valued functions

Example 2.1. Suppose $\mathbf{r}(t) = \left\langle \frac{4t}{t^2+4}, \frac{2t^2}{t^2+4} \right\rangle$. Find $\lim_{t \to \infty} \mathbf{r}(t)$.

Solution: Because $4t/(t^2+4) \to 0$ and $2t^2/(t^2+4) \to 2$ as $t \to \infty$, we have that $\lim_{t \to \infty} \mathbf{r}(t) = \langle 0, 2 \rangle$. ∎

This particular $\mathbf{r}(t)$ arises from the stereographic projection of t onto the circle (see Section 1.3). As t gets larger and larger, that projection heads toward the point $(0, 2)$.

Solution
On-line

Limits of vector valued functions at finite time

Example 2.2. Suppose $\mathbf{r}(t) = \frac{\sin 2t}{t}\mathbf{i} + (t^2 - 5)\mathbf{j} + e^{7t}\mathbf{k}$. Find $\lim_{t \to 0} \mathbf{r}(t)$.

Answer: $\lim_{t \to 0} \mathbf{r}(t) = 2\mathbf{i} - 5\mathbf{j} + \mathbf{k}$. ∎

As in the scalar-valued setting, we say that a vector-valued function is *continuous* where its limit value is the same as its actual value.

Definition: Suppose the vector-valued function $\mathbf{r}$ is defined in an open interval I, which includes c. We say that $\mathbf{r}$ is **continuous** at c if

$$\lim_{t \to c} \mathbf{r}(t) = \mathbf{r}(c). \tag{2.3}$$

Further, we say that $\mathbf{r}$ is continuous on (over) the interval I when it's continuous at each $t \in I$. (We can extend this definition to the case of a closed interval by using the appropriate one-sided limits at the end points.)

Because the limit of a vector-valued function is determined by the limits of its component functions, we have the following relationship between the continuity of a vector-valued function and the continuity of its component functions.

Theorem: The vector-valued function $\mathbf{r}(t) = \langle x(t), y(t), z(t) \rangle$ is continuous at $t = c$ if and only if all of its component functions are continuous at $t = c$.

Continuity of a vector function

Example 2.3. Is $\mathbf{r}(t) = \left\langle 3 + t^2, \frac{\sin(t)}{t}, \ln(1 + t) \right\rangle$ continuous at $t = 0$?

Solution: Although the first and third components of $\mathbf{r}(t)$ are continuous at $t = 0$, the second component is not defined there. So $\mathbf{r}(t)$ is not continuous at $t = 0$ as written. However, the discontinuity is removable because $\lim_{t \to 0} \sin(t)/t = 1$. So we can *make* $\mathbf{r}(t)$ continuous by adding $t = 0$ into the domain, and writing

$$\mathbf{r}(t) = \begin{cases} \langle 1 + t^2, \sin(t)/t, e^t \rangle & \text{if } t \neq 0 \\ \langle 3, 1, 0 \rangle & \text{if } t = 0. \end{cases}$$ ∎

❖ Derivatives of Vector-Valued Functions

In our study of scalar-valued functions, we interpreted the first derivative of position as velocity and the second as acceleration. Now we extend those interpretations and techniques to vector-valued functions. Our preliminary discussion will focus on two-dimensional vectors, so that the equations are closely related to the accompanying two-dimensional diagrams, but the math extends easily to 3-vectors simply by including a third component.

Suppose the location of an object is described by the position vector $\mathbf{r}(t) = \langle x(t), y(t) \rangle$. Then the object's displacement between times t and $t + \Delta t$ is

$$\Delta \mathbf{r} = \mathbf{r}(t + \Delta t) - \mathbf{r}(t) = \begin{bmatrix} x(t + \Delta t) \\ y(t + \Delta t) \end{bmatrix} - \begin{bmatrix} x(t) \\ y(t) \end{bmatrix} = \begin{bmatrix} x(t + \Delta t) - x(t) \\ y(t + \Delta t) - y(t) \end{bmatrix},$$

which is depicted in the top image of Figure 2.2. The bottom image of that figure depicts the object's **average velocity** over that interval of time,

$$\frac{\Delta \mathbf{r}}{\Delta t} = \frac{1}{\Delta t} \Delta \mathbf{r} = \frac{1}{\Delta t} \begin{bmatrix} x(t + \Delta t) - x(t) \\ y(t + \Delta t) - y(t) \end{bmatrix} = \begin{bmatrix} \frac{x(t+\Delta t)-x(t)}{\Delta t} \\ \frac{y(t+\Delta t)-y(t)}{\Delta t} \end{bmatrix}.$$

As you might expect, the magnitude of the average velocity vector has dimensions of speed. For example, if distance is measured in meters and time in seconds,

$$\left\| \frac{\Delta \mathbf{r}}{\Delta t} \right\| = \frac{\|\Delta \mathbf{r}\|}{|\Delta t|} \quad \begin{matrix} \leftarrow \text{meters} \\ \leftarrow \text{seconds} \end{matrix}.$$

As in our study of scalar-valued functions, we say that the limit of average velocity is **instantaneous velocity**, and we denote it by $\mathbf{r}'(t)$.

$$\mathbf{r}'(t) = \lim_{\Delta t \to 0} \frac{\Delta \mathbf{r}}{\Delta t} = \begin{bmatrix} \lim\limits_{\Delta t \to 0} \frac{x(t+\Delta t)-x(t)}{\Delta t} \\ \lim\limits_{\Delta t \to 0} \frac{y(t+\Delta t)-y(t)}{\Delta t} \end{bmatrix} = \begin{bmatrix} x'(t) \\ y'(t) \end{bmatrix}.$$

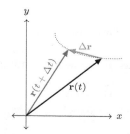

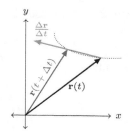

Figure 2.2: (top) Calculating $\Delta \mathbf{r}$ for a specific $\Delta t > 0$; (bottom) the same $\mathbf{r}(t)$ and $\mathbf{r}(t+\Delta t)$, but this time pictured with $\Delta \mathbf{r}/\Delta t$ when $\Delta t \in (0, 1)$.

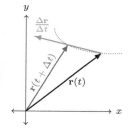
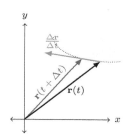
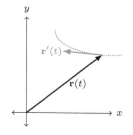

Figure 2.3: (all) The dotted curve is parameterized by $\mathbf{r}(t)$. The vectors $\Delta \mathbf{r}/\Delta t$ converge to $\mathbf{r}'(t)$ as $\Delta t \to 0$. (right) The vector $\mathbf{r}'(t)$ points along the tangent line to the curve at $\mathbf{r}(t)$.

More generally, we refer to $\Delta \mathbf{r}/\Delta t$ as the **difference quotient** and interpret it as an **average rate of change**, and we refer to the limit of the difference quotient as the **derivative** of the function $\mathbf{r}$.

Definition: Suppose $\mathbf{r}$ is a vector-valued function, and $\lim_{\Delta t \to 0} \frac{\Delta \mathbf{r}}{\Delta t}$ exists at t. Then we say that $\mathbf{r}$ is **differentiable** at t, and define

$$\mathbf{r}'(t) = \lim_{\Delta t \to 0} \frac{\Delta \mathbf{r}}{\Delta t}.$$

Further, we say that $\mathbf{r}$ is differentiable on (over) the interval (a, b) when it's differentiable at each $t \in (a, b)$.

Note that this definition does not specify whether $\mathbf{r}$ is a 2-vector or a 3-vector. That's because it doesn't matter. The definition and interpretation of the derivative is the same in both cases.

Because $\mathbf{r}'(t)$ is defined as a limit, the limit laws allow us to calculate it by differentiating the component functions of $\mathbf{r}$, as you saw previously.

Recall that the limit of a sum is the sum of the limits, when those limits exist.

> **Theorem:** Suppose $x(t), y(t)$ and $z(t)$ are differentiable functions on some open interval I. Then $\mathbf{r}(t) = x(t)\mathbf{i} + y(t)\mathbf{j} + z(t)\mathbf{k}$ is differentiable on I, and
>
> $$\mathbf{r}'(t) = x'(t)\mathbf{i} + y'(t)\mathbf{j} + z'(t)\mathbf{k}.$$

Note: The derivative of a vector function is another vector function, so $\mathbf{r}'(t)$ has both a direction and a magnitude. You can adapt this theorem to vector-valued functions in 2-space by omitting all mention of the third component.

The various notations for the derivative that were introduced in Chapter 3 are also used with vectors, so you'll often see $\dot{\mathbf{r}}$ and $\frac{d\mathbf{r}}{dt}$.

Velocity in 3-space

Example 2.4. Suppose the car of a roller coaster moves across a circular helix according to $\mathbf{r}(t) = \langle 50t, -20\cos 2t, 20\sin 2t \rangle$, where distance is measured in feet and time in seconds. Determine the car's velocity and speed at time $t = \pi$ seconds.

Solution: Differentiating $\mathbf{r}(t)$ gives us the velocity vector,

$$\mathbf{v}(t) = \frac{d}{dt}\mathbf{r}(t) = \frac{d}{dt}\begin{bmatrix} 50t \\ -20\cos 2t \\ 20\sin 2t \end{bmatrix} = \begin{bmatrix} 50 \\ 40\sin 2t \\ 40\cos 2t \end{bmatrix},$$

This formula allows us to calculate $\mathbf{v}(\pi) = \langle 50, 0, 40 \rangle$, so the speed of the car is $\|\mathbf{v}(\pi)\| = 10\sqrt{41} \approx 64.031$ feet per second (roughly 44 miles per hour). ∎

The units associated with this numbers arise from the difference quotient.

Calculating a velocity vector

Example 2.5. Suppose distance is measured in meters and time in seconds, and an object's position vector is $\mathbf{r}(t) = \langle 1 + 0.5t^2,\ 1 - 0.5t + 0.5t^2 \rangle$. (a) Find the velocity vector of the object at time $t = 0.25$, and (b) determine the object's speed.

Answer: (a) $\langle 0.25, -0.25 \rangle$. (b) $0.25\sqrt{2} \approx 0.354$ m/sec. ∎

Solution On-line

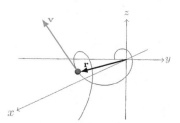

Figure 2.4: The position and velocity vector for Example 2.4.

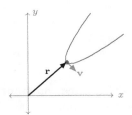

Figure 2.5: The vectors $\mathbf{r}(0.25)$ and $\mathbf{v}(0.25)$ in Example 2.5.

▷ Rules of Differentiation

The rules governing the differentiation of vector functions are similar to those you saw in Chapter 3, including analogs of the Product Rule for dot and cross products.

Differentiation of Vector-Valued Functions: Suppose $\mathbf{u}$ and $\mathbf{v}$ are differentiable vector-valued functions, and f is a differentiable scalar-valued function. Then

$$(\mathbf{u} \pm \mathbf{v})' = \mathbf{u}' \pm \mathbf{v}' \tag{2.4}$$

$$(f\mathbf{u})' = f\,\mathbf{u}' + f'\,\mathbf{u} \tag{2.5}$$

$$(\mathbf{u} \cdot \mathbf{v})' = \mathbf{u} \cdot \mathbf{v}' + \mathbf{u}' \cdot \mathbf{v} \tag{2.6}$$

$$(\mathbf{u} \times \mathbf{v})' = (\mathbf{u} \times \mathbf{v}') + (\mathbf{u}' \times \mathbf{v}) \tag{2.7}$$

> Order is important in equation (2.7) because $\mathbf{v} \times \mathbf{u}'$ and $\mathbf{u}' \times \mathbf{v}$ are opposites. Note that all three terms have the same order of terms, $\mathbf{u}$ then $\mathbf{v}$, as we read left-to-right.

Proof. You'll address equations (2.4) and (2.5) in the exercise set. Here we focus on establishing equations (2.6) and (2.7), in that order. In both cases, we'll write $\mathbf{u}(t) = \langle u_1(t), u_2(t), u_3(t) \rangle$ and $\mathbf{v}(t) = \langle v_1(t), v_2(t), v_3(t) \rangle$.

Equation (2.6): The derivative of the dot product is

$$(\mathbf{u} \cdot \mathbf{v})' = \big(u_1 v_1 + u_2 v_2 + u_3 v_3\big)' = (u_1 v_1)' + (u_2 v_2)' + (u_3 v_3)',$$

so the Product Rule tells us that

$$(\mathbf{u} \cdot \mathbf{v})' = (u_1 v_1' + u_1' v_1) + (u_2 v_2' + u_2' v_2) + (u_3 v_3' + u_3' v_3).$$

Now we gather the terms in which some component of $\mathbf{u}$ is differentiated, and group those in which some component of $\mathbf{v}$ is differentiated. This brings us to

$$(\mathbf{u} \cdot \mathbf{v})' = (u_1 v_1' + u_2 v_2' + u_3 v_3') + (u_1' v_1 + u_2' v_2 + u_3' v_3)$$
$$= \langle u_1, u_2, u_3 \rangle \cdot \langle v_1', v_2', v_3' \rangle + \langle u_1', u_2', u_3' \rangle \cdot \langle v_1, v_2, v_3 \rangle$$
$$= \mathbf{u} \cdot \mathbf{v}' + \mathbf{u}' \cdot \mathbf{v}.$$

Equation (2.7): Again using the Product Rule

$$(\mathbf{u} \times \mathbf{v})' = \frac{d}{dt} \begin{bmatrix} u_2 v_3 - u_3 v_2 \\ u_3 v_1 - u_1 v_3 \\ u_1 v_2 - u_2 v_1 \end{bmatrix} = \begin{bmatrix} u_2 v_3' + u_2' v_3 - (u_3 v_2' + u_3' v_2) \\ u_3 v_1' + u_3' v_1 - (u_1 v_3' + u_1' v_3) \\ u_1 v_2' + u_1' v_2 - (u_2 v_1' + u_2' v_1) \end{bmatrix}.$$

When we collect the terms that have v' and the terms that have u', we see

$$(\mathbf{u} \times \mathbf{v})' = \begin{bmatrix} u_2 v_3' - u_3 v_2' \\ u_3 v_1' - u_1 v_3' \\ u_1 v_2' - u_2 v_1' \end{bmatrix} + \begin{bmatrix} u_2' v_3 - u_3' v_2 \\ u_3' v_1 - u_1' v_3 \\ u_1' v_2 - u_2' v_1 \end{bmatrix} = \mathbf{u}' \times \mathbf{v} + \mathbf{u} \times \mathbf{v}'. \qquad \blacksquare$$

Derivative of a dot product (functions of constant magnitude)

Example 2.6. Suppose $\mathbf{u}(t)$ is a differentiable function with a constant magnitude. Show that $\mathbf{u}(t)$ is orthogonal to its derivative.

Solution: Since $\|\mathbf{u}(t)\|$ is constant, so is $\|\mathbf{u}(t)\|^2$, which means that its derivative is zero. That is,

$$0 = \frac{d}{dt} \|\mathbf{u}(t)\|^2 = \frac{d}{dt}\big(\mathbf{u}(t) \cdot \mathbf{u}(t)\big) \tag{2.8}$$

$$= \mathbf{u}(t) \cdot \mathbf{u}'(t) + \mathbf{u}'(t) \cdot \mathbf{u}(t) = 2\mathbf{u}(t) \cdot \mathbf{u}'(t), \tag{2.9}$$

which can only happen when $\mathbf{u}(t)$ and $\mathbf{u}'(t)$ are orthogonal. $\qquad \blacksquare$

> We pass from equation (2.8) to (2.9) using equation use (2.6), and finish the calculation using the fact that the dot product is commutative.

▷ The second derivative and acceleration

In our study of scalar-valued functions we defined the word *acceleration* to mean the instantaneous rate of change in velocity. We continue to use that meaning in the vector-valued setting, and see again that acceleration is the second derivative of position with respect to time:

$$\mathbf{a}(t) = \frac{d}{dt}\mathbf{v}(t) = \frac{d}{dt}\mathbf{r}'(t) = \mathbf{r}''(t).$$

Acceleration in 3-space

Example 2.7. Determine the acceleration experienced by the car in Example 2.4 at time $t = \pi$ seconds.

Solution: In Example 2.4 we determined that $\mathbf{v}(t) = \langle 50, 40\sin 2t, 40\cos 2t\rangle$. Differentiating this vector-valued function gives us

$$\mathbf{a}(t) = \frac{d}{dt}\mathbf{v}(t) = \frac{d}{dt}\begin{bmatrix} 50 \\ 40\sin 2t \\ 40\cos 2t \end{bmatrix} = \begin{bmatrix} 0 \\ 80\cos 2t \\ -80\sin 2t \end{bmatrix}.$$

So $\mathbf{a}(\pi) = \langle 0, 80, 0\rangle$, and the passengers in this car experience an acceleration of $\|\mathbf{a}(\pi)\| = 80\,\frac{\text{ft}}{\text{sec}}$ per second. ■

Calculating acceleration

Example 2.8. Suppose you're walking through the xy-plane, and your position is given by $\mathbf{r}(t)$ from Example 2.5. Calculate your acceleration vector at $t = 0.25$, and determine which way you're turning.

Answer: $\mathbf{a}(0.25) = \langle 1, 1\rangle$ points left of $\mathbf{v}(0.25)$, so you're turing left. ■

Solution
On-line

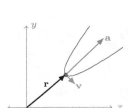

Figure 2.6: The vectors from Example 2.7, $\mathbf{r}$, $\mathbf{v}$ and $\mathbf{a}$ at $t = \pi$.

Figure 2.7: The vectors from Example 2.8, $\mathbf{r}$, $\mathbf{v}$ and $\mathbf{a}$ at $t = 0.25$.

Figures 2.6 and 2.7 show the velocity and acceleration vectors from Examples 2.7 and 2.8. Note that the vector $\mathbf{a}$ is pointing *into* the turn in both figures. This will always happen because $\mathbf{a}(t)$ tells us about the change in both the magnitude of $\mathbf{v}(t)$ and its *direction*.

Derivative of a cross product (conservation of angular momentum)

Example 2.9. The angular momentum of an object is $\mathbf{L}(t) = \mathbf{r}(t) \times m\mathbf{v}(t)$, where $\mathbf{r}$ is the object's position vector, $\mathbf{v}$ is its linear velocity vector, and m is the object's (constant) mass. Suppose the only force acting on a moving object is a central force (i.e., always pointing toward the origin). Show that $\mathbf{L}(t)$ is constant.

Solution: We're going to show that angular momentum is constant by verifying that $\mathbf{L}'(t)$ is always $\mathbf{0}$. Now that we understand $\mathbf{v} = \mathbf{r}'$, we can write the object's angular momentum as $\mathbf{L}(t) = \mathbf{r}(t) \times m\mathbf{r}'(t)$. Then using the Product Rule,

$$\mathbf{L}' = \mathbf{r}' \times m\mathbf{r}' \; + \; \mathbf{r} \times m\mathbf{r}''.$$

Since m is a constant scalar and $\mathbf{r}' \times \mathbf{r}' = \mathbf{0}$, this reduces to $\mathbf{L}'(t) = \mathbf{r}(t) \times m\mathbf{r}''(t)$. Further, Newton's Second Law tells us that $\mathbf{F} = m\mathbf{a} = m\mathbf{r}''$ where $\mathbf{F}$ is the net force acting on the object, so we can rewrite this equation as

$$\mathbf{L}'(t) = \mathbf{r}(t) \times \mathbf{F}(t). \tag{2.10}$$

Since $\mathbf{r}$ points from the origin to the object, and $\mathbf{F}$ points from the object toward the origin, the angle between them is π radians. Therefore, $\mathbf{r} \times \mathbf{F} = \mathbf{0}$. ∎

> Recall that *torque* is defined to be $\boldsymbol{\tau} = \mathbf{r} \times \mathbf{F}$, so we could rewrite equation (2.10) as
>
> $$\frac{d\mathbf{L}}{dt} = \boldsymbol{\tau},$$
>
> which says that, just as *force* is the derivative of *momentum*, *torque* is the derivative of *angular momentum*.

❖ Integrals of Vector-Valued Functions

In earlier chapters, we calculated an object's net change in position by integrating its velocity, and the same is done in the vector-valued setting for the same reasons; when an object's velocity is $\mathbf{v}(t)$, we can estimate the net change in its position over $[a, b]$ by defining a regular partition $a = t_0 < t_1 < \cdots < t_n = b$ and sampling $\mathbf{v}(t)$ in each subinterval. Then the object's

$$\text{net change in position} \approx \sum_{k=1}^{n} \mathbf{v}(t_k^*)\, \Delta t, \tag{2.11}$$

where t_k^* is the specific time in the kth subinterval at which we sample $\mathbf{v}$, and Δt is the length of the subinterval. We refer to the right-hand side of (2.11) as a ***Riemann sum*** of $\mathbf{v}(t)$, and when these sums converge to a particular vector as $n \to \infty$, regardless of the particular sampling scheme we use, we say that $\mathbf{v}(t)$ is ***integrable*** and define the ***definite integral*** of $\mathbf{v}$ over $[a, b]$ to be that limit. We denote the definite integral of a vector-valued function with the same integral notation you're accustomed to seeing, so the statement that *"the definite integral is the limit of Riemann sums"* is written concisely as

$$\int_a^b \mathbf{v}(t)\, dt = \lim_{n \to \infty} \sum_{k=1}^{n} \mathbf{v}(t_k^*)\, \Delta t$$

> As with scalar-valued functions, the subintervals could have different lengths, mathematically speaking. In that case, we define the definite integral to be the limit of the Riemann sums as the the norm of the partition tends to 0, just as we did in Chapter 5.

> The subscript of k tells us which subinterval we're talking about, and the asterisk indicates that this time is "special" (if only because we chose to check the velocity at that specific time).

> Note that we're scaling and adding vectors to make the Riemann sum, so the result of this limit is a vector.

when working with a regular partition. In the case when $\mathbf{v}(t)$ is the velocity of an object at position $\mathbf{r}(t)$, we have that $\mathbf{v}(t) = \mathbf{r}'(t)$, so our discussion about displacement leads us to write

$$\mathbf{r}(b) - \mathbf{r}(a) = \int_a^b \mathbf{r}'(t)\, dt.$$

In practice, the limit laws allow us to calculate definite integrals of vector functions in a component-by-component fashion.

Theorem (Definite Integrals of Vector Functions): Suppose f, g and h are integrable over $[a, b]$. Then $\mathbf{v}(t) = f(t)\mathbf{i} + g(t)\mathbf{j} + h(t)\mathbf{k}$ is integrable over $[a, b]$, and

$$\int_a^b \mathbf{v}(t)\, dt = \left(\int_a^b f(t)\, dt \right) \mathbf{i} + \left(\int_a^b g(t)\, dt \right) \mathbf{j} + \left(\int_a^b h(t)\, dt \right) \mathbf{k}. \tag{2.12}$$

> It's important to note that the integral of a vector function is a vector.

Proof. Since the definite integral is the limit of Riemann sums, we consider

$$\lim_{n\to\infty} \sum_{k=1}^{n} \begin{bmatrix} f(t_k^*) \, \Delta t \\ g(t_k^*) \, \Delta t \\ h(t_k^*) \, \Delta t \end{bmatrix} = \lim_{n\to\infty} \begin{bmatrix} \sum_{k=1}^{n} f(t_k^*) \, \Delta t \\ \sum_{k=1}^{n} g(t_k^*) \, \Delta t \\ \sum_{k=1}^{n} h(t_k^*) \, \Delta t \end{bmatrix} = \begin{bmatrix} \lim_{n\to\infty} \sum_{k=1}^{n} f(t_k^*) \, \Delta t \\ \lim_{n\to\infty} \sum_{k=1}^{n} g(t_k^*) \, \Delta t \\ \lim_{n\to\infty} \sum_{k=1}^{n} h(t_k^*) \, \Delta t \end{bmatrix}$$

Since f, g and h are integrable, we know that their respective limits of Riemann sums converge (see Section 5.2), thereby yielding equation (2.12). ∎

Calculating a definite integral

Example 2.10. Suppose an object's velocity is $\mathbf{v}(t) = \langle 2t^2, \cos t, e^{-t} \rangle$ m/sec. Find the net distance it travels when $t \in [3, 10]$.

Solution: Since $\mathbf{v} = \mathbf{r}'$, the definite integral tells us that the object's displacement vector over this interval of time is

$$\mathbf{r}(10) - \mathbf{r}(3) = \int_3^{10} \mathbf{v}(t) \, dt = \left\langle \int_3^{10} 2t^2 \, dt, \int_3^{10} \cos(t) \, dt, \int_3^{10} e^{-t} \, dt \right\rangle$$

$$= \left\langle \frac{1946}{3}, \sin(10) - \sin(3), e^{-3} - e^{-10} \right\rangle.$$

So the object has traveled a net distance of $\|\mathbf{r}(10) - \mathbf{r}(3)\| \approx 648.667$ meters. ∎

▷ Antiderivatives and indefinite integrals of vector functions

The terms *antiderivative* and *indefinite integral* are used in this setting just as they were in Chapter 5. We say $\mathbf{r}(t)$ is an **antiderivative** of $\mathbf{v}(t)$ whenever $\mathbf{r}'(t) = \mathbf{v}(t)$, and the **indefinite integral** of $\mathbf{v}(t)$ is the collection of all its antiderivatives. Using the standard integral notation,

$$\mathbf{r}'(t) = \mathbf{v}(t) \quad \Leftrightarrow \quad \int \mathbf{v}(t) \, dt = \mathbf{r}(t) + \mathbf{c},$$

where $\mathbf{c}$ can be any vector that's independent of t. As with definite integrals, antiderivatives and indefinite integrals can be found in a component-by-component fashion (because that's how we differentiate $\mathbf{r}(t)$).

Indefinite integral of a vector-valued function

Example 2.11. Determine an antiderivative of $\mathbf{r}'(t) = \langle 2, 15t^2, -\sin t \rangle$ for which $\mathbf{r}(0) = \langle 7, 1, 9 \rangle$.

Solution: Because $\int 2 \, dt = 2t + c_1$, $\int 15t^2 \, dt = 5t^3 + c_2$ and $\int -\sin(t) \, dt = \cos(t) + c_3$, we know that

$$\int \mathbf{r}'(t) \, dt = \langle 2t, 5t^3, \cos t \rangle + \mathbf{c}.$$

To determine the correct $\mathbf{c}$ we note that our formula results in $\langle 0, 0, 1 \rangle + \mathbf{c}$ when $t = 0$, but $\mathbf{r}(0) = \langle 7, 1, 9 \rangle$.

$$\begin{bmatrix} 0 \\ 0 \\ 1 \end{bmatrix} + \mathbf{c} = \begin{bmatrix} 7 \\ 1 \\ 9 \end{bmatrix} \quad \Rightarrow \quad \mathbf{c} = \begin{bmatrix} 7 \\ 1 \\ 8 \end{bmatrix}.$$

∎

Indefinite integrals of vector-valued functions

Example 2.12. Suppose $\mathbf{v}(t) = \langle 3t^2, \sin t, 3 - t \rangle$. Calculate $\int \mathbf{v}(t) \, dt$.

Answer: $\langle t^3 + c_1, -\cos t + c_2, 3t - 0.5t^2 + c_3 \rangle$. ∎

Solution On-line

❖ Connections to Single-Variable Theorems

Here we pause to compare the ideas presented in this section to the concepts developed in previous chapters. We begin by noting a difference: there is no direct analog of the Intermediate Value Theorem for vector-valued functions.

The lack of a simply stated IVT for vector-valued functions

Example 2.13. Suppose $\mathbf{r}(t) = \langle t, 1+(t-1)^4 \rangle$. Then $\mathbf{r}(1) = \langle 1, 1 \rangle$ and $\mathbf{r}(3) = \langle 3, 9 \rangle$. Show that there is no time at which $\mathbf{r}(t) = \langle 2, 4 \rangle$ even though $1 < 2 < 3$ and $1 < 4 < 9$.

Solution: Were it true that $\mathbf{r}(t) = \langle 2, 4 \rangle$, we would have $t = 2$ (since $x(t) = t$), but $y(2) = 2$ instead of 4. So $\mathbf{r}(t)$ is never $\langle 2, 4 \rangle$. In short, although the Intermediate Value Theorem guarantees that $x(t) = 2$ at some time, and also that $y(t) = 4$ at some time, those events happen at different times. ■

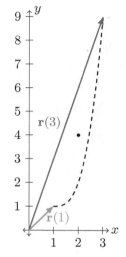

Figure 2.8: Graph to accompany Example 2.13.

Although there is no simple analog of the Intermediate Value Theorem, there *is* a version of the Mean Value Theorem that applies to vector functions. Specifically, in Section 4.5 you saw Cauchy's extension of the Mean Value Theorem. We cite here the version that you proved in the exercise set.

> **Cauchy's Mean Value Theorem:** Suppose the functions f and g are continuous on $[a,b]$ and differentiable on (a,b). Then there is a number $c \in (a,b)$ at which
> $$ f'(c)\big(g(b) - g(a)\big) = g'(c)\big(f(b) - f(a)\big). $$

To understand how this theorem is related to vector-valued functions, suppose $\mathbf{r}(t) = \langle f(t), g(t) \rangle$ is the position of an object at time t. Then the object's net displacement between $t = a$ and $t = b$ is

$$ \Delta\mathbf{r} = \mathbf{r}(b) - \mathbf{r}(a) = \langle f(b) - f(a), \ g(b) - g(a) \rangle. $$

When we rewrite Cauchy's Mean Value Theorem as

$$ 0 = g'(c)\left(f(b) - f(a)\right) - f'(c)\left(g(b) - g(a)\right) = \langle g'(c), -f'(c) \rangle \cdot \Delta\mathbf{r} $$

we see that the object's net displacement is orthogonal to $\langle g'(c), -f'(c) \rangle$. The vector $\mathbf{r}'(c) = \langle f'(c), g'(c) \rangle$ is also orthogonal to $\langle g'(c), -f'(c) \rangle$, so we conclude that $\mathbf{r}'(c)$ is parallel to $\Delta\mathbf{r}$. Intuitively speaking, this means that when an object moves from one location to another, its velocity vector must point in the direction of the net displacement at least once.

❖ A connection to Kepler's laws of planetary motion

In the project called *Planetary Orbits* in Chapter 9 you established Kepler's Second Law based on the assertion that the product $mr^2 \frac{d\theta}{dt}$ is constant, where the planet's mass is m and its polar coordinates at time t are (r, θ). The truth of that assertion is tightly tied to Example 2.9, in which you saw that $\mathbf{L} = \mathbf{r} \times m\mathbf{v}$ is constant when an object experiences only a central force. In the current discussion, the central force is the pull of the sun's gravity. Since the direction of $\mathbf{L}$ is constant and orthogonal to the planet's position vector, $\mathbf{r}$, the planet must remain in the same plane throughout its orbit. And since the magnitude of $\mathbf{L}$ is unchanging, we know that

$$ \|\mathbf{L}\| = m\|\mathbf{r} \times \mathbf{v}\| = m\|\mathbf{r}\| \, \|\mathbf{v}\| \sin\phi \qquad (2.13) $$

is constant, where ϕ is the angle between $\mathbf{r}$ and $\mathbf{v}$ (the planet's orbit might not be circular, so $\mathbf{r}$ and $\mathbf{v}$ might not be orthogonal).

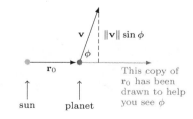

Figure 2.9: A planet with position vector $\mathbf{r}_0$ and velocity vector $\mathbf{v}$.

Back in Chapter 9, we might have said that the planet's polar coordinates are (r_0, θ_0) at time t, and (r_1, θ_1) a moment later, at time $t + \Delta t$. Now that we have vectors at our disposal, let's say that the position vectors at these times are $\mathbf{r}_0$ and $\mathbf{r}_1$, which are separated by an angle of $\Delta\theta$. Figures 2.9 and 2.10 depict this situation when the distance between the sun and planet is increasing, and for the sake of simplicity we'll limit the scope of our discussion to that scenario. More specifically, let's assume that

$$0 < \frac{d}{dt}\|\mathbf{r}\|^2 = \frac{d}{dt}(\mathbf{r} \cdot \mathbf{r}) = 2\mathbf{r} \cdot \mathbf{v},$$

from which we conclude that $\phi \in [0, \pi/2)$.

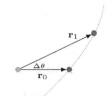

Figure 2.10: The trajectory of a planet is shown as a dotted curve.

The displacement that occurs over these Δt seconds is $\Delta\mathbf{r}$, and as you see in the left-hand image of Figure 2.11, we'll denote by α the angle between $\Delta\mathbf{r}$ and $\mathbf{r}_0$. The angles α and ϕ are not the same, but α converges to ϕ as $\Delta t \to 0^+$ because the vector $\Delta\mathbf{r}/\Delta t$ converges to $\mathbf{v}$ in the limit. Therefore, we'll proceed under the assumption that $\alpha \in [0, \pi/2)$.

Also in Figure 2.11 you see that $\|\mathbf{r}_0\|\Delta\theta$ and $\|\mathbf{r}_1\|\Delta\theta$ are lengths of circular arcs, and between them is $\|\Delta\mathbf{r}\|\sin\alpha$, which is the length of a line segment. Because the planet is moving away from the sun we know that $\|\mathbf{r}_0\| \leq \|\mathbf{r}_1\|$, as in the figures, so

> We're using the fact that $\Delta\mathbf{r}/\Delta t$ points in the same direction as $\Delta\mathbf{r}$ when $\Delta t > 0$. The technical details of this argument change if $\Delta t < 0$, but the important outcomes remain the same.

$$\|\mathbf{r}_0\|\Delta\theta \leq \|\Delta\mathbf{r}\|\sin\alpha \leq \|\mathbf{r}_1\|\Delta\theta.$$

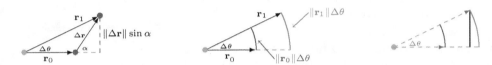

Figure 2.11: (left) The vector $\Delta\mathbf{r}$ and its relationship to $\mathbf{r}_0$; (middle) circular arcs with radii $\|\mathbf{r}_0\|$ and $\|\mathbf{r}_1\|$; (right) the line segment is longer than one circular arc and shorter than the other.

When we divide this string of inequalities by the positive Δt we see

$$\|\mathbf{r}_0\| \frac{\Delta\theta}{\Delta t} \leq \left\|\frac{\Delta\mathbf{r}}{\Delta t}\right\| \sin\alpha \leq \|\mathbf{r}_1\| \frac{\Delta\theta}{\Delta t}, \tag{2.14}$$

which provides useful information in the limit. Since $\mathbf{r}_1 = \mathbf{r}(t + \Delta t)$ and $\mathbf{r}_0 = \mathbf{r}(t)$, we know that $\lim_{\Delta t \to 0} \mathbf{r}_1 = \mathbf{r}_0$. And from our study of derivatives we know that

> There are minor differences in the technical details when $\|\mathbf{r}_0\| > \|\mathbf{r}_1\|$ or $\Delta t < 0$. (e.g., dividing by Δt reverses the inequalities), but the basic ideas are the same and lead to the same conclusions via the Squeeze Theorem.

$$\lim_{\Delta t \to 0} \frac{\Delta\theta}{\Delta t} = \frac{d\theta}{dt} \qquad \text{and} \qquad \lim_{\Delta t \to 0} \frac{\Delta\mathbf{r}}{\Delta t} = \mathbf{v}.$$

By combining these facts with inequality (2.14) and the Squeeze Theorem as $\Delta t \to 0$ we see that

$$r\frac{d\theta}{dt} = \|\mathbf{v}\| \sin\phi,$$

where $r = \|\mathbf{r}(t)\|$. This allows us to write equation (2.13) as

$$\|\mathbf{L}\| = m \|\mathbf{r}\| \|\mathbf{v}\| \sin\phi = mr\left(r\frac{d\theta}{dt}\right) = mr^2\frac{d\theta}{dt}.$$

Since $\|\mathbf{L}\|$ is constant, so is $mr^2\frac{d\theta}{dt}$.

You should know

- the terms *derivative, velocity, acceleration, definite integral, indefinite inte-*

gral, and *antiderivative;*
- the rules of differentiation.

You should be able to

- calculate velocity and acceleration vectors;
- integrate a vector-valued function;
- use a velocity vector, $\mathbf{v}(t)$, to calculate displacement over a definite interval of time.

✣ 12.2 Skill Exercises

In #1–4 calculate the specified limit or explain why it doesn't exist.

1. $\lim_{t\to 4} \left\langle \frac{t^2-6t+8}{t^2-3t-4}, \frac{t^2-5t+8}{t^2+8t-9} \right\rangle$

2. $\lim_{t\to 4} \left\langle \frac{t^2-6t+8}{\sin(2t-8)}, \frac{\cos(\pi t^2)}{6t+8} \right\rangle$

3. $\lim_{t\to 2} \frac{t-3}{t^2+8t+1}\mathbf{i} + \frac{t^2-4t+4}{t^2-3t+2}\mathbf{j} + \frac{t^2-6t-8}{\sin \pi t}\mathbf{k}$

4. $\lim_{t\to 0} \frac{\sin t}{t}\mathbf{i} + t\ln(t)\mathbf{j} + e^{-1/t}\mathbf{k}$

In #5–8 determine $\lim_{t\to\infty} \mathbf{r}(t)$ or explain why it doesn't exist.

5. $\mathbf{r}(t) = \left\langle \cos t, \sin \frac{1}{t} \right\rangle$

6. $\mathbf{r}(t) = \left\langle t^6 e^{-2t}, \frac{\sin t}{5t} \right\rangle$

7. $\mathbf{r}(t) = e^{-t}\mathbf{i} + \frac{\ln t}{1+\sqrt{t}}\mathbf{j} + \cos(t^{2-t})\mathbf{k}$

8. $\mathbf{r}(t) = \arctan(t)\mathbf{i} + \frac{1}{1+t^2}\mathbf{j} + \ln\left(\frac{t+3}{t+19}\right)\mathbf{k}$

In exercises #9–14 draw the vectors $\mathbf{r}(c)$, $\mathbf{r}'(c)$ and $\mathbf{r}''(c)$.

9. $\mathbf{r}(t) = \langle 1+t^2, 3te^t \rangle$, $c = 0$

10. $\mathbf{r}(t) = \langle 1-4t^2, 5te^{-t} \rangle$, $c = 0$

11. $\mathbf{r}(t) = \langle \sin 2t, \cos 2t \rangle$, $c = \pi/4$

12. $\mathbf{r}(t) = \langle \sin^2 4t, \cos^2 4t \rangle$, $c = \pi/16$

13. $\mathbf{r}(t) = \langle t+e^{-t}, t^2 - e^{-t^2} \rangle$, $c = 0$

14. $\mathbf{r}(t) = \langle t\ln t, \arctan t \rangle$, $c = 1$

In exercises #15–18 calculate the derivative at the specified time. In all these exercises, $\mathbf{u}(t) = \langle 3t^2, e^t, t \rangle$, $\mathbf{v}(t) = \langle 6t, 7t, 10t \rangle$ and $\mathbf{w}(t) = \langle \sin t, \cos t, t \rangle$.

15. $\frac{d}{dt}\big(\mathbf{u}(t) + \mathbf{v}(t)\big)$ at $t = 2$

16. $\frac{d}{dt}\big(\mathbf{u}(t) - \mathbf{w}(t)\big)$ at $t = \pi/3$

17. $\frac{d}{dt}\big(t^2\mathbf{u}(t)\big)$ at $t = 3$

18. $\frac{d}{dt}\big(\cos(3t)\mathbf{v}(t)\big)$ at $t = \pi$

In exercises #19–24 calculate the derivative of the product at the specified time. In all these exercises, $\mathbf{u}(t) = \langle 3t^2, e^t, t \rangle$, $\mathbf{v}(t) = \langle 6t, 7t, 10t \rangle$, and $\mathbf{w}(t) = \langle t, 0, 3t^2 \rangle$.

19. $\frac{d}{dt}\big(\mathbf{v}(t) \cdot \mathbf{u}(t)\big)$ at $t = 1.5$

20. $\frac{d}{dt}\big(\mathbf{u}(t) \cdot \mathbf{w}(t)\big)$ at $t = 0$

21. $\frac{d}{dt}\big(\mathbf{v}(t) \cdot \mathbf{w}(t)\big)$ at $t = 3$

22. $\frac{d}{dt}\big(\mathbf{u}(t) \times \mathbf{v}(t)\big)$ at $t = 2$

23. $\frac{d}{dt}\big(\mathbf{u}(t) \times \mathbf{w}(t)\big)$ at $t = 0$

24. $\frac{d}{dt}\big(\mathbf{w}(t) \times \mathbf{v}(t)\big)$ at $t = 1$

In exercises #25–30 calculate the specified definite integral.

25. $\int_0^2 \langle 3t, 2t+8, 9t^2+4t \rangle \, dt$

26. $\int_0^1 \langle 20t-1, 12t^2+5t \rangle \, dt$

27. $\int_1^2 \langle 3t\sqrt{t^2-1}, 6t^2 \sin(\pi t^3) \rangle \, dt$

28. $\int_0^1 \left(\sec^2(0.25\pi t)\mathbf{i} - \frac{2}{9t^2+1}\mathbf{j} \right) dt$

29. $\int_0^1 \big(\ln(t+1)\mathbf{i} + t\sin(\pi t/2)\mathbf{j} + te^t\mathbf{k} \big) dt$

30. $\int_0^1 \left(t\cos(7t)\mathbf{i} + \frac{8t+1}{t^2-5t+6}\mathbf{j} + \frac{7}{10t+3}\mathbf{k} \right) dt$

In exercises #31–34 determine the specified antiderivative of $\mathbf{r}'$.

31. $\mathbf{r}'(t) = \langle te^{3t^2}, t^6 - t, \sin 8t \rangle$; $\mathbf{r}(0) = \langle 2, 1, -7 \rangle$

32. $\mathbf{r}'(t) = \langle 20t^4 + t, \ln 6t \rangle$; $\mathbf{r}(1) = \langle 17, 2, 0 \rangle$

33. $\mathbf{r}'(t) = \langle \arctan t, t + 1, \cos 9t \rangle$; $\mathbf{r}(0) = \langle 3, 1, -1 \rangle$

34. $\mathbf{r}'(t) = \langle \frac{3}{t^2+6t+8}, \sec 9t \tan 9t \rangle$; $\mathbf{r}(0) = \langle 3, 8, -10 \rangle$

In exercises #35–38 determine the indefinite integral of $\mathbf{v}$.

35. $\mathbf{v}(t) = \langle 8t + 1, e^{2t} \sin 3t, 3t^2 - 8t \rangle$

36. $\mathbf{v}(t) = \langle t^2 e^{7t}, (t - 7)^6, -\sec^2 t \rangle$

37. $\mathbf{v}(t) = \langle -\frac{1}{1+t}, \frac{1}{1+t^2}, \sec^3 t \rangle$

38. $\mathbf{v}(t) = \langle \frac{9}{t^3-6t^2+5t}, -\frac{6}{1+8t^2}, \cos 9t \rangle$

❖ 12.2 Concept and Application Exercises

39. Suppose $\mathbf{r}(t) = \langle x(t), y(t) \rangle$.

    (a) Sketch the graph of a function $x(t)$ that's continuous at $t = 3$.

    (b) Sketch the graph of a function $y(t)$ with a jump discontinuity at $t = 3$.

    (c) In complete sentences, explain what your graphs in parts (a) and (b) say about $\lim_{t \to 3^{\pm}} \mathbf{r}(t)$.

40. Suppose $\mathbf{r}(t) = \frac{4t}{4+t^2}\mathbf{i} + \frac{2t^2}{4+t^2}\mathbf{j}$.

    (a) Verify that $\lim_{t \to \infty} \mathbf{r}(t) = \langle 0, 2 \rangle$ by calculating the limits of the component functions.

    (b) Draw the position vectors $\mathbf{r}(t), \langle 0, 2 \rangle$, and their difference, $\mathbf{r}(t) - \langle 0, 2 \rangle$, at times $t = 1, 5$ and 10.

    (c) In complete sentences, explain what's happening to $\mathbf{r}(t) - \langle 0, 2 \rangle$ as t grows arbitrarily large.

41. Suppose $\mathbf{r}(t) = \left\langle \frac{9t}{4-t}, e^{-t} \right\rangle$.

    (a) Show that $\lim_{t \to 4^-} x(t) = \infty$ but $\lim_{t \to 4^-} y(t) = e^{-4}$.

    (b) If we think of $\mathbf{r}(t)$ as the position vector for an object, describe what's happening to the object as $t \to 4^-$.

42. Suppose $\mathbf{r}(t) = \langle 3t - \ln(2), 9e^{-t} \rangle$.

    (a) Find the range of $x(t)$ during $0 \le t \le \ln(4)$.

    (b) Find the range of $y(t)$ during $0 \le t \le \ln(4)$.

    (c) Verify that $x(t)$ and $y(t)$ are both continuous during the specified time frame, yet $\mathbf{r}(t)$ is never $\langle 0, 5 \rangle$.

    (d) Why doesn't part (c) contradict the Intermediate Value Theorem?

43. The **signum function**, $\text{sgn}(x)$, is defined to be

$$\text{sgn}(x) = \begin{cases} 1 & \text{when } x > 0 \\ 0 & \text{when } x = 0 \\ -1 & \text{when } x < 0. \end{cases}$$

Suppose $\mathbf{r}(t) = \text{sgn}(\cos \pi t)\mathbf{i} + \text{sgn}(\sin 1.5\pi t)\mathbf{j}$.

    (a) Describe what happens to $\mathbf{r}(t)$ as time evolves forward.

(b) Determine the times at which $\mathbf{r}(t)$ is discontinuous.

44. Suppose $\mathbf{r}(t) = \text{sgn}(\cos p\pi t)\mathbf{i} + \text{sgn}(\sin q\pi t)\mathbf{j}$, where p and q are rational numbers and sgn is the signum function (see #43). Determine the times at which $\mathbf{r}(t)$ is discontinuous.

In exercises #45–48 determine the net displacement of an object whose velocity vector is $\mathbf{v}$ over the specified time interval.

45. $\mathbf{v}(t) = \langle 3t, 4t \rangle$, $[3, 7]$

46. $\mathbf{v}(t) = \langle 4t^3, 4t \rangle$, $[2, 6]$

47. $\mathbf{v}(t) = \langle e^{4t}, e^{5t}, e^{6t} \rangle$, $[0, 1]$

48. $\mathbf{v}(t) = \langle \ln t, t \ln t, 4 \rangle$, $[1, e]$

In exercises #49–52 an object's position is given by $\mathbf{r}(t)$. Determine (a) the object's velocity and acceleration vectors at the given time, and (b) whether the object is turning to its left or to its right (assuming it's facing in the direction of its velocity).

49. $\mathbf{r}(t) = \langle \sin t, \cos t \rangle$; $t = \pi/4$

50. $\mathbf{r}(t) = \langle t, \tan t \rangle$; $t = \pi/6$

51. $\mathbf{r}(t) = \langle t^3 - 4t + 1, t^2 + 1 \rangle$; $t = 1$

52. $\mathbf{r}(t) = \langle t \sin t, 8t \rangle$; $t = 2$

53. Suppose the velocity an object is $\mathbf{v}(t) = \cos(t)\mathbf{i} + \sin(t)\mathbf{j}$.

    (a) Verify that $\int_0^{2\pi} \mathbf{v}(t)\, dt = \mathbf{0}$.

    (b) What does part (a) tell us about the object's position at times $t = 0$ and $t = 2\pi$?

54. Suppose an object's position is $\mathbf{r}(t) = \langle x(t), y(t) \rangle$, and $s(t) = \|\mathbf{r}(t)\|^2$.

    (a) In complete sentences, explain why the object is approaching the origin when $s(t)$ is decreasing.

    (b) By writing $s(t)$ as $\mathbf{r}(t) \cdot \mathbf{r}(t)$, show that $s'(t) < 0$ when $\langle x, y \rangle \cdot \langle x', y' \rangle < 0$.

    (c) Show that $\langle x, y \rangle \cdot \mathbf{r}(3) = s(3)$ describes a line in the Cartesian plane.

    (d) What's the (geometric) relationship between the position vector $\mathbf{r}(3)$ and the line $\langle x, y \rangle \cdot \mathbf{r}(3) = s(3)$?

    (e) The line $\langle x, y \rangle \cdot \mathbf{r}(3) = s(3)$ separates the plane into a pair of half-planes. If $ds/dt < 0$ at time $t = 3$, does $\mathbf{r}'(t)$ point into the half-plane that contains the origin, or the other half-plane? Use parts (a)-(d) to explain your answer in complete sentences.

55. Suppose $\mathbf{v}(t) = \langle x'(t), y'(t) \rangle$, where the graphs of $x'(t)$ and $y'(t)$ are shown in Figures 2.12 and 2.13. Calculate $\int_1^8 \mathbf{v}(t)\, dt$.

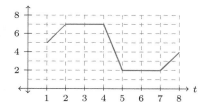

Figure 2.12: Graph of $x'(t)$ for #55

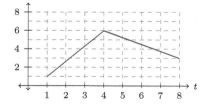

Figure 2.13: Graph of $y'(t)$ for #55

56. Suppose your position is described by $\mathbf{u}(t)$, and your friend's by $\mathbf{v}(t)$.

    (a) In complete sentences, explain the physical meaning of the equation $\mathbf{u}'(t) = \mathbf{v}'(t)$.

(b) Use a definite integral to show that the displacement between you is the same at times $t = a$ and $t = b$ if $\mathbf{u}'(t) = \mathbf{v}'(t)$ over $[a, b]$.

57. Design a function $\mathbf{r}(t)$ for which velocity and acceleration always point in the same direction.

58. Design a function $\mathbf{r}(t)$ for which $\mathbf{r}'$ and $\mathbf{r}''$ always point in opposite directions.

59. Suppose $\mathbf{r}(t) = \cos(5t)\sin(3t)\mathbf{i} + \cos(5t)\cos(3t)\mathbf{j} + \sin(5t)\mathbf{k}$.

   (a) Show that $\|\mathbf{r}(t)\| = 1$ at all times t.

   (b) Based on part (a), what *should* be true about $\mathbf{r}(t)$ and $\mathbf{r}'(t)$?

   (c) Calculate $\mathbf{r}'(t)$ and check your assertion from part (b).

60. Recall that $\|\mathbf{r}(t)\|^2 = \mathbf{r}(t) \cdot \mathbf{r}(t)$.

   (a) Verify that $\frac{d}{dt}\|\mathbf{r}(t)\|^2 = 2\mathbf{r}(t) \cdot \mathbf{r}'(t)$.

   (b) Based on part (a), what happens to the magnitude of $\mathbf{r}(t)$ when the vectors $\mathbf{r}(t)$ and $\mathbf{r}'(t)$ point in the same direction?

61. Suppose you own a fixed number of shares in each of three companies, X, Y and Z. We will denote the investment portfolio by $\mathbf{r}(t) = \langle x(t), y(t), z(t) \rangle$, where the value of your shares in these companies are $x(t), y(t)$ and $z(t)$ respectively. | Business |

   (a) What does $\|\mathbf{r}(t)\|$ tell you?

   (b) Suppose the angle between $\mathbf{r}'$ and $\mathbf{r}$ is acute. What is happening to the value of your three-company investment portfolio?

   (c) Could it happen that $\frac{d}{dt}\|\mathbf{r}(t)\| > 0$ but one of the companies has a falling stock price? If not, why not? If so, provide an example.

62. You invest x dollars in company X, which pays a weekly rate of return of $p_x\%$. Similarly for companies Y and Z. Suppose $\mathbf{p} = \langle p_x/100, p_y/100, p_z/100 \rangle$ and $\mathbf{r} = \langle x, y, z \rangle$. | Business |

   (a) Explain what the number $\mathbf{r} \cdot \mathbf{p}$ tells you.

   (b) Determine a formula for $\frac{d}{dt}(\mathbf{r} \cdot \mathbf{p})$, and explain the practical meaning of each summand in your formula.

63. Newton's Second Law tells us that an object of (constant) mass of m undergoes an acceleration of $\mathbf{a}$ when it experiences a net force of $\mathbf{F}$, and further, that $\mathbf{F} = m\mathbf{a} = m\mathbf{r}''$. As we did in Section 7.4, we can use this to calculate the resulting change in the object's kinetic energy by introducing $\mathbf{r}'$ into the equation. Specifically, we "multiply" $\mathbf{r}'$ onto the equation with the dot product: | Physics |

$$\mathbf{F} \cdot \mathbf{r}'(t) = m\mathbf{r}'(t) \cdot \mathbf{r}''(t),$$

from which it follows that

$$\int_0^T \mathbf{F} \cdot \mathbf{r}'(t) \, dt = \int_0^T m\mathbf{r}'(t) \cdot \mathbf{r}''(t) \, dt.$$

   (a) Verify that the integrand on the right-hand side of the equation is the derivative of $\frac{1}{2}\,m\|\mathbf{r}'(t)\|^2$.

   (b) Use the Fundamental Theorem of Calculus to show that the value of the integral on the right-hand side of the equation is $\frac{1}{2}m\|\mathbf{r}'(T)\|^2 - \frac{1}{2}m\|\mathbf{r}'(0)\|^2$, which is the change in kinetic energy between times $t = 0$ and $t = T$.

(c) Show that the left-hand side of the equation is $\mathbf{F} \cdot (\mathbf{r}(T) - \mathbf{r}(0))$ when $\mathbf{F}$ is constant, which is the dot product of force with displacement.

64. The forces involved in combat maneuvers of modern fighter aircraft can exceed human tolerance, at which point a pilot can experience G-force induced loss of consciousness (G-LOC). In this exercise we consider a *barrel roll,* in which the pilot flies the plane around the surface of a cylinder with the canopy facing the cylinder's central axis (i.e., if the central axis were a physical object, the pilot could see it by looking up—see Figure 2.14). Specifically, suppose the aircraft flies along the path $\mathbf{r}(t) = \langle \alpha t, \beta \cos(\omega t), \beta \sin(\omega t) \rangle$, where distance is measured in meters and time in seconds.

Aviation

(a) In complete sentences, explain how each of the numbers α, β and ω affect the path followed by the plane.

(b) G-LOC can occur when pilots sustain 6 G or more (i.e., when the magnitude of acceleration exceeds 58.8 m/sec per second). If $\beta = 50$ and $\alpha = 200$ determine the value of ω at which $\|\mathbf{a}(t)\| = 58.8$, and the corresponding air speed.

Figure 2.14: Schematic of a barrel roll.

65. When a ball is spinning as it passes through the air, it experiences the *Magnus force,* which is an important part of pitching in baseball and cricket, and allows soccer players to "bend" the path of the soccer ball. In Section 11.4 (exercise #48) we characterized the Magnus force as $\mathbf{F} = c(\boldsymbol{\omega} \times \mathbf{v})$, where c is a positive constant, $\boldsymbol{\omega}$ is the ball's angular velocity, and $\mathbf{v}$ is its translational velocity, which depends on time.

Sports

(a) Suppose that the position of the ball is $\mathbf{r}(t) = \langle x(t), y(t), z(t) \rangle$, and $\boldsymbol{\omega} = w\mathbf{k}$. Show that the Magnus force affects $x(t)$ and $y(t)$ but not $z(t)$.

(b) If the only forces acting on the ball during its flight are gravity and the Magnus force, show that $\|\mathbf{v}_\perp\|$ is constant, where $\mathbf{v}_\perp = \langle v_1, v_2, 0 \rangle$ is the part of $\mathbf{v}$ that's orthogonal to $\boldsymbol{\omega} = w\mathbf{k}$. *(Hints: It's often easier to work with $\|\mathbf{u}\|^2$ rather than $\|\mathbf{u}\|$. A differentiable function is constant when its derivative is always 0. Newton's Second Law is helpful here.)*

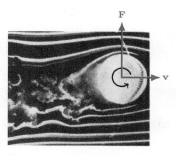

Figure 2.15: Smoke filaments show the wake of the ball deflecting the air flow on one side.

66. We say that $\lim_{t \to \infty} \mathbf{r}(t) = \mathbf{L}$ when $\mathbf{r}(t)$ gets close and stays close to $\mathbf{L}$, eventually. Mathematically speaking, for each $\varepsilon > 0$ there is a T so that

$$\|\mathbf{r}(t) - \mathbf{L}\| < \varepsilon \quad \text{when} \quad t > T.$$

The number ε quantifies "close."   The number T quantifies "eventually."

In this exercise you'll prove that $\mathbf{r}(t) \to \mathbf{L}$ as $t \to \infty$ when $\mathbf{L} = \langle 3, 2 \rangle$ and $\mathbf{r}(t) = \left\langle \frac{9t^2 + 7}{3t^2 + 8}, \frac{2t + 53}{t + 21} \right\rangle$.

(a) Use the fact that $\sqrt{a^2 + b^2} \leq |a| + |b|$ to show that $\|\mathbf{r}(t) - \mathbf{L}\| \leq \frac{17}{3t^2+8} + \frac{11}{t+21}$.

(b) Suppose that $\varepsilon \in (0,1)$ is an arbitrary, but fixed number. Determine a value of T so that

$$\frac{17}{3t^2 + 8} < \frac{\varepsilon}{2} \quad \text{and} \quad \frac{11}{t+21} < \frac{\varepsilon}{2}$$

when $t > T$ (you should get a formula in terms of ε).

(c) Combine your answers from parts (a) and (b) to show that $\|\mathbf{r}(t) - \mathbf{L}\| < \varepsilon$ when $t > T$. (This proves that $\lim_{t \to \infty} \mathbf{r}(t) = \mathbf{L}$.)

67. Use the technique from #66 to prove that $\mathbf{r}(t) \to \langle 2, 5 \rangle$ as $t \to \infty$ when $\mathbf{r}(t) = \left(\frac{4t^2+t+1}{2t^2+3t+5} \right) \mathbf{i} + \left(\frac{15t+42}{3t+1} \right) \mathbf{j}$.

68. Think about the resolution of your computer screen. Higher resolutions mean that you are better able to distinguish between points that are close together. In this exercise, we will say that we can distinguish between numbers when they differ by more than ε, so ε serves as a kind of "resolution parameter." We say that $\lim_{t \to c} \mathbf{r}(t) = \mathbf{L}$ if we are unable to resolve the difference between $\mathbf{r}$ and $\mathbf{L}$ when t is "sufficiently close" to c. Mathematically speaking, for each $\varepsilon > 0$ there is a positive number δ so that

$$\underbrace{\|\mathbf{r}(t) - \mathbf{L}\| < \varepsilon}_{} \quad \text{when} \quad \underbrace{0 < |t - c| < \delta}_{}.$$

Because this number is $< \varepsilon$, it looks like 0.   The number δ quantifies "sufficiently close."

In this exercise you'll prove that $\lim_{t \to 1} \mathbf{r}(t) = \mathbf{L}$ when $\mathbf{L} = \langle 2, 5 \rangle$ and $\mathbf{r}(t) = \langle t^2 + 1, 5t \rangle$.

(a) Write the Taylor expansion for $y(t) = 5t$ about $c = 1$.

(b) Show that $|y(t) - 5| < \varepsilon/2$ when $|t - 1| < \varepsilon/10$.

(c) Write the Taylor expansion for $x(t) = t^2 + 1$ about $c = 1$.

(d) Show that $|x(t) - 2| < 3|t - 1|$ by using the facts that $|a + b| \leq |a| + |b|$, and $|t - 1|^2 < |t - 1|$ when $|t - 1| < 1$.

(e) Show that $|x(t) - 2| < \varepsilon/2$ when $|t - 1| < \varepsilon/6$.

(f) Determine a formula for δ in terms of ε.

69. Use the technique of #68 to show that $\lim_{t \to 2} \langle t^3, t + 5 \rangle = \langle 8, 7 \rangle$.

Checking the details

70. Suppose $\mathbf{u}(t) = \langle u_1(t), u_2(t) \rangle$ and $\mathbf{v}(t) = \langle v_1(t), v_2(t) \rangle$, and all the component functions are differentiable. Show that $(\mathbf{u} + \mathbf{v})' = \mathbf{u}' + \mathbf{v}'$.

71. Suppose $\mathbf{v}(t) = \langle v_1(t), v_2(t) \rangle$. Show that $(f \mathbf{v})' = f \mathbf{v}' + f' \mathbf{v}$ when f and the component functions of $\mathbf{v}(t)$ are all differentiable.

12.3   Arc Length and Curvature

In Section 12.2 we discussed the velocity and acceleration of things that move, and now we turn our discussion to the *path along which* they move. So instead of talking about a roller-coaster car, for example, we'll talk about the *track*. While the car might travel fast or slow, the shape of the track is always the same.

✤ Arc Length in the Vector-Valued Setting

Extending the language of Chapter 11, we will say that the vector-valued function $\mathbf{r}(t)$ is a **parameterization** of the curve $\mathcal{C}$, or that it **parameterizes** $\mathcal{C}$, if an object with the position vector $\mathbf{r}(t)$ would traverse the curve. Further, the function $\mathbf{r}$ is said to be **regular** if $\mathbf{r}'(t)$ exists but is never $\mathbf{0}$, and if $\mathbf{r}'$ is also continuous we'll say that $\mathbf{r}$ is **smooth**. A smooth parameterization cannot stop, pivot, and then proceed in a new direction, so the curve it parameterizes cannot have any corners. We can calculate the length of such a parameterized curve by using a definite integral, much as we did in Chapter 9.

> **Calculating Arc Length:** Suppose $\mathbf{r}(t)$ is a smooth parameterization of a curve $\mathcal{C}$, and $\mathcal{C}$ is traversed once as t increases from a to b. Then the **arc length** of $\mathcal{C}$, which we denote by $|\mathcal{C}|$, is
>
> $$|\mathcal{C}| = \int_a^b \|\mathbf{r}'(t)\| \, dt. \tag{3.1}$$

Calculating arc length

Example 3.1. Suppose we design a segment of roller-coaster track so that the base of a car traverses the circular helix parameterized by $\mathbf{r}(t) = \langle 10t, 5\cos t, 5\sin t \rangle$, where $0 \le t \le 3\pi$ and length is measured in meters. Determine the length of the segment.

Solution: Since $\mathbf{r}'(t) = \langle 10, -5\sin t, 5\cos t \rangle$, which has a constant magnitude of $\|\mathbf{r}'(t)\| = \sqrt{125}$, this segment of the track has a length of

$$|\mathcal{C}| = \int_0^{3\pi} \sqrt{125} \, dt = 3\pi\sqrt{125} \approx 105.372 \text{ meters.} \qquad \blacksquare$$

A curve's arc length is independent of parameterization

Example 3.2. Suppose $\mathcal{C}$ is the line segment in the xy-plane that extends from $(-1, 6)$ to $(2, 10)$. (a) Show that $\langle -1 + 3t, 6 + 4t \rangle$ parameterizes $\mathcal{C}$ when $t \in [0, 1]$, and $\langle 2 - 0.6t, 10 - 0.8t \rangle$ parameterizes $\mathcal{C}$ when $t \in [0, 5]$. Then (b) show that the integral in equation (3.1) results in the same number with both parameterizations.

Answer: (b) both calculations result in a length of 5 units. $\blacksquare$

▷ Parameterizing by Arc Length

We've been parameterizing curves with vector-valued functions $\mathbf{r}(t)$ that describe position in terms of how much time has elapsed, but time has to do with the rate at which we cross the curve, not the curve itself. If we want to use a parameter that's intrinsic to the curve, a natural choice is the distance that one must travel along the curve (from one end or the other) to arrive at a point. Equation (3.1) can be adapted to this purpose.

Sidebar notes:

Key Idea(s): *Arc length is calculated with an integral, much in the same way that distance is the integral of speed with respect to time.*

The unit tangent vector to a curve is a vector of magnitude 1, denoted by $\mathbf{T}$, that is tangent to the curve.

The curvature of the curve $\mathcal{C}$ quantifies the instantaneous rate of change in $\mathbf{T}$ as we traverse $\mathcal{C}$ at unit speed.

In Section 12.2 we interpreted $\mathbf{r}'(t)$ as a velocity. So you can think of $\|\mathbf{r}'(t)\|$ as a speed, and

$$\|\mathbf{r}'(t)\| \, dt = (\text{rate}) \times (\text{time}).$$

Solution On-line

If the curve is a loop, it won't have endpoints. In this case, you have to pick a reference point and designate a direction of travel.

Let's think of $\mathbf{r}'(t)$ as a velocity with units of meters per second, and denote by $s(t)$ the distance traveled by an object between time 0 and time t seconds. Then

$$s(t) = \int_0^t \overbrace{\|\mathbf{r}'(\tau)\|}^{\text{m/sec}} \overbrace{d\tau}^{\text{sec}} .$$

(3.2)

$$\underbrace{}_{\text{sum}} \underbrace{\phantom{\|\mathbf{r}'(\tau)\| \, d\tau}}_{\text{units of meters}}$$

Notice that, according to the Fundamental Theorem of Calculus,

$$\frac{ds}{dt} = \frac{d}{dt} \int_0^t \|\mathbf{r}'(\tau)\| \, d\tau = \|\mathbf{r}'(t)\|,$$

(3.3)

which is always positive when $\mathbf{r}(t)$ is a smooth parameterization. It follows that s is an increasing function of t, so its graph passes the Horizontal Line Test (see Figure 3.1). This means the relationship between t and s can be inverted, in principle, so we can treat time as a function of distance along the curve and rewrite $\mathbf{r}$ as a function of arc length. When we do this, we say that a curve is ***parameterized by arc length.***

Parameterizing a curve with respect to arc length

Example 3.3. Suppose $\mathcal{C}$ is the helix parameterized by $\mathbf{r}(t) = 10t\mathbf{i} + 5\cos(t)\mathbf{j} + 5\sin(t)\mathbf{k}$, where $0 \le t \le 3\pi$. Determine a parameterization of $\mathcal{C}$ by arc length.

Solution: Because $\mathbf{r}'(t) = \langle 10, -5\sin t, 5\cos t \rangle$ has a constant magnitude of $\|\mathbf{r}'(t)\| = \sqrt{125}$, the time interval $[0, t]$ corresponds to a length of

$$s = \int_0^t \sqrt{125} \, dt = \sqrt{125} \, t.$$

Now using the fact that $t = s/\sqrt{125}$, we can rewrite the components of $\mathbf{r}$ in terms of s, and so parameterize the helix in terms of the distance we travel along it:

$$\mathbf{r}(s) = \tfrac{10s}{\sqrt{125}}\mathbf{i} + 5\cos\left(\tfrac{s}{\sqrt{125}}\right)\mathbf{j} + 5\sin\left(\tfrac{s}{\sqrt{125}}\right)\mathbf{k}. \qquad \blacksquare$$

Parameterizing a curve with respect to arc length

Example 3.4. Suppose $\mathcal{C}$ is the ray parameterized by $\mathbf{r}(t) = \langle \sqrt{6}\,t, 8 - 3t, 7t + 1 \rangle$, where $0 \le t$. Determine a parameterization of $\mathcal{C}$ by arc length.

Answer: $\mathbf{r}(s) = \left\langle \tfrac{\sqrt{6}}{8}s, \; 8 - \tfrac{3s}{8}, \tfrac{7s}{8} + 1 \right\rangle.$ $\qquad \blacksquare$

Notice that $\|d\mathbf{r}/ds\| = 1$ in both Examples 3.3 and 3.4. Intuitively, this happens when you parameterize by arc length because each unit increment of the parameter s is exactly a unit increment of arc length, so the ratio of $\Delta(\text{length})$ to $\Delta(\text{parameter})$ is 1. Mathematically, you can understand it in terms of the Chain Rule. Because $ds/dt = \|\mathbf{r}'(t)\|$ is a positive number when $\mathbf{r}$ is smooth,

$$\left\| \frac{d\mathbf{r}}{dt} \right\| = \left\| \frac{d\mathbf{r}}{ds}\frac{ds}{dt} \right\| = \left\| \frac{d\mathbf{r}}{ds} \right\| \frac{ds}{dt} \quad \Rightarrow \quad \left\| \frac{d\mathbf{r}}{ds} \right\| = \frac{\|d\mathbf{r}/dt\|}{ds/dt} = 1.$$

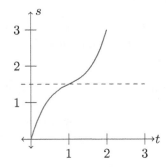

Figure 3.1: An example graph of $s(t)$, which passes the Horizontal Line Test because $s'(t) > 0$.

Solution On-line

Don't just read it! Check for yourself that $\|d\mathbf{r}/ds\| = 1$ in both examples.

❖ Curvature

Earlier in this section we introduced the idea of a *smooth* parameterization, $\mathbf{r}(t)$. In essence, a smooth parameterization of a curve never stops or reverses itself, and the direction of $\mathbf{r}'(t)$ changes continuously so the curve parameterized by $\mathbf{r}$ has no corners or cusps. This allows us to define the ***unit tangent vector*** as

$$\mathbf{T}(t) = \frac{\mathbf{r}'(t)}{\|\mathbf{r}'(t)\|}. \tag{3.4}$$

Intuitively speaking, the unit tangent vector changes slowly where a curve is relatively straight, and its rate of change will be large at tight curves (see Figure 3.2), so we quantify the *curvature* of a path by measuring the rate of change in $\mathbf{T}$.

Figure 3.2: The vector $\mathbf{T}$ changes relatively quickly where a curve is tight (left) and slowly when the curve is not (right).

Imagine yourself sitting on a merry-go-round that's revolving slowly, so the change in $\mathbf{T}$ *per second* is small. Then your friend pushes the merry-go-round so that it spins rapidly. Provided that you hang on, your unit tangent vector is now changing a great deal per second, even though the path on which you're traveling is the same as it was before your friend gave his mighty push. This thought experiment is meant to raise the point that, in order to properly define curvature, we need to use something other than *time* as the independent variable for our calculation. Instead, we measure the rate of change in $\mathbf{T}$ with respect to *length along the curve*.

Definition: Suppose $\mathbf{T}$ is the unit tangent vector to the curve $\mathcal{C}$. The ***curvature*** of $\mathcal{C}$ (which can vary from point to point) is the number

$$\kappa = \left\| \frac{d\mathbf{T}}{ds} \right\|. \tag{3.5}$$

Although curvature is defined as a rate of change with respect to arc length along a curve, as a practical matter it's often difficult to work with arc length. This leads us to search for equivalent formulations of κ. The Chain Rule allows us to rewrite equation (3.5) as

$$\kappa = \underbrace{\left\| \frac{d\mathbf{T}}{ds} \right\| = \left\| \frac{d\mathbf{T}}{dt}\frac{dt}{ds} \right\|}_{\text{Since } t \text{ is a function of } s} = \underbrace{\left\| \frac{d\mathbf{T}}{dt}\frac{1}{ds/dt} \right\| = \left\| \mathbf{T}'(t)\frac{1}{\|\mathbf{r}'(t)\|} \right\|}_{\text{From equation (3.3)}} = \frac{\|\mathbf{T}'(t)\|}{\|\mathbf{r}'(t)\|}. \tag{3.6}$$

The curvature of a circle

Example 3.5. The function $\mathbf{r}(t) = \langle R\sin 5t, R\cos 5t \rangle$ is a smooth parameterization of the circle of radius R centered at the origin. Determine the curvature of this circle.

Solution: Differentiating $\mathbf{r}$ with respect to time yields $\mathbf{r}'(t) = \langle -5R\sin 5t, 5R\cos 5t \rangle$, which has a magnitude of $\|\mathbf{r}'\| = 5R$, so the unit tangent vector is

$$\mathbf{T} = \frac{1}{\|\mathbf{r}'\|}\mathbf{r}' = \frac{1}{5R}\begin{bmatrix} -5R\sin 5t \\ 5R\cos 5t \end{bmatrix} = \begin{bmatrix} -\sin 5t \\ \cos 5t \end{bmatrix}.$$

Differentiating again with respect to time,

$$\mathbf{T}' = \frac{d}{dt}\begin{bmatrix} -\sin 5t \\ \cos 5t \end{bmatrix} = \begin{bmatrix} -5\cos 5t \\ -5\sin 5t \end{bmatrix},$$

which has a magnitude of $\|\mathbf{T}'\| = 5$. Therefore, the curvature of the circle is

$$\kappa = \frac{\|\mathbf{T}'\|}{\|\mathbf{r}'\|} = \frac{5}{5R} = \frac{1}{R}.$$

Notice that the number 5 does not appear in our final formula, although it appears in the definition of $\mathbf{r}(t)$. That's because the number 5 controls the speed at which $\mathbf{r}(t)$ travels around the circle, but the curvature of a path is independent of the speed at which you traverse it. Instead, we see here that the curvature of a circle depends on its radius (larger circles have smaller curvatures). ∎

     Generally speaking, calculating curvature using equation (3.6) can be arduous since it involves differentiating $\mathbf{T} = \mathbf{r}'/\|\mathbf{r}'\|$. This motivates us to continue our search for equivalent formulations of κ, and in the discussion that follows we'll use a simple geometric argument involving $\mathbf{r}''$ and the area of a parallelogram to establish that

$$\|\mathbf{T}'\| = \frac{\|\mathbf{r}' \times \mathbf{r}''\|}{\|\mathbf{r}'\|^2}. \tag{3.7}$$

Once this equation is established, we'll be able to combine it with equation (3.6) to write curvature as

$$\kappa = \frac{\|\mathbf{r}' \times \mathbf{r}''\|}{\|\mathbf{r}'\|^3}.$$

Next, we present the geometric argument that leads us to equation (3.7). Since $\mathbf{r}' = \|\mathbf{r}'\|\mathbf{T}$, the Product Rule tells us that

$$\mathbf{r}'' = \frac{d\|\mathbf{r}'\|}{dt}\,\mathbf{T} + \|\mathbf{r}'\|\,\mathbf{T}'. \tag{3.8}$$

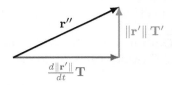

Figure 3.3: You know from Section 12.2 that $\mathbf{T}$ and $\mathbf{T}'$ are orthogonal because $\mathbf{T}$ has a constant magnitude.

Figure 3.3 depicts the scenario described by equation (3.8). You can see that the height of the triangle is $\|\mathbf{r}'\|\,\|\mathbf{T}'\|$. This is also the height of the parallelogram defined by $\mathbf{r}''$ and $(d\|\mathbf{r}'\|/dt)\mathbf{T}$, and because $\mathbf{r}'$ points in the same direction as $\mathbf{T}$, this same number is the height of the parallelogram defined by $\mathbf{r}'$ and $\mathbf{r}''$ (see Figure 3.4).

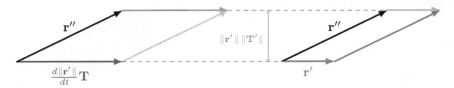

Figure 3.4: (left) The vector $\mathbf{r}''$ is the sum of orthogonal vectors; (right) the vector $\mathbf{T}$ points in the direction of $\mathbf{r}'$.

So to calculate $\|\mathbf{T}'\|$ we can determine the area of the parallelogram defined by $\mathbf{r}'$ and $\mathbf{r}''$, and then divide that area by its width. That is

We could use this strategy with either of the parallelograms in Figure 3.4, but it's much easier to calculate $\mathbf{r}'$ than $(d\|\mathbf{r}'\|/dt)\mathbf{T}$.

$$\underbrace{\|\mathbf{r}'\| \, \|\mathbf{T}'\|}_{\text{(height)} \times \text{(width)}} \|\mathbf{r}'\| = (\text{area of parallelogram}) = \|\mathbf{r}' \times \mathbf{r}''\|,$$

from which we get equation (3.7). Substituting that formula into equation (3.6) yields the following.

Calculating Curvature: Suppose $\mathbf{r}(t)$ is a smooth parameterization of $\mathcal{C}$, and $\mathbf{r}'$ is differentiable. Then

$$\kappa = \frac{\|\mathbf{r}' \times \mathbf{r}''\|}{\|\mathbf{r}'\|^3}. \tag{3.9}$$

Calculating curvature

Example 3.6. Suppose $\mathcal{C}$ is the circular helix parameterized by the function $\mathbf{r}(t) = \langle 10t, 5\cos t, 5\sin t \rangle$. (a) Use equation (3.9) to show that the curvature of $\mathcal{C}$ is constant, and (b) compare it to the curvature of the circular cross section of the cylinder around which $\mathcal{C}$ is wrapped.

Solution: (a) To use equation (3.9) we need formulas for $\mathbf{r}'$ and $\mathbf{r}''$. These are $\mathbf{r}' = \langle 10, -5\sin t, 5\cos t \rangle$ and $\mathbf{r}'' = \langle 0, -5\cos t, -5\sin t \rangle$, which we use to calculate $\|\mathbf{r}' \times \mathbf{r}''\| = \sqrt{3125}$ (constant). When we combine this with the fact that $\|\mathbf{r}'\| = \sqrt{125}$, equation (3.9) tells us that $\kappa = \sqrt{3125}/(\sqrt{125})^3 = 1/25$.

(b) This helix is driven down the x-axis by the first component, and the other components of $\mathbf{r}$ wrap it around a circular cylinder of radius 5 (see Figure 3.5). Since the radius of this cylinder is 5, the curvature of its circular cross section is $1/5$, which is greater than that of the helix. You can understand this intuitively by thinking of a segment of the helix as a circle that's been clipped and stretched, the latter of which reduces its curvature. ∎

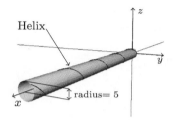

Figure 3.5: The helix in Example 3.6 wraps around a cylinder of radius 5.

Calculating curvature

Example 3.7. Suppose $\mathcal{C}$ is the curve parameterized by $\mathbf{r}(t) = \langle \ln t, t^3, t \rangle$ when $t \geq 1/2$. Determine the curvature of $\mathcal{C}$ at $\mathbf{r}(1)$.

Answer: $\kappa = \frac{\sqrt{1298}}{121}$. ∎

Solution On-line

When $\mathcal{C}$ is a curve of the form $y = f(x)$ we can parameterize it as $\mathbf{r}(t) = \langle t, f(t), 0 \rangle$, which allows us to calculate its curvature using equation (3.9). Since

$$\mathbf{r}'(t) = \langle 1, f'(t), 0 \rangle \quad \text{and} \quad \mathbf{r}''(t) = \langle 0, f''(t), 0 \rangle$$

we have $\|\mathbf{r}'\| = \sqrt{1 + \left(f'(t)\right)^2}$ and $\|\mathbf{r}' \times \mathbf{r}''\| = |f''(t)|$. Then recognizing that $t = x$ in this parameterization, and using equation (3.9) we arrive at the following fact.

Curvature of the Graph of a Function: Suppose $\mathcal{C}$ is the curve $y = f(x)$ in the Cartesian plane, where f is a twice-differentiable function. The curvature of $\mathcal{C}$ at the point $(x, f(x))$ is

$$\kappa = \frac{|f''(x)|}{\left[1 + \left(f'(x)\right)^2\right]^{3/2}}. \tag{3.10}$$

Curvature of the graph of a function

Example 3.8. Suppose $\mathcal{C}$ is the curve $y = 1 + x^4$. Determine the maximum and minimum curvature of $\mathcal{C}$.

Solution: When $f(x) = 1 + x^4$ we have $f'(x) = 4x^3$ and $f''(x) = 12x^2$, so equation (3.10) tells us that

$$\kappa(x) = \frac{12x^2}{\left(1 + 16x^6\right)^{3/2}}.$$

This is never negative but vanishes at $x = 0$, so the minimum value of κ is 0. To determine the maximum value of κ, we look for critical points of $\kappa(x)$. Using the relative-rate-of-change formula for the derivative of a quotient (see Section 3.5), we find that

$$\kappa'(x) = \kappa(x)\left[\frac{2}{x} - \frac{144x^5}{1 + 16x^6}\right] = \kappa(x)\left[\frac{2 - 112x^6}{x(1 + 16x^6)}\right],$$

which is graphed together with f in Figure 3.6. We already know that $\kappa(0) = 0$, so $x = 0$ is a critical point. To find the others, we solve the equation $2 - 112x^6 = 0$ for $x = \pm 56^{-1/6}$. At these points we have a curvature of

$$\kappa(56^{-1/6}) = \frac{12(56)^{-1/3}}{\left(1 + \frac{2}{7}\right)^{3/2}} \approx 2.151. \qquad \blacksquare$$

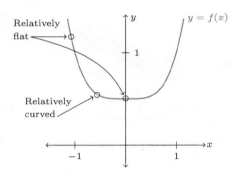 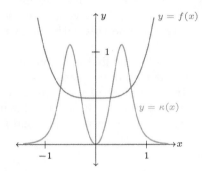

Figure 3.6: (left) The graph of f from Example 3.8; (right) the graphs of f and κ.

You should know

- the terms *smooth, arc length, unit tangent vector,* and *curvature;*
- what it means to *parameterize by arc length;*
- curvature is never negative;
- curvature is defined as the change in $\mathbf{T}$ per unit of arc length.

You should be able to

- calculate arc length;
- parameterize a curve by arc length;
- calculate the unit tangent vector;
- calculate curvature.

❖ **12.3 Skill Exercises**

In exercises #1–6 determine a formula for $\mathbf{T}(t)$.

1. $\mathbf{r}(t) = \langle 3t + 1, 8t - 9 \rangle$

2. $\mathbf{r}(t) = \langle 5t + 2, 3t + 1 \rangle$

3. $\mathbf{r}(t) = \langle \sin 5t, \cos 5t \rangle$

4. $\mathbf{r}(t) = \langle e^t, e^{-t} \rangle$

5. $\mathbf{r}(t) = \langle 9, \ln|\sec t|, t \rangle$

6. $\mathbf{r}(t) = \langle \sin 4t, 3t, \cos 5t \rangle$

In exercises #7–12 determine whether the given parameterization is smooth.

7. $\mathbf{r}(t) = t^2\mathbf{i} + \cos(t)\mathbf{j}$

8. $\mathbf{r}(t) = (e^{t+1} - t)\mathbf{i} + (t^2 + 2t + 1)\mathbf{j}$

9. $\mathbf{r}(t) = (t^3 + 7t)\mathbf{i} + 5\sin(t)\mathbf{j}$

10. $\mathbf{r}(t) = \langle t^4 + 3t + 1, e^{\cos t}, \ln(t^2 + 1)\rangle$

11. $\mathbf{r}(t) = \langle \sec 3t, e^t + e^{-t}, t^4\rangle$

12. $\mathbf{r}(t) = \langle t^4 - t^2, t^5, (t + 1)\ln(t + 1) - t\rangle$

In #13–18 use equation (3.1) to determine the length of the curve parameterized by $\mathbf{r}$. Additionally in #13 and #14, show that $\mathbf{r}$ parameterizes a line segment, and use geometry to check your calculation of length.

13. $\mathbf{r}(t) = \langle 8 - 2t, 3 + 4t\rangle, \; t \in [1, 3]$

14. $\mathbf{r}(t) = \langle 1 + 9t, 2 - 6t\rangle, \; t \in [0, 2]$

15. $\mathbf{r}(t) = \langle 9, 5t^3, 1 + 8t^3\rangle, \; t \in [-1, 1]$

16. $\mathbf{r}(t) = \langle 0.5t^2, 4 + \sqrt{2}\,t, \ln t\rangle, \; t \in [1, 2]$

17. $\mathbf{r}(t) = \langle e^t - t, 2e^{t/2}, 2\sqrt{3}\,e^{t/2}\rangle, \; t \in [0, 1]$

18. $\mathbf{r}(t) = \langle t, -3, \ln(\sec t)\rangle, \; t \in [0, \pi/4]$

In exercises #19–24 calculate the curvature of the curve parameterized by $\mathbf{r}$ at the specified point.

19. $\mathbf{r}(t) = \langle 8t + 1, 9t - 4\rangle; \; \mathbf{r}(2)$

20. $\mathbf{r}(t) = \langle t, t^2\rangle; \; \mathbf{r}(0)$

21. $\mathbf{r}(t) = \langle 8t + 1, 5t^3 - 2t\rangle; \; (9, 3)$

22. $\mathbf{r}(t) = \langle 4t^2 + 12t, t^3 - 8t\rangle; \; (40, 3)$

23. $\mathbf{r}(t) = \langle 8t + t^2, \sin 3t, e^t\rangle; \; \mathbf{r}(0)$

24. $\mathbf{r}(t) = \langle \cos^2 t, \sin^2 t, 8t\rangle; \; \mathbf{r}(\pi/3)$

A function of a single variable is specified in exercises #25–30. Determine the curvature of its graph at the given point.

25. $f(x) = x^2; \; (0, 0)$

26. $f(x) = x^3 - 3x; \; (1, 0)$

27. $f(x) = \cos x; \; (0, 1)$

28. $f(x) = \sin x; \; (\pi, 0)$

29. $f(x) = e^x; \; (1, e)$

30. $f(x) = \sqrt{x}; \; (1, 1)$

In exercises #31–36 a curve is parameterized by $\mathbf{r}(t)$ when $t \geq 0$. Reparameterize the curve by arc length.

31. $\mathbf{r}(t) = \langle 3t + 4, 8t - 1\rangle$

32. $\mathbf{r}(t) = \langle 8 + 3t^2, 13 - 4t^3\rangle$

33. $\mathbf{r}(t) = \langle e^t + e^{-t}, 2t - 3\rangle$

34. $\mathbf{r}(t) = \left\langle \int_0^t \sin\left(\frac{\tau^2}{2}\right)\, d\tau, \int_0^t \cos\left(\frac{\tau^2}{2}\right)\, d\tau \right\rangle$

35. $\mathbf{r}(t) = \langle 4t^{3/2}, 5 + 3t^2, 3t - 8\rangle$

36. $\mathbf{r}(t) = \langle 3t, 5\sqrt{1 - t^2}, 4t - 2\rangle$

✧ 12.3 Concept and Application Exercises

37. Suppose $\mathbf{r}(t) = \langle 4 + t, 8 - 9t, 3 + 2t\rangle$.

    (a) Show that $\mathbf{r}'(t)$ is constant, and explain what that means about the curve parameterized by $\mathbf{r}$.

    (b) Based on your answer to part (a), what should be true about the curvature of the path described by $\mathbf{r}(t)$?

    (c) Use equation (3.9) to calculate κ and compare it to your answer from part (b).

38. Suppose $f(x) = \sqrt{R^2 - x^2}$ where $R > 0$.

    (a) Describe the graph of f.

    (b) Based on your answer to part (a), what should be true about κ?

    (c) Use equation (3.10) to calculate κ and compare it to your answer in part (b).

39. Suppose that you use equation (3.9) to calculate the curvature of the graph of a function, and your friend uses equation (3.10). Your calculation results in an answer of 2, and his in -2. Who made a mistake, and how do you know?

40. Suppose $\mathbf{r}(t) = \langle 2\cos t,\ 6\sin t \rangle$.

    (a) Verify that $\mathbf{r}(t)$ always sits on the ellipse $\frac{x^2}{4} + \frac{y^2}{36} = 1$ in the xy-plane.

    (b) Based on part (a), at what times to you expect the curvature, $\kappa(t)$, to be greatest and smallest?

    (c) Determine a formula for $\kappa(t)$ and use it to determine the times at which it's maximized and minimized. Do these times agree with your predictions in part (b)?

41. Suppose $\mathbf{r}(t) = \langle a\cos t,\ b\sin t \rangle$, where $|a| > |b| > 0$.

    (a) Verify that $\mathbf{r}(t)$ always sits on the ellipse $\frac{x^2}{a^2} + \frac{y^2}{b^2} = 1$ in the xy-plane.

    (b) Determine the maximum and minimum values of $\|\mathbf{r}(t)\|$.

    (c) Based on parts (a) and (b) what do you anticipate about the maximum and minimum values of κ?

    (d) Determine a formula for $\kappa(t)$ and use it validate the conjecture you made in part (c).

42. Suppose $\mathbf{r}(t) = \langle \cos t,\ \sin t,\ \beta t \rangle$, where $\beta > 0$.

    (a) Describe the path parameterized by $\mathbf{r}(t)$.

    (b) Based solely on intuition, do you expect β to affect curvature? If so, how? If not, why not?

    (c) Determine a formula for the curvature of the path parameterized by $\mathbf{r}(t)$. How does your answer compare with your prediction in part (b)?

43. Suppose $\mathcal{C}$ is the circular helix parameterized by $\mathbf{r}(t) = \langle \cos(\alpha t), \sin(\alpha t), \beta t \rangle$, where α and β are positive numbers.

    (a) Explain how α and β affect the shape of $\mathcal{C}$.

    (b) Show that, although the numbers α and β can change the shape of $\mathcal{C}$ independently, the curvature of $\mathcal{C}$ is determined by their ratio, and explain what this means in terms of the structure of $\mathcal{C}$.

44. The ***Cornu spiral*** is the curve parameterized by $\mathbf{r}(t) = a\left(\int_0^t \cos(\tau^2)d\tau\right)\mathbf{i} + a\left(\int_0^t \sin(\tau^2)d\tau\right)\mathbf{j}$, where $a \neq 0$ is constant.

    (a) The spiral is shown in Figure 3.7 when $a = 2$. In complete sentences, explain how increasing the value of a will affect the curve.

    (b) Based on your answer to part (a), how do you think increasing a will affect the curvature?

    (c) Determine a formula for κ in terms of a, and compare it to your answer from part (b).

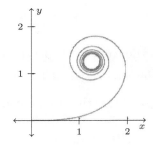

Figure 3.7: A Cornu spiral when $a = 2$.

45. Suppose $\mathcal{C}$ is the curve parameterized by $\mathbf{r}(t) = \langle t^2, -t^3 \rangle$.

    (a) Show that $\mathbf{r}'(t)$ is continuous.

    (b) Determine whether $\mathbf{r}(t)$ is a smooth parameterization of $\mathcal{C}$, and explain your reasoning.

(c) Use a graphing utility to render a plot of $\mathcal{C}$, and explain what you see at the origin in light of your answer to part (b).

46. The piecewise-linear curve $\mathcal{C}$ is shown in Figure 3.8. Parameterize $\mathcal{C}$ with a vector-valued function $\mathbf{r}(t)$ for which $\mathbf{r}'(t)$ is continuous at all times, and which remains at the point $(2, -1)$ when $t \in (0, 1)$.

47. A telecommunications company needs to run a fiber-optic cable along a winding road described by

$$\mathbf{r}(t) = \frac{1}{100} \begin{bmatrix} 2t \sin t - (t^2 - 2) \cos t \\ 2t \cos t + (t^2 - 2) \sin t \\ 10 - 0.1t^2 \end{bmatrix}.$$

Determine the length of the cable needed to connect $\mathbf{r}(0)$ to $\mathbf{r}(10)$. Assume distance is measured in miles.

48. Suppose a power company plans to run a power line between a pair of substations. The cable follow the path parameterized by $\mathbf{r}(t) = 20t\mathbf{i} + 20 \sin\left(\frac{t}{2}\right)\mathbf{j} + t^2\mathbf{k}$ when $t \in [-3, 3]$, where distance is measured in miles.

(a) Write the integral that would calculate the length of cable needed to follow this path.

(b) Determine an over-estimate of the length of cable needed by recalling that $0 \le \cos^2 \theta \le 1$.

(c) Determine an under-estimate of the length of cable needed by, again, recalling that $0 \le \cos^2 \theta \le 1$.

(d) Use a CAS to evaluate the integral from part (a), and determine which of the two estimates is closer to the actual value.

49. In Section 12.2 (exercise #65) you worked with the *Magnus force* on a spinning ball, which is responsible for "bending" the ball's trajectory. Here we continue with $\boldsymbol{\omega}$ and $\mathbf{v}_\perp$ as in that exercise, and define $\mathbf{r}_\perp = \langle x, y, 0 \rangle$. Distance will be measured in meters and time in seconds.

(a) Show that when the ball is affected by only gravity and the Magnus force, the path parameterized by $\mathbf{r}_\perp$ has constant curvature.

(b) Because the path parameterized by $\mathbf{r}_\perp$ is planar and has constant curvature, it's a circle. Determine the radius of this circle, R, in terms of the mass of the ball, m, the parameters w and c, and the magnitude of $\mathbf{v}_\perp$ (which is constant, see #65 of Section 12.2).

(c) Suppose a soccer ball is placed at the point $(a, 0, 0)$, and then kicked in the direction of $\mathbf{j}$ with a speed of v_2 meters per second. Determine a formula for $\mathbf{r}_\perp(t)$.

(d) Now we incorporate the third component and the effect of gravity. Suppose a soccer ball is placed at the point $(a, 0, 0)$, and kicked with an initial velocity of $\mathbf{v} = \langle 0, v_2, v_3 \rangle$ meters per second. Determine a formula for the ball's trajectory in space, $\mathbf{r}(t)$.

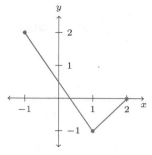

Figure 3.8:   The curve $\mathcal{C}$ for exercise #46.

Civil Engineering

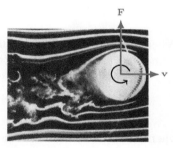

Figure 3.9:   A ball spinning counterclockwise in an air flow. Smoke filaments show that the wake of the ball shifts to one side of the ball, deflecting the air flow on that side.

12.4   Motion in Space

Key Idea(s): *When an object is moving, the unit vector* **T** *points in the direction it's traveling, and the unit vector* **N** *points in the direction it's turning.*

The vectors **T, N** *and* **B** *form a natural frame of reference for a moving object.*

Whether walking, driving a car, or riding a roller coaster, there are three directions that are important when you're moving: forward-backward, side-to-side, and up-down. These directions provide a natural frame of reference for a moving object, and in this section we discuss them in some detail. In brief, these directions are defined by the unit tangent vector, **T**, the *unit normal vector,* **N**, and the *unit binormal vector,* **B**.

In Section 12.3 we introduced **T** as the unit vector that points in the direction of **r′** (provided that **r′** ≠ **0**). If we think of **r** as the position of a moving object, the vector **r′** is the object's velocity, so let's denote it by **v** and write

$$\mathbf{T}(t) = \frac{\mathbf{v}(t)}{\|\mathbf{v}(t)\|}. \tag{4.1}$$

In this section we'll focus on the other vectors that complete the natural frame of reference when $\mathbf{r}(t)$ is smooth. We'll develop methods of calculating **N** and **B**, and we'll use them in conjunction with **T** to better understand curves, velocity, and acceleration in space.

✣ The Unit Normal Vector

Whereas **T** tells us something important about velocity (its direction), the *unit normal vector* arises naturally in a discussion of acceleration, which we calculate next. After rewriting equation (4.1) as $\mathbf{v}(t) = \|\mathbf{v}(t)\|\mathbf{T}$, we can calculate the acceleration vector by differentiating:

$$\mathbf{a}(t) = \frac{d}{dt}\mathbf{v}(t) = \frac{d}{dt}\left(\|\mathbf{v}(t)\|\mathbf{T}(t)\right) = \underbrace{\left(\frac{d\|\mathbf{v}(t)\|}{dt}\right)}_{\text{Rate of change in speed}}\mathbf{T}(t) + \|\mathbf{v}(t)\|\underbrace{\mathbf{T}'(t)}_{\text{Rate of change in direction}}. \tag{4.2}$$

When $\mathbf{T}' \neq \mathbf{0}$, the unit vector that points in the direction of $\mathbf{T}'$ is called the **principal unit normal vector**, and is denoted by **N** (people often omit the word *principal,* and refer to **N** as the unit normal vector). That is,

In Example 2.6 we showed that **u** is orthogonal to **u′** when ∥**u**∥ is constant.

$$\mathbf{N} = \frac{1}{\|\mathbf{T}'\|}\mathbf{T}' \tag{4.3}$$

The word "normal" is being used in the sense of "orthogonal," as it was when we talked about lines and planes.

when $\|\mathbf{T}'\| \neq 0$. This allows us to rewrite equation (4.2) more simply as

$$\mathbf{a} = a_\mathrm{T}\mathbf{T} + a_\mathrm{N}\mathbf{N} \tag{4.4}$$

where

$$a_\mathrm{T} = \frac{d\|\mathbf{v}\|}{dt} \quad\text{and}\quad a_\mathrm{N} = \|\mathbf{v}\|\|\mathbf{T}'\|. \tag{4.5}$$

The diagram in Figure 4.1 depicts the main point of equation (4.4)—that the vector **a** can be "built" by scaling and adding the vectors **T** and **N**. The scale factors are are a_T and a_N respectively, and we'll say more about them later in this section. Also in the figure you see that **T** and **N** are orthogonal. This happens because **T** has a constant magnitude, so **T** and **T′** are orthogonal.

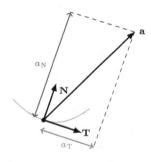

Figure 4.1: A point is moving along the gray curve. This diagram shows the relationship between **a**, **T** and **N**.

Using equation (4.3) to compute **N** can be a grueling endeavor, even in simple cases. So although we *define* **N** using the ideas and notation of calculus, it's often easier to *calculate* it using the algebra of vectors. As you'll see in the next example, because the vectors **a** and $a_\mathrm{T}\mathbf{T}$ are relatively easy to calculate, we can determine the direction of **N** by rewriting equation (4.4) as

$$a_\mathrm{N}\mathbf{N} = \mathbf{a} - a_\mathrm{T}\mathbf{T}$$

Then normalizing this vector gives us $\mathbf{N}$.

Calculating $\mathbf{T}$ and $\mathbf{N}$

Example 4.1. Suppose $\mathbf{r}(t) = \langle t, t^4, 1 - t^2 \rangle$. Determine the unit tangent and unit normal vectors at $\mathbf{r}(1)$.

Solution: When position is described by $\mathbf{r}(t)$, velocity and acceleration are

$$\mathbf{v}(t) = \mathbf{r}'(t) = \langle 1, 4t^3, -2t \rangle$$
$$\mathbf{a}(t) = \mathbf{v}'(t) = \langle 0, 12t^2, -2 \rangle,$$

so the unit tangent vector at $t = 1$ is

$$\mathbf{T}(1) = \frac{1}{\|\mathbf{v}(1)\|}\mathbf{v}(1) = \frac{1}{\sqrt{21}}\langle 1, 4, -2 \rangle.$$

To use the strategy for finding $\mathbf{N}(1)$ that was outlined prior to this example, we need to know the number a_T at $t = 1$. Luckily, it's value can be determined quickly by using the dot product. Since $\mathbf{T} \cdot \mathbf{T} = \|\mathbf{T}\|^2 = 1$ and $\mathbf{T} \cdot \mathbf{N} = 0$,

$$\underbrace{\mathbf{a} \cdot \mathbf{T} = (a_\mathrm{T}\mathbf{T} + a_\mathrm{N}\mathbf{N}) \cdot \mathbf{T}}_{\text{From equation (4.4)}} = a_\mathrm{T}\underbrace{\mathbf{T} \cdot \mathbf{T}}_{\|\mathbf{T}\|^2=1} + a_\mathrm{N}\underbrace{\mathbf{N} \cdot \mathbf{T}}_{=0} = a_\mathrm{T}. \qquad (4.6)$$

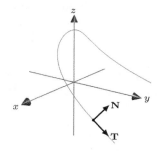

Figure 4.2: The path parameterized by $\mathbf{r}(t)$ in Example 4.1. The vector $\mathbf{N}(1)$ points in the direction of the side-to-side force at time $t = 1$.

Using the vectors $\mathbf{T}(1)$ and $\mathbf{a}(1)$ specified above, this equation gives us $a_\mathrm{T} = {}^{52}\!/\sqrt{21}$ when $t = 1$.

Now that we know the vectors $\mathbf{a}, \mathbf{T}$ and the number a_T when $t = 1$, equation (4.4) tells us that

$$a_\mathrm{N}\mathbf{N} = \mathbf{a} - a_\mathrm{T}\mathbf{T} = \begin{bmatrix} 0 \\ 12 \\ -2 \end{bmatrix} - \frac{52}{\sqrt{21}}\frac{1}{\sqrt{21}}\begin{bmatrix} 1 \\ 4 \\ -2 \end{bmatrix} = \frac{2}{21}\begin{bmatrix} -26 \\ 22 \\ 31 \end{bmatrix}.$$

Since this vector points in the direction of $\mathbf{N}(1)$, we need only normalize it to determine the unit normal vector:

$$\mathbf{N} = \frac{a_\mathrm{N}\mathbf{N}}{\|a_\mathrm{N}\mathbf{N}\|} = \frac{1}{\sqrt{2121}}\begin{bmatrix} -26 \\ 22 \\ 31 \end{bmatrix}. \qquad \blacksquare$$

> The effect of normalizing a nonzero vector is to make its magnitude 1 (without changing its direction), regardless of the original magnitude, so we can make our calculation of magnitude easier by disregarding the factor of ²/21. The magnitude of $\langle -26, 22, 31 \rangle$ is $\sqrt{2121}$.

$\mathbf{N}$ points in the direction of side-to-side force

Example 4.2. Suppose the position vector of a 10-kg object is $\mathbf{r}(t) = \langle t, t^4, 1 - t^2 \rangle$. If distance is measured in meters and time in seconds, determine the side-to-side force experienced by this object at time $t = 1$.

Solution: Newton's Second Law tells us that $\mathbf{F} = (\text{mass}) \times (\text{acceleration}) = 10\mathbf{a}$, and we know from equation (4.4) that $\mathbf{a} = a_\mathrm{T}\mathbf{T} + a_\mathrm{N}\mathbf{N}$, so

$$\mathbf{F} = 10(a_\mathrm{T}\mathbf{T} + a_\mathrm{N}\mathbf{N}) = 10a_\mathrm{T}\mathbf{T} + 10a_\mathrm{N}\mathbf{N}.$$

Since $\mathbf{T}$ points in the "forward" direction (the direction of $\mathbf{v}$) and $\mathbf{N}$ is orthogonal to it, this equation shows us that the side-to-side component of the force experienced by the object is $10a_\mathrm{N}\mathbf{N}$. We found that $a_\mathrm{N}\mathbf{N}(1) = \frac{2}{21}\langle -26, 22, 31 \rangle$ in Example 4.1, so the side-to-side force is $\frac{20}{21}\langle -26, 22, 31 \rangle$, which has units of newtons. $\qquad \blacksquare$

Example 4.3. Suppose $\mathbf{r}(t) = \langle t^3, 8 \ln t, t \rangle$ is the position vector for a 5-kg object. If distance is measured in meters and time in seconds, determine the side-to-side force experienced by this object at time $t = 2$.

Answer: $\frac{10}{161} \langle 150, -433, -68 \rangle$. ∎

Solution
On-line

▷ Tangential and Normal Components of Acceleration

In Examples 4.2 and 4.3 you determined the side-to-side force experienced by a moving object, but before you arrived at the final answer you had to proceed through the lengthy preliminary steps demonstrated in Example 4.1. If we only need the magnitude of the side-to-side force, there's a quicker way. Because

$$\mathbf{F} = m\mathbf{a} = m\big(a_{\mathrm{T}}\mathbf{T} + a_{\mathrm{N}}\mathbf{N}\big),$$

we need simple techniques for determining a_{T} and a_{N}. We've already seen that a_{T} can be quickly calculated with a dot product,

$$a_{\mathrm{T}} = \mathbf{a} \cdot \mathbf{T} = \mathbf{a} \cdot \frac{\mathbf{v}}{\|\mathbf{v}\|} = \frac{\mathbf{a} \cdot \mathbf{v}}{\|\mathbf{v}\|}. \tag{4.7}$$

Interestingly, the number a_{N} can be easily calculated with a cross product. Consider the parallelogram defined by $\mathbf{a}$ and $\mathbf{T}$, which is depicted in Figure 4.3. Its area can be calculated as (base)×(height)$= 1 \times a_{\mathrm{N}} = a_{\mathrm{N}}$, or as $\|\mathbf{a} \times \mathbf{T}\|$, so

$$a_{\mathrm{N}} = \|\mathbf{a} \times \mathbf{T}\| = \left\| \mathbf{a} \times \frac{1}{\|\mathbf{v}\|}\mathbf{v} \right\| = \frac{1}{\|\mathbf{v}\|}\|\mathbf{a} \times \mathbf{v}\| = \frac{\|\mathbf{a} \times \mathbf{v}\|}{\|\mathbf{v}\|}. \tag{4.8}$$

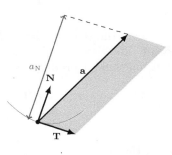

Figure 4.3: The parallelogram defined by $\mathbf{a}$ and $\mathbf{T}$. Compare to Figure 4.1.

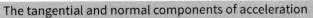

Example 4.4. Suppose $\mathbf{r}(t) = \langle 2 - \cos \pi t, 5 - t^3, t^4 - t \rangle$. Determine the numbers a_{T} and a_{N} when $t = 1$.

Solution: Let's begin by calculating the acceleration vector.

$$\mathbf{v}(t) = \mathbf{r}'(t) = \langle \pi \sin(\pi t), -3t^2, \ 4t^3 - 1 \rangle$$
$$\mathbf{a}(t) = \mathbf{v}'(t) = \langle \pi^2 \cos(\pi t), -6t, 12t^2 \rangle.$$

So $\mathbf{v}(1) = \langle 0, -3, 3 \rangle$ and $\mathbf{a}(1) = \langle -\pi^2, -6, 12 \rangle$. According to equation (4.7),

$$a_{\mathrm{T}} = \mathbf{a} \cdot \mathbf{T} = \mathbf{a} \cdot \frac{\mathbf{v}}{\|\mathbf{v}\|} = \frac{\mathbf{a} \cdot \mathbf{v}}{\|\mathbf{v}\|} = 9\sqrt{2}.$$

And since $\mathbf{a} \times \mathbf{v} = \langle -18, -3\pi^2, -3\pi^2 \rangle$ when $t = 1$, equation (4.9) tells us that

$$a_{\mathrm{N}} = \frac{\|\langle -18, -3\pi^2, -3\pi^2 \rangle\|}{\sqrt{18}} = \sqrt{18 + \pi^4}.$$ ∎

Although we have introduced the technique determining a_{N} with a cross product, it can also be calculated with a dot product:

$$\mathbf{a} \cdot \mathbf{N} = (a_{\mathrm{T}}\mathbf{T} + a_{\mathrm{N}}\mathbf{N}) \cdot \mathbf{N} = a_{\mathrm{T}}\mathbf{T} \cdot \mathbf{N} + a_{\mathrm{N}}\mathbf{N} \cdot \mathbf{N} = a_{\mathrm{T}}(0) + a_{\mathrm{N}}(1) = a_{\mathrm{N}}. \tag{4.9}$$

$\boxed{\mathbf{T} \cdot \mathbf{N} = 0 \text{ because the vectors are orthogonal, and } \mathbf{N} \cdot \mathbf{N} = 1 \text{ because } \mathbf{N} \text{ is a unit vector.}}$

Equations (4.7) and (4.9) are important because they provide us with a geometric way of understanding a_{T} and a_{N}:

$$a_{\mathrm{T}} = \mathbf{a} \cdot \mathbf{T} = \|\mathbf{a}\| \underbrace{\cos \theta}_{} = \mathrm{comp}_{\mathbf{T}}\mathbf{a} \quad \text{and} \quad a_{\mathrm{N}} = \mathbf{a} \cdot \mathbf{N} = \|\mathbf{a}\| \underbrace{\cos \theta}_{} = \mathrm{comp}_{\mathbf{N}}\mathbf{a}.$$

θ = angle between $\mathbf{a}$ and $\mathbf{T}$ θ = angle between $\mathbf{a}$ and $\mathbf{N}$

Because of this, we refer to a_{T} and a_{N} as the *tangential component* and *normal component* of acceleration, respectively. When traveling in a vehicle, the tangential component of acceleration is what presses the seat against your back, and the normal component of acceleration is what makes you slide sideways.

> **Tangential and Normal Components of Acceleration:** Suppose $\mathbf{r}(t)$ is a twice-differentiable, smooth vector-valued function. Then an object whose position is $\mathbf{r}(t)$ has a velocity of $\mathbf{v}(t) = \mathbf{r}'(t)$ and experiences an acceleration of $\mathbf{a} = a_{\mathrm{T}}\mathbf{T} + a_{\mathrm{N}}\mathbf{N}$, where $\mathbf{T}$ and $\mathbf{N}$ are the unit tangent and unit normal vectors,
>
> $$a_{\mathrm{T}} = \frac{\mathbf{a}\cdot\mathbf{v}}{\|\mathbf{v}\|}, \quad \text{and} \quad a_{\mathrm{N}} = \frac{\|\mathbf{a}\times\mathbf{v}\|}{\|\mathbf{v}\|}. \tag{4.10}$$

Tangential and normal components of acceleration

Example 4.5. Suppose $\mathbf{r}(t) = \langle 3t^2, 2\cos 4t, 5\sin 4t\rangle$. Write $\mathbf{a}$ as a sum of $\mathbf{T}$ and $\mathbf{N}$ when $t = \pi$.

Answer: $\mathbf{a} = \dfrac{36\pi}{\sqrt{400+36\pi^2}}\mathbf{T} + \sqrt{\dfrac{424{,}000+36{,}864\pi^2}{400+36\pi^2}}\,\mathbf{N}$ when $t = \pi$. ∎

Solution On-line

We close this introduction to $\mathbf{N}$ by returning to equation (4.5), where we first defined $a_{\mathrm{N}} = \|\mathbf{v}\|\,\|\mathbf{T}'\|$. At this stage, we also know that $a_{\mathrm{N}} = \mathbf{a}\cdot\mathbf{T}$, so we can conclude that

$$\mathbf{a}\cdot\mathbf{N} = \|\mathbf{v}\|\|\mathbf{T}'\| > 0$$

during a turn, which means that the angle between $\mathbf{a}$ and $\mathbf{N}$ is acute. Consequently, the vector $\mathbf{N}$ always points into a turn (since the vector $\mathbf{a}$ does). You see this depicted in Figure 4.4, in which $\mathbf{r}(t) = \langle x(t), y(t)\rangle$ parameterizes the graph of a scalar-valued function, say $y = f(x)$. Note that $\mathbf{N}$ must flip at an inflection point in order to continue pointing into a turn.

> The vector $\mathbf{T}$ is nonconstant during a turn, so $\mathbf{T}' \neq \mathbf{0}$.

> Because $\|\mathbf{N}\|$ is always 1, it cannot switch sides of a curve by shrinking to $\mathbf{0}$ and then poking out the other side.

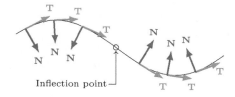

Figure 4.4: On the curve $y = f(x)$, jump discontinuities in $\mathbf{N}$ happen at inflection points.

❖ The Osculating Plane and the Binormal Vector

We've seen that the motion described by $\mathbf{r}(t)$ heads in the direction of $\mathbf{T}$ and turns in the direction of $\mathbf{N}$. It's almost as if the path "wants" to stay in the plane described by $\mathbf{T}$ and $\mathbf{N}$, which is called the *osculating plane* of the curve. (The Latin word *osculum* means "to kiss.") In order to write the equation of the osculating plane, we need a vector that's orthogonal to it; since $\mathbf{T}$ and $\mathbf{N}$ lie in the plane, the vector $\mathbf{T}\times\mathbf{N}$ does that job. This vector is called the *binormal* vector of the curve, and is denoted by $\mathbf{B}$.

Let us remark that since $\mathbf{T}$ and $\mathbf{N}$ are orthogonal unit vectors,

$$\|\mathbf{B}\| = \|\mathbf{T}\times\mathbf{N}\| = \|\mathbf{T}\|\,\|\mathbf{N}\|\sin\tfrac{\pi}{2} = 1\cdot 1\cdot 1 = 1.$$

And since $\mathbf{B}$ is orthogonal to both $\mathbf{T}$ and $\mathbf{N}$, the binormal vector completes the "natural" frame of reference for an object that's moving in three dimensions—insofar as

T points in the direction of motion, and **N** points "sideways" (in the direction of the turn), the vector **B** indicates which direction is "up." In practice we find **B** by normalizing the vector $\mathbf{r}' \times \mathbf{r}''$, which works because (as you'll show in the exercises) $\mathbf{r}' \times \mathbf{r}''$ points in the direction of $\mathbf{T} \times \mathbf{N}$.

> **TNB Frame of Reference:** Suppose that $\mathbf{r}(t)$ is a smooth vector-valued function that's twice differentiable. Then
>
> $$\mathbf{T} = \tfrac{1}{\|\mathbf{r}'\|}\mathbf{r}', \qquad \mathbf{N} = \tfrac{1}{\|\mathbf{T}'\|}\mathbf{T}' \text{ when } \mathbf{T}' \neq \mathbf{0}, \text{ and} \qquad \mathbf{B} = \mathbf{T} \times \mathbf{N}.$$
>
> Equivalently,
>
> $$\mathbf{B} = \tfrac{1}{\|\mathbf{r}' \times \mathbf{r}''\|}(\mathbf{r}' \times \mathbf{r}'') \qquad \text{and} \qquad \mathbf{N} = \tfrac{1}{a_{\mathrm{N}}}\left(\mathbf{r}'' - a_{\mathrm{T}}\mathbf{T}\right)$$
>
> when $a_{\mathrm{T}} = \mathbf{T} \cdot \mathbf{r}''$, and $a_{\mathrm{N}} = \|\mathbf{r}' \times \mathbf{r}''\|/\|\mathbf{r}'\|$ is nonzero.

Calculating the binormal vector

Example 4.6. Suppose $\mathbf{r}(t) = \langle 2 - 4t + 4t^3, 1 - 2t + 3t^2 - t^4, 3t - t^3 \rangle$. Determine (a) the vector **B** at $t = 0$, and (b) the equation of the osculating plane at $\mathbf{r}(0)$.

Solution: (a) The binormal vector points in the direction of $\mathbf{r}' \times \mathbf{r}''$ and has unit length, so we begin by calculating

$$\mathbf{r}'(t) = \langle -4 + 12t^2, -2 + 6t - 4t^3, 3 - 3t^2 \rangle \quad \Rightarrow \quad \mathbf{r}'(0) = \langle -4, -2, 3 \rangle$$
$$\mathbf{r}''(t) = \langle 24t, 6 - 12t^2, -6t \rangle \quad \Rightarrow \quad \mathbf{r}''(0) = \langle 0, 6, 0 \rangle.$$

These allow us to calculate $\mathbf{r}' \times \mathbf{r}'' = -18\mathbf{i} - 24\mathbf{k}$ at $t = 0$. The magnitude of this vector is $\|-18\mathbf{i} - 24\mathbf{k}\| = 30$, so the binormal vector is

$$\mathbf{B} = \frac{1}{\|\mathbf{r}' \times \mathbf{r}''\|}(\mathbf{r}' \times \mathbf{r}'') = \frac{1}{30}\langle -18, 0, -24 \rangle = \frac{1}{5}\langle -3, 0, -4 \rangle.$$

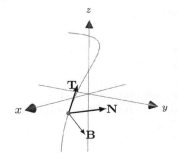

(b) To write the equation of a plane, we need two pieces of information: a point that's on the plane, and a vector that's orthogonal to the plane. Based on the work in part (a), we know that $\mathbf{n} = \langle -3, 0, -4 \rangle$ is orthogonal to the osculating plane, and the point at $\mathbf{r}(0) = \langle 2, 1, 0 \rangle$ is on the plane. Since $\mathbf{n} \cdot \mathbf{r}(0) = -6$, the equation of the plane is $-3x + 0y - 4z = -6$. ∎

Figure 4.5: The curve in Example 4.6, with **T**, **N** and **B** at a point.

▷ The Osculating Circle

Suppose $P = (a, b, c)$ is a point on the curve $\mathcal{C}$. The ***osculating circle*** to $\mathcal{C}$ at P is the circle that (a) lies in the osculating plane at P, (b) is tangent to the curve at P, (c) has the same curvature at P as the curve $\mathcal{C}$, and for which (d) its center is found in the direction of **N** (so the curve and the circle turn the same way).

> Whereas the tangent line approximates the direction that a curve is headed, the osculating circle approximates both its direction *and* curvature.

Determining an osculating circle

Example 4.7. Suppose $\mathcal{C}$ is the curve parameterized by $\mathbf{r}(t) = (2 - 4t + 4t^3)\mathbf{i} + (1 - 2t + 3t^2 - t^4)\mathbf{j} + (3t - t^3)\mathbf{k}$. (a) Locate the center of the osculating circle at $\mathbf{r}(0)$, and (b) parameterize the osculating circle.

Solution: (a) The position vector $\mathbf{r}(0) = \langle 2, 1, 0 \rangle$ locates the point that lies on both $\mathcal{C}$ and the osculating circle. From there, the circle's center lies in the direction of $\mathbf{N}(0)$. To determine that direction, we make use of the right-handed nature of the TNB frame of reference. Specifically, since $\mathbf{B} = \mathbf{T} \times \mathbf{N}$, the vector **N** points in the direction of $\mathbf{B} \times \mathbf{T}$. In Example 4.6 saw that **B** points in the direction of $\langle -3, 0, -4 \rangle$, and **T** in the direction of $\langle -4, -2, -3 \rangle$, so the direction in which we find the center is $\langle -3, 0, -4 \rangle \times \langle -4, -2, -3 \rangle = \langle -8, 25, 6 \rangle$. We recover the vector $\mathbf{N}$ by normalizing this result:

$$\mathbf{N} = \frac{1}{5\sqrt{29}} \langle -8, 25, 6 \rangle.$$

Now that we know the direction from $\mathbf{r}(0)$ in which the center of the circle is located, we need to know how far it is from $\mathbf{r}(0)$. That is, we need to know the radius of the circle. We know from Section 12.3 that the radius of a circle is the reciprocal of its curvature, $R = 1/\kappa$, where

$$\kappa = \frac{\|\mathbf{r}' \times \mathbf{r}''\|}{\|\mathbf{r}'\|^3}.$$

> This is equation (3.9).

Using $\mathbf{r}'(0) = \langle -4, -2, 3 \rangle$ and $\mathbf{r}''(0) = \langle 0, 6, 0 \rangle$, which were determined in Example 4.6, this formula allows us to calculate $\kappa = 30/29\sqrt{29}$. So we can locate the center of the circle by starting at $\mathbf{r}(0)$ and traveling a distance of $R = 29\sqrt{29}/30$ in the direction of $\mathbf{N}$ (see Figure 4.6). That is, the position vector for the center is

> Recall that a circle of radius R has a curvature of $\kappa = 1/R$. So when we know κ we can determine $R = 1/\kappa$.

$$\mathbf{c} = \mathbf{r}(0) + R\mathbf{N} = \begin{bmatrix} 2 \\ 1 \\ 0 \end{bmatrix} + \frac{29}{150} \begin{bmatrix} -8 \\ 25 \\ 6 \end{bmatrix}.$$

(b) The key to parameterizing this circle is that, just as we can use the unit vectors $\mathbf{i}$ and $\mathbf{j}$ to build all vectors in the xy-plane, we can use the unit vectors $\mathbf{T}$ and $\mathbf{N}$ to build all vectors that lie in the osculating plane, including the displacement vectors that reach from the center of the circle to its edge. In fact, since $\mathbf{T}$ and $\mathbf{N}$ are orthogonal, every such displacement vector takes the form

$$R\cos(\theta)\mathbf{N} + R\sin(\theta)\mathbf{T},$$

> Position vectors in the xy-plane of the form $R\cos(\theta)\mathbf{i} + R\sin(\theta)\mathbf{j}$ locate points on the circle of radius R that's centered at the origin. This is the analogous formula for a plane containing the orthogonal unit vectors $\mathbf{T}$ and $\mathbf{N}$.

where R is the radius of the circle and $\theta \in [0, 2\pi]$ is a parameter that moves us around the circle. This fact allows us to parameterize the circle as

$$\mathbf{u}(\theta) = \underbrace{\mathbf{c}}_{} + \underbrace{R\cos(\theta)\mathbf{N} + R\sin(\theta)\mathbf{T}}_{}$$

Start at the center, and then move to the edge

Now incorporating the number R and the vectors $\mathbf{c}, \mathbf{T}$ and $\mathbf{N}$, we have

$$\mathbf{u}(\theta) = \begin{bmatrix} 2 \\ 1 \\ 0 \end{bmatrix} + \frac{29}{150} \begin{bmatrix} -8 \\ 25 \\ 6 \end{bmatrix} + \frac{29}{150}\cos(\theta) \begin{bmatrix} -8 \\ 25 \\ 6 \end{bmatrix} + \frac{29}{30}\sin(\theta) \begin{bmatrix} -4 \\ -2 \\ -3 \end{bmatrix}. \qquad \blacksquare$$

> Note that we pass through $\mathbf{r}(0)$ when $\theta = \pi$. Compare to Figure 4.6.

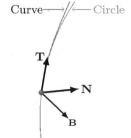

Figure 4.6: (all) The curve parameterized by $\mathbf{r}(t)$ is show in blue; (left) the center of the osculating circle is at $\mathbf{r}(0) + R\mathbf{N}$; (middle) displacement vectors that reach from the center to the edge of the osculating circle can be written in terms of $\mathbf{N}$ and $\mathbf{T}$; (right) zoomed in on the middle image, we see that the osculating circle approximates the curve.

Determining an osculating circle

Example 4.8. Determine the center and radius of the osculating circle at $\mathbf{r}(1)$ when $\mathbf{r}(t) = \langle t^2, t, t^4 \rangle$.

Answer: $R = 21\sqrt{21/404}$, $\mathbf{c} = \langle 1, 1, 1 \rangle + \frac{21}{202}\langle -31, -26, 22 \rangle$. ∎

You should know

- the terms *unit tangent, unit normal, unit binormal, normal and tangential components of acceleration, osculating plane,* and *osculating circle;*
- the normal component of acceleration is never negative;
- curvature is defined as the change in $\mathbf{T}$ per unit of arc length.

You should be able to

- calculate the vectors $\mathbf{T}$, $\mathbf{N}$, and $\mathbf{B}$;
- determine the equation of the osculating plane;
- parameterize the osculating circle.

✤ 12.4 Skill Exercises

In #1–4 determine the tangential and normal components of acceleration at the specified value of t.

1. $\mathbf{r}(t) = \langle 3t^4, t^{-1}, 8 \rangle$; $t = 1$

2. $\mathbf{r}(t) = \langle 7t^2 - t, -2, 8t + 4 \rangle$; $t = 3$

3. $\mathbf{r}(t) = \langle e^t, e^{-t}, \sin \pi t \rangle$; $t = 0$

4. $\mathbf{r}(t) = \langle \sin 4t, \cos 2t, \tan t \rangle$; $t = \pi/4$

In #5–8 determine $\mathbf{T}$, $\mathbf{N}$, and $\mathbf{B}$ from the given information.

5. $\mathbf{v} = \langle 0, 3, 0 \rangle$, $\mathbf{a} = \langle 1, 0, 1 \rangle$

6. $\mathbf{v} = \langle 1, 3, -2 \rangle$, $\mathbf{a} = \langle 2, 3, 1 \rangle$

7. $\mathbf{v} = \langle 2, 0, -3 \rangle$, $\mathbf{a} = \langle 10, 1, 9 \rangle$

8. $\mathbf{v} = \langle 5, 1, 1 \rangle$, $\mathbf{a} = \langle 0, 1, -3 \rangle$

In #9–14 determine formulas for $\mathbf{T}(t)$, $\mathbf{N}(t)$, and $\mathbf{B}(t)$ that are valid when $t > 0$. *(Hint: by using $\mathbf{v}$ and $\mathbf{a}$ (or scaled versions of them) to determine the appropriate directions you can avoid introducing normalization factors until the very last step.)*

9. $\mathbf{r}(t) = \langle t^3, t, 1 \rangle$

10. $\mathbf{r}(t) = \langle 3, t^4, t \rangle$

11. $\mathbf{r}(t) = \langle t + 2, 3t^4, \ln t \rangle$

12. $\mathbf{r}(t) = \langle e^t, 3t, 8t^2 \rangle$

13. $\mathbf{r}(t) = \langle \sin 2t, \cos 2t, t \rangle$

14. $\mathbf{r}(t) = \langle 3\cos t, 5\sin t, -2t \rangle$

15. Suppose $\mathbf{r} = \langle 2, 5, 0 \rangle$, and the osculating circle is the intersection of the plane $z = 0$ and the cylinder $(x - 8)^2 + (y - 5)^2 = 36$. If $\mathbf{T} = -\mathbf{j}$, determine $\mathbf{N}$ and $\mathbf{B}$.

16. Suppose $\mathbf{r} = \langle 0, 3, 7 \rangle$, and the osculating circle is the intersection of the plane $x = 0$ and the cylinder $(y - 3)^2 + (z + 3)^2 = 100$. If $\mathbf{B} = -\mathbf{i}$, determine $\mathbf{T}$ and $\mathbf{N}$.

In #17–20 determine the equation of the osculating plane at the specified t.

17. $\mathbf{r}(t) = \langle t^3, t, -t^3 \rangle$; $t = 2$

18. $\mathbf{r}(t) = \langle t, t^4, t \rangle$; $t = 3$

19. $\mathbf{r}(t) = \langle \sin t, \sin^2 t, 0 \rangle$; $t = \pi/6$

20. $\mathbf{r}(t) = \langle \cos t, 6t - 1, \cos^2 t \rangle$; $t = \pi/6$

In #21–24 determine the (a) radius and (b) center of the osculating circle at the specified t.

21. $\mathbf{r}(t) = \langle \cos \pi t, \sin \pi t, 4t \rangle$; $t = 2$

22. $\mathbf{r}(t) = \langle 5t, 3 \sin \pi t, 3 \cos \pi t \rangle$; $t = 1$

23. $\mathbf{r}(t) = \langle t, t^2, t^3 \rangle$; $t = 1$

24. $\mathbf{r}(t) = \langle t, \sqrt{t}, t^2 \rangle$; $t = 9$

In #25–28 parameterize the osculating circle to the curve at the point $\mathbf{r}(c)$.

25. $\mathbf{r}(t) = \langle t, t, e^t \rangle$; $c = 0$

26. $\mathbf{r}(t) = \langle 2t, 3 - t, t^3 \rangle$; $c = 1$

27. $\mathbf{r}(t) = \langle \ln t, 3 - t^2, t^4 \rangle$; $c = 1$

28. $\mathbf{r}(t) = \langle \sqrt{t}, 3t, t^2 - t \rangle$; $c = 4$

❖ 12.4 Concept and Application Exercises

29. Suppose $\mathbf{r}(t) = \langle x(t), y(t) \rangle$ is the trajectory of an object, and $\mathbf{v}(0) = \langle 0, 3 \rangle$ and $\mathbf{a}(0) = \langle 2, c \rangle$, where c is unknown. Determine the unit tangent and unit normal vectors to the object's trajectory at $\mathbf{r}(0)$.

30. Suppose $\mathbf{r}'(1) = \langle 3, 1, 7 \rangle$ is an object's velocity, in $\frac{m}{sec}$. (a) Characterize the set of acceleration vectors, $\mathbf{a}(1)$, that do not affect the object's speed. (b) Characterize the set of acceleration vectors, $\mathbf{a}(1)$, that effect an instantaneous rate of change in the object's speed of *at least* $4 \frac{m}{sec}$ per second.

31. Suppose the curve in Figure 4.7 is traversed from right to left at unit speed. (a) Draw the vector $\mathbf{N}$ at each of the specified points. (b) Determine the direction of $\mathbf{B}$ at each of the specified points.

32. Describe the effect of $\mathbf{a}$ on the magnitude and direction of velocity (a) when $\text{comp}_{\mathbf{T}}\mathbf{a} = 0$, and (b) when the normal component of acceleration is zero.

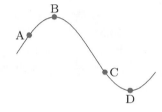

Figure 4.7: The curve for exercise #31.

33. Explain why $\langle 1, 1, -2 \rangle$ cannot be the acceleration vector when $\mathbf{N} = \frac{1}{\sqrt{29}} \langle 2, 3, 4 \rangle$.

34. Suppose $\mathcal{C}$ is a curve in 3-space that connects points P_1 and P_2, and Q is a point on $\mathcal{C}$ in between. You travel one way along $\mathcal{C}$, say from $P_1 \to P_2$, and a friend travels in the other direction. Determine whether the following statements are true or false, and explain your reasoning in complete sentences.

    (a) Your normal vectors are the same at Q.

    (b) Your binormal vectors are opposites at Q.

35. Suppose $\mathbf{r}(t) = \langle 4t^3 + 2t, te^{-t}, \sin t \rangle$. Determine the volume of the parallelepiped defined by $\mathbf{T}(2)$, $\mathbf{N}(2)$, and $\mathbf{B}(2)$.

36. Suppose $\mathbf{r}(t) = t\mathbf{i} + (1 - e^{-t})\mathbf{j}$. Show that $\mathbf{N}(t)$ always points toward the 4th quadrant. *(Hint: this $\mathbf{r}$ parameterizes the graph of a function.)*

37. Suppose $\mathbf{r}(t) = \langle t, t^3 - 4t^2 + 3t \rangle$.

    (a) Show that $\mathbf{N}(t)$ points toward the lower half plane (3rd and 4th quadrants) when $t = 0$, but points into the upper half plane when $t = 2.5$. *(Hint: this $\mathbf{r}$ parameterizes the graph of a function.)*

    (b) When does $\mathbf{N}(t)$ change from pointing into the lower half plane to pointing into the upper half plane, and what does that have to do with the curve $y = x^3 - 4x^2 + 3x$?

38. In complete sentences, explain why a line does not have an associated osculating circle at any point.

39. Imagine that a stream of smoke travels eastward because of the wind. Its path is called a **streamline**, and in this exercise you'll approximate the path of a streamline in the xy-plane from information at a specified point. Suppose x and y are measured in miles from a weather monitoring station. When $x \in [-2, 2]$ and $y \in [1, 4]$ a westerly wind typically blows along paths for which $\frac{dy}{dx} = \frac{1}{y} + x$. Use the osculating circle to approximate the location of the point on the streamline through $(-1/2, 3/2)$ that lies a half mile to the east (i.e., at $x = 0$). *(Hint: you can use implicit differentiation to derive a formula for $\frac{d^2y}{dx^2}$.)*

Meteorology

40. The vector **B** is always perpendicular to a curve (because it's orthogonal to **T**), but it can spin around the curve. This exercise introduces you to the *torsion* of a curve, which measures the rate at which **B** spins around it.

    (a) Suppose the curve $\mathcal{C}$ is parameterized by arc length. Verify that $\frac{d\mathbf{B}}{ds}$ is orthogonal to **B**.

    (b) Explain why $\frac{d\mathbf{T}}{ds} \times \mathbf{N} = \mathbf{0}$.

    (c) Show that $\frac{d\mathbf{B}}{ds}$ is orthogonal to **T** by differentiating $\mathbf{B} = \mathbf{T} \times \mathbf{N}$.

    (d) Since $\frac{d\mathbf{B}}{ds}$ is orthogonal to both **T** and **B**, it must be scaled version of **N**. That is, $\frac{d\mathbf{B}}{ds} = \tau \mathbf{N}$. The scalar τ is called the **torsion** of the curve, and it can change from point to point. Use the facts that $\tau = \mathbf{N} \cdot \frac{d\mathbf{B}}{ds}$ and $\frac{d\mathbf{B}}{ds} = \frac{1}{\|\mathbf{r}'\|} \frac{d\mathbf{B}}{dt}$ to show that, when $\mathbf{r}(t)$ is a smooth parameterization of $\mathcal{C}$,

    $$\tau = -\frac{(\mathbf{r}' \times \mathbf{r}'') \cdot \mathbf{r}'''}{\|\mathbf{r}' \times \mathbf{r}''\|^2}$$

    The negative sign is a vestige of the historical development of this material, and is now a convention.

    (e) Use part (d) to calculate the torsion at $\mathbf{r}(0)$ when $\mathbf{r}(t) = \langle t^3, t^2, \sin t \rangle$.

41. Suppose $\mathbf{r}(t) = \langle \cos 2t, \sin 2t, 3t \rangle$. Show that the torsion of the curve is constant. (See #40.)

42. Suppose $\mathbf{r}(t)$ parameterizes a curve $\mathcal{C}$ in 3-space that happens to lie in the xy-plane, and that κ is always positive.

    (a) Explain why the torsion, τ, must always be zero. (See #40)

    (b) Do you think it matters that $\mathcal{C}$ is in the xy-plane, specifically, or would $\tau = 0$ as long as it lay entirely in *some* plane? Explain.

    (c) Suppose $\mathbf{r}(t) = (6\cos t - 8\sin t)\mathbf{i} + (3\cos t + 12\sin t)\mathbf{j} - (\sqrt{3}\cos t + 4\sqrt{3}\sin t)\mathbf{k}$. Determine whether $\mathbf{r}(t)$ parameterizes a planar curve. If not, how do you know? If so, what's the equation of the plane that contains it?

43. Show that $\mathbf{T}' = \kappa \mathbf{N}$ if $\|\mathbf{r}'(t)\|$ is always 1.

Checking the details

44. By using the fact that $\mathbf{a} = a_T \mathbf{T} + a_N \mathbf{N}$, where $a_N \geq 0$, show that $\mathbf{v} \times \mathbf{a}$ points in the direction of $\mathbf{T} \times \mathbf{N}$ whenever $\|\mathbf{v}\| \neq 0$.

Chapter 12 Review

❖ True or False

1. The functions $\mathbf{p}(t) = \langle 2+4t, 3-8t \rangle$ and $\mathbf{q}(t) = (6-4t)\mathbf{i} + (9+8t)\mathbf{j}$ parameterize parallel lines.

2. The line parameterized by $\mathbf{r}(t) = \langle 3+4t, 5+6t, 7+8t \rangle$ is the same as the line described by the symmetric equations $\frac{x+1}{4} = \frac{y+1}{6} = \frac{z+1}{8}$.

3. We say that $\mathbf{r}(t)$ is continuous at c when $\lim_{t \to c} \mathbf{r}(t) = \mathbf{r}(\lim_{t \to c} t)$.

4. Suppose $\mathbf{r}(t)$ is a continuous vector-valued function for which $\mathbf{r}(0) = \mathbf{0}$ and $\mathbf{r}(2) = \langle 2, 2, 2 \rangle$. Then there is some time $t^* \in (0, 2)$ at which $\mathbf{r}(t^*) = \langle 1, 1, 1 \rangle$.

5. Suppose $\mathbf{r}(t) = \langle x(t), y(t), z(t) \rangle$ is a differentiable vector-valued function. Then there is some time $t^* \in (a, b)$ at which $\mathbf{r}'(t^*) = \frac{\mathbf{r}(b) - \mathbf{r}(a)}{b-a}$.

6. Suppose $\mathbf{r}(t) = \langle x(t), y(t), z(t) \rangle$ is a differentiable function. Then each of $x(t)$, $y(t)$, and $z(t)$ are differentiable functions.

7. Suppose $\mathbf{r}(t)$ is smooth and $\mathbf{r}''(t)$ is continuous. Then $\mathbf{r}''(t)$ is always antiparallel to $\mathbf{r}(t)$.

8. Suppose $\mathbf{r}(t)$ is smooth and $\mathbf{r}''(t)$ is continuous. Then $\mathbf{r}''(t)$ is always perpendicular to $\mathbf{r}'(t)$.

9. Suppose $\mathbf{r}(t)$ is smooth and $\mathbf{r}''(t)$ is continuous. Then $\mathbf{r}''(t)$ always points *into* a turn.

10. $(\mathbf{u} \cdot \mathbf{v})' = \mathbf{u}' \cdot \mathbf{v} + \mathbf{v}' \cdot \mathbf{u}$

11. $(\mathbf{u} \times \mathbf{v})' = \mathbf{u}' \times \mathbf{v} + \mathbf{v}' \times \mathbf{u}$

12. Suppose $\mathbf{r}(t)$ is a differentiable position function that always locates points on the sphere of radius 1 that's centered at the origin (in 3-space). Then $\mathbf{r}'$ is always orthogonal to $\mathbf{r}$.

13. $\int \langle 3t^2, -\sin t \rangle \, dt = \langle t^3, \cos t \rangle$.

14. The *normal component* of acceleration can be negative.

15. The *tangential component* of acceleration can be negative.

16. When $\mathbf{r}'' = 4\mathbf{N}$, the object with position $\mathbf{r}(t)$ remains at the same speed.

17. The *normal component* of acceleration is $\frac{\|\mathbf{v} \times \mathbf{a}\|}{\|\mathbf{a}\|^3}$

18. The osculating circle lies in the osculating plane.

❖ Multiple Choice

19. By saying that $\mathbf{r}(t)$ is a *regular* vector-valued function, we mean ...

   (a) it's nothing special.   (c) $\mathbf{r}'(t)$ exists, and is never $\mathbf{0}$.
   (b) it's periodic.   (d) none of the above.

20. The *normal component* of acceleration is...

   (a) the component that we see usually.
   (b) the nonzero component of acceleration.
   (c) the number β in $\mathbf{a} = \alpha \mathbf{T} + \beta \mathbf{N}$.
   (d) none of the above.

21. The *osculating plane*...

(a) contains $\mathbf{T}$ and $\mathbf{N}$.

(b) contains $\mathbf{T}$ and $\mathbf{B}$.

(c) contains $\mathbf{B}$ and $\mathbf{N}$.

(d) none of the above.

22. Suppose $\mathbf{r}(t)$ parameterizes the curve $\mathcal{C}$. The osculating circle to $\mathcal{C}$ at $\mathbf{r}(t_0)$ is centered at...

(a) $\mathbf{r}(t_0) + x\mathbf{T}(t_0)$ for some number $x > 0$.

(b) $\mathbf{r}(t_0) + x\mathbf{N}(t_0)$ for some number $x > 0$.

(c) $\mathbf{r}(t_0) + x\mathbf{B}(t_0)$ for some number $x > 0$.

(d) none of the above.

23. The curvature of a circle...

(a) is directly proportional to R.

(b) is inversely proportional to R.

(c) is directly proportional to R^2.

(d) is inversely proportional to R^2.

(e) is independent of radius.

(f) none of the above.

24. The curvature of the helix $\mathbf{r}(t) = \langle \cos 3t, \sin 3t, 5t \rangle$ is ...

(a) $15/34$

(b) $8/34$

(c) $9/34$

(d) $25/34$

(e) $1/9$

(f) none of the above.

❖ Exercises

25. Suppose distance is measured in meters and time in seconds. A particle is at the point $(3, -1, -2)$ at time $t = 0$, and heads in the direction of $\langle 6, 5, -1 \rangle$ at 1000 meters per second. Parameterize the linear motion of this particle.

26. Parameterize the helix of radius 5 around the z-axis that completes 4 full cycles for every unit it rises.

27. When we developed the parameterization of the cycloid in Section 12.1, we assumed that the wheel did not slip as it rolled. If it *were* to slip, the center of the wheel would either (i) not travel as far for each revolution, or (ii) travel farther than expected during each revolution of the wheel. We can accomplish this numerically by inserting a parameter β, and writing

$$\mathbf{r}(\theta) = \beta \begin{bmatrix} \theta R \\ R \end{bmatrix} + \begin{bmatrix} -R\sin\theta \\ -R\cos\theta \end{bmatrix} = \begin{bmatrix} \beta\theta R - R\sin\theta \\ \beta R - R\cos\theta \end{bmatrix}.$$

In full English sentences, describe a situation in which (a) $0 < \beta < 1$, (b) $\beta > 1$, (c) $\beta < 0$.

28. Parameterize the line that is the intersection of the planes $4x + 9y - 5z = 2$ and $1x - 2y + z = 3$.

29. Find a parameterization of the line that is the intersection of the planes $10x + 2y + 1z = 4$ and $20x - 2y + 3z = 1$.

30. Find a parameterization of the line $\frac{x-4}{2} = \frac{y+10}{12} = \frac{z-1}{8}$.

Calculate the following limits.

31. $\displaystyle\lim_{t\to\infty} \left\langle \frac{t^6}{e^{\sqrt{t}}}, \frac{8t}{13t+2} \right\rangle$

32. $\displaystyle\lim_{t\to 7} \left\langle \frac{1-\cos(t-7)}{t^2-14t+49}, \frac{8t}{13t+2} \right\rangle$

33. $\displaystyle\lim_{t\to 0^+} \left\langle t\sin\frac{1}{t}, t\cos\frac{1}{t}, t \right\rangle$

34. Suppose $\mathbf{r}(t) = \langle t^2 - 3, t^3 + 1, t - 15 \rangle$. Show that $\lim_{t\to 2} \mathbf{r}(t) = \langle 1, 9, -13 \rangle$ by finding a formula that will produce an appropriate δ for any $\varepsilon \in (0, 1)$.

In #35–36 suppose an object's position is $\mathbf{r}(t) = \langle 3t^2, \sin \pi t, e^{8t} \rangle$, where distance is measured in meters and time in seconds.

35. Find the object's velocity vector at time $t = 1/2$, and determine its speed.

36. Find the acceleration vector for the object at time $t = 4.5$.

In #37–42 use $\mathbf{u}(t) = \langle 3t, 8t^2, 4t + t^3 \rangle$ and $\mathbf{v}(t) = \langle -8t, 4, 8t^4 \rangle$ to calculate.

37. $\frac{d}{dt}(\mathbf{u} \times \mathbf{v})$ 39. $\int \mathbf{u}(t)\, dt$.   41. $\int_2^4 \mathbf{u}(t)\, dt$.

38. $\frac{d}{dt}(\mathbf{u} \cdot \mathbf{v})$.   40. $\int \mathbf{v}(t)\, dt$.   42. $\int_1^8 \mathbf{v}(t)\, dt$

43. Calculate $\mathbf{T}(1)$, $\mathbf{B}(1)$, and $\kappa(1)$ when $\mathbf{r}(t) = t^3 \mathbf{i} + 8t \mathbf{j} + \ln(t) \mathbf{k}$.

44. Determine a formula for the curvature of the helix $\mathbf{r}(t) = \langle \cos pt, \sin pt, qt \rangle$.

Exercises #45–47 investigate what happens as we move away from the point $(1, 1, 4)$ while remaining in the plane $2x + 3y + 5z = 25$.

45. In this exercise we move away from the point while keeping $y = 1$ fixed.

   (a) If x increases, how does z change so the point stays in the plane?

   (b) In the equation for the plane, substitute $y = 1$, $x = 1 + \Delta x$ and $z = 4 + \Delta z$, then determine $\frac{\Delta z}{\Delta x}$. How might we interpret this ratio?

   (c) Find a parameterization for a line that stays in the plane, where $y = 1$ is fixed. *(Hint: how can you ensure your line stays in the plane?)*

46. In this exercise we move away from the point while keeping $x = 1$ fixed.

   (a) If y increases, how does z change so the point stays in the plane?

   (b) Repeat #45(b) with $x = 1$, $y = 1 + \Delta y$ and $z = 4 + \Delta z$.

   (c) Repeat #45(c) but keep $x = 1$ fixed instead of y.

47. How are the components of the direction vectors of the lines produced in #45(c) and #46(b) related to the coefficients in the equation for the plane?

48. The point $(2, 3, 4)$ sits on the plane $7x + y + 3z = 29$. Use your answer to #47 to write the equations of two lines that stay in the plane, one where $x = 2$ is fixed, and another where $y = 3$ is fixed.

49. Suppose $\mathbf{r}(t) = \langle t, t^3 - 12t^2 + 1 \rangle$. Find all discontinuities in $\mathbf{N}$. *(Hint: this $\mathbf{r}$ parameterizes the graph of a function.)*

50. Find the equation of the osculating plane for $\mathbf{r}(t) = \langle t^3, 8t - t^2, \ln t \rangle$.

51. Suppose the curve $\mathcal{C}$ is parameterized by $\mathbf{r}(t) = \langle t^{2/3}, -t^2 \rangle$. Determine the equation of the osculating circle to $\mathcal{C}$ at the point $\mathbf{r}(1)$.

52. Suppose the curve $\mathcal{C}$ is parameterized by $\mathbf{r}(t) = \langle t^{2/3}, -t^2, 3 + 8(t - 1)^3 \rangle$. Determine the center and radius of the osculating circle to $\mathcal{C}$ at the point $\mathbf{r}(1)$.

53. Suppose the curve $\mathcal{C}$ is parameterized by $\mathbf{r}(t) = \langle t^2 - t, 3t + 1, t^3 \rangle$. Find a parameterization of the osculating circle to $\mathcal{C}$ at the point $\mathbf{r}(2)$.

Chapter 12 Projects and Applications

✤ Path of NYC around the sun

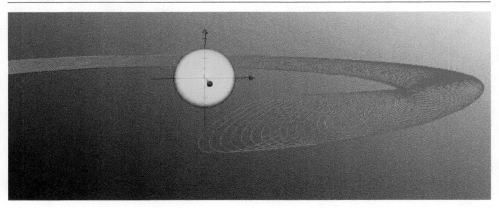

In the exercise set of Section 12.1 you parameterized the path of New York City through one day's rotation of the planet (#22). Now, parameterize the path of New York City around the *sun*.

- For simplicity, assume that the earth's orbit is circular and that its speed around the sun is constant.

- The earth should complete one full rotation every 24 hours, and it should orbit the sun in 365.25 days.

- You should incorporate the tilt of the earth's axis. (The exercises in Appendix F introduce rotation matrices, which make this easier to accomplish.)

- You'll need to know the radius of the earth. (The earth is *not* a sphere, but treat it like one in order to simplify your calculations.)

- You'll need to know the average distance from the sun to the earth (which will be the radius of the circular orbit).

All of this information is readily available online (e.g., at the NASA website). You should cite all your sources in your report.

✤ Low point of a rotating ellipse

When a football is kicked toward the goal posts, it spins end over end as it moves forward. For simplicity, we're going to model the football as an ellipse and suppose that it's "upright," on the ground at time $t = 0$, as shown above.

1. Write the equation for an ellipse centered at the point $(0, 0.5)$ that has height of 1 and a width of 0.5866 (lengths measured in feet).

2. Suppose that the x and y-coordinates (measured in feet) of the football's center are determined by

$$
\begin{aligned}
x(t) &= 120t & (6.1) \\
y(t) &= -16t^2 + 69.282t + 0.5. & (6.2)
\end{aligned}
$$

Parameterize the path of the tip of the ball that starts "on top," indicated by • in the Figure 6.1 (don't worry about when the ball hits the ground). Assume that the ball is spinning in a counter-clockwise direction, and that it completes one rotation once every 2 seconds.

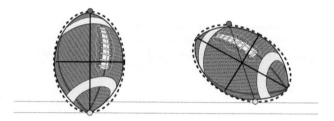

Figure 6.1: When the football is upright, its lowest point is directly below the center; when the football rotates, its lowest point is usually *not* directly below the center.

3. The ball will hit the ground when its lowest point has a y-coordinate of zero. In order to determine when that happens, we need to know where the lowest point is at any given time. For example, at time $t = 0$ the lowest point is directly below the center of the ball (this is the point • in Figure 6.1), but when the ball is rotated a little in the counter-clockwise direction, the lowest point is *not* directly under the center. In order to find it, you need to know the equation for a rotated ellipse. Determine the equation of the ellipse after it's rotated through θ radians, counter-clockwise. *(Hint: the exercise set of Appendix F introduces rotation matrices, which make this easy.)*

4. Now that you have the equation for the rotated ellipse, you can find the lowest point by using horizontal lines. Specifically, the horizontal line $y = h$ will intersect the ellipse only once at the lowest and highest points, and it will intersect the ellipse twice in between them. Use this idea to find the y-coordinate of the lowest point (it will depend on θ).

5. Now that you have the y-coordinate of the lowest point, use the equation of the rotated ellipse to find its x-coordinate.

6. Now that you have the components of the position vector that finds the lowest point, as functions of θ, combine this information with equations (6.1) and (6.2) in order to parameterize the location of the lowest point of the rotating ellipse with respect to time (remember that the ball completes one rotation once every 2 seconds).

7. Determine when the lowest point hits the ground (assuming a level surface).

Chapter 13
Surfaces and Multivariable Functions

The order of topics in this chapter parallels your mathematical education heretofore. We'll begin with relations, functions, and graphs; then we'll discuss limits, continuity, and finally differentiability. Integrals will be developed in the next chapter.

Key Idea(s): *Quadric surfaces are analogs of parabolas, ellipses, and hyperbolas.*

Surfaces called paraboloids occur in two types, named according to the shape of a cross section (elliptic or hyperbolic).

Surfaces called hyperboloids occur in two types (one "sheet" or two).

You can tell what type of surface an equation describes by the exponents on its variables (1 or 2) and the signs of its coefficients.

13.1 Cylinders and Quadric Surfaces

You saw planar surfaces and the equations that describe them in Chapter 11. Here we extend our discussion to surfaces that are not flat, but which can still be described by relatively simple equations. As with planes, the point (x, y, z) is on a surface if the numbers x, y and z satisfy its defining equation.

Defining equation of a surface

Example 1.1. Suppose $\mathcal{S}$ is the sphere described by $x^2 + y^2 + z^2 = 16$. Determine whether the point $(1, 2, 3)$ is on $\mathcal{S}$.

Solution: The point is not on $\mathcal{S}$ because $1^2 + 2^2 + 3^2 \neq 16$. ∎

❖ Cylinders

Because the equation $x^2 + y^2 = 1$ places no constraint on z, it defines a surface in 3-space that extends vertically forever (see Figure 1.1). We call the surface a *cylinder*. When the word cylinder is used in everyday language it typically refers to a shape with a circular cross section, but the mathematical definition is more

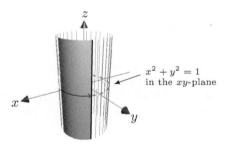

Figure 1.1: (left) A segment of the cylinder described by the equation $x^2 + y^2 = 1$ in three dimensions. The cylinder extends across all values of z. (right) Sweeping out the cylinder by sliding (translating) a line around the circle $x^2 + y^2 = 1$ in the xy-plane.

1004

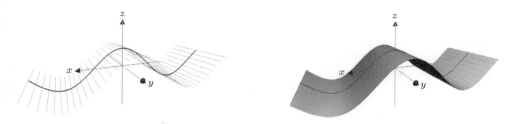

Figure 1.2: (left) A line that's parallel to the y-axis is placed at various points on the curve $z = \cos x$ in the xz-plane; (right) when the line is translated continuously along the curve, it seeps out the cylinder surface described by $z = \cos x$.

general. Toward understanding that generalization, we're going to describe the cylinder $x^2 + y^2 = 1$ in a different way.

You know that the point $(1, 0, 0)$ is on the cylinder $x^2 + y^2 = 1$ because it satisfies the equation, as does $(1, 0, z)$ for each z. That is, the entire vertical line through $(1, 0, 0)$ is part of the cylinder. As shown in Figure 1.1, the cylinder is the set of points swept out by translating that line around the circle in the xy-plane, and therein lies the central idea.

Generally speaking, a **_cylinder_** is any surface that's generated by translating a line over a planar curve. The line that we translate in order to generate a cylinder can extend in any direction, and the curve along which we translate it can lie in any plane.

> The mathematical meaning of the word "translating" is "sliding without changing orientation, or shape, or size."

Cylinder

Example 1.2. Describe the cylinder $z = \cos x$

Solution: This equation describes a curve in the xz-plane. Since the equation makes no mention of y, the cylinder extends forever in that direction. Alternatively, you can think of making this shape by translating a line in the direction of $\mathbf{j}$ along that curve in the xz-plane. The result is shown in Figure 1.2. ∎

In the previous example (and discussion) you saw that cylinders are described by equations that omit a variable. In the next example you'll see how a cylinder can be described an equation in which two variables enter (only) linearly.

A cylinder described by an equation with all three variables

Example 1.3. Describe the cylinder $z + y - 2x(x - 1)^2 = 0$.

Solution: When we rewrite this equation as $y = 2x(x - 1)^2 - z$ it's easier to see that each value of z corresponds to a translation of the familiar curve $y = 2x(x - 1)^2$.

$$
\begin{aligned}
z = 0 &\;\Rightarrow\; y = 2x(x - 1)^2 \\
z = 1 &\;\Rightarrow\; y = 2x(x - 1)^2 - 1 \\
z = 2 &\;\Rightarrow\; y = 2x(x - 1)^2 - 2
\end{aligned}
$$

Each time we lift the curve (in z) we shift it back (in y) by the same amount. Up, back, up, back... if done incrementally gives us a collection of curves (Figure 1.3), but when done continuously yields the surface (see Figure 1.4). So if you start at a point on the curve $y = 2x(x - 1)^2$, in the xy-plane, you can stay on the surface by moving along the line through $(x, 2x(x - 1)^2, 0)$ that heads in the direction of $\langle 0, -1, 1 \rangle$. Alternatively, we could say that the surface is constructed by translating that line along the curve, so the surface is a cylinder. ∎

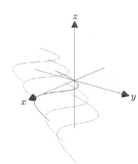

Figure 1.3: The curve $y = 2x(x - 1)^2$ in the xy-plane is shown in red. The other curves are found by shifting it up (in z) and back (in y).

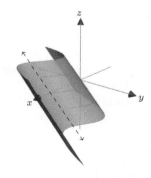

Figure 1.4: A surface is generated by translating a line along the curve $y = 2x(x - 1)^2$ in the xy-plane.

✢ Quadric Surfaces

The analogs of parabolas, ellipses and hyperbolas in 3-space are surfaces called *paraboloids, ellipsoids,* and *hyperboloids* (respectively). Figure 1.5 shows several examples. Generally speaking, all of these surfaces are described by an equation of the form

$$Ax^2 + By^2 + Cz^2 + Dxy + Exz + Fyz + Gx + Hy + Iz + J = 0, \qquad (1.1)$$

and we refer to them as **quadric surfaces**. Our discussion of quadric surfaces begins by examining equations in which D, E, and F are all zero because these describe surfaces that align nicely with the standard xyz-frame of reference.

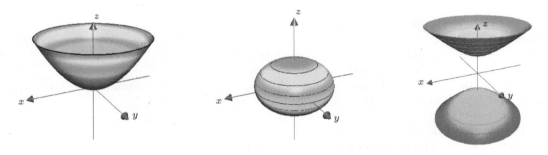

Figure 1.5: (all) Examples of quadric surfaces. (left) A paraboloid; (middle) an ellipsoid; (right) a hyperboloid.

▷ Paraboloids

An equation in which one variable enters linearly while the other two appear quadratically, such as

$$z = x^2 + y^2 \text{ or} \qquad (1.2)$$

$$40z = 3x^2 - 5y^2 \text{ or} \qquad (1.3)$$

$$13x = 9y^2 + 8z^2, \qquad (1.4)$$

describes a surface called a **paraboloid**. The paraboloid described by equation (1.2) is shown in the left-hand image of Figure 1.5, and the saddle-shaped surface corresponding to equation (1.3) appears in the left-hand image of Figure 1.6. Although the surfaces appear quite different, they have something in common: if you hold one of the quadratic variables constant, the defining equation describes a parabola in the other two variables. For example, fixing $x = 1$ reduces equations (1.2) and (1.3) to

$$z = 1 + y^2 \quad \text{and} \quad 40z = 3 - 5y^2.$$

Geometrically speaking, holding a variable constant is the same as intersecting the surface with a plane (see Figures 1.6 and 1.7), the result of which is a curve called a **trace**. Much as the cylinder in Figure 1.1 can be understood of as a "stack" of circles, each at a different value of z, you can often get a good idea about the shape of a surface by thinking of it as a "stack" of its traces.

Traces help us to distinguish between paraboloids that are fundamentally like the one you see in Figure 1.5, and paraboloids that have the shape displayed in Figure 1.6. When we hold the linear variable constant, the resulting equation describes either an ellipse or a hyperbola in the remaining variables; we classify paraboloids as being either **elliptic** or **hyperbolic** accordingly (see Figure 1.7).

> In Section 13.8 we'll see something called a *saddle point*. The origin is such a point on the paraboloid shown in Figure 1.6.

> For instance, the equation $x = 1$ is the same as
>
> $$1x + 0y + 0z = 1$$
>
> which describes a plane through $(1, 0, 0)$ with normal vector $\mathbf{n} = \mathbf{i}$.

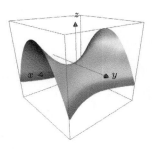 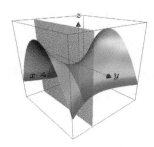 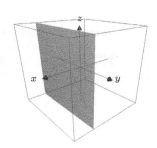 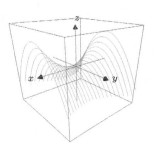

Figure 1.6: (All) A bounding box has been included to help with perspective. (left) The paraboloid described by equation (1.3); (middle left) the paraboloid and the plane $x = 1$; (middle right) the trace of the paraboloid on the plane $x = 1$; (right) a collection of traces allows us to see the shape of the paraboloid.

Classifying paraboloids

Example 1.4. Determine whether equations (1.2) and (1.3) describe elliptic or hyperbolic paraboloids.

Solution: When we set the linear variable to 1 in equation (1.2) we see $1 = x^2 + y^2$, which describes an ellipse (a circle, more specifically). So equation (1.2) describes an elliptic paraboloid. By contrast, setting the linear variable to 1 in equation (1.3) leaves us with $40 = 3x^2 - 5z^2$, which describes a hyperbola (see Figure 1.7). So equation (1.2) describes a hyperbolic paraboloid. ∎

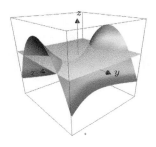 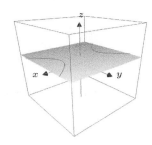

Figure 1.7: The intersection of the plane $z = 1$ with the paraboloid described by equation (1.3) is a trace that's a hyperbola.

Classifying paraboloids

Example 1.5. Determine whether equation (1.4) describes an elliptic or a hyperbolic paraboloid.

Answer: Elliptic. ∎

Solution
On-line

Using traces to sketch a paraboloid

Example 1.6. Here we address the paraboloid $y = -3x^2 - 5z^2$. (a) Sketch the traces of the surface on the planes $y = -1, y = -5$ and $y = -10$, and (b) determine the axis along which the paraboloid opens.

Solution: (a) When $y = -1, -5$ and -10 we see

$$\underbrace{1 = 3x^2 + 5z^2}_{y=-1} \qquad \underbrace{5 = 3x^2 + 5z^2}_{y=-5} \qquad \underbrace{10 = 3x^2 + 5z^2}_{y=-10}$$

In Figure 1.8 you can see that the ellipses described by these equations all have the same aspect ratio (width to height ratio) and grow larger with $|y|$. So as we move farther from the origin along the y-axis, the cross section of this paraboloid is growing wider and taller. The surface is essentially a "stack" of these cross sections (one for each value of $y \leq 0$), three of which are shown in Figure 1.9. ∎

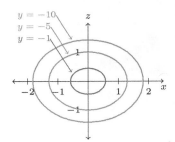

Figure 1.8: The ellipses defined by choosing different values of y in Example 1.6. This image depicts the same structure as the left-hand image of Figure 1.9, but here you're looking from a point far down the negative-y-axis.

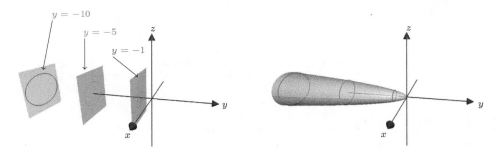

Figure 1.9: (left) Each cross section of the paraboloid is a curve that's found by fixing one variable and letting the others vary; (right) the paraboloid shown with three of the cross sectional curves.

Using paraboloids to visualize energy

Example 1.7. Suppose an m-kg object is attached to a linear spring with spring constant $k > 0$. In Chapter 7 showed that the potential energy in the spring is $\frac{k}{2}x^2$ joules when it has been extended or compressed by x meters from its natural length, and that the kinetic energy of the object is $\frac{1}{2}my^2$ when it's moving at y m/sec. So if we write the system's total mechanical energy as z,

$$z = \frac{k}{2}x^2 + \frac{m}{2}y^2. \tag{1.5}$$

(a) Interpret the equation as a surface, and (b) explain what happens when force is applied to the system.

Solution: (a) Since one variable enters this equation linearly, and the other two are squared, the equation describes an elliptic paraboloid. (b) In the absence of external force the total mechanical energy of the system is constant, so z is constant and equation (1.5) describes an elliptical trace on the paraboloid. This means that as x (position) and y (velocity) change, they change together in such a way that (x, y, z) remains on a particular ellipse (see Figure 1.10). On the other hand, external force will change the overall amount of energy in our system: z decreases if the system loses energy, and z increases if energy is gained. In this case, the point (x, y, z) will continue to travel around the paraboloid but will descend or rise along the surface according to whether energy was lost or gained (see Figure 1.11). ∎

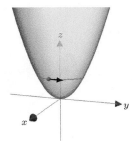

Figure 1.10: The point (x, y, z) moves along the paraboloid at a fixed height when energy is constant.

▷ Ellipsoids

Like an ellipse, the shape of an ***ellipsoid*** is described by an equation in which all variables appear quadratically. More specifically, the numbers A, B and C are all nonzero in equation (1.1) and all have the same sign. In the same sense that a circle is a special case of an ellipse, a sphere is a special case of an ellipsoid ($A = B = C$).

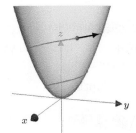

Figure 1.11: The point (x, y, z) ascends the paraboloid when energy is gained.

Traces of an ellipsoid

Example 1.8. Draw several traces of the ellipsoid $\frac{x^2}{16} + \frac{y^2}{25} + \frac{z^2}{10} = 1$ corresponding to fixed values of x and fixed values of y.

Solution: Any point (x, y, z) on this surface must have $|x| \leq 4$, and for such values of x we can rewrite the equation as

$$\frac{y^2}{25} + \frac{z^2}{10} = 1 - \frac{x^2}{16}. \left.\right\} \begin{array}{l} \text{This is a non-negative} \\ \text{number when } |x| \leq 4. \end{array}$$

So each $x \in (-4, 4)$ corresponds to an ellipse in y and z. Several of these traces are shown in Figure 1.12. Similarly, the equation dictates that $|y| \leq 5$, in which case

$$\frac{x^2}{16} + \frac{z^2}{10} = 1 - \frac{y^2}{25}. \left.\right\} \begin{array}{l} \text{This is a non-negative} \\ \text{number when } |y| \leq 5. \end{array}$$

So each $y \in (-5, 5)$ corresponds to an ellipse in x and z. We see the same thing when we examine admissible values of z; each $z \in (-\sqrt{10}, \sqrt{10})$ corresponds to an ellipse in x and y. ∎

> If $|x| > 4$ the value of
> $$\frac{x^2}{16} + \frac{y^2}{25} + \frac{z^2}{10}$$
> is certainly larger than 1.

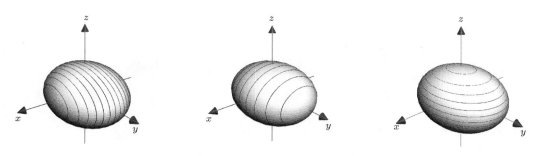

Figure 1.12: (all) Traces of the ellipsoid in Example 1.8; (left) traces with $x = c$; (middle) traces with $y = c$; (right) traces with $z = c$.

▷ Hyperboloids

The three-dimensional analog of a hyperbola is a surface called a ***hyperboloid***, which is described by equation (1.1) when the numbers A, B and C are nonzero and do *not* all have the same sign. The right-hand image of Figure 1.5 shows an example of a hyperboloid. You might expect a hyperboloid to comprise two disjoint surfaces (much like a hyperbola comprises two disjoint curves), but in some cases they join together to make a single surface. This leads us to classify hyperboloids as having either one ***sheet*** or two.

Determining the number of sheets

Example 1.9. Determine whether the hyperboloids have one sheet or two: (a) $x^2 - y^2 - z^2 = 1$, and (b) $-x^2 + y^2 + z^2 = 1$.

Solution: Our strategy for making this determination is based on the simple idea that if a hyperboloid has two sheets, there is a plane that passes between them.

(a) When we rewrite the equation so that all its coefficients are positive, we see

$$x^2 = 1 + y^2 + z^2,$$

from which it's clear that $x^2 \geq 1$. This allows $x \leq -1$ and $x \geq 1$, but prohibits x from being any number in $(-1, 1)$. For example, $x = 0$ is impossible. This separation of the possible x-values means that the surface has two disjoint parts so it is a hyperboloid of two sheets (see Figure 1.13).

(b) Like before, we can gain insight by rewriting the equation so that all its coefficients are positive:

$$y^2 + z^2 = 1 + x^2.$$

At each fixed value of x, this equation describes a circle (larger values of $|x|$ result in larger circles). Since all values of x (and y and z) are admissible, this surface has one sheet. ∎

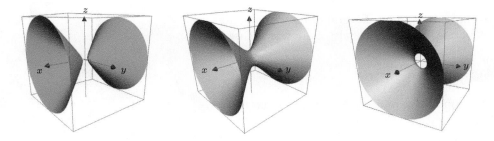

Figure 1.13: (all) Hyperboloids from Example 1.9; (left) from part (a), note that the yz-plane ($x = 0$) passes between the two sheets; (middle and right) the hyperboloid from part (b).

Transitioning from one sheet to two

Example 1.10. Discuss how the surface $b = -x^2 + y^2 + z^2$ depends on b.

Solution: Let's begin by rewriting the equation as $b + x^2 = y^2 + z^2$. When $b > 0$, each value of x corresponds to a circle in y and z, and the smallest of them happens when $x = 0$. Since all values of x are admissible, this is a hyperboloid with one sheet, but as b decreases, the circle at $x = 0$ shrinks. The hyperboloid continues to have one sheet until (and including) $b = 0$, in which case the "circle" at $x = 0$ is a single point (see Figure 1.14). As b descends into negative values, we see that x can no longer be zero, so the equation describes a surface with two sheets. ∎

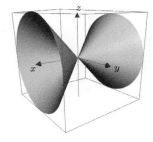

Figure 1.14: The surface from Example 1.10 when $b = 0$. This hyperboloid of one sheet is called a cone.

The hyperboloid of one sheet that's depicted in Figure 1.14 is "pointed" and "straight" rather than "smooth" and "rounded." This is a kind of degenerate hyperboloid called a ***cone*** and it happens when the constant term in the equation of a hyperboloid is zero.

In Example 1.10 the coefficients of y^2 and z^2 have the same sign; the coefficient of x^2 is different, and Figure 1.14 shows that the axis of the hyperboloid is the x-axis. This is a particular instance of a more general fact: a hyperboloid's ***axis*** is determined by which of A, B and C has the "different" sign in equation (1.1).

Determining the number of sheets

Example 1.11. Consider the hyperboloid $10 = -17x^2 + 3y^2 - 8z^2$. Determine (a) whether the hyperboloid has one sheet or two, and (b) its axis.

Answer: (a) two sheets; (b) y-axis. ∎

Solution
On-line

❖ Translated Surfaces

The equation $x^2 + y^2 = 1$ describes a circle of radius 1 in the xy-plane, centered at the origin. When we translate it away from the origin, so that it's centered at the point $(3, 4)$, the equation becomes $(x - 3)^2 + (y - 4)^2 = 1$. Similarly, translating quadric surfaces can be accomplished by employing additive constants.

A translated surface

Example 1.12. Determine the kind of surface described by the equation $1 = x^2 - 2y^2 - 4z^2 - 4x - 2y^2 + 4y - 8z$, and how it's been translated away from the origin.

Solution: All of the variables appear quadratically but they have different signs, so this equation describes a hyperboloid. Since two of the quadratic terms are negative, our experience with Example 1.9 tempts us to say that this is a hyperboloid of two sheets, but after completing the square in each variable we'll see that this is incorrect. Let's begin by gather our variables together so that we see $1 = x^2 - 4x - 2y^2 + 4y - 4z^2 - 8z$. Completing the square in each variable brings us to

$$1 = (x-2)^2 - 2(y-1)^2 - 4(z+1)^2 + 2,$$

which is equivalent to

$$1 = -(x-2)^2 + 2(y-1)^2 + 4(z+1)^2.$$

This equation tells us that the hyperboloid is centered at the point $(2,1,-1)$. With the quadratic terms on the same side of the equation, we can see that the coefficient of the x-term has the "different" sign, so the axis of the surface is parallel to the x-axis. And since each value of x corresponds to an ellipse in y and z (i.e., no values of x are prohibited) this is a hyperboloid of one sheet (see Figure 1.15). ■

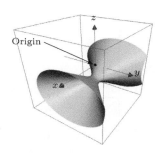

Figure 1.15: The graph of the surface in Example 1.12.

A translated surface

Example 1.13. Determine the kind of surface described by the equation $5x^2 + 6y^2 + 2z^2 = 40x - 36y + 4z - 135$.

Answer: An ellipsoid centered at $(4,-3,1)$. ■

Solution On-line

✥ Rotation by $\pi/4$

A host of phenomena are described by equations of the form $z = xy$, where one quantity depends on the product of two others. In the next example we'll show that this equation describes a quadric surface that has been rotated by $\pi/4$ radians away from the standard axis.

Momentum: $p = mv$
Newton's Law: $F = ma$
Hooke's Law: $F = kx$
Ohm's Law: $V = IR$

A rotation by $\pi/4$ can be revealed by a substitution

Example 1.14. The Ideal Gas Law tells us that the relationship among pressure (P), volume (V), and temperature (T) is $PV = Nk_{\text{B}}T$, where N is the number of atoms in the gas, and k_{B} is a number called Boltzmann's constant. Show that for each fixed N, this equation describes a quadric surface in 3-space.

Solution: Let's start by defining $z = Nk_{\text{B}}T$, so that the equation looks a little simpler: $z = PV$. The equation becomes even less complicated when pressure and volume are the same: $z = P^2$. Mathematically, we can also examine the case when P and V are opposites, in which case $z = -P^2$. Since the equation $z = PV$ describes a concave-up parabola in one direction (when $P = V$) and a concave-down parabola in another (when $P = -V$), it seems that the surface described by $z = PV$ is a hyperbolic paraboloid. That's correct (see Figure 1.16), and we can establish it algebraically by introducing variables x and y as follows:

$$P = x + y \quad \text{and} \quad V = x - y.$$

By making this choice, each value of P corresponds to a line in the xy-plane with a slope of -1, and each value of V corresponds to a line of slope 1. Taken together,

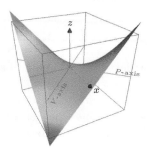

Figure 1.16: The hyperbolic paraboloid described by the Ideal Gas Law. (The y-axis is covered by the surface.)

each (P, V) pair identifies a point in the xy-plane. Figure 1.17 shows that by working in terms of x and y rather than P and V we effectively rotate our frame of reference by $\pi/4$ radians. And algebraically, since $PV = (x+y)(x-y)$, our equation becomes simply $z = x^2 - y^2$, which describes a hyperbolic paraboloid in this new frame of reference. (Changing our frame of reference didn't change the relationship among P, V and T, just our ability to recognize it as something familiar.)   ∎

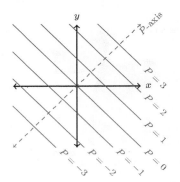
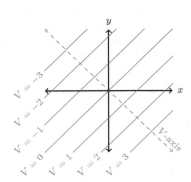
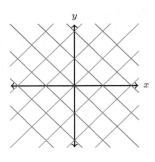

Figure 1.17: (left and middle) Each value of P and V corresponds to a line in the xy-plane; (right) the xy-frame of reference and the PV-frame of reference differ by a rotation of $\pi/4$ radians.

❖ In Closing

Much of this section was devoted to understanding equations of the form $Ax^2 + By^2 + Cz^2 + Gx + Hy + Iz + J = 0$, in which some of the coefficients are 0. Provided that the equation is solvable, you've see that the surface it describes depends on the number of quadratic variables and the sign of their coefficients:

> The equation $x^2 + y^2 + z^2 + 1 = 0$ has no solution (unless we allow the variables to be complex numbers).

0 or 1 quadratic variable	$\Rightarrow$	cylinder
2 quadratic variables	$\Rightarrow$	paraboloid
3 quadratic variables	$\Rightarrow$	ellipsoid or hyperboloid

Table 13.1 provides a quick reference for the quadric surfaces we've discussed.

You should know

- the terms *elliptic paraboloid, hyperbolic paraboloid, ellipsoid, hyperboloid, sheets,* and *cylinder;*
- that cones are hyperboloids.

You should be able to

- determine the kind of surface described by equation (1.1) based on the sign of its coefficients;
- determine whether a paraboloid is elliptic or hyperbolic;
- determine whether a hyperboloid has one sheet or two;
- determine the axis of elliptic paraboloids, and hyperboloids.

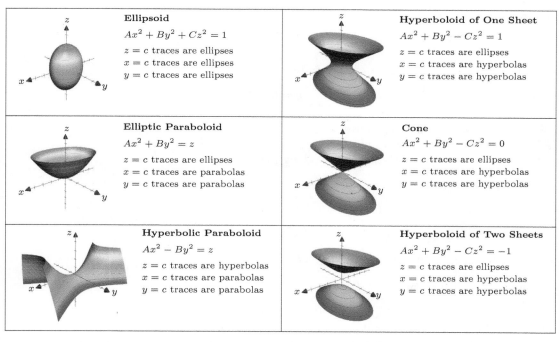

Table 13.1: Examples of Quadric Surfaces (A, B and C are positive constants)

✥ 13.1 Skill Exercises

In each of #1–10 determine whether the equation describes a cylinder, ellipsoid, hyperboloid, paraboloid, or none of the above. If the surface is a cylinder, determine the direction in which it extends and the shape of its cross section. If the surface is a hyperboloid, determine the number of sheets. If it's a paraboloid, describe its axis.

1. $6x^2 + 1 = 4y^2 - 3z^2$

2. $6x^2 + 2 = 3z^2$

3. $6x^2 + 3 = 4y^2 + 3z^2$

4. $6x^2 + 4 = 4y + 3z^2$

5. $y^2 = 8 + xz$

6. $6x^2 + 1 = zy$

7. $2x^2 + 7y^2 + z^2 = 9$

8. $8x^2 + 1 = 3y^2 - 1z^2$

9. $3y + 9 = 9x^2$

10. $7y^2 = 3x^2 - 8z^2$

The surfaces in #11–18 have been translated away from the origin. Determine (a) whether each equation describes an ellipsoid, hyperboloid, paraboloid, or none of the above, and (b) how it's translated away from the origin. (c) If the surface is a hyperboloid, determine the number of sheets. If it's a paraboloid, describe its axis.

11. $6x^2 - 3 = -4y^2 + y + 3z^2$

12. $6x^2 + 24x + 7 = -4y^2 - 3z^2$

13. $7z^2 - 3 = -8y^2 + x$

14. $6x + 1 = -4y^2 - 3z^2 + 6z$

15. $8x^2 + 16x + 1 = 3y^2 - 1z^2$

16. $3x^2 + 9x + 2 = y - y^2 - 9z^2$

17. $7z^2 - 3y = -8x^2 + x - 4z$

18. $x^2 - 2y^2 - 2z^2 = 4x - 4y + 4z$

In #19–26 (a) draw the specified traces, and (b) sketch the surface.

19. $z = x^2 + 4y^2$; $z = 1, 4, 9$

20. $y = 2x^2 + z^2$; $y = 2, 4, 9$

21. $1 = 3x^2 + y^2 - z^2$; $z = 1, 2, 3$

22. $1 = 9x^2 + y^2$; $z = -1, 0, 2$

23. $100 = x^2 + y^2 + 2z^2$; $x = \pm 3, \pm 5, \pm 7$

24. $4 = -x^2 + y^2 - 2z^2$; $y = \pm 3, \pm 4, \pm 5$

25. $10 = x^2 - z^2$; $z = 4, 5, 6$

26. $25 = 5x^2 + y^2 + 5z^2$; $y = 0, \pm 2, \pm 3$

In the general definition of a cylinder, we translate a line over a planar curve. When that planar curve is also a line, the resulting surface is a plane. In #27–30 determine the equation of the plane that's swept out by translating line ℓ_1 along line ℓ_2.

27. ℓ_1: $(x-1)/2 = (y-4)/5 = (z+2)/7$ and ℓ_2: $(x-5)/1 = (y-14)/2 = (z-12)/3$

28. ℓ_1: $(x-3)/1 = (y+1)/2 = (z-8)/3$ and ℓ_2: $(x+3)/4 = (y+13)/5 = (z+10)/6$

29. ℓ_1: $(x-4)/2 = (y-5)/1 = (z-1)/1$ and ℓ_2: $\mathbf{r}(t) = \langle 4 + 8t, 5 - 7t, 1 + 3t \rangle$.

30. ℓ_1: $(x-5)/3 = (y-1)/5 = (z+6)/2$ and ℓ_2: $\mathbf{r}(t) = \langle 5 - t, 1 + 11t, -6 - 2t \rangle$

In #31–34 write the equation of the specified surface.

31. An ellipsoid on which $-4 \leq x \leq 4$, $-3 \leq y \leq 3$, and $-7 \leq z \leq 7$. (Meaning that there is a point on the ellipse with $x = 4$, and another with $x = -4$, but no point has an x-coordinate with a magnitude larger than 4. Similarly for y- and z-coordinates.)

32. An ellipsoid on which $10 \leq x \leq 14$, $2 \leq y \leq 13$, and $-7 \leq z \leq -1$. (Meaning that there is a point on the ellipse with $x = 10$, and another with $x = 14$, but no point has an x-coordinate smaller than 10 or larger than 14. Similarly for y- and z-coordinates.)

33. An elliptic paraboloid with vertex at the point $(2, -7, -1)$, its axis parallel to the y-axis, including only points with $y \geq -7$

34. An elliptic paraboloid with vertex at the point $(-1, 3, 10)$, its axis parallel to the x-axis, including only points with $x \leq -1$

In #35–38 write the equation of a hyperboloid for which the given condition is true.

35. $|x| \geq 3$.　　　36. $|y| \geq 0.2$.　　　37. $|z - 7| \geq 2.3$.　　　38. $|x + 8| \geq 4.8$.

❖ 13.1 Concept and Application Exercises

39. Suppose $\mathcal{S}$ is the ellipsoid described by $1 = kx^2 + ky^2 + kz^2$. (a) Let $k = 1/4$. Draw several traces of $\mathcal{S}$ corresponding to different values of z, and (b) describe $\mathcal{S}$ when $k = 1/4$. Then (c) explain how the value of k affects $\mathcal{S}$.

40. Determine all values of k (if any) for which the equation $1 = x^2 + y^2 + z^2 + kxy$ describes a sphere.

41. Consider the equation $(x - a)^2 + (y - b)^2 + z^2 = a + b$. For what values of a and b does this equation describe an ellipsoid that's entirely contained in the first octant? (Answer in terms of the position of the point (a, b) in 2-space.)

42. Consider the equation $(x - a)^2 + b(y - 1)^2 + (z - c)^2 = c^2 + a^2 - 1$. For what values of a, b and c does this equation describe an ellipsoid that's entirely contained in the first octant? (Answer in terms of the position of the point (a, b, c) in 3-space.)

43. Suppose $\mathcal{S}$ is the quadric surface described by $z^2 = (y - 0.1x)(2x - y)$.

    (a) Suppose $\mathbf{r}$ is the position vector for a point on $\mathcal{S}$. Show that the position vector $k\mathbf{r}$ also locates a point on $\mathcal{S}$ for every constant k.

    (b) Draw the trace of $\mathcal{S}$ on the plane $z = 0$, and determine what points in the xy-plane have correspond to points (x, y, z) on $\mathcal{S}$. *(Hint: z^2 is never negative.)*

    (c) Based on parts (a) and (b), describe the surface $\mathcal{S}$. Then use a graphing utility to check your answer.

    (d) Suppose $m_2 > m_1$. Describe the surface $z^2 = (y - m_1 x)(m_2 x - y)$, including how the constants m_1 and m_2 affect its shape.

44. Determine the equation of the central axis of the surface described by $z^2 = 7xy - 12x^2 - y^2$. *(Hint: see #43d.)*

45. The function $f(t) = at^2 + bt + c$ has exactly one root when $0 = b^2 - 4ac$. Show that this equation describes a cone in the abc-parameter space.

46. Suppose a rectangular box has length ℓ cm, width w cm, and height h cm.

Packaging

    (a) Write an equation that says the surface area of the box is 30 cm^2.

    (b) Show that $\langle 1, 1, 1 \rangle, \langle 1, -1, 0 \rangle$ and $\langle 1, 1, -2 \rangle$ are mutually orthogonal.

    (c) Show that the equation from part (a) describes a hyperboloid with its axis parallel to $\langle 1, 1, 1 \rangle$ by making the change of variables $x = 1\ell + 1w + 1h$, $y = 1\ell - 1w + 0h$, and $z = 1\ell + 1w - 2h$ (solve these three equations for ℓ, w and h, and then substitute into the surface area equation).

47. Use the technique of #46 to show that $15 = ab + ac - bc$ describes a hyperboloid of one sheet in (a, b, c)-space. Then determine the axis of this hyperboloid. *(Hint: Find two vectors that, along with $\langle 1, -1, -1 \rangle$, are mutually perpendicular. Then define a new set of variables based on them.)*

48. Use the technique of #46 to show that $15 = ab - ac - bc$ describes a hyperboloid of two sheets in (a, b, c)-space. Then determine the axis of this hyperboloid.

49. Consider the circle $x^2 + y^2 = 1$ in the xy-plane, and the line in the direction of $\mathbf{v} = \langle 1, 0, 1 \rangle$ that passes through the point $(1, 0, 0)$ on the circle. If we translate that line around the circle we make a cylinder. Looking back at the origin from the point $(1, 0, 1)$, as in Figure 1.18, we see that the cylinder has an elliptical cross section (taken with planes orthogonal to $\mathbf{v}$). Determine the aspect ratio (width to height ratio) of that ellipse.

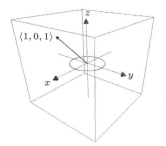
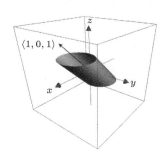
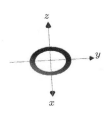

Figure 1.18: (left) The unit circle in the xy-plane, and the vector $\mathbf{v}$; (middle) a portion of the cylinder made by sliding the line in the direction of $\mathbf{v}$ around the circle; (right) looking back at the origin from the point $(1, 0, 1)$, the cylinder has elliptical cross sections (taken with planes orthogonal to $\langle 1, 0, 1 \rangle$).

50. Suppose $\mathcal{C}$ is the ellipse $0.25x^2 + y^2 = 1$ in the xy-plane, $\mathbf{v} = \langle 1, 0, b \rangle$, and ℓ is the line that passes through $(2, 0, 0)$ in the direction of $\mathbf{v}$. We denote by $\mathcal{S}$ the cylinder made by translating ℓ around the ellipse. Suppose we look back at the origin from the point $(1, 0, b)$. Determine a value of b for which the cross section is circular (taken with planes orthogonal to $\mathbf{v}$).

51. Neglecting the effect of gravity, Bernoulli's Law for a two-dimensional fluid flow says $0.5\rho u^2 + 0.5\rho v^2 + P = \rho k$, where $\langle u, v \rangle$ is the velocity of the flow (which changes from point to point), P is the pressure of the fluid (which also depends on location), k is a constant that has only to do with the material properties of the fluid, and ρ is the density of the fluid (which we'll assume to be constant).

    (a) The components of the fluid velocity, u and v, have units of $\frac{\text{m}}{\text{sec}}$, P has units of $\frac{\text{N}}{\text{m}}$, and ρ has units of $\frac{\text{kg}}{\text{m}^2}$. What are the units of k?

    (b) Determine what type of surface in uvP-space is described by Bernoulli's law, and whether it's been translated away from the origin. If so, where has the surface been translated to?

52. Ohm's Law tells us that $V = IR$, where I denotes current, R is resistance, and V is voltage. Show that Ohm's Law describes a paraboloid in IRV-space.

53. Suppose an object of mass m kg is spinning at ω radians per second and traveling with a velocity of $\langle u, v \rangle$. Then its translational kinetic energy is $0.5m\|\langle u, v \rangle\|^2$, and its rotational kinetic energy is $0.5I\omega^2$, where I is a constant called the moment of inertia that depends on the object's distribution of mass.

    (a) Write an equation in terms of u, v and ω that says the object's total kinetic energy is constant.

    (b) Determine what quadric surface is described by the equation.

    (c) In complete sentences, explain how m and I affect the shape.

54. Suppose an object of mass m kg starts from rest, and rolls s meters down an inclined plane that makes an angle of $\pi/6$ with the horizontal. If the object rotates at ω radians per second, and travels at a speed of v meters per second,

$$mv^2 + I\omega^2 = mgs,$$

where g is the acceleration per unit mass due to gravity, and I is a constant called the moment of inertia that depends on the object's distribution of mass.

    (a) Determine what kind of surface is described by this equation.

    (b) Use complete sentences to describe the way that $\mathbf{r}(t) = \langle v(t), \omega(t), s(t) \rangle$ changes in time.

Physics

13.2 Functions of More Than One Variable

In the previous section we broadened our understanding of surfaces in 3-space, and in this section we use surfaces to develop ideas about functions of two or more variables. Just as the graph of a single-variable function is a curve in 2-space, you'll see that the graph of a two-variable function is a surface in 3-space.

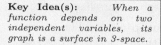

Key Idea(s): *When a function depends on two independent variables, its graph is a surface in 3-space.*

A "level set" is a set of points in the domain on which the function maintains a constant value, like curves on a topographic map indicate paths of constant altitude.

❖ Multivariable Functions and Their Graphs

Imagine a rectangle in the xy-plane as a stovetop griddle, having warmer and cooler regions depending on the intensity of the stove's heating elements. The distribution of heat can be clearly communicated by an image that relates temperature, T, to location. To make such an image, we can

(a) *use color:* paint the point (x,y) red if T is large, blue if T is small, and use a range of colors in between to indicate intermediate temperatures (see the left-hand image of Figure 2.1); or

(b) *use height:* raise the point (x,y) up high if T is large, keep it low if T is small, and raise it to some intermediate height for temperatures in between; or

(c) use both height and color, as seen in the right-hand image of Figure 2.1.

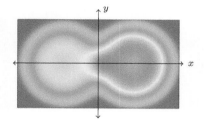

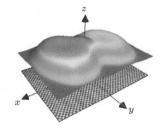

Figure 2.1: (left) Unevenly distributed heat; (middle) a stovetop griddle; (right) using the z-direction to show value—higher points correspond to larger function values.

Since T is a function of two independent variables, x and y, we write it as $T(x,y)$. In general, functions that depend on more than one independent variable are called **multivariable** (or **multivariate**) functions. The **range** of a multivariable function is the set its outputs, and the **domain** of a multivariable function is the collection of input values for which there's an associated output. When a formula for the function is available, domain restrictions for multivariable functions are found in the same way you've always found them—avoid zeros in denominators and logarithms, negatives under even roots or in logarithms, etc.

Domain of a multivariable function

Example 2.1. Determine the domain of $f(x,y) = \ln(xy)/(y-x)$.

Solution: Because of the logarithm in the numerator, we know that $xy > 0$, which happens in the first and third quadrants. And the denominator excludes point on the line $y = x$. This leaves us with the region shown in Figure 2.2. ∎

When f is a function of x and y, the equation the equation $z = f(x,y)$ defines a surface in 3-space called the **graph** of the function. As with functions of a single variable, the graph of $f(x,y)$ allows us to visualize the relationship between the function's domain and range.

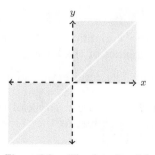

Figure 2.2: The domain of f in Example 2.1.

Graphs of familiar multivariable functions

Example 2.2. The perimeter and area of a rectangle depend on its length, x, and width, y. Describe the graphs of these functions.

Solution: The perimeter and area of the rectangle are $p(x,y) = 2x + 2y$ and $a(x,y) = xy$, respectively. Their graphs are generated by letting them determine corresponding values of z:

$$z \;=\; 2x + 2y \;\; \text{is the graph of } p(x,y), \text{ and} \tag{2.1}$$
$$z \;=\; xy \;\; \text{is the graph of } a(x,y). \tag{2.2}$$

Equation (2.1) can be rewritten as $0 = 2x + 2y - z$, which describes a plane through the origin with a normal vector $\mathbf{n} = \langle 2, 2, -1 \rangle$, and in Example 1.14 of Section 13.1 we saw that equation (2.2) describes a hyperbolic paraboloid that has been rotated $\pi/4$ radians away from the standard axes. The graphs of these functions are shown in Figure 2.3. Only positive x and y are physically meaningful. ■

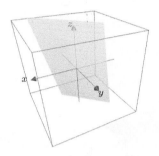 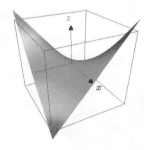

Figure 2.3: Graphs of functions in Example 2.2; (left) the surface $z = p(x,y)$; (right) the surface $z = a(x,y)$.

Graphs of familiar multivariable functions

Example 2.3. (a) Describe the perimeter of an isosceles triangle as a function of its side lengths, and (b) describe the graph of the function.

Answer: (a) $p(x,y) = 2x + y$; (b) a plane through the origin with $\mathbf{n} = \langle 2, 1, -1 \rangle$. ■

▷ The technique of vertical slicing

In Examples 2.2 and 2.3 you saw functions with relatively familiar graphs (planes, paraboloids). In other cases, you can often get a sense of a graph's shape by considering its traces on vertical planes.

Method of vertical slicing

Example 2.4. Suppose $f(x,y) = 3x^2 - 4y - 1$. Describe the traces of its graph on vertical planes of the form $y = c$.

Solution: The intersection of this graph with the plane $y = c$ is the curve $z = 3x^2 - 4c - 1$, which is a parabola on which the lowest point has $z = -4c - 1$ (see Figure 2.4). You can think of the graph of f as a "stack" of such parabolas, their vertices descending as the value of c increases. ■

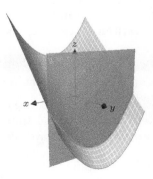

Figure 2.4: The intersection of $z = 3x^2 - 4y - 1$ with the plane $y = c$ results in a parabola.

Method of vertical slicing

Example 2.5. Suppose $f(x,y) = 0.3x^2 - 0.5y - 1$. (a) Describe the traces of its graph on planes of the form $x = c$, and (b) explain how the value of c affects them.

Answer: These are lines. See the online solution for part (b) and a graph.   ∎

Vertical slices of a graph are not only helpful when trying to understand the shape of the surface, but can also have practical meaning. For example, suppose a loud noise is generated at $x = 0$ on the x-axis, half of the acoutsitc energy travels down the axis to the left, and half travels to the right. Let's denote the intensity of the sound at position x at time t by $I(x,t)$. The graph of the intensity function is shown in Figure 2.5. Intersecting it with the vertical plane $t = c$ shows us the intensity of the sound at every position at time $t = c$. The traces of the surface on $t = 0$ and $t = 0.5$ indicate that an observer at $x = 0$ hears sound, but when $t = 1.25$ all the sound energy has propagated away from that position. Observers at other positions don't hear the sound until the wave of sound energy reaches and washes over them.

> Here we're calling the second variable t because using the letter y for time seems awkward.

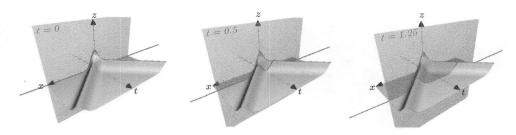

Figure 2.5: In these images you see sound energy propagate left and right away from its source. At later times, the energy pulses have traveled farther apart.

❖ Level Sets

Think about the surface $z = f(x,y)$ as a landscape for a moment, and suppose that you want to walk on it without changing altitude. Your path is the trace of the surface on a plane $z = c$, and the set of points in the xy-plane that lies directly beneath it is called a **level curve** (or more generally, a **level set**) of the function. In various application fields, the level curves of a function are also called **contours**, or are named by joining the prefix *iso* to a word that communicates the nature of the quantity that is constant along the curve; examples include *isobar* (equal barometric pressure), *isotherm* (equal temperature), and *isoquant* (equal quantity).

> The prefix *iso* comes from the ancient Greek word for "equal."

Example of level sets

Example 2.6. Draw level curves of the function $f(x,y) = 2x + y$.

Solution: A level set is just a collection of points over which the value of f remains constant. So let's pick a value in the range of f and fix it, say 1. The equation $f(x,y) = 1$ is $2x + y = 1$, which is a line in the xy-plane. Similarly, the function value is always c along the line $2x + y = c$ in the xy-plane. So the level sets of f are lines, all with different y-intercepts (depending on the value of c) but all with a slope of -2.   ∎

In Figure 2.6 you see several level curves of a function f, and the function's value on consecutive contours always differs by 2. When several contours are drawn

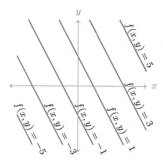

Figure 2.6: A contour map of the planar surface $z = f(x, y)$.

together and the change in the function's value from one to the next is always the same, called the ***contour increment***, we refer to the collection of level curves as a ***contour map***.

Example of level curves

Example 2.7. Draw a contour map of the surface $z = f(x, y)$ when $f(x, y) = \ln(1 + 3x^2 + y^2)$.

Solution: A contour of this surface is a curve along which $f(x, y)$ constant. For example, $f(x, y)$ is 1 whenever $1 = \ln(1 + 3x^2 + y^2)$. We can rewrite this equation is a more familiar form by exponentiating both sides and subtracting 1, thereby arriving at $3x^2 + y^2 = (e^1 - 1)$, which is the equation of an ellipse. In general, the level set of f corresponding to a height of $z = c$ on its graph is described by $3x^2 + y^2 = (e^c - 1)$. This is an ellipse when $c > 0$, but is nothing at all when $c < 0$ (because $f(x, y)$ is never negative). Level curves corresponding to $z = 1, 1.5, 2, 2.5$ and $z = 3$ (i.e., a contour increment of $\Delta f = 0.5$) are shown in Figure 2.7.   ■

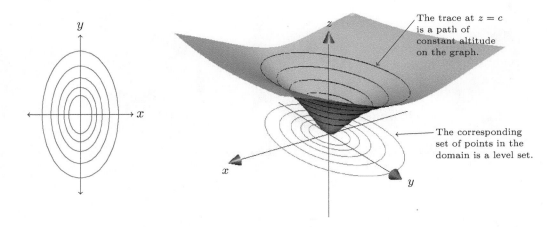

Figure 2.7: (left) A contour map of the surface $z = f(x, y)$ in Example 2.7, with a contour increment of $\Delta f = 0.5$; (right) paths of constant "altitude" on the graph of f.

In Figure 2.7 you see that the level curves enclose the point $(x, y) = (0, 0)$, which corresponds to the lowest point of a basin on the graph of f. In the next example you'll see level curves enclose points that correspond to the peaks of hills on the graph of f.

Example of level sets

Example 2.8. Use a computer to produce a contour map of the surface $z = f(x, y)$ when

$$f(x, y) = 7e^{-0.1(x-4)^2 - 0.2(y-5)^2} + 5e^{-0.15(x-10)^2 - 0.08(y-8)^2},$$

and use it to determine where the graph of f is steep.

Solution: The graph of f is shown in Figure 2.8, where the paths of constant altitude differ by a contour increment of $\Delta f = 0.9$. The points in the xy-plane directly below those paths are level sets of f, several of which are depicted in the right-hand image of the figure. Moving in the xy-plane from one of these curves to the next causes the value of f to change by 0.9 units.

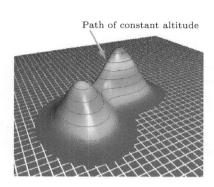

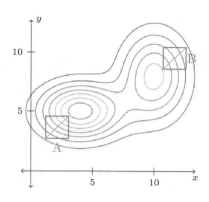

Figure 2.8: (left) The graph of f (from Example 2.8) as seen from above the first quadrant of the xy-plane; (right) a contour map of the surface $z = f(x, y)$.

The contour map in Figure 2.8 also includes congruent boxes. Note that the level curves in box A are closer together than those in box B, so if we step *across* the curves instead of along them (e.g., along the diagonal), we cross more contours in box A than in box B—the function value increments by 0.9 more times in box A than in box B, which means the graph is steeper above box A than it is above box B.■

The idea of a level set is closely related to the idea of a trace, but they're not the same. Whereas a trace lies on the graph of f, a level set is the corresponding set of points in the domain. So a trace on the graph of $f(x, y)$ is a curve that sits in 3-space, and a level set of $f(x, y)$ is a curve in 2-space (the xy-plane). This dimensional difference has practical importance when working with functions of three variables, $f(x, y, z)$. Because all three of our spacial dimensions are used for the domain, we need a fourth independent variable to represent the function value, say $w = f(x, y, z)$. Consequently, the graph of such a function sits in 4-space, which most people find very difficult to visualize. However, the level sets of f are surfaces in its three-dimensional domain. We refer to them as **level surfaces**.

Some people use the word "contour" to mean a trace on a surface, instead of how we've used it here (as a synonym for "level set"). However, the term "level set" always refers to a set of points in the domain of a function, never on its graph.

Level Surfaces

Example 2.9. Describe the level surfaces of $f(x, y, z) = x + 5y + 5z$.

Solution: A level surface is a set of points in the domain (3-space) on which the function is constant. For example, the function value is always 3 where $x + 5y + 5z = 3$, and this equation describes a plane. In fact, the function f is constant on any plane for which $\mathbf{n} = \langle 1, 5, 5 \rangle$ is a normal vector (see Figure 2.9). ■

Level surfaces

Example 2.10. Describe the level surfaces of $f(x, y, z) = x^2 + y^2 + z^2$.

Answer: Spheres. ■

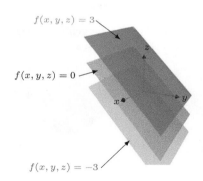

Figure 2.9: Level surfaces of $f(x, y, z) = x + 5y + 5z$.

You should know

- the terms *multivariable, multivariate, level curve,* and *level surface;*
- that the graph of $f(x, y)$ is a surface in 3-space;
- that functions are constant on level curves (surfaces).

You should be able to

- write the equations of level curves (surfaces) of a given multivariate function;
- tell where the graph of a function is steep from a graph of its level sets.

❖ 13.2 Skill Exercises

In exercises #1–6 determine the domain of the given function.

1. $f(x,y) = \sqrt{xe^{y^2-x^2}}$

2. $f(x,y) = e^{-x^{-2}-y^{-2}}$

3. $f(x,y) = \sqrt{(x-1)(y-4)-1}$

4. $f(x,y) = \sin^{-1}(x^2 + x - y^2 + 7y)$

5. $f(x,y) = \ln(y - x^3)$

6. $f(x,y) = \frac{\arcsin(xy)}{(2x-1)(4y-1)}$

In exercises #7–10 determine the range of the given function.

7. $f(x,y) = \ln(1 + x^2 + y^2)$

8. $f(x,y) = e^{-x^2-y^2}$

9. $f(x,y) = \sin(xy)$

10. $f(x,y) = -x - 3y$

In exercises #11–16 draw the level curves $f(x,y) = k$ when $k = 1, 2, 3, 4, 5$ and 6.

11. $f(x,y) = 3x + 2y$

12. $f(x,y) = -4x + 5y$

13. $f(x,y) = x + y^2$

14. $f(x,y) = x^2 + y$

15. $f(x,y) = \frac{x^2}{4} + \frac{y^2}{25}$

16. $f(x,y) = \frac{x^2}{4} - \frac{y^2}{25}$

17. Suppose $f(x,y) = \min\{1/x,\, 1/y\}$ when (x,y) is in the first quadrant, and is zero otherwise. Draw several level curves of f.

18. Describe the level sets of $g(x,y) = \lfloor f(x,y) \rfloor$, where $f(x,y)$ is from #17 and $\lfloor\ \rfloor$ denotes the greatest integer function (also called the "floor" function).

19. Match the graphs of the functions in (a)–(d) with plots of their corresponding level curves in (i)–(iii), if present.

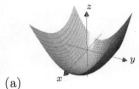 (a)   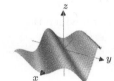 (b)    (c)   (d)

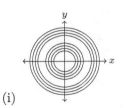 (i)   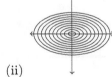 (ii)   (iii)

20. Match the graphs of the functions in (a)–(d) with plots of their corresponding level curves in (i)–(iii), if present.

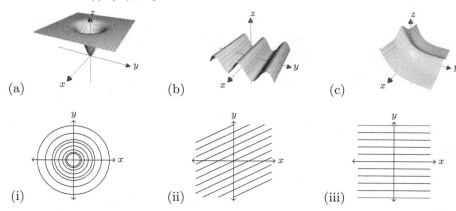

(a)   (b)   (c)   (d)

(i)   (ii)   (iii)

✛ 13.2 Concept and Application Exercises

Answer #21–27 in complete sentences.

21. Suppose c is some number in the range of f. Explain how the set $f(x, y) = c$ differs from the trace of the graph of f on the plane $z = c$.

22. Can the disk $x^2 + y^2 \leq 1$ be a level set of $f(x, y)$? If not, explain why not. If so, what does that tell us about the graph of f?

23. Describe the graph of $f(x, y) = 19x - 20y$ as a surface in 3-space.

24. Describe the graph of $f(x, y) = 5x^2 + 3y^2$ as a surface in 3-space.

25. Explain how the graphs of $f(x, y) = 3x + 7y$ and $g(x, y) = 3x + 7y + 2$ differ.

26. Describe the relationship between the graphs of $f(x, y) = 1 + x^2 + 7y^2$ and $g(x, y) = -1 - x^2 = y^2$.

27. Explain why the graph of a function of two variables cannot be an ellipsoid.

28. (a) Show that level surfaces of $f(x, y, z) = 7x^2 + 8y^2 + 3z^2$ are ellipsoids. (b) Does part (a) contradict #27? If so, explain how. If not, why not?

29. Figure 2.10 shows the level curves $f(x, y) = 1, 2, 3, \ldots, 10$. At which point, A or B, is the graph of f steeper? How can you tell?

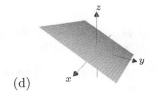

Figure 2.10: Level curves for #29

30. Figure 2.11 shows the level curves $f(x, y) = 1, 2, 3, \ldots, 6$. At which point, A or B, is the graph of f steeper?

In #31–34 (a) describe the trace of the graph of f on the plane $x = 9$, and (b) explain how it differs from the trace on the plane $x = 10$.

31. $f(x, y) = x + y^2$ 33. $f(x, y) = 1 + x \sin 2\pi y$

32. $f(x, y) = 3x + 8y$ 34. $f(x, y) = x + \cos \pi y$

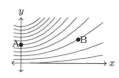

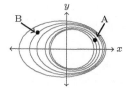

Figure 2.11: Level curves for #30

In #35–38 (a) describe the trace of the graph of f on the plane $y = 3$, and (b) explain how it differs from the trace on the plane $y = 4$.

35. $f(x,y) = x + y^2$

37. $f(x,y) = e^x y$

36. $f(x,y) = 3x + 8y$

38. $f(x,y) = xy$

For #39-44 (a) determine the (practical) domain of the function, (b) describe its level sets, and (c) describe the physical significance of the level sets.

39. The kinetic energy of an object with mass m kg and speed of $v \frac{\text{m}}{\text{sec}}$ is $K(m, v) = 0.5mv^2$.

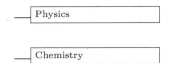

Physics

40. The Ideal Gas Law says that temperature is a function of pressure, P, and volume, V. Specifically, $T(P, V) = \frac{PV}{k_B N}$, where N is the number of atoms in the gas (which is constant here), and k_B is Boltzmann's constant.

Chemistry

41. The perimeter of a rectangle $p(x, y)$ with width x and length y.

42. A solid ball of radius r has a mass of $m(r, \rho) = \frac{4\pi}{3} r^3 \rho$ when it's made of a material with uniform density $\rho \frac{\text{kg}}{\text{m}^3}$.

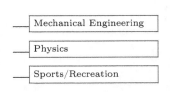

Physics

43. Rework #40 but treat N as a third variable.

Chemistry

44. The electrostatic force between two ions has a magnitude of $F(q, Q, r) = \frac{qQ}{r^2}$ where q and Q are the charges on the ions, and r is the distance between them.

Chemistry

For questions #45-46 explain the physical significance of the level curves.

45. The temperature, $T(x, y)$, on a car's disk brake.

Mechanical Engineering

46. Suppose $I(x, t)$ is the intensity of light at position x at time t.

Physics

47. In soccer, a foul outside the penalty box can result in a *direct free kick* at the 8-yard wide goal. As drawn in Figure 2.12, defenders can prevent direct-line shots at the $4 + q$ yards on the ball-side of the goal ($q \geq 0$) by standing shoulder-to-shoulder in a "wall," 10 yards away from the ball (placed where the foul occurred). The width of the wall depends on q and the polar coordinates where the foul occurred (where the center of the goal is the origin, and θ is measured from the goal line).

Sports/Recreation

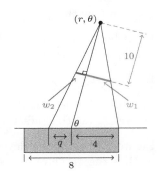

(a) Use similar triangles to show that the width of the wall is $w = w_1 + w_2$,

$$\text{where} \quad w_1 = \frac{40\sin\theta}{r - 4\cos\theta} \quad \text{and} \quad w_2 = \frac{10q\sin\theta}{r + q\cos\theta}.$$

(b) Determine the (practical) domain of $w(r, \theta, q)$.

(c) Determine a formula for the minimum number of players in a defensive wall. (The CDC provides data about average shoulder-to-shoulder breadth at `http://www.cdc.gov/nchs/data_access/ftp_data.htm`)

Figure 2.12: Diagram of the goal and ball placement for #47.

48. Fixing $q = 2$ in #47 reduces w to a function of position. (a) Explain the practical significance of setting $q = 2$. (b) Figure 2.13 shows the level curves of w. Is w changing more quickly at A or at B?

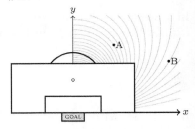

Figure 2.13: Level curves for #48.

49. Suppose your company has three plants, X, Y and Z, that supply a commodity to a specific market. Due to shipping contracts signed by your company, it costs $200 per unit to ship from plant X, $321 per unit to ship from Plant Y, and $250 per unit to ship from Z. Let x, y and z denote the units shipped to this market from plants X, Y and Z respectively, and denote by C the total cost of shipping to this market. (a) Write C as a function of x, y and z. (b) Use complete sentences to describe the level surfaces of C.

Business

50. In Chapter 10 we introduced the "sales equation," which predicts the equilibrium sales level of a product as $s(a, p, k) = {}^{ap}/_k$, where $a, p, k > 0$. The company's monthly advertising expenditure promoting its product is a, the effectiveness of the advertising campaign is quantified by p, and k determines the rate at which sales fall off in the absence of advertising. Describe the level surfaces of s in apk-space, and explain what they mean to us.

Marketing

51. Suppose you invest in a portfolio of three independent stocks, S_1, S_2 and S_3. To describe your confidence in the distribution of money among the stocks in the portfolio, we combine information about the stocks' average rates of return, their volatilities, and your aversion to risk.

Finance

    (a) Suppose r_1, r_2 and r_3 are the mean rates of return for the respective stocks (which we take to be constant), and x, y and z are the fractions of your investment designated for S_1, S_2 and S_3 respectively. What does the number $r_1 x + r_2 y + r_3 z$ tell us about the investment portfolio?

    (b) The *variance* of a return rate quantifies the extent to which it deviates from its average. Suppose the return rates have variances of σ_1^2, σ_2^2 and σ_3^2 respectively. Then $\sqrt{(\sigma_1 x)^2 + (\sigma_2 y)^2 + (\sigma_3 z)^2}$ quantifies the volatility of the portfolio. With this formula, we define *confidence* as

$$c = (r_1 x + r_2 y + r_3 z) - a\sqrt{\sigma_1^2 x^2 + \sigma_2^2 y^2 + \sigma_3^2 z^2}$$

    where a is a constant that quantifies your aversion to risk. Use the fact that $x + y + z = 1$ to reduce c to a function of x and y and determine the (practical) domain of $c(x, y)$.

    (c) Suppose $a = 1, r_1 = 0.03, r_2 = 0.05, r_3 = 0.04, \sigma_1 = 0.01, \sigma_2 = 0.03$ and $\sigma_3 = 0.02$. Use a graphing utility to plot several level curves of $c(x, y)$.

    (d) Based on part (c), estimate values of x and y that maximize c.

Exericses #52–54 extend the scenario from #51.

52. Suppose that you're considering including a new stock in place of S_1. The new stock has the same volatility as S_1, but its rate of return is 0.035.

Finance

    (a) Based on the meaning of r_1, predict how this change will affect your answer from #51(d).

    (b) Check your answer from part (a) by repeating #51(c)–(d) with $r_1 = 0.035$. (Keep all other parameters as indicated in #51(c).)

53. Suppose σ_2 decreases to $\sigma_2 = 0.01$ over the next year.

Finance

    (a) Based on the meaning of σ_2, predict the effect of this change in S_2 on your answer to #51(d). (All other parameters as indicated in #51(c).)

    (b) Check your answer to part (a) by repeating #51(c)–(d) with $\sigma_2 = 0.01$.

54. Suppose the number a increases to 2 over the next year.

Finance

    (a) Based on the meaning of a, predict the effect of this change on your answer to #51(d). (All other parameters as indicated in #51(c).)

    (b) Check your answer to part (a) by repeating #51(c)–(d) with $a = 2$.

55. A *production function* describes the quantity that can be produced, Q, as a function of labor units, L, and units of capital investment, K. (a) Intersecting the graph of $Q(K, L)$ with a plane of the form $L=$constant results in a curve in 3-space. What does this curve tell us? (b) What practical significance is there to a given level curve Q (often called an *isoquant*).

Economics

13.3   Limits and Continuity

As in single-variable calculus, the *limit* is the fundamental precursor to continuity and differentiability in the multivariable setting. So in this section we define limits of multivariable functions, discuss continuity and explore some of its consequences.

Key Idea(s): *The basic ideas of limits and continuity are the same as in single-variable calculus, and the limit laws you learned in Chapter 2 still apply.*

When dealing with single-variable functions, a limit value depends only on one-sided limits from the left and the right. In the multivariable setting, it depends on limit values as we approach the target point from all directions, along all paths.

✢ Limits

The idea of a limit is fundamentally the same in the single-variable and multivariable settings, but to communicate it concisely we need to adapt our notation to the new context. By writing $(x, y) \to (a, b)$ we will mean that $x \to a$ and $y \to b$.

> **Definition:** Suppose the domain of the function f includes points arbitrarily close to (a, b). We say that the number L is the **limit** of $f(x, y)$, or that $f(x, y)$ **converges** to L as $(x, y) \to (a, b)$, and write
>
> $$\lim_{(x,y)\to(a,b)} f(x, y) = L \qquad (3.1)$$
>
> if the value of f becomes arbitrarily close to L as the point $(x, y) \to (a, b)$.

This definition is made technically precise at the end of the section.

In the single-variable setting, we calculate limits *from the left* and *from the right,* and say that the limit exists if and only if those two calculations result in the same value. In the multivariable context (x, y) can approach (a, b) along a linear path (e.g. $y = 5x$), a quadratic path (e.g., $y = -x^2$), a transcendental path (e.g., $y = \cos x$), etc. The approach doesn't even have to be along a *path.* The point (x, y) could hop around in the plane as it approaches (a, b) as long as it remains in the domain of f (so that $f(x, y)$ makes sense). In order for the limit to exist, the value of $f(x, y)$ must converge to the same number, L, every time, no matter how (x, y) approaches (a, b). Otherwise, we say that the limit *does not exist.*

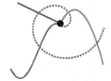

Figure 3.1: In the multivariable setting, we must get the same value regardless of the path we use to approach a point.

Simple limits

Example 3.1. Suppose f is the piecewise function defined below. Determine (a) $\lim_{(x,y)\to(1,1)} f(x, y)$, (b) $\lim_{(x,y)\to(-1,-0.2)} f(x, y)$, and (c) $\lim_{(x,y)\to(0,0)} f(x, y)$.

$$f(x, y) = \begin{cases} 3 & \text{if } |y| \geq x/5 \\ 0 & \text{otherwise} \end{cases}$$

Solution: Figure 3.2 shows the level sets of f. The xy-plane has been shaded where $f(x, y) = 3$, and is white where $f(x, y) = 0$.

(a) Because the function value is always 3 near the point $(1, 1)$, we see that $f(x, y) \to 3$ as $(x, y) \to (1, 1)$, regardless of how it proceeds through the domain. Therefore, $\lim_{(x,y)\to(1,1)} f(x, y) = 3$.

(b) The value of f remains 0 as we approach the point $(-1, -0.2)$ from the left, along the line $y = -0.2$, and it remains 3 as we approach the point along the same line, but from the right. This disagreement along different paths means that the limit does not exist.

(c) The function value is constantly 3 as we approach the origin along the y-axis, which leads us to think that the limit value is 3. However, the function value is constantly 0 as we approach the origin along the x-axis. This disagreement along different paths means that the limit does not exist. ∎

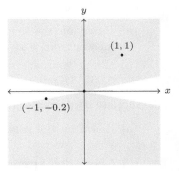

Figure 3.2: Level sets of f in Example 3.1.

Calculating a limit

Example 3.2. Suppose that $f(x, y) = \frac{x^2 - 7x - y^2 + 7y}{x - y}$ when $x \neq y$. Show that $\lim_{(x,y)\to(1,1)} f(x, y) = -5$.

Solution: Before contemplating $(x, y) \to (1, 1)$ along all possible paths, let's try to simplify $f(x, y)$: when $x \neq y$,

$$\frac{x^2 - 7x - y^2 + 7y}{x - y} = \frac{x^2 - y^2}{x - y} - \frac{7x - 7y}{x - y} = \frac{(x - y)(x + y)}{x - y} - \frac{7(x - y)}{x - y} = x + y - 7.$$

Now regardless of how (x, y) proceeds through the domain of f toward $(1, 1)$, we see $x \to 1$ and $y \to 1$, so $\lim_{(x,y) \to (1,1)} x + y - 7 = 1 + 1 - 7 = -5$.   ∎

> The phrase "regardless of how (x, y) proceeds through the domain of f" is extremely important in this context!

Determining whether a limit exists

Example 3.3. Suppose $f(x, y) = \frac{xy}{x^2 + y^2}$. Determine $\lim_{(x,y) \to (0,0)} f(x, y)$ or show that it does not exist.

Solution: Many people check this limit by approach the origin along the x-axis, and then the y-axis. We see a value of 0 in both cases (check!), but that's not enough for us to make a conclusion because the resulting value must be the same along *all* paths. So let's expand our investigation by considering limit values along arbitrary lines through the origin. Along the line $y = mx$ we see

$$f(x, y) = \frac{xy}{x^2 + y^2} = \frac{x(mx)}{x^2 + (mx)^2} = \frac{mx^2}{x^2 + m^2 x^2} = \frac{m}{1 + m^2}.$$

> You can think of this function as having a strange kind of jump discontinuity at the origin, where the jump you see depends on how you approach the discontinuity.

The function value is always $m/(1+m^2)$ when $y = mx$, so the limit is $m/(1+m^2)$ when we approach the origin along that line. Because this depends on *which* line we use (i.e., which m), the limit does not exist.   ∎

A limit that does not exist

Example 3.4. Suppose $f(x, y) = xy^{-1/3}$. (a) Show that $f(x, y) \to 0$ as $(x, y) \to (0, 0)$ along any line $y = mx$ or parabola $y = mx^2$ with $m \neq 0$, and (b) determine what happens to $f(x, y)$ as $(x, y) \to (0, 0)$ along the curve $y = x^3$. Then (c) based on parts (a) and (b), what can we say about $\lim_{(x,y) \to (0,0)} f(x, y)$?

Answer: (b) 1, and (c) the limit does not exist.   ∎

Solution
On-line

In these examples we have emphasized that $\lim_{(x,y) \to (a,b)} f(x, y)$ exists only if we get the same number by approaching (a, b) along every possible path. In all but the simplest examples, this must be done using the precise definition of the limit (discussed at the end of this section). Showing that a limit does *not* exist is often the easier proposition, because we need only find two paths along which we get different numbers for the limit.

▷ Limit Laws

The limit laws that you learned in Chapter 2 transition into the multivariable setting with only typographical changes.

The Limit Laws: Suppose that k is a constant,

$$\lim_{(x,y)\to(a,b)} f(x,y) = L, \quad \text{and} \quad \lim_{(x,y)\to(a,b)} g(x,y) = M.$$

Then the following are true:

1. $\displaystyle\lim_{(x,y)\to(a,b)} k = k$

2. $\displaystyle\lim_{(x,y)\to(a,b)} x = a \text{ and } \lim_{(x,y)\to(a,b)} y = b$

3. $\displaystyle\lim_{(x,y)\to(a,b)} \big(k f(x,y)\big) = kL$

4. $\displaystyle\lim_{(x,y)\to(a,b)} \big(f(x,y) + g(x,y)\big) = L + M$

5. $\displaystyle\lim_{(x,y)\to(a,b)} \big(f(x,y) - g(x,y)\big) = L - M$

6. $\displaystyle\lim_{(x,y)\to(a,b)} \big(f(x,y) g(x,y)\big) = LM$

7. $\displaystyle\lim_{(x,y)\to(a,b)} \left(\frac{f(x,y)}{g(x,y)}\right) = \frac{L}{M}$, when $M \neq 0$

Using the Limit Laws

Example 3.5. Use the limit laws to determine the value of $\lim_{(x,y)\to(0,0)} \frac{(1-\cos y)\sin x}{xy}$.

Solution: We know from our study of single-variable calculus (see Chapter 2) that

$$\lim_{x\to 0} \frac{\sin x}{x} = 1 \quad \text{and} \quad \lim_{y\to 0} \frac{1 - \cos y}{y} = 0.$$

Since both of these limits exist as $(x,y) \to (0,0)$, Limit Law 6 tells us that

$$\lim_{(x,y)\to(0,0)} \frac{(1 - \cos y)\sin x}{xy} = 1 \times 0 = 0. \qquad \blacksquare$$

❖ Continuity

As in Chapter 2, we say that a multivariable function is continuous where its limit and function value are the same.

Definition: We say that f is ***continuous*** at (a, b) when

$$\lim_{(x,y)\to(a,b)} f(x,y) = f(a,b). \tag{3.2}$$

Further, we say that the function f is ***continuous on a set*** R if it's continuous at each point in R. If the limit in equation (3.2) exists but differs from $f(a,b)$, perhaps because f is not defined at (a,b), we say that f has a ***removable discontinuity*** at (a, b).

Removable discontinuity

Example 3.6. Suppose $f(x,y) = \frac{x^2 + y^2 - \tan(x^2 + y^2)}{(x^2 + y^2)^3}$ away from the origin. (a) Show that f has a removable discontinuity at $(0,0)$, and (b) determine how we should define f at $(0,0)$ in order to make the function continuous there.

Solution: (a) To show that f has a removable discontinuity at the origin, we need to show that $\lim_{(x,y)\to(0,0)} f(x,y)$ exists, even though $f(x,y)$ is not defined at the origin. The term $x^2 + y^2$ is common in this expression, and it tends to 0 as $(x,y) \to (0,0)$ regardless of how (x,y) approaches the origin. By using this to our advantage we can treat our limit with the methods of single variable calculus. If we write $u = x^2 + y^2$,

$$\lim_{(x,y)\to(0,0)} \frac{x^2 + y^2 - \tan(x^2 + y^2)}{(x^2 + y^2)^3} = \lim_{u\to 0} \frac{u - \tan u}{u^3} = -\frac{1}{3}.$$

> The value of $-1/3$ can determined by writing the first few terms of the Maclaurin series for $\tan(u)$ or by repeated applications of L'Hôpital's Rule.

(b) In order to make f continuous at the origin, we set $f(0,0) = -1/3$. ∎

As you saw in our earlier discussion of continuity (Chapter 2), algebraic combinations of continuous functions are continuous on their domains. The following theorem addresses the composition of continuous functions.

> The term "algebraic combinations of ..." means "sums, products, quotients, and roots of ..."

Theorem (Composition of Continuous Functions): Suppose $f(x,y)$ is continuous at (a,b).

Part I: If $g(t)$ is continuous at $t = f(a,b)$, the function $g \circ f$ is continuous at (a,b), meaning

$$\lim_{(x,y)\to(a,b)} g\big(f(x,y)\big) = g\big(f(a,b)\big). \tag{3.3}$$

Part II: Suppose $x(t)$ and $y(t)$ are continuous at $t = c$ with $x(c) = a$ and $y(c) = b$, and the point $(x(t), y(t))$ remains in the domain of f when t is sufficiently close to c. Then the composition of f with $x(t)$ and $y(t)$ is also continuous at $t = c$. That is,

$$\lim_{t\to c} f\big(x(t), y(t)\big) = f(a,b). \tag{3.4}$$

Composition of continuous functions

Example 3.7. (a) Use the previous theorem to show that $\cos(0.25y^2 e^{5xy})$ is continuous, and (b) use that fact to determine its limit as $(x,y) \to (0, \sqrt{\pi})$.

Solution: (a) Limit Law 6 allows us to conclude that $5xy$ is a continuous function of x and y, and we know from our study of single-variable calculus that the exponential function is continuous, so by virtue of the previous theorem we conclude that e^{5xy} is a continuous function of x and y. For similar reasons, $f(x,y) = 0.25y^2 e^{5xy}$ is continuous. Now using $g(t) = \cos(t)$, which is continuous at all values of t, we can calculate the limit as

$$\lim_{(x,y)\to(0,\sqrt{\pi})} g\big(f(x,y)\big) = g\big(f(0,\sqrt{\pi})\big) = g(\pi/4) = \frac{\sqrt{2}}{2}. \qquad ∎$$

Continuity

Example 3.8. Determine whether $f(x,y) = \frac{x^2 - 7x - y^2 + 7y}{x - y}$ is continuous at $(2, 13)$.

Answer: It is. ∎

Solution On-line

✥ Extreme and Intermediate Value Theorems

In Chapter 2 you saw the Extreme Value Theorem, which says that a continuous function on an interval $[a, b]$ achieves maximum and minimum values. You also saw the Intermediate Value Theorem, which says that a continuous function on an interval cannot jump over values in its range. These theorems are consequences of continuity, to be sure, but also depend on the fact that an interval $[a, b]$ is *connected*, *closed* and *bounded*, which we define below.

▷ Connected

When R is a collection of points, any one of which can be reached from any other by traveling along a continuous path that remains in R, we will say that R is ***connected***. Unless otherwise specified, whenever we talk about a ***region*** we will mean a connected set of points. This vocabulary allows us to state a familiar result.

> **Intermediate Value Theorem:** Suppose f is a continuous function on the region R, and that f achieves a value of m at some point in R and a value of M at another, where $m < M$. Then for each $c \in [m, M]$ there is at least one point in R where the value of f is c.

Proof. Suppose (x_1, y_1) and (x_2, y_2) are the points in R at which f achieves values of m and M, respectively. Because R is connected, there is a continuous path through R that extends between them. Suppose this path is parameterized by the continuous function $\mathbf{r}(t) = \langle x(t), y(t) \rangle$ over $[a, b]$. Then $f(x(t), y(t))$ is a continuous function on $[a, b]$ that achieves values of m and M. When $c \in [m, M]$, the Intermediate Value Theorem from Chapter 2 guarantees some $t^* \in [a, b]$ at which $f(x(t^*), y(t^*)) = c$. The certain existence of $(x(t^*), y(t^*))$ proves the theorem. (Note that the theorem guarantees at least one point, there may be several.) ∎

▷ Closed and bounded

Suppose (a, b) is a point in the region R. We say that (a, b) is an ***interior point*** of R when there is some circle centered at (a, b) that encloses only points in the region, as seen in Figure 3.3. In the same figure, you can see that every circle around (c, d) encloses both points that are in R and points that are not, which is what we mean by saying that (c, d) is a ***boundary point*** of the region. (If R is in 3-space, we use spheres instead of circles, but otherwise the definitions are the same.)

Instead of describing one point at a time, it's often convenient to say something about all the points in R together. We say that R is ***open*** when all of its points are interior points, and ***closed*** when it contains all of its boundary points.

Describing points and regions

Example 3.9. Use the terms defined above to describe the regions (a) $x^2 + y^2 \leq 1$, (b) $x^2 + y^2 < 1$, and (c) $x^2 + y^2 = 1$, which are shown in Figure 3.4

Solution: (a) All points the region's boundary are included, so this region is closed. (b) This region is open since all points of $x^2 + y^2 < 1$ are interior points. (c) This region includes all of its boundary points, so it's closed. (As an aside, note that this set is composed of only boundary points.) ∎

In Example 3.9 we said that the disk $x^2 + y^2 \leq 1$ is closed. The half-plane $x \geq 0$ is too, but it extends forever while the disk does not. To distinguish between such cases, we say that a set R is ***bounded*** when it can be circumscribed by a circle (or sphere, if R is a set in 3-space).

> A *continuous path* is one that's parameterized by a continuous position function, $\mathbf{r}(t)$.
>
> If you study a subject called *topology* in a later course, you'll refine the idea of connectedness and will refer to this definition as *path connectedness*.

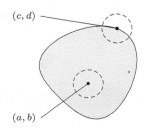

(c, d)

(a, b)

Figure 3.3: The point (a, b) is an interior point of R, and (c, d) is a boundary point.

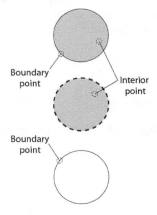

Boundary point

Interior point

Boundary point

Figure 3.4: (top to bottom) The regions in parts (a), (b), and (c) of Example 3.9.

The role of the interval $[a, b]$ in the Extreme Value Theorem of Chapter 2 is played by closed and bounded regions in higher-dimensions, as seen below.

> **Extreme Value Theorem:** Suppose the region R is closed and bounded, and f is continuous over R. Then f achieves a maximum value at some point in R, and also achieves a minimum value at some point in R.

✢ Precise Definition of a Limit

When we say that $f(x, y)$ converges to L as $(x, y) \to (a, b)$ we mean that the difference between $f(x, y)$ and L can be made arbitrarily small by considering points in the domain of f that are "close enough" to (a, b). In the definition below, "small" is quantified by $\varepsilon > 0$, and the number $\delta > 0$ defines "close enough."

> **Precise Definition of the Limit:** Suppose the domain of f includes points arbitrarily close to (a, b)—here we mean to exclude (a, b) itself, even if it's in the domain of f. We say that L is the **limit** of $f(x, y)$ as $(x, y) \to (a, b)$ when each $\varepsilon > 0$ is associated with a distance $\delta > 0$ such that
>
> $$|f(x, y) - L| < \varepsilon \tag{3.5}$$
>
> whenever (x, y) is a point in the domain of f for which
>
> $$0 < \sqrt{(x - a)^2 + (y - b)^2} < \delta. \tag{3.6}$$

Note: Equation (3.6) says that (x, y) is within δ units of (a, b), but the displacement vector between them could point in any direction. Because of that fact, the number δ defines a *disk* centered at (a, b), such as you see in Figure 3.5.

| The phrase "arbitrarily small" means that we can choose ε to be any positive number, as small as we want. |

| Equation (3.5) says that the difference between the numbers $f(x, y)$ and L is "small."

Equation 3.6 says that (x, y) is "close enough" to (a, b). |

Figure 3.5: The number δ is the radius of a disk.

Working with the definition of the limit

Example 3.10. Suppose $f(x, y) = x^2 + y^4$. Use the definition of the limit to show that $\lim_{(x,y) \to (3,1)} f(x, y) = 10$.

Solution: Intuitively speaking, the limit value is 10 because $x^2 \to 9$ and $y^4 \to 1$ as $(x, y) \to (3, 1)$. This leads us to measure the difference between $f(x, y)$ and 10 as

$$|f(x, y) - 10| = |x^2 - 9 + y^4 - 1| \le |x^2 - 9| + |y^4 - 1|, \tag{3.7}$$

so $|f(x, y) - 10| < \varepsilon$ when both $|x^2 - 9| < \varepsilon/2$ and $|y^4 - 1| < \varepsilon/2$. We consider these inequalities one at a time, below.

The Taylor expansion of x^2 about $x = 3$ is useful in this context because it shows us explicitly how the function value depends on $(x - 3)$, which is vanishing in the limit, so let's rewrite x^2 as $9 + 6(x - 3) + (x - 3)^2$. This allows us to see that

$$|x^2 - 9| = |6(x - 3) + (x - 3)^2| \le 6|x - 3| + |x - 3|^2.$$

The number $|x - 3| < 1$ when $x \approx 3$, so $|x - 3|^2 < |x - 3|$. Therefore,

$$|x^2 - 9| \le 6|x - 3| + |x - 3| = 7|x - 3|,$$

from which we conclude that $|x^2 - 9| < \varepsilon/2$ when $|x - 3| < \varepsilon/14$.

Similarly, we rewrite y^4 as $1 + 4(y - 1) + 6(y - 1)^2 + 4(y - 1)^3 + (y - 1)^4$, which allows us to see that

$$
\begin{aligned}
|y^4 - 1| &= |4(y - 1) + 6(y - 1)^2 + 4(y - 1)^3 + (y - 1)^4| \\
&\le 4|(y - 1)| + 6|y - 1|^2 + 4|y - 1|^3 + |y - 1|^4.
\end{aligned}
$$

| We're using the *triangle inequality:*

$$|a + b| \le |a| + |b|,$$

with $a = x^2 - 9$ and $b = y^4 - 1$. |

| Here we're using the triangle inequality. |

| When a positive number is less than 1, squaring it makes it smaller. |

| This is the Taylor expansion of the function y^4 about $y = 1$. |

Since $|y - 1| < 1$ when $y \approx 1$, we know that $|y-1|^2$, $|y-1|^3$ and $|y-1|^4$ are all less than $|y - 1|$. It follows that

$$|y^4 - 1| \le 4|(y - 1)| + 6|y - 1| + 4|y - 1| + |y - 1| = 15|y - 1|,$$

from which we conclude that $|y^4 - 1| < \varepsilon/2$ when $|y - 1| < \varepsilon/30$.

Lastly, we set $\delta = \min\{\varepsilon/14,\ \varepsilon/30\} = \varepsilon/30$. Then

$$\|\langle x, y\rangle - \langle 3, 1\rangle\| < \delta \Rightarrow \begin{cases} |x - 3| < \varepsilon/14 & \Rightarrow & |x^2 - 9| < \varepsilon/2 \\ |y - 1| < \varepsilon/30 & \Rightarrow & |y^4 - 1| < \varepsilon/2, \end{cases}$$

so that equation (3.7) guarantees $|f(x, y) - 10| < \varepsilon$.   ■

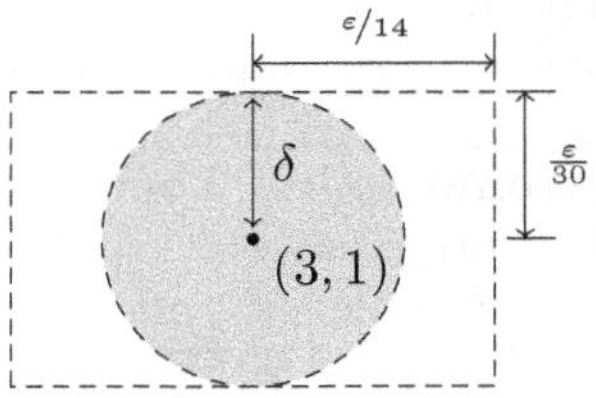

Figure 3.6: Choosing δ so that $|x-3|$ and $|y-1|$ are both small enough.

You should know

- the terms *continuous*, *region*, *interior point*, *boundary point*, *open*, *closed*, and *bounded*;
- the notation $\lim_{(x,y)\to(a,b)} f(x, y) = L$;
- the limit laws;
- that algebraic combinations of, and compositions of continuous functions are continuous on their domains;
- the Extreme Value Theorem, and the Intermediate Value Theorem;
- the precise definition of $\lim_{(x,y)\to(a,b)} f(x, y) = L$.

You should be able to

- verify that a limit does not exist;
- apply the limit laws to evaluate a limit;
- determine a formula for δ in terms of ε.

❖ 13.3 Skill Exercises

In #1–6 use the limit laws (including equation (3.3)) to verify the specified limit. Specify which limit laws you use, and where you use them.

1. $\lim_{(x,y)\to(1,8)} \frac{3x}{x^6 - 4xy^2} = -\frac{3}{255}$

2. $\lim_{(x,y)\to(2,-5)} \frac{5x+10y}{6xy+x^2+y^2+1} = 0$

3. $\lim_{(x,y)\to(7,13)} e^{x^2-y} = e^{56}$

4. $\lim_{(x,y)\to(0.25,\pi)} \cos xy = \sqrt{2}/2$

5. $\lim_{(x,y)\to(2,3)} \left[3x + \sin(0.5\pi y)\right] = 5$

6. $\lim_{(x,y)\to(7,13)} e^x \cos \pi y = -e^7$

In #7–12 calculate the limit by writing it as the product of limits.

7. $\lim_{(x,y)\to(0,0)} \frac{e^y - 1 - y}{y \cos(x)}$

8. $\lim_{(x,y)\to(0,0)} \frac{\sin y - y}{y^3 \sec x}$

9. $\lim_{(x,y)\to(0,0)} \frac{6x \sin y - 6xy}{4y^3 \sin x}$

10. $\lim_{(x,y)\to(1,2)} \frac{\ln x \, \ln y}{(y-1)(x-1)}$

11. $\lim_{(x,y)\to(\pi/2,0)} y(x - \frac{\pi}{2}) \tan x \cot y$

12. $\lim_{(x,y)\to(3,\pi)} (1 + \sec y)(yx - x\pi)$

Determine each limit in exercises #13–18.

13. $\lim_{(x,y)\to(0,0)} \frac{\sin(x+y)}{x+y}$

14. $\lim_{(x,y)\to(0,0)} \frac{1-\cos(3x+4y)}{3x+4y}$

15. $\lim_{(x,y)\to(0,0)} \frac{e^{9x+2y}-1}{18x+4y}$

16. $\lim_{(x,y)\to(0,0)} (x^2 + y^2) \ln(x^2 + y^2)$

17. $\lim_{(x,y)\to(1,0)} \frac{(x+y)^2 - 1}{x+y-1}$

18. $\lim_{(x,y)\to(1,1)} \frac{(x+y)^3 - 8}{x+y-2}$

In #19–22 approximate $\lim_{(x,y)\to(a,b)} f(x,y)$ (which exists) by using a graphing utility to render a graph of f over the line through (a,b) that extends in the direction of **u**.

19. $f(x,y) = \cos(x^3 - \pi y^{-1/3})$; $(a,b) = (0,27)$; $\mathbf{u} = \langle 4, -3 \rangle$

20. $f(x,y) = \sin(0.25\pi x + y^3)$; $(a,b) = (4,0)$; $\mathbf{u} = \langle 1, 2 \rangle$

21. $f(x,y) = \frac{\ln(1+x+y)\sin(x+y)}{|x+y|^{3/2}}$; $(a,b) = (2,-2)$; $\mathbf{u} = \langle 2, 1 \rangle$

22. $f(x,y) = \frac{1-\sqrt{2x+1+y}}{\cos(2x+y)-1}$; $(a,b) = (-3,3)$; $\mathbf{u} = \langle 8, -1 \rangle$

In #23 and #24 Determine $\lim_{(x,y)\to(a,b)} f(x,y)$ at the specified points, or explain why it doesn't exist.

23. (a) the point $(1/2, 1/4)$, and (b) the point $(0,0)$, with $f(x,y) = \begin{cases} 1 & \text{if } y \leq x(1-x) \\ 1 & \text{if } y \geq e^x - 1 \\ 0 & \text{otherwise} \end{cases}$

24. (a) the point $(0,1)$, and (b) the point $(0,0)$, with $f(x,y) = \begin{cases} 1 & \text{if } y \leq 0 \text{ or } x \leq 0 \\ e^{-xy} & \text{otherwise} \end{cases}$

In #25–26 calculate $\lim_{(x,y)\to(0,0)} f(x,y)$ by switching into polar coordinates.

25. $f(x,y) = \frac{5}{x^2+y^2} e^{-1/\sqrt{x^2+y^2}}$

27. $f(x,y) = \frac{2x^4 - x^2 + 4x^2y^2 - y^2 + 2y^4}{x^4 + x^2 + 2x^2y^2 + y^2 + y^4}$

26. $f(x,y) = \frac{\ln(x^2+1+y^2)}{x^2 + \sin(x^2+y^2) + y^2}$

28. $f(x,y) = \frac{3x^4 - 2x^2 + 6x^2y^2 - 2y^2 + 3y^4}{5x^4 + 3x^2 + 10x^2y^2 + 3y^2 + 5y^4}$

✥ 13.3 Concept and Application Exercises

29. Draw a region that is (a) open and bounded, (b) open and unbounded, (c) closed and bounded, (d) closed and unbounded.

30. Can a bounded region be (a) neither open nor closed? (b) both open and closed? If so, draw such a region. If not, explain why not.

31. Determine whether the curve $y = x^2$ is (a) open, or closed, or neither, and (b) whether the curve is bounded or unbounded. Explain your conclusion in complete sentences.

32. Determine whether the curve $1 = y^2 + x^2$ is (a) open, or closed, or neither, and (b) whether the curve is bounded or unbounded. Explain your conclusion in complete sentences.

33. Suppose that R is the disk $x^2 + y^2 < 1$ and $f(x,y) = x$. Verify that f does *not* achieve a maximum value on R, and explain why this does not contradict the Extreme Value Theorem.

34. Suppose that R is the half-plane $y \geq 0$ and $f(x,y) = 1/(1+y^2)$. Show that f does *not* achieve a minimum value on R, and explain why this does not contradict the Extreme Value Theorem.

In exercises #35–40 determine what value should be assigned to the function at the specified point in order to make it continuous there.

35. $f(x,y) = x \ln \frac{1}{x} + y^2 \csc^2 y$; $(0,0)$

38. $f(x,y) = \frac{xy^2 - xy - 20x}{y^2 + 2y - 35}$; $(3,5)$

36. $f(x,y) = e^{-x^{-2} - y^{-2}}$; $(0,0)$

39. $f(x,y) = \frac{9 + x^2 \sin^2 y + 6x \sin y}{x \sin y + 3}$; $(3, 1.5\pi)$

37. $f(x,y) = \frac{x^2 - 7x + 12}{yx^2 - yx - 6y}$; $(3,7)$

40. $f(x,y) = \frac{y^3 \sin x}{-xy + x \sin y}$; $(0,0)$

41. Suppose $f(x, y) = \frac{xy}{x^2+y^2}$.

    (a) Show that $f(x, y) \to 0$ when $(x, y) \to (0, 0)$ along any path of the form $y = k\, x^2$, where $k \neq 0$.

    (b) Explain why $\lim_{(x,y)\to(0,0)} f(x, y)$ does not exist, in spite of part (a).

42. Suppose $f(x, y) = \frac{xy+3x-2y-6}{x^2+y^2-4x+6y+13}$. Show that $\lim_{(x,y)\to(2,-3)} f(x, y)$ does not exist. *(Hint: factor the numerator, and complete squares in the denominator.)*

In #43–44 evaluate the limit of $f(x, y)$ as $(x, y) \to (0, 0)$ along the specified paths (see Example 3.3). Then make a conjecture about $\lim_{(x,y)\to(0,0)} f(x, y)$ based on that evidence.

43. $f(x, y) = \frac{x^2 y}{x^4+y^2}$; (a) $y = 3x$, (b) $y = x^2$.

44. $f(x, y) = \frac{x^9 y}{3x^{12}+y^4}$; (a) $y = 2x$, (b) $y = 2x^3$.

In #45–46 design a function f so that as $(x, y) \to (0, 0)$ along the given paths (as in Example 3.3) the value of $f(x, y)$ converges to the specified numbers.

45. $f(x, y) \to 0$ along $y = 7x$, and $f(x, y) \to 3/11$ along $y = 2x^6$

46. $f(x, y) \to 0$ along $y = 3x^2$, and $f(x, y) \to 5/971$ along $y = 4x^5$

As with the limit laws, the **Squeeze Theorem** extends easily into the multivariable setting. It says that when $g(x, y) \to L$ and $h(x, y) \to L$ as $(x, y) \to (a, b)$, and $g(x, y) \leq f(x, y) \leq h(x, y)$, it must also be true that $\lim_{(x,y)\to(a,b)} f(x, y) = L$. Exercises #47–50 make use of this fact.

47. Prove that $\ln(xy)/(xy-1) \to 1/2$ as $(x, y) \to (4, 1/4)$ by using the fact that

$$(xy - 1) - \tfrac{1}{2}(xy - 1)^2 \leq \ln xy \leq (xy - 1) - \tfrac{1}{2}(xy - 1)^2 + \tfrac{1}{3}(xy - 1)^3$$

    when (x, y) is near $(4, 1/4)$.

48. Use the fact that $1 - \frac{x^2 y^2}{2} \leq \cos xy \leq 1$ to determine $\lim_{(x,y)\to(0,0)} \frac{1-\cos xy}{xy}$.

49. Use the Squeeze Theorem to determine $\lim_{(x,y)\to(0,0)} x \cos(1/y)$.

50. Use the Squeeze Theorem to determine $\lim_{(x,y)\to(0,0)} y \arctan(1/x)$.

51. Use the Taylor-series method of Example 3.10 to prove that $\lim_{(x,y)\to(-1,2)} f(x, y) = 58$ when $f(x, y) = 2x^2 + 7y^3$.

52. Use the Taylor-series method of Example 3.10 to prove that $\lim_{(x,y)\to(1,3)} f(x, y) = 27$ when $f(x, y) = 9x^4 + 2y^2$.

In each of #53–56 use the precise definition of the limit to verify the equation.

53. $\lim_{(x,y)\to(3,4)} \left(2x^3 + 4y^2\right) = 118$　　　55. $\lim_{(x,y)\to(0,0)} e^{x+y} = 1$

54. $\lim_{(x,y)\to(-1,3)} 5x^2 y = 15$　　　56. $\lim_{(x,y)\to(0,0)} e^{\sin(x+y)} = 1$

13.4   Partial Derivatives

In this section we extend the idea of differentiation to functions of more than one variable by introducing a *partial derivative,* which tells us about slope and rate of change when only one of the independent variables changes.

✤ First Partial Derivatives

In Chapter 3 we used the phrase "with respect to..." to identify the independent variable in cases where it was unclear. For example, a rectangular box with a square base (see Figure 4.1) has a volume of $(area\ of\ base) \times (height)$, so we write $V(x, y) = x^2 y$. It's easy enough to see that a box with base length of $x = 3$ cm and a height of $y = 4$ cm has a volume of $V = 36$ cm^3, but how sensitive is that number to changes in the dimensions? In order to answer that question by using the differentiation techniques of Chapter 3, we need to know whether we're talking about changes in x with fixed y, or vice versa.

1. Suppose the height of the box is fixed at $y = 4$, but we can adjust the size of the square base. Then volume depends only on the dimensions of the base, $V(x, 4) = 4x^2$, and its rate of change with respect to x is $8x$ (the derivative), which is 24 when $x = 3$. More formally, the rate of change is

$$\lim_{\Delta x \to 0} \frac{\Delta V}{\Delta x} = \lim_{\Delta x \to 0} \frac{V(3 + \Delta x, 4) - V(3, 4)}{\Delta x} = 8x \bigg|_{x=3} = 24 \ \frac{\text{cm}^3 \text{ of volume}}{\text{cm of base length}}.$$

2. Suppose we're talking about a box with a fixed base length of $x = 3$, but we can vary the height. Then volume depends only on the height, $V(3, y) = 9y$, and its rate of change with respect to y is

$$\lim_{\Delta y \to 0} \frac{\Delta V}{\Delta y} = \lim_{\Delta y \to 0} \frac{V(3, 4 + \Delta y) - V(3, 4)}{\Delta y} = 9 \ \frac{\text{cm}^3 \text{ of volume}}{\text{cm of height}}.$$

Although we held one dimension fixed in each of these calculations, we know that both x and y *can* change together. In this sense, each of the numbers we calculated above tells us only part of the story, and we call them *partial derivatives.*

The key idea to take away from this discussion is that we can effectively reduce a function of two variables to a single-variable function simply by holding one variable constant. That allows us to use our techniques from single-variable calculus to talk about rates of change, one variable at a time.

> **Definition:** Suppose f is a function of two variables, x and y. The **partial derivative of f with respect to x** is denoted by
>
> $$\frac{\partial f}{\partial x}, \quad \text{or} \quad f_x, \quad \text{or} \quad \partial_x f,$$
>
> and its value at the point (a, b) is
>
> $$f_x(a, b) = \lim_{\Delta x \to 0} \frac{f(a + \Delta x, b) - f(a, b)}{\Delta x}, \tag{4.1}$$
>
> provided that the limit exists.

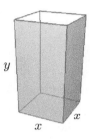

Figure 4.1: A rectangular box with a square base.

The number $y = b$ is held fixed in equation (4.1). Only the first argument of f changes.

Key Idea(s):   *We make use of the single-variable calculus by allowing only one argument of a function to vary at a time.*

A partial derivative tells us rate of change and the slope of a tangent line, but only in one direction at a time.

The basic rules of differentiation that you learned in Chapter 3 still apply.

The concavity of a graph is detected by two applications of partial differentiation (a second partial derivative).

We hold the value of y fixed when calculating f_x, which effectively reduces f to a function of a single variable. Similarly, we can effectively reduce f to a single-variable function of y by holding x fixed. This allows us to find the instantaneous rate of change of f with respect to y.

Definition: Suppose f is a function of two variables, x and y. The **partial derivative of f with respect to y** is denoted by

$$\frac{\partial f}{\partial y}, \quad \text{or} \quad f_y, \quad \text{or} \quad \partial_y f,$$

and its value at the point (a, b) is

$$f_y(a, b) = \lim_{\Delta y \to 0} \frac{f(a, b + \Delta y) - f(a, b)}{\Delta y}, \qquad (4.2)$$

provided that the limit exists.

> The number $x = a$ is held fixed in equation (4.2). Only the second argument of f changes.

We don't typically calculate f_x and f_y as limits of difference quotients. Instead, because only one variable changes at a time, we use the techniques of differentiation that we developed for functions of a single variable.

Partial derivatives

Example 4.1. The box in Figure 4.1 has a surface area of $A(x, y) = 2x^2 + 4xy$ cm^2. Determine (a) $A_x(3, 4)$, and (b) a general formula for A_x.

Solution: (a) It's important to remember that the value of y is constant when we calculate the partial derivative with respect to x. So for the purposes of this calculation, we'll write the surface area as $A(x, 4) = 2x^2 + 16x$. This allows us to use the techniques from single-variable calculus to determine that

$$\frac{\partial A}{\partial x} = 4x + 16 \quad \text{so} \quad A_x(3, 4) = 28 \ \frac{\text{cm}^2 \text{ of surface area}}{\text{cm of base length}}.$$

(b) Here we generalize the previous calculation by allowing y to be any fixed number. In this case, although $A(x, y)$ appears to be a function of two variables, we know that y is actually a specific constant, so

$$A_x(x, y) = \partial_x \big(2x^2 + 4xy\big) = 4x + 4y. \qquad \blacksquare$$

Partial derivatives

Example 4.2. The box in Figure 4.1 has a volume of $V(x, y) = x^2 y$ cm^3. Determine (a) $V_y(2, 5)$, and (b) general formulas for V_x and V_y.

Answer: (a) 2; (b) $V_x(x, y) = 2xy$ and $V_y(x, y) = x^2$. $\qquad \blacksquare$

Solution On-line

In Examples 4.1 and 4.2 you saw that the general formula for the partial derivative of a two-variable function is, generally speaking, also a function of two variables. In the next examples we calculate more complicated partial derivatives by using differentiation rules that we established in the single-variable setting.

Partial derivatives and the Product Rule

Example 4.3. Calculate (a) f_x and (b) f_y when $f(x, y) = x^2 e^{xy^3}$.

Solution: (a) Since f is a product of factors involving x, we use the Product Rule.

> The Chain Rule tells us that the derivative of e^u with respect to x is $e^u u'$.

$$\frac{\partial f}{\partial x} = \frac{\partial}{\partial x}\left(x^2\, e^{xy^3}\right) = e^{xy^3}\frac{\partial}{\partial x}\left(x^2\right) + x^2\frac{\partial}{\partial x}\left(e^{xy^3}\right)$$

$$= 2x\, e^{xy^3} + x^2\, e^{xy^3}\underbrace{\frac{\partial}{\partial x}\left(xy^3\right)}_{\text{From the chain rule}} = 2xe^{xy^3} + x^2y^3e^{xy}.$$

(b) Holding x fixed effectively reduces f to a function of y, so

$$\frac{\partial f}{\partial y} = \frac{\partial}{\partial y}\left(x^2 e^{xy^3}\right) = x^2 e^{xy^3}\underbrace{\frac{\partial}{\partial y}\left(xy^3\right)}_{\text{From the chain rule}} = x^2 e^{xy^3}\, 3xy^2 = 3x^3y^2 e^{xy^3}. \qquad\blacksquare$$

Partial derivatives and the Quotient Rule

Example 4.4. Calculate f_x and f_y when $f(x,y) = x^2/(2x+3y)$.

Answer: $f_x = \frac{2x^2+6xy}{(2x+3y)^2}$, and $f_y = -\frac{3x^2}{(2x+3y)^2}$. $\qquad\blacksquare$

Partial derivatives and level curves

Example 4.5. Use the level curves of f in Figure 4.2 to approximate $f_y(1,0)$.

Solution: We know that $f_y(1,0)$ is defined to be

$$f_y(1,0) = \lim_{\Delta y \to 0}\frac{f(1,0+\Delta y) - f(1,0)}{\Delta y},$$

but we cannot compute this limit without more information. However, we can approximate it by using what we know of f at the points $(1, 0.5)$ and $(1, -1)$. When $\Delta y = 0.5$,

$$f_y(1,0) \approx \left.\frac{f(1,0+\Delta y) - f(1,0)}{\Delta y}\right|_{\Delta y = 0.5} = \frac{f(1,0.5) - f(1,0)}{0.5} = \frac{2.3 - 2}{0.5} = \frac{3}{5}.$$

Similarly, when $\Delta y = -1$,

$$f_y(1,0) \approx \left.\frac{f(1,0+\Delta y) - f(1,0)}{\Delta y}\right|_{\Delta y = -1} = \frac{f(1,-1) - f(1,0)}{-1} = \frac{1 - 2}{-1} = 1.$$

It seems reasonable that the actual value of $f_y(1,0)$ should be between these estimates, so for a simple approximation we might use their average:

$$f_y(1,0) \approx \frac{1}{2}\left(\frac{3}{5} + 1\right) = \frac{4}{5}.$$

Note that in this average we've given equal weight to both of our initial estimates. A more sophisticated scheme might weight the average according to our confidence in each approximation. For example, because one of the points that we used in our approximation is twice as close to $(1,0)$ as the other, you might have twice the confidence in that estimate of $f_y(1,0)$ and so choose to calculate the average as

$$\frac{2}{3}\left(\frac{3}{5}\right) + \frac{1}{3}\,(1) = \frac{11}{15}. \qquad\blacksquare$$

In the next example you'll see that partial derivatives can exist even where a function is not continuous. This seems contrary what you learned in earlier chapters, but it's not. Fundamentally, a partial derivative tells us about a function's behavior a single direction, but continuity in the multivariable context requires consistent behavior in *all* directions.

Solution
On-line

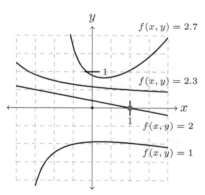

Figure 4.2: Level curves of f for Example 4.5.

Partial derivatives do not imply continuity

Example 4.6. Suppose f is the function shown below. Show that f is not continuous at $(0,0)$ but that f_x and f_y both exist there.

$$f(x,y) = \begin{cases} \frac{xy}{x^2+y^2} & \text{if } x \neq 0 \text{ or } y \neq 0 \\ 0 & \text{otherwise.} \end{cases}$$

Solution: We showed that $\lim_{(x,y)\to(0,0)} f(x,y)$ does not exist in Section 13.3 (Example 3.3), so f is not continuous at $(0,0)$. However, equation (4.1) allows us to see that

$$f_x(0,0) = \lim_{\Delta x \to 0} \frac{f(0+\Delta x, 0) - f(0,0)}{\Delta x} = \lim_{\Delta x \to 0} \frac{0-0}{\Delta x} = 0.$$

Similarly, the limit of difference quotients shows that $f_y(0,0) = 0$. ∎

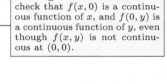

You might find it instructive to check that $f(x,0)$ is a continuous function of x, and $f(0,y)$ is a continuous function of y, even though $f(x,y)$ is not continuous at $(0,0)$.

▷ Tangent Lines

When we talked about graphs of functions in Section 13.2, we introduced the technique of vertical slicing as a way of understanding them as a collection of traces. That idea is closely related to our current discussion because intersecting the surface $z = f(x,y)$ with a vertical plane of the form $y = b$ effectively holds y constant (see Figure 4.3), and that's exactly what we do when calculating $f_x(a,b)$. So the number $f_x(a,b)$, which is the limit of the difference quotient in x, is the slope of a line that passes through the point $(a, b, f(a,b))$ and is tangent to the trace of $z = f(x,y)$ on the plane $y = b$.

Similarly, the number $f_y(a,b)$ is the slope of a line that's tangent to the the trace of $z = f(x,y)$ on the plane $x = a$ (also at the point $(a, b, f(a,b))$).

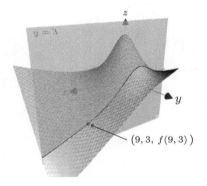 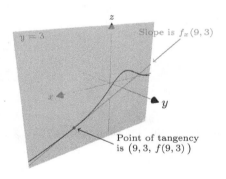

Figure 4.3: (left) The trace of the surface $z = f(x,y)$ on a vertical plane (in this case $y = 3$) is a curve; (right) a line that's tangent to the curve at the point $(9, 3, f(9,3))$.

Using f_x to parameterize a tangent line

Example 4.7. Suppose f is the function defined below. Parameterize the line in the plane $y = 3$ that's tangent to the graph of f at the point $(9, 3, f(9,3))$.

$-4.2 = f(9,3)$

$$f(x,y) = \frac{100}{10 + x^2 + y^2} - \frac{xy}{10} - \frac{5}{2}$$

Solution: The graph of f and the tangent line are shown in Figure 4.3. We're going to parameterize the line as $\mathbf{r}(t) = \mathbf{u} + t\mathbf{v}$, where $\mathbf{u}$ is the position vector for a point on the line, and $\mathbf{v}$ points in the direction of its extension.

Since $f(9,3) = -4.2$, let's set $\mathbf{u} = \langle 9, 3, -4.2 \rangle$. In order to determine $\mathbf{v}$ we need to know the rise-to-run ratio of this line in the $y = 3$ plane. Since y is constant, that information is carried in

$$f_x(x,y) = \frac{\partial}{\partial x}\left(\frac{100}{10 + x^2 + y^2} - \frac{xy}{10} - \frac{5}{2}\right) = -\frac{200x}{(10 + x^2 + y^2)^2} - \frac{y}{10}.$$

The function f_x tells us that the slope of the line is $f_x(9,3) = -0.48$. That is, when x increases by 1, the height of the line will decrease by 0.48 units. So our line will head in the direction

$$\overbrace{\phantom{x \text{ increases by 1}}}^{x \text{ increases by } 1}$$
$$\mathbf{v} = \langle \; 1 \; , \quad 0 \quad , -0.48 \; \rangle.$$
$$\underbrace{\phantom{y \text{ doesn't change at all}}}_{y \text{ doesn't change at all}}$$

Therefore, the tangent line is parameterized by

$$\mathbf{r}(t) = \mathbf{u} + t\mathbf{v} = \begin{bmatrix} 9 \\ 3 \\ -4.2 \end{bmatrix} + t\begin{bmatrix} 1 \\ 0 \\ -0.48 \end{bmatrix} = \begin{bmatrix} 9 + t \\ 3 \\ -4.2 - 0.48t \end{bmatrix}. \qquad \blacksquare$$

> Note that increasing t also increases x, but decreases z. Compare to Figure 4.3.

Using f_y to parameterize a tangent line

Example 4.8. Suppose $f(x,y) = x^2 + x(y-1)^3$. Parameterize the line in the plane $x = 4$ that's tangent to graph at the point $(4, 2, f(4,2))$.

Answer: $\mathbf{r}(t) = \langle 4, 2 + t, 20 + 12t \rangle.$ $\qquad \blacksquare$

Solution
On-line

▷ Functions of more than two variables

When f is a function of three or more variables, the basic notion of a partial derivative is the same: hold all variables fixed except for one. The basic techniques are also the same.

Computing partial derivatives of a function of three variables

Example 4.9. Suppose $f(x,y,z) = y^4 + x^2z + e^{5yz}$. Determine a general formula for $f_z(x,y,z)$, and use it to calculate $f_z(1,2,0)$.

Solution: Thinking of x and y as constant, we compute the partial derivative with respect to z as

$$\frac{\partial f}{\partial z} = 0 + x^2 + 5ye^{5yz}.$$

This allows us to calculate $f_z(1,2,0) = 1^2 + 10e^0 = 11.$ $\qquad \blacksquare$

> The factor of $5y$ in the second term arises from differentiating the exponential function, treating $5y$ as constant.

Interpreting partial derivatives of a function of three variables

Example 4.10. The Ideal Gas Law tells us that $P = {}^{nRT}/V$, where R is the *universal gas constant*, P is pressure, V is volume, T is the temperature of the gas, and n is the amount of gas (measured in mols). Determine and interpret formulas for the partial derivatives of P with respect to V, T and n.

Solution: By letting only one variable change at a time, we find that

$$\frac{\partial P}{\partial V} = -\frac{nRT}{V^2} \qquad\qquad \frac{\partial P}{\partial T} = \frac{nR}{V} \qquad\qquad \frac{\partial P}{\partial n} = \frac{RT}{V}.$$

Since P, V, T, n and R are all positive, these formulas tell us that P_T and P_n are positive, meaning that the pressure will increase if the temperature is raised or more

> Temperature is positive because it's measured in kelvins.

gas is injected. The fact that P_V is negative means that we can lower the pressure by increasing the volume of the container that's holding the gas. ■

Partial derivatives of a function of three variables

Example 4.11. Determine the first partial derivatives of $f(x, y, z) = yz^2 + x^z$.

Answer: $f_x = zx^{z-1}$, $f_y = z^2$, $f_z = 2yz + x^z \ln x$. ■

Solution
On-line

✦ Higher Order Partial Derivatives

We've talked about $f_x(a, b)$ as the slope of a tangent line to the trace of $z = f(x, y)$ on the plane $y = b$. If we want to determine the concavity of that trace, we differentiate f_x with respect to x (just as we did in single-variable calculus). The result is called the ***second order partial derivative*** of f with respect to x, and is commonly written as

$$(f_x)_x , \quad \text{or} \quad f_{xx} , \quad \text{or} \quad \frac{\partial}{\partial x} f_x , \quad \text{or} \quad \frac{\partial f_x}{\partial x} , \quad \text{or} \quad \frac{\partial^2 f}{\partial x^2} .$$

Similarly, the second order partial derivative of f with respect to y is denoted by

$$(f_y)_y , \quad \text{or} \quad f_{yy} , \quad \text{or} \quad \frac{\partial}{\partial y} f_y , \quad \text{or} \quad \frac{\partial f_y}{\partial y} , \quad \text{or} \quad \frac{\partial^2 f}{\partial y^2} ,$$

and its sign tells us about the concavity of the graph of f in the y-direction.

Concavity in the y-direction

Example 4.12. Determine whether the trace of the surface $z = 3 \sin(\pi x) e^{-0.25y^2}$ on the plane $x = 1.25$ is concave up or concave down (in the y-direction) near $y = 1$.

Solution: This surface is the graph of $f(x, y) = 3 \sin(\pi x) e^{-0.25y^2}$, so let's begin by calculating $f_y(x, y) = 3 \sin(\pi x) e^{-0.25y^2} \left(-\frac{1}{2} y \right)$, and

$$f_{yy}(x, y) = 3 \sin(\pi x) e^{-0.25y^2} \left(-\frac{1}{2} y \right)^2 - 3 \sin(\pi x) e^{-0.25y^2} \left(\frac{1}{2} \right)$$

$$= 3 \sin(\pi x) e^{-0.25y^2} \left(\frac{1}{4} y^2 - \frac{1}{2} \right)$$

Since $x = 1.25$ is fixed, we are concerned with the sign of

$$f_{yy}(1.25, y) = 3 \sin(1.25\pi) e^{-0.25y^2} \left(\frac{1}{4} y^2 - \frac{1}{2} \right)$$

which is a continuos function of y. When $y = 1$, we see that

$$f_{yy}(1.25, 1) = 3 \sin(1.25\pi) e^{-0.25} \left(\frac{1}{4} - \frac{1}{2} \right) = \frac{3\sqrt{2}}{8} e^{-0.25} > 0.$$

Since $f_{yy}(1.25, y)$ is a continuous function of y, it remains positive near $y = 1$, so the graph of f is concave up in the y-direction. (See Figure 4.4.) ■

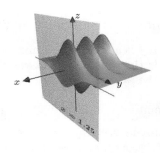

Figure 4.4: The graph of f in Example 4.12.

Because the exponential is always positive, the sign of this product · is controlled by the quadratic polynomial.

Concavity in the x-direction

Example 4.13. Determine whether the trace of $z = 0.1y^2 \sin x$ on the plane $y = 3$ is concave up (in the x-direction) near $x = 2.5$ radians.

Answer: Concave down. ∎

Instead of taking two derivatives in x or two in y, which are sometimes called the second **pure** partials, sometimes it's necessary to calculate the partial derivative of f_x with respect to y, or the partial derivative of f_y with respect to x. The resulting functions are called the second **mixed** partial derivatives of f. We typically write them as

$$(f_y)_x \;, \quad \text{or } f_{yx} \;, \quad \text{or } \frac{\partial}{\partial x} f_y \;, \quad \text{or } \frac{\partial f_y}{\partial x} \;, \quad \text{or } \frac{\partial^2 f}{\partial x \partial y}$$

and

$$(f_x)_y \;, \quad \text{or } f_{xy} \;, \quad \frac{\partial}{\partial y} f_x \;, \quad \text{or } \frac{\partial f_x}{\partial y} \;, \quad \text{or } \frac{\partial^2 f}{\partial y \partial x}.$$

In the subscript notation, the order that you read the subscripts from left to right is the order in which the derivatives are taken.

Since f_x tells us the slope of the tangent line in the x-direction, you can understand f_{xy} as the rate at which that slope changes when we move in the y direction.

Mixed derivatives and change in slope

Example 4.14. Suppose $f(x,y) = 1 + 0.2x^2 - 0.1y^2 + 0.15x(1 - y^2)$, and $c = 1.25$. (a) Determine the slope of the line in the plane $y = c$ that's tangent to the graph of f at $\big(1, c, f(1,c)\big)$, and (b) explain what happens to the slope as c increases.

Solution: The intersection of the surface $z = f(x,y)$ with the vertical plane $y = c$ is a curve (see Figure 4.5). To determine the slope of its tangent line, we can use $f_x(x,y) = 0.4x + 0.15(1 - y^2)$. Specifically, $f_x(1, {}^5/_4) = {}^{101}/_{320} > 0$, so this tangent line rises as x increases.

(b) To determine how f_x changes as we increase y from ${}^5/_4$ we calculate

$$\frac{\partial f_x}{\partial y} = \frac{\partial}{\partial y}\big(0.4x + 0.15(1 - y^2)\big) = -0.3y.$$

This continuous function of y has a negative value at (and near) $y = {}^5/_4$, from which we conclude that f_x (the slope of the tangent line in the x-direction) is decreasing. This can be seen in Figure 4.5. ∎

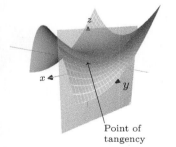

Point of tangency

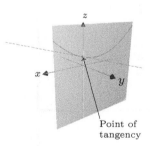

Point of tangency

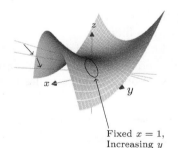

Fixed $x = 1$, Increasing y

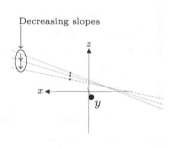

Decreasing slopes

Figure 4.5: (left) the graph of f from Example 4.14, with the plane $y = {}^5/_4$ and a tangent line in that plane; (middle-left) the trace on the plane $y = {}^5/_4$, and the tangent line; (middle-right) the graph of f with the tangent lines at three points $(1, y)$; (right) the same three points and tangent lines, seen from a different perspective.

Mixed derivatives and changing slope

Example 4.15. Suppose f is the function in Example (4.14), and $c = 1$. (a) Determine the slope of the line in the plane $x = c$ that's tangent to the graph of f at $\left(c, {}^5\!/_4, f(c, {}^5\!/_4)\right)$, and (b) use f_{yx} to determine what happens to that slope as c increases.

Solution On-line

Answer: (a) $-{}^1\!/_8$; (b) it will decrease.   ■

Many people have trouble remembering whether f_{xy} means to differentiate first in x or first in y. The following fact, which you saw manifest in Examples 4.14 and 4.15, and which you'll prove in the exercises, makes the question moot in many cases.

> **Clairaut's Theorem:** Suppose f_{xy} and f_{yx} are both continuous in an open disk about the point (a, b). Then $f_{xy}(a, b) = f_{yx}(a, b)$.

The name *Clairaut* is pronounced "klair-OH."

Checking Clairaut's Theorem

Example 4.16. Verify that $f_{xy} = f_{yx}$ when $f(x, y) = x + 2xy + \sin xy$.

Solution: Since $f_{xy} = \frac{\partial}{\partial y} f_x$ and $f_{yx} = \frac{\partial}{\partial x} f_y$,

$$f_{xy} = \frac{\partial}{\partial y}\left(1 + 2y + y\cos xy\right) = 2 + \cos xy - xy\sin xy$$

$$f_{yx} = \frac{\partial}{\partial x}\left(2x + x\cos xy\right) = 2 + \cos xy - xy\sin xy \qquad ■$$

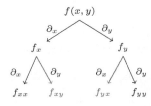

Figure 4.6: The symbol ∂_x means to differentiate with respect to x. Similarly for ∂_y. Clairaut's Theorem says the mixed partial derivatives will be equal if they are continuous.

As with functions of a single variable, in principle we can continue differentiating to determine higher order partial derivatives.

Third partial derivatives

Example 4.17. Determine (a) f_{xxy} and (b) f_{xyz} when $f(x, y, z) = x^2 y e^{5z}$.

Solution: In both cases we begin by calculating $f_x = 2xye^{5z}$. (a) Here we continue by calculating $f_{xx} = 2ye^{5z}$, and then $f_{xxy} = 2e^{5z}$. (b) In this case we continue by differentiating $f_{xy} = 2xe^{5z}$, and then $f_{xyz} = 10xe^{5z}$.   ■

You should know

- the terms *partial derivative* and *second partial derivative (pure and mixed)*;
- that f_x and f_y are defined as limits;
- that f_x and f_y are functions of two variables when f is;
- that the formulas for f_x and f_y provide information about what happens to the graph of f when *only one* of the variables is allowed to change;
- Clairaut's Theorem.

You should be able to

- calculate $f_x, f_{xx}, f_y, f_{yy}, f_{yx}$, and f_{xy} at a point (a, b);
- determine general formulas for partial derivatives;

- describe the tangent line to the graph of f in either the x or the y direction;
- determine whether the graph of f is concave up or concave down in the x-direction, and in the y-direction.

✦ 13.4 Skill Exercises

In exercises #1–10 determine f_x, f_y, f_{xx}, and f_{yy}.

1. $f(x,y) = x^4 - y^6$

2. $f(x,y) = 7x + 9y$

3. $f(x,y) = 3x^2 e^y$

4. $f(x,y) = xe^{x/y} + y^2$

5. $f(x,y) = 5x^3 y + 2$

6. $f(x,y) = 2y - x^3 \tan(0.1y)$

7. $f(x,y) = e^{x^3 y + y^2}$

8. $f(x,y) = x\sin(y) + y\sin(x)$

9. $f(x,y) = \sin(x^2)\cos(y)$

10. $f(x,y) = \tan^{-1}\left(\frac{y}{x}\right)$

In exercises #11–18 verify that $\frac{\partial}{\partial x} f_y = \frac{\partial}{\partial y} f_x$.

11. $f(x,y) = 7x + 9y$

12. $f(x,y) = 10x^{27} - 5y^{72}$

13. $f(x,y) = \cos xy$

14. $f(x,y) = \ln(1 + x^2 + y^2)$

15. $f(x,y) = \sqrt{x^4 + y^4 + 2}$

16. $f(x,y) = x^6 y \sin xy$

17. $f(x,y) = e^{x^2 + 3y}$

18. $f(x,y) = x^2 e^{\cos y}$

In #19–24 determine the specified derivative.

19. f_{xxyy} when $f(x,y) = e^{3x}\cos 2y$

20. f_{xyy} when $f(x,y) = \ln(x + y^2)$

21. f_{xxy} when $f(x,y) = \arctan(5x + 2y)$

22. f_{xyz} when $f(x,y,z) = z/xy$

23. f_{xzyz} when $f(x,y,z) = x^2 z + z^3 y$

24. f_{zzy} when $f(x,y,z) = x^z \sec z$

The equation $f_{xx} + f_{yy} = 0$, is an example of something called a *partial differential equation*. This particular equation is called **Laplace's Equation**, and it arises in mathematical descriptions of electrostatics and fluid flow. In #25–28 (a) determine the second pure partial derivatives of f and (b) determine whether they sum to 0.

25. $f(x,y) = xy + 4$

26. $f(x,y) = x^2 + 17xy - y^2$

27. $f(x,y) = \ln(x^2 + y^2)$

28. $f(x,y) = e^{-x}\cos y$

✦ 13.4 Concept and Application Exercises

Exercises #29–30 refer to the following table of function values, $f(x,y)$.

$y = 5.4$	1.2	1	1.3	1.6
$y = 5.3$	2.9	2.5	2.7	2.6
$y = 5.2$	5.1	5	3.9	3.1
$y = 5.1$	4.3	4.5	4.6	4.7
$y = 5$	4	4.1	4.3	4.6
	$x = 2$	$x = 2.01$	$x = 2.02$	$x = 2.03$

29. Approximate $f_x(2.01, 5.1)$ and $f_y(2.01, 5.1)$.

30. Approximate $f_x(2.02, 5.2)$ and $f_y(2.02, 5.2)$.

31. Use the level curves of f shown in Figure 4.7 to approximate (a) f_x and f_y at point A, (b) f_y at B, and (c) f_y at C.

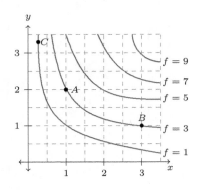

Figure 4.7: The level curves of f for #31.   Figure 4.8: The level curves of f for #32.

32. Use the level curves of f shown in Figure 4.8 to approximate (a) f_x at point A, (b) f_x at B, (c) f_y at C, and (d) f_y at D.

In exercises #33–38 determine a parameterization of the tangent line to the graph of f at the specified point in the specified direction.

33. $f(x,y) = x^3 - y^2 \sin(x)$; $(\pi/2, 3)$; x-direction

34. $f(x,y) = \sin(x^2 + y^2)$; $(1,0)$; y-direction

35. $f(x,y) = 3x^2 + 7xy^3$; $(-2, -5)$; x-direction

36. $f(x,y) = 3xy^2 \csc(x+y)$; $(\pi/2, \pi/3)$; x-direction

37. $f(x,y) = 3(x+y)^2 e^y$; $(1,4)$; y-direction

38. $f(x,y) = \cos(x^2 + y^2)$; $(1,0)$; y-direction

In exercises #39–44 determine whether the graph of f is concave up or concave down in the specified direction, in the vicinity of the given point.

39. $f(x,y) = x^3 - y^2 \sin(x)$; $(\pi/2, 3)$; y-direction

40. $f(x,y) = \sin(x^2 + y^2)$; $(1,0)$; x-direction

41. $f(x,y) = xy^3$; $(-2, 3)$; y-direction

42. $f(x,y) = \tan(\pi xy)$; $(1, -1)$; y-direction

43. $f(x,y) = -x^3 y^5$; $(4, -2)$; x-direction

44. $f(x,y) = \cos(x^2 + y^2)$; $(1,0)$; x-direction

A function f and a point (a, b) is specified in each of #45–50. Determine the tangent line to the trace of f (i) on the plane $y = b$, and (ii) on the plane $x = a$ at the point $(a, b, f((a, b)))$, and then (iii) determine the equation of the plane that contains both. (Hint: use the cross product for part (c).)

45. $f(x,y) = 5x^3 - 4y$; $(1, 4)$

46. $f(x,y) = x^2 y^2$; $(3, 2)$

47. $f(x,y) = \sqrt{x} - \sqrt{y}$; $(9, 4)$

48. $f(x,y) = y^3/(7x + 8y)$; $(-1, 1)$

49. $f(x,y) = \ln(5x - 3y)y^3$; $(2, 3)$

50. $f(x,y) = x^2\sqrt{3x + 4y}$; $(1, 3)$

51. The vertex of the parabola $y = ax^2 + bx + 1$ (in the xy-plane) has an x-coordinate of $-\frac{b}{2a}$, which we'll denote by $v(a, b)$.

    (a) Fix $b = 3$ and graph the parabola when $a = 4.9, 4.95, 5.05, 5.1$.

    (b) Based on part (a), is $\frac{\partial v}{\partial a}$ positive or negative at $(a, b) = (5, 3)$?

    (c) Fix $a = 5$ and graph the parabola when $b = 2.9, 2.95, 3.05, 3.1$.

    (d) Based on part (c), is $\frac{\partial v}{\partial b}$ positive or negative at $(a, b) = (5, 3)$?

52. The vertex of the parabola $y = ax^2 + bx + 1$ (in the xy-plane) has a y-coordinate of $1 - \frac{b^2}{4a}$, which we'll denote by $v(a, b)$.

    (a) Fix $b = 4$ and graph the parabola when $a = 6.9, 6.95, 7.05, 7.1$.

(b) Based on part (a), is $\frac{\partial v}{\partial a}$ positive or negative at $(a, b) = (7, 4)$?

(c) Fix $a = 7$ and graph the parabola when $b = 3.9, 3.95, 4.05, 4.1$.

(d) Based on part (c), is $\frac{\partial v}{\partial b}$ positive or negative at $(a, b) = (7, 4)$?

53. Consider the curve $y = x^a + x^b$ over $(0, \infty)$ when $a < 0$ and $b > 0$. Such a curve has a global minimum at some $x > 0$. We'll denote that minimum value by $m(a, b)$ [so $m(a, b)$ is a y-coordinate of a point on the curve].

(a) Fix $b = 1$ and graph the curve when $a = -2.1, -2.05, -1.95, -1.95$.

(b) Based on part (a), is $m_a(-2, 1)$ positive or negative?

(c) Fix $a = -2$ and graph the curve when $b = 0.9, 0.95, 1.05, 1.1$.

(d) Based on part (c), is $m_b(-2, 1)$ positive or negative?

54. Consider the curve $y = x^a e^{-bx}$ over $[0, \infty)$ when $a > 0$ and $b > 0$. Such a curve has a global maximum at some $x > 0$. We'll denote the location of that maximum by $M(a, b)$.

(a) Fix $b = 1$ and graph the curve when $a = 0.9, 1, 1.1, 1.2$.

(b) Based on part (a), is $M_a(1.05, 1)$ positive or negative?

(c) Fix $a = 1.05$ and graph the curve when $b = 0.9, 0.95, 1.05, 1.1$.

(d) Based on part (c), is $M_b(1.05, 1)$ positive or negative?

55. Suppose $f(x, y) = x^2 - y^2$.

(a) Identify the graph of f as one of the quadric surfaces.

(b) Verify that the graph of f is concave up in the x-direction by calculating the relevant derivative.

(c) Verify that the graph of f is concave down in the y-direction by calculating the relevant derivative.

56. Design a bivariate function for which both of the following statements are true in the vicinity of $(2, 7)$, and verify your design by calculating the relevant derivatives.

(a) $f(x, y)$ is increasing and concave up in the x-direction;

(b) $f(x, y)$ is increasing and concave down in the y-direction.

57. The stereographic projection was introduced in Section 1.3 during our discussion of rational functions. In that discussion we projected points from the x-axis onto a circle of radius 1 centered at $(0, 1)$. Here we consider a circle of radius r centered at $(0, r)$ instead. The stereographic projection of t onto that circle (see Figure 4.9) has an x-coordinate of $\frac{4r^2 t}{4r^2 + t^2}$, which we denote by $x(t, r)$.

(a) Determine a formula $\frac{\partial x}{\partial t}$ and explain what it tells us.

(b) Determine a formula $\frac{\partial x}{\partial r}$ and explain what it tells us.

(c) Find a formula for $\frac{\partial^2 x}{\partial r \partial t}$ and evaluate it when $t = 2$ and $r = 3$.

(d) Calculate $x_t(2, 3)$, and based on part (c), make a prediction about $x_t(2, 3 + \Delta r)$ when $\Delta r > 0$ is small.

(e) Find a formula for $\frac{\partial^2 x}{\partial t^2}$ and evaluate it when $t = 2$ and $r = 3$.

(f) Based on part (e), make a prediction about $x_t(2 + \Delta t, 3)$ when $\Delta t > 0$ is small.

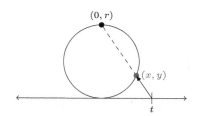

Figure 4.9: The stereographic projection of t onto the circle of radius r, as in #57. The stereographic projection was introduced on p. 19.

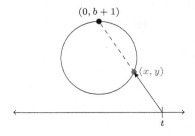

58. Repeat the steps of #57 but use the y-coordinate of the stereographic projection instead, $y(t,r) = \frac{2rt^2}{4r^2+t^2}$.

59. This exercise extends #58. Suppose we center a circle of radius 1 at (0,b), where $b > 1$ (see Figure 4.10).

    (a) Find a formula for the y-coordinate of the stereographic projection of t onto the circle, $y(t,b)$.

    (b) Calculate $\frac{\partial y}{\partial t}$ at $(t,b) = (2,3)$ and explain what it tells us.

    (c) Now let's allow the circle's center to move. What does $\frac{\partial^2 y}{\partial b \partial t}$ tell us?

    (d) Find a formula for $\frac{\partial^2 y}{\partial b \partial t}$ and evaluate it when $t = 2$ and $b = 3$.

    (e) Use your answer from part (c) to make a prediction about $y_t(2, 3 + db)$.

Figure 4.10: The stereographic projection of t onto the circle of radius 1 centered at $(0, b)$, as in #59

60. This exercise extends #57. Repeat the steps of #59, but this time work with the x-coordinate of the stereographic projection of t onto the circle.

61. In Chapter 1 we introduced the idea of modeling a traveling pressure wave as a translating cosine curves: $y = \cos(kx - \omega t)$, where the constants k and ω affect the wavelength of the traveling wave and the rate at which it moves (respectively).

    (a) Show that $\left(\frac{k}{\omega}\right)^2 y_{xx} = y_{tt}$.

    (b) Suppose x is measured in meters and t in seconds. What are the units of $\frac{k}{\omega}$, and what do you think it tells us, physically?

62. Suppose a spherical droplet of liquid comes to rest on a flat surface, as shown in Figure 4.11.

    (a) Determine a formula for the volume of the drop as a function of its radius, r, and the distance between the sphere's center and the solid surface, h.

    (b) Determine the area of the (circular) solid-liquid interface.

    (c) Determine the area of the liquid-gas interface.

    (d) If $V(r, h)$ is the function from part (a), determine formulas for V_r and V_h and compare them to your answers for parts (b) and (c).

Figure 4.11: The droplet in #62.

63. In Section 13.2 (exercise #47) you showed that the wall of soccer players defending a direct free kick must have a width of

$$w(r, \theta, q) = 10 \sin(\theta) \left(\frac{4}{r - 4\cos\theta} + \frac{q}{r + q\cos\theta} \right) \text{ yards.}$$

    (a) Draw the direct kick scenario when $\theta = \pi/3$, $r = 23$ and $q = 2$.

    (b) Make a conjecture about whether $\frac{dw}{d\theta}$ is positive or negative when $(r, \theta, q) = (23, \pi/3, 2)$ and explain your reasoning.

    (c) Check your conjecture from part (b) by calculating $\frac{dw}{d\theta}$ at the point $(r, \theta, q) = (23, \pi/3, 2)$.

Sports/Recreation

64. This exercise is an extension of #63. (a) Make a conjecture about whether $\frac{dw}{dr}$ is positive or negative when $(r, \theta, q) = (23, \pi/3, 2)$ and explain your reasoning. (b) Check your conjecture from part (a) by calculating $\frac{dw}{dr}$ at the point $(r, \theta, q) = (23, \pi/3, 2)$.

Sports/Recreation

65. A *production function* describes the quantity that can be produced, Q, as a function of labor units, L, and units of capital investment, K. Intersecting the graph of $Q(K, L)$ with a plane of the form K=constant results in a curve in 3-space. (a) What does $\partial Q/\partial L$ tell us about this curve? (b) Based on its practical significance, what should be true about the number $\partial Q/\partial L$?

    Economics

66. In #65 we defined a *production function*, $Q(K, L)$. What is be the practical significance of the inequalities $Q_L > 0$ and $Q_{LL} < 0$?

    Economics

67. The *wind chill index* estimates the perceived temperature based on actual air temperature, T, and wind speed, s, provided that $s \geq 3$ mph and $T \leq 50$ °F. Here we approximate the wind chill index as $w(T, s) = 35.74 + 0.6215T - 35.75s^{0.16} + 0.4275Ts^{0.16}$. If the air temperature is 45 °F and the wind is blowing at 3.5 mph, (a) show that $\partial w/\partial s$ is negative but $\partial w/\partial T$ is positive, and (b) explain the practical significance of that fact.

    Meteorology

68. The *heat index* estimates the perceived temperature based on actual air temperature, $T \geq 80$ °F, and relative humidity, $r \in [0, 100]$. Here we approximate it with

    Meteorology

$$h(T, r) = -42.37 + 2.05T + 10.14r - 0.23rT - (6.84 \times 10^{-3})T^2$$
$$- (5.48 \times 10^{-3})r^2 + (1.23 \times 10^{-3})T^2r + (8.53 \times 10^{-4})Tr^2.$$

Determine which of $\partial h/\partial T$ and $\partial h/\partial r$ is larger when $T = 83$ °F and $r = 65$ (i.e, 65% relative humidity), and explain the practical significance of that fact.

69. This exercise refers to #51 in Section 13.2, in which you used level curves of $c(x, y)$ to investigate the distribution of assets across an investment portfolio.

    Finance

   (a) Determine formulas for c_x and c_y.

   (b) Graph the level curve $c_x(x, y) = 0$.

   (c) Draw the line $y = 0.1$ on your graph from part (b), and use it to estimate where the function $c(x, 0.1)$ has its maximum value. Then repeat the process for the line $y = 0.25$.

   (d) Based on part (c), explain what the curve $c_x(x, y) \doteq 0$ tells us.

   (e) Graph the level curve $c_y(x, y) = 0$ and explain what it tells us.

   (f) Graph several level sets of $c(x, y)$ with the curves from parts (b) and (e), and explain the practical meaning of the resulting image.

70. In #51 of Section 13.2 you investigated the distribution of assets in an investment portfolio; the parameters r_1, σ_2 and a were changed in following exercises. In this exercise, we think of the the distribution of assets as fixed (so x and y are constant) and treat c as a function of r_1, σ_2 and a. Determine which (if any) of $\partial c/\partial r_1$, $\partial c/\partial \sigma_2$ and $\partial c/\partial a$ is positive, and based on their contextual meaning, explain why the others are not.

    Finance

Checking the details

71. Suppose R is the rectangle defined by $a \leq x \leq a+\Delta x$ and $b \leq y \leq b+\Delta y$, and that R resides inside the region where f_{yx} and f_{xy} are continuous. In the steps below, you'll show that every such R contains a pair of points, say (k_1, k_2) and (m_1, m_2), where $f_{xy}(k_1, k_2) = f_{yx}(m_1, m_2)$. Then, since the second mixed partial derivatives are continuous,

$$f_{xy}(a, b) = \lim_{\max\{\Delta x, \Delta y\} \to 0} f_{xy}(k_1, k_2) = \lim_{\max\{\Delta x, \Delta y\} \to 0} f_{xy}(m_1, m_2) = f_{yx}(a, b).$$

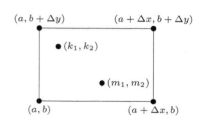

Figure 4.12: The rectangle R..

The proof will revolve around the differences

$$\mathcal{D}_1 \;=\; f(a+\Delta x, b+\Delta y) - f(a+\Delta x, b)$$
$$\mathcal{D}_2 \;=\; f(a, b+\Delta y) - f(a, b)$$

(a) Show that $\mathcal{D}_1$ is the change in the value of f from the bottom to the top of the rectangle at the rightmost edge of R. Similarly for $\mathcal{D}_2$ at the leftmost edge.

(b) Denote by $g(x)$ the change in f from the bottom to the top of the rectangle, at x. Show $g(a+\Delta x) - g(a) = \mathcal{D}_1 - \mathcal{D}_2$.

(c) Use the Mean Value Theorem (check its hypotheses!) to conclude that there must be some k_1 between a and $a+\Delta x$ for which

$$\mathcal{D}_1 - \mathcal{D}_2 = g'(k_1)\Delta x = \Big(f_x(k_1, b+\Delta y) - f_x(k_1, b) \Big)\Delta x.$$

(d) Denote by $h(y) = f_x(k_1, y)$. Use the Mean Value Theorem to show that there is some k_2 for which $h(b+\Delta y) - h(b) = h'(k_2)\Delta y$.

(e) Use the result from part (d) to verify that

$$\mathcal{D}_1 - \mathcal{D}_2 = g'(k_1)\Delta x = f_{xy}(k_1, k_2)\Delta y \Delta x.$$

(f) Repeat parts (a)–(e) to show $\mathcal{D}_3 - \mathcal{D}_4 = f_{yx}(m_1, m_2)\Delta x \Delta y$ when

$$\mathcal{D}_3 \;=\; f(a+\Delta x, b+\Delta y) - f(a, b+\Delta y)$$
$$\mathcal{D}_4 \;=\; f(a+\Delta x, b) - f(a, b).$$

(g) Conclude that $f_{yx}(m_1, m_2) = f_{xy}(k_1, k_2)$ by showing that $\mathcal{D}_3 - \mathcal{D}_4 = \mathcal{D}_1 - \mathcal{D}_2$.

In Section 14.1 we will prove Clairaut's Theorem using something called the *double integral.*

13.5 Linear Approximation, Tangent Planes, and Differentiability

You know that $f_x(a, b)$ tells us the slope of the tangent line that extends in the direction of increasing x. So when x changes by some small amount, say from a to $a + \Delta x$, the height on the graph of f changes by approximately

$$\left(\frac{\text{rise}}{\text{run}}\right) \times (\text{run}) = f_x(a, b) \, \Delta x.$$

Similarly, the value of f changes by approximately $f_y(a, b)\Delta y$ when y changes by some small amount, Δy. If x and y change simultaneously, the simplest approximation of the resulting change in f is arguably

$$\Delta f \approx \underbrace{f_x(a, b)\Delta x}_{\text{...due to the change in } x} + \underbrace{f_y(a, b)\Delta y}_{\text{...and due to the change in } y}. \tag{5.1}$$

In the discussion that follows, we develop a geometric understanding of this approximation, and investigate its practical utility.

> **Key Idea(s):** *Tangent planes to graphs of two-variable functions play the same role as tangent lines to graphs of single-variable functions.*
>
> *A function of two variables is differentiable at a point when its tangent plane is a good approximation of its graph near that point.*
>
> *Just as we used the tangent line to make a linear approximation in the single-variable case, we use the tangent plane in this context.*
>
> *The total differential of a function approximates change using the tangent plane.*
>
> *The Newton-Raphson method is a multivariable analog of Newton's method.*

✤ Linear Approximation, Tangent Planes, and the Total Differential

We can use approximation (5.1) to estimate the value of f at points near (a, b). Specifically, when $x = a + \Delta x$ and $y = b + \Delta y$,

$$f(x, y) = f(a, b) + \Delta f$$
$$\approx f(a, b) + f_x(a, b) \, (x - a) + f_y(a, b) \, (y - b).$$

Because the variables x and y enter only linearly, this is called the **linear approximation** of f at (a, b). The graph of the linear approximation is the surface described by

$$z = f(a, b) + f_x(a, b) \, (x - a) + f_y(a, b) \, (y - b).$$

This equation is crowded with notation, but most of its terms are constants that depend on the point (a, b). The variables in the equation are x, y and z, all of which occur to the first power (only), so the graph of the linear approximation is a plane. This fact plays a key role in understanding what it means for a function of several variables to be *differentiable*, which we'll discuss at the end of this section. Until then, you should understand *differentiability* to mean that the graph of f has no discontinuity, cusp, or crease at (a, b), in which case the graph of the linear approximation is a good approximation of the graph of f, and we call it the *tangent plane*. (The formal definition below includes a preliminary statement that, as you'll see later in this section, guarantees differentiability.)

> This equation has the form
>
> $$z = C + A(x - a) + B(y - b)$$
>
> where A, B and C are constants; they depend on (a, b) but that point is fixed.

> In single-variable calculus you saw that the tangent line through $(c, f(c))$ is a good approximation of the graph of f (at least when x is close to c). This is the same idea. The word "good" will be made technically precise when we discuss the definition of differentiability at the end of this section.

> **Definition:** Suppose the partial derivatives of f are continuous in an open set containing the point (a, b). Then the **tangent plane** to the surface $z = f(x, y)$ at the point $(a, b, f(a, b))$ is the graph of the linear approximation,
>
> $$z = f(a, b) + f_x(a, b) \, (x - a) + f_y(a, b) \, (y - b). \tag{5.2}$$

Calculating the tangent plane

Example 5.1. Suppose $f(x, y) = 5 + 2x^2 + 6y^2$. (a) Determine the equation of the tangent plane to the graph of f at the point $(-3/2, -2)$. Then (b) use the linear approximation of f at $(-3/2, -2)$ to approximate $f(-1.4, -2.1)$.

Solution: (a) Since $f_x(x, y) = 4x$ and $f_y(x, y) = 12y$, we can calculate

$$f\left(-3/2, -2\right) = 33.5 \quad , \quad f_x\left(-3/2, -2\right) = -6 \quad , \quad f_y\left(-3/2, -2\right) = -24.$$

So equation (5.2) tells us that the tangent plane is described by

$$z = 33.5 - 6\left(x + \frac{3}{2}\right) - 24\left(y + 2\right).$$

The graph of f is shown with this tangent plane in Figure 5.1. Because it will be helpful later, let's note that the equation of the plane can be written as

$$6x + 24y + z = -25.5,$$

so the vector $\mathbf{n} = \langle 6, 24, 1 \rangle$ is normal to the plane.

   (b) The tangent plane is the graph of the linear approximation, so

$$f(x, y) \approx 33.5 - 6\left(x + \frac{3}{2}\right) - 24\left(y + 2\right)$$

when (x, y) is near $(-3/2, -2)$. This allows us to approximate

$$f(-1.4, -2.1) \approx 33.5 - 6(0.1) - 24(-0.1) = 35.3.$$ ∎

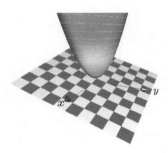
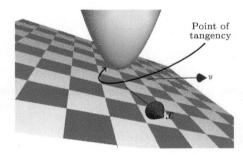

Point of
tangency

Figure 5.1: (left) The graph of f from Example 5.1 with its tangent plane at $(-1/4, -2/3, 91/144)$; (right) the same surface and tangent plane, but closer up and seen from slightly above the fourth quadrant.

Calculating the tangent plane

Example 5.2. Suppose $f(x, y) = x^2(x+y)^3$. Determine the equation of the tangent plane to the graph of f at $(1, 0)$.

Answer: $-5x - 3y + z = -4$, which has a normal vector of $\mathbf{n} = \langle -5, -3, 1 \rangle$. ∎

Solution
On-line

   In both Examples 5.1 and 5.2 you saw that the tangent plane has a normal vector of the form $\mathbf{n} = \langle -f_x(a, b), -f_y(a, b), 1 \rangle$. This happens in general, which we see by rewriting equation (5.2) as

$$-f_x(a, b)\ x - f_y(a, b)\ y + z = f(a, b) - f_x(a, b)\ a - f_y(a, b)\ b$$

$$\mathbf{n} \cdot \langle x, y, z \rangle = \underbrace{\mathbf{n} \cdot \langle a, b, f(a, b) \rangle}_{\text{constant}}$$

The tangent plane to the graph of f at (a, b) has a normal vector of

$$\mathbf{n} = \left\langle -f_x(a, b), -f_y(a, b), 1 \right\rangle. \tag{5.3}$$

▷ The total differential

At the beginning of this section we asserted that the simplest approximation of the change in f due to changes in x and y is arguably

$$\underbrace{f_x(a,b)\Delta x}_{\substack{\text{Approximate change in } f \\ \text{due to the change in } x}} \quad + \quad \underbrace{f_y(a,b)\Delta y}_{\substack{\text{Approximate change in } f \\ \text{due to the change in } y}}.$$

This linear approximation of change is called the **total differential** of f, and is denoted by df. It's often used in the sciences to approximate the effect of uncertainty in measurements on subsequent calculations. We typically write dx instead of Δx, and dy instead of Δy, which reminds us that the approximation is only good when the changes in x and y are small. Using this notation, the total differential is

$$df = f_x(a,b)\ dx + f_y(a,b)\ dy, \tag{5.4}$$

or in Leibniz notation,

$$df = \frac{\partial f}{\partial x}\ dx + \frac{\partial f}{\partial y}\ dy.$$

Using the total differential

Example 5.3. Suppose the shadow of a building is measured to be $x = 100$ meters long, and the angle of elevation from the tip of the shadow to the top of the building is measured to be $\theta = \pi/3$ radians (see Figure 5.2). (a) Calculate the height of the building. (b) If the instruments used to measure x and θ have a precision of at most 0.01 meters and 0.001 radians respectively, estimate the possible error in the calculated height found in part (a).

Solution: (a) By using the fact that $h = x\tan\theta$ we calculate the height of the building to be $100\sqrt{3}$ meters. (b) The total differential of h allows us to estimate the uncertainty in our calculation:

$$dh = \underbrace{\frac{\partial h}{\partial x}\ dx}_{\substack{\text{Variation in our calculation of } h \text{ due} \\ \text{to the error in our measurement of } x}} + \underbrace{\frac{\partial h}{\partial \theta}\ d\theta}_{\substack{\text{Variation in our calculation of } h \text{ due} \\ \text{to the error in our measurement of } \theta}}. \tag{5.5}$$

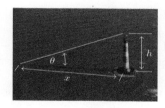

Figure 5.2: The height of a tower can be determined using trigonometry.

Since $\partial h/\partial x = \tan\theta$ and $\partial h/\partial \theta = x\sec^2\theta$, equation (5.5) becomes $dh \doteq \sqrt{3}\ dx + 400\ d\theta$ when $x = 100$ and $\theta = \pi/3$.

    We don't know whether our measurements of x and θ are larger or less than their true values, but we have a sense of how big the error might be, so let's talk in terms of magnitudes. Since the actual value of x within 0.01 meters of our measurement, we know $|dx| \leq 0.01$. Similarly, we know $|d\theta| \leq 0.001$, so the triangle inequality tells us

> The triangle inequality says
>
> $$|a+b| \leq |a| + |b|.$$

$$|dh| = \left|\sqrt{3}\ dx + 400\ d\theta\right| \leq \sqrt{3}\ |dx| + 400\ |d\theta| \leq \frac{\sqrt{3}}{100} + 4 \leq 4.0174 \text{ meters.} \quad \blacksquare$$

Using the total differential

Example 5.4. When an m-kg object is traveling at a speed of v m/sec, its kinetic energy is $K = 0.5mv^2$ joules. Determine (a) the kinetic energy of the object when $m = 2$ kg and $v = 6$ m/sec, and (b) how much error could be in that calculation if our measurement of m is off by most 1 gram, and our measurement of velocity is off by at most 1 mm/sec.

Answer: (a) 36 J; (b) 0.03 J.

Solution
On-line

$\blacksquare$

▷ Newton-Raphson method

In Chapter 3 you saw Newton's method, which uses linear approximation to find the roots of a function. The **Newton-Raphson method** is an adaption of the technique to multivariable functions, but instead of solving one equation in one variable, we solve two equations in two variables.

Suppose we want to find a point (x, y) at which $f(x, y) = 0$ and $g(x, y) = 0$, but an exact solution is elusive. As in Chapter 3, we begin with an educated guess, (a, b), which is close to the simultaneous root. After that, we rely on linear approximations to drive toward the solution:

$$f(x, y) \approx f(a, b) + f_x(a, b)\Delta x + f_y(a, b)\Delta y$$
$$g(x, y) \approx g(a, b) + g_x(a, b)\Delta x + g_y(a, b)\Delta y,$$

where $\Delta x = x - a$ and $\Delta y = y - b$. Since we want $f(x, y) = 0$ and $g(x, y) = 0$, we set both linear approximations equal to 0 and solve the resulting system of equations for Δx and Δy.

> The Newton-Raphson method can be extended to work with any number of variables. Here we focus on functions of two variables for the sake of simplicity.

Using the Newton-Raphson method in a familiar setting

Example 5.5. Use the Newton-Raphson method to approximate a point that's a root of both $f(x, y) = x^2 + y^2 - 4$ and $g(x, y) = y + x^2 - 1$.

Solution: Based on Figure 5.3, which shows the curves $f(x, y) = 0$ and $g(x, y) = 0$, we guess that $(1.5, -1.5)$ is near a simultaneous root. A quick check reveals that $f(1.5, -1.5) = 0.5$ and $g(1.5, -1.5) = -0.25$, so we've not found the solution. We proceed by calculating the partial derivatives of our functions at $(1.5, -1.5)$:

$$f_x = 3, \qquad f_y = -3, \qquad g_x = 3, \qquad g_y = 1.$$

Based on these values we construct the linear approximations

$$f(x, y) \approx 0.5 + 3\Delta x - 3\Delta y \qquad \text{and} \qquad g(x, y) \approx -0.25 + 3\Delta x + 1\Delta y.$$

Since we're looking for a point at which both $f(x, y)$ and $g(x, y)$ are 0, we set both approximations to 0 and solve the system of equations

$$0 = 0.5 + 3\Delta x - 3\Delta y$$
$$0 = -0.25 + 3\Delta x + 1\Delta y$$

for $\Delta x = 1/48$ and $\Delta y = 3/16$. So our next guess is that f and g are simultaneously 0 at (x_1, y_1), where

$$x_1 = a + \Delta x = \frac{3}{2} + \frac{1}{48} = \frac{73}{48} \qquad \text{and} \qquad y_1 = b + \Delta y = -\frac{3}{2} + \frac{3}{16} = -\frac{21}{16}.$$

A quick check reveals that $f(x_1, y_1) = 41/1152$ and $g(x_1, y_1) = 1/2304$, both of which are closer to 0 than the corresponding function values at (a, b). That's a good sign, so let's perform a second iteration of the method. At (x_1, y_1) we have

$$f = \tfrac{41}{1152}, \qquad f_x = \tfrac{73}{24}, \qquad f_y = -\tfrac{21}{8}$$
$$g = \tfrac{1}{2304}, \qquad g_x = \tfrac{73}{24}, \qquad g_y = 1$$

so the linear approximations of f and g at (x_1, y_1) are

$$f(x, y) \approx \tfrac{41}{1152} + \tfrac{73}{24}\Delta x - \tfrac{21}{8}\Delta y \qquad \text{and} \qquad g(x, y) \approx \tfrac{1}{2304} + \tfrac{73}{24}\Delta x + 1\Delta y.$$

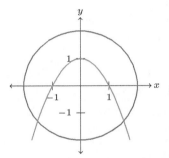

Figure 5.3:   The curves $f(x, y) = 0$ and $g(x, y) = 0$ in Example 5.5.   These curves were chosen because we can use precalculus methods to check our work.   The curves intersect when $y = (1 - \sqrt{13})/2 \approx -1.3026$. In the first step of our solution we find $y_1 \approx -1.3125$, and in the second that $y_2 \approx -1.3028$.

> This system of equations can be written in matrix form as
>
> $$\begin{bmatrix} -0.5 \\ 0.25 \end{bmatrix} = \begin{bmatrix} 3 & -3 \\ 3 & 1 \end{bmatrix} \begin{bmatrix} \Delta x \\ \Delta y \end{bmatrix}.$$
>
> Then we can solve it by multiplying both sides by the inverse matrix (see Appendix F).

We want $f = 0$ and $g = 0$, so we solve the system of equations

$$0 = \tfrac{41}{1152} + \tfrac{73}{24}\Delta x - \tfrac{21}{8}\Delta y$$

$$0 = \tfrac{1}{2304} + \tfrac{73}{24}\Delta x + 1\Delta y$$

for $\Delta x = -677/203232$ and $\Delta y = 9/928$, and our next guess is that f and g share a root at (x_2, y_2), where

$$x_2 = x_1 + \Delta x = \frac{308405}{203232} \qquad \text{and} \qquad y_2 = y_1 + \Delta y = -\frac{1209}{928}.$$

The function values at this point are

$$f(x_2, y_2) = \frac{2171585}{20651622912} \qquad \text{and} \qquad g(x_2, y_2) = \frac{458329}{41303245824},$$

which are even closer to 0. Further iterations will bring us closer to the actual root but we're unlikely to find it exactly, so at some stage we have to decide that the values of f and g are "close enough" to 0 for our purposes. ∎

> The structure of these equations is the same as what we saw in the first step, so the algebra of solving them will be the same. Because each step of the process follows the same pattern, it's easy to program this method into a spreadsheet.

Using the Newton-Raphson method

Example 5.6. Suppose $f(x, y) = 9x^2 + 4y^2 - 36$ and $g(x, y) = y^2 - x^2 - 1$. (a) Graph the curves $g(x, y) = 0$ and $f(x, y) = 0$, and (b) starting from $(1.75, 1.5)$, make one step of the Newton-Raphson method to approximate the point where both $f(x, y) = 0$ and $g(x, y) = 0$, simultaneously.

Answer: (b) $x_1 = 1149/728$ and $y_1 = 99/52$. ∎

*Solution
On-line*

✥ Differentiability (Local Linearity)

Toward the beginning of this section we said that the tangent plane is a good approximation of the surface $z = f(x, y)$ near points where f is differentiable. In fact, that's fundamentally what differentiability means—the crux of the matter is stating precisely what we mean by "good," and for motivation we revisit the relationship between the graph of a single-variable function and its tangent line at a point of differentiability.

In Chapter 3 we said that when the single-variable function f is differentiable at $x = c$, the tangent line to its graph at $x = c$ is $y = f(c) + f'(c)(x - c)$, which is the graph of the linear approximation of f. Then during our proof of the Chain Rule, we established that

$$f(x) - \underbrace{\big(f(c) + f'(c)\Delta x\big)}_{\text{The linear approximation of } f} = \varepsilon\Delta x, \tag{5.6}$$

> This is a rewritten version of equation (6.5) from Section 3.6.

where $\Delta x = x - c$, and $\varepsilon \to 0$ as $\Delta x \to 0$. Since ε and Δx converge to 0 together, the product $\varepsilon\Delta x \to 0$ faster than Δx alone. So equation (5.6) says that the difference between f and its linear approximation (i.e., between the curve $y = f(x)$ and its tangent line) vanishes faster than Δx alone. That's the sense in which we mean that the tangent line is a "good" approximation of the graph near a point of differentiability.

Now let's adapt this idea to the multivariable setting. By saying that the tangent plane is a "good" approximation of the graph of f near (a, b) we mean that *the difference between f and its linear approximation vanishes faster than the magnitude of $\Delta \mathbf{r} = \langle x - a, y - b \rangle$.* This statement is made rigorous in the formal definition below.

Definition: Suppose (a, b) is an interior point in the domain of f at which f_x and f_y both exist, and $L(x, y)$ is the linear approximation of f:

$$L(x, y) = f(a, b) + f_x(a, b)(x - a) + f_y(a, b)(y - b).$$

We say that f is **differentiable** at (a, b) if

$$f(x, y) - L(x, y) = \|\Delta \mathbf{r}\| \; \varepsilon(x, y), \tag{5.7}$$

where $\Delta \mathbf{r} = \langle x - a, y - b \rangle$ and $\varepsilon(x, y) \to 0$ as $(x, y) \to (a, b)$.

> On the left-hand side of equation (5.7) you see the difference between the function value and the linear approximation. On the right-hand side you see a product that's vanishing faster than $\|\Delta \mathbf{r}\|$ alone. This is the analog of equation (5.6).

Differentiability means that the tangent plane is a good approximation of the graph in *all* directions, but the existence of f_x and f_y guarantees only that it's a good approximation in the directions of **i** and **j**. For this reason, a function can fail to be differentiable at a point even when its first partial derivatives exist there. This fact is reminiscent of Example 4.6, in which you saw that f may fail to be continuous at a point even when f_x and f_y exist.

A function that's not differentiable at $(0, 0)$.

Example 5.7. Show that $f(x, y) = 1 - \sqrt{|xy|}$ is not differentiable at the origin, even though both partial derivatives exist there.

Solution: Intuitively, this function is not differentiable at the origin because it looks like $1 - |x|$ when $y = x$ (and you know $|x|$ is not differentiable at zero, see Figure 5.4). However, the goal of this example is to use the definition, so let's do that. Since $f(x, 0) = 1$ for all values of x, the limit of difference quotients yields

$$f_x(0, 0) = \lim_{\Delta x \to 0} \frac{f(0 + \Delta x, 0) - f(0, 0)}{\Delta x} = \lim_{\Delta x \to 0} \frac{1 - 1}{\Delta x} = 0.$$

Similarly, $f_y(0, 0) = 0$, so both partial derivatives exist at the origin (and both are zero). Therefore, the linear approximation of f at the origin is

$$L(x, y) = 1 + 0(x - 0) + 0(y - 0) = 1 \quad \text{(a constant function).}$$

The difference between f and its linear approximation is

$$f(x, y) - L(x, y) = \left(1 - \sqrt{|xy|}\right) - 1 = -\sqrt{|xy|}. \tag{5.8}$$

When $(x, y) \to (0, 0)$ along the line $y = x$ this is just $-|x|$. Since the distance from (x, x) to $(0, 0)$ is $\|\Delta \mathbf{r}\| = \sqrt{x^2 + x^2} = \sqrt{2}|x|$, we can rewrite equation (5.8) as

$$f(x, x) - L(x, x) = -|x| = -\frac{1}{\sqrt{2}}\|\Delta \mathbf{r}\|,$$

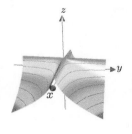  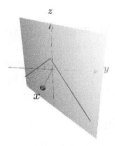

Figure 5.4: (left) the graph of $f(x, y) = 1 - \sqrt{|xy|}$, and the plane $z = 1$, (middle) the graph of $f(x, y)$ intersected with the plane $y = x$, and the line $y = x$ superimposed in the domain of f, (right) the restriction of f to the plane $y = x$ shows why f is not differentiable at zero.

which means that $\varepsilon(x,x) = -1/\sqrt{2}$. The function f is not differentiable at $(0,0)$ because $\lim_{x \to 0} \varepsilon(x,x) \neq 0$. ∎

Many students find the definition of differentiability difficult to read, and even harder to work with. The next theorem, proved in the End Notes for this chapter, provides some relief. In essence, it says that the orientation of the tangent plane changes continuously as we move over the graph of a differentiable function.

> Recall that the vector $\mathbf{n} = \langle -f_x, -f_y, 1 \rangle$ is normal to the tangent plane.

> **Theorem:** Suppose both f_x and f_y exist and are continuous on an open disk about the point (a,b). Then f is differentiable at (a,b).

Checking partial derivatives (this complements Example 5.7)

Example 5.8. Verify that f_x is not continuous in any disk about $(0,0)$ when $f(x,y) = 1 - \sqrt{|xy|}$.

> In light of the previous theorem and Example 5.7, this fact is not surprising.

Solution: It's easiest to work in the first quadrant, where $x > 0$ and $y > 0$, since the formula for f simplifies to $f(x,y) = 1 - \sqrt{xy}$. In this case,

$$f_x(x,y) = \frac{\partial}{\partial x}\left(1 - \sqrt{xy}\right) = -\frac{1}{2\sqrt{xy}}y = -\frac{\sqrt{y}}{2\sqrt{x}},$$

which grows arbitrarily large (in magnitude) as $x \to 0$. Said formally, since $\lim_{x \to 0^+} f_x(x,y)$ does not exist when $y > 0$, the function f_x is not continuous at $(0,y)$ when $y > 0$. This lack of continuity means that f falls outside the scope of the previous theorem. Since the theorem doesn't apply, we can't make any conclusions about differentiability at $(0,0)$ based on it. ∎

> Though we already know it's not differentiable because of our work in Example 5.7.

Checking partial derivatives

Example 5.9. Is $f(x,y) = x^2y$ differentiable at $(3,4)$?

Solution: Since $f_x(x,y) = 2xy$ and $f_y(x,y) = x^2$ are both continuous everywhere, the function is differentiable at $(3,4)$. ∎

We close our discussion of differentiability with a familiar fact.

> **Differentiability Implies Continuity:** Suppose f is differentiable at the point (a,b). Then f is continuous at (a,b).

> Compare to Example 4.6, in which we showed that the existence of partial derivatives is insufficient to guarantee continuity.

Proof. Let's begin by use the definition of the linear approximation, $L(x,y)$, to rewrite equation (5.7) as

$$\Delta f = f_x(a,b)\Delta x + f_y(a,b)\Delta y + \varepsilon(x,y)\|\langle \Delta x, \Delta y \rangle\|,$$

where $\Delta f = f(x,y) - f(a,b)$, $\Delta x = x - a$ and $\Delta y = y - b$. Since $\varepsilon(x,y)\|\langle \Delta x, \Delta y \rangle\| \to 0$ with $\|\langle \Delta x, \Delta y \rangle\|$, this equation shows us that $\lim_{(x,y)\to(a,b)} \Delta f = 0$, which is the definition of continuity. ∎

❖ Life in 3-D

When a function depends on more than two variables, the results we've established in this section still hold (you just need to write more terms). For example, when f is a function x, y and z, the total differential is

$$df = \frac{\partial f}{\partial x}\,dx + \frac{\partial f}{\partial y}\,dy + \frac{\partial f}{\partial z}\,dz,$$

and its linear approximation about the point $(x, y, z) = (a, b, c)$ is

$$f(a,b,c) + f_x(a,b,c)(x - a) + f_y(a,b,c)(y - b) + f_z(a,b,c)(z - c).$$

You should know

- the terms *differentiable, linear approximation, tangent plane,* and *total differential;*
- the vector $\langle -f_x, -f_y, 1 \rangle$ is normal to the tangent plane.

You should be able to

- determine the equation of a tangent plane;
- write a formula for the linear approximation to f near (a, b);
- use the total differential to approximate error;
- implement the Newton-Raphson method;
- determine whether a function of two variables is differentiable at a given point.

❖ 13.5 Skill Exercises

In #1–8 determine the equation of the tangent plane at the specified point.

1. $f(x, y) = x^2 - y^4$; $(1, -1)$

2. $f(x, y) = 4x^2 + y^2$; $(-3, 7)$

3. $f(x, y) = 6x - 4y^2$; $(5, 2)$

4. $f(x, y) = 3/x^2 - 9\sqrt{y}$; $(-3, 7)$

5. $f(x, y) = 6\sqrt{xy}$; $(-3, -7)$

6. $f(x, y) = x \ln y$; $(3, 7)$

7. $f(x, y) = e^{xy^2}$; $(2, -1)$

8. $f(x, y) = \sqrt{3 + x^4 y^2}$; $(-1, 7)$

In exercises #9–12 make two steps of the Newton-Raphson method to approximate values of x and y that solve the given equations, starting at the specified (a, b).

9.
$\begin{cases} 5x^2 + 8y^2 - 100 = 0 \\ y - x^3 + 1 = 0 \\ \left(\frac{3}{2}, \frac{7}{2}\right) \end{cases}$

10.
$\begin{cases} 5x^2 + y - 1 = 0 \\ x - y^2 + 12 = 0 \\ \left(1, -\frac{7}{2}\right) \end{cases}$

11.
$\begin{cases} \sin(x) + \cos(y) = 1 \\ x^3 + xy + y^3 = 2 \\ (0.5, 1) \end{cases}$

12.
$\begin{cases} xe^y + \ln(x) = y \\ x^5 - xy + y^5 = 3 \\ (0.5, 1.3) \end{cases}$

In #13–20 write the total differential of f at the given point.

13. $f(x, y) = 3x^2 y - 9xy^4$; $(x, y) = (2, 5)$

14. $f(x, y) = -2xy^2 + 3x + 9y$; $(x, y) = (-1, 7)$

15. $f(x, y) = 12x \ln(x + 2y)$; $(x, y) = (1, 3)$

16. $f(x, y) = 5x \arctan y$; $(x, y) = (3, 1)$

17. $f(x, y, z) = x^2 y^3 - z^4$; $(x, y, z) = (3, 1, -1)$

18. $f(x, y, z) = xyz$; $(x, y, z) = (2, 3, 4)$

19. $f(x, y, z) = x \sin y \cos z$; $(x, y, z) = (3, \pi, 0.25\pi)$

20. $f(x, y, z) = xe^z + ze^y$; $(x, y, z) = (1, 0, 1)$

In #21–26 approximate the specified function value using the total differential. Relevant data is provided in the tables below.

$y = 3$	14	13	12
$y = 2$	13	11	9
$y = 1$	12	10	11
	$x = 4$	$x = 5$	$x = 6$

values of $f_x(x, y)$

$y = 3$	2	0	-2
$y = 2$	3	1	-1
$y = 1$	4	3	0
	$x = 4$	$x = 5$	$x = 6$

values of $f_y(x, y)$

21. Approximate $f(4.1, 1.01)$ when $f(4, 1) = 7$.

22. Approximate $f(5.01, 2.1)$ when $f(5, 2) = 10$.

23. Approximate $f(5.99, 2.98)$ when $f(6, 3) = 1$.

24. Approximate $f(4.95, 0.99)$ when $f(5, 1) = -3$.

25. Approximate $f(5.02, 2.97)$ when $f(5, 3) = -6$.

26. Approximate $f(3.95, 0.99)$ when $f(4, 1) = 9$.

✥ 13.5 Concept and Application Exercises

In each of #27–34 (a) determine the value of f at P_0, and (b) use the total differential at that point to estimate the value of f at P_1

27. $f(x, y) = xy + \sqrt{y}$; $P_0 = (-1, 1)$; $P_1 = (-0.7, 1.2)$

28. $f(x, y) = x^2 - y^2$; $P_0 = (2, -3)$; $P_1 = (1.99, 2.93)$

29. $f(x, y) = xy^3$; $P_0 = (4, 1)$; $P_1 = (4.1, 0.9)$

30. $f(x, y) = \sin(x + \sqrt{1 + y})$; $P_0 = (0, 0)$; $P_1 = (0.1, -0.1)$

31. $f(x, y, z) = xy^2z$; $P_0 = (1, 1, 1)$; $P_1 = (1.2, 1.01, 0.99)$

32. $f(x, y, z) = x^3y^8z$; $P_0 = (2, 0, 3)$; $P_1 = (2.01, 0.1, 2.95)$

33. $f(x, y, z) = xe^{\sin y}\cos z$; $P_0 = (3, 0, 0)$; $P_1 = (3.1, -0.1, 0.02)$

34. $f(x, y, z) = x/(5y+3z)$; $P_0 = (1, 2, 10)$; $P_1 = (1.3, 1.99, 10.2)$

In #35–40 determine the distance between P_0 and the tangent plane to the graph of f at P_1 (see Section 11.5).

35. $f(x, y) = 3x^2 + 5y^2$; $P_0 = (1, 4, 7)$; $P_1 = (1, 1, 8)$

36. $f(x, y) = 9x - 3y^5$; $P_0 = (0, 0, 10)$; $P_1 = (2, 1, 15)$

37. $f(x, y) = \frac{x}{y^2+5}$; $P_0 = (3, 1, 5)$; $P_1 = (12, 1, 2)$

38. $f(x, y) = \frac{y}{x^3}$; $P_0 = (2, 0, 7)$; $P_1 = (1, 1, 1)$

39. $f(x, y) = x^2 \ln y$; $P_0 = (3, 1, 5)$; $P_1 = (3, 1, 0)$

40. $f(x, y) = y\sin x$; $P_0 = (13, 2, 10)$; $P_1 = (\pi, 4, 0)$

41. Suppose $f(x, y) = 7x + 9y$. Show that the linear approximation of f about $(0, 0)$ is exactly the same as $f(x, y)$.

42. Suppose $f(x, y) = -2x + 17y$. Show that the linear approximation of f about $(2, -4)$ is exactly the same as $f(x, y)$.

43. A person's *body mass index* (BMI) is $I = m/h^2$ where h is the person's height (in meters), m is his mass (in kilograms). Suppose a child is 1.4 meters tall, and his mass is 35 kg.

    | Medical Sciences |

    (a) Calculate the child's BMI.

    (b) Determine I_m and I_h when $m = 35$ and $h = 1.4$.

    (c) Write the equation of the tangent plane to the graph of $I(m, h)$ at $(35, 1.4)$.

    (d) Use the linear approximation of I to estimate the change in the child's BMI if his mass increases by 250 grams and he grows by 1 cm.

44. A pendulum's period of oscillation is $T = 2\pi\sqrt{\ell/g}$ seconds, where ℓ is the length of the pendulum (in meters) and g is the acceleration due to gravity.

    | Physics |

    (a) Determine the period when $\ell = 2$ m, using $g = 9.8$.

    (b) Determine T_ℓ and T_g when $\ell = 2$ and $g = 9.8$

    (c) Write the equation of the tangent plane to the graph of $T(\ell, g)$ at $(2, 9.8)$.

(d) Use the linear approximation of T at $(2, 9.8)$ to estimate the period if we let the value of g change from 9.8 to 9.81.

(e) Use the linear approximation of T at $(2, 9.8)$ to estimate the period assume a 0.1% error in our measurement of ℓ.

45. A cylinder of radius r and height h has a volume of $V = \pi r^2 h$.

                                                                                             Manufacturing

(a) Determine the volume of the cylinder if its radius is measured as 2 cm, and its height is measured as 5 cm.

(b) Use the total differential of V to approximate the error in part (a) if the measurement of r has at most 0.1 cm of error, and the error in the measurement of h is at most 0.01 cm.

46. The surface area of a closed cylinder of radius r centimeters and height h centimeters is $S = 2\pi r^2 + 2\pi rh$ cubic centimeters.

                                                                                              Manufacturing

(a) Determine the surface of the cylinder if its radius is measured as 2 cm, and its height is measured as 5 cm.

(b) Use the total differential of S to approximate the error in part (a) if the measurement of r has at most 0.01 cm of error, and the error in the measurement of h is at most 0.001 cm.

47. *Aa* is a Hawiian word (pronounced "ah-ah") for a type of flow lava. When aa lava is ejected from a volcanic vent at an average rate of q m^3/sec, the length of the flow is $L(q) = k\sqrt{q}$ meters, where k is a constant that depends on the physical properties of the lava at the front of the flow.

                                                                                          Volcanology

(a) Suppose that a particular flow of aa lava on Mt. Etna has $k = 830$ and q is measured to be 95.3 m^3/sec. How long do we project the flow to be?

(b) Suppose there's an uncertainty of 2 m^3/sec in the measurement of q, and an error of at most 2 units in our measurement of k. Use the total differential of L to estimate the possible error in the projected flow length.

48. When we talked about a single-slit diffraction experiment in Chapter 3, we said the line connecting the slit to the first *fringe* is separated from vertical by an angle of $\theta = \sin^{-1}(\lambda/a)$, where λ is the wavelength of the light being used, and a is the width of the slit through which is passes (see Figure 5.5).

                                                                                        Physics

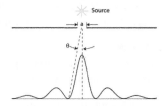

(a) Determine the angular separation of the first fringe from the vertical if the slit has a width of $a = 1 \times 10^{-6}$ meters, and the light has a wavelength of $\lambda = 460 \times 10^{-9}$ meters.

(b) Use the total differential of $\theta(a, \lambda)$ to approximate the error in part (a) if the machine that produces the light can only guarantee the wavelength to within 1 nanometer (1×10^{-9} meter), and the width of the slit may differ from the manufacturer's specifications by at most 1 micron.

Figure 5.5:   Diagram of a single-slit diffraction experiment.

49. Suppose that, because of your performance in a given academic term, your grade in a particular class will be calculated as a decimal according to

                                                                                        Student Life

$$g(F, P) = \frac{375 + PF}{420 + F},$$

where F is the number of points on the final exam, and P is the fraction of them that you earn. The teacher has said that the exam will be worth 125 points ($\pm$ 25 points), and based on previous experience with this teacher, you expect that you can earn 88% ($\pm$ 5%).

(a) Using the values you expect ($F = 125$ and $P = 0.88$) what do you estimate your final grade will be?

(b) Use the total differential and the estimated error in your values to determine the best and worst grade you anticipate.

(c) Which will have the larger effect on your grade? The possible ± 5 percentage points in your score, or the possible ± 25 points in the possible points on the exam?

50. The current (in amperes) in an AC circuit is given by

| Electrical Engineering |

$$I = \frac{E}{\sqrt{R^2 + X^2}}.$$

where E represents the total voltage on the circuit, R is the total resistance on the circuit, and X is a quantity called the *capacitive reactance* that depends on the frequency of the alternating current. Suppose the voltage is rated at $E = 100$ volts, but in actuality will fluctuate by 1.5 volts. Similarly, the resistance is rated at $R = 10.0$ ohms with an expected fluctuation of 0.2 ohms, and the capacitive reactance is rated at $X = 8.0$ ohms but will fluctuate by as much as 0.1 ohms.

(a) Using the values of 100, 10 and 8 for voltage, resistance and capacitive reactance, what is the calculated value of the current.

(b) Use the total differential to estimate how much larger the actual current value could be than the calculated value.

51. In economics, a *production function* is used to model the level of production as a function of such quantities as labor hours, available capital, etc. In the exercise, we work with

| Economics |

$$Q = 240 L^{1/3} K^{1/4}$$

where Q is the number of items produced during a single work day, L is the number of labor hours available that day, and K is the amount of capital (in dollars) that is available for production. Suppose that currently there are 1728 labor hours and \$50,625 in capital. Use the total differential of the production function to estimate answers to the following questions.

(a) Which would have a greater impact on production, an increase of 100 labor hours, or \$100 of capital?

(b) Suppose, as the production manager, you have the option of calling in workers for over-time shifts to help you meet your production quotas. Each worker who comes in for over-time will work an 8-hour shift at a rate \$18 per hour (time and a half). To pay them, you have to spend some of the capital available for this production run. Would you call in any extra workers? Explain how you make your decision.

52. A *consumption function* describes consumer spending (in dollars). One simple version of this function has the form

| Economics |

$$C(I, T) = c_0 + c_1(I - T),$$

where I is the total income of the population, T are the total taxes paid, and the constants c_0 and c_1 are positive.

(a) Find the total differential of consumption.

(b) When income increases, so does the amount paid in taxes. That is, $T = T(I)$. Use this fact to show that the total differential found in part (a) can be written

$$dC = \left(C_I + C_T \frac{dT}{dI} \right) dI$$

(c) Explain the practical significance of the inequality $\frac{dT}{dI} < 1$.

(d) What does the equation of differentials assert about the relationship between income and consumption when $\frac{dT}{dI} < 1$?

Exercises #53–56 are about the relationship between differentiability and partial derivatives.

Mathematics

53. Determine whether $f(x,y) = xy + y^3$ is differentiable at $(9, 12)$.

54. Determine whether $f(x,y) = 8y/(x^2 + 4)$ is differentiable at $(-1, 5)$.

55. In this exercise you'll show that $f(x,y) = (xy)^{1/3}$ is not differentiable at the origin, even though both partial derivatives exist.

    (a) Show that $f_x(0,0) = 0$ using the limit of difference quotients.

    (b) Show that $f_y(0,0) = 0$ using the limit of difference quotients.

    (c) Use the definition of differentiability to show that if f *were* differentiable at $(0,0)$, it would be true that $\lim_{x \to 0} \frac{f(x,x)}{x}$ would be 0.

    (d) Show that f is not differentiable by verifying that $\lim_{x \to 0} \frac{f(x,x)}{x} \neq 0$.

    (e) Use a graphing utility to render a graph of f, and use the surface to explain the function's non-differentiability.

56. In this exercise you'll show that a function is not differentiable at the origin, even though both partial derivatives exist. Specifically, suppose

$$f(x,y) = \begin{cases} \frac{2xy(x+y)}{x^2+y^2} & \text{away from the origin} \\ 0 & \text{when both } x = 0 \text{ and } y = 0 \end{cases}$$

    which, you can verify, is continuous at $(0,0)$.

    (a) Show that $f_x(0,0) = 0$ using the limit of difference quotients.

    (b) Show that $f_y(0,0) = 0$ using the limit of difference quotients.

    (c) Use the definition of differentiability to show that if f *were* differentiable at $(0,0)$, it would be true that $\lim_{x \to 0} \frac{f(x,x)}{x}$ would be 0.

    (d) Show that f is not differentiable by verifying that $\lim_{x \to 0} \frac{f(x,x)}{x} \neq 0$.

    (e) Use a graphing utility to render a graph of f, and use the surface to explain the function's non-differentiability.

57. Suppose we want to use the Newton-Raphson Method to approximate the solution to the system of equations $f(x,y) = 0$ and $g(x,y) = 0$, starting at the point $(x,y) = (a,b)$. Explain in geometric terms why the method fails when $f_x(a,b)$ and $f_y(a,b)$ are both zero.

Mathematics

58. Suppose we want to use the Newton-Raphson Method to approximate the solution to the system of equations $f(x,y) = 0$ and $g(x,y) = 0$, starting at the point $(x,y) = (a,b)$. Explain in geometric terms why the method fails when $f_x(a,b) = g_x(a,b)$ and $f_y(a,b) = g_y(a,b)$.

Mathematics

13.6   The Gradient and Directional Derivatives

In Section 13.4 we introduced f_x and f_y, which tell us the rate at which f changes in the x and the y directions, respectively. In this section we extend this idea by developing a vector called the *gradient* of f that allows us to calculate the function's instantaneous rate of change in any direction, and tells us the direction in which the function's value increases most rapidly.

> **Key Idea(s):** *The gradient of a function f is a vector in its domain that tells us the direction in which the value of f changes most rapidly.*
>
> *The gradient of a function can be used to calculate its instantaneous rate of change in any direction.*
>
> *The gradient of f is orthogonal to level sets of f.*
>
> *The Chain Rule allows us to calculate the rate of change in $f(x, y)$ as the point $x(t)$ and $y(t)$ moves in the plane.*

❖ The Gradient

The *gradient* is a vector that arises naturally from linear approximations of change. For instance, suppose a company's monthly profit is $f(x, y)$, where x is the sale price of its product, and y is the combined cost of making and marketing the product. At $x = a$ and $y = b$ the company is making a certain amount of profit, but what happens if we make a small change in price, say dx, and a small change in manufacturing or marketing costs, say dy? We know from Section 13.5 that the resulting change in profit is approximated by the total differential,

$$df = f_x(a, b) \ dx + f_y(a, b) \ dy, \tag{6.1}$$

The right-hand side of this equation is the dot product of two vectors,

$$df = \langle f_x(a, b), f_y(a, b) \rangle \cdot \langle dx, dy \rangle. \tag{6.2}$$

The first of these vectors, $\langle f_x(a, b), f_y(a, b) \rangle$, is called the *gradient* of f at (a, b) and is denoted by $\nabla f(a, b)$.

> We know that the dot product of two vectors is defined to be the product of their lengths and the cosine of the angle between them, so we conclude from equation (6.2) that df is maximized when $\langle dx, dy \rangle$ points in the same direction as $\langle f_x(a, b), f_y(a, b) \rangle$.

> **Definition:** Suppose f is a function of two variables, and its partial derivatives exist at (a, b). The **gradient** of f at the point (a, b) is the vector
>
> $$\nabla f(a, b) = \langle f_x(a, b), \ f_y(a, b) \rangle.$$
>
> If f is a function of three variables, and its partial derivatives exist at (a, b, c),
>
> $$\nabla f(a, b, c) = \langle f_x(a, b, c), \ f_y(a, b, c), \ f_z(a, b, c) \rangle.$$

> The symbol ∇ is called *nabla* (which comes from the Greek word for a Hebrew harp), but many people read ∇ as **del** or **grad**.

Calculating the gradient

Example 6.1. Find a formula for $\nabla f(2, \pi)$ when $f(x, y) = yx^4 + \sin y$.

Solution: The gradient comprises the first partial derivatives of f, in order: $f_x = 4yx^3$ and $f_y = x^4 + \cos y$ so $\nabla f(x, y) = \langle 4yx^3, x^4 + \cos y \rangle$. When $x = 2$ and $y = \pi$, this becomes $\nabla f(2, \pi) = \langle 32\pi, 15 \rangle$. ∎

Calculating the gradient

Example 6.2. Determine the vector $\nabla f(\pi/3, \pi/6)$ when $f(x, y) = 4x + \sin(x - 2y)$.

Answer: $\nabla f(\pi/3, \pi/6) = \langle 5, -2 \rangle$. ∎

Solution
On-line

We calculated the gradient at specific points in Examples 6.1 and 6.2, but it's also common to leave the point unspecified and write

$$\nabla f = \left\langle \frac{\partial f}{\partial x}, \frac{\partial f}{\partial y}, \frac{\partial f}{\partial z} \right\rangle,$$

much as we write f' when working with a function of a single variable, rather than writing $f'(c)$. Because the components of ∇f are derivatives, the gradient obeys some of the basic rules of differentiation that you first saw in Chapter 3.

Properties of the Gradient: Suppose that the partial derivatives of f and g exist, and k is any constant. Then

1. $\nabla(f \pm g) = \nabla f \pm \nabla g$

2. $\nabla(kf) = k\nabla f$

3. $\nabla(fg) = f\nabla g + g\nabla f$

Further, if F is a scalar-valued function of a single variable, the gradient of its composition with f is

4. $\nabla(F \circ f) = (F' \circ f)\nabla f$.

In the list above, Property 4 is a statement of the Chain Rule in this context. The following example arrives at the result through methods you already know, and provides an indication of why Property 4 is true.

Gradient of a composition

Example 6.3. Suppose $F(s) = s^5$ and $f(x, y) = 3y + \sin x$. Determine $\nabla(F \circ f)$.

Solution: The composition $(F \circ f)(x, y) = (f(x, y))^5 = (3y + \sin x)^5$. The partial derivatives of this composition are

$$\frac{\partial}{\partial x}(3y + \sin x)^5 = 5(3y + \sin x)^4 \cos x, \quad \text{and} \quad \frac{\partial}{\partial y}(3y + \sin x)^5 = 5(3y + \sin x)^4(3),$$

so the gradient of $F \circ f$ is

$$\nabla(F \circ f) = \begin{bmatrix} 5(3y + \sin x)^4 \cos x \\ 5(3y + \sin x)^4(3) \end{bmatrix} = 5(3y + \sin x)^4 \begin{bmatrix} \cos x \\ 3 \end{bmatrix}.$$

Note that $\nabla f(x, y) = \langle \cos x, 3 \rangle$ and $F'(s) = 5s^4$, so this expression has the form $F'\big(f(x, y)\big)\nabla f(x, y)$, as stated in Property 4 above. ∎

❖ Directional derivatives

In Section 13.4 we used $f_x(a, b)$ to determine the rate at which f changes when we move away from (a, b) in the direction of increasing x—that is, in the direction of the vector **i**. Graphically speaking, the number $f_x(a, b)$ is the slope of the line in the plane $y = b$ that's tangent to graph of f at the point $\big(a, b, f(a, b)\big)$. Similarly, the number $f_y(a, b)$ tells us the rate at which the function changes when we move away from (a, b) in the direction of the vector **j**, and it can also be interpreted as the slope of a tangent line.

At this point in our discussion, we're ready to generalize this idea. To determine the rate at which f changes when we move away from (a, b) in the direction of the vector $\hat{\mathbf{u}}$ we intersect the surface $z = f(x, y)$ with a vertical plane that contains the vector $\hat{\mathbf{u}}$ (see Figure 6.1). The tangent line to the resulting curve lies in the tangent plane, and its slope tells us the desired rate of change. The calculation of that slope is made by using the gradient. When $\mathbf{u} = \langle dx, dy \rangle$, equation (6.2) tells us that $df = \nabla f \cdot \mathbf{u}$. Since this linear approximation of the change in f corresponds to a step of length $\|\mathbf{u}\|$, we have a rise-to-run ratio of

$$\frac{df}{\|\mathbf{u}\|} = \frac{\nabla f \cdot \mathbf{u}}{\|\mathbf{u}\|} = \nabla f \cdot \hat{\mathbf{u}},$$

Recall that $\hat{\mathbf{u}}$ denotes the unit vector in the direction of **u**.

If we change our frame of reference so that one of our coordinate axes extends in the direction of $\hat{\mathbf{u}}$, and denote by u the variable along that axis, the partial derivative of f with respect to u is $D_{\mathbf{u}} f$.

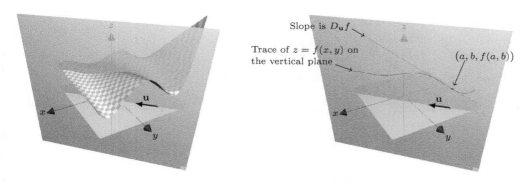

Figure 6.1: (left) The surface $z = f(x, y)$ intersected with the vertical plane through $(a, b, 0)$ that extends in the direction of $\mathbf{u}$; (right) the trace of the surface on that plane, and its tangent line at $(a, b, f(a, b))$.

which leads us to the following definition.

Definition: Suppose f is differentiable at (a, b). The ***directional derivative*** of f in the direction of $\mathbf{u}$ is denote by $D_{\mathbf{u}}f$ or $\partial_{\mathbf{u}}f$ and is defined to be

$$D_{\mathbf{u}}f(a, b) = \nabla f(a, b) \cdot \hat{\mathbf{u}}.$$

Note: $D_{\mathbf{u}}f$ is f_x when $\mathbf{u} = \mathbf{i}$, and is f_y when $\mathbf{u} = \mathbf{j}$.

Calculating and using the gradient

Example 6.4. Suppose $f(x, y) = x^3 y + \cos(6x + 2y)$. Use the directional derivative to determine whether the function value will increase or decrease when we move away from $(-1, 3)$ in the direction $\mathbf{u} = \langle -2, 3 \rangle$.

Solution: To calculate the directional derivative we need to know the gradient, so we begin by finding the partial derivatives:

$$\frac{\partial f}{\partial x} = 3x^2 y - 6 \sin(6x + 2y) \quad \text{and} \quad \frac{\partial f}{\partial y} = x^3 - 2 \sin(6x + 2y).$$

These allow us to determine $\nabla f(-1, 3) = \langle 9, -1 \rangle$, so the directional derivative of f in the direction of $\mathbf{u} = \langle -2, 3 \rangle$ is

$$D_{\mathbf{u}}f = \frac{\nabla f(-1, 3) \cdot \mathbf{u}}{\|\mathbf{u}\|} = \frac{\langle 9, -1 \rangle \cdot \langle -2, 3 \rangle}{\sqrt{13}} = -\frac{21}{\sqrt{13}}.$$

Because this derivative is negative, the function value will decrease (at least initially) when we move away from $(-1, 3)$ in the direction of $\langle -2, 3 \rangle$. ∎

Calculating and using the gradient

Example 6.5. Suppose $f(x, y) = -x/y + 2y^2 \cos x$. (a) Determine the vector $\nabla f(0, 1)$, and (b) use it to determine whether the function value will increase or decrease when we start at $(0, 1)$ and head in the direction $\mathbf{v} = \langle -2, 3 \rangle$.

Answer: The function will increase. ∎

Solution On-line

Tangent line in a direction other than i and j

Example 6.6. Suppose $f(x, y) = 192 + (1 + y)\left(x^4 - 12x^2 + 24\right)$. (a) Determine $D_{\mathbf{u}}f$ at the point $(-2, 3)$ when $\mathbf{u} = \langle 1, -1 \rangle$, and (b) write symmetric equations for the line that's tangent to the graph of f at $\left(-2, 3, f(-2, 3)\right)$ and lies in the vertical plane $x + y = 1$ (which contains the vector $\langle 1, -1, 0 \rangle$).

Solution: We begin by calculating the partial derivatives of f,

$$f_x(x,y) = (y+1)\left(4x^3 - 24x\right) \quad \text{and} \quad f_y(x,y) = x^4 - 12x^2 + 24,$$

which we use to determine $\nabla f(-2,3) = \langle 64, -8 \rangle$. So the directional derivative of f in the direction of $\mathbf{u}$ is

$$D_{\mathbf{u}}f = \nabla f \cdot \hat{\mathbf{u}} = \frac{\langle 64, -8 \rangle \cdot \langle 1, -1 \rangle}{\sqrt{2}} = \frac{72}{\sqrt{2}}$$

(b) This is similar to Example 4.7, except that we're heading in the direction of $\mathbf{u}$ instead of $\mathbf{i}$. We know from part (a) that when we step 1 unit away from $(-2,3)$ in the direction of $\mathbf{u}$, the z-coordinate on our line will increase by $72/\sqrt{2}$. That is, the line extends in the direction of

$$\underbrace{\left\langle \tfrac{1}{\sqrt{2}}, -\tfrac{1}{\sqrt{2}}, \right.}_{\text{unit of "run"}} \underbrace{\left. \tfrac{72}{\sqrt{2}} \right\rangle,}_{\text{resulting "rise"}} \quad \text{which is parallel to} \quad \mathbf{v} = \langle 1, -1, 72 \rangle.$$

And since $f(-2,3) = 160$, we know that the line passes through the point $(-2,3,160)$. Therefore,

$$\frac{x+2}{1} = \frac{y-3}{-1} = \frac{z-160}{72},$$

are symmetric equations for this tangent line.   ∎

Tangent line in a "skew" direction

Example 6.7. Parameterize the line that's tangent to the graph of $f(x,y) = 4x^{-2} + y^5$ at the point $(1, -1, f(1,-1))$ and lies in the vertical plane containing the vector $\mathbf{u} = \langle -2, 5, 0 \rangle$.

Answer: $\mathbf{r}(t) = \langle 1 - 2t, -1 + 5t, 3 + 41t \rangle$.   ∎

Solution On-line

Because $D_{\mathbf{u}}f = \nabla f \cdot \hat{\mathbf{u}} = \|\nabla f\| \, \|\hat{\mathbf{u}}\| \, \cos\theta = \|\nabla f\| \cos\theta$, where θ is the angle between ∇f and $\mathbf{u}$, the directional derivative is maximized when $\theta = 0$ and minimized when $\theta = \pi$.

> **Steepest Ascent/Descent:** Suppose f is differentiable at (a,b), and at least one of f_x and f_y is not zero. Then f increases most quickly in the direction of $\nabla f(a,b)$, and decreases most quickly in the direction of $-\nabla f(a,b)$.

Maximizing the rate of change

Example 6.8. Suppose $f(x,y) = x^2 + 3y^2$. (a) Determine the direction to proceed from $(1, 1/2)$ in order to effect the most rapid increase in the value of f. Then (b) plot several level curves of f, and a ray in the direction of ∇f at the point $(1, 1/2)$.

Solution: (a) The value of f increases most rapidly when we proceed in the direction of $\nabla f = \langle 2x, 6y \rangle$, so we should move away from the point $(1, 1/2)$ in the direction of $\langle 2, 3 \rangle$ in order to effect the most rapid change in f.

(b) Level curves of f have the form $x^2 + 3y^2 = k$ where k is constant. Several of these ellipses have been graphed in Figure 6.2. Note that the vectors $\hat{\mathbf{u}}$, $\hat{\mathbf{v}}$ and $\hat{\mathbf{w}}$ in the figure all have the same length, but $\mathbf{w}$ (which points in the direction of ∇f) crosses more level curves than the other two. This happens because the change in f per unit length is greatest is the direction of ∇f.   ∎

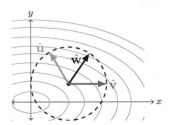
Figure 6.2: The vector $\hat{\mathbf{w}}$ crosses more level curves than either $\hat{\mathbf{u}}$ or $\hat{\mathbf{v}}$.

❖ The Chain Rule for Paths

We started this section by recalling the total differential, which is a linear approximation of the change in f due to changes in x and y. If x and y are changing because they're functions of time (e.g., parameterizing a path in the xy-plane), equation (6.1) might lead you to conjecture that f changes at a rate of

$$\frac{df}{dt} = f_x(a,b)\,\frac{dx}{dt} + f_y(a,b)\,\frac{dy}{dt},$$

and that is exactly what happens when f is differentiable.

> **Chain Rule for Paths:** Suppose f is a differentiable function of x and y, both of which are differentiable functions of t. Then
>
> $$\frac{df}{dt} = \frac{\partial f}{\partial x}\frac{dx}{dt} + \frac{\partial f}{\partial y}\frac{dy}{dt}. \qquad (6.3)$$

Note: In the special case when f depends only on x, equation (6.3) reduces to the Chain Rule from Chapter 3.

Proof. We're going to focus our attention at an arbitrary but fixed value of $t = t_0$, at which $x = a$ and $y = b$. Because x and y are functions of t, they change by Δx and Δy (respectively) when t changes by Δt. Because f is differentiable, we can use equation (5.7) to write the resulting change in f as

$$\Delta f = f_x(a,b)\Delta x + f_y(a,b)\Delta y + \|\Delta \mathbf{r}\|\varepsilon,$$

so the average rate of change in f with respect to t is

$$\frac{\Delta f}{\Delta t} = f_x(a,b)\frac{\Delta x}{\Delta t} + f_y(a,b)\frac{\Delta y}{\Delta t} + \frac{\|\Delta \mathbf{r}\|}{\Delta t}\varepsilon. \qquad (6.4)$$

Let's consider the last term on the right-hand side. When $\Delta t > 0$, its first factor is

$$\frac{\|\Delta \mathbf{r}\|}{\Delta t} = \frac{\sqrt{(\Delta x)^2 + (\Delta y)^2}}{\Delta t} = \sqrt{\left(\frac{\Delta x}{\Delta t}\right)^2 + \left(\frac{\Delta y}{\Delta t}\right)^2},$$

which converges to $\sqrt{\left(x'(t_0)\right)^2 + \left(y'(t_0)\right)^2}$ as $\Delta t \to 0^+$. Similarly, the fraction $\|\Delta \mathbf{r}\|/\Delta t$ remains bounded as $\Delta t \to 0^-$. Since $\|\Delta \mathbf{r}\|/\Delta t$ remains bounded as $\Delta t \to 0$ but $\varepsilon \to 0$ (because Δx and Δy vanish as $\Delta t \to 0$), the rightmost term in equation (6.4) vanishes in the limit, and the result follows. ∎

Using the Chain Rule for Paths

Example 6.9. Suppose $f(x,y) = x^4 e^{-2\sin(\pi y/4)}$, and x and y change according to the parameterization $\mathbf{r}(t) = \langle 2t^3 + 1, -4t^3 + 2\rangle$. Determine whether the value of f is increasing or decreasing when t is near 1.

Solution: We need the first partial derivatives of f in order to calculate df/dt with the Chain Rule for Paths:

$$f_x(x,y) = 4x^3 e^{-2\sin(\pi y/4)} \quad \text{and} \quad f_y(x,y) = -\frac{\pi}{2}x^4 e^{-2\sin(\pi y/4)}\cos\left(\frac{\pi y}{4}\right).$$

Since $\mathbf{r}(1) = \langle 3, -2\rangle$, we use these formulas to calculate

$$f_x(3,-2) = 108e^2 \quad \text{and} \quad f_y(3,-2) = 0.$$

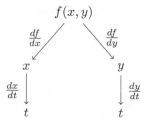

$$f(x,y)$$

Figure 6.3: The value of f depends on x and y, each of which depends on t. To determine df/dt, multiply the derivatives that you find along each path in the diagram from f to t, and then add the results together.

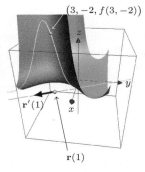

Figure 6.4: The line in the xy-plane parameterized by $\mathbf{r}(t)$, and the trace of the graph of f over that line (in yellow). The point $\mathbf{r}(1)$ is shown in the xy-plane, and the vector next to it points in the direction of $\mathbf{r}'(1)$.

Lastly, note that $\mathbf{r}'(t) = \langle 6, -12 \rangle$, so $x'(1) = 6$ and $y'(1) = -12$. Therefore,

$$\left.\frac{df}{dt}\right|_{t=1} = f_x(3, -2)x'(1) + f_y(3, -2)y'(1) = (108e^2)(6) + (0)(-12) = 648e^2 > 0$$

Further, because the terms of our calculation are continuous, the value of $\frac{df}{dt}$ varies continuously with t. So we know that it remains positive in some interval about $t = 1$. This allows us to conclude that the value of f is increasing with t. ∎

> f_x and f_y are continuous functions of x and y, which are differentiable functions of t; their derivatives are continuous, so df/dt is a sum of products of continuous functions.

Using the Chain Rule for Paths

Example 6.10. Suppose $f(x,y) = x^4(2x + 5y)^3$, and x and y change according to $\mathbf{r}(t) = \langle 3t - 10, 7 - 2t^2 \rangle$. Use the Chain Rule for Paths to determine whether f is increasing when t is near 2.

Answer: It's decreasing. ∎

Solution On-line

The Chain Rule for Paths and the Chain Rule for single-variable functions

Example 6.11. Suppose you're walking down a hallway when the fire alarm goes off. The acoustic power experienced by your ear is $f(x,y) = k/(x^2+y^2)$ watts, where k is a positive constant, and (x,y) is your position relative to the alarm (distance measured in meters). (a) Verify that the rate of change in f according to the Chain Rule for Paths agrees with the Chain Rule from single-variable calculus, and (b) perform a dimensional analysis of its terms.

Solution: (a) The Chain Rule from single-variable calculus tells us that

$$\frac{d}{dt}(k\,u^{-1}) = -k\,u^{-2}\,\frac{du}{dt}.$$

In this case $u = x^2 + y^2$, where x and y change with time as you move. So

$$\begin{aligned}
\frac{df}{dt} &= -k(x^2 + y^2)^{-2}\,\frac{d}{dt}(x^2 + y^2) \\
&= -k(x^2 + y^2)^{-2}\,(2x\,x' + 2y\,y') \\
&= -\frac{2k\,x}{(x^2 + y^2)^2}\,x' - \frac{2k\,y}{(x^2 + y^2)^2}\,y'
\end{aligned} \qquad (6.5)$$

Because

$$\frac{\partial f}{\partial x} = -\frac{2k\,x}{(x^2 + y^2)^2} \quad \text{and} \quad \frac{\partial f}{\partial y} = -\frac{2k\,y}{(x^2 + y^2)^2}$$

equation (6.5) is exactly the Chain Rule for Paths. (b) In order to perform a dimensional analysis, let's assume that length is measured in meters, and time in seconds. Then at $(x,y) = (a,b)$ we have

$$\frac{\partial f}{\partial x} = \lim_{\Delta x \to 0} \frac{f(a + \Delta x, b) - f(a, b)}{\Delta x} \quad \begin{matrix}\leftarrow \text{watts} \\ \leftarrow \text{m}\end{matrix}$$

and dx/dt has units of meters per second, so $\frac{\partial f}{\partial x}\frac{dx}{dt}$ has units of $\left(\frac{\text{W}}{\text{m}}\right) \times \left(\frac{\text{m}}{\text{sec}}\right) = \frac{\text{W}}{\text{sec}}$. Similarly for the product $\frac{\partial f}{\partial y}\frac{dy}{dt}$, so their sum has units of watts per second, which is what we expect from df/dt. ∎

▷ Level curves and the gradient

Suppose $\mathbf{r}(t) = \langle x(t), y(t) \rangle$ is a smooth parameterization of a level curve of f, so that $f(x, y)$ remains constant. Since f is constant along the curve, the Chain Rule tells us

$$0 = \frac{df}{dt} = \frac{\partial f}{\partial x}\frac{dx}{dt} + \frac{\partial f}{\partial y}\frac{dy}{dt} = \nabla f \cdot \langle x', y' \rangle = \nabla f \cdot \mathbf{r}' \tag{6.6}$$

at each value of t. Since the vector $\mathbf{r}'$ is tangent to the level curve, equation (6.6) tells us that the gradient is orthogonal to the level curve. This result is stated formally below.

> **Theorem:** Suppose f is a function of two variables with partial derivatives that are continuous in an open disk about the point (a, b), and the vector $\nabla f(a, b) \neq \mathbf{0}$. Then $\nabla f(a, b)$ is orthogonal to the level curve of f that passes through (a, b).

    Intuitively speaking, this theorem is true because the value of f is constant along a level curve, and ∇f points in the direction of most rapid increase (i.e., in the most "f-not-constant" direction there is). The result can be proved rigorously using the Implicit Function Theorem, which will be introduced in the next section but is established in advanced courses.

The gradient is orthogonal to level curves

Example 6.12. Suppose $f(x, y) = x^2 + 2y$. (a) Draw several level curves of f, and (b) draw ∇f at several points in the plane. Then (c) discuss the relationship between the gradient and the level curves of f.

Solution: (a) Level curves of f are described by equations of the form $x^2 + 2y = k$, where k is constant. Several of these parabolas are shown in Figure 6.5. (b) The gradient of this function is $\nabla f(x, y) = \langle 2x, 2 \rangle$. This formula has been used to generate the vectors in Figure 6.5. Finally, (c) Figure 6.5 suggests that $\nabla f(a, b)$ is perpendicular to the level curve through (a, b). To verify this, let's rewrite the equation of the level curve as $y = -\frac{1}{2}x^2 + \frac{k}{2}$. This allows us to see that $\frac{dy}{dx} = -x$, so the line that's tangent to the curve at (a, b) has a slope of $-a$. That is, the line extends in the direction of the vector $\mathbf{v} = \langle 1, -a \rangle$, and

$$\nabla f(a, b) \cdot \mathbf{v} = \langle 2a, 2 \rangle \cdot \langle 1, -a \rangle = 2a - 2a = 0.$$

That is, the gradient is orthogonal to the direction in which tangent line extends. Said differently, the gradient is normal to the level curve. ∎

The gradient is orthogonal to level curves

Example 6.13. (a) Plot several level curves of $f(x, y) = x^2 + y^2$, (b) draw ∇f at several points in the plane, and (c) discuss the relationship between them.

Answer: See on-line solution. ∎

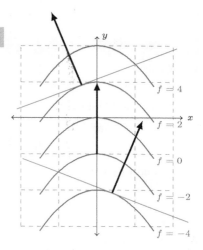

Figure 6.5: Level curves (blue) and gradient vectors (black) of f on a grid of 1×1 squares. In Example 6.12 you see that $\nabla f(a, b)$ is normal to the (red) tangent line through (a, b).

Solution On-line

✧ Life in 3-D

When a function depends on three or more variables, the results we've established in this section still hold (you just need to write more terms). For example, when f is a function of x, y and z, its gradient is the vector

$$\nabla f = \langle f_x, f_y, f_z \rangle,$$

and the directional derivative of f in the direction of the 3-vector $\mathbf{u}$ is calculated as

$$D_{\mathbf{u}}f = \nabla f \cdot \hat{\mathbf{u}}.$$

As before, because $D_{\mathbf{u}}f$ is a dot product we know that it's maximized when $\mathbf{u}$ points in the direction of ∇f.

Gradients of functions of more than 2 variables

Example 6.14. Suppose $f(x, y, z) = 3x + 8y^2 - 7z^4$. Determine the direction we should move away from $(2, 4, -1)$ in order to increase the function value most rapidly.

Solution: The gradient of f is $\langle f_x, f_y, f_z \rangle = \langle 3, 16y, -28z^3 \rangle$. So moving away from $(2, 4, -1)$ in the direction of $\nabla f(2, 4, -1) = \langle 3, 64, 28 \rangle$ will effect the most rapid increase in the function value. ∎

The extension of the Chain Rule for Paths to functions of several variables is also straightforward. We state it below in generality.

Chain Rule for Paths: Suppose f is a differentiable function of $x_1, x_2, \ldots, x_n$, all of which are differentiable functions of t. Then

$$\frac{df}{dt} = \frac{\partial f}{\partial x_1}\frac{dx_1}{dt} + \frac{\partial f}{\partial x_2}\frac{dx_2}{dt} + \cdots + \frac{\partial f}{\partial x_n}\frac{dx_n}{dt}. \qquad (6.7)$$

Using the Chain Rule when f depends on more than two variables

Example 6.15. Suppose $f(x, y, z) = x^2 + yz$, where $x(t) = 3t + 4$, $y(t) = t^2 - 1$, and $z(t) = \sin \pi t$. Determine df/dt when $t = 3$.

Solution: The Chain Rule tells us that

$$\frac{df}{dt} = \frac{\partial f}{\partial x}\frac{dx}{dt} + \frac{\partial f}{\partial y}\frac{dy}{dt} + \frac{\partial f}{\partial z}\frac{dz}{dt} = \nabla f \cdot \langle x', y', z' \rangle.$$

So we begin by calculating

$$\frac{\partial f}{\partial x} = 2x, \quad \frac{\partial f}{\partial y} = z, \quad \frac{\partial f}{\partial z} = y$$

At $t = 1$ we have $x = 7$, $y = 0$, $z = 0$, and $\langle x'(1), y'(1), z'(1) \rangle = \langle 3, 2, -\pi \rangle$, so

$$\frac{df}{dt} = \nabla f \cdot \langle x', y', z' \rangle = \langle 14, 0, 0 \rangle \cdot \langle 3, 2, -\pi \rangle = 42. \qquad ∎$$

The Chain Rule when f depends on more than two variables

Example 6.16. Suppose $f(x, y, z) = \arctan(x + yz)$, where $x(t) = \sqrt{t^2 + 24}$, $y(t) = \ln(t - 4)$, and $z(t) = 8t + 2$. Determine df/dt when $t = 5$.

Answer: $df/dt = 229/350$. ∎

Solution On-line

When working with functions of two variables we saw that ∇f is orthogonal to level curves. When f is a differentiable function of three variables, the equation $f(x, y, z) = k$ describes a surface, and as you might suspect, the vector ∇f is orthogonal to it. The reasoning is virtually the same: suppose that $\mathbf{r}(t) = \langle x(t), y(t), z(t) \rangle$ is a smooth parameterization of some curve on the surface $f(x, y, z) = k$. Because the value of f is constant on the surface, it's constant along such a curve, so

$$0 = \frac{df}{dt} = \frac{\partial f}{\partial x}\frac{dx}{dt} + \frac{\partial f}{\partial y}\frac{dy}{dt} + \frac{\partial f}{\partial z}\frac{dz}{dt} = \nabla f \cdot \mathbf{r}'(t)$$

at every value of t. Since $\mathbf{r}(t)$ can parameterize any regular curve on the surface, the vector $\mathbf{r}'(t)$ can be any vector that's tangent to the surface at $\mathbf{r}(t)$. The only way for ∇f to be orthogonal to all of them is for it to be orthogonal to the tangent plane of the surface. The result is stated formally as follows.

> **Theorem:** Suppose f is a function of three variables, the partial derivatives of f are continuous inside a sphere about the point (a, b, c), and $\nabla f(a, b, c) \neq \mathbf{0}$. Then $\nabla f(a, b, c)$ is orthogonal to the level surface of f that passes through (a, b, c).

The gradient of f is orthogonal to level surfaces of f

Example 6.17. Suppose $f(x, y, z) = x^2 + y^2 - z$. (a) Describe the surface $f(x, y, z) = 0$, and (b) determine the equation of the tangent plane to the surface at the point $(1, 1, 2)$.

Solution: (a) The equation $x^2 + y^2 - z = 0$ is equivalent to $z = x^2 + y^2$, which describes an elliptic paraboloid. (b) Since $\nabla f = \langle 2x, 2y, -1 \rangle$, we know that the vector $\langle 2, 2, -1 \rangle$ is orthogonal to the surface at the point $(1, 1, 2)$. Said differently, the vector $\langle 2, 2, -1 \rangle$ is normal to the tangent plane, so the equation of the plane is

See Section 11.5 to review equations of planes.

$$\langle 2, 2, -1 \rangle \cdot \langle x, y, z \rangle = \langle 2, 2, -1 \rangle \cdot \langle 1, 1, 2 \rangle$$
$$2x + 2y - z = 2$$

∎

✧ Common Difficulties with the Gradient

Many students erroneously think that ∇f is a vector *on* the graph of f. It's not. For example, when f is a function of two variables, $\nabla f = \langle f_x, f_y \rangle$ is a 2-vector in the domain of f (see Figure 6.5).

You should know

- the terms *gradient* and *directional derivative;*
- that ∇f is a vector in the domain of f (not on its graph);
- that ∇f points in the direction of most rapid change in f;
- that $D_{\mathbf{u}} f$ is the slope of a tangent line;
- that $D_{\mathbf{u}} f$ tells us the instantaneous rate of change in f in the direction of $\mathbf{u}$;
- the Chain Rule for Paths.

You should be able to

- calculate ∇f (both at a point, and as a general formula);
- determine the direction in which function value increases most rapidly;
- calculate the directional derivative of f in any direction;
- parameterize a tangent line to the graph of f in any direction.

✧ 13.6 Skill Exercises

In exercises #1–8 determine a formula for ∇f.

1. $f(x, y) = 7x + 8y$

2. $f(x, y) = 3yx^2 - 4xy^5$

3. $f(x, y) = \frac{x}{x^2 + y}$

4. $f(x, y) = xye^y$

5. $f(x, y, z) = 6x - 7y + 10z$ 7. $f(x, y, z) = xyz$

6. $f(x, y, z) = x - zy - xy$ 8. $f(x, y, z) = \frac{x \sin xy}{y + z^2}$

In exercises #9–16 determine ∇f at the specified point.

9. $f(x, y) = 3xy^2 + x^2$; $(2, 4)$ 13. $f(x, y, z) = 3x - 2y + 8z$; $(1, 2, -2)$

10. $f(x, y) = \cos(x + \pi y)$; $(\pi, 2)$ 14. $f(x, y, z) = x^2 + 4y^2 - 5z^2$; $(3, 1, 0)$

11. $f(x, y) = e^{xy} y \arctan x$; $(1, -2)$ 15. $f(x, y, z) = e^{xy} \sin yz$; $(1, 0, -2)$

12. $f(x, y) = \frac{\ln x}{y}$; $(1, 8)$ 16. $f(x, y, z) = \frac{3x + 2y}{8z + 4x}$; $(2, 1, 3)$

In exercises #17–24 determine the directional derivative of f at the specified point in the direction of $\mathbf{u}$.

17. $f(x, y) = xy$; $(2, -3)$; $\mathbf{u} = \langle 5, 1 \rangle$ 21. $f(x, y, z) = xyz$; $(2, 3, 4)$; $\mathbf{u} = \langle 2, 5, 1 \rangle$

18. $f(x, y) = x^2 + xy^3$; $(2, 1)$; $\mathbf{u} = \langle -1, 3 \rangle$ 22. $f(x, y, z) = x^2 - yz$; $(1, 1, 1)$; $\mathbf{u} = \langle 1, 3, 8 \rangle$

19. $f(x, y) = \sin xy$; $(\pi, 1)$; $\mathbf{u} = \langle 2, 5 \rangle$ 23. $f(x, y, z) = y \cos(x - z)$; $(\pi, 8, 0.25\pi)$; $\mathbf{u} = \langle 1, -1, 1 \rangle$

20. $f(x, y) = y \ln(x^2 + 1)$; $(0, 2)$; $\mathbf{u} = \langle 1, 4 \rangle$ 24. $f(x, y, z) = x \sin zy$; $(2, \pi, 1)$; $\mathbf{u} = \langle 1, 2, 3 \rangle$

In exercises #25–30 determine the symmetric equations for the line that's tangent to the graph of f at the point $\big(a, b, \ f(a, b)\big)$ and lies in the specified vertical plane.

25. $f(x, y) = x^2 y$; $(a, b) = (3, 5)$; $4x + 2y = 22$ 28. $f(x, y) = x - y^2$; $(a, b) = (1, 2)$; $x + y = 3$

26. $f(x, y) = xy^3$; $(a, b) = (6, 1)$; $3x + y = 19$ 29. $f(x, y) = x^2 \cos y$; $(a, b) = (1, \pi/2)$; $4x - 26y = 4 - 13\pi$

27. $f(x, y) = x^2 + y^2$; $(a, b) = (2, 1)$; $x - 4y = -2$ 30. $f(x, y) = x^3 \sin y$; $(a, b) = (1, \pi)$; $2x + y = 2 + \pi$

In each of #31–34 the point (x, y) moves according to $\langle x(t), y(t) \rangle = \mathbf{r}(t)$. Use the Chain Rule for Paths to calculate df/dt at the given time.

31. $\mathbf{r}(t) = \langle 3t + 1, 11 - 5t \rangle$; $f(x, y) = x^2 + x \ln y$, $t = 2$

32. $\mathbf{r}(t) = \langle 2 - 7t, 5t - 2 \rangle$; $f(x, y) = (y + 6)^2 e^{x+5}$, $t = 1$

33. $\mathbf{r}(t) = \langle \sqrt{t}, \frac{4}{3t+1} \rangle$; $f(x, y) = 8x + 5y$, $t = 4$

34. $\mathbf{r}(t) = \langle e^t, t \cos t \rangle$; $f(x, y) = 13x - 7y$, $t = 0$

In each of #35–38 use the Chain Rule for Paths to calculate df/dt at the specified time, given that the point (x, y, z) moves according to $\langle x(t), y(t), z(t) \rangle = \mathbf{r}(t)$.

35. $\mathbf{r}(t) = \langle 8t - 1, 1 - 2t, 2 + 8t \rangle$, $f(x, y, z) = z + \sin(\pi x + y)$, $t = 0.5$

36. $\mathbf{r}(t) = \langle 3 \cos(t), t^3 - t - 1, \sin(t) \rangle$, $f(x, y, z) = \ln(z + x + y)$, $t = \pi$

37. $\mathbf{r}(t) = \langle \frac{t}{t^2+1}, t3^t, t^2 \sin \pi t \rangle$, $f(x, y, z) = xe^{7z+5y}$, $t = 2$

38. $\mathbf{r}(t) = \langle \frac{3t}{t^2+1}, e^{6t/(t+5)}, \ln t \rangle$, $f(x, y, z) = \frac{x}{z^4 + \sqrt{y}}$, $t = 1$

In #39–44 the variables x and y change according to $\mathbf{r}(t)$. Use the Chain Rule for Paths to determine df/dt at the specified value of t. The following tables provide data regarding the partial derivatives of f at points in the plane.

$y = 3$	14	13	12
$y = 2$	13	11	9
$y = 1$	12	10	11
	$x = 4$	$x = 5$	$x = 6$

Values of $f_x(x,y)$

$y = 3$	2	0	-2
$y = 2$	3	1	-1
$y = 1$	4	3	0
	$x = 4$	$x = 5$	$x = 6$

Values of $f_y(x,y)$

39. $\mathbf{r}(t) = \langle -10 + 2t, 10 - t \rangle; \ t = 7$ 42. $\mathbf{r}(t) = \langle \frac{5t^2 - 2}{t+4}, t^2 - 2t + 3 \rangle; \ t = 2$

40. $\mathbf{r}(t) = \langle 5t - 4, t - 1 \rangle; \ t = 2$ 43. $\mathbf{r}(t) = \langle 5t + \ln t, \cos(\ln t) \rangle; \ t = 1$

41. $\mathbf{r}(t) = \langle 4 + t^2, 4 + \cos \pi t \rangle; \ t = 1$ 44. $\mathbf{r}(t) = \langle \frac{8t+4}{t+1}, e^{t-1} \rangle; \ t = 1$

✤ 13.6 Concept and Application Exercises

45. Suppose $\mathbf{r}_1(t) = \langle \cos t, \sin t \rangle$, $\mathbf{r}_2(t) = \langle \cos 2t, \sin 2t \rangle$, and $f(x, y) = 3x + 4y$.
    (a) Verify that $\mathbf{r}_1(t)$ and $\mathbf{r}_2(t)$ parameterize the same curve, and that $\mathbf{r}_1(\pi/4) = \mathbf{r}_2(\pi/8)$.
    (b) Calculate df/dt at time $t = \pi/4$ when the point (x, y) moves according to $\mathbf{r}_1(t)$.
    (c) Calculate df/dt at time $t = \pi/8$ when the point (x, y) moves according to $\mathbf{r}_2(t)$.
    (d) Explain why the numbers you found in parts (b) and (c) are different, in spite of part (a).

46. Suppose $\mathbf{r}_1(t) = \langle 5 + 2t, 7 - 3t \rangle$, $\mathbf{r}_2(t) = \langle 15 - 2t, -8 + 3t \rangle$, and $f(x, y) = 6x + 4y + 1$.
    (a) Eliminate the parameter to show that $\mathbf{r}_1(t)$ and $\mathbf{r}_2(t)$ parameterize the same curve.
    (b) Verify that $\mathbf{r}_1(2) = \mathbf{r}_2(3)$, and $\|\mathbf{r}_1'(t)\| = \|\mathbf{r}_2'(t)\|$.
    (c) Calculate df/dt at time $t = 2$ when the point (x, y) moves according to $\mathbf{r}_1(t)$.
    (d) Calculate df/dt at time $t = 3$ when the point (x, y) moves according to $\mathbf{r}_2(t)$.
    (e) Explain why the numbers you found in parts (c) and (d) are different, in spite of parts (a) and (b).

In exercises #47–54 determine the direction we should move away from the given point in order to affect the most rapid increase in f.

47. $f(x, y) = xy^3 - x^3 y; \ (-4, 2)$ 51. $f(x, y, z) = x \ln(x) + y^4 z; \ (1, 2, 3)$

48. $f(x, y) = x/\sqrt{x+y}; \ (1, 2)$ 52. $f(x, y, z) = x/(y+z); \ (5, -7, 9)$

49. $f(x, y) = xy \sin x; \ (\pi/4, 2)$ 53. $f(x, y, z) = \sin(x^2 + y^2 + z^2); \ (0, 3, -1)$

50. $f(x, y) = y^2 \cos x; \ (\pi/4, 2)$ 54. $f(x, y, z) = \cos(x^2 - 6y^2 + 8z^2); \ (3, 5, 0)$

Exercises #55–56 refer the values of $f(x, y)$ shown in the table below.

$y = 3.3$	4.9	5.5	4.7	4.6
$y = 3.2$	5.1	5	4.9	5.1
$y = 3.1$	4.3	4.5	4.6	4.7
$y = 3$	4	4.1	4.3	4.6
	$x = 1$	$x = 1.1$	$x = 1.2$	$x = 1.3$

55. Use the table of data above to approximate the direction in which f is increasing most rapidly at the point $(1.2, 3.1)$.

56. Use the table of data above to approximate the direction in which f is increasing most rapidly at the point $(1.1, 3.2)$.

57. Several level curves of f are shown in Figure 6.6. Determine whether $D_\mathbf{u} f$, $D_\mathbf{v} f$ and $D_\mathbf{w} f$ are positive, negative, or zero.

58. The level curves of f are shown in Figure 6.7. Determine (a) $D_\mathbf{u} f$ at $(0, 0)$ when $\mathbf{u} = \langle 1, 1 \rangle$, (b) $D_\mathbf{u} f$ at $(0, 0)$ when $\mathbf{u} = \langle -1, 1 \rangle$. (c) What do your answers from parts (a) and (b) tell you about $\nabla f(0, 0)$?

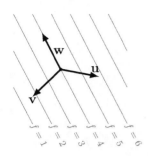

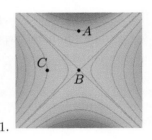

Figure 6.6: Level curves of f in #57.   Figure 6.7: Level curves of f in #58.

In each of #59–62 level curves of a function $f(x, y)$ are shown. Draw the vector ∇f at each of the points $\mathbf{A}$, $\mathbf{B}$, and $\mathbf{C}$. (The planes are colored so that blue corresponds to low function value, green corresponds to medium function value, and red corresponds to high function value.)

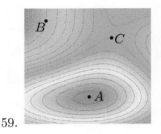

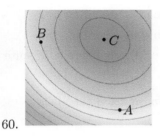

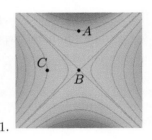

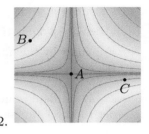

59.   60.   61.   62.

63. Suppose $f(x, y) = e^{x^2 + y^2}$.

   (a) Draw the level curve of f that passes through $(1, 0)$, and draw ∇f at the point $(1, 0)$.
   (b) Verify that $\mathbf{r}(t) = \langle \cos(t), \sin(t) \rangle$ parameterizes the curve you drew in part (a).
   (c) Draw the vector $\mathbf{r}'(0)$ at $(1, 0)$ on your graph from part (a).
   (d) Based on geometry displayed in part (c), what should be true about df/dt at $t = 0$? Calculate df/dt and see if your prediction is right.

64. Suppose x and y change according to $\mathbf{r}(t) = \langle 3 + 4t, -7 + t^2 \rangle$, and $f(x, y) = x^2 - y^2$.

   (a) Draw the path that's parameterized by $\mathbf{r}(t)$.
   (b) Plot the vector $\mathbf{r}'(2)$ with its tail at $\mathbf{r}(2)$.
   (c) Draw the level curve of f that passes through $\mathbf{r}(2)$.
   (d) Draw the vector $\nabla f(x(2), y(2))$ with its tail at $\mathbf{r}(2)$.
   (e) Based on the vectors that you determined in parts (b) and (d), calculate df/dt at $t = 2$.

65. Suppose $D_{\mathbf{u}} f = 3$ and $D_{\mathbf{v}} f = 4$ at $(1, 22)$ when $\mathbf{u} = \langle 3, 5 \rangle$ and $\mathbf{v} = \langle -2, 7 \rangle$. Determine $\frac{d}{dt} f(x(t), y(t))$ at time $t = 3$ when $x(t) = 7 - 2t$ and $y(t) = 9t - 5$.

66. Suppose $f(x, y) = x^3 - 4y^2$.

   (a) Show that $\mathbf{u}(t) = \langle 3 + 2t, 5 + 4t \rangle$ and $\mathbf{v}(t) = \langle -5 + 6t, -9 + 12t \rangle$ parameterize the same line, moving in the same direction,
   (b) Show that $\mathbf{u}(2) = \mathbf{v}(2)$, and determine ∇f at that point.
   (c) Determine $\mathbf{u}'(2)$ and $\mathbf{v}'(2)$.

(d) Suppose x and y change according to $\mathbf{u}(t)$. Use ∇f from (b) and $\mathbf{u}'(2)$ from part (c) to determine df/dt when $t = 2$.

(e) Suppose x and y change according to $\mathbf{v}(t)$. Use ∇f from (b) and $\mathbf{v}'(2)$ from part (c) to determine df/dt when $t = 2$.

(f) Explain why your answers to parts (c) and (d) are different, in spite of the fact that $\mathbf{u}(2) = \mathbf{v}(2)$.

67. Suppose $f(x, y) = 3x^2 + y^2$, where x and y change according to $\mathbf{r}(t) = \langle 14 + 2t, -1 + 8t \rangle$.

   (a) Use the formulas for $x(t)$ and $y(t)$ to rewrite f as a function of t.

   (b) Determine the value of t that minimizes f, which we'll call t^*.

   (c) Determine $\mathbf{r}'(t^*)$ and ∇f at $(x(t^*), y(t^*))$.

   (d) Show that the vectors from part (c) are orthogonal.

68. Figure 6.8 shows level curves of f, and the linear path parameterized by $\mathbf{r}(t) = \langle x(t), y(t) \rangle$.

   (a) Locate the point at which $df/dt = 0$, and label it as P.

   (b) Suppose $P = (x(t^*), y(t^*))$. Assuming that $x'(t^*) > 0$, draw $\mathbf{r}'(t^*)$ and ∇f at P.

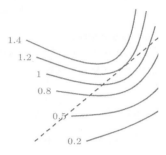

Figure 6.8: The graph for #68. Gray curves are level curves of f, labeled with the associated function value. The blue, dashed line is the path parameterized by $\mathbf{r}(t)$.

69. Suppose f is a differentiable function, and x and y change according to $\mathbf{r}(t) = \langle 1 + 7t, 2 + 8t \rangle$. Then we can think of f as a function of t along the line parameterized by $\mathbf{r}(t)$. (a) Determine $\mathbf{r}'(t)$, and (b) use the Chain Rule to show that $df/dt = 0$ when ∇f and $\mathbf{r}'(t)$ are orthogonal.

70. Suppose f is a differentiable function, and x and y change according to $\mathbf{r}(t) = \langle a + \alpha t, b + \beta t \rangle$, where $a, b, \alpha, \beta \in \mathbb{R}$ are arbitrary, nonzero constants. Then we can think of f as a function of t along the line parameterized by $\mathbf{r}(t)$. (a) Determine $\mathbf{r}'(t)$, and (b) use the Chain Rule to show that $df/dt = 0$ when ∇f and $\mathbf{r}'(t)$ are orthogonal.

71. Verify that $\nabla f(a, b) \cdot \langle 1, 0 \rangle = f_x(a, b)$, and explain this fact geometrically.

72. Suppose $f(x, y)$ is a differentiable function.

   (a) What's the normal vector for the tangent plane to the graph of f at $(a, b, f(a, b))$?

   (b) Suppose we define $g(x, y, z) = f(x, y) - z$. What's the relationship between the graph of f, and the level surface $g(x, y, z) = 0$?

   (c) Compare the formula for ∇g to your answer from part (a).

73. Determine ∇f if $D_{\mathbf{u}} f = 2$ and $D_{\mathbf{v}} f = 5$, where $\mathbf{u} = \langle 2, 7 \rangle$ and $\mathbf{v} = \langle 3, -4 \rangle$.

74. Determine ∇f if $D_{\mathbf{u}} f = 3$ and $D_{\mathbf{v}} f = -1$, where $\mathbf{u} = \langle 4, 5 \rangle$ and $\mathbf{v} = \langle -3, 2 \rangle$.

75. Suppose $f(3, 2) = 7$, $D_{\mathbf{u}} f = 12$ and $D_{\mathbf{v}} f = 51$, where $\mathbf{u} = \langle 1, -1 \rangle$ and $\mathbf{v} = \langle 1, 1 \rangle$. Parameterize the tangent line to the graph of f in the x-direction that passes through the point $(3, 2, 7)$.

76. Suppose $f(-4, 1) = 8$, $D_{\mathbf{u}} f = 21$ and $D_{\mathbf{v}} f = 15$, where $\mathbf{u} = \langle -2, -6 \rangle$ and $\mathbf{v} = \langle 10, 1 \rangle$. Parameterize the tangent line to the graph of f in the y-direction that passes through the point $(-4, 1, 8)$.

77. The Ideal Gas Law describes pressure as a function of temperature T, and volume V, by $P(T,V) = Nk_{\mathrm{B}}\frac{T}{V}$, where N is the (fixed) number of atoms in the gas, and k_{B} is Boltzmann's constant. If the temperature in a piston is 300 kelvins, and the current volume is 0.3 m^3, how should we change the temperature and volume (together) in order to affect the most rapid rise in pressure? Be exact.

78. The Ideal Gas Law describes pressure as a function of temperature T, volume V, and the number of mols of a gas, n, by $P(T,V,n) = R\frac{nT}{V}$, where R is the Ideal Gas Constant. If an ideal gas in a piston has a temperature of 427 kelvins, its current volume is 0.2 m^3, and there are 7 mols of gas present, how should we change the pressure, volume, and number of atoms (together) in order to affect the most rapid rise in pressure?

      ⎯ | Chemistry |

79. The stereographic projection was introduced in Section 1.3 during our discussion of rational functions. In that discussion we projected points from the x-axis onto a circle of radius 1 centered at $(0,1)$. Now let's project onto the circle of radius r that's centered at $(0,b)$, where $0 < r < b$. We'll denote by $x_1(r,b)$ the x-coordinate of the stereographic projection of 1 onto that circle, as seen in Figure 6.9.

   (a) Derive a formula for $x_1(r,b)$.

   (b) Suppose $b = 0.5$ and $r = 0.5$ (in which case the circle rests on the x-axis). How should we change r and b simultaneously in order to affect the most rapid increase in $x_1(r,b)$?

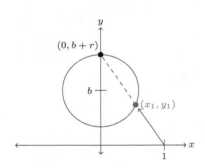

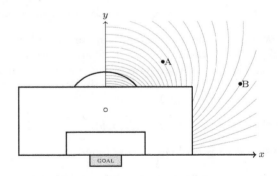

Figure 6.9: The stereographic projection, as in exercise #79.   Figure 6.10: The level curves for exercise #80.

80. Exercise #47 in Section 13.2 introduced a formula for the width, w, of a wall of soccer players defending against a free kick. (a) The formula for w was expressed in terms of r and θ. Multiply it by r/r and then rewrite w in terms of x and y. (b) Level curves of $w(x,y)$ are shown in Figure 6.10. Draw a vector at points A and B indicating the direction of $\nabla w(x,y)$. (c) Determine a formula for ∇w.

      ⎯ | Sports/Recreation |

81. Figure 6.11 depicts the temperature on a metal plate in degrees Fahrenheit, where distance is measured in centimeters. Suppose a lady bug lands at the point $(-1,0)$ and walks toward the point A at 0.5 cm/sec, and the temperature is held steady at all points on the plate.

   (a) If the temperature at (x,y) is $T(x,y)$, use the level curves of T to approximate the ∇T at the point A.

   (b) Uses the Chain Rule for paths to approximate the rate of change in the temperature experienced by the lady bug as it passes through point A.

82. This exercise is a variation of #81. Suppose the lady bug lands at $(-1, 0)$ and walks toward point B at 0.5 cm/sec. Figure 6.11 shows the temperature of the plate at the moment the lady bug lands, but the plate is cooling uniformly at 2 °F per second. Approximate the rate of change in the temperature experienced by the bug as it passes through point A.

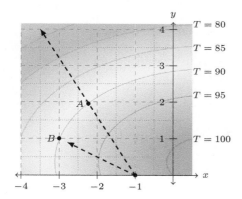

Figure 6.11: Point A is for #81, and point B for #82.

83. The annual cost of storing goods in a warehouse is $c(n, N) = 50n + 32\frac{N}{n}$ when we take N units of inventory (per year) from our supplier in n orders ($50 is the handling fee per order, and $32N/n$ is the cost of floor space in the warehouse). Suppose we currently restock the warehouse 12 times per year, and order 13,000 units with each order. How should we change our procedures in order to make the most aggressive reduction in the cost associated with warehousing our product?

       Business

84. A person's *body mass index* (BMI) is $I = m/h^2$ where h is the person's height (in meters), m is his mass (in kilograms). Suppose a child is 1.75 meters tall, and his mass is 70 kg.

       Medical Sciences

   (a) Calculate the child's BMI.

   (b) Determine ∇I at $(m, h) = (70, 1.75)$.

   (c) Based on part (b), determine the rate of weight gain (in kg/month) needed to maintain his BMI if the child is growing at a rate of 1 cm per month.

85. When three resistors with resistance x, y and z ohms are wired in parallel, their combined resistance is $R = \frac{xyz}{yz+xz+xy}$ ohms.

       Electrical Engineering

   (a) Determine R when $x = 20$ ohms, $y = 30$ ohms, and $z = 40$ ohms.

   (b) Calculate $\nabla R(20, 30, 40)$.

   (c) Based on your answer from (b), if $x = 20$ remains fixed but z decreases at a rate of 0.01 ohms per second, determine the rate of change in y necessary to maintain R.

86. Suppose we want to use the Newton-Raphson Method to approximate the solution to the system of equations $f(x, y) = 0$ and $g(x, y) = 0$, starting at the point (a, b). Show that if $f(a, b) = 0$ but $g(a, b) \neq 0$ the first iteration of the method will move us away from (a, b) in a direction that's tangent to the curve $f(x, y) = 0$.

       Mathematics

13.7   The Chain Rule

The arguments of a multivariable function can themselves be multivariable functions. For example, economists often describe an individual's satisfaction as a function (called a *utility function*) of consumption, c. If we partition a person's life into two stages, say young and old, we could write utility as $U(c_1, c_2)$. The consumption in the first stage of life depends on both how much wealth is earned and how much is saved, so we write it as $c_1(w_1, s)$. The consumption in the second stage depends on how much wealth is earned, and s, so we write it as $c_2(w_2, s)$. In this section we develop the mathematical ideas and techniques that allow us to investigate, for example, how utility changes (and at what rate) as s increases.

> **Key Idea(s):** *When x and y depend on several independent variables, we can hold all but one fixed and so calculate the rate of change in $f(x, y)$ using the Chain Rule for Paths from the previous section.*
>
> *The level curve $f(x, y) = 0$ may define y as a function of x. In such cases, the partial derivatives of f can be used to determine dy/dx.*
>
> *These ideas extend seamlessly to functions of more than two variables.*

❖ The Chain Rule

In the previous section we introduced the Chain Rule for Paths, which says that

$$\frac{d}{dt}f(x, y) = \frac{\partial f}{\partial x}\frac{dx}{dt} + \frac{\partial f}{\partial y}\frac{dy}{dt} \tag{7.1}$$

when x and y are differentiable functions of t. In the discussion that follows we generalize this fact by considering the case when x and y are themselves functions of more than a single variable, say t_1 and t_2. Since there is more than one independent variable, each "d" in equation (7.1) becomes a "∂," and we write

$$\frac{\partial}{\partial t_1}f(x, y) = \frac{\partial f}{\partial x}\frac{\partial x}{\partial t_1} + \frac{\partial f}{\partial y}\frac{\partial y}{\partial t_1}.$$

> You might find it helpful to think of t_1 as quantifying some physical characteristic of an object, such as the roughness of its surface (which affects aerodynamic forces), and to think of t_2 as time. Then in order to talk about an object's position (which depends on time) along a trajectory (which depends on the object's physical features), we need $x(t_1, t_2)$ and $y(t_1, t_2)$.

This may appear to be a mere typographic change, but the notation communicates an important idea. Although $x(t_1, t_2)$ and $y(t_1, t_2)$ depend on two independent parameters, we're holding t_2 fixed, which effectively makes x and y functions of a single variable, t_1, so they parameterize a curve in the xy-plane and we can use the Chain Rule for Paths to calculate the rate of change in f as (x, y) traverses it. This idea is stated in general below.

Chain Rule: Suppose f is a differentiable function of $x_1, x_2, \ldots, x_n$, all of which are differentiable functions of $t_1, t_2, \ldots, t_m$. Then

$$\frac{\partial f}{\partial t_j} = \frac{\partial f}{\partial x_1}\frac{\partial x_1}{\partial t_j} + \frac{\partial f}{\partial x_2}\frac{\partial x_2}{\partial t_j} + \cdots + \frac{\partial f}{\partial x_n}\frac{\partial x_n}{\partial t_j}. \tag{7.2}$$

> The notation ∂t_j indicates that all of the t-variables except t_j are being held fixed, so this equation the result of the Chain Rule for Paths.

Using the Chain Rule with a function of two variables

Example 7.1. Suppose the xy-coordinates of a runner are $x = 30\cos\left(2t_1/(35+t_2)\right)$ and $y = 50\sin\left(2t_1/(35+t_2)\right)$, where t_1 is the length of time she's been running (in seconds), and $35 + t_2$ is the air temperature (in °C). If the runner is on a hill where the altitude is described by $f(x, y) = 0.2y - 0.3x$, and length is measured in meters, determine a formula for $\partial f/\partial t_1$ and explain what it tells us.

Solution: In this case the Chain Rule tells us that

$$\frac{\partial f}{\partial t_1} = \frac{\partial f}{\partial x}\frac{\partial x}{\partial t_1} + \frac{\partial f}{\partial y}\frac{\partial y}{\partial t_1} = -0.3\frac{\partial x}{\partial t_1} + 0.2\frac{\partial y}{\partial t_1} = \frac{18\sin\left(\frac{2t_1}{35+t_2}\right)}{35 + t_2} + \frac{20\cos\left(\frac{2t_1}{35+t_2}\right)}{35 + t_2}.$$

Based on the units of f and t_1, this partial derivative has units of $\frac{\text{m}}{\text{sec}}$. It's the rate at which the runner's altitude is changing with respect to time.   ∎

Using the Chain Rule with a function of three variables

Example 7.2. Suppose $f(x, y, z) = x^2 + yz$, where $x = st^2$, $y = s^4 + t^4$, and $z(t) = s + e^{st}$. Use the Chain Rule to determine $\partial f / \partial t$ when $t = 3$ and $s = 0$.

Solution: The Chain Rule tells us that

$$\frac{\partial f}{\partial t} = \frac{\partial f}{\partial x}\frac{\partial x}{\partial t} + \frac{\partial f}{\partial y}\frac{\partial y}{\partial t} + \frac{\partial f}{\partial z}\frac{\partial z}{\partial t}.$$

We begin by determining formulas for the relevant partial derivatives,

$$\frac{\partial f}{\partial x} = 2x \qquad\qquad \frac{\partial f}{\partial y} = z \qquad\qquad \frac{\partial f}{\partial z} = y$$

$$\frac{\partial x}{\partial t} = 2st \qquad\qquad \frac{\partial y}{\partial t} = 4t^3 \qquad\qquad \frac{\partial z}{\partial t} = se^{st}.$$

When $t = 3$ and $s = 0$, we find that $x = 0$, $y = 81$ and $z = 1$. Then using the formulas above, we see that $x_t = 0$, $y_t = 108$, $z_t = 0$, $f_x = 0$, $f_y = 1$, and $f_z = 81$. Now we calculate

$$\frac{\partial f}{\partial t} = \nabla f \cdot \langle x_t, y_t, z_t \rangle = \langle 0, 1, 81 \rangle \cdot \langle 0, 108, 0 \rangle = 108. \qquad \blacksquare$$

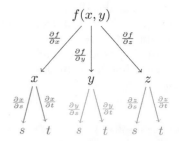

Figure 7.1: The dependence structure for Example 7.2. The value of f depends on x, y and z, each of which depends on s and t. To calculate df/dt, multiply the derivatives along each path in the diagram from f to t, and then add the results together.

Using the Chain Rule with a function of three variables

Example 7.3. Suppose $f(x, y, z) = x + y^2 + z \ln x$, where $x = s + t$, $y = s^2 + t^{-1}$, and $z(t) = \ln st$. Use the Chain Rule to determine $\partial f / \partial s$ when $t = 2$ and $s = 1$.

Answer: $\frac{\partial f}{\partial s} = 7 + \frac{1}{3} \ln 54$ $\qquad\qquad \blacksquare$

Solution On-line

✣ Implicit Differentiation

We opened this section by discussing a utility function, $U(c_1, c_2)$, which models an individual's satisfaction as a function of consumption. Suppose you want to consume less in the first half of life but maintain your overall satisfaction, meaning that c_1 changes but the value of U remains constant. Intuitively speaking, this can only happen if c_2 varies in response to changes in c_1, which leads us to think of c_2 as a function of c_1. This kind of thinking is correct in many cases, as specified by the following theorem.

> **Implicit Function Theorem (for two variables):** Suppose (a, b) is an interior point of the domain of f, and $k = f(a, b)$. If $f_y(a, b) \neq 0$ and the partial derivatives of f are continuous, the level curve $f(x, y) = k$ implicitly defines y as a differentiable function of x near (a, b). Moreover, $y'(x)$ is continuous, and the slope of the tangent line to the curve at (a, b) is
>
> $$\left.\frac{dy}{dx}\right|_{(a,b)} = -\frac{f_x(a, b)}{f_y(a, b)}. \qquad (7.3)$$

The rigorous proof of the Implicit Function Theorem is substantial, and is usually presented in advanced classes, but you can remember equation (7.3) by applying some simple algebra to the total differential. Since the value of f remains constant as the point (x, y) moves along the level curve $f(x, y) = k$, the linear approximation of change in f is $df = 0$. That is,

$$0 = f_x \, dx + f_y \, dy \quad \Rightarrow \quad \frac{dy}{dx} = -\frac{f_x}{f_y}.$$

For a rigorous proof of the Implicit Function Theorem, see *Principles of Mathematical Analysis* by Walter Rudin.

Clearly, we cannot divide by f_y if it's 0, but you can also understand the hypothesis that $f_y(a,b) \neq 0$ in geometric way. We know from Section 13.6 that $\nabla f(a,b)$ is orthogonal to the level curve of f that runs through (a,b). More specifically, the vector ∇f is orthogonal to the curve's tangent line. So intuitively speaking, the tangent line is vertical when $\nabla f(a,b)$ is a multiple of $\mathbf{i}$ (which happens when $f_y(a,b) = 0$). The slope of such a line is undefined, and as you see in Figure 7.2, the curve might not even define y as a function of x near such a point.

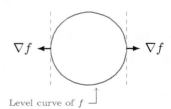

Figure 7.2: A curve might not define y as a function of x where its tangent line is vertical, as in the case of the circle.

Using the Implicit Function Theorem for two variables

Example 7.4. The point $(2,1)$ is on the level curve $f(x,y) = 8$ when $f(x,y) = yx^3 + x\sin\pi y$. (a) Show that this curve defines y as a function of x near $(2,1)$, and (b) determine the slope of the tangent line at $(2,1)$.

Solution: (a) We begin by checking the partial derivatives, $f_x = 3yx^2 + \sin\pi y$ and $f_y = x^3 + \pi x\cos\pi y$. These are both continuous, and $f_y(2,1) \neq 0$, so the Implicit Function Theorem guarantees that y is a function of x near $(2,1)$. (b) Since $f_x(2,1) = 12$ and $f_y(2,1) = 8 - 2\pi$, the tangent line to $f(x,y) = 8$ at the point $(2,1)$ has a slope of

$$\left.\frac{dy}{dx}\right|_{(2,1)} = -\frac{f_x(2,1)}{f_y(2,1)} = -\frac{12}{8-2\pi}. \qquad \blacksquare$$

Using the Implicit Function Theorem for two variables

Example 7.5. The point $(-1,3)$ is on the level curve $f(x,y) = 29$ when $f(x,y) = y + x^2y^3 + x^5$. (a) Show that this curve defines y as a function of x near $(-1,3)$, and (b) determine the slope of the tangent line at $(-1,3)$.

Answer: (b) $\left.\frac{dy}{dx}\right|_{(-1,3)} = \frac{7}{4}$. $\qquad \blacksquare$

Solution On-line

Application to economics (utility functions and the marginal rate of substitution)

Example 7.6. In the introduction to this section we discussed the relationship among wealth, savings, consumption, and utility, which we denote by w, s, c and U respectively. Suppose that consumption in the first half of life is $c_1(w_1, s) = w_1 - s$, and in the second half of life is $c_2 = w_2 + (1+r)s$, where r is the prevailing interest rate expected on savings. Use the Implicit Function Theorem to derive a formula for the rate at which c_2 changes in response to increasing c_1 (due to a reduction in savings) when an individual maintains constant utility.

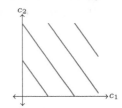

When economists quantify satisfaction, they call it utility.

Solution: The term "constant utility" means that an individual makes changes that do not affect the value of U, which is a function of c_1 and c_2. In order to remain on a level curve of U in the c_1c_2-plane (called an *indifference curve*), the Implicit Function Theorem tells us that c_2 changes with c_1 at a rate of

$$\frac{dc_2}{dc_1} = -\frac{\partial U/\partial c_1}{\partial U/\partial c_2}. \qquad (7.4)$$

We can simplify this equation by using the Chain Rule. Since c_1 is increasing because s is changing, and the value of U is constant during this change,

$$0 = \frac{dU}{ds} = \frac{\partial U}{\partial c_1}\frac{\partial c_1}{\partial s} + \frac{\partial U}{\partial c_2}\frac{\partial c_2}{\partial s} = \frac{\partial U}{\partial c_1}(-1) + \frac{\partial U}{\partial c_2}(1+r),$$

from which we conclude that

$$\frac{\partial U/\partial c_1}{\partial U/\partial c_2} = 1 + r.$$

Figure 7.3: Lines along which $\frac{dc_2}{dc_1} = -(1+r)$.

By substituting this into equation (7.4) we see that $dc_2/dc_1 = -(1+r)$, which means that we "trade away" $\$(1+r)$ of spending when old for each $\$1$ increase of spending when young. The ratio $(1+r):1$ is called the *marginal rate of substitution*. ∎

▷ Life in 3-D

The same ideas can be applied to functions of three variables. In this case, the surface $f(x,y,z) = k$ defines z as a function of x and y (implicitly) provided that the tangent plane is not vertical. Since ∇f is orthogonal to the tangent plane, that's the same as saying that $f_z \neq 0$.

> **Implicit Function Theorem (for three variables):** Suppose (a,b,c) is an interior point of the domain of f, and $k = f(a,b,c)$. If $f_z(a,b,c) \neq 0$ and the partial derivatives of f are continuous, the surface $f(x,y,z) = k$ implicitly defines z as a differentiable function of x and y near (a,b,c). Moreover, z_x and z_y are continuous, and
>
> $$z_x(a,b) = -\frac{f_x(a,b,c)}{f_z(a,b,c)} \quad \text{and} \quad z_y(a,b) = -\frac{f_y(a,b,c)}{f_z(a,b,c)}. \qquad (7.5)$$

Using the Implicit Function Theorem for three variables

Example 7.7. The point $(1,4,0)$ is on the surface $f(x,y,z) = 20$ when $f(x,y,z) = y^2 e^z + y\sqrt{x} + xz\sqrt{y}$. (a) Show that this surface defines z as a function of x and y near $(1,4,0)$, and (b) determine the partial derivatives of $z(x,y)$ at $(1,4)$.

Solution: (a) The partial derivatives of f are

$$f_x = \frac{y}{2\sqrt{x}} + z\sqrt{y}, \quad f_y = 2ye^z + \sqrt{x} + \frac{xz}{2\sqrt{y}}, \quad \text{and} \quad f_z = y^2 e^z + x\sqrt{y},$$

all of which are continuous near $(1,4,0)$, and $f_z(1,4,0) \neq 0$, so the Implicit Function Theorem guarantees that z is a function of x and y near the point $(1,4,0)$. (b) The Implicit Function Theorem tells us that the values of z_x and z_y at $(1,4)$ are

$$z_x(1,4) = -\frac{f_x(1,4,0)}{f_z(1,4,0)} = -\frac{1}{9}, \quad \text{and} \quad z_y(1,4) = -\frac{f_y(1,4,0)}{f_z(1,4,0)} = -\frac{1}{2}. \qquad ∎$$

Using the Implicit Function Theorem for three variables

Example 7.8. The point $(4,38,8)$ is on the surface $f(x,y,z) = 5$ when $f(x,y,z) = \frac{1}{x} + \frac{y}{z}$. (a) Show that the equation $f(x,y,z) = 5$ defines z as a function of x and y near $(4,38,8)$, and (b) determine the partial derivatives of $z(x,y)$.

Answer: (b) $z_x = 2/19$ and $z_y = -4/19$. ∎

Solution On-line

Tangent plane to the graph of an implicit function

Example 7.9. Suppose $f(x,y,z) = (x-z)^4 + \ln z + \sin(y-z)$. Then the point $(2,1,1)$ is on the surface described by $f(x,y,z) = 1$. (a) Show that z is a function of x and y in the vicinity of the point. Then determine (b) z_x and z_y at the point $(2,1)$, and (c) the tangent plane to the surface at $(2,1,1)$.

Solution: The domain of f all of 3-space, so $(2,1,1)$ is certainly an interior point, and the partial derivatives of f are

$$f_x = 4(x-z)^3, \quad f_y = \cos(y-z), \quad \text{and} \quad f_z = -4(x-z)^3 + \frac{1}{z} - \cos(y-z),$$

which are continuous near $(2, 1, 1)$. Further, since $f_z(2, 1, 1) = -4 \neq 0$, the Implicit Function Theorem tells us that z is a function of x and y.

(b) We can use equation (7.5) to determine z_x and z_y at the given point. Specifically, since $f_x(2, 1, 1) = 4$, $f_y(2, 1, 1) = 1$ and $f_z(2, 1, 1) = -4$, we know that

$$z_x(2, 1) = -\frac{f_x(2, 1, 1)}{f_z(2, 1, 1)} = 1 \quad \text{and} \quad z_y(2, 1) = -\frac{f_y(2, 1, 1)}{f_z(2, 1, 1)} = \frac{1}{4}.$$

(c) Since the surface is a level set of f, the vector $\nabla f(2, 1, 1) = \langle 4, 1, -4 \rangle$ is normal to the tangent plane. And since the point $(2, 1, 1)$ is on the plane, we know that its equation is

$$\langle 4, 1, -4 \rangle \cdot \langle x, y, z \rangle = \langle 4, 1, -4 \rangle \cdot \langle 2, 1, 1 \rangle$$
$$4x + y - 4z = 5. \tag{7.6}$$

We can arrive at the same equation by using our calculations in part (b). Since $z_y(2, 1) = 1/4$, the tangent line in the y-direction rises 1 unit for every 4-unit increase in y, so the vector $\mathbf{v} = \langle 0, 4, 1 \rangle$ points along it. Similarly, because $z_x(2, 1) = 1$ the tangent line that extends in the x-direction has a slope of 1. That is, it extends in the direction of $\mathbf{u} = \langle 1, 0, 1 \rangle$. Since $\mathbf{v}$ and $\mathbf{u}$ are tangent to the surface, the vector $\mathbf{v} \times \mathbf{u} = \langle 4, 1, -4 \rangle$ is normal to the tangent plane (compare to equation (7.6)).   ∎

You should know

- the Chain Rule;
- the Implicit Function Theorem (for two and three variables).

You should be able to

- use the Chain Rule to determine $\partial f/\partial t$ when f is a function of two or more variables, all of which depend on t and other variables;
- use the Implicit Function Theorem to determine dy/dx, $\partial z/\partial y$, and $\partial z/\partial y$.

✤ 13.7 Skill Exercises

In #1–4 (a) determine ∇f at the point $\big(x(r, \theta), y(r, \theta)\big)$, and (b) use the Chain Rule to calculate f_r and f_θ at the given point, where $x(r, \theta) = r\cos(\theta)$ and $y(r, \theta) = r\sin(\theta)$.

1. $f(x, y) = 3x + 6y$; $(r, \theta) = (2, \pi/6)$
3. $f(x, y) = x^2\sqrt{y}$; $(r, \theta) = (1, \pi/4)$

2. $f(x, y) = 4x - 7y$; $(r, \theta) = (8, \pi/4)$
4. $f(x, y) = x^{1/3}e^y$; $(r, \theta) = (1, \pi)$

In #5–10 (a) determine ∇f at the point $(x(s, t), y(s, t))$, and (b) use the Chain Rule to calculate f_s and f_t at the given point.

5. $f(x, y) = 13x + 9y$; $x = 3s + 2t$, $y = 5s - 8t$; $(s, t) = (2, 3)$

6. $f(x, y) = 8x - 7y$; $x = 13s - 6t$, $y = 2s + 18t$; $(s, t) = (1, 2)$

7. $f(x, y) = x^2\sqrt{x + y}$; $x = 10s - 3t$, $y = 3s + 2t$; $(s, t) = (2, 1)$

8. $f(x, y) = y^2\sqrt{5x + 4y}$; $x = 2s + 8t$, $y = 5s - t$; $(s, t) = (3, 2)$

9. $f(x, y) = \sin(\pi x + 0.5\pi y)$; $x = st^2$, $y = s\sqrt{t}$; $(s, t) = (2, 4)$

10. $f(x,y) = \cos(0.25\pi\sqrt{7x + 2y})$; $x = 2s/t$, $y = 10s - 4t$; $(s,t) = (0.5, 1)$

In #11–16 the variables x, y, and z depend on s and t. At the specified point (s,t) determine (a) x, y and z, (b) the partial derivatives f_x, f_y and f_z, and then (c) use the Chain Rule to determine f_s and f_t.

11. $f(x,y,z) = 5x - 4y + 11z$; $\langle x,y,z \rangle = \langle 19s + 2t, 3 + 2s, -9t + 1 \rangle$; $(s,t) = (1, -1)$

12. $f(x,y,z) = 2x + 9y - 3z$; $\langle x,y,z \rangle = \langle 20st, s - t, s + t \rangle$; $(s,t) = (2,2)$

13. $f(x,y,z) = x^2 + 4y - z^3$; $\langle x,y,z \rangle = \langle s/t, \ t/s, 5s + 8t \rangle$; $(s,t) = (4,8)$

14. $f(x,y,z) = x^2 y - z\sqrt{z} + 7y$; $\langle x,y,z \rangle = \langle 1 - st, \sin(0.5\pi t), s^3 + t^4 \rangle$; $(s,t) = (1,2)$

15. $f(x,y,z) = z^2 - xe^{3z+xy}$; $\langle x,y,z \rangle = \langle t\cos st, s\cos t, s\sin t \rangle$; $(s,t) = (3,0)$

16. $f(x,y,z) = \ln(z^2 + \sqrt{1 + x^2 + 8y})$; $\langle x,y,z \rangle = \langle te^{ts}, s\sqrt{s^2 + 9t}, \cos(s^2 + t^2) \rangle$; $(s,t) = (0,0)$

In #17–20 use the Implicit Function Theorem to (a) show that the specified level curve of f defines y as function of x, and (b) determine dy/dx at the specified point.

17. $f(x,y) = 7$ when $f(x,y) = 6x^2 + 0.25y^2$; $(x,y) = (1,2)$

18. $f(x,y) = 23$ when $f(x,y) = x^2 - 0.125y^2$; $(x,y) = (5,4)$

19. $f(x,y) = 1$ when $f(x,y) = x^2 + xy\sin(y)$; $(x,y) = (1,\pi)$

20. $f(x,y) = 0.5$ when $f(x,y) = yx/\sqrt{3x + y^2}$; $(x,y) = (1,1)$

In #21–24 use the Implicit Function Theorem to (a) show that the specified level surface of f defines z as function of x and y, and (b) determine $\partial z/\partial x$ and $\partial z/\partial y$ at the specified point.

21. $f(x,y,z) = 2$ when $f(x,y,z) = x^2 e^{-yz} + z$; $(x,y,z) = (-1,0,1)$

22. $f(x,y,z) = 4$ when $f(x,y,z) = z^2\sqrt{x + yz}$; $(x,y,z) = (0,2,2)$

23. $f(x,y,z) = -1$ when $f(x,y,z) = \dfrac{xy}{x^2 + 4y + 3z}$; $(x,y,z) = (1,1,-2)$

24. $f(x,y,z) = 6$ when $f(x,y,z) = \dfrac{24x + 5zy}{7x + 2y - 3z}$; $(x,y,z) = (1,0,1)$

In #25–28 the variables x and y depend on s and t as specified in the tables below. Use this information to calculate the specified derivative of f at the given point.

values of $x(s,t)$			values of $\partial x/\partial s$			values of $\partial x/\partial t$			values of $f_x(x,y)$			
$s = 7$	5	6	$s = 7$	2	3	$s = 7$	1	-2	$y = 3$	14	13	12
$s = 6$	4	5	$s = 6$	1	0	$s = 6$	1	3	$y = 2$	13	11	9
$s = 5$	4	6	$s = 5$	0	-1	$s = 5$	2	-3	$y = 1$	12	10	11
	$t = 8$	$t = 9$		$t = 8$	$t = 9$		$t = 8$	$t = 9$		$x = 4$	$x = 5$	$x = 6$

$s = 7$	1	1	$s = 7$	1	-3	$s = 7$	0	4	$y = 3$	2	0	-2
$s = 6$	1	3	$s = 6$	-1	0	$s = 6$	2	5	$y = 2$	3	1	-1
$s = 5$	3	2	$s = 5$	-2	1	$s = 5$	-1	1	$y = 1$	4	3	0
	$t = 8$	$t = 9$		$t = 8$	$t = 9$		$t = 8$	$t = 9$		$x = 4$	$x = 5$	$x = 6$

values of $y(s,t)$ values of $\partial y/\partial s$ values of $\partial y/\partial t$ values of $f_y(x,y)$

25. $\dfrac{\partial f}{\partial s}$ at $(s,t) = (5,8)$ 27. $\dfrac{\partial f}{\partial t}$ at $(s,t) = (7,8)$

26. $\dfrac{\partial f}{\partial s}$ at $(s,t) = (6,9)$ 28. $\dfrac{\partial f}{\partial t}$ at $(s,t) = (5,9)$

In #29–32 (a) show that z is an implicitly defined function of x and y near the specified point, and (b) determine the equation of the tangent plane there.

29. $4(x + z)^6 + yz + \sin z = 4$; $(1,2,0)$ 31. $z\arctan yz = -\sin xz$; $(\pi, 0, 1)$

30. $ye^{xz} - \ln(y + z) = 2$; $(0,2,-1)$ 32. $\dfrac{yz}{1 + xz} + \arcsin(x - z) = 1$; $(1,2,1)$

❖ 13.7 Concept and Application Exercises

At the beginning of this chapter you saw that the mathematical statements of some physical laws can be visualized as surfaces that have been rotated by $\pi/4$ radians from the standard axis. Exercises #33 and 34 explore the consequences of rotating our coordinate system to match.

33. Suppose we define $x = s + t$ and $y = s - t$. Use the Chain Rule to show

$$\frac{\partial f}{\partial s}\frac{\partial f}{\partial t} = \left(\frac{\partial f}{\partial x}\right)^2 - \left(\frac{\partial f}{\partial y}\right)^2.$$

34. Suppose $x = \cos(\theta)t + \sin(\theta)s$ and $y = \sin(\theta)t - \cos(\theta)s$, where θ is a fixed angle of rotation. Use the Chain Rule to show

$$\frac{\partial f}{\partial s}\frac{\partial f}{\partial t} = \left(\cos(\theta)\frac{\partial f}{\partial x}\right)^2 - \left(\sin(\theta)\frac{\partial f}{\partial y}\right)^2.$$

35. Suppose $x = e^s \cos(t)$ and $y = e^s \sin(t)$, and $f(x,y) = 2x + 3y$.

   (a) Sketch the curve parameterized by x and y when $s = 0$ (the parameter is t).
   (b) Verify that $f_y(1,0)$ and $\partial f/\partial t$ at $(s,t) = (0,0)$ are the same.
   (c) Explain why part (b) makes sense from a geometric point of view.

36. Suppose $x = -\ln(s)\sin t$ and $y = \ln(s)\cos t$, and $f(x,y) = 5x - 7y$.

   (a) Sketch the curve parameterized by x and y when $s = e$ is constant (the parameter is t).
   (b) Verify that $f_x(0,-1)$ and $\partial f/\partial t$ at $(s,t) = (e,\pi)$ are the same.
   (c) Explain why part (b) makes sense from a geometric point of view.

37. When $f(tx, ty) = t^n f(x,y)$ we say that the function f is **homogeneous** of degree n.

   (a) Show that $f(x,y) = 3x - 8y$ is homogeneous of degree 1.
   (b) Show that $f(x,y) = 8x^2 + 2xy - y^2$ is homogeneous of degree 2.
   (c) Suppose f is a differentiable function that's homogeneous of degree n. Show that $xf_x + yf_y = nf(x,y)$.

38. Suppose $x = r\cos\theta$ and $y = r\sin\theta$.

   (a) Use the Chain Rule to show that

$$\frac{\partial f}{\partial r} = \cos(\theta)\frac{\partial f}{\partial x} + \sin(\theta)\frac{\partial f}{\partial y} \qquad (7.7)$$

$$\frac{\partial f}{\partial \theta} = -r\sin(\theta)\frac{\partial f}{\partial x} + r\cos(\theta)\frac{\partial f}{\partial y} \qquad (7.8)$$

   (b) Multiply equation (7.7) by $r\sin\theta$, and equation (7.8) by $\cos\theta$. Then add them together to show that $f_y = \sin(\theta)f_r + \frac{1}{r}\cos(\theta)f_\theta$.
   (c) Multiply equation (7.7) by $r\cos\theta$, and equation (7.8) by $\sin\theta$. Then subtract them to show that $f_x = \cos(\theta)f_r - \frac{1}{r}\sin(\theta)f_\theta$.
   (d) Use the result of parts (b) and (c) to explain the meaning of the equations

$$\frac{\partial}{\partial x} = \cos(\theta)\frac{\partial}{\partial r} - \frac{1}{r}\sin(\theta)\frac{\partial}{\partial \theta} \quad \text{and} \quad \frac{\partial}{\partial y} = \sin(\theta)\frac{\partial}{\partial r} + \frac{1}{r}\cos(\theta)\frac{\partial}{\partial \theta}.$$

   (e) Suppose $f(r,\theta) = r^3\sqrt{3.5 + \sin\theta}$. Determine the values of $\partial f/\partial x$ and $\partial f/\partial y$ at $(r,\theta) = (3, \pi/6)$.

13.8   Optimization

You know from Chapter 4 that when f is a continuous function of a single variable, its extrema in $[a, b]$ can occur only at critical points in (a, b) or at the endpoints of the interval. Similarly, the extrema of a continuous function over a closed and bounded region occur either on the region's boundary or at *critical points* in its interior (see Figure 8.1). In this section we define the term *critical point,* and formalize a method for locating the extrema of continuous functions. For the sake of simplicity, much of our discussion will be devoted to functions of two variables.

> **Key Idea(s):** *The extrema of f inside an open region happen where f is not differentiable or where $\nabla f = \mathbf{0}$.*
>
> *An extension of the Second Derivative Test allows us to classify critical points based on concavity.*
>
> *In simple situations, we can find the extrema of f along the boundary of a region by parameterizing it.*

Figure 8.1: (left) The graph of f over a rectangle in the xy-plane; (middle) the graph of f over the rectangle's edge suggests local extrema occur along the edge; (right) level curves of f show us (roughly) the location of a local extremum in the rectangle's interior.

✤ Local Extrema and Critical Points

In Chapter 4 we said that a function f has a local maximum at c if $f(x)$ is not larger than $f(c)$ in the vicinity of c. For functions of a single variable, "the vicinity" refers to an an open interval about c. When we talk about functions of two variables, we understand "the vicinity" to be a disk about the critical point, but the basic idea remains the same.

> **Definition:** Suppose (a, b) is point in the domain of the function f. We say that (a, b) is a ...
>
> - *local minimum* of f if $f(a, b) \leq f(x, y)$ for all domain points (x, y) in some open disk about (a, b).
>
> - *local maximum* of f if $f(a, b) \geq f(x, y)$ for all domain points (x, y) in some open disk about (a, b).
>
> In either case, we say that (a, b) is a *local extremum* of the function f.

Intuitively speaking, you can imagine the graph of a two-variable function f as a rolling landscape (see Figure 8.2). The tangent plane to that landscape is horizontal at the top of a hill (a maximum) and at the bottom of a basin (a minimum), so we expect extrema to occur where the tangent plane's normal vector is a multiple of $\mathbf{k}$. Since the vector $\mathbf{n} = \langle f_x, f_y, -1 \rangle$ is normal to the tangent plane, our first step toward locating extrema will be finding points at which $f_x = 0$ and $f_y = 0$. This leads us to make the following definition:

No smaller values of f near by: local minimum   No larger values of f near by: local maximum

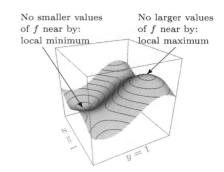

Figure 8.2: Traces on the surface $z = f(x, y)$.

> **Definition:** Suppose (a, b) is an interior point of the domain of f. We say (a, b) is a *critical point* of f when $\nabla f(a, b) = \mathbf{0}$ or f is not differentiable at (a, b).

> A maximum might occur at the tip of a cone, for example, where a function is not differentiable.

Detecting a critical point

Example 8.1. Suppose $f(x, y) = x^3 + 12xy + y^3$. Determine whether $(-4, -4)$ is a critical point.

Solution: The gradient of f at any point (x, y) is $\nabla f(x, y) = \langle 3x^2 + 12y, 12x + 3y^2 \rangle$, which is $\mathbf{0}$ when $x = -4$ and $y = -4$. So $(-4, -4)$ is a critical point. ∎

Detecting a critical point

Example 8.2. Suppose $f(x, y) = 2x^2 + 3xy + x + 8y$. Find all critical points of f.

Answer: $(-8/3, 29/9)$ ∎

Solution On-line

As in Chapter 4, the multivariable analog of Fermat's Theorem tells us that local extrema and critical points are closely related (but not the same).

Fermat's Theorem: Suppose the function f has a local extremum at (a, b), which is in the interior of its domain. Then (a, b) is a critical point of f.

As with single-variable functions, a critical point of a multivariable function can be a local maximum, a local minimum, or neither. For example, Figure 8.3 depicts the graphs of three functions, each with a critical point at $(0, 0)$. The first has a local maximum at the origin because its graph is concave down in all directions, the second has a local minimum there because its graph is concave up in all directions, and the origin is not an extremum of the last function because its graph is concave up in one direction but concave down in another. (Such a critical point is called a **saddle point** of the function.)

The discussion below develops the *second directional derivative*, which allows us to check a graph's concavity in any given direction, and then introduces a quick numerical test to determine whether its sign depends on direction.

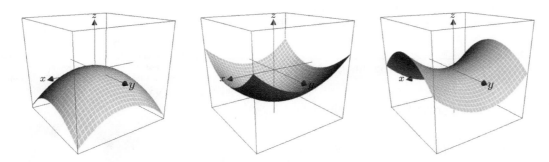

Figure 8.3: Graphs of functions with a critical point at the origin. (left) A local maximum; (middle) a local minimum; (right) a saddle.

▷ The Second Directional Derivative

You already know that $f_{xx}(a, b)$ tells us about the concavity of the surface $z = f(x, y)$ in the direction of increasing x. Similarly, $f_{yy}(a, b)$ tells us about the graph's concavity in the direction of increasing y. That is, we can already determine the concavity of a surface when we intersect it with the vertical planes $y = b$ or $x = a$, thereby creating a curve over a horizontal or vertical line in the xy-plane. In the discussion that follows, we develop a method of determining the concavity of the surface over *any* line through (a, b).

Toward developing this method, recall that the line in the xy-plane that passes through the point (a, b) and extends in the direction of the unit vector $\hat{\mathbf{u}} = \langle \alpha, \beta \rangle$ can be parameterized by

$$x(t) = a + \alpha t \quad \text{and} \quad y(t) = b + \beta t.$$

This line lies on a vertical plane that intersects the surface $z = f(x, y)$ in a curve. By considering the value of f along this line, we effectively reduce f to a function of the single variable t, and the Chain Rule for Paths allows us to calculate

$$\frac{df}{dt} = \frac{\partial f}{\partial x}\frac{dx}{dt} + \frac{\partial f}{\partial y}\frac{dy}{dt} = \alpha f_x(x, y) + \beta f_y(x, y). \tag{8.1}$$

> If light were traveling in the direction of $-\mathbf{k}$, the line in the xy-plane would be the shadow of the curve on the graph of f.

at any point (x, y) on the line. The concavity of the graph in the direction of our motion is determined by the sign of the second derivative, so we differentiate equation (8.1) to find

$$\frac{d}{dt}\left(\frac{df}{dt}\right) = \frac{d}{dt}\Big(\alpha f_x(x, y) + \beta f_y(x, y)\Big) = \alpha\frac{df_x}{dt} + \beta\frac{df_y}{dt}. \tag{8.2}$$

> Recall that α and β are constant.

Since f_x is a function of x and y,

$$\frac{df_x}{dt} = \frac{\partial f_x}{\partial x}\frac{dx}{dt} + \frac{\partial f_x}{\partial y}\frac{dy}{dt} = \alpha f_{xx} + \beta f_{xy}.$$

Similarly, $\frac{df_y}{dt} = \alpha f_{yx} + \beta f_{yy}$, so we can rewrite equation (8.2) as

$$\frac{d^2 f}{dt^2} = \alpha^2 f_{xx} + \alpha\beta f_{xy} + \beta\alpha f_{yx} + \beta^2 f_{yy}. \tag{8.3}$$

This leads us to make the following definition.

Definition: The **second directional derivative** of $f(x, y)$ at the point (a, b) in the direction of the unit vector $\hat{\mathbf{u}} = \langle \alpha, \beta \rangle$ is

$$D_{\mathbf{u}}^2 f(a, b) = \alpha^2 f_{xx}(a, b) + \alpha\beta f_{xy}(a, b) + \beta\alpha f_{yx}(a, b) + \beta^2 f_{yy}(a, b).$$

> It's important that $\mathbf{u}$ is a unit vector, so that it corresponds to a "run" of 1 unit in the xy-plane, regardless of its direction.

Many people find it easier to remember equation (8.3) when it's written with matrix notation:

$$D_{\mathbf{u}}^2 f(a, b) = \begin{bmatrix} \alpha \\ \beta \end{bmatrix} \cdot \begin{bmatrix} f_{xx}(a, b) & f_{xy}(a, b) \\ f_{yx}(a, b) & f_{yy}(a, b) \end{bmatrix} \begin{bmatrix} \alpha \\ \beta \end{bmatrix}. \tag{8.4}$$

The matrix of second partial derivatives in equation (8.4) is called the **Hessian** matrix of f, and in this text we'll typically denote it by H or $H(a, b)$.

> The word *Hessian* is pronounced "HESH-un."

Calculating the second directional derivative

Example 8.3. Suppose $f(x, y) = 3x^2 + 7xy + 4y^3$. Determine the second directional derivative of f in the direction of $\mathbf{u} = \langle 2, 3 \rangle$ at the point $(1, 1/2)$.

Solution: Because we don't want the magnitude of $\mathbf{u}$ to affect our calculation (we work with unit vectors), we normalize it to get $\hat{\mathbf{u}} = \langle 2/\sqrt{13}, 3/\sqrt{13} \rangle$. Since $f_{xx}(x, y) = 6$, $f_{xy}(x, y) = 7$ and $f_{yy}(x, y) = 24y$, equation (8.3) tells us that

> Recall that f_{xy} and f_{yx} are equal where they are continuous.

$$D_{\mathbf{u}}^2 f(1, 1/2) = 6\left(\frac{2}{\sqrt{13}}\right)^2 + 14\left(\frac{2}{\sqrt{13}}\right)\left(\frac{3}{\sqrt{13}}\right) + 12\left(\frac{3}{\sqrt{13}}\right)^2 = \frac{216}{13}. \quad \blacksquare$$

▷ The Second Derivative Test

Equation (8.4) shows the central role that the Hessian matrix plays in calculating the second directional derivative of f. In the context of classifying extrema, we care whether the sign of that derivative depends on direction, and as you'll see in the following theorem, that is determined by the determinant of the Hessian when f is a function of two variables. Note that, much as the Second Derivative Test from Chapter 4 makes no assertion when the second derivative of a single-variable function is 0, this two-variable version makes no assertions when the determinant of the Hessian is 0 (there are functions for which extrema occur at such points, and others for which such a point is a saddle point).

Theorem (Second Derivative Test): Suppose (a, b) is a critical point of the differentiable function f, the second partial derivatives of f are continuous on an open disk about (a, b), and H is the Hessian matrix of f at (a, b).

($\star$) If the determinant of H is positive, the point (a, b) is a ...

    – local minimum of f when $f_{xx}(a, b)$ is positive;

    – local maximum of f when $f_{xx}(a, b)$ is negative.

($\star\star$) If the determinant of H is negative, the point (a, b) is a saddle point.

> Although it's not obvious from our discussion, here, a study of linear algebra reveals that the determinant of this Hessian matrix is the product of the maximum and minimum second directional derivatives, say $\lambda_{\min}$ and $\lambda_{\max}$. If that product is negative, it must be that $\lambda_{\min} < 0$ and $\lambda_{\max} > 0$, which means that there's a change in concavity. If the product is positive, it could be $\lambda_{\min}$ and $\lambda_{\max}$ are both positive, or both negative; in either case, concavity is the same in all directions.

Note: Part ($\star$) of this theorem is proved in the End Notes, and you'll investigate ($\star\star$) in the exercise set.

Second derivative test

Example 8.4. Suppose $f(x, y) = 12xy - x^3 - y^3$. Classify the critical point at $(4, 4)$ as either a local minimum, local maximum, or saddle point.

Solution: We begin by calculating the Hessian matrix:

$$H(x, y) = \begin{bmatrix} f_{xx} & f_{xy} \\ f_{yx} & f_{yy} \end{bmatrix} = \begin{bmatrix} -6x & 12 \\ 12 & -6y \end{bmatrix}$$

which has a determinant of $\det\big(H(x, y)\big) = 36xy - 144$. When $x = 4$ and $y = 4$ this becomes $\det\big(H(4, 4)\big) = 432 > 0$, so the Second Derivative Test tells us that $(4, 4)$ is either a local min or a local max. To determine which, we note that $f_{xx}(4, 4) < 0$, so the graph of f is concave down in the x-direction. Therefore, f has a local maximum at $(4, 4)$. ∎

Second derivative test

Example 8.5. Show that $f(x, y) = \sin xy$ has a saddle point at the origin.

Answer: $\det\big(H(0, 0)\big) = -1 < 0$. ∎

Solution
On-line

✦ Optimization

Now let's apply what we know of critical points to a simple example.

Maximizing volume

Example 8.6. Suppose you're designing a rectangular box with a top and bottom made of material that costs $\$5/\text{ft}^2$, and sides made of material that costs $\$1/\text{ft}^2$. If your company has budgeted $\$30$ for materials (per box), what's the largest volume your design can enclose?

Solution: The volume of this box is $V = xyz$ where x and y are its length and width, respectively, and is z its height (we take these to be positive, since we're discussing a physical object). The top of the box has an area of xy, so it costs $\$5xy$. Similarly for the bottom, so the combined cost of these two surfaces is $\$10xy$. Additionally, the box has two sides with an area of xz, and two with an area of yz, so the total cost of the sides is $\$(2xz + 2yz)$. Since \$30 is budgeted for such a box, we set

$$10xy + 2xz + 2yz = 30 \quad \Rightarrow \quad z = \frac{15 - 5xy}{x + y}.$$

This relationship among x, y and z shows us that $xy \leq 3$, and

$$V = xyz = xy\left(\frac{15 - 5xy}{x + y}\right) = \frac{15xy - 5x^2y^2}{x + y}.$$

Because we want to maximize V, we look for points at which $\nabla V = \mathbf{0}$. This leads us to calculate

$$\frac{\partial V}{\partial x} = \frac{5y^2(3 - 2xy - x^2)}{(x + y)^2} \quad \text{and} \quad \frac{\partial V}{\partial y} = \frac{5x^2(3 - 2xy - y^2)}{(x + y)^2}.$$

These are 0 where

$$5y^2\left(3 - 2xy - x^2\right) = 0 \quad \text{and} \quad 5x^2\left(3 - 2xy - y^2\right) = 0.$$

Since x and y are positive, these equations can only be true where

$$\underbrace{3 - 2xy - x^2 = 0}_{} \quad \text{and} \quad \underbrace{3 - 2xy - y^2 = 0}_{}. \qquad (8.5)$$

$$\underset{\text{same}}{\longleftarrow\longrightarrow}$$

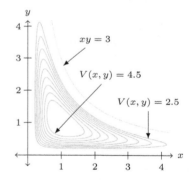

Figure 8.4: Level curves of $V(x, y)$ shown in blue, and the curve $xy = 3$ in black.

From these equations we conclude that $x^2 = y^2$ at critical points of V. Since x and y are positive numbers, that means $x = y$. It follows from equation (8.5) that $x = 1$ at such a point, so $y = 1$ and $V(1, 1) = 5$ ft^3.

Because the second derivatives of V are

$$V_{xx} = -\frac{10y^2(y^2+3)}{(x+y)^3} \qquad V_{xy} = -\frac{10xy(x^2+3xy+y^2-3)}{(x+y)^3} \qquad V_{yy} = -\frac{10x^2(x^2+3)}{(x+y)^3},$$

the Hessian matrix at $(x, y) = (1, 1)$ is

$$H = \begin{bmatrix} -5 & -2.5 \\ -2.5 & -5 \end{bmatrix} \quad \Rightarrow \quad \det(H) = \frac{75}{4} > 0.$$

This tells us that $(1, 1)$ is the location of an extremum, not a saddle point of V. Because $V_{xx}(1, 1) < 0$, we know that we've found a maximum of V. The maximum volume of a box, given the cost of materials and the budget cited above, is $V(1, 1) = 5$ ft^3. In Figure 8.4 you see that the level curves of $V(x, y)$ enclose $(1, 1)$, and curves closer to $(1, 1)$ correspond to larger function values. ∎

The next example investigates a case when extrema can occur on the boundary of a region. As you'll see, we address this possibility by parameterizing the boundary and using what we know of single-variable calculus.

Optimizing over a rectangle

Example 8.7. Suppose $f(x, y) = 12xy - x^3 - y^3$. Determine whether f has achieves a maximum value on the set of points for which $-5 \leq x \leq 5$ and $-5 \leq y \leq 5$ (which is a square of side length 10), and if so, find it.

Solution: Since f is a continuous function, and the domain is closed and bounded, the Extreme Value Theorem guarantees that f achieves a maximum value. Our strategy for finding it will be to compare the value of f at critical points in the interior of the square, and at extrema along the boundary.

Step 1 (finding critical points in the interior): The partial derivatives of f are $f_x(x, y) = 12y - 3x^2$ and $f_y(x, y) = 12x - 3y^2$, which are simultaneously 0 only at the points $(0, 0)$ and $(4, 4)$.

Step 2 (checking the boundary): Next we find the maximum values of f on the boundary of the square, along which f is effectively a function of a single variable.

- On the boundary segment where $y = -5$ and $-5 \leq x \leq 5$, the function takes the form $f(x, -5) = -60x - x^3 + 125$. This function of x is decreasing because its derivative is $-60 - 3x^2 < 0$, so it has extrema at $x = \pm 5$.

- On the boundary segment where $y = 5$ and $-5 \leq x \leq 5$, we see that $f(x, 5) = 60x - x^3 - 125$. The derivative of this function of x is $60 - 3x^2$, which vanishes at $x = \pm 2\sqrt{5}$. So $f(x, 5)$ can have extrema at $x = \pm 5$ and $x = \pm 2\sqrt{5}$.

- On the boundary segment where $x = -5$ and $-5 \leq y \leq 5$, the function takes the form $f(-5, y) = -60y - 125 - y^3$. This function of y is decreasing because its derivative is $-60 - 3y^2 < 0$, so it has extrema at $y = \pm 5$.

- On the boundary segment where $x = 5$ and $-5 \leq y \leq 5$, we see $f(5, y) = 60y + 125 - y^3$. The derivative of this function (of y) is $60 - 3y^2$, which is 0 at $y = \pm 2\sqrt{5}$.

Step 3 (comparing values): When we compare the function values at the points we've identified, $(0, 0), (4, 4), (5, \pm 5), (-5, \pm 5), (5, \pm 2\sqrt{5})$ and $(\pm 2\sqrt{5}, 5)$, we find that the largest function value is 550. ∎

In Example 8.4 we used the determinant of the Hessian matrix to show that $(4, 4)$ is a local maximum of f. And since $\det(H)$ is negative when both x and y are 0, the origin is a saddle point (i.e., neither a local max nor a local min).

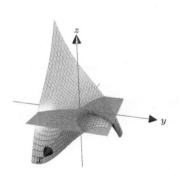
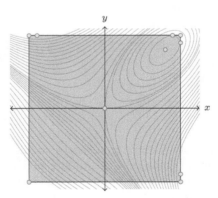

Figure 8.5: For Example 8.7; (left) the graph of f over the specified domain; (right) level curves of f, along with the local extrema specified in the example (indicated by yellow dots).

Optimizing over a rectangle

Example 8.8. Suppose $f(x, y) = (y - 1)^2 - 0.5x + \sin x$. Find the minimum value of f when $-2 \leq x \leq 1.5$ and $0 \leq y \leq 2$.

Answer: $f\left(-\frac{\pi}{3}, 1\right) = \frac{\pi}{6} - \frac{\sqrt{3}}{2}$. ∎

Solution On-line

Optimizing over a circle (using numerical methods)

Example 8.9. Determine the maximum value of $h(x, y) = 0.05x^2 + y \sin xy + y^2$ over the disk $x^2 + y^2 \leq (1.5)^2$.

Solution: Since $h_x = 0.1x + y^2 \cos xy$ and $h_y = xy \cos xy + \sin xy + 2y$, the function h has critical points where

$$0.1x + y^2 \cos xy = 0 \tag{8.6}$$

$$xy \cos xy + \sin xy + 2y = 0. \tag{8.7}$$

Figure 8.6 depicts the curves defined by equations (8.6) and (8.7), and you can see that they intersect at three points inside the disk: at the origin, and in the second and third quadrants. To find the points of intersection in the second and third quadrants, we employ the Newton-Raphson method (see Section 13.5) with

$$f(x, y) = 0.1x + y^2 \cos xy$$
$$g(x, y) = xy \cos xy + \sin xy + 2y.$$

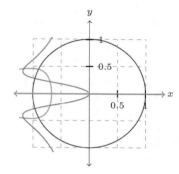

Figure 8.6: The curves defined by equations (8.6) and (8.7) intersect inside the unit circle.

Figure 8.6 indicates that one of the simultaneous root is near $(x_1, y_1) = (-0.75, 0.2)$. The following table reflects data from a spreadsheet implementation of the Newton-Raphson method started there.

n	x_n	y_n	$f(x_n, y_n)$	$g(x_n, y_n)$
1	-0.75	0.2	-0.0354	0.1022
2	-1.3456	0.4448	0.0289	-0.1683
$\vdots$	$\vdots$	$\vdots$	$\vdots$	$\vdots$
6	-1.0413	0.3327	1.6445×10^{-13}	-1.5528×10^{-12}
7	-1.0413	0.3327	0	0

The values of zero in the last columns of row 7 indicate that the values of f and g are 0 to within the computer's precision.

Figure 8.6 indicates (and the equations verify) that another simultaneous root of f and g occurs at $(x, y) \approx (-1.0413, -0.3327)$.

Now we check the value of h at the interior critical points:

$$h(0, 0) = 0$$
$$h(-1.0413, 0.3327) \approx 0.0519$$
$$h(-1.0413, -0.3327) \approx 0.0519.$$

Lastly, we check h along the boundary. When we parameterize the circle of radius 1.5 with $x(\theta) = 1.5 \cos \theta$ and $y(\theta) = 1.5 \sin \theta$, we effectively reduce h to a function of a single variable,

$$h(x(\theta), y(\theta)) = 0.05(1.5 \cos \theta)^2 + 1.5 \sin \theta \sin((1.5 \cos \theta)(1.5 \sin \theta)) + (1.5 \sin \theta)^2,$$

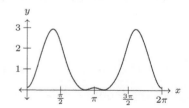

Figure 8.7: The graph of h over the circle (parameterized by $\theta \in [0, 2\pi]$).

which we'll denote simply by $h(\theta)$. Based on the graph of $h(\theta)$ shown in Figure 8.7, we see that the function achieves a maximum value of $h \approx 3$ when $\theta \approx 0.4\pi$ and when $\theta \approx 1.6\pi$. In order to determine this value of h more precisely (and where it happens), we use Newton's Method to search for a value of θ near $\theta_1 = 0.4\pi$ at which $h'(\theta) = 0$. After seven iterations, Newton's method converges to $\theta_8 = 1.2121894 \approx 0.386\pi$, and we calculate $h(\theta_8) \approx 2.9332$. When we start Newton's method at $\theta_1 = 1.6\pi$ it converges to $\theta_{14} = 5.070995909 \approx 1.614\pi$ where (again) the value of h is ≈ 2.9332. This is larger than the value of h at the interior critical points, so we conclude that the function's maximum is $h \approx 2.9332$. ∎

When searching for a root of $h'(\theta)$, Newton's method takes the form

$$\theta_{n+1} = \theta_n - \frac{h'(\theta_n)}{h''(\theta_n)}.$$

❖ Quadratic Approximations

In Chapter 8 we used Taylor polynomials to approximate functions. For example, when we know $f(a)$, $f'(a)$ and $f''(a)$, we can use the second-degree Taylor polynomial of f about $x = a$ to approximate

$$f(x) \approx f(a) + f'(a)(x - a) + \frac{f''(a)}{2}(x - a)^2 \tag{8.8}$$

when x is near a. Notice that the approximation depends on $x - a$, which is the displacement between x and the expansion point, a. To make the same kind of approximation in the two-variable setting we use directional derivatives. Let's denote by $\mathbf{v}$ the displacement vector that extends from (a, b) to the point (x, y). The directional derivative of f at (a, b) in the direction of $\mathbf{v}$ is $\nabla f(a, b) \cdot \hat{\mathbf{v}}$, so the linear approximation of the change in f between (a, b) and (x, y) is

$$(\text{slope}) \times (\text{step length}) = \nabla f(a, b) \cdot \hat{\mathbf{v}} \, \|\mathbf{v}\| = \nabla f(a, b) \cdot \mathbf{v}.$$

$$\underbrace{\qquad\qquad\qquad}_{\text{slope} \longrightarrow} \quad \underset{\text{step length}}{\big\lfloor} \quad \underset{\mathbf{v} = \|\mathbf{v}\|\hat{\mathbf{v}}}{\big\lfloor}$$

> These are the first three terms in the Taylor series generated by f at $x = a$. Notice that there are two factors of $(x - a)$ in the last summand.

And according to equation (8.4) the second directional derivative of f in the direction of $\mathbf{v}$ is $\hat{\mathbf{v}} \cdot H\hat{\mathbf{v}}$, where H is the Hessian matrix of f at (a, b), so the analog of the quadratic term in (8.8) is

$$\frac{\hat{\mathbf{v}} \cdot H\hat{\mathbf{v}}}{2}\|\mathbf{v}\|^2 = \frac{1}{2}\|\mathbf{v}\|\hat{\mathbf{v}} \cdot H\,\hat{\mathbf{v}}\|\mathbf{v}\| = \frac{1}{2}\mathbf{v} \cdot H\,\mathbf{v}.$$

By combining this with the linear approximation of change, we arrive at the two-variable analog of (8.8),

$$f(x, y) \approx f(a, b) + \nabla f(a, b) \cdot \mathbf{v} + \frac{1}{2}\mathbf{v} \cdot H\mathbf{v}.$$

Finally, by writing $\mathbf{v} = \langle x - a, y - b\rangle$ we arrive at the following.

Definition: Suppose the two-variable function f is continuous in an open disk about the point (a, b), as are its first- and second-order partial derivatives. The **quadratic approximation** of f about the point (a, b) is

$$f(a, b) + \nabla f(a, b) \cdot \begin{bmatrix} x - a \\ y - b \end{bmatrix} + \frac{1}{2}\begin{bmatrix} x - a \\ y - b \end{bmatrix} \cdot H \begin{bmatrix} x - a \\ y - b \end{bmatrix},$$

where H denotes the Hessian matrix of f at (a, b).

Quadratic approximation

Example 8.10. Determine the quadratic approximation of $f(x, y) = \sin(x^2 + 3y) + x^2$ about the point $(0, \pi/2)$.

Solution: We begin by calculating derivatives.

$$f_x = 2x\cos(x^2 + 3y) + 2x \qquad\qquad f_y = 3\cos(x^2 + 3y)$$

$$f_{xx} = 2\cos(x^2 + 3y) - 4x^2\sin(x^2 + 3y) + 2 \qquad f_{yy} = -9\sin(x^2 + 3y)$$

and $f_{xy} = -6x\sin(x^2 + 3y)$. When we evaluate these at $(0, \pi/2)$, and set $\mathbf{v} = \langle x - 0, y - \pi/2\rangle$ we get the quadratic approximation

$$f(x, y) \approx -1 + \langle 0, 0\rangle \cdot \mathbf{v} + \frac{1}{2}\mathbf{v} \cdot \begin{bmatrix} 2 & 0 \\ 0 & 9 \end{bmatrix} \mathbf{v}$$

$$= -1 + \frac{1}{2}\langle x - 0, y - \pi/2\rangle \cdot \langle 2x, 9y - 9\pi/2\rangle = -1 + x^2 + \frac{9}{2}\left(y - \frac{\pi}{2}\right)^2. \quad\blacksquare$$

Quadratic approximation

Example 8.11. Find the quadratic approximation of $f(x,y) = 4xe^y$ about $(3,0)$.

Answer: $f(x,y) \approx 4x + 4xy + 6y^2$　　　　　　　　　　　　　　■

You should know

- the terms *critical point, saddle point, second directional derivative, Hessian matrix,* and *quadratic approximation;*
- the Second Derivative Test.

You should be able to

- find critical points using algebraic or numerical methods;
- classify a critical point (as a min, max, or saddle) using $\det(H)$;
- calculate the second directional derivative of a function;
- determine the quadratic approximation of a function of two variables.

✤ 13.8 Skill Exercises

In each of 1–8 find any/all critical points of the given function.

1. $f(x,y) = 2x - 5y$

2. $f(x,y) = 8x + 9y^2$

3. $f(x,y) = x^3 - 9xy^2$

4. $f(x,y) = yx^2 + 3y^3 - y$

5. $f(x,y) = x^3 - 6x^2 + 9x + y^2$

6. $f(x,y) = (x-y)^2(y-1)$

7. $f(x,y) = \sin x \cos y$

8. $f(x,y) = xe^{-x^2-y^2}$

In exercises #9–12 determine a general formula for the Hessian matrix of f.

9. $f(x,y) = 8x - 2y^2$

10. $f(x,y) = x^4\sqrt{3+y^2}$

11. $f(x,y) = x \sin \pi y$

12. $f(x,y) = 3x^2y + y^3 \cos x$

In exercises #13–16 the Hessian matrix of f (at a specific, but undisclosed point) is provided. Use it to determine whether f is concave up or concave down in the direction **u**.

13. $H = \begin{bmatrix} 3 & 7 \\ 7 & 10 \end{bmatrix}$; $\mathbf{u} = \langle -2, 1 \rangle$

14. $H = \begin{bmatrix} 2 & 4 \\ 4 & 1 \end{bmatrix}$; $\mathbf{u} = \langle 6, -7 \rangle$

15. $H = \begin{bmatrix} 8 & 6 \\ 6 & 3 \end{bmatrix}$; $\mathbf{u} = \langle 5, -8 \rangle$

16. $H = \begin{bmatrix} 1 & 3 \\ 3 & 5 \end{bmatrix}$; $\mathbf{u} = \langle 1, 4 \rangle$

In exercises #17–20 determine the second directional derivative of f in the direction of **u** at the specified point.

17. $f(x,y) = 2x^3 + xy^{-2}$ at $(3,-1)$; $\mathbf{u} = \langle 2, 1 \rangle$

18. $f(x,y) = \cos(xy)y^{-2}$ at $(0,3)$; $\mathbf{u} = \langle -1, 4 \rangle$

19. $f(x,y) = x \ln y$ at $(0.1, 0.2)$; $\mathbf{u} = \langle 1, 1 \rangle$

20. $f(x,y) = \frac{xy}{x^2+y^2}$ at $(2,5)$; $\mathbf{u} = \langle 3, -1 \rangle$

In exercises #21–24 use the Hessian matrix H to classify the given critical point as a local maximum, local minimum, or saddle point.

21. $(-3,5)$; $H = \begin{bmatrix} x^2 & xy \\ xy & 10y^2 \end{bmatrix}$

23. $(1,0)$; $H = \begin{bmatrix} -5 & xy \\ xy & \cos(y) \end{bmatrix}$

22. $(0,1)$; $H = \begin{bmatrix} y^2 & 3x+y \\ 3x+y & \sin(x) \end{bmatrix}$

24. $(2,3)$; $H = \begin{bmatrix} 20 & xy \\ xy & -4\sin(\frac{\pi y}{2}) \end{bmatrix}$

In #25–30 (a) find the critical point(s) of f, and (b) report the conclusion of the Second Derivative Test at each.

25. $f(x,y) = x^3 - xy^2$

28. $f(x,y) = y^4 - x^2 y$

26. $f(x,y) = x^2 - y^2 + x + 3y$

29. $f(x,y) = x^2 + 5y^2 - 2x - 20y$

27. $f(x,y) = x^3 - xy^2 + 1$

30. $f(x,y) = xe^{-x} - y^2 + 2y$

In #31–40 determine the quadratic approximation of f about the given point.

31. $f(x,y) = 13 - 9x + 2y$; $(7,3)$

36. $f(x,y) = 2x^3 + 3y^3 \ln x$; $(1,4)$

32. $f(x,y) = 4 + 5x - 8y$; $(1,10)$

37. $f(x,y) = \arctan(4x^2 - 3y^5)$; $(1,1)$

33. $f(x,y) = 1 - 3x + 2x^2 + 8y^2$; $(0,0)$

38. $f(x,y) = \arcsin(\frac{2x+y}{4x+2y})$; $(2,-3)$

34. $f(x,y) = 4x^2 - 5y^2$; $(0,0)$

39. $f(x,y) = \frac{xy}{x^2+y^2}$; $(3,4)$

35. $f(x,y) = xy + y^3 + e^{-x}$; $(-2,3)$

40. $f(x,y) = \frac{\sin x}{e^y + 1}$; $(\pi, 0)$

In #41–44 use three steps of the Newton-Raphson method to approximate the location of the critical point that's nearest to the given location. A spreadsheet can expedite calculations.

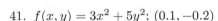

41. $f(x,y) = 3x^2 + 5y^2$; $(0.1, -0.2)$

43. $f(x,y) = x^2 - y^2 + y^3\sqrt{x} - 3x$; $(1.5, -0.5)$

42. $f(x,y) = (x+1)^2 + y^2 - xy/2$; $(-1,0)$

44. $f(x,y) = x^2 \sin y + y^2 + x$; $(1,-1)$

45. Find the maximum value of $f(x,y) = 5x + 2y$ over the rectangle $1 \le x \le 2$ and $-3 \le y \le 1$.

46. Find the minimum value of $f(x,y) = 3x - y^2$ over the rectangle $-1 \le x \le 4$ and $-0.5 \le y \le 0.5$.

47. Find the maximum value of $f(x,y) = 3xy^2 + \sin(x)$ over the rectangle $-1 \le x \le 2$ and $-3 \le y \le 1$. (*Hint: start by finding out where $f_y = 0$.*)

48. Find the minimum value of $f(x,y) = e^{\sin x} \sin y$ over the rectangle $0 \le x \le 3$ and $-1 \le y \le 2.5$.

49. Find the maximum value of $f(x,y) = x \sin xy$ over the triangle connecting $(5,1)$, $(-1,1)$ and $(-1,-2)$.

50. Find the maximum value of $f(x,y) = xe^{-x^2}(y - y^3)$ over the triangle connecting $(0,1)$, $(2,1)$, and $(0,-1)$.

51. Find the maximum value of $f(x,y) = 4x^2 - 3xy + x$ over the disk $x^2 + y^2 \le 1$. (*Hint: use trigonometric functions to parameterize the boundary.*)

52. Find the minimum value of $f(x,y) = 3x + x^2 y - y^2$ over the elliptical region $2x^2 + 5y^2 \le 1$. (*Hint: use trigonometric functions to parameterize the boundary.*)

❖ 13.8 Concept and Application Exercises

53. Design a function $f(x, y)$ that has a saddle point at $(2, 3)$, and no other critical points.

54. Your friend is having trouble finding the critical points of a function, so he asks you, "Where are $f_x(x, y) = 3x + 7y^2$ and $f_y(x, y) = 15xy^5 + 2$ both zero at the same time?" Explain how you know, based on Clairaut's Theorem (see Section 13.4), that he's made a mistake somewhere.

In #55–56 you see the level sets of a differentiable function. (a) Determine whether each point is a critical point, and if so (b) classify each as an extremum or saddle point. Explain your reasoning.

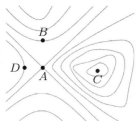   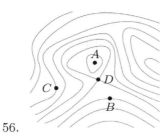

55.   56.

57. Suppose (x, y, z) is a point on the plane $2x + y - z = 3$.

                                                                     `Geometry`

(a) Write the distance from (x, y, z) to the point $(1, -1, 1)$ as a function of x and y. (Hint: start by writing the distance in terms of all three variables, and then write z in terms of x and y.)

(b) Use the methods of this section to determine what point on the plane is closest to $(1, -2, 1)$. Then check your answer by using the geometric methods of Chapter 11.

58. Find the point on the surface $z = x^2 + y + 3$ that is closest to the origin.   `Geometry`

59. When the numbers a and b are positive, the plane $ax + by + z = c$ that passes through the point $(2, 3, 4)$ slices off the corner of the first octant that includes the origin. Determine the equation of the plane through $(2, 3, 4)$ that slices off the minimum volume of the first octant. (Hint: you can use the method of slicing from Chapter 7 to develop a formula in terms of a and b for the volume that's sliced off by the plane.)   `Geometry`

60. When the numbers a and b are positive and the point (α, β, γ) is in the first octant, the plane $ax + by + z = c$ that passes through (α, β, γ) slices off the corner of the first octant that includes the origin. Determine the minimum volume of such a slice. (Your answer will depend on α, β and γ.)   `Geometry`

61. Suppose $Q(k, \ell)$ is the quantity of some commodity that can be produced with ℓ hours of labor and k dollars of capital. The *average quantity produced per labor hour* is $A = Q/\ell$. Show that $A(k, \ell)$ is maximized when $A = Q_\ell$, assuming a maximum exists.   `Economics`

62. Suppose a long metal strip 12 cm wide is to be bent into the shape of three sides of an isosceles trapezoid (see Figure 8.8). What are the lengths of the three sides so that the cross-sectional area of the trapezoid is maximized?   `Manufacturing`

63. A rectangular cardboard package is being designed to encompass 2880 cubic centimeters. The package will have a double layer of cardboard on the bottom for reinforcement. What dimensions minimize the amount of material needed?   `Packaging Science`

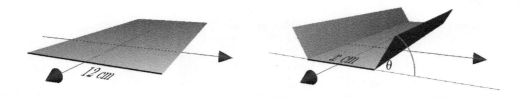

Figure 8.8: Bending a metal strip, as in #62.

64. This exercise is an extension of #63.   Packaging Science

   (a) Suppose the packaging is redesigned so that one side has a 24 cm² "win-dow" of clear plastic (so the product can be seen). Can the overall dimensions of the package be adjusted to further minimize the amount of cardboard that is used? If so, what are the new dimensions?

   (b) Suppose the interior of the package must be separated into two com-partments with a vertical sheet of cardboard. Determine the dimensions that minimize the amount of material needed. (Assume that the interior divider does not affect the interior volume.)

65. In #51 of Section 13.2 you quantified your confidence in the distribution   Finance
    of money across an investment portfolio as $c(x, y)$. Using the parameters specified in that exercise, determine the values of x and y that maximize c.

66. In this exercise you'll work with $c(x, y)$ from #51 of Section 13.2, but without   Finance
    using specified values of the parameters $r_1, r_2, r_3, \sigma_1, \sigma_2, \sigma_3$ and a (at least initially).

   (a) Assuming that the parameters have different values, solve the equations $c_x = 0$ and $c_y = 0$ to show that $c(x, y)$ has a critical point on the line

$$y = \frac{\left((r_2 - r_3)\sigma_1^2 + (r_2 - r_1)\sigma_3^2\right)x + (r_1 - r_2)\sigma_3^2}{(r_1 - r_3)\sigma_2^2 + (r_1 - r_2)\sigma_3^2}.$$

   (b) Show that this line passes through $(1, 0)$ when $\sigma_1 = 0$ and explain why that makes sense based on the meaning of x, y and σ_1.

   (c) The parameter a does not appear in the equation of the line from part (a). Based on the meaning of the number a, make a conjecture about the way it affects the location of the critical point.

   (d) Use a graphing utility to render the line from part (a) when the values
       of the parameters are as specified in #51 of Section 13.2, along with the level curves $c_x = 0$ and $c_y = 0$. Change the value of a and see whether the corresponding change in the location of the critical point is what you predicted in part (c).

67. The Hessian matrix is **symmetric**, meaning it has the form $\begin{bmatrix} a & b \\ b & c \end{bmatrix}$. Show   Mathematics
    that $\det(H) = 0$ describes a cone in abc-space.

68. Suppose $(0, 0)$ is a critical point of f.   Mathematics

   (a) Show that the graph of the quadratic approximation of f about $(0, 0)$ has the form $z = z_0 + ax^2 + 2bxy + cy^2$.

(b) When none of a, b, c are zero, this quadratic approximation describes either an elliptic or a hyperbolic paraboloid. Explain how this is determined by the numbers a, b, c.

(c) Based on your answer above, determine which (if either) of $1 = x^2 + 10xy + 6y^2$ and $1 = x^2 + 6xy + 10y^2$ is an ellipse, and which (if either) is a hyperbola.

69. Suppose we mix molecules of types X and Y with water. The *intensive free energy* of the solution depends on the relative concentrations of X and Y, which we'll call x and y (measured as number densities between 0 and 1) respectively. The *regular solution model* describes the free energy of a particular aqueous mixture as

$$g(x, y) = x \ln x + y \ln y + (1 - x - y) \ln(1 - x - y) + x^2 - 10.5xy + y^2$$

Chemistry

(these numbers are contrived for simplicity, but the form of $g(x, y)$ is accurate).

(a) Determine the quadratic approximation of g about $(1/4, 1/2)$.

(b) Draw several level curves of the quadratic portion, $\langle x - \frac{1}{4}, y - \frac{1}{2} \rangle \cdot H \langle x - \frac{1}{4}, y - \frac{1}{2} \rangle$.

(c) Though the *average* concentrations in the solution may be $x = 1/4$ and $y = 1/2$, the density of X and Y molecules varies throughout the solution. These random fluctuations away from the average concentration result in so-called "energy penalties." Directions away from $(1/4, 1/2)$ in which the quadratic portion of g is steep incur a greater penalty per step, and so are less likely. Using your formula and graph from part (b), determine the direction in which fluctuation away from $(1/4, 1/2)$ are *least* likely.

(d) Determine the direction in which fluctuation away from $(1/4, 1/2)$ are *most* likely.

70. In #69 you learned a little bit about the intensive free energy, which the regular solution model describes as $g(x, y) = x \ln x + y \ln y + (1 - x - y) \ln(1 - x - y) + ax^2 + bxy + cy^2$, where x and y are the average concentrations of two types of molecules. If the graph of g at (x, y) is concave down in any direction, the solution will undergo a phase transition, separating into two different solutions (think "oil and water"); but if the graph of g is concave up in all directions, the solution is stable. Separating these regions of stability and instability is a locus of points called the *spinodal*, where $\det(H) = 0$. What conditions on a, b, and c are necessary for a spinodal?

Chemistry

Exercises #71–76 are about the **steepest descent** method for finding critical points. The basic idea is simple: suppose that (a, b) is near a critical point of f. Since f changes most rapidly in the direction of $\nabla f(a, b)$, parameterize a line through (a, b) in the direction of $\nabla f(a, b)$, say

$$\mathbf{r}_0(t) = \mathbf{u}_0 + t\,\mathbf{v}_0 = \underbrace{\langle a, b \rangle}_{\text{constant}} + t\,\underbrace{\nabla f(a, b)}_{\text{constant}}.$$

Then we use methods from single-variable calculus to find a critical point of $f(\mathbf{r}(t))$ near $t = 0$, say t_1. The point at $\mathbf{r}_0(t_1)$ is our next approximation of the critical point of f, and we repeat the process starting there. For notational simplicity, let's write $\mathbf{r}_0(t_1)$ as $\mathbf{u}_1$, and the gradient of f at that point will be denoted by $\mathbf{v}_1$. Then $\mathbf{r}_1(t) = \mathbf{u}_1 + t\mathbf{v}_1$ parameterizes a line along which f decreases most rapidly. Minimize f along that line, and repeat the process.

71. Use the Chain Rule for Paths to show that $\mathbf{r}_0(t_1)$ is a point where ∇f is orthogonal to $\mathbf{v}_0$.

72. Suppose the first step of a steepest descent optimization algorithm takes us from $(4, 7)$ to $(9.12, 3.7872)$. Based on the result of #71, determine the equation of the line along which we'll travel in the second step of the algorithm.

In each of 73–76 use three steps of the steepest descent algorithm to approximate the location the critical point nearest to the given location. Remember that each step is a single-variable calculus problem, so you can use techniques such as Newton's method when necessary. (Consider using a spreadsheet to expedite calculations.)

73. $f(x, y) = 0.5y^2 + x^2$; $(1, 3)$

74. $f(x, y) = \frac{1}{2}y^3 - 2y^2 + x^2 - 3x$; $(1, 5)$

75. $f(x, y) = e^{\sin x} \cos y$; $(0, 3)$

76. $f(x, y) = y^2 \sin^2(\frac{xy}{10}) + 2\cos^2 x$; $(-6, 2)$

Checking the details

77. Suppose f_{xy} and f_{yx} are continuous in an open disk centered at (a, b), and $\det(H)$ is positive. Show that $f_{xx}(a, b) \neq 0$.

78. Show that the directions in which the second directional derivative is maximized and minimized are $\pi/2$ radians apart.

79. In the steps below you'll show that (a, b) is a saddle point if $\det(H) < 0$.

(a) Read the proof of the Second Derivative Test in the End Notes. Then explain the coefficients in the following equation, and the role it plays

$$A\left(\cos\theta\right)^2 + B\cos\theta + C = 0. \tag{8.9}$$

(b) Show that when both $f_{xx} = 0$ and $f_{yy} = 0$ the second directional is certainly positive is some directions and negative in others, and the determinant of the Hessian matrix is negative.

(c) We proceed by examining equation (8.9) in the case when $A = f_{xx} \neq 0$ (a similar argument works if we know that $f_{yy} \neq 0$). After subtracting C and dividing by A, complete the square in equation (8.9) to show that

$$\left(\frac{B}{2A} + \cos\theta\right)^2 = \frac{B^2 - 4AC}{4A^2}. \tag{8.10}$$

(d) Prove that the right-hand side of equation (8.10) is certainly positive when $\det(H) < 0$. It follows that any solution, θ, must satisfy the equation

$$\cos\theta = \frac{-B \pm \sqrt{B^2 - 4AC}}{2A}. \tag{8.11}$$

(e) By using the definitions of A, B and C, show that equation (8.11) is satisfied when

$$\cos\theta = -\frac{f_{xy} \pm \det(H)}{f_{xx}}\sin\theta. \tag{8.12}$$

(f) Use your knowledge of the cotangent to prove that equation (8.12) has four solutions (two for "+" that are π radians apart, and two for "−" that are π radians apart).

13.9   Lagrange Multipliers

In Section 13.8 we discussed a procedure for finding the extrema of a function over a closed and bounded region. Part of that process involves parameterizing the region's boundary, which allows us to apply the tools of single-variable calculus. In this section we introduce a method for finding extrema along a curve when no parameterization is available. The same method will allow us to locate the extrema of 3-variable functions on surfaces in 3-space.

> **Key Idea(s):** *Lagrange multipliers are numbers that help us find the extrema of a function along a curve when no parameterization of the curve is readily available.*
>
> *The extreme values of f along the curve $g(x, y) = 0$ happen where ∇f is a multiple of ∇g.*

✣ The Basic Idea

Suppose we want to find the extreme values of $f(x, y)$ along a curve $\mathcal{C}$, but a parameterization of the curve is either impractical or impossible to find. The intuitive motivation for the method outlined below lies in the relationship between $\mathcal{C}$, called the ***constraint curve***, and level curves of the ***objective function*** f. Figure 9.1 depicts the intersection of such curves at the point P. As we'll explain in just a moment, the fact that this intersection is transverse allows us to conclude that P is not the location of a local extremum of f on $\mathcal{C}$. Here's why: the magnified section of the figure depicts ∇f and a vector $\mathbf{u}$, which is a small displacement from P to another point on $\mathcal{C}$. Since the angle between them is acute, the directional derivative $D_{\mathbf{u}} f = \nabla f \cdot \hat{\mathbf{u}} > 0$, which indicates that we can increase the value of f by moving along $\mathcal{C}$ in the direction of $\mathbf{u}$. A similar argument can be made at any point where a level curve of f intersects $\mathcal{C}$ transversely.

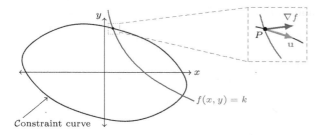

Figure 9.1: A level curve of the objective function intersects the constraint curve transversely. The vector $\mathbf{u}$ is a small displacement along $\mathcal{C}$, and ∇f is orthogonal to the level curve.

By contrast, Figure 9.2 shows a level curve of f that intersects $\mathcal{C}$ tangentially at the point Q. In this case, any small move to another point on $\mathcal{C}$ requires a displacement $\mathbf{u}$ for which the directional derivative is $D_{\mathbf{u}} f = \nabla f \cdot \hat{\mathbf{u}} \leq 0$. That is, small displacements away from Q only reduce the function's value, so this point of tangency is a local maximum of f along $\mathcal{C}$.

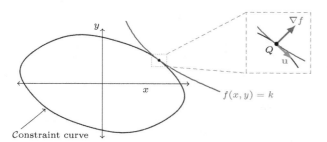

Figure 9.2: A level curve of the objective function intersects the constraint curve tangentially. The vector $\mathbf{u}$ is a displacement along $\mathcal{C}$, and ∇f is orthogonal to the level curve.

⚜ The Method of Lagrange Multipliers

Based on the discussion of Figures 9.1 and 9.2, our strategy for locating the extrema of f on a constraint curve $\mathcal{C}$ will be to find points where ∇f is orthogonal to the curve. When searching for these points, it's helpful to treat the constraint as a level curve of some function, say g, because we know that ∇g is always orthogonal to $\mathcal{C}$. So ∇f is orthogonal to the constraint curve where ∇f is a multiple of ∇g. That is, the vector ∇f is orthogonal to the constraint curve when there is some constant λ (called a ***Lagrange multiplier***) for which

$$\nabla f(x, y) = \lambda \nabla g(x, y). \tag{9.1}$$

Note: Equation (9.1) may be satisfied at several different points on the constraint curve, and the number λ can be different at each.

> **Method of Lagrange Multipliers:** Suppose $\mathcal{C}$ is a level set of the differentiable function g, and $\nabla g \neq \mathbf{0}$ on $\mathcal{C}$. To find the extreme values of the differentiable function f on $\mathcal{C}$ (assuming that these values exist),
>
> (a) locate points P on the curve where $\nabla f(P) = \lambda \nabla g(P)$, and
>
> (b) evaluate f at the points from part (a).
>
> The largest number calculated in part (b) is the maximum value of f on $\mathcal{C}$, and the smallest is the function's minimum value on $\mathcal{C}$.

The following examples demonstrate this method in practice.

> If $\mathcal{C}$ is not closed an bounded, there might not be any extreme values to find. For instance, consider the value of $f(x, y) = x^3 + y^3$ along the line $y - x = 0$ (which is a level set of $g(x, y) = y - x$). Both f and g are differentiable. The value of f grows arbitrarily large in one direction along the line, and drops below every negative number in the other. And although f has a critical point at $(0, 0)$, that critical point is not an extreme point. In fact, there are no extreme values of f on this line.

A linear objective function

Example 9.1. Use Lagrange multipliers to find the maximum value of $f(x, y) = 4x - y$ on the circle $x^2 + y^2 = 1$.

Solution: First let's note that f is continuous, and the constraint curve (the circle) is a closed and bounded set, so the Extreme Value Theorem guarantees that f will achieve a maximum. Our job is to find it, and toward that end we'll treat the circle as a level curve of $g(x, y) = x^2 + y^2$. Since $\nabla f = \langle 4, -1 \rangle$ and $\nabla g(x, y) = \langle 2x, 2y \rangle$, we look for points where

$$\begin{bmatrix} 4 \\ -1 \end{bmatrix} = \lambda \begin{bmatrix} 2x \\ 2y \end{bmatrix}. \tag{9.2}$$

This happens when $4 = 2\lambda x$ and $-1 = 2\lambda y$. Note that these equations guarantee $\lambda \neq 0$, so we can divide by λ and rewrite them as

$$\frac{x}{2} = \frac{1}{\lambda} \quad \text{and} \quad -2y = \frac{1}{\lambda} \quad \Rightarrow \quad y = -\frac{x}{4}.$$

Since our constraint curve is the unit circle, we look for points at which the line $y = -x/4$ intersects it. There are two:

$$(x_1, y_1) = \left(\frac{4\sqrt{17}}{17}, -\frac{\sqrt{17}}{17} \right) \quad \text{and} \quad (x_2, y_2) = \left(-\frac{4\sqrt{17}}{17}, \frac{\sqrt{17}}{17} \right).$$

Evaluating f at these points, we find that its maximum value is $\sqrt{17}$. ∎

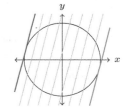

Figure 9.3: Level curves of f are shown passing over the constraint curve (the circle). Since $\nabla f = \langle 4, -1 \rangle$ is constant in this case, we maximize f by moving as far as possible in the direction $\langle 4, -1 \rangle$ while staying on the circle.

> Note that $\lambda > 0$ at (x_1, y_1) but $\lambda < 0$ at (x_2, y_2).

Solution On-line

A linear objective function

Example 9.2. Maximize $f(x, y) = -2x + 8y$ over the curve $5x^2 + y^2 = 1$.

Answer: $\max f = {}^{162}/\sqrt{405}$ at $\left(-1/\sqrt{405}, {}^{20}/\sqrt{405} \right)$ ∎

When $\lambda = 0$ is a possibility

Example 9.3. Use the technique of Lagrange multipliers to find the extreme values of $f(x, y) = (8y - 1)^2$ on the ellipse $5x^2 + 7y^2 = 1$.

Solution: First let's note that f is continuous, and the constraint curve (the ellipse) is a closed and bounded set, so the Extreme Value Theorem guarantees that f will achieve a maximum and a minimum. In order to find them, we'll treat the ellipse as a level curve of $g(x, y) = 5x^2 + 7y^2$. Then the equation $\nabla f = \lambda \nabla g$ is

$$\begin{bmatrix} 0 \\ 128y - 16 \end{bmatrix} = \lambda \begin{bmatrix} 10x \\ 14y \end{bmatrix}, \tag{9.3}$$

from which we conclude that $0 = 10\lambda x$ and $128y - 16 = 14\lambda y$. The first of these equations is true when either $x = 0$ or $\lambda = 0$, so we proceed by considering two cases.

> Notice that the minimum value of f is 0, and the level curve $f(x, y) = 0$ is the horizontal line $y = 1/8$, which meets the ellipse transversely (see Figure 9.4). Nonetheless, the technique works!

Case 1: When $\lambda = 0$ equation (9.3) becomes $\nabla f = \langle 0, 0 \rangle$ which happens when $y = 1/8$. Such a point on the ellipse has an x-coordinate of $\pm 3\sqrt{5}/40$. So we check

$$f\left(\frac{3\sqrt{5}}{40}, \frac{1}{8}\right) = 0 \quad \text{and} \quad f\left(-\frac{3\sqrt{5}}{40}, \frac{1}{8}\right) = 0$$

Case 2: When $\lambda \neq 0$ equation (9.3) can only be solved with $x = 0$. Such a point on the ellipse has $y = \pm 1/\sqrt{7}$. So we check

$$f\left(0, \frac{1}{\sqrt{7}}\right) = \frac{71 - 16\sqrt{7}}{7} \approx 4.0954 \quad \text{and} \quad f\left(0, -\frac{1}{\sqrt{7}}\right) = \frac{71 + 16\sqrt{7}}{7} \approx 16.1903.$$

> The Lagrange multipliers at the points $(0, 1/\sqrt{7})$ and $(0, -1/\sqrt{7})$ are $\lambda = (32-4\sqrt{7})/7$ and $\lambda = -(32+4\sqrt{7})/7$, respectively.

The minimum value occurs at both $(\pm 3\sqrt{5}/40, 1/8)$, and the maximum value at $(0, -1/\sqrt{7})$. The point we found at $(0, 1/\sqrt{7})$ is a local (but not a global) maximum of f along the curve (see Figure 9.4). ∎

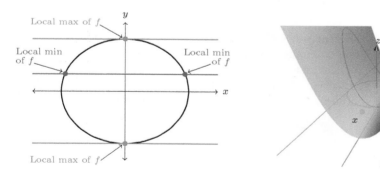

Figure 9.4: (left) The ellipse $5x^2 + 7y^2 = 1$ and level curves of f from Example 9.3; (right) the graph of f over the ellipse. The lines in the xy-plane are the same in both figures.

Working algebraically with λ

Example 9.4. Determine where $f(x, y) = 3x^2 + xy + y^2$ achieves its maximum and minimum values on the circle $x^2 + y^2 = 1$.

Solution: First let's note that f is continuous, and the circle is a closed and bounded set, so the Extreme Value Theorem guarantees that f will achieve a maximum and a minimum. Our job is to find those extrema. The level curves of f are rotated ellipses, as shown in Figure 9.5. And when we treat the circle as a level curve of $g(x, y) = x^2 + y^2$, the equation $\nabla f = \lambda \nabla g$ becomes

$$\begin{bmatrix} 6x + y \\ x + 2y \end{bmatrix} = \lambda \begin{bmatrix} 2x \\ 2y \end{bmatrix} \Rightarrow \begin{cases} 6x + y = 2\lambda x \\ x + 2y = 2\lambda y. \end{cases}$$

These equations can be rewritten as

$$y = (2\lambda - 6)x \quad \text{and} \quad (2\lambda - 2)y = x,$$

which describe a pair of lines through the origin. These lines intersect at the origin (which is not on our constraint curve) unless $(2\lambda - 6)$ and $(2\lambda - 2)$ are reciprocals (in which case the equations describe the same line), so we solve the equation

$$(2\lambda - 6)(2\lambda - 2) = 1 \quad \Rightarrow \quad 4\lambda^2 - 16\lambda + 11 = 0 \quad \Rightarrow \quad \lambda = \frac{4 \pm \sqrt{5}}{2}.$$

When $\lambda = \frac{4+\sqrt{5}}{2}$ the line $y = (2\lambda - 6)x$ intersects the unit circle at

$$(x_1, y_1) = \left(\frac{1}{\sqrt{10-4\sqrt{5}}}, \frac{1}{\sqrt{10+4\sqrt{5}}} \right) \quad \text{and} \quad (x_2, y_2) = \left(-\frac{1}{\sqrt{10-4\sqrt{5}}}, -\frac{1}{\sqrt{10+4\sqrt{5}}} \right).$$

When $\lambda = \frac{4-\sqrt{5}}{2}$ the line $y = (2\lambda - 6)x$ intersects the unit circle at

$$(x_3, y_3) = \left(\frac{1}{\sqrt{10+4\sqrt{5}}}, -\frac{1}{\sqrt{10-4\sqrt{5}}} \right) \quad \text{and} \quad (x_4, y_4) = \left(-\frac{1}{\sqrt{10+4\sqrt{5}}}, \frac{1}{\sqrt{10-4\sqrt{5}}} \right).$$

Now we compare the function values:

$$\begin{aligned} f(x_1, y_1) &\approx 0.882 & f(x_3, y_3) &\approx 3.137 \\ f(x_2, y_2) &\approx 0.882 & f(x_4, y_4) &\approx 3.137 \end{aligned}$$

So the maximum value of f occurs at (x_3, y_3) and (x_4, y_4), and the minimum value occurs at (x_1, y_1) and (x_2, y_2). ∎

In these introductory examples we've seen three different ways of solving the equation $\nabla f = \lambda \nabla g$. In Example 9.1 the particular value of λ played virtually no role in our work, in Example 9.3 we had to account for the fact that λ could be 0, and in Example 9.4 we treated λ algebraically. When the equations become too difficult to handle analytically, we employ numerical methods.

Incorporating the Newton-Raphson method

Example 9.5. Determine the maximum value of $f(x, y) = y^2 + 3xy$ on the curve $0.125x^2 + y^2 + \sin xy = 2$.

Solution: Because the objective function is continuous, and the constraint curve is closed and bounded, the Extreme Value Theorem guarantees that f achieves a maximum. To find it, we set $g(x, y) = 0.125x^2 + y^2 + \sin xy$ and write equation $\nabla f = \lambda \nabla g$ as a pair of equations:

$$3y = \lambda(0.25x + y \cos xy) \tag{9.4}$$

$$2y + 3x = \lambda(2y + x \cos xy) \tag{9.5}$$

If λ were 0 these equations would require $x = 0$ and $y = 0$, but the origin is not on the constraint curve. So we proceed under the assumption that $\lambda \neq 0$. Note that ∇f is $\mathbf{0}$ only at the origin, so at least one of its components is nonzero along the constraint curve. For the sake of discussion, let's assume that $3y \neq 0$.

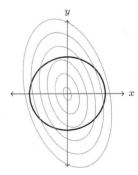

Figure 9.5: The level curves of f and the unit circle.

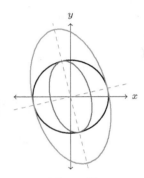

Figure 9.6: The curves $f(x, y) = 0.88197$ and $f(x, y) = 3.13654$, shown with the unit circle. Notice that the lines $y = (2\lambda - 6)x$ are the major and minor axes of the rotated ellipses!

There's a certain art to determining which approach will work for a given problem, and it comes with practice.

Equation (9.4) says that the value of $3y$ is the same as the value of $\lambda(0.25x + y\cos xy)$. Whatever this (nonzero) value is, let's multiply both sides of equation (9.5) by it. On the left-hand side we'll write the value as $\lambda(0.25x + y\cos xy)$, and on the right-hand side we'll write it as $3y$. This brings us to

$$\lambda(0.25x + y\cos xy)(2y + 3x) = 3y\lambda(2y + x\cos xy).$$

And since $\lambda \neq 0$, this can only happen when

$$(0.25x + y\cos xy)(2y + 3x) = 6y^2 + 3xy\cos xy. \qquad (9.6)$$

This equation is graphed with the constraint curve in Figure 9.7, and the points we want are at their intersection. One of the intersections, which we'll denote by (x^*, y^*), is in the the first quadrant near $(2, 1)$. Equation (9.6) and the constraint equation, $g(x, y) = 2$, constitute two equations in two variables; we can approximate the solution of these equations by starting the Newton-Raphson method at $(2, 1)$. This quickly brings us to $x_* \approx 1.85921$ and $y_* \approx 0.76151$, where $f \approx 4.8273$. The same value occurs at the intersection point in the third quadrant, but the value of f is less at the intersections in quadrants 2 and 4 because $xy < 0$. ∎

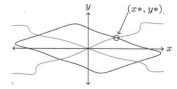

Figure 9.7: The graphs of equations (9.6) and $g(x, y) = 2$.

✢ Life in 3-D

The ideas motivating Lagrange multipliers continue to apply, and the techniques continue to work when we move from two variables to three. We need only replace the word *curve* with the word *surface* in our discussion. The technique is demonstrated in the following examples of continuous objective functions over closed and bounded surfaces (note that the Extreme Value Theorem applies).

Lagrange multipliers in 3-D

Example 9.6. Determine the minimum value of $f(x, y, z) = 4x + y + 2z$ on the ellipsoid $2x^2 + y^2 + z^2 = 1$.

Solution: Let's treat the ellipsoid as a level surface of $g(x, y, z) = 2x^2 + y^2 + z^2$. Then the equation $\nabla f = \lambda \nabla g$ is $\langle 4, 1, 2 \rangle = \lambda \langle 4x, 2y, 2z \rangle$. Note that the equation cannot be solved when $\lambda = 0$, so we can safely proceed under the assumption that $\lambda \neq 0$, and write

$$x = \frac{1}{\lambda} \qquad y = \frac{1}{2\lambda} \qquad z = \frac{1}{\lambda}.$$

Because (x, y, z) must be a point on the ellipse, these equations tell us that

$$2\left(\frac{1}{\lambda}\right)^2 + \left(\frac{1}{2\lambda}\right)^2 + \left(\frac{1}{\lambda}\right)^2 = 1 \quad \Rightarrow \quad \lambda = \pm\frac{\sqrt{13}}{2}.$$

Because f grows with x, y and z, we can minimize f by choosing the negative value of λ. This choice corresponds to the point $(x, y, z) = (-2\sqrt{13}/13, -\sqrt{13}/13, -2\sqrt{13}/13)$, at which the value of f is $-14\sqrt{13}/13$. ∎

Lagrange multipliers in 3-D (including numerical methods)

Example 9.7. Use Lagrange multipliers to determine the extreme values of the function $f(x, y, z) = z + x - y - x^2 - y^2$ over the unit sphere in 3-space.

Solution: The unit sphere is described by $g(x, y, z) = 1$ when $g(x, y, z) = x^2 + y^2 + z^2$. In this case the equation $\nabla f = \lambda \nabla g$ is

$$\begin{bmatrix} 1 - 2x \\ -1 - 2y \\ 1 \end{bmatrix} = \lambda \begin{bmatrix} 2x \\ 2y \\ 2z \end{bmatrix} \quad \Rightarrow \quad \begin{cases} 1 - 2x = 2x\lambda \\ -1 - 2y = 2y\lambda \\ 1 = 2z\lambda \end{cases}$$

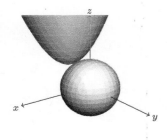
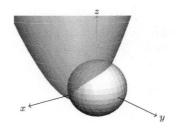
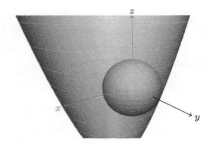

Figure 9.9: (left) When M is the maximum value of f on the sphere, the level surface $f(x, y, z) = M$ is tangent to the sphere; (middle) the level surface $f(x, y, z) = 0$ intersects the sphere transversely, so we can move along the sphere (away from the curve of intersection) to increase or decrease the value of f; (right) when m is the minimum value of f on the sphere, the level surface $f(x, y, z) = m$ is tangent to the sphere.

The first two equations can be rewritten as

$$1 = 2x(\lambda + 1)$$
$$-1 = 2y(\lambda + 1)$$

from which we conclude that $\lambda \neq -1$, neither x nor y is 0, and

$$y = -x. \tag{9.7}$$

Similarly, the third equation guarantees that $z \neq 0$. Solving it for λ and combining the result with the first equation yields $1/z = (1-2x)/x$, from which we conclude that $x \neq 1/2$. This fact allows us to rewrite the equation as

$$z = \frac{x}{1 - 2x}. \tag{9.8}$$

A point of the form $x, y, z = (x, -x, {}^x/(1-2x))$ on the unit sphere satisfies the equation

$$1 = x^2 + y^2 + z^2 = x^2 + (-x)^2 + \left(\frac{x}{1 - 2x} \right)^2 = 2x^2 + \frac{x^2}{(1 - 2x)^2},$$

which we can rewrite as $1 - 4x + x^2 + 8x^3 - 8x^4 = 0$. Based on the graph in Figure 9.8 we look for roots of this equation by starting Newton's method at $x = 0$, and again at $x = -1$. In the first case Newton's method converges to $x_1 \approx 0.3203$, where equations (9.7) and (9.8) tell us that the corresponding y and z values are $y_1 \approx -0.3203$ and $z_1 \approx 0.8912$. In the second case Newton's method converges to $x_2 \approx -0.6772$, where $y_2 \approx 0.6772$ and $z_2 \approx -0.2876$. So the extreme values of f on the surface are (approximately)

$$f(x_1, y_1, z_1) \approx 1.3266 \quad \text{and} \quad f(x_2, y_2, z_2) \approx -2.5592. \qquad \blacksquare$$

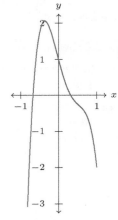

Figure 9.8: The graph of $y = 1 - 4x + x^2 + 8x^3 - 8x^4$. Since x is a coordinate of a point on the unit sphere, we're looking for roots with $|x| \leq 1$.

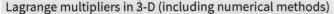

Lagrange multipliers in 3-D (including numerical methods)

Example 9.8. Determine the extreme values of $f(x, y, z) = z^2 - x + 3y - y^2$ over the ellipsoid $2x^2 + 3y^2 + z^2 = 1$.

Answer: Max $f \approx 1.688$, min $f \approx -2.168$. $\blacksquare$

*Solution
On-line*

❖ Multiple Constraints

The method of Lagrange multipliers can be extended to handle cases with more than one constraint. Here we discuss the case of two constraints, $g(x, y, z) = 0$ and $h(x, y, z) = 0$, where g and h are differentiable functions. As depicted in Figure

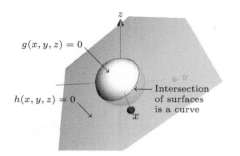
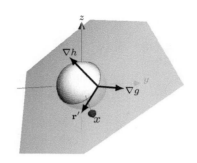

Figure 9.10: (left) The intersection of surfaces $g(x,y,z) = 0$ and $h(x,y,z) = 0$ is a curve; (right) the vectors ∇g and ∇h are orthogonal to $\mathbf{r}'$ at each point on the curve.

9.10, these constraints define surfaces in 3-space. Imagine that their intersection is a curve $\mathcal{C}$, and that $\mathbf{r}(t)$ is a smooth parameterization of $\mathcal{C}$. Because ∇g is orthogonal to the surface $g(x,y,z) = 0$, on which the curve resides, the vectors ∇g and $\mathbf{r}'$ are orthogonal. Similarly for ∇h and $\mathbf{r}'$. Now let's consider a differentiable objective function, f. If f has an extremum along $\mathcal{C}$ at $\mathbf{r}(t_0)$ we know that

$$0 = \frac{d}{dt} f\big(x(t), y(t), z(t)\big) = \frac{\partial f}{\partial x}\frac{\partial x}{\partial t} + \frac{\partial f}{\partial y}\frac{\partial y}{\partial t} + \frac{\partial f}{\partial z}\frac{\partial z}{\partial t} = \nabla f \cdot \mathbf{r}'(t_0).$$

This equation tells us that, like ∇g and ∇h, the vector ∇f is orthogonal to $\mathbf{r}'(t_0)$. The collection of such vectors constitutes a plane, so the three gradient vectors are coplanar. For the sake of discussion let's suppose that, as shown in Figure 9.11, none of ∇g, ∇h, and ∇f is a multiple of another. In that case we can scale and add any two of these vectors to make the third. So we expect that there are numbers λ and μ such that

$$\nabla f = \lambda \nabla g + \mu \nabla h. \qquad (9.9)$$

This equation plays the role of equation (9.1) in a two-constraint problem.

> As above, it's often the case that no formula for $\mathbf{r}(t)$ is readily available. We're using $\mathbf{r}(t)$ to motivate an idea.
>
> By saying that $\mathbf{r}$ is smooth, we mean that $\mathbf{r}'$ is continuous and never $\mathbf{0}$ (see Section 12.3).

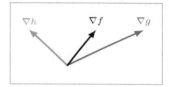

Figure 9.11: Three coplanar vectors. No vector is a multiple of any other, but ∇f can be made by scaling and adding ∇g and ∇h.

> These constraint surfaces are seen together in Figure 9.10.

Two constraints

Example 9.9. Determine the maximum value of $f(x,y,z) = x + y$ subject to the constraints $x^2 + y^2 = 1 - z^2$ and $3x - 4y + 5z = 2$.

Solution: By setting $g(x,y,z) = x^2 + y^2 + z^2 - 1$ and $h(x,y,z) = 2 - 3x + 4y - 5z$ we can write the constraints as $g(x,y,z) = 0$ and $h(x,y,z) = 0$. The first of these equations defines a sphere, and the second a plane, the intersection of which is a circle in 3-space. Because the intersection curve is closed and bounded, the continuous function f achieves a maximum (and a minimum) value on it, and the method of Lagrange multipliers enables us to find it. With g and h as defined above, equation (9.9) becomes

$$\begin{bmatrix} 1 \\ 1 \\ 0 \end{bmatrix} = \lambda \begin{bmatrix} 2x \\ 2y \\ 2z \end{bmatrix} + \mu \begin{bmatrix} -3 \\ 4 \\ -5 \end{bmatrix} \quad \Rightarrow \quad \begin{cases} 1 = 2\lambda x - 3\mu \\ 1 = 2\lambda y + 4\mu \\ 0 = 2\lambda z - 5\mu \end{cases}$$

from which it follows that $\lambda \neq 0$. This fact allows us to write $x = \frac{(1+3\mu)}{2\lambda}$, $y = \frac{(1-4\mu)}{2\lambda}$ and $z = \frac{5\mu}{2\lambda}$. Using these formulas, the constraint $h(x,y,z) = 0$ becomes

$$2 - 3\left(\frac{1+3\mu}{2\lambda}\right) + 4\left(\frac{1-4\mu}{2\lambda}\right) - 5\left(\frac{5\mu}{2\lambda}\right) = 0 \quad \Rightarrow \quad 4\lambda - 50\mu = -1, \qquad (9.10)$$

and the constraint that $x^2 + y^2 + z^2 = 1$ becomes

$$2 - 2\mu + 50\mu^2 = 4\lambda^2. \tag{9.11}$$

By rewriting equation (9.10) as $\lambda = {(50\mu - 1)}/4$ and substituting that formula into equation (9.11), we find that $2300\mu^2 - 92\mu - 7 = 0$. Solving this with the quadratic formula yields

$$\mu = \frac{23 \pm 3\sqrt{506}}{1150} \quad \Rightarrow \quad \lambda = \pm\frac{3\sqrt{506}}{92}.$$

Using the "+" values of μ and λ allows us to calculate

$$x = \frac{759}{6325} + \frac{53\sqrt{506}}{1650}, \quad y = \frac{23\sqrt{506} - 132}{825}, \quad z = \frac{1518 + 23\sqrt{506}}{15180},$$

where the value of f is $x + y \approx 1.3097$. ∎

The "+" version of λ corresponds to the "+" version of μ.

We're using only the "+" values of μ and λ because that makes x and y positive (remember that we're maximizing the sum $x + y$).

Another case of multiple constraints

Example 9.10. Find the maximum value of $f(x, y, z) = 3x + 4y - 2z$ on the intersection of the cylinder $x^2 + y^2 = 1$ and the plane $2x - y + 8z = 1$.

Answer: $\max f \approx 4.8796$ ∎

Solution
On-line

Lagrange multipliers in the case of multiple constraints

Example 9.11. The equation $x^2 + (y - 3)^2 - 1 = 0$ describes the circle of radius 1 centered at $(0, 3)$. Use Lagrange multipliers to find the minimum distance between the line $y - x + 4 = 0$ and the circle.

Solution: This problem could be solved with geometric methods, which makes it a good one for practicing because we can check our answer (see Figure 9.12). In order to apply the technique of Lagrange multipliers, let's rephrase the goal as follows: suppose (x, y) is on the circle, and (s, t) is on the line. How close can two such points get? That is, what's the

$$\text{minimum of} \quad \sqrt{(x - s)^2 + (y - t)^2}$$
$$\text{when} \quad x^2 + (y - 3)^2 - 1 = 0$$
$$\text{and} \quad t - s + 4 = 0 \ ?$$

In previous examples we've used the Extreme Value Theorem to establish that a minimum (or maximum) value exists before we begin searching for it. Here, we appeal to elementary geometric intuition.

To make the algebra of this easier, let's minimize $(x - s)^2 + (y - t)^2$ instead of its square root. That is, our objective function will be

$$f(x, y, s, t) = (x - s)^2 + (y - t)^2,$$

and the constraint functions are

$$g(x, y, s, t) = x^2 + (y - 3)^2 - 1$$
$$h(x, y, s, t) = t - s + 4.$$

Now we're dealing with four variables instead of three, but the same techniques work. After calculating formulas for ∇f, ∇g, and ∇h, we write equation (9.9) as

$$\begin{bmatrix} 2(x - s) \\ 2(y - t) \\ 2(s - x) \\ 2(t - y) \end{bmatrix} = \lambda \begin{bmatrix} 2x \\ 2(y - 3) \\ 0 \\ 0 \end{bmatrix} + \mu \begin{bmatrix} 0 \\ 0 \\ -1 \\ 1 \end{bmatrix}. \tag{9.12}$$

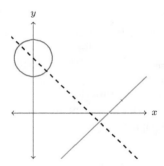

Figure 9.12: The constraint circle, and the constraint line. We can determine the distance between them with analytic geometry: the line through the center of the circle that's perpendicular to the constraint line is described by $y = 3 - x$. That line intersects the circle at $(\frac{\sqrt{2}}{2}, 3 - \frac{\sqrt{2}}{2})$ and the constraint line at $(3.5, -0.5)$. The distance between these points is $(7\sqrt{2} - 2)/2 \approx 3.95$ units.

Equation (9.12) separates into two pairs, involving λ and μ respectively.

$$\left.\begin{array}{rcl} 2(x-s) &=& 2\lambda(x) \\ 2(y-t) &=& 2\lambda(y-3) \end{array}\right\} \qquad (9.13)$$

$$\left.\begin{array}{rcl} 2(s-x) &=& -\mu \\ 2(t-y) &=& \mu \end{array}\right\} \qquad (9.14)$$

Note that equation (9.14) requires $x = s$ and $y = t$ when $\mu = 0$; this cannot happen because no point lies on both the circle and the line, so $\mu \neq 0$. With this fact in hand, equation (9.14) tells us that $x \neq s$ and $y \neq t$, and applying these facts to equation (9.13) allows us to see that neither λ nor x is 0, and $y \neq 3$.

Now since $2(x - s)$ is the same nonzero number as $2\lambda x$, we can multiply it onto the second equation in (9.13). On the left we write it as $2\lambda x$, and on the right as $2(x - s)$, thereby arriving at $(y - t)(2\lambda x) = 2\lambda(y - 3)(x - s)$. And since $2\lambda \neq 0$, this is only true when

$$(y - t)(x) = (y - 3)(x - s). \qquad (9.15)$$

Further, equation (9.14) tells us that $s - x = y - t$. By applying this fact to equation (9.15) we see

$$y = 3 - x.$$

The points on $x^2 + (y - 3)^2 - 1 = 0$ that also sit on the line $y = 3 - x$ are $\left(\frac{\sqrt{2}}{2}, \frac{6-\sqrt{2}}{2}\right)$ and $\left(-\frac{\sqrt{2}}{2}, \frac{6+\sqrt{2}}{2}\right)$. When we substitute the second of these ordered pairs into equation (9.14), we see

$$s + \frac{\sqrt{2}}{2} = \frac{6 + \sqrt{2}}{2} - t,$$

which, since (s, t) must also sit on the line $t = s - 4$, means that $s = {}^7/_2$ and $t = -{}^1/_2$. We get the same values of s and t when we use the other point from the circle. Now we have only to check the function values:

$$f\left(\frac{\sqrt{2}}{2}, \frac{6-\sqrt{2}}{2}, \frac{7}{2}, -\frac{1}{2}\right) \approx 15.60 \quad \text{and} \quad f\left(-\frac{\sqrt{2}}{2}, \frac{6+\sqrt{2}}{2}, \frac{7}{2}, -\frac{1}{2}\right) \approx 35.40.$$

So the minimum value of f is ≈ 15.6. That means the minimum distance between the line and the circle is $\sqrt{15.6} \approx 3.95$ units, which agrees with the answer we get using geometric methods (see Figure 9.12). ∎

You should know

- the terms *Lagrange multiplier*, *constraint curve*, and *objective function*;
- what motivates us to look for $\nabla f = \lambda \nabla g$

You should be able to

- use Lagrange multipliers to find local extrema of $f(x, y)$ over a curve;
- use Lagrange multipliers to find local extrema of $f(x, y, z)$ over a surface;
- use Lagrange multipliers to find local extrema of an objective function when multiple constraints are imposed.

❖ 13.9 Skill Exercises

In #1–8 (a) use a graphing utility to render a plot of the constraint curve with several level curves of f, and (b) use the method of Lagrange multipliers to maximize f over the given constraint curve.

1. $f(x, y) = 3x + y$; $0.1x^2 + y^2 = 1$

2. $f(x, y) = x + 4y$; $x^2 + 7y^2 = 1$

3. $f(x, y) = y - 3x$; $x^2 - y^2 = 1$ $(x > 0)$

4. $f(x, y) = -8x - y$; $xy = 1$ $(x > 0)$

5. $f(x, y) = 7x - 2y^2$; $x + y = -1$

6. $f(x, y) = 2y - x^2$; $y - 0.125x = 1$

7. $f(x, y) = x^3 + y^3$; $(x + y)^2 + 2(x - y)^2 = 1$

8. $f(x, y) = ye^{x^2}$; $x^4 + y^2 = 1$

In exercises #9–12 use the method of Lagrange multipliers in conjunction with a numerical method to determine the maximum value of f over the given curve.

9. $f(x, y) = e^y \sin x$; $x^2 + y^2 = 1$

10. $f(x, y) = x^2 \sin y$; $3x^2 + 0.1y^2 = 1$

11. $f(x, y) = x + e^y + \sec \frac{x}{4}$; $\sin x + 2 \cos y = 2.5$ where $0 \le x \le 1$ and $-1 \le y \le 1$ (the constraint equation defines multiple loops)

12. $f(x, y) = x + e^{-x} + 2 \sin \frac{y}{2}$; $\cos y + 3 \sin x = 3.2$ where $0 \le x \le 3$ and $-2 \le y \le 2$ (the constraint equation defines multiple loops)

In exercises #13–18 minimize f over the given surface.

13. $f(x, y, z) = 2x - y + z$; $x^2 + y^2 + z^2 = 1$

14. $f(x, y, z) = 3x + 9y - z$; $x^2 + y^2 + z^2 = 1$

15. $f(x, y, z) = x - y$; $3x^2 + 6y^2 + 2z^2 = 18$

16. $f(x, y, z) = 2y + 8z$; $5x^2 + 8y^2 + z^2 = 20$

17. $f(x, y, z) = x^2 y - z$; $x^4 + y^4 + z^2 = 1$

18. $f(x, y, z) = xy - z^2$; $3x^4 + 4y^4 + 2z^4 = 12$

In exercises #21–26 use Lagrange multipliers to maximize $f(x, y, z) = x^2 + y^2 - z^2$ subject to the given constraints.

19. $\begin{cases} 4x + 2y + z = 0 \\ 3x - 2y - z = 3 \end{cases}$

20. $\begin{cases} x - 2y + z = 1 \\ 2x - y - 8z = 4 \end{cases}$

21. $\begin{cases} x^2 + y^2 + z^2 = 1 \\ x + y - z = 0 \end{cases}$

22. $\begin{cases} x^2 + y^2 + z^2 = 4 \\ x - y + z = 0 \end{cases}$

23. $\begin{cases} xy = 1 \\ 1 = z^2 + y^2 \end{cases}$

24. $\begin{cases} xyz = 1 \\ 1 = x^2 + y^2 \end{cases}$

25. $\begin{cases} x^2 + 4y^2 + 6z^2 = 24 \\ z = x^2 + y^2 \end{cases}$

26. $\begin{cases} 3x^2 + y^2 + 6z^2 = 72 \\ x = z^2 - y^2 \end{cases}$

❖ 13.9 Concept and Application Exercises

27. Suppose a friend is trying to maximize $f(x, y) = 3x - 4y$ over the curve $g(x, y) = 0$, and finds a point where both components of ∇g are positive. Explain how you know that he's not found the location of an extreme point.

28. Suppose $\nabla f = \lambda \nabla g$ is solved at (x_*, y_*) when the Lagrange multiplier is $\lambda = 0$. Explain why (x_*, y_*) must be a critical point of the objective function.

29. Based on the level curves shown in the left-hand image of Figure 9.13 determine the maximum value of f subject to the constraint that $g(x, y) = 0$.

30. Based on the level curves shown in Figure 9.14 determine the minimum value of f subject to the constraint that $g(x, y) = 0$.

31. Figure 9.15 shows level curves of f. Draw a curve so that, when constrained to your curve, the function f achieves a global maximum of 9 and a global minimum of 6.

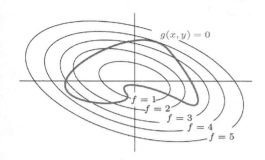

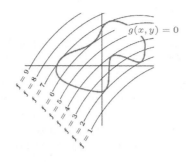

Figure 9.13: Level curves of f, and the constraint curve for #29

Figure 9.14: Level curves of f, and the constraint curve for #30

32. Figure 9.16 shows the level curves of f. Draw a constraint curve on which f has a local (but not a global) minimum of -2, and achieves a global maximum of 2 at two different points.

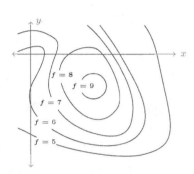

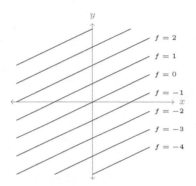

Figure 9.15: Level curves of f for #31

Figure 9.16: Level curves of f for #32

33. Suppose $f(x, y) = x^2 + 0.2y^2$.

(a) Graph the level curves $f(x, y) = k$ for $k = 1/5, 1/2, 1, 3/2$, and 2

(b) On the same graph, draw the unit circle.

(c) Based part (b), geometrically determine where f achieves its maximum and minimum value on the unit circle.

(d) Now that you know what *should* happen, use Lagrange multipliers to locate the extrema of f along the unit circle.

34. Suppose $f(x, y) = 0.4x^2 - y^2$.

(a) Graph the level curves $f(x, y) = k$ for $k = 5, 4, 3, 2$ and 1

(b) On the same graph, draw the unit circle.

(c) Based on the progression of level curves from part (a), determine where f achieves its maximum and minimum value on the unit circle.

(d) Use Lagrange multipliers to confirm your answer from part (a).

In #35–38 use the technique of Lagrange multipliers to solve the geometric problem.

35. Find the point on the curve $y = 3x + 4$ that's closest to $(-1, -2)$.

36. Find the point on the curve $y = x^2$ that's closest to $(4, 7)$.

37. Determine the minimum distance between the curves $y = x^2$ and $3x - y = 3$.

38. Determine the minimum distance between the curves $(x+2y)^2 + 0.1(2x-y)^2 = 2$ and $6 = x - 2y$.

Many of the optimization problems in Chapter 4 required a substitution in order to arrive at a function of a single variable. Such problems can often be solved without that preliminary step by using Lagrange multipliers. Exercises #39–46 are examples of such problems. (a) Draw the constraint curve, and several level curves of the objective function, and (b) solve the problem using the method of Lagrange multipliers.

39. Determine the maximum product of two numbers that sum to 10.

40. Determine the maximum product of two numbers that differ by 7.

41. A closed cylinder is being designed with reinforced ends. The material for the top and bottom costs \$10/ft^2, and the material for the sides costs \$4/ft^2. Find the minimum cost of a cylinder that encloses a volume of 1 ft^3.

_____ | Manufacturing |

42. Using the costs specified in #41, determine the maximum volume of a container if the cost cannot exceed \$40.

_____ | Manufacturing |

43. A fence that is 8 feet tall runs parallel to the face of a building 4 feet away. What is the length of the shortest ladder that will reach from the ground, over the fence, to the side of the building?

_____ | Security |

44. Suppose you intend to enclose 4 mi^2 of wetlands bordering a lake. The enclosed region must be rectangular, and fencing will cost \$10/ft^2 (you don't need to fence the lakeside). What's the smallest level of funding required?

_____ | Ecology |

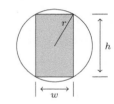

45. The strength of a rectangular beam is proportional to the product of its width and the square of its height. Consider a beam of height h and width w that's cut from a circular log of radius r, as shown in Figure 9.17. What are the dimensions (in terms of r) of the beam that maximize its strength?

46. Find the dimensions of the largest cylinder that has a 100 in^2 surface area.

Figure 9.17: For #45.

A *production function* describes the quantity that can be produced, Q, as a function of labor hours, ℓ, and short-term capital investment, k. Exercises #47 and #48 address the *Cobb-Douglas* production model, which assumes that Q has the form $Q(k, \ell) = \gamma k^\alpha \ell^\beta$, where α, β and γ are positive constants.

47. Suppose $\alpha = 0.4$, $\beta = 0.6$, $\gamma = 100$, labor costs \$15 per hour, and capital investment costs \$1.07 per dollar (i.e., investors require a 7% return on investment). (a) Write the total cost of a production run, $C(k, \ell)$, and (b) use Lagrange multipliers to determine the values of k and ℓ at which we can produce 90,000 units at minimum cost.

_____ | Economics |

48. Show that the cost of a production run is minimized where $C_\ell / C_k = Q_\ell / Q_k$.

_____ | Economics |

Exercises #49–52 are about a consumer's *utility function*, which quantifies the benefit to the consumer from purchasing items. The consumer attempts to maximize the cumulative utility of purchases subject to financial constraints.

_____ | Economics |

49. Suppose a consumer can purchase two kinds of products, say X and Y. If the benefit to the consumer from purchasing x units of X, and y units of Y is quantified by the *utility function* $U(x, y)$, the consumer's goal is to maximize $U(x, y)$ with a finite amount of money, M.

(a) We're going to work under the assumption that $\partial U/\partial x > 0$ and $\partial U/\partial y > 0$. What is the practical significance of these inequalities?

(b) If the price of product X is p and the price of product Y is q, explain the meaning of the equation $px + qy = M$.

(c) The *indirect utility function*, $V(p, q, M)$, tells us the maximum value of $U(x, y)$ subject to the constraint $px + qy = M$. Use Lagrange multipliers to show that $V(p, q, M)$ is calculated where $U_x/p = U_y/q$.

(d) The Lagrange multiplier that arises in the determination of $V(p, q, M)$ is called the *marginal utility of money*. Explain its practical meaning.

50. Suppose $U(x, y) = xy + x$. Determine $V(10, 3, 100)$.

51. Suppose $U(x, y) = 2y + xy^2$. Determine $V(6, 3, 100)$.

52. Suppose $U(x, y) = x^2 - x + xy + 3y^2$. Determine $V(3, 5, 50)$.

53. Suppose there are towns at $(0, 0)$ and $(12, -16)$, where length is measured in kilometers, and the segment of turnpike that passes near them follows the curve $y = 30e^{-\sqrt{x}}$. The Turnpike Authority has been directed to establish a new entrance point to service these towns. Assuming that straight roads can be laid between the towns and the entrance point, use Lagrange multipliers to determine where the entrance should be built in order to minimize the amount of new road that will be needed. *(Hint: if $f(x, y)$ is the cumulative distance from (x, y) to the towns, the level curves of f are ellipses.)*

            Civil Engineering

54. Suppose there are factories at $(0, 0)$ and $(1, -3)$, where distance is measured in km, and a river near them follows the curve $y = \cos(\pi x/2)$. The factories have agreed to build a water treatment facility on the river that will service both of them. If each factory will be connected to the treatment facility by a straight stretch of pipeline, where should the facility be built in order to minimize the amount of pipe that will be needed to connect it to the factories?

            Civil Engineering

55. The *information entropy* of a random event with three possible outcomes is $H(x, y, z) = -x \log_2(x) - y \log_2(y) - z \log_2(z)$, where x, y and z are the probabilities of each possible outcome and sum to 1. Use Lagrange multipliers to prove that H is maximized when x, y and z are equal.

            Coding Theory

56. When a 1-microliter droplet rests on a surface (e.g., a droplet of ink on a piece of paper), it takes a spherical shape that minimizes its *surface energy*. In brief, surface energy depends on the areas of the solid-liquid interface ($A_{s\ell}$), the solid-gas interface (A_{sg}), and the gas-liquid interface ($A_{g\ell}$). Specifically, the surface energy is

            Surface Chemistry

$$\mathcal{E} = \sigma_{s\ell} A_{s\ell} + \sigma_{sg} A_{sg} + \sigma_{g\ell} A_{g\ell},$$

where $\sigma_{s\ell}, \sigma_{sg}$ and $\sigma_{g\ell}$ are constants with dimensions of energy per unit area. Suppose $\sigma_{s\ell} = 86$, $\sigma_{sg} = 70$ and $\sigma_{g\ell} = 75$. If the drop sits at the center of a circular solid with diameter 1 cm (see Figure 9.18), use Lagrange multipliers to determine the values of r and h that minimize the surface energy. *(Hint: the volume of the droplet is the same for all possible values of r and h.)*

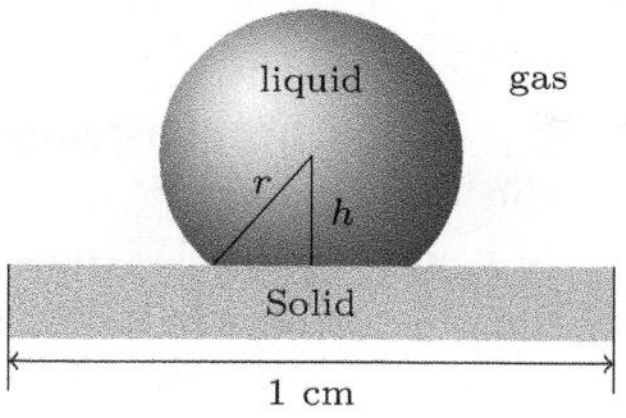

Figure 9.18: A droplet sitting on a flat surface, as in exercise #56 (not to scale!)

57. Suppose a soccer player dribbles the ball along the line through the penalty spot (12 yards in front of the goal's center) toward the corner flag 30 yards right of the goal's center (see Figure 9.19). (a) Use the method of Lagrange multipliers to determine the point along this path where the shooting angle, θ, is largest, (b) show that your answer from part (a) is *not* the point along the path where the player is closest to the goal's center (nor to either post).

            Sports/Recreation

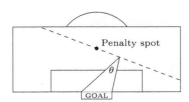

Figure 9.19: A player's path in front of goal in #57.

58. When a soccer player causes the ball to follow a curved trajectory by imparting
    spin during the kick, the ball's energy is described by $E = 0.5mv^2 + 0.5I\omega^2$,
    where v is the ball's speed, ω is its rate of rotation, m is its mass, and I
    is a number called the ball's *moment of inertia*. For the sake of discussion,
    consider the following model of the probability of scoring a goal on a free kick:
    $P(\text{goal}) = \gamma v^\alpha \omega^\beta$, where α, β and γ are positive constants.

    Sports/Recreation

    (a) Show that for a given amount of energy, the probability of scoring is
        maximized when the spin to speed ratio is the geometric mean of the
        ratio of β to α and the ratio of m to I.

    (b) What does this model predict as the probability of scoring a goal if the
        speed is zero, or if no spin is imparted to the ball? Do you believe it? If
        not, how might you improve the model?

When we think of a matrix A as a function (see Appendix F), we can gauge the
"size" of A using the **operator norm**, denoted by $\|A\|_*$ and defined as:

Mathematics

$$\|A\|_* = \text{maximum value of } \|A\mathbf{u}\| \text{ when } \mathbf{u} \text{ is a unit vector.}$$

The operator norm answers the question, "How much can A stretch a unit vector?"
Determine the operator norm of the matrix in #59–64 by maximizing $\|A\mathbf{u}\|$ subject
to the constraint $\|\mathbf{u}\| = 1$. *(Hint: it's often easier to work with $\|A\mathbf{u}\|^2$ instead of
$\|A\mathbf{u}\|$ because you avoid the square roots.)*

59. $A = \begin{bmatrix} 2 & 3 \\ -1 & 1 \end{bmatrix}$ 61. $A = \begin{bmatrix} 5 & -2 \\ 3 & 0 \end{bmatrix}$ 63. $A = \begin{bmatrix} -4 & 0 & 1 \\ 2 & 2 & 0 \end{bmatrix}$

60. $A = \begin{bmatrix} 3 & 2 \\ 0 & 8 \end{bmatrix}$ 62. $A = \begin{bmatrix} 1 & 3 \\ -1 & 2 \end{bmatrix}$ 64. $A = \begin{bmatrix} 4 & 1 & 0 \\ 1 & 5 & -1 \end{bmatrix}$

65. Consider the constrained optimization problem in which we want to find
    the extrema of $f(x, y, z)$ subject to the constraints that $g(x, y, z) = 0$ and
    $h(x, y, z) = 0$. We can rewrite this as an *unconstrained* optimization prob-
    lem by using the the **Lagrangian** associated with this problem, which is a
    function of the variables x, y, z, λ, μ. Specifically,

    $$L(x, y, z, \lambda, \mu) = f(x, y, z) + \lambda\, g(x, y, z) + \mu\, h(x, y, z).$$

    Explain what the critical points of L tell us about the extrema of f (subject
    to the given constraints).

66. In Example 9.1 we used the method of Lagrange multipliers to determine the
    maximum value of $f(x, y) = 4x - y$ on the circle $x^2 + y^2 = 1$. A minor change
    in the equation describing the curve can have a significant effect. Show that
    the method fails to find a maximum value of f on the curve $x^2 - y^2 = 1$, and
    explain why it happens.

Chapter 13 Review

✤ True or False

1. The equation $ax^2 + by^2 + cz^2 = 1$ describes either an ellipsoid or a hyperboloid when the coefficients a, b and c are nonzero.

2. The hyperboloid $x^2 - y^2 + z^2 = 1$ has one sheet.

3. The axis of the paraboloid $x^2 + 2x + y + z^2 = 2$ is parallel to the y-axis.

4. The two kinds of hyperboloids are *elliptic* and *parabolic*.

5. A cone is a kind of hyperboloid.

6. A level set is a collection of points in the domain of $f(x, y)$ over which its graph has a constant altitude.

7. The level curves $f(x, y) = 1$ and $f(x, y) = 2$ can intersect transversely.

8. The level curves $f(x, y) = 1$ and $f(x, y) = 2$ can intersect tangentially.

9. The plane $z = 10$ can intersect the graph of $f(x, y)$ in more than one place.

10. An ellipsoid can be the graph of a bivariate function.

11. An ellipsoid can be the level surface of a bivariate function.

12. A paraboloid can be the graph of a bivariate function.

13. A paraboloid can be the level surface of a multivariate function.

14. When all the limits in question exist, $\lim_{(x,y)\to(2,4)} f(x)g(y) = \left(\lim_{x\to 2} f(x) \right) \left(\lim_{x\to 4} g(y) \right)$.

15. When f_x and f_y exist, the bivariate function f is differentiable.

16. When $f(x, y)$ is differentiable, the normal vector to its tangent plane is $\mathbf{n} = \langle f_x, f_y, 1 \rangle$.

17. The numbers $\frac{\partial^2 f}{\partial x \partial y}$ and $\frac{\partial^2 f}{\partial y \partial x}$ are always the same.

18. The directional derivative, $D_{\mathbf{u}} f$, is never larger than $\|\nabla f\|$.

19. If $\det(H) > 0$ at (a, b), where H is the Hessian matrix of f, the graph of f has the same concavity in all directions.

20. A Lagrange multiplier can be 0.

✤ Multiple Choice

21. The equation $x^2 - y^2 + z^2 + 2x - 4y = 0$ describes ...

    (a) a hyperboloid of one sheet   (c) an ellipsoid

    (b) a cone   (d) none of the above

22. The equation $x^2 + y^2 - z^2 + 8x + 10y = -36$ describes ...

    (a) a hyperboloid of one sheet   (c) a paraboloid

    (b) a hyperboloid of two sheets   (d) none of the above

23. The (nonzero) gradient of $f(x,y)$ ...

    (a) is a 3-vector   (c) is tangent to a level curve
    (b) is a 2-vector   (d) none of the above

24. The level curve $f(x,y) = 2$ ...

    (a) always encloses the level curve $f(x,y) = 1$
    (b) is always enclosed by the level curve $f(x,y) = 1$
    (c) is perpendicular to ∇f at each point
    (d) none of the above

25. Suppose the bivariate function f is differentiable. Then ...

    (a) f_x exists, guaranteed   (c) both (a) and (b)
    (b) f_y exists, guaranteed   (d) neither (a) nor (b)

26. When $\det(H) = 0$ at the critical point (a,b) ...

    (a) we have found a local maximum
    (b) we have found a local minimum
    (c) we have found a saddle point
    (d) we don't know what kind of critical point it is

27. Lagrange multipliers

    (a) are never zero   (c) are used to find extrema on curves
    (b) are used to find critical points   (d) none of the above

28. The second directional derivative of f at (a,b) in the direction of $\mathbf{u}$

    (a) tells us the concavity of the graph of f in the direction of $\mathbf{u}$
    (b) only makes sense when (a,b) is a critical point of f
    (c) is the same in all directions
    (d) has the same sign in all directions

❖ Exercises

29. Consider the equation $(x-a)^2 + (y-b)^2 + (z-c)^2 = ab$. For what values of a, b and c (if any) does this equation describe an ellipsoid that's entirely contained in the first octant?

30. Consider the equation $Ax^2 + Bx + Cy^2 + Dy + Ez^2 + Fz = G$. What must be true about the coefficients in order for this equation to describe (a) a hyperboloid? (b) a paraboloid?

31. Sketch several level curves of $f(x,y) = 3x + 5y$.

32. Sketch several level curves of $f(x,y) = 3x^2 + 5y^2$.

33. Describe the level surfaces of $f(x,y,z) = 7x^2 + y^2 + z$

34. Describe the level surfaces of $f(x,y,z) = 7x^2 - y^2 + z$

35. Suppose $f(x,y) = 3x^4 - y^2$. Determine the rate at which f changes in the direction of increasing x at the point $(1, 2)$.

36. Suppose $f(x,y) = 8x^2 + 4\sin y$. Determine a parameterization of the tangent line to the graph of f that lies in the plane $y = \pi$ and passes through the point $(1, \pi, 8)$.

37. Suppose $f(x,y) = 4x^3 - e^{5y} + x^2y^3$. Determine (a) f_{xx}, and (b) f_{yx}.

38. Suppose $f(x,y,z) = \sin(xz) + \cos(yz)$. Determine (a) f_{zz}, and (b) f_{xy}.

39. Use Clairaut's theorem to show that $\langle 3x + y, -4y + 7x \rangle$ is *not* the gradient of a function.

40. Suppose $f(2,5) = -7$, $f_x(2,5) = 10$ and $f_y(2,5) = 6$. Write the equation of the tangent plane to the graph of f.

41. Suppose $f(x,y) = 2x^2 + 0.1y^2$. Write the equation of the tangent plane to the graph of f at $(1, 10, 12)$.

42. Suppose $f(11, -3) = 2$, $f_x(11, -3) = 1$ and $f_y(11, -3) = -4$. Write the formula for the linear approximation of f about $(11, -3)$.

43. Suppose $f(1,3) = 4$ and $\nabla f(x,y) = \langle 2x^3 + y, x - y \rangle$. Use linear approximation to estimate $f(1.01, 3.02)$.

44. Suppose $f(x,y) = 3x^2 + 0.01y^2$. Write the formula for the linear approximation of f about $(-1, 10)$.

45. Suppose $f(x,y) = 2x - 3y^2$, and the point (x,y) is moving according to $x(t) = 3\sin t$, $y(t) = 2t - 7$. Use the Chain Rule for Paths to determine df/dt when $t = \pi$.

46. Suppose $f(x,y) = x^2 + 0.13y - z^2$, and the point (x,y,z) is moving according to $x(t) = t^3$, $y(t) = \cos^2 t$, and $z(t) = t^{1/3}$. Use the Chain Rule for Paths to determine df/dt when $t = 2$.

47. Suppose that $f(x,y) = 2x^2 - 3y^4$. Determine the direction away from $(1, -2)$ in which the rate of increase in f is greatest.

48. Suppose that $f(x,y) = 3x - y^2 + (z+2)^3$. Determine the direction away from $(1, 4, 0)$ in which the rate of decrease in f is greatest.

49. Suppose that $(3, -4)$ is a critical point of f and $H = \begin{bmatrix} 1 & 2 \\ 2 & 7 \end{bmatrix}$. Determine whether $(3, -4)$ is a local minimum, local maximum, or saddle point.

50. Suppose $H = \begin{bmatrix} 1 & 2 \\ 2 & 7 \end{bmatrix}$. Determine the direction in which the second directional derivative of f is largest. *Hint: remember to use __unit__ vectors in the calculation.*

51. Explain why $(f_{xy})_x$ and $(f_{xx})_y$ have to be the same when they're continuous. Then show that
$$\begin{bmatrix} xy^2 & 3x \\ 3x & 4\cos y \end{bmatrix}$$
is not the Hessian matrix of a function, even though it's symmetric.

In #52–56 find the maximum value of f subject to the given constraint.

52. $f(x, y) = (x + 2)^3(y + 0.5)^2$; $x^2 + y^2 \leq 9$

53. $f(x, y) = (x - 1)^2(y + 1)^3$; $x^2 + 2y^2 \leq 20$

54. $f(x, y) = 3x + \sin(y)$; the curve $0.5x^2 - \cos y = 1$ that surrounds the origin

55. $f(x, y, z) = 3x - y^2 + z$; $x^2 + 3y^2 + 0.1z^2 = 1$

56. $f(x, y, z) = x^2 + y - z$; both $x^2 + 2y^2 = 3z^2 = 1$ and $4x + 3y + 2z = 0$

In #57–60 calculate the maximum value of $\|A\mathbf{u}\|$ subject to the constraint $\|\mathbf{u}\| = 1$ (see Appendix F).

57. $A = \begin{bmatrix} 5 & 2 \\ 1 & 1 \end{bmatrix}$

58. $A = \begin{bmatrix} 1 & 2 \\ 3 & 4 \end{bmatrix}$

59. $A = \begin{bmatrix} 1 & -1 & 2 \\ 0 & 5 & 1 \\ 0 & 0 & 8 \end{bmatrix}$

60. $A = \begin{bmatrix} 0 & 1 & 2 \\ 3 & 0 & 4 \\ 1 & 1 & 0 \end{bmatrix}$

Chapter 13 Projects and Applications

✤ Game Theory: Matching Pennies

Game theory is a branch of mathematics that deals with situations in which the outcome depends on the choices of two independent "players" whose interests are opposed. The players could be individuals, companies, or countries ... and each tries to maximize their "payoff," the value of which could be measured in political, economic, or military capital, etc. One of the simplest examples is a game that's commonly called *matching pennies.*

Suppose you and a friend each place a penny on the table. You get to keep the pair if *both* pennies show heads or *both* show tails, but he keeps them if one shows heads and the other shows tails.

> This is an example of something called a **zero-sum game**, since players' outcomes sum to zero: one player is 1 penny richer (+1) and the other has lost one penny (−1).

Here's a bit of strategic advice: if you play according to a pattern, such as **H, H, T, H, H, T, H, H, T** ... your opponent will quickly recognize what you're doing and exploit it to his advantage. Instead of a pattern, play heads with some *probability,* say x (then your probability of playing tails is $1 - x$). Your opponent will do likewise. For the sake of discussion, suppose he plays heads 56 times, and tails 44 times in a 100-turn game. The cumulative payoff that you expect from the turns on which he plays heads is

$$\underbrace{(56)\ x}\ +\ \underbrace{(-56)\,(1-x)}.$$

Probability (think "percentage of the   Probability (think "percentage of the
time") that you play heads also   time") that you play tails

Similarly, the payoff that you expect from the times that he plays tails is

$$\underbrace{(-44)x} + \underbrace{(44)(1-x)}\,. \tag{11.1}$$

He plays tails but you play heads (you lose)   He plays tails and you do too (you win)

When we add your winnings, we see that your payoff for this game is

$$56\Big((1)x + (-1)(1-x)\Big) + 44\Big((-1)x + (1)(1-x)\Big).$$

Since you played 100 rounds, your average payoff *per round,* called the **expected value** of your strategy, is

$$0.56\Big((1)x + (-1)(1-x)\Big) + 0.44\Big((-1)x + (1)(1-x)\Big).$$

Notice that your opponent played heads with a probability of 0.56 (56 times out of 100) in this hypothetical game, and tails with probability $0.44 = 1 - 0.56$. In general, if he plays heads with a probability of y, the expected value of your strategy is

$$E(x,y) = y\Big((1)x + (-1)(1-x)\Big) + (1-y)\Big((-1)x + (1)(1-x)\Big),$$

which we usually write as

$$E(x,y) = \begin{bmatrix} y \\ 1-y \end{bmatrix} \cdot \begin{bmatrix} 1 & -1 \\ -1 & 1 \end{bmatrix} \begin{bmatrix} x \\ 1-x \end{bmatrix}. \tag{11.2}$$

The matrix in (11.2) is called your **payoff matrix**. Of course, you want to maximize $E(x,y)$, and your opponent wants to minimize it. Suppose you play your best strategy, x^*, and he plays his best strategy, y^*.

1. Intuitively speaking, if you change away from your *best* strategy by adding or subtracting a little from x^*, you should do worse.

   (a) Explain what this tells us about E_x at (x^*, y^*).

   (b) Explain what this tells us about the concavity of the graph of E in the x-direction. *(Hint: adding a little bit to x^* has the same effect as subtracting a little bit.)*

2. Intuitively speaking, if he changes away from his *best* strategy by adding or subtracting a little from y^*, you should do better.

   (a) Explain what this tells us about E_y at (x^*, y^*).

   (b) Explain what this tells us about the concavity of the graph of E in the y-direction.

3. We say that (x^*, y^*) is a ***Nash equilibrium*** when $E(x^*, y) \geq E(x^*, y^*) \geq E(x, y^*)$, and say that $E(x^*, y^*)$ is the ***value*** of the game.

   (a) Locate the Nash equilibrium of the matching pennies game.

   (b) Determine the value of the matching pennies game.

> The Nash equilibrium is named after John Forbes Nash, who won the 1994 Nobel Prize in Economics for his work in game theory.

4. We say that a game is ***fair*** (meaning "unbiased toward either player") if its value is zero. Is matching pennies a fair game?

5. There's no need for the payoffs of a game to all have the same magnitude. Determine whether the payoff matrices below result in fair games.

$$A = \begin{bmatrix} 3 & -2 \\ -1 & 4 \end{bmatrix} \quad B = \begin{bmatrix} 3 & -5 \\ -4 & 6 \end{bmatrix} \quad C = \begin{bmatrix} 3 & -2 \\ -6 & 4 \end{bmatrix}$$

6. Calculate the determinants of matrices $A, B,$ and C above, and compare those numbers to your conclusions about the fairness of the game. What do you notice? Make a conjecture about the relationship and prove that you're right.

✣ Energy Functions and Least-squares Optimization

Least-squares optimization is a technique that's often used to fit lines (or curves) to data. It's especially important when working with data that are gathered from experiments, because such data always contain error—if not from the experimenter, then from the finite precision of the instruments that are used—so even when quantities are related linearly, measurements result in data that are *not* colinear.

Toward understanding the basic mathematical idea behind least-squares optimization, suppose we want to find a line that passes through the points $(0.5, 2.75)$, $(4, 5)$, $(6, 3.95)$, $(6.5, 5.25)$, shown in Figure 11.1. The points aren't collinear, so no line can pass through all of them, but consider the following thought experiment: take 4 identical springs, and screw them into the Cartesian plane so that their natural lengths end at the given points (see the left-hand image of Figure 11.2). Secure the springs to the plane tightly enough that they cannot pivot, but can only stretch in the y-direction. Then stretch the springs and connect them to a meter stick.

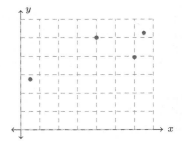

Figure 11.1: Suppose we want to fit a line to these points.

Remember from our discussion of integral calculus that when a linear spring (with spring constant 2) is stretched Δy, it has a potential energy of $(\Delta y)^2$. So when the meter stick is described by $y = mx + b$, the springs have a combined energy of

$$E(m, b) = \underbrace{\left(2.75 - (0.5m + b)\right)^2}_{\Delta y \text{ for the spring at } x = 0.5} + \left(5 - (4m + b)\right)^2 + \underbrace{\left(3.95 - (6m + b)\right)^2}_{\Delta y \text{ for the spring at } x = 6} + \left(5.25 - (6.5m + b)\right)^2.$$

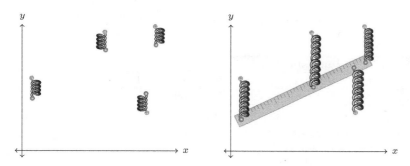

Figure 11.2: Screws, springs, a meter stick, and potential energy

Our thought experiment ends as the springs quickly tug the meter stick to a height and angle that minimizes the total potential energy of the system, $E(m, b)$.

1. Find the critical point of $E(m, b)$, use the Hessian matrix to verify that it's a minimum, and then plot the line $y = mx + b$ along with the data.

Because we're minimizing E, which is a sum of squares, we refer to the line you found in #1 as the **least-squares** linear regression of the data.

2. Find the least-squares linear regressions of the following data sets, and calculate the minimum value of E.

x	1	2.3	4.7	5.1	6.3	7	7.2	8.9	9.2
y	3.010	4.014	4.320	4.633	4.799	5.311	5.201	5.479	6.021

x	1	2.3	4.7	5.1	6.3	7	7.2	8.9	9.2
y	4.130	6.899	12.011	12.863	15.419	16.91	17.336	20.957	21.596

3. What does it mean when $E(m, b) = 0$ for a particular data set, (x_1, y_1), (x_2, y_2), ..., (x_n, y_n)?

4. For any particular data set, (x_1, y_1), (x_2, y_2), ..., (x_n, y_n), can there be two different pairs, (m_1, b_1) and (m_2, b_2), at which E is zero? If so, give an example. If not, explain why not.

5. Suppose we insist that $m = 0$.

   (a) Show that $E(0, b)$ is minimized when $b =$ the average (mean) y-value in the data set.

   (b) We denote the average y-value of the data set by $\langle y_j \rangle$. Show that $E(0, \langle y_j \rangle) = n\text{Var}(y_j)$, where $\text{Var}(y_j)$ is the variance of $\{y_1, y_2, \ldots, y_n\}$ (see p. 951).

6. After plotting the following data set, explain why linear regressions are irrelevant.

x	1	2.3	4.7	5.1	6.3	7	7.2	8.9	9.2
y	5.56	9.11	6.41	5.01	-1.44	-6.7	-8.00	-23.01	-24.94

7. Use the least-squares technique with the data from #6 to find numbers a, b and c for which $y = ax^2 + bx + c$ minimizes E.

In all the examples so far, the arguments of E (a, b, c and m, respectively) occur linearly in ∇E, which makes finding critical points relatively easy. Of course, that doesn't always happen.

8. The website `www.weather.com` reports the following averages for monthly highs in Rochester, NY:

	Jan	Feb	Mar	Apr	May	Jun	Jul	Aug	Sep	Oct	Nov	Dec
Month	1	2	3	4	5	6	7	8	9	10	11	12
Avg. High	31	33	43	55	68	77	81	79	71	60	47	36

The yearly average of the high temperatures in this list is 56.75, and it seems reasonable that the temperatures should repeat this up-down cycle every year, which makes us think of a cosine function with a period of 12:

$$T(t) = 56.75 + a\cos\left(\frac{\pi}{6}(t - b)\right).$$

Determine the values of a and b that minimize $E(a, b)$. Then plot the cosine curve along with the given data.

9. Repeat #8 with weather data from your home town.

Chapter 14
Multiple Integrals

In Chapter 13 you saw that differentiability is truly a two-dimensional aspect of a function of two variables, but as a practical matter we differentiate with respect to one variable at a time. Similarly, in this chapter we'll see that the integral of $f(x, y)$ is a two-dimensional calculation, but computing that number will often be done by integrating one variable at a time.

14.1 Double Integrals Over Rectangles

Imagine that some quantity is spread over a region, and we want to know how much there is all together. For example, Figure 1.1 represents a day's distribution of solar radiation across the state of Colorado. The red in the southern part of the state

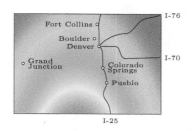

Figure 1.1: A map representing the *direct normal solar radiation* received across Colorado each day. Red corresponds to 8 kW-hrs/m^2 per day, and blue corresponds to 5 kW-hrs/m^2.

indicates nearly 8 kW-hrs of power per square meter, and Colorado has a land area of approximately 268.66×10^9 m^2, so we could estimate that an average of

$$\left(8\frac{\text{kW-hr}}{\text{m}^2}\right) 268.66 \times 10^9 \text{ m}^2 = 2.1493 \times 10^{12} \text{ kW-hrs}$$

of solar power falls on the state each day. On the other hand, the blue in the northeast corner of the state indicates about 5 kW-hrs of power per square meter each day, so we could also estimate the total power as

$$\left(5\frac{\text{kW-hr}}{\text{m}^2}\right) 268.66 \times 10^9 \text{ m}^2 = 1.3433 \times 10^{12} \text{ kW-hrs}.$$

Both of these calculations assume that the solar radiation that falls on Colorado is the same across the entire state, but in reality the intensity of solar radiation differs from one part of the state to another, so the actual amount of solar power received by Colorado lies somewhere between our estimates. As you can see in Figure 1.2, the plan for improving our approximation is to partition Colorado into smaller rectangles. Then we pick a location in each of the rectangles at which to measure the solar radiation, and treat it as constant throughout that rectangle.

Key Idea(s): *When something (e.g., mass, energy, population) is spread over a region, we approximate the net total by subdividing the region into small rectangles and measuring the density in each. This is the two-dimensional version of a Riemann sum.*

The net total is calculated exactly with a limit, which we call the double integral.

The properties of double integrals are similar to those of definite integrals that you saw in Chapter 5.

Fubini's Theorem allows us to evaluate a double integral by integrating first in x (with y held as constant) and then in y, or vice versa. This allows us to employ techniques from single-variable integration.

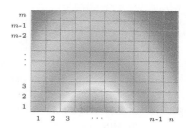

Figure 1.2: Partitioning a region with a grid of rectangles.

1119

For the sake of formulating this idea mathematically, suppose we use a grid of rectangles having m rows and n columns. We'll say that the rectangle at the intersection of row i and column j has an area of ΔA_{ij}, and we'll denote by (x_{ij}^*, y_{ij}^*) the point in that rectangle where we measure the intensity of solar radiation, $f(x_{ij}^*, y_{ij}^*)$. Using this notation, the amount of solar radiation that falls on row i of the grid is approximately

$$\sum_{j=1}^{n} \overbrace{f(x_{ij}^*, y_{ij}^*)}^{\text{Solar radiation, in kW-hrs/m}^2} \underbrace{\Delta A_{ij}}_{\text{Area of a rectangle, in m}^2}$$

The sigma notation tells us that the column index increments from $j = 1$ to $j = n$, but no part of this expression changes the row number, i, so this is a sum across row i of the grid.

Adding the sums from all the rows gives us an approximation of the cumulative amount of solar energy,

$$\sum_{i=1}^{m} \sum_{j=1}^{n} f(x_{ij}^*, y_{ij}^*)\, \Delta A_{ij}. \tag{1.1}$$

We refer to the number in (1.1) as a **Riemann sum** of f. Generally speaking, Riemann sums allow us to approximate the net total of *any* quantity that's distributed over an area, whether it's energy, charge, mass, etc.

Riemann sums and accumulation

Example 1.1. Suppose $f(x, y)$ has units of bacteria per mm^2, where x and y are measured in mm. What does the Riemann sum $\sum_{i=1}^{9} \sum_{j=1}^{11} f(x_{ij}^*, y_{ij}^*)\Delta A_{ij}$ tell us?

Solution: The units of $f(x_{ij}, y_{ij})\Delta A_{ij}$ are $\left(\frac{\text{bacteria}}{\text{mm}^2}\right) \times (\text{mm}^2) = \text{bacteria}$. This Riemann sum approximates the number of bacteria in a region. ∎

❖ A Double Integral is the Limit of Riemann Sums

In our preliminary discussion we approximated the cumulative total of a quantity (energy, population) by treating a function as constant over rectangles. Intuitively speaking, grids with smaller rectangles should give us better approximations of that cumulative total, and based on our prior experience with Riemann sums, we expect to determine the exact value in a limit. The following paragraphs introduce vocabulary that will help us to be precise when discussing such limits.

We'll use the notation $[a, b] \times [c, d]$ to mean the rectangle in the xy-plane consisting of all points (x, y) for which $x \in [a, b]$ and $y \in [c, d]$, where we assume that $a < b$ and $c < d$. By partitioning the width and height of $[a, b] \times [c, d]$, say

$$a = x_0 < x_1 < \cdots < x_n = b$$
$$c = y_0 < y_1 < \cdots < y_m = d,$$

we define a grid with m rows and n columns, as in Figure 1.3. This grid of rectangles, which we'll denote by P, constitutes a **partition** (or **mesh**) of $[a, b] \times [c, d]$. The rectangle at the intersection of row i and column j has a height of $\Delta y_i = y_i - y_{i-1}$, a width of $\Delta x_j = x_j - x_{j-1}$, and an area of $\Delta A_{ij} = \Delta x_i \Delta y_j$. The **norm** of P, also called the **mesh size**, is

$$\|P\| = \text{ the largest of all the } \Delta x_i \text{ and } \Delta y_j,$$

and we say that P is **regular** when all its rectangles are congruent.

When the Riemann sums of f converge to a particular number as $\|P\| \to 0$, regardless of where we choose to sample f along the way, we say that f is **integrable**,

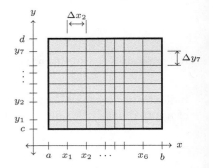

Figure 1.3:   A non-regular mesh of $[a, b] \times [c, d]$ having $n = 7$ columns and $m = 8$ rows. The intersection of column 2 and row 7 is a rectangle. We denote its width by Δx_2 and its height by Δy_8.

The mesh size is either the *width* of the widest rectangle, or the *height* of the tallest rectangle—whichever is larger.

and that the limit value is the ***double integral*** of f over R. We typically use a tandem pair of integral signs to denote the double integral:

$$\iint_R f(x,y)\, dA = \lim_{\|P\|\to 0} \sum_{i=1}^{m} \sum_{j=1}^{n} f(x_{ij}^*, y_{ij}^*)\, \Delta A_{ij}. \qquad (1.2)$$

The differential of area, dA, that you see on the left-hand side of equation (1.2) is often called the ***area element***.

> When R is a rectangle and f is the constant function $f(x,y) \equiv 1$, the Riemann sum on the right-hand side tells us the area of R.

The following theorem identifies an important class of functions that are integrable, and is often proved in advanced courses using the same basic techniques that establish its single-variable analog.

Theorem: Suppose the function f is continuous over $R = [a,b] \times [c,d]$ in the xy-plane, except perhaps at a finite number of points or along a finite number of smooth curves, and that f is bounded over R (meaning that there is a number M for which $|f(x,y)| < M$ at all points in R). Then f is integrable over R.

Calculating a double integral as the limit of Riemann sums

Example 1.2. Calculate $\iint_R f(x,y)\, dA$ when $f(x,y) = 1+xy$ and R is the rectangle $[2,4] \times [5,8]$, depicted in Figure 1.4.

Solution: Our strategy will be to approximate the double integral by sampling f on a regular mesh, and then apply the limit as $\|P\| \to 0$.

Suppose we partition R with a regular mesh that has m rows and n columns. Then because R is 2 units wide and 3 units tall, each of the rectangles in our mesh has a width of $\Delta x = 2/n$, a height of $\Delta y = 3/m$, and an area of $\Delta A = \Delta x \Delta y = 6/mn$.

Since it doesn't matter where we sample the function in each rectangle, let's sample f in the upper-right corner of each. To write that out precisely, we'll have to index the rectangles of our mesh. We'll use j to index the columns from left to right, and i to denote the rows from bottom to top (see Figure 1.4). Then the upper-right corner of the rectangle in column j of row i is at

$$x_j = 2 + j\Delta x = 2 + \frac{2j}{n} \quad \text{and} \quad y_i = 5 + i\Delta y = 5 + \frac{3i}{m}.$$

The function value there is

$$f\left(2 + \frac{2j}{n}, 5 + \frac{3i}{m}\right) = 1 + \left(2 + \frac{2j}{n}\right)\left(5 + \frac{3i}{m}\right) = 11 + \frac{6i}{m} + \frac{10j}{n} + \frac{6ji}{mn}.$$

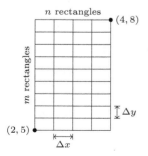
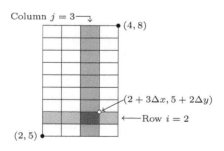

Figure 1.4: (left) Partitioning the rectangle R into a mesh of m rows and n columns; (right) the sample point for the rectangle in row $i = 2$, column $j = 3$ is in its upper, right-hand corner.

To add the contributions from all the rectangles in row i, we calculate

$$\sum_{j=1}^{n} f(x_j, y_i)\, \Delta A.$$

The row index, i, is not changing

Using our formulas for x_j and y_i, this is

$$\sum_{j=1}^{n} f(x_j, y_i)\Delta A = \sum_{j=1}^{n}\left(11 + \frac{6i}{m} + \frac{10j}{n} + \frac{6ji}{mn}\right)\Delta A.$$

Since we're going to sum over j, let's group our terms according to how many factors of j they have:

$$\sum_{j=1}^{n} f(x_j, y_i)\Delta A = \sum_{j=1}^{n}\left(\left[11 + \frac{6i}{m}\right] + \left[\frac{10}{n} + \frac{6i}{mn}\right]j\right)\Delta A.$$

The number ΔA is constant since we're using a regular mesh (i.e., it's independent of i and j), so we can factor it out of the sum and write

$$\sum_{j=1}^{n} f(x_j, y_i)\Delta A = \left(\sum_{j=1}^{n}\left[11 + \frac{6i}{m}\right] + \left[\frac{10}{n} + \frac{6i}{mn}\right]\sum_{j=1}^{n}j\right)\Delta A.$$

Since $\left[11 + \frac{6i}{m}\right]$ does not depend on j, this is

$$\sum_{j=1}^{n} f(x_j, y_i)\Delta A = \left(\left[11 + \frac{6i}{m}\right]n + \left[\frac{10}{n} + \frac{6i}{mn}\right]\frac{n(n+1)}{2}\right)\Delta A$$

$$= \left(16n + 5 + \frac{9n+3}{m}i\right)\Delta A.$$

That's the sum we get by adding across row i. Next we'll add the contribution from all of the rows, so let's collect terms according to how many factors of i they have, and write

$$\sum_{i=1}^{m}\left(\sum_{j=1}^{n} f(x_j, y_i)\Delta A\right) = \sum_{i=1}^{m}\left(16n + 5 + \frac{9n+3}{m}i\right)\Delta A$$

$$= \left(16nm + 5m + \left[\frac{9n+3}{m}\right]\frac{m(m+1)}{2}\right)\Delta A$$

$$= \left(\frac{41}{2}nm + \frac{9}{2}n + \frac{13}{2}m + \frac{3}{2}\right)\Delta A.$$

Now since $\Delta A = {}^{6}/_{nm}$ (calculated above), this becomes

$$\sum_{i=1}^{m}\left(\sum_{j=1}^{n} f(x_j, y_i)\Delta A\right) = 123 + \frac{27}{m} + \frac{39}{n} + \frac{9}{nm}.$$

That's the value of a Riemann sum with nm rectangles (in n columns and m rows). Since both $m \to \infty$ and $n \to \infty$ as $\|P\| \to 0$, the limit of Riemann sums is

$$\iint_R f(x,y)\, dA = \lim_{\|\Delta A\|\to 0}\left(123 + \frac{27}{m} + \frac{39}{n} + \frac{9}{nm}\right) = 123. \qquad \blacksquare$$

Recall that

$$\sum_{j=1}^{n} j = \frac{n(n+1)}{2}.$$

and

$$\sum_{j=1}^{n} k = kn.$$

Calculate a double integral as the limit of Riemann sums

Example 1.3. Suppose $f(x,y) = x^2 - y^2$ and R is the rectangle $3 \leq x \leq 4$ and $1 \leq y \leq 5$. Calculate $\iint_R f(x,y)\, dA$.

Answer: $\iint_R f(x,y)\, dA = 8.$ $\qquad \blacksquare$

Solution On-line

❖ Volume and Surface Area

Just as we calculated area and arc length using integrals in the single-variable setting, we calculate volume and surface area using the double integral.

▷ Volume

In Chapter 5 you saw that a Riemann sum can be understood as the cumulative area of rectangles when $f(x) \geq 0$, so in the limit we get the area between the graph of f and the x-axis. An analogous interpretation of the double integral is valid when $f(x,y) \geq 0$. Since we make the graph of f by using $f(x,y)$ to determine a height (i.e., z-coordinate), each term in a Riemann sum can be understood as

> When $f(x)$ can be negative, we talk about *net* area.

$$f(x_j, y_i)\, \Delta A = \text{(height)} \times \text{(area of the base)} = \text{(volume of a tower)}.$$

So a Riemann sum approximates the volume between the graph of f and the xy-plane, and we determine the volume exactly in the limit as $\|P\| \to 0$ (see Figure 1.5). As in single-variable calculus, the limit of Riemann sums is said to be a **net volume** in the case when $f(x,y)$ can be negative.

Volume: Suppose the function f is integrable over the region $R = [a,b] \times [c,d]$. The net volume between the surface $z = f(x,y)$ and the region R is

$$V = \iint_R f(x,y)\, dA.$$

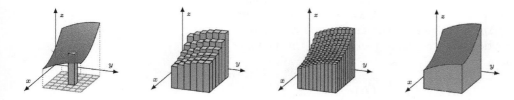

Figure 1.5: (left) The height of a tower is determined by the graph of f; (middle pair) approximating the volume between the graph of f and the xy-plane by using more and more towers; (right) in the limit.

Net Volume

Example 1.4. Suppose $f(x,y) = 4+x-y$ when $x \in [0,1]$ and $y \in [3,5]$. Determine whether the graph of f bounds more volume above or below the xy-plane.

> Note that $f(0,5) < 0$ but $f(3,0) > 0$. So the graph of this function is above the xy-plane at some points, and below at others.

Solution: In the end, this is just a question about whether the net volume is positive or negative. So let's partition our domain with a regular mesh of rectangles that has n columns and m rows. Then $\Delta x = 1/n$ and $\Delta y = 2/m$, so we set

$$x_j = 0 + \frac{j}{n} \quad \text{and} \quad y_i = 3 + \frac{2i}{m}, \quad \text{and calculate} \quad f(x_j, y_i) = 1 - \frac{2i}{m} + \frac{j}{n}.$$

The net volume of the towers in row i of the mesh is

$$\sum_{j=1}^{n} f(x_j, y_i)\, \Delta A = \sum_{j=1}^{n} \left(1 - \frac{2i}{m} + \frac{j}{n}\right) \Delta A = \left(\left[1 - \frac{2i}{m}\right] n + \frac{1}{n}\left[\frac{n(n+1)}{2}\right]\right) \Delta A = \left(\frac{3n}{2} + \frac{1}{2} - \frac{2ni}{m}\right) \Delta A.$$

Our next step is to add the contributions from all the rows, which we do by summing as i increases from 1 to m.

$$\sum_{i=1}^{m} \sum_{j=1}^{n} f(x_i, y_j)\, \Delta A = \sum_{i=1}^{m} \left(\frac{3n}{2} + \frac{1}{2} - \frac{2ni}{m}\right) \Delta A. = \left(\frac{3nm}{2} + \frac{m}{2} - \frac{2n}{m}\frac{m(m+1)}{2}\right) \Delta A.$$

After distributing $\Delta A = \Delta x \, \Delta y = 2/mn$, this becomes

$$\sum_{i=1}^{m} \sum_{j=1}^{n} f(x_i, y_j) \, \Delta A = 3 + \frac{1}{n} - 2\left(\frac{m+1}{m}\right).$$

Since $m \to \infty$ and $n \to \infty$ as $\|P\| \to 0$, the net volume between the graph of f and the xy-plane is

$$\iint_R f(x, y) \, dA = 1.$$

Because the double integral is positive, the graph of f bounds more volume above the xy-plane than below it.   ∎

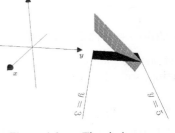

Figure 1.6:   The dark gray rectangle in the xy-plane is the region R for Example 1.4, and the graph of f. The lines $y = 3$ and $y = 5$ are shown in the xy-plane for reference.

Net volume

Example 1.5. Suppose $R = [-1, 2] \times [-3, 1]$, and $f(x, y) = x + 2y$. Determine whether the graph of f bounds more volume above or below the xy-plane.

Answer: Below; $\iint_R f(x, y) \, dA = -18$.   ∎

Solution On-line

▷ Surface Area

Because we already know how to calculate the area of a parallelogram, our method of determining the surface area of a function's graph begins by approximating the surface as a collection of small parallelogram-shaped facets (the actual surface area is found in a limit). Consider a small rectangle in the xy-plane, say $x \in [a, a + \Delta x]$ and $y \in [b, b + \Delta y]$, with an area of $\Delta A = \Delta x \, \Delta y$. When f is a differentiable function, the vector $\langle 1, 0, f_x(a, b) \rangle$ is tangent to the graph. Scaling this vector so that it corresponds to a step of Δx in the x-direction gives us $\mathbf{u} = \langle \Delta x, 0, f_x(a, b)\Delta x \rangle$. Similarly, the vector $\mathbf{v} = \langle 0, \Delta y, f_y(a, b)\Delta y \rangle$ is tangent to the graph, and corresponds to a step of length Δy in the y-direction. So the small rectangle in the xy-plane corresponds to a parallelogram of area

$$\begin{aligned}
\|\mathbf{u} \times \mathbf{v}\| &= \sqrt{\left(\Delta x \, \Delta y\right)^2 + \left(f_x(a, b) \, \Delta x \, \Delta y\right)^2 + \left(f_x(a, b) \, \Delta x \, \Delta y\right)^2} \\
&= \sqrt{1 + \left(f_x(a, b)\right)^2 + \left(f_y(a, b)\right)^2} \, \Delta A.
\end{aligned}$$

that's tangent to the graph of f (see Figure 1.7). To approximate the surface area of the graph of f over a larger rectangular region, R, we partition R with a mesh and write

$$\text{surface area} \approx \sum_{i=1}^{m} \sum_{j=1}^{n} \sqrt{1 + \left(f_x(x_{ij}^*, y_{ij}^*)\right)^2 + \left(f_y(x_{ij}^*, y_{ij}^*)\right)^2} \, \Delta A_{ij}.$$

Here we're restricting our discussion to graphs of functions. More general surfaces are considered in Chapter 15.

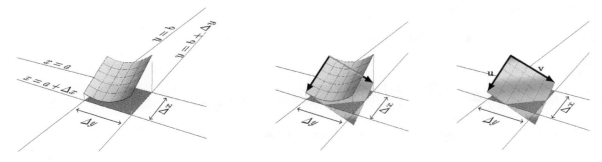

Figure 1.7: (left) a patch of the graph of f over a rectangle in the xy-plane. Vertical line segments have been added at the corners of the patch in order to help communicate perspective; (middle) the graph of f with a patch of the tangent plane at $(a, b, f(a, b))$; (right) the area of the parallelogram is $\|\mathbf{u} \times \mathbf{v}\|$.

Approximation becomes equality in the limit as $\|P\| \to 0$, which brings us to the following statement.

Surface Area: Suppose $R = [a,b] \times [c,d]$, and f is a function with continuous first-partial derivatives. Then the graph of f over R has a surface area of

$$\iint_R \sqrt{1 + \big(f_x(x,y)\big)^2 + \big(f_y(x,y)\big)^2}\, dA.$$

Approximating surface area

Example 1.6. Suppose $f(x,y) = x^2 + 7y^2$, and $R = [0,4] \times [5,6]$, where length is measured in cm. Estimate the surface area of the graph of f over R by using a regular mesh with 10 columns and 8 rows.

Solution: Since $f_x = 2x$ and $f_y = 14y$, the surface has an area of

$$\iint_R \sqrt{1 + (2x)^2 + (14y)^2}\, dA = \iint_R \sqrt{1 + 4x^2 + 196y^2}\, dA.$$

By using our mesh of 80 rectangles (10 wide, 8 high) we can estimate

$$\iint_R \sqrt{1 + 4x^2 + 196y^2}\, dA \approx \sum_{i=1}^{8} \sum_{j=1}^{10} \sqrt{1 + 4x_j^2 + 196y_i^2}\, \Delta A,$$

where ΔA is the area of the rectangle at the intersection of row i and column j, and (x_j, y_i) is its upper-right corner (as in Figure 1.4). More specifically, $\Delta A = \Delta x\, \Delta y$ where $\Delta x = {(4-0)}/{10} = 0.4$ is the width of each rectangle in the mesh, and $\Delta y = {(6-5)}/{8} = 0.125$ is its height. So

> All the rectangles have the same area because we're using a regular mesh.

$$\sum_{i=1}^{8} \sum_{j=1}^{10} \sqrt{1 + 4x_j^2 + 196y_i^2}\, \Delta A = \sum_{i=1}^{8} \sum_{j=1}^{10} \sqrt{1 + 4x_j^2 + 196y_i^2}\, (0.05)$$

Generating and adding 80 function values is manually intensive, but we can make the process very fast with a spreadsheet. Since the $x \in [0,4]$ and $\Delta x = 0.4$, the right-hand sides of the rectangles in our mesh are at $0.4, 0.8, \ldots, 3.96, 4$ respectively. Similarly, since $y \in [5,6]$ and $\Delta y = 0.125$, the tops of the rectangles are at $y = 5.125, 5.25, \ldots, 5.875, 6$ respectively. We begin by listing these in spreadsheet.

> After putting the number 6 in cell **A1** you can quickly fill in the rest of the y-coordinates by entering the formula =A1-0.125 in cell **A2** and using the drag technique presented in earlier discussions to copy it into the rest of the rows in column **A**. Similarly for the x-coordinates. This technique of entering data becomes important when you have many more than 8 rows or 10 columns.

	A	B	C	D	E	F	G	H	I	J	K
1	6										
2	5.875										
3	5.75										
4	5.625										
5	5.5										
6	5.375										
7	5.25										
8	5.125										
9		0.4	0.8	1.2	1.6	2	2.4	2.8	3.2	3.6	4

$\leftarrow$ x-values

$\uparrow$
y-values

In cell **B1** we enter the formula for calculating $\sqrt{1 + 4x_j^2 + 196y_i^2}\, (0.05)$ at the point $(x_j, y_i) = (0.4, 6)$, but recall that we refer to the numbers x_j and y_i by their location in the spreadsheet rather than their value; since 0.4 is found in cell **B9**, and 6 is found in cell **A1**, in cell **B1** we type

The symbol $ "locks" whatever row or column follows; typing B$9 locks the row at 9 but allows the column to change from B to C, to D, ..., to K when using the "drag" technique to populate the cells in the spreadsheet. Similarly, by typing $A1 (instead of just A1) we lock the column at A but allow the row to change from 1 to 2, to 3, ..., to 8.

$$= \texttt{sqrt(1 + 4*B\$9\^2 + 196*\$A1\^2)*0.05}$$

This tells the spreadsheet to put the number $\sqrt{1 + 4 * 6^2 + 196 * 0.4^2}(0.05)$ into cell B1. We can copy this formula to the rest of the cells in the first row by using the "drag" technique presented in earlier discussions, and then to the rest of the cells by dragging the first row down to the eighth. This results in

	A	B	C	D	E	F	G	H	I	J	K
1	6	4.20049	4.20106	4.20201	4.20334	4.20506	4.20715	4.20962	4.21247	4.21570	4.21930
2	5.875	4.11280	4.11358	4.11455	4.11591	4.11766	4.11980	4.12232	4.12523	4.12853	4.13221
3	5.75	4.02551	4.02611	4.02710	4.02849	4.03028	4.03246	4.03504	4.03801	4.04138	4.04514
4	5.625	3.9380	3.93863	3.93965	3.94107	3.94289	3.94512	3.94776	3.95080	3.95424	3.95808
5	5.5	3.85053	3.85116	3.85219	3.85365	3.85552	3.85780	3.86049	3.86360	3.86712	3.87105
6	5.375	3.76304	3.76368	3.76475	3.76623	3.76814	3.77048	3.77324	3.77641	3.78001	3.78403
7	5.25	3.67556	3.67621	3.67730	3.67882	3.68078	3.68317	3.68599	3.68924	3.69293	3.69704
8	5.125	3.58807	3.58874	3.58985	3.59141	3.59342	3.59587	3.59876	3.60209	3.60586	3.61008
9		0.4	0.8	1.2	1.6	2	2.4	2.8	3.2	3.6	4

Lastly, we add all of these numbers by typing $= \texttt{sum(B1:K8)}$ in any empty cell. The result is that the surface area is

$$\iint_R \sqrt{1 + 4x^2 + 196y^2}\, dA \approx 312.159 \text{ cm}^2 \qquad \blacksquare$$

✣ Iterated Integrals Over Rectangles

Imagine that you want to paint a rectangular wall. You might be able to paint it all at once with a very large, fine-grained sponge, but doing the job with a roller brush or sprayer is more practical—moving it horizontally to paint rows, or vertically to paint columns. A similar idea is often helpful in the case of double integrals: instead of calculating a limit of Riemann sums, determine the value by integrating in one variable at a time—first in x (to find the net totals over the "rows" of the rectangle) and then in y (to obtain a single, cumulative value by adding the row totals), or vice versa. The details of this method are presented below in the case of a continuous function f, and a rectangular region $R = [a, b] \times [c, d]$.

You know that the double integral of f over the rectangle R is the limit of Riemann sums,

$$\iint_R f(x, y)\, dA = \lim_{\|P\| \to 0} \sum_{i=1}^{m} \sum_{j=1}^{n} f(x_j, y_i)\, \Delta x \Delta y.$$

The notation of this Riemann sum indicates that the partition is regular (since Δx and Δy are independent of i and j), and that we are sampling f in the upper-right corner of each small rectangle of the mesh.

Note that taking $\|P\| \to 0$ forces both $\Delta x \to 0^+$ and $\Delta y \to 0^+$ simultaneously. Now let's consider what happens when we send $\Delta x \to 0^+$ and $\Delta y \to 0^+$ *separately*. For example, suppose $\Delta x \to 0^+$ while Δy remains fixed, so that $n \to \infty$ while m remains constant. Then

$$\lim_{n \to \infty} \sum_{i=1}^{m} \sum_{j=1}^{n} f(x_j, y_i)\, \Delta x \Delta y = \sum_{i=1}^{m} \left(\lim_{n \to \infty} \sum_{j=1}^{n} f(x_j, y_i)\, \Delta x \right) \Delta y$$

And because y_i remains constant as $n \to \infty$,

Because y_i is fixed, this integration takes place over a line segment that reaches from the left to the right boundary of the region.

$$\sum_{i=1}^{m} \left(\lim_{n \to \infty} \sum_{j=1}^{n} f(x_j, y_i)\, \Delta x \right) \Delta y = \sum_{i=1}^{m} \left(\int_a^b f(x, y_i)\, dx \right) \Delta y \qquad (1.3)$$

Note that the value of this sum depends only on the y_i, because x is a dummy variable in the integral. Now sending $\Delta y \to 0^+$ by letting $m \to \infty$, this Riemann sum (in y) becomes a definite integral (in y):

$$\lim_{m \to \infty} \sum_{i=1}^{m} \left(\int_{a}^{b} f(x, y_i) \, dx \right) \Delta y = \int_{c}^{d} \left(\int_{a}^{b} f(x, y) \, dx \right) \, dy. \qquad (1.4)$$

Had we reversed the order of our limits, first sending $\Delta y \to 0^+$ and then $\Delta x \to 0^+$, we would have arrived at

$$\lim_{n \to \infty} \left(\lim_{m \to \infty} \sum_{i=1}^{m} \sum_{j=1}^{n} f(x_j, y_i) \, \Delta x \Delta y \right) = \int_{a}^{b} \left(\int_{c}^{d} f(x, y) \, dy \right) \, dx. \qquad (1.5)$$

The value of x is constant in first of these nested integrals (integrating in y), so the integration happens along a line segment that extends from the lower to the upper boundary of the region.

The nested integrals on the right-hand side of equations (1.4) and (1.5) are called *iterated integrals,* and the key to their calculation is indicated by the parentheses: *we leave y as constant when integrating in x,* and vice versa. With that said, it's common practice to omit parentheses from the notation, so

This is reminiscent of partial differentiation, in which one variable is treated as constant, so it might seem reasonable to call this technique *partial integration.* Alas, that terminology is not standard.

$$\int_{a}^{b} \int_{c}^{d} f(x, y) \, dy \, dx \quad \text{means} \quad \int_{a}^{b} \left(\int_{c}^{d} f(x, y) \, dy \right) \, dx.$$

Evaluating an iterated integral

Example 1.7. Calculate $\int_{3}^{4} \int_{1}^{5} (xy + x^2) \, dx \, dy$.

Solution: We begin by calculating the "inner" integral. Since the variable of integration is x (indicated by the differential dx), we treat y as a constant and see

Including the variable name in the limits of integration helps to avoid errors.

$$\int_{1}^{5} (xy + x^2) \, dx = \left(\frac{1}{2} y x^2 + \frac{1}{3} x^3 \right) \Big|_{x=1}^{x=5}$$

$$= \left(\frac{25}{2} y + \frac{125}{3} \right) - \left(\frac{1}{2} y + \frac{1}{3} \right) = \frac{24}{2} y + \frac{124}{3} = 12y + \frac{124}{3}.$$

Now we complete the calculation by writing

$$\int_{3}^{4} \left(\int_{1}^{5} (xy + x^2) \, dx \right) \, dy = \int_{3}^{4} \left(12y + \frac{124}{3} \right) \, dy = \left(6y^2 + \frac{124}{3} y \right) \Big|_{3}^{4} = \frac{250}{3}. \quad \blacksquare$$

In Example 1.7 we wrote the steps of integration on separate lines in order to emphasize that only one of the variables is integrated at a time, but it's common practice to keep them together by writing the calculation as follows:

$$\int_{3}^{4} \int_{1}^{5} (xy + x^2) \, dx \, dy = \int_{3}^{4} \underbrace{\left[\frac{1}{2} x^2 y + \frac{1}{3} x^3 \right]_{x=1}^{x=5}}_{} \, dy = \int_{3}^{4} \left[12y + \frac{124}{3} \right] \, dy = \frac{250}{3}.$$

The square braces delimit the first step of integration, and also act as the vertical evaluation bar

Evaluating an iterated integral

Example 1.8. Calculate $\int_{1}^{5} \int_{3}^{4} (xy + x^2) \, dy \, dx$.

Answer: $250/3$ $\blacksquare$

Solution On-line

▷ Fubini's Theorem

We arrived at the number $250/3$ in both Examples 1.7 and 1.8, even though the order of integration was reversed. This happened because the iterated integrals in these examples are both equal to the *double integral* over the rectangle R (remember the roller-brush idea from the section opener). The following theorem, due to the Italian mathematician Guido Fubini (1879–1943), generalizes this idea.

The name *Fubini* is pronounced "foo-BEE-nee."

Fubini's Theorem for Rectangular Regions: Suppose f is continuous over the rectangle $R = [a,b] \times [c,d]$. Then

$$\int_a^b \int_c^d f(x,y)\,dy\,dx = \iint_R f(x,y)\,dA = \int_c^d \int_a^b f(x,y)\,dx\,dy. \qquad (1.6)$$

Fubini's Theorem gives us a relatively quick and easy way to calculate double integrals in lieu of using the definition (i.e., computing the limit of Riemann sums).

Calculating a double integral

Example 1.9. Suppose $f(x,y) = 1 + xy$ and R is the rectangle $[2,4] \times [5,8]$. Use Fubini's theorem to calculate $\iint_R f(x,y)\,dA$.

Solution: Fubini's theorem tells that the order of the iterated integral doesn't matter (provided that the bounds of integration are properly matched with the differentials). So we can write the double integral as

This agrees with our calculation in Example 1.2.

$$\iint_R (1+xy)\,dA = \int_2^4 \int_5^8 (1+xy)\,dy\,dx = \int_2^4 \left(\int_5^8 (1+xy)\,dy \right) dx$$

$$= \int_2^4 \left[y + \frac{1}{2}xy^2 \right]_{y=5}^{y=8} dx = \int_2^4 \left[3 + \frac{39}{2}x \right] dx = 123. \quad \blacksquare$$

Choosing which iterated integral to compute

Example 1.10. Suppose $f(x,y) = ye^{xy}$ and $R = [0,4] \times [0,1]$. Determine the volume between the xy-plane and the graph of f over R.

Solution: Fubini's Theorem tells us that, in principle, we can calculate this volume with either of two integrals:

$$\int_0^1 \int_0^4 ye^{xy}\,dx\,dy = \iint_R ye^{xy}\,dA = \int_0^4 \int_0^1 ye^{xy}\,dy\,dx.$$

Our choice of which iterated integral to compute is influenced by practical concerns. The iterated integral on the left requires simpler techniques than the integral on the right, so we compute

$$\text{Volume} = \int_0^1 \int_0^4 ye^{xy}\,dx\,dy = \int_0^1 \left[e^{xy} \right]_0^4 dy = \int_0^1 \left(e^{4y} - 1 \right) dy = \frac{1}{4}(e^4 - 5). \quad \blacksquare$$

Don't just read it. Try computing

$$\int_0^4 \int_0^1 ye^{xy}\,dy\,dx,$$

starting with an integration by parts (with respect to y), just to see what happens!

Calculating surface area

Example 1.11. Suppose $f(x,y) = 3 + 2x + 9y$, and $R = [0,5] \times [0,3]$, where length is measured in meters. Determine the surface area of the graph of f over the rectangle R.

Answer: $15\sqrt{86}$ m^2 ⬛

Solution On-line

✢ Properties of the Double Integral

The properties of double integrals are closely related to the properties of definite integrals (see Chapter 5), and can be understood using similar intuition. Suppose R is a rectangular region in the xy-plane, f and g are integrable functions, and k is a scalar. Then

$$\iint_R \left(f(x,y) \pm g(x,y) \right) dA = \iint_R f(x,y)\,dA \pm \iint_R g(x,y)\,dA \qquad (1.7)$$

$$\iint_R k\,f(x,y)\,dA = k \iint_R f(x,y)\,dA \qquad (1.8)$$

Properties (1.7) and (1.8) are often referred to as the *linearity* of the double integrals. Further, if $f(x,y) \in [m, M]$ at all points in R, and $|R|$ denotes the area of R,

$$m\,|R| \leq \iint_R f(x,y)\,dA \leq M\,|R| \tag{1.9}$$

A special case of (1.9) happens in the case of constant functions,

$$\iint_R k\,dA = k\,|R|. \tag{1.10}$$

If R is the union of rectangles R_1 and R_2 that are disjoint except at their boundaries,

$$\iint_R f(x,y)\,dA = \iint_{R_1} f(x,y)\,dA + \iint_{R_2} f(x,y)\,dA. \tag{1.11}$$

Compare equation (1.10) to Example 1.11.

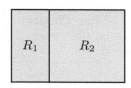

▷ The Mean Value Theorem

In Chapter 7 you saw the Mean Value Theorem for Integrals, which guarantees that a continuous function over $[a, b]$ achieves its average value at some point in the interval. The extension of this fact to functions of two variables is relatively straightforward once we define the notion of *average value* in this context.

For the sake of discussion, suppose that 2 coulombs of charge is distributed across the face of a 4-mm^2 metal plate. What's the average (mean) charge density? And if the mass of that same plate is 5 grams, what's the average (mean) mass density? We answer both questions with a simple ratio,

$$\frac{\text{net total charge} \to}{\text{area} \to} \frac{2}{4}\frac{\text{C}}{\text{mm}^2}, \quad \text{and} \quad \frac{\text{net total mass} \to}{\text{area} \to} \frac{5}{4}\frac{\text{g}}{\text{mm}^2}.$$

Recall that a Riemann sum (and so in the limit, the double integral) is used to measure the net total of *any* quantity that's distributed over an area. This leads us to the following definition.

Figure 1.8: An example of partitioning R into R_1 and R_2.

> **Definition:** When f is integrable over $R = [a, b] \times [c, d]$, the ***average value*** of f over R is
>
> $$\langle f \rangle = \frac{\iint_R f(x,y)\,dA}{|R|} \quad \begin{array}{l} \leftarrow \text{net total} \\ \leftarrow \text{area of } R \end{array}$$
>
> where $|R|$ denotes the area of R.

We're dealing with only rectangular regions in this section, but we'll learn how to handle more general regions in Section 14.2.

As in the single-variable case, the average value of a function can also be interpreted geometrically.

Average value and net volume

Example 1.12. Suppose $R = [a, b] \times [c, d]$, and $f(x, y)$ is a continuous function. Further, suppose R is the base of a rectangular box that encloses the same (net) volume as the graph of f over R. Show that the height of the box is $\langle f \rangle$.

The statement that $|R| > 0$ is meant to avoid division by 0.

Solution: If the height of the box is denoted by z, its volume is

$$(\text{area of the base}) \times (\text{height}) = |R|z.$$

Since this is equal to the net volume of f over R, we have that

$$|R|z = \iint_R f(x,y)\,dA \quad \Rightarrow \quad z = \frac{1}{|R|}\iint_R f(x,y)\,dA = \langle f \rangle. \qquad \blacksquare$$

Note: If $\langle f \rangle < 0$, we understand $z < 0$ to mean that the box is below the xy-plane.

Now suppose that f is continuous function on the rectangle R. Since R is closed and bounded, you know from Chapter 12 that f achieves a minimum value, say m, and a maximum value, say M. So property (1.9) assures us that

$$m \, |R| \leq \iint_R f(x,y) \, dA \leq M \, |R|.$$

Dividing this string of inequalities by $|R| > 0$, results in

$$m \leq \langle f \rangle \leq M.$$

Since $\langle f \rangle$ is a number between the minimum and maximum values of f, and f is continuous on R, the Intermediate Value Theorem guarantees at least one point in R at which f achieves its average (mean) value.

> **Mean Value Theorem for Double Integrals:** Suppose f is a continuous function on the rectangle R in the xy-plane. Then there is some point (a, b) in R at which $f(a, b) = \langle f \rangle$.

The Mean Value Theorem asserts the existence of *at least* one point at which a continuous function achieves its average value, but the equation $f(x, y) = \langle f \rangle$ defines a level curve of f. The Mean Value Theorem guarantees that this curve intersects R.

Mean Value Theorem

Example 1.13. Suppose the region R and the function f are as in Example 1.4. Show that $\langle f \rangle$ intersects R.

Solution: In Example 1.4 we showed that $\iint_R f(x,y) \, dA = 1$, and the rectangle R has an area of 2 square units, so $\langle f \rangle = 0.5$. In Figure 1.9 you can see that the line $4 + x - y = 0.5$ intersects the rectangle R. ∎

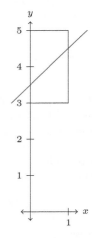

Figure 1.9: The rectangular region R and the level curve $f(x, y) = \langle f \rangle$.

> ### You should know
>
> - the terms *Riemann sum, regular mesh, mesh size, integrable, area element, double integral, net volume* and *average value*;
> - basic properties of the double integral;
> - that all continuous functions are integrable;
> - that the double integral can be understood as a (net) volume, or as the accumulation of some quantity (e.g., mass, energy, . . .);
> - the Mean Value Theorem for Double Integrals

> ### You should be able to
>
> - calculate the value of (simple) double integrals using sums and limits;
> - approximate a double integral with a Riemann sum;
> - determine $\langle f \rangle$;
> - use a Riemann sum to approximate the surface area of the graph of $f(x, y)$ (or a double integral to calculate it exactly in simple cases).

❖ 14.1 Skill Exercises

In #1–2 the region R is the rectangle in which $x \in [1, 5]$ and $y \in [5, 8]$. Use the values of f shown in Figure 1.10 to approximate $\iint_R f(x, y)\, dA$ with a Riemann sum using the specified sampling scheme.

1. Sampling in the upper-right corner of each square.

2. Sampling in the lower-left corner of each square.

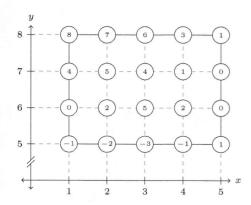

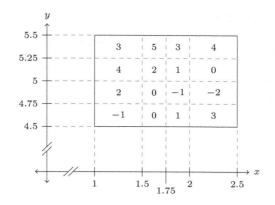

Figure 1.10: Function values in R for #1–2.   Figure 1.11: Function values in R for #3–4.

Figure 1.11 shows $f(x, y)$ at several points in the rectangle R, where $x \in [1, 2.5]$ and $y \in [4.5, 5.5]$. Use this data for #3–4.

3. Approximate the net volume bounded by the graph of f over R.

4. Approximate the average value of f over R.

In #5–12 determine the double integral of f over the given rectangle using the definition (i.e., by calculating a limit of Riemann sums).

5. $x \in [0, 5]$, $y \in [0, 5]$; $f(x, y) = 1 + 3x + 17y$
6. $x \in [1, 4]$, $y \in [1, 4]$; $f(x, y) = 2 - 13x - 9y$
7. $x \in [-1, 1]$, $y \in [-2, 4]$; $f(x, y) = x + 9y^2$
8. $x \in [0, 7]$, $y \in [-3, -1]$; $f(x, y) = 2 + 5x + y^2$

9. $x \in [-4, -3]$, $y \in [0, 2]$; $f(x, y) = x^2 - 2y$
10. $x \in [0, 1]$, $y \in [-2, 0]$; $f(x, y) = -1 + 9x^2 + y$
11. $x \in [-1, 5]$, $y \in [1, 4]$; $f(x, y) = 1 + x^2 + 7y^2$
12. $x \in [7, 12]$, $y \in [10, 13]$; $f(x, y) = x^2 - y^2$

Calculate the iterated integral in #13–30.

13. $\displaystyle\int_6^8 \int_1^8 3\, dx\, dy$

14. $\displaystyle\int_{-2}^3 \int_4^9 -5\, dy\, dx$

15. $\displaystyle\int_1^5 \int_2^4 6x\, dx\, dy$

16. $\displaystyle\int_0^2 \int_1^8 4y\, dx\, dy$

17. $\displaystyle\int_7^9 \int_{-1}^1 y\, dy\, dx$

18. $\displaystyle\int_2^3 \int_{-1}^1 x^2\, dy\, dx$

19. $\displaystyle\int_0^1 \int_0^2 (3x + 9y)\, dx\, dy$

20. $\displaystyle\int_0^3 \int_0^1 (x^2 - y)\, dx\, dy$

21. $\displaystyle\int_0^1 \int_0^3 xy^2\, dy\, dx$

22. $\displaystyle\int_1^9 \int_2^4 y\sqrt{x}\, dy\, dx$

23. $\displaystyle\int_1^5 \int_{-1}^1 x\cos(\pi y/2)\, dy\, dx$

24. $\displaystyle\int_4^5 \int_\pi^{3\pi/2} \sin(xy)\, dy\, dx$

25. $\displaystyle\int_3^4 \int_1^2 (3xy + y^2 + x)\, dx\, dy$

26. $\displaystyle\int_1^7 \int_2^5 (x^2 - 7xy + y)\, dx\, dy$

27. $\displaystyle\int_4^6 \int_3^6 (x^2 y^2 - 8x - 2y)\, dy\, dx$

28. $\displaystyle\int_1^3 \int_2^5 (6xy^2 - 10x - 4y)\, dy\, dx$

29. $\displaystyle\int_0^1 \int_0^1 \frac{y^2}{1 + (xy)^2}\, dx\, dy$

30. $\displaystyle\int_1^2 \int_0^1 \frac{1}{y^3} e^{x/y}\, dx\, dy$

In #31–36 (a) determine the average value of f over R, denoted by $\langle f \rangle$, and (b) graph R with curve $f(x, y) = \langle f \rangle$.

31. $f(x, y) = 8x - y$, $x \in [1, 5]$ and $y \in [0, 3]$

32. $f(x, y) = x + 3y$, $x \in [-1, 1]$ and $y \in [1, 2]$

33. $f(x, y) = x^2 + y$, $x \in [0, 1]$ and $y \in [-1, 3]$

34. $f(x, y) = x - y^2$, $x \in [1, 2]$ and $y \in [-2, 0]$

35. $f(x, y) = 1 - xy$, $x \in [-2, 0]$ and $y \in [2, 5]$

36. $f(x, y) = x^2 + y^2$, $x \in [-1, 1]$ and $y \in [-2, 2]$

❖ 14.1 Concept and Application Exercises

In #37–40 calculate $\iint_R \rho(x, y)\, dA$, where R is the specified rectangle and length is measured in cm. Include proper units in your answer.

37. $x \in [1, 3]$, $y \in [2, 4]$; $\rho(x, y) = 8x \ \frac{g}{cm^2}$

38. $x \in [2, 7]$, $y \in [8, 9]$; $\rho(x, y) = 12y \ \frac{kW\text{-}min}{cm^2}$

39. $x \in [1, 3]$, $y \in [5, 7]$; $\rho(x, y) = xy + x \ \frac{J}{cm^2}$

40. $x \in [1, 3]$, $y \in [0, 4]$; $\rho(x, y) = yx + y \ \frac{molecules}{cm^2}$

In #41–44 determine the region R for which $\iint_R f(x, y)\, dA$ is maximized.

41. $f(x, y) = 1 - x^2 - 7y^2$

42. $f(x, y) = 4 - |x| - |y|$

43. $f(x, y) = \sin x - \sin y$; R is contained in the rectangle $[0, 2\pi] \times [0, \pi]$

44. $f(x, y) = \cot y - \tan x$; R is contained in the rectangle $[0, 0.5\pi] \times [0, 0.5\pi]$

45. Suppose R is a rectangular region in the xy-plane. Use the double integral to write an inequality that says, "The graph of f bounds more volume below R than above it."

46. Suppose $R = [0, 2] \times [0, 4]$. (a) Partition R using a regular mesh with three horizontal and two vertical lines. (b) Calculate $\|P\|$ for this partition. (c) Draw several more horizontal and/or vertical lines but keep $\|P\|$ constant.

47. Suppose $R = [0, 2] \times [0, 4]$, and $f(x, y) = e^{-x^2 - y^2}$. If we approximate $\iint_R f(x, y)\, dA$ with a Riemann sum in which f is sampled at the lower-left corner of each sub-rectangle, have we overestimated or underestimated the value of the integral? Explain, in light of f_x and f_y.

48. Suppose R is a rectangle in the xy-plane and f is continuous. Put the following numbers in order from least to greatest.

$$\iint_R |f(x, y)|\, dA \qquad \iint_R f(x, y)\, dA \qquad \left| \iint_R f(x, y)\, dA \right|$$

49. Suppose $R = [0, 10] \times [-7, -6]$. Design a continuous function $f(x, y)$ for which $\iint_R f(x, y)\, dA = 0$.

50. Suppose $f(x, y)$ is 1 if either of x or y is rational, and is 0 otherwise. The function f is not continuous, but is it integrable over the square in which $x \in [0, 1]$ and $y \in [0, 1]$?

51. Figure 1.12 shows the depth of water (in meters) in a particular patch of ocean. (a) Use the depth values at the specified points to approximate the average depth of water. (b) The figure indicates that the patch of ocean is a square with a side length of 100 m. If the side length were 1000 m instead, how would the answer to part (a) change, if at all?

Oceanography

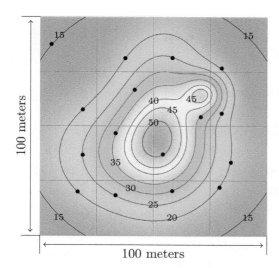

Figure 1.12: Water depth for #51.

52. Suppose $R = [1,3] \times [-1,0]$, and $f(x,y) = 6x - y$. If R is the base of a rectangular box, B, that encloses the same volume as that between R and the graph of f, how tall is B?

_____ | Average Height |

53. Suppose $R = [6,7] \times [1,8]$, where length is measured in mm. If thermal energy is distributed across R according to the density function $\sigma(x,y) = 2x + 5y$, measured in J/mm^2, determine the average energy density on R.

_____ | Average Energy |

54. Suppose $R = [3,8] \times [0,2]$, where length is in cm. If R has an embedded charge of $\sigma(x,y) = x+y$ coulombs per cm^2, determine the average charge density on R.

_____ | Average Charge |

In #55–58 determine the volume between the xy-plane and the graph of f over the given rectangle, assuming all lengths are measured in millimeters.

_____ | Volume |

55. $[0,1] \times [0,1]$; $f(x,y) = 1 - 0.5x$ 57. $[3,5] \times [1,2]$; $f(x,y) = xy$

56. $[1,3] \times [2,4]$; $f(x,y) = 8 - y$ 58. $[2,7] \times [-1,0]$; $f(x,y) = x^2 - y$

In #59–62 (a) calculate $\iint_R f(x,y) \, dA$, and (b) determine whether the graph of f bounds more volume above or below R.

_____ | Net Volume |

59. $R = [2,3] \times [2,3]$; $f(x,y) = -4 + x + y$ 62. $R = [0,3] \times [0,1]$; $f(x,y) = -8 + 2x^2 + 3y$

60. $R = [2,3] \times [2,3]$; $f(x,y) = 6 - 2x - y$ 63. $R = [0,3] \times [0,\pi]$; $f(x,y) = 3x\sin y$

61. $R = [1,3] \times [1,2]$; $f(x,y) = 7 - x^2 - 2y^2$ 64. $R = [1,3] \times [-2,0]$; $f(x,y) = 3x^2y + y^2$

In #65–68 estimate the surface area of f over the given rectangle by using a regular mesh that's n rectangles wide and m rectangles high, and sampling the integrand in the upper right-hand corner of each subrectangle. All lengths are measured in centimeters. (A spreadsheet can make the calculations much quicker!)

_____ | Surface Area |

65. $[1,4] \times [3,9]$; $n = 2$, $m = 3$; $f(x,y) = x^2 + y$

66. $[5,7] \times [3,11]$; $n = 4$, $m = 2$; $f(x,y) = 1 + xy$

67. $[-1,6] \times [-9,-1]$; $n = 20$, $m = 30$; $f(x,y) = {}^x\!/y$

68. $[-3,-2] \times [-1,8]$; $n = 15$, $m = 25$; $f(x,y) = xy^3$

In #69–72, find the surface area of f over the given rectangle if lengths are in inches.   Surface Area

69. $[1,4] \times [3,9]$; $f(x,y) = 10 - x - y$ 74. $[-5,8] \times [-1,3]$; $f(x,y) = \sqrt{16 - y^2}$

70. $[5,7] \times [3,11]$; $f(x,y) = 2 - 2x - 5y$ 75. $[-1,0] \times [1,5]$; $f(x,y) = 4 + 8x^2 + y$

71. $[-1,6] \times y \in [-8,0]$; $f(x,y) = 7 + 4x - 2y$ 76. $[-1,0] \times [1,5]$; $f(x,y) = -3 + 2x - 7y^2$

72. $[-3,-2] \times [-1,8]$; $f(x,y) = 3 + 6x - 4y$ 77. $[8,9] \times [2,3]$; $f(x,y) = 13x - \ln y$

73. $[-1,2] \times [0,4]$; $f(x,y) = \sqrt{9 - x^2}$ 78. $[2,5] \times [1,3]$; $f(x,y) = 4y + 2\ln x$

79. Suppose $R = [0,5] \times [0,5]$, where length is measured in cm. A colony of bacteria lives in R, and because of nutrient placement the population density is $\sigma(x,y) = 1000(x+y)$ bacteria per cm^2. Determine (a) the units of $\sigma(x,y)\,dA$, (b) the number of bacteria in R, and (c) the average population density of the colony.   Biology

80. This exercise is about the production rate at a given company, which depends on the skill levels of the employees, x, and the time spent on task, t (in hours). Here we take $x = 0$ to indicate the lowest skill level of employees, and $x = 1$ the highest. If the production density is $p(x,t) = 0.25(8xt - xt^2 + 8t - t^2)\frac{\text{items/hr}}{\text{skill level}}$, determine (a) the units of $\int_0^8 \int_0^1 p(x,t)\,dx\,dt$, and (b) the number of items produced by this company in an 8-hour work day.   Business

81. Suppose $R = [a,b] \times [c,d]$, and f and g are continuous functions of a single variable. Show that   Mathematics

$$\iint_R f(x)g(y)\,dA = \left(\int_a^b f(x)\,dx \right) \left(\int_c^d g(y)\,dy \right).$$

82. Recall that Clairaut's Theorem guarantees $f_{xy}(a,b) = f_{yx}(a,b)$ when the second mixed partial derivatives of f are continuous in an open set containing the point (a,b). We used a somewhat involved application of the Mean Value Theorem to prove this in the exercise set for Section 13.4. Here we use a simpler proof that relies on Fubini's Theorem instead. Suppose that Δx and Δy are chosen sufficient small that the rectangle $R = [a, a + \Delta x] \times [b, b + \Delta y]$ is entirely contained inside the open set where f_{xy} and f_{yx} are continuous. Fubini's Theorem allows us to calculate double integrals over R as iterated integrals.   Mathematics

  (a) Determine a formula for $\iint_R f_{xy}\,dA = \int_a^{a+\Delta x} \int_b^{b+\Delta y} f_{xy}(x,y)\,dy\,dx$.

  (b) Determine a formula for $\iint_R f_{yx}\,dA = \int_b^{b+\Delta y} \int_a^{a+\Delta x} f_{yx}(x,y)\,dx\,dy$.

  (c) Use parts (a) and (b) to argue that $\iint_R (f_{xy} - f_{yx})\,dA = 0$.

  (d) Since the second mixed partial derivatives of f are continuous, so is their difference. So if $(f_{xy} - f_{yx})$ were positive (or negative) at (a,b), it would remain positive (negative) throughout a small disk centered at (a,b). Based on what we've shown in this exercise, explain why this cannot happen.

14.2   Double Integrals Over More General Regions

Key Idea(s):   *Fubini's Theorem applies to non-rectangular regions, provided that they are sufficiently simple.*

In the previous section we discussed the cumulative total of solar power that falls on the state of Colorado each day; the shape of the state led us to the ideas and methods of double integrals over rectangles. Since most shapes are not rectangles, in this section we extend our understanding of double integrals to non-rectangular regions, subject to some mild constraints. Specifically, we will address bounded regions with **simple** boundaries, meaning that the boundary curve does not intersect itself, and we will assume that the boundary curve is part of the region. Further, we will limit the scope of our discussion to regions with **piecewise smooth** boundaries, meaning that a region's boundary is composed of a finite collection of smooth curves. Figure 2.2 shows some examples of bounded regions with simple, piecewise smooth boundaries.

Figure 2.1: Examples of non-rectangular regions with simple, piecewise smooth boundaries.

Now suppose that we want to calculate the double integral of a continuous function f over such a region, D. Since we already understand double integrals over rectangles, let's enclose D in a rectangle, say R. As you see in Figure 2.2, our plan is to partition the rectangle with a grid of rectangles, P, and to determine a limit as $\|P\| \to 0$.

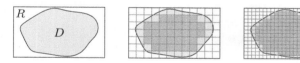

Figure 2.2: (left) A region D enclosed by a rectangle R; (middle) a partition of R naturally partitions D; (right) as $\|P\|$ is reduced, the union of rectangles inside of D becomes a better approximation of D.

Although f might be defined in the entire rectangle, we want to ignore its value at all points outside of D. We accomplish this by making our calculation with a "helper" function:

$$\tilde{f}(x,y) = \begin{cases} f(x,y) & \text{if } (x,y) \text{ is a point in } D \\ 0 & \text{otherwise.} \end{cases}$$

Because $\tilde{f}$ is continuous on R, except perhaps at the piecewise smooth boundary of D, it is integrable. This allows us to define the double integral of f over D as

$$\iint_D f(x,y)\,dA = \iint_R \tilde{f}(x,y)\,dA. \tag{2.1}$$

It is important to understand that the double integral of f over D is the limit of Riemann sums, because there are cases when using analytical methods to evaluate integrals is either impractical or impossible. With that said, in the remainder of this section we will focus on using an the extension of Fubini's Theorem to non-rectangular regions.

Note that the height and width of R are irrelevant (provided that it encloses D) because $\tilde{f}$ is 0 outside of D.

✧ Fubini's Theorem

In Section 14.3 we introduced Fubini's Theorem, which tells us that we can calculate a double integral as an iterated integral. Fubini's theorem can also be used for non-rectangular regions of the plane, as long as they are simple. In this case, the word "simple" means more than just "uncomplicated." Intuitively speaking, the region R is **simple** when it amounts to a collection of parallel line segments that extend between its left and right boundaries, or between its lower and upper boundaries. In such cases we can integrate over slices of R in the x- or the y-direction (depending on the region's geometry), and then aggregate the results by integrating in the other variable.

> Here we mean that the left and right boundaries can be easily characterized as different curves. We mean to exclude cases when horizontal line segments extend from a curve to itself (although the technique demonstrated below does, sometimes, work in that case too). Similarly, the lower and upper boundaries are intended to be distinct curves.

▷ Regions that are simple in the y-direction

We'll say that a region in the xy-plane is simple in the y-direction, or more concisely that it's y-**simple** if secant lines parallel to the y-axis intersect the boundary twice— once as it enters the region and once as it exits. The left and middle regions in Figure 2.3 are y-simple, but the rightmost region is not.

> Some other authors refer to this kind of region as *type I*.

Figure 2.3: The left and middle regions are y-simple, but the rightmost region is not.

When a region D is y-simple, we can often calculate $\iint_D f(x,y)\,dA$ using an iterated integral of the $dy\,dx$ variety—i.e., integrating first in y and then in x. For instance, suppose D is the bounded region that lies above the curve $y = g_1(x)$, below $y = g_2(x)$, and extends from $x = a$ to $x = b$ as shown in Figure 2.4. When we enclose D in the rectangle $R = [a,b] \times [c,d]$, Fubini's Theorem tells us that

> Think back to the idea of painting a wall with a roller brush. You can think of integrating in y as making a vertical stroke. Then integrating with respect to x moves us from left to right across the region.

$$\iint_D f(x,y)\,dA = \iint_R \tilde{f}(x,y)\,dA = \int_a^b \int_c^d \tilde{f}(x,y)\,dy\,dx. \qquad (2.2)$$

And because $\tilde{f}$ is 0 when $y > g_2(x)$ or $y < g_1(x)$, this reduces to

$$\iint_D f(x,y)\,dA = \int_a^b \int_{g_1(x)}^{g_2(x)} \tilde{f}(x,y)\,dy\,dx. = \int_a^b \int_{g_1(x)}^{g_2(x)} f(x,y)\,dy\,dx, \qquad (2.3)$$

> The function $\tilde{f}$ might not be continuous over R, as required by Fubini's Theorem, but we can justify equation (2.2) nonetheless. The integral
> $$\int_c^d \tilde{f}(x,y)\,dy$$
> exists since $\tilde{f}$ has at most two discontinuities along each vertical line, and the value of the integral varies continuously with x.

where the final equality is true because $\tilde{f}$ is identical to f inside D. We demonstrate this technique in the following examples.

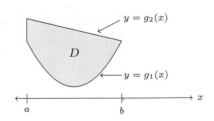 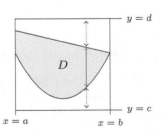

Figure 2.4: (left) A y-simple region D; (right) the region D is enclosed by the rectangle $[a,b] \times [c,d]$. Note that $\tilde{f}(x,y) = 0$ on the dotted portion of the vertical line segment, so the integral over this segment contributes nothing to the total.

Integrating over a y-simple region

Example 2.1. Suppose D is the bounded region defined by the curves $y = 2x^2$ and $y = x^2 + 4$. Use Fubini's theorem to calculate $\iint_R (2xy + 3)\, dA$.

Solution: The region D is shown in Figure 2.5, and the bounding curves meet at the points $(\pm 2, 8)$. This region is y-simple, so we begin by integrating in y. The lower curve (and so the *lower* bound of this integral) is $y = 2x^2$. The upper curve (and so the *upper* bound of this integral) is $y = x^2 + 4$. So

$$\iint_D f(x,y)\, dA = \int_{-2}^{2} \int_{2x^2}^{x^2+4} (2xy + 3)\, dy\, dx = \int_{-2}^{2} \left[xy^2 + 3y \right]_{y=2x^2}^{y=x^2+4} dx$$

$$= \int_{-2}^{2} \left[x\left((x^2+4)^2 - (2x^2)^2 \right) + 12 - 3x^2 \right] dx$$

Because $x\left((x^2+4)^2 - (2x^2)^2 \right)$ is an odd function of x, its integral over $[-2, 2]$ is 0. This leaves us with

$$\iint_D f(x,y)\, dA = \int_{-2}^{2} \left[12 - 3x^2 \right] dx = 32. \qquad \blacksquare$$

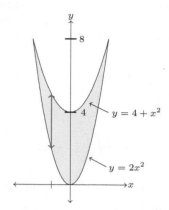

Figure 2.5: At each value of x, the vertical "stroke" through this region extends from $y = 2x^2$ to $y = 4 + x^2$.

Integrating over a y-simple region

Example 2.2. Suppose D is the region bounded above by $y = \cos x$ and below by $y = -x$, where $0 \le x \le \pi$. Use Fubini's theorem to calculate $\iint_D (3y - x)\, dA$.

Answer: $\iint_R (3y - x)\, dA = 2 + \frac{3}{4}\pi - \frac{5}{6}\pi^3$ $\qquad \blacksquare$

Solution On-line

▷ Regions that are simple in the *x*-direction

We will say that a region in the xy-plane is simple in the x-direction, or more concisely that it's x-**simple** if secant lines parallel to the x-axis intersect the boundary twice—once as it enters the region, and once as it exits. For example, the left-hand and righthand regions in Figure 2.6 are x-simple, but the middle region is not.

Some other authors refer to this kind of region as *type II*.

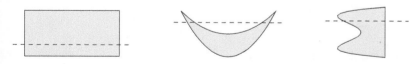

Figure 2.6: The left and right regions are x-simple, but the middle region is not.

When a region D is x-simple, we can calculate $\iint_D f(x,y)\, dA$ using an iterated integral of the $dx\, dy$ variety—i.e., integrating first in x and then in y. For instance, when D is the bounded region that lies to the right of the curve $x = h_1(y)$, to the left of $x = h_2(y)$, and extends between the lines $y = c$ and $y = d$, the ideas that led us to equation (2.3) also show us that

Integrating in x is like making a horizontal stroke with "the roller brush." Then integrating in y moves us from bottom to top across the region.

$$\iint_D f(x,y)\, dA = \int_c^d \int_{h_1(x)}^{h_2(x)} \tilde{f}(x,y)\, dy\, dx. = \int_c^d \int_{h_1(x)}^{h_2(x)} f(x,y)\, dy\, dx. \qquad (2.4)$$

We demonstrate this technique in the examples below.

Integrating over a x-simple region

Example 2.3. Suppose D is the bounded region defined by $-2 \le x \le y^2$ and $-1 \le y \le 1$. Calculate $\iint_R (x - y^2)\, dA$.

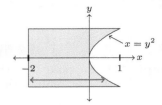

Solution: The region D is shown in Figure 2.7. It's x-simple, so we begin by integrating in x. The left-most boundary, and so the starting point of our integration is $x = -2$. The rightmost boundary is $x = y^2$, which is the upper bound of our integral in x. So,

$$\iint_D (x - y^2)\, dA = \int_{-1}^{1} \int_{-2}^{y^2} (x - y^2)\, dx\, dy = \int_{-1}^{1} \left[\frac{1}{2}x^2 - xy^2 \right]_{x=-2}^{x=y^2} dy.$$

This leaves us with

$$\iint_D (x - y^2)\, dA = \int_{-1}^{1} \left[-\frac{1}{2}y^4 - 2y^2 - 2 \right] dy = -\frac{83}{15}. \qquad \blacksquare$$

Figure 2.7: At each value of y, the horizontal "stroke" through this region extends from the line $x = -2$ to the parabola $x = y^2$.

Integrating over a x-simple region

Example 2.4. Suppose D is the bounded region defined by the curves $x = -y^2$, $y = -0.5x + 1$, $y = 1$ and $y = 0$. Calculate $\iint_R (x^2 + y^2)\, dA$.

Answer: $\iint_D (x^2 + y^2)\, dA = {}^{344}/_{35}$ $\blacksquare$

Solution
On-line

▷ Regions that are both *x*- and *y*-simple

When a region is both x- and y-simple, it's sometimes advantageous to change the order of integration.

Using Fubini's Theorem to facilitate calculation

Example 2.5. Determine the value of $\int_0^4 \int_{3x}^{12} e^{y^2}\, dy\, dx$.

Solution: We cannot find an antiderivative of e^{y^2}, so we cannot calculate this integral in its present form. This leads us to rewrite it using Fubini's Theorem. In the original integral we see that $x \in [0, 4]$, and at each value of x the variable y ranges from $y = 3x$ to $y = 12$. When we draw these curves, we see the region in Figure 2.9. When we rewrite this integral in the $dx\, dy$ form, the outer integral will be in y, so its lower and upper bounds must be the minimum and maximum values of y:

$$\int_0^{12} \int_?^? e^{y^2}\, dx\, dy.$$

To fill in the question marks, think about what happens to x at each value of $y \in [0, 12]$. It can be as small as 0 and as large as $y/3$, so our integral is

$$\int_0^{12} \int_0^{y/3} e^{y^2}\, dx\, dy = \int_0^{12} \left[xe^{y^2} \right]_{x=0}^{x=y/3} dy = \int_0^{12} \frac{1}{3}ye^{y^2}\, dy = \frac{1}{6}\left(e^{144} - 1 \right). \quad \blacksquare$$

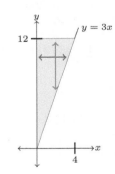

Figure 2.8: At each x a vertical line segment through this region extends from $y = 3x$ to $y = 12$. At each y, a horizontal line segment through this region extends from $x = 0$ to $x = y/3$.

Using Fubini's Theorem to switch the order of integration

Example 2.6. Change the order of integration for $\int_0^4 \int_0^{\sqrt{y}} f(x, y)\, dx\, dy$.

Solution: Rewriting this integral is matter of understanding the region over which the integration takes place. When we rewrite it as

$$\int_0^4 \int_0^{\sqrt{y}} f(x, y)\, dx\, dy$$

the outer integral (dy) tells us that y ranges from $y = 0$ to $y = 4$. The inner integral tells us that at each value of $y \in [0, 4]$, the variable x ranges from $x = 0$ to $x = \sqrt{y}$, which is the parabola $y = x^2$. These equations allow us to graph the bounding curves of this region (see Figure 2.9).

When we rewrite this integral in the $dy\,dx$ form, the outer integral will be in x, so its lower and upper bounds must be the minimum and maximum values of x:

$$\int_0^2 \int_?^? f(x,y)\,dy\,dx.$$

To fill in the question marks, think about what happens to y at each value of $x \in [0,2]$. At each x in $[0,2]$ the variable y can be as small as x^2 and grow as large as 4, so these are the bounds of integration and our answer is

$$\int_0^2 \int_{x^2}^4 f(x,y)\,dy\,dx. \qquad \blacksquare$$

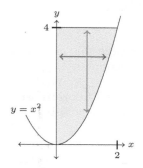

Figure 2.9: At each x a vertical line segment through this region extends from $y = x^2$ to $y = 4$. At each y a horizontal line segment extends from $x = 0$ to $x = \sqrt{y}$.

Understanding the region of integration

Example 2.7. Change the order of integration for $\int_0^2 \int_{y^3}^{4y} f(x,y)\,dx\,dy$.

Answer: $\int_0^8 \int_{x/4}^{x^{1/3}} f(x,y)\,dy\,dx$. $\qquad \blacksquare$

Changing the order of integration is not always practical, even for regions that are both x- and y-simple. For example, Figure 2.10 shows the bounded region between $y = x \sin x$ and the x-axis. From a practical standpoint we cannot treat the region as x-simple because we cannot determine a general formula that tells us how the left and right bounds of integration (in x) depend on y. We have to treat the region in Figure 2.10 as y-simple.

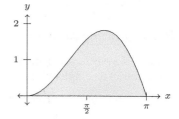

Figure 2.10: A region that's both y- and x-simple

▷ Regions that are neither x- nor y-simple

When a region is neither x- nor y-simple, we can either (1) subdivide the region into a collection of simple subregions, or (2) work with Riemann sums.

A region that's neither x- nor y-simple

Example 2.8. Suppose D is the bounded region defined by the x-axis, the lines $y = (x-2)/3$ and $x = 4$, the parabola $x = 4y(y-1)$, and the curve $y = 1.5 - 0.5\cos \pi x$. Write the double integral of f over D as the sum of iterated integrals over simple regions.

Solution: As seen in Figure 2.11, we begin by using the lines $y = 1$ and $x = 2$ to partition D into the subregions D_1, D_2 (which are y-simple) and D_3 (which is x-simple). Then a straightforward extension of property (1.11) from Section 14.1 yields

$$\iint_D f(x,y)\,dA = \iint_{D_1} f(x,y)\,dA + \iint_{D_2} f(x,y)\,dA + \iint_{D_3} f(x,y)\,dA.$$

We conclude by writing the double integrals over the subregions as iterated integrals.

$$\iint_{D_1} f(x,y)\,dA = \int_0^2 \int_1^{1.5-0.5\cos \pi x} f(x,y)\,dy\,dx$$

$$\iint_{D_2} f(x,y)\,dA = \int_2^4 \int_{(x-2)/3}^{1.5-0.5\cos \pi x} f(x,y)\,dy\,dx$$

$$\iint_{D_3} f(x,y)\,dA = \int_0^1 \int_{4y(y-1)}^2 f(x,y)\,dx\,dy \qquad \blacksquare$$

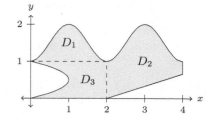

Figure 2.11: Subdividing D into simple regions.

We close this part of our discussion with summary of the techniques presented in the examples.

Fubini's Theorem for Simple Regions: Suppose D is a region with a simple, piecewise smooth boundary, and f is continuous over D.

If D is the y-simple region between the lines $x = a$ and $x = b$ that extends from the curve $y = g_1(x)$ to the curve $y = g_2(x)$, where $a \leq b$ and $g_1(x) \leq g_2(x)$,

$$\iint_D f(x,y)\, dA = \int_a^b \int_{g_1(x)}^{g_2(x)} f(x,y)\, dy\, dx.$$

On the other hand, if D is the x-simple region between the lines $y = c$ and $y = d$ that extends from the curve $x = h_1(y)$ to the curve $x = h_2(y)$, where $c \leq d$ and $h_1(y) \leq h_2(y)$,

$$\iint_D f(x,y)\, dA = \int_c^d \int_{h_1(y)}^{h_2(y)} f(x,y)\, dx\, dy.$$

Note: Instead of memorizing these two equations, you should focus on the single idea they communicate: when a region is simple, we slice it horizontally or vertically (depending on its geometry).

✤ Calculating Area with Double Integrals

Volume and area are dimensionally different but numerically the same when a solid has a uniform height of 1 (see Figure 2.12) because

$$\text{volume} = (\text{area of the base}) \times (\text{height}) = (\text{area of the base}) \times (1).$$

So we can calculate the area of a region D, denoted by $|D|$, with a double integral.

Area: Suppose D is a region with a simple, piecewise smooth boundary. The area of D is

$$|D| = \iint_D 1\, dA. \qquad (2.5)$$

Using double integrals to calculate area

Example 2.9. Suppose D is the region between the curves $y = 3 + \sin^2(x-1)$ and $y = 3 - \sin^2(x-1)$ when $x \in [1, 1+\pi]$. Calculate the area of D.

Solution: The region D is both x-simple and y-simple, but we must treat it as y-simple due to the boundary. So we determine its area by calculating

$$|D| = \iint_D 1\, dA = \int_1^{1+\pi} \int_{3-\sin^2(x-1)}^{3+\sin^2(x-1)} 1\, dy\, dx = \int_1^{1+\pi} \left[\, y\, \right]_{y=3-\sin^2(x-1)}^{y=3+\sin^2(x-1)} dx$$

$$= \underbrace{\int_1^{1+\pi} 2\sin^2(x-1)\, dx = \int_0^{\pi} 2\sin^2(u)\, du}_{\text{Using the substitution } u=x-1,\, du=dx} = \pi \qquad \blacksquare$$

✤ Properties of the Double Integral Over More General Regions

In Example 2.8 we used a straightforward extension of equation (1.11). In fact, all of the properties of the double integral listed in Section 14.1 are fundamentally the same for bounded regions with simple, piecewise smooth boundaries as they

> In order to be dimensionally consistent, the 1 must be dimensionless, so that the integrand is really "one dA" rather than $1 \times dA$. Some people prefer to write this integral as
>
> $$\iint_R dA.$$

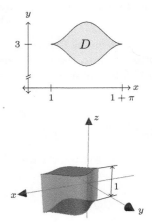

Figure 2.12: The region D in Example 2.9; (right) a solid with a uniform height of 1 unit over the region R.

are for rectangles. In particular, equations (1.7)–(1.11) are all valid if we replace R with D, and change the word rectangle to the phrase "bounded region with a simple, piecewise smooth boundary." Similarly, the definition of average value of an integrable function f over such a region is

$$\langle f \rangle = \frac{1}{|D|} \int_D f(x, y)\, dA,$$

where $|D|$ is the area of D. Moreover, when f is continuous over D, the average-value argument that led us to the Mean Value Theorem for Double Integrals still applies. The theorem remains true!

You should know

- the terms *iterated integral, partial integration, y-simple, x-simple,* and *two-dimensional advection-diffusion equation;*
- Fubini's theorem.

You should be able to

- write a double integral as an iterated integral;
- calculate iterated integrals;
- use Fubini's Theorem to change the order of integraion;
- use double integrals to calculate area.

14.2 Skill Exercises

In #1–12 the given iterated integral is equal to an integral of the form $\iint_D f(x, y)\, dA$. Draw the region D.

1. $\int_3^7 \int_1^2 f(x, y)\, dx\, dy$
2. $\int_{-1}^3 \int_{-2}^5 f(x, y)\, dy\, dx$
3. $\int_0^3 \int_0^{\sqrt{x}} f(x, y)\, dy\, dx$
4. $\int_1^2 \int_0^{7x} f(x, y)\, dy\, dx$
5. $\int_2^6 \int_3^{8x} f(x, y)\, dy\, dx$
6. $\int_{-2}^6 \int_{-2x}^{13} f(x, y)\, dy\, dx$
7. $\int_3^7 \int_{\sin x}^{x+2} f(x, y)\, dy\, dx$
8. $\int_{-2}^2 \int_{4-x^2}^{5+\cos x} f(x, y)\, dy\, dx$
9. $\int_4^9 \int_0^{\sqrt{y}} f(x, y)\, dx\, dy$
10. $\int_1^e \int_0^{\ln y} f(x, y)\, dx\, dy$
11. $\int_2^5 \int_{0.5(1-y)}^{\ln y} f(x, y)\, dx\, dy$
12. $\int_0^1 \int_{\sqrt{y}}^{2y-0.5} f(x, y)\, dx\, dy$

In #13–18 the given integral is equal to $\iint_D f(x, y)\, dA$ where D is a region that's both x- and y-simple. If the given integral has a $dx\, dy$ form, rewrite it using a $dy\, dx$ form, and vice versa.

13. $\int_0^7 \int_{3x}^{21} f(x, y)\, dy\, dx$
14. $\int_0^4 \int_{x^2}^{4x} f(x, y)\, dy\, dx$
15. $\int_1^e \int_{\ln y}^1 f(x, y)\, dx\, dy$
16. $\int_0^1 \int_{\arcsin y}^1 f(x, y)\, dx\, dy$
17. $\int_0^{0.5\sqrt{2}} \int_{\pi/4}^{\arccos y} f(x, y)\, dx\, dy$
18. $\int_{0.5\sqrt{2}}^1 \int_0^{\arccos y} f(x, y)\, dx\, dy$

In #19–24 the number $\iint_D f(x, y)\, dA$ is written as a sum of iterated integrals. (a) Draw the region D, and (b) write $\iint_D f(x, y)\, dA$ as a single iterated integral.

19. $\displaystyle\int_{-3}^{0}\int_{0}^{2x+6} f(x,y)\ dy\ dx + \int_{0}^{6}\int_{0}^{6-x} f(x,y)\ dy\ dx$

20. $\displaystyle\int_{0}^{1}\int_{0}^{x^3} f(x,y)\ dy\ dx + \int_{1}^{2}\int_{0}^{1-(x-2)^2} f(x,y)\ dy\ dx$

21. $\displaystyle\int_{-4}^{0}\int_{0}^{4+x} f(x,y)\ dy\ dx + \int_{0}^{16}\int_{\sqrt{x}}^{4} f(x,y)\ dy\ dx$

22. $\displaystyle\int_{-\pi/2}^{0}\int_{0}^{y+0.5\pi} f(x,y)\ dx\ dy + \int_{0}^{1}\int_{0}^{\arccos y} f(x,y)\ dx\ dy$

23. $\displaystyle\int_{0.1}^{1}\int_{-1+1/y}^{9} f(x,y)\ dx\ dy + \int_{1}^{e^9}\int_{\ln y}^{9} f(x,y)\ dx\ dy$

24. $\displaystyle\int_{0}^{3}\int_{0}^{\sqrt{y}} f(x,y)\ dx\ dy + \int_{3}^{9}\int_{0.5(y-3)}^{\sqrt{y}} f(x,y)\ dx\ dy$

In #25–30 the bounded region D is neither x- nor y-simple. Write $\iint_D f(x,y)\ dA$ as the sum of iterated integrals over x-simple and/or y-simple subregions.

25. D is bounded by $x = y(y^2 - 1)(y+2)$, $y = 0.5x(x-2)+1$, $x = 2$ and $y = -2$

26. D is the region inside the square $2 = |x|+|y|$ but outside the square $1 = |x|+|y|$

27. D is the region in the first quadrant between the circle of radius 2 centered at the origin, and the polygon with vertices at $(0,0), (0, 1/2), (1,1)$ and $(1/2, 0)$

28. D is the X-shaped region including the origin that's bounded by the curves $y = \pm(1+x^2)$, $x = \pm(1+y^2)$, and the circle of radius 4 centered at the origin

29. D is the region in the fourth quadrant bounded by the curves $x = \sin y$, $y = \sin x$, and the parabola $\pi^2 y = 4(\pi - 1)x^2 - \pi^3$

30. D is made by omitting the circle of radius $1/8$ centered at $(0.75, 0.6)$ from the square $[0,1] \times [0,1]$.

✥ 14.2 Concept and Application Exercises

31. Draw a region that's x-simple but not y-simple.

32. Draw a region that's y-simple but not x-simple.

In #33–36 the given curves define a bounded region D. (a) Write the area of D as a single iterated integral, and (b) use the integral to calculate the area of D.

____ | Area |

33. $y = 0$, $x = 0$, and $x + y = 5$ 35. $2x - y = 0$, $x - y = 0$, and $y = 3$

34. $y = 0$, $x = 0$, and $2x - y = 3$ 36. $x + y = 3$, $x = 3 + 2y - y^2$

In #63–40 use an iterated integral to calculate the net volume between the the graph of f and the bounded region D, specified by the given lines and/or curves.

____ | Net Volume |

37. $f(x,y) = y^2 x e^x$; D is defined by $y = 3x$, $y = x$, and $x = 6$

38. $f(x,y) = 4 + x^2 \cos(\pi xy)$; D is defined by $y = -3x$, $y = x$, and $x = 1$

39. $f(x,y) = y + x \sin \pi y$; D is defined by $y = x^2$, $y = -2x - 1$ and $y = 2x - 1$

40. $f(x,y) = x e^{xy}$; D is defined by $y = \cos x$, $y = -\cos x$, where $-\pi \le x \le \pi$

In #41–42 calculate the average value of f over D.

____ | Average Value |

41. f and D from #37   42. f and D from #38

Exercises #43–44 are about the production rate at a given company, which depends on the skill levels of the employees, x, and the time spent on task, t (in hours). Here we take $x = 0$ to indicate the lowest skill level of employees, and $x = 1$ the highest. (You might find it helpful to read (or complete) exercise #43 in Section 14.1, but it is not required.)

43. Suppose the company elects to reduce labor costs by offering more time to low-skilled workers (which cost less per hour) and less time to highly-skilled workers (which cost more). Specifically, a worker with a skill level of x is assigned to a shift that is $t = 9 - 2x$ hours long. If the production density function is $p(x,t) = 85 + xt + 0.5x - t^2 \frac{\text{items/hr}}{\text{skill level}}$, determine the number of items produced by the company each day.

⎯⎯ Business

44. Suppose the company's production density is $p(x,t) = 10 + 2x - t \frac{\text{items/hr}}{\text{skill level}}$. When all employees work an 8-hour day, they produce 56 items. In order to provide financial incentives for workers to increase their skill level, the company decides to offer more hours to highly-skilled workers. Specifically, a worker with a skill level of x is assigned to a shift that is $t = mx + b$ hours long.

⎯⎯ Business

    (a) Explain why m and b must be positive.

    (b) If the company intends to maintain a production level of 56 items per day, and cap the maximum shift length at 10 hours, what are the values of m and b?

45. Suppose D is the bounded region in the xy-plane between the parabolas $x = 4y(1 - y)$ and $x = y(y - 1)$, where length is measured in cm. A short wall extends vertically from the parabolas so that a thin pool of fluid can be held over the region D. An incompressible fluid is seeping into the pool through D at a rate that varies from point to point. Suppose the fluid enters at a rate of $f(x,y) = 1 + x^2$ g/sec per cm^2. After the pool fills up, at what rate does this fluid spill over its boundary? (Answer in g/sec.)

⎯⎯ Fluids

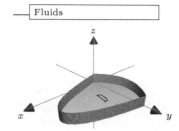

Figure 2.13:   The tank over D holds a pool of fluid.

46. This exercise is like #45. Suppose D is the bounded region in the first quadrant of the xy-plane between the curves $x - y = 0$, $y = x(x - 1.75)$ and $y - x^3 = x$, where length is measured in cm, and $f(x,y) = 1 + x^2$ g/sec per cm^2. After the pool fills up, at what rate does this fluid spill over its boundary? (Answer in g/sec.)

⎯⎯ Fluids

47. Suppose the triangular region in the xy-plane between the lines $y - x = 1$, $y + x = 1$ and $x = 0.5$ is a partially-silvered shard of a mirror. The fraction of incident light that is reflected by at (x,y) is $(x + y)/2$. Assuming that a uniform intensity of light falls on the shard, determine the fraction of it that's reflected.

⎯⎯ Physics

48. Suppose D is the bounded region in the xy-plane between the parabola $x = 250 - y^2$ and the y-axis, where length is measured in kilometers. If the annual rainfall at (x,y) is $120 - 0.1x - 0.2y$ cm, determine the volume of rain that falls on D each year.

⎯⎯ Ecology

14.3   Double Integrals in Polar Coordinates

The region shown in Figure 3.1 is neither y-simple nor x-simple, so using the methods of Section 14.2 to calculate the double integral of $f(x, y)$ over R would require us to segment the region into several subregions. However, in the right-hand image of the figure you see that the region is ***radially simple***, by which we mean that any secant ray from the origin intersects the region's boundary at most twice (once when it enters and once when it leaves). Double integrals over such regions can often be computed with an iterated integral when we switch into polar coordinates.

Key Idea(s): *Switching into polar coordinates can sometimes expedite the integration process.*

The area of a "polar rectangle" depends on how far it is away from the origin.

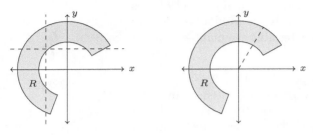

Figure 3.1: The region R is neither y- nor x-simple, but is radially simple.

✦ A Double Integral in Polar Coordinates is the Limit of Riemann Sums

As with all integrals in this book, a double integral in polar coordinates is the limit of Riemann sums, but each of the Riemann sums in this context corresponds to a mesh of "polar rectangles" (see Figures 3.2 and 3.3):

$$\sum_{k=1}^{n} f(r_k^*, \theta_k^*) \, \Delta A_k,$$

where (r_k^*, θ_k^*) are the polar coordinates of the point at which we sample f in the kth polar rectangle, and ΔA_k is the area of that rectangle. As you see in the left-hand image of Figure 3.3, two polar rectangles that have the same polar dimensions (i.e., both have a width of Δr and both subtend $\Delta\theta$ radians) might not have the same area, so our next step is to understand the relationship among ΔA, Δr and $\Delta\theta$.

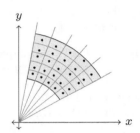

Figure 3.2: To generate a Riemann sum we partition a radially simple region with polar rectangles and sample f somewhere in each of them.

Suppose a polar rectangle extends from $r = r_1$ to $r = r_2$, so its width is $\Delta r = r_2 - r_1$ (see the right-hand image of Figure 3.3). The area of this polar rectangle

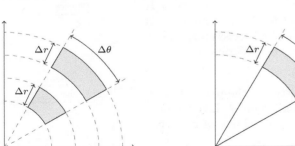

Figure 3.3: (left) Two polar "rectangles" that are Δr wide and subtend an angle of $\Delta\theta$, but have different areas; (right) a polar rectangle is the difference of two circular wedges.

is the difference in the areas of circular wedges with radii r_2 and r_1. The area of a circular wedge of radius r that subtends $\Delta\theta$ radians is $\frac{1}{2}r^2\Delta\theta$, so the area of the polar rectangle is

$$\frac{1}{2}r_2^2\Delta\theta - \frac{1}{2}r_1^2\Delta\theta = \frac{1}{2}(r_2^2 - r_1^2)\Delta\theta.$$

By factoring this difference of squares we can write the area as

$$\frac{1}{2}(r_2 + r_1)(r_2 - r_1)\Delta\theta = \frac{1}{2}(r_2 + r_1)\Delta r \; \Delta\theta = r \; \Delta r \; \Delta\theta$$

where r is the average of r_1 and r_2.

Now suppose that we partition the polar rectangle R with a grid of polar rectangles. If the width of the kth rectangle is Δr_k and it subtends $\Delta\theta_k$ radians, we can approximate the double integral of f over R with the Riemann sum

$$\sum_{k=1}^{n} f(r_k^*, \theta_k^*) \; r_k \; \Delta r_k \; \Delta\theta_k.$$

As you expect by now, the limit of these Riemann sums converges when f is continuous. Specifically, we define the double integral

$$\iint_R f(r,\theta) \; dA = \lim_{\|P\|\to 0} \sum_{k=1}^{n} f(r_k^*, \theta_k^*) \; r_k \; \Delta r_k \; \Delta\theta_k \tag{3.1}$$

when this limit exists, where similar to our discussion in Section 14.1, we define

$$\|P\| = \text{ the largest of all the } \Delta r_k \text{ and } \Delta\theta_k.$$

> The number $n \to \infty$ as the mesh size $\|P\| \to 0$.

❖ Iterated Integrals

The work we did to express ΔA in terms of Δr and $\Delta\theta$ led us to equation (3.1), but it's also the key to making calculations with iterated integrals. In the limit,

$$\Delta A = r \; \Delta r \; \Delta\theta \quad \text{becomes} \quad dA = r \; dr \; d\theta,$$

which leads us to the following fact.

Fubini's Theorem for Polar Rectangles: Suppose R is a region in the plane consisting of all points with polar coordinates (r,θ), where $\theta \in [\alpha, \beta]$, $r \in [r_1, r_2]$, $0 \le r_1$ and $\beta - \alpha \le 2\pi$. When f is a continuous function,

$$\int_{r_1}^{r_2} \int_\alpha^\beta f(r,\theta) \; r \; d\theta \; dr = \iint_R f(r,\theta) \; dA = \int_\alpha^\beta \int_{r_1}^{r_2} f(r,\theta) \; r \; dr \; d\theta.$$

> Caution! You must remember the factor of r in the polar form of the area element $dA = r \; dr \; d\theta$.

Calculating volume

Example 3.1. Determine the volume between the paraboloid $z = 3 + x^2 + y^2$ and the disk $x^2 + y^2 \le 1$ in the xy-plane when length is measured in feet.

Solution: The volume is the double integral of $f(x,y) = 3 + x^2 + y^2$ over the disk. When written in polar coordinates, the disk is the polar rectangle in which $0 \le r \le 1$ and $0 \le \theta \le 2\pi$, and the value of f at (r,θ) is $3 + x^2 + y^2 = 3 + r^2$. So we calculate

$$\iint_R f \; dA = \int_0^{2\pi} \int_0^1 \underbrace{(3 + r^2)}_{\text{ft}} \; \underbrace{r \; dr \; d\theta}_{\text{ft}^2} = \frac{7}{2}\pi \text{ ft}^3. \qquad \blacksquare$$

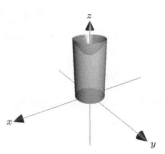

Figure 3.4: The cylindrical solid for Example 3.1.

Calculating cumulative value (of thermal energy)

Example 3.2. Suppose R is the metal plate for which $1 \leq x^2 + y^2 \leq 4$ and $y \geq 0$, where distance is measured in cm (see Figure 3.5). Thermal energy is distributed across R according to the density function $\rho(x, y) = 1 + e^{-x^2 - y^2}$ joules per square cm. Determine the cumulative amount of thermal energy in R.

Solution: The cumulative amount of thermal energy in R is determined by calculating the double integral of ρ over R. Since R is a polar rectangle with $1 \leq r \leq 2$ and $0 \leq \theta \leq \pi$, Fubini's Theorem allows us to calculate

$$\iint_R \rho \, dA = \int_0^\pi \int_1^2 \underbrace{(1 + e^{-r^2})}_{\text{J/cm}^2} \underbrace{r \, dr \, d\theta}_{\text{cm}^2} = \left(3 + e^{-1} - e^{-4} \right) \frac{\pi}{2} \text{ J.} \quad \blacksquare$$

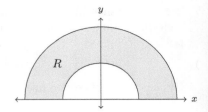

Figure 3.5: The region R for Example 3.2.

In a polar rectangle, the inner radius and the outer radius are constant. More generally, the inner and outer bounding curves of a radially simple region can depend on θ (see Figure 3.6). Much as we did in Section 14.2, we can extend our ability to calculate double integrals to such regions by enclosing them in polar rectangles and using a helper function, $\tilde{f}$. This brings us to the following statement:

Fubini's Theorem for Radially Simple Regions: Suppose D is a region in the plane consisting of all points with polar coordinates (r, θ), where $\theta \in [\alpha, \beta]$, $r \in [r_1(\theta), r_2(\theta)]$, $0 \leq r_1(\theta)$ and $\beta - \alpha \leq 2\pi$. When r_1 and r_2 are continuous on $[\alpha, \beta]$, and f is continuous on D,

$$\iint_D f(r, \theta) \, dA = \int_\alpha^\beta \int_{r_1(\theta)}^{r_2(\theta)} f(r, \theta) \, r \, dr \, d\theta. \qquad (3.2)$$

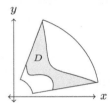

Figure 3.6: A radially simple region D enclosed by a polar rectangle.

Calculating area

Example 3.3. Suppose R is the region in the first quadrant between the curves $r = 5$ and $r = 2 + 2\cos\theta$. If length is measured in mm, determine the area of R.

Solution: As discussed in Section 14.2, we can calculate this area by integrating the constant function $f(r, \theta) = 1$ over R. Because the region extends from $r = 2 + 2\cos\theta$ to $r = 5$, and $\theta \in [0, \pi/2]$ in the first quadrant,

$$\iint_R 1 \, dA = \int_0^{\pi/2} \int_{2+2\cos\theta}^5 1r \, dr \, d\theta = \int_0^{\pi/2} \left[\frac{25}{2} - \frac{1}{2}(2 + 2\cos\theta)^2 \right] d\theta$$

$$= \int_0^{\pi/2} \left[\frac{21}{2} - 4\cos\theta - \underbrace{2\cos^2\theta}_{\text{Use the half-angle identity}} \right] d\theta = \frac{19\pi}{4} - 4 \text{ mm}^2. \quad \blacksquare$$

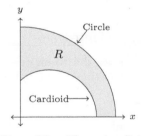

Figure 3.7: The region R in Example 3.3 lies between the cardioid and the circle.

Recall that the 1 is dimensionless in this calculation, as is $d\theta$ (radians are dimensionless). Both r and dr have units of mm, so the units of the integral are mm^2.

Integrating over a polar region

Example 3.4. Suppose R is the bounded region enclosed by $r = 2 + \sin\theta$. Calculate $\iint_R (x + y) \, dA$.

Answer: $17\pi/4$. $\blacksquare$

Solution On-line

Changing coordinate systems

Example 3.5. Calculate the following iterated integral.

$$\int_1^2 \int_0^{\sqrt{4-x^2}} \sqrt{x^2 + y^2} \, dy \, dx.$$

Solution: We begin by drawing the region. Since the first of these iterated integrals is in y, the bounds tell us that y ranges between the x-axis and the circular arc $y = \sqrt{4 - x^2}$. The second of these iterated integrals tells us that x ranges between $x = 1$ and $x = 2$. The region of integration is shown in Figure 3.8.

In order to calculate this integral using polar coordinates, we need to describe the boundaries of R in terms of r and θ (see Figure 3.9). To understand the range of θ, think about traveling along the outer, circular boundary. The value of θ begins at $\theta = 0$, and increases until we reach the point P. Because P has an x-coordinate of 1, and is 2 units away from the origin, its polar coordinates are $(r, \theta) = \left(2, \arccos(1/2)\right) = (2, \pi/3)$. So $0 \le \theta \le \pi/3$; at each of these values of θ a ray from the origin extends between the line $x = 1$ and the circular arc. Since $x = r \cos \theta$, the equation $x = 1$ is the same as writing $r = \sec \theta$, so our bounds on r are $\sec \theta \le r \le 2$. Lastly, we note that $\sqrt{x^2 + y^2} = r$, so

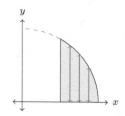

Figure 3.8: The region R indicated by the bounds of integration in Example 3.5.

$$\int_1^2 \int_0^{\sqrt{4-x^2}} \sqrt{x^2 + y^2} \; dy \; dx = \iint_R \sqrt{x^2 + y^2} \; dA = \int_0^{\pi/3} \int_{\sec \theta}^2 r \; r \; dr \; d\theta$$

$$= \int_0^{\pi/3} \left[\frac{1}{3} r^3\right]_{r=\sec \theta}^{r=2} d\theta = \frac{1}{3} \int_0^{\pi/3} \left[8 - \sec^3 \theta\right] d\theta.$$

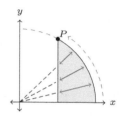

Figure 3.9: Thinking of the region R in terms of polar coordinates.

Using the integral of $\sec^3 \theta$ that we determined in Chapter 6, we see that

$$\frac{1}{3} \int_0^{\pi/3} \left[8 - \sec^3 \theta\right] d\theta = \frac{1}{3} \left(8\theta - \frac{1}{2} \sec \theta \tan \theta - \frac{1}{2} \ln |\sec \theta + \tan \theta|\right) \Bigg|_0^{\pi/3}$$

$$= \frac{8\pi}{9} - \frac{\sqrt{3}}{3} - \frac{1}{6} \ln \left|2 + \sqrt{3}\right|.$$ ■

Changing coordinate systems

Example 3.6. Calculate the following definite integral.

$$\int_1^3 \int_y^{\sqrt{3}y} \frac{8y}{x} \; dx \; dy.$$

Solution
On-line

Answer: $16 \ln 3$. ■

You should know

- the term *radially simple;*
- Fubini's Theorem for polar coordinates;
- that $dA = r \; dr \; d\theta$

You should be able to

- convert iterated integrals from Cartesian to polar coordinates;
- calculate integrals using polar coordinates.

❖ 14.3 Skill Exercises

In #1–6 an annular region R is shown in which r ranges from 1 to 2. Write $\iint_R f \, dA$ as an iterated integral in polar coordinates.

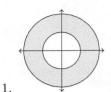

1.

3.

5.

7.

2.

4.

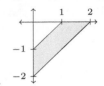

6.

8.

In #9–16 sketch the region of integration.

9. $\displaystyle\int_0^{\pi/4} \int_2^3 f(r,\theta) \, r \, dr \, d\theta$

10. $\displaystyle\int_{-\pi/6}^{\pi/6} \int_1^3 f(r,\theta) \, r \, dr \, d\theta$

11. $\displaystyle\int_0^1 \int_{\pi/4}^{2\pi/3} f(r,\theta) \, r \, d\theta \, dr$

12. $\displaystyle\int_1^2 \int_{\pi/2}^{4\pi/3} f(r,\theta) \, r \, d\theta \, dr$

13. $\displaystyle\int_0^{\pi/6} \int_{\cos(3\theta)}^2 f(r,\theta) \, r \, dr \, d\theta$

14. $\displaystyle\int_{\pi/2}^{\pi} \int_{\sin(\theta)}^1 f(r,\theta) \, r \, dr \, d\theta$

15. $\displaystyle\int_0^{\pi/3} \int_{1/2}^{\cos(\theta)} f(r,\theta) \, r \, dr \, d\theta$

16. $\displaystyle\int_0^{\pi/3} \int_{1.5\sin(2\theta)}^{1+\cos(\theta)} f(r,\theta) \, r \, dr \, d\theta$

In #17–22 convert the iterated integral from Cartesian to polar coordinates.

17. $\displaystyle\int_0^{3/\sqrt{2}} \int_{-\sqrt{9-y^2}}^{-y} f \, dx \, dy$

18. $\displaystyle\int_{-50\sqrt{2}}^0 \int_{-y}^{\sqrt{100-y^2}} f \, dx \, dy$

19. $\displaystyle\int_0^{\sqrt{21}} \int_2^{\sqrt{25-x^2}} f \, dy \, dx$

20. $\displaystyle\int_{-\sqrt{8}}^{\sqrt{8}} \int_{-\sqrt{9-x^2}}^{-1} f \, dy \, dx$

21. $\displaystyle\int_0^4 \int_y^{8-y} f \, dx \, dy$

22. $\displaystyle\int_0^1 \int_{\sqrt{1-y^2}}^{\sqrt{16-y^2}} f \, dx \, dy$

In #23–28 use an iterated integral in polar coordinates to calculate $\iint_R f \, dA$.

23. $f(r,\theta) = r + \cos\theta$ and R is the region between the cardioid $r = 1 + \cos\theta$ and the circle $r = 7$ that lies in the first quadrant.

24. $f(r,\theta) = \theta$ and R is the region between the cardioids $r = 1 + \cos\theta$ and $r = 2 + 2\cos\theta$ that lies in the second quadrant.

25. $f(x,y) = x^2 + y^2$ and R is the region bounded by the curve $r = 3 + \cos\theta$.

26. $f(x,y) = xy$ and R is the region in the third quadrant bounded by the curve $r = \cos 3\theta$.

27. $f(x,y) = xy$ and R is the region bounded by the lower leaf of $r = \sin 3\theta$.

28. $f(x,y) = x$ and R is the region in the first quadrant bounded by the cardioids $r = 1 + \sin\theta$ and $r = 1 + \cos\theta$.

✤ 14.3 Concept and Application Exercises

29. The region R is shaded in Figure 3.10. It has been partitioned with a mesh of polar rectangles, and the function f has been evaluated at the center of each polar rectangle. (a) Write $\iint_R f \; dA$ as an iterated integral using polar coordinates, and (b) approximate the double integral of f over R using a center-sampled Riemann sum.

30. The region R is shaded in Figure 3.11. It has been partitioned with a mesh of polar rectangles, and the function f has been evaluated at the center of each polar rectangle. (a) Write $\iint_R f \; dA$ as an iterated integral using polar coordinates, and (b) approximate the double integral of f over R using a center-sampled Riemann sum.

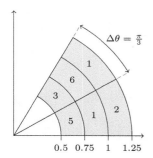

Figure 3.10: The region for exercise #29   Figure 3.11: The region for exercise #30

31. Suppose R is the disk of radius 4 centered at the origin, and $\langle\|\mathbf{r}\|\rangle$ is the average distance between points in R and the origin. (a) Explain why $\langle\|\mathbf{r}\|\rangle$ *should* be larger than 2, and (b) determine the value of $\langle\|\mathbf{r}\|\rangle$.

32. Suppose R is the disk of radius a centered at the origin. Determine the average distance of points in R to the origin (in terms of a).

33. Suppose the mass density in a disk of radius a is $\rho(r,\theta) = 1 + r$ g/cm^2, where r is measured in cm. Determine the average mass density of the disk. | Physics |

34. Suppose that the charge density in a disk of radius a is given by $\sigma(r,\theta) = 1/r$. Determine the average charge density on the disk. | Physics |

35. Suppose R is the disk of radius 1. By converting to polar coordinates, explain why $\iint_R (x^2 + y^2)^{-1.5} \; dA$ is a number but $\iint_R (x^2 + y^2)^{-2.1} \; dA$ is not.

36. This exercise is about the improper integral $\iint_R e^{-x^2 - y^2} \; dA$, in which the region R is the entire xy-plane.

    (a) Explain why $\iint_R e^{-x^2-y^2} \; dA = \lim_{L\to\infty} \int_0^L \int_0^{2\pi} e^{-r^2} \; r \; d\theta \; dr$.

    (b) Calculate the value of the integral.

In #37–40 determine the area of the specified region. | Area |

37. Between the curves $r = \theta$ and $r = e^\theta$ when $0 \le \theta \le 2\pi$.

38. In the first quadrant, between the curves $r = 1.5\sin\theta$ and $r = 1 + \sin\theta$.

39. Between the circles $r = A\sin\theta$ and $r = B\sin\theta$ where $0 < A < B$.

40. Enclosed by the cardioid $r = A + A\cos\theta$, but outside the circle $r = 1$, where $0 < 1 < A$.

In #41–44 determine the volume of the given solid.   Volume

41. The region between the xy-plane and the planar surface $z = 1 + x + 6y$ and R, where R is the quarter of the disk $x^2 + y^2 \leq 4$ in which $x \geq 0$ and $y \geq 0$

42. The region between the xy-plane and the cone $z = 4 - \sqrt{x^2 + y^2}$ when (x, y) is a point at which $x^2 + y^2 \leq 16$.

43. The region above the surface $z = 1 - x^2 - y^2$ and below the surface $z = 3 + 2x^2 + 2y^2$ when $x^2 + y^2 \leq 1$.

44. The region above the surface $z = -3x^2 - 3y^2$ and below the surface $z = 2 + 5x^2 + 5y^2$ when $1 \leq x^2 + y^2 \leq 2$.

Exercises #45–48 ask you to calculate the surface area of a graph. (See Section 14.1 for a review of surface area.)   Surface Area

45. Suppose R is the disk $x^2 + y^2 \leq 4$, and S is the portion of the paraboloid $z = x^2 + y^2$ that sits over R. Determine the surface area of S.

46. Suppose R is the portion of the disk $x^2 + y^2 \leq 5$ in which $x \geq 0$ and $y \geq 0$, and S is the portion of the graph of $f(x, y) = 2x + 3y + 4$ that sits over R. Determine the surface area of S.

47. Suppose R is the portion of the disk $x^2 + y^2 \leq 7$ in which $x \leq 0$ and $y \geq 0$, and S is the portion of the graph of $f(x, y) = 5x - 2y$ that sits over R. Determine the surface area of S.

48. Suppose S is the portion of the cone $z^2 = 4x^2 + 4y^2$ that lies below the plane $z = 6$. Calculate the surface area of S.

49. Suppose R is the disk of radius 50 in the xy-plane, where length is measured in kilometers. If the annual rainfall at (x, y) is $120 - 0.07x - 0.15y$ cm, use an iterated integral in polar coordinates to determine the volume of rain that falls on R each year.   Ecology

50. Suppose R is the disk of radius 5 cm in the xy-plane. A colony of bacteria lives in R, and because of nutrient placement the population density is $\rho(x, y) = 100 - 3x + 6y$ bacteria per cm^2. Use an iterated integral in polar coordinates to determine the number of bacteria in the disk.   Biology

51. Suppose there is a police station at the origin, and distance is measured in miles. Crime rates depend on distance from the station, and because of socioeconomic factors, the direction. Specifically, annual records show that, on average, police incidents are distributed according to the density function $\rho(r, \theta) = \frac{1}{10\pi}(1 + \cos\theta)r^2$ crimes/mi^2 when $r \in [0, 5]$. Determine the number of crimes within 5 miles of the station each year, on average.   Sociology

52. Suppose the lower half of the xy-plane is a lake (i.e., $y < 0$), and a community lives in the upper half of the plane. The community resides between a beltway described by $r = 1 + \sin\theta$, and an inner loop at $r = 0.25$ (which surrounds the harbor). If annual income in the community is distributed according to $\rho(r, \theta) = (1 + \theta/r) \times 10^6$ \$/mi^2, determine the total annual income of the community.   Socioeconomics

14.4   Applications of the Double Integral

In Section 14.1 we said that Riemann sums (and therefore the double integral) tell us about the net total of *any* quantity that's distributed over an area, whether it's energy, charge, mass, etc. As you've seen in our previous discussions, a function that describes such a distribution is called a *density*. Perhaps the most familiar density is a distribution of mass, so we begin with it.

> **Key Idea(s):** *The double integral of a density tells us the total (or net) amount of a quantity that's distributed over an area.*

❖ Mass

When length is measured in centimeters, for example, and $\rho(x,y)$ is a mass density measured in grams per square centimeter, the double integral of ρ tells us the total amount of mass in a region because

$$\iint_R \rho(x,y)\, dA = \lim_{\|P\|\to 0} \sum_{k=1}^{n} \overbrace{\rho(x_k^*, y_k^*)}^{\text{g/cm}^2} \underbrace{\overbrace{\Delta A_k}^{\text{cm}^2}}_{\text{g}},$$

> Recall $n \to \infty$ as $\|\Delta A\| \to 0$.

where as usual, we mean ΔA_k to be the area of the kth rectangle in a partition of R, and (x_k^*, y_k^*) to be some point in it.

Calculating mass from density

Example 4.1. Suppose length is measured in centimeters, and R is the bounded region between the line $y = 2x$ and the parabola $y = x(1-x)$ for which $0 \le x \le 1$ (see Figure 4.1). If the density in R is $\rho(x,y) = 1 + xy$ grams per square centimeter, determine the mass of the slab.

Solution: Because R is a y-simple region, we can write its mass as

$$\iint_R (1 + xy)\, dA = \int_0^1 \int_{x-x^2}^{2x} (1 + xy)\, dy\, dx = \int_0^1 \left[y + \frac{1}{2}xy^2 \right]_{y=x-x^2}^{y=2x} dx$$

$$= \int_0^1 \left[x + x^2 + \frac{1}{2}\left(3x^3 + 2x^4 - x^5\right) \right] dx = \frac{53}{40}\ \text{g.} \qquad \blacksquare$$

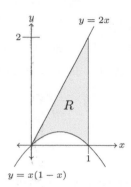

Figure 4.1: The region R for Example 4.1.

Calculating mass from density

Example 4.2. Suppose R is the bounded region enclosed by the lines $y = {}^{x}\!/\!{}_2$, $y = 2x$ and $x = 1$, where length is measured in meters. If the density in R is $\rho(x,y) = 2 + 7x + 3y$ kg/m^2 determine the mass of the region.

Answer: $\iint_R \rho(x,y) = {}^{55}\!/\!{}_8$ kg. $\qquad \blacksquare$

Solution On-line

❖ Center of Mass

Recall from Chapter 7 that calculating the center of mass for a lamina requires us to determine its *first moments,* and that the *first moment*) with respect to an axis is the product of mass and distance to that axis. Because the points in a lamina are at various distances from the x- and y-axes (see Figure 4.2), and its mass density varies from one point to the next, the points of a lamina have different first moments. The double integral allows us to calculate the cumulative total of those first moments.

> Said loosely, the first moments of a lamina tell us about how its mass is distributed across its geometry.

For example, when the mass density in R is the continuous function $\rho(x,y)$, the first moment of R with respect to the y-axis is

$$M_y = \lim_{\|P\|\to 0} \sum_{k=1}^{n} \underbrace{x_k^*}_{} \underbrace{\rho(x_k^*, y_k^*)\,\Delta A_k}_{} = \iint_R x\,\rho(x,y)\,dA,$$

(Distance from (x_k^*, y_k^*) to the y-axis) $\times$ ($\approx$ mass of the kth rectangle)

where ΔA_k is the area of the kth rectangle in a partition of R, and (x_k^*, y_k^*) is some point in it. A similar formula (shown below) allows us to calculate the region's first moment with respect to the x-axis.

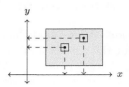

Figure 4.2:　The points in a region are at different distances from the axes.

First Moments of a Lamina: Suppose the continuous function $\rho(x,y)$ is the mass density in a region R. Then the region's first moments with respect to the x- and y-axes are

$$\underbrace{M_x = \iint_R y\,\rho(x,y)\,dA,}_{\text{First moment with respect to the } x\text{-axis}} \quad \text{and} \quad \underbrace{M_y = \iint_R x\,\rho(x,y)\,dA\,.}_{\text{First moment with respect to the } y\text{-axis}}$$

Calculating first moments

Example 4.3. Suppose R is the lamina defined by $1 \le x \le 2$ and $2 \le y \le 5$, where length is measured in meters, and the mass density at $(x,y) \in R$ is described by $\rho(x,y) = x^2 + y$ kg/m^2. Calculate M_y.

Solution: The first moment with respect to the y-axis is

$$M_y = \iint_R x\,\rho(x,y)\,dA = \int_1^2 \int_2^5 (x^3 + xy)\,dy\,dx$$

$$= \int_1^2 \left[x^3 y + \frac{1}{2}xy^2 \right]_{y=2}^{y=5} dx = \int_1^2 \left[3x^3 + \frac{21}{2}x \right] dx = 27. \qquad \blacksquare$$

Now that we can calculate the first moments of a lamina when its mass density depends on both x and y, we can locate its center of mass. The formulas for the x- and y-coordinates of the center of mass are the same as you saw in Chapter 7.

Center of Mass of a Lamina: Suppose R is a lamina with mass m, and first moments M_y and M_x. Then its center of mass is at the point $(\overline{x}, \overline{y})$, where

$$\overline{x} = \frac{M_y}{m} \quad \text{and} \quad \overline{y} = \frac{M_x}{m}.$$

Calculating center of mass

Example 4.4. Suppose R is the lamina described in Example 4.3. (a) Calculate the value of M_x, and (b) determine the location of its center of mass.

Answer: (a) $M_x = \frac{127}{2}$, and (b) $(\overline{x}, \overline{y}) = (^{54}/_{35}, \, ^{127}/_{35})$. $\qquad \blacksquare$

Solution
On-line

❖ Rotational Kinetic Energy and Moments of Inertia

Suppose R is a lamina in the xy-plane. If R spins about the x-axis (like a fan blade on a turbine), how much energy is required to stop it—that is, to reduce its kinetic energy to 0? Generally speaking, the kinetic energy of an object is $K = \frac{1}{2}mv^2$, where v is the object's speed and m is its mass; but the mass of this lamina is distributed over an area, and points that are farther away from the axis of rotation move faster than points that are closer to the axis.

More specifically, suppose that R is revolving about the x-axis at ω radians per second, and that distance is measured in meters. Then the point at (x, y) is y meters from the axis of revolution, and so travels at a speed of ωy. Therefore, the lamina's kinetic energy is

$$K = \lim_{\|P\| \to 0} \sum_{k=1}^{n} \frac{1}{2} \underbrace{(\omega y_k^*)^2}_{\text{(squared speed of the point }(x_k^*, y_k^*)\text{)}} \underbrace{\rho(x_k^*, y_k^*) \, \Delta A_k}_{(\approx \text{ mass of the } k^{\text{th}} \text{ rectangle})} = \iint_R \frac{1}{2} \omega^2 y^2 \rho(x, y) \, dA.$$

The constant factor of $\frac{1}{2}\omega^2$ is often moved out of the double integral so that the final formula is reminiscent of $K = \frac{1}{2}mv^2$.

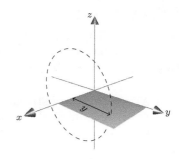

Figure 4.3: When R spins around the x-axis, the point (x, y) travels along a circle of radius y, which has a circumference is $2\pi y$. If R revolves about the axis N times per second, the point (x, y) travels a distance of $2\pi N y$ each second. The number $2\pi N$ is what we call ω.

Rotational Kinetic Energy and Moment of Inertia: Suppose R is a lamina with a mass density of $\rho(x, y)$. When R revolves about the x-axis at ω radians per second, its rotational kinetic energy is

$$K = \frac{1}{2}I_x \, \omega^2, \quad \text{where} \quad I_x = \iint_R y^2 \rho(x, y) \, dA$$

is called the lamina's **moment of inertia** (or **second moment**) with respect to the x-axis. Similarly, if we were to spin R about the y-axis, the rotational kinetic energy would be

$$K = \frac{1}{2}I_y \, \omega^2, \quad \text{where} \quad I_y = \iint_R x^2 \rho(x, y) \, dA$$

is called the lamina's moment of inertia with respect to the y-axis. The lamina's moment of inertia with respect to the origin is

$$I_o = I_x + I_y$$

since the squared-distance between (x, y) and the origin is $x^2 + y^2$.

Calculating rotational kinetic energy

Example 4.5. Suppose R is the bounded region in the first quadrant of the xy-plane between the curves $y = x^4$ and $y = \sqrt{x}$ (see Figure 4.4), and the mass density at each point in R is given by $\rho(x, y) = 5 - xy \, \frac{\text{kg}}{\text{m}^2}$. Determine the kinetic energy of R as a function angular velocity when it revolves about the y-axis.

Solution: The kinetic energy of R is $K = 0.5 I_y \, \omega^2$, where

$$I_y = \iint_R x^2(5 - xy) \, dA = \int_0^1 \int_{x^4}^{\sqrt{x}} (5x^2 - x^3 y) \, dy \, dx = \int_0^1 \left[5x^2 y - \frac{1}{2}x^3 y^2 \right]_{y=x^4}^{y=\sqrt{x}} dx$$

$$= \int_0^1 \left[5x^{5/2} - 5x^6 - \frac{1}{2}x^4 + \frac{1}{2}x^{11} \right] dx = \frac{551}{840}. \qquad \blacksquare$$

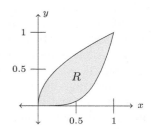

Figure 4.4: The region R for Example 4.5.

Calculating moments of inertia

Example 4.6. Suppose R is the lamina in Example 4.5. Calculate its moment of inertia with respect to the x-axis.

Answer: $I_x = {}^{917}/_{1872}$ $\qquad \blacksquare$

Solution
On-line

✤ Probability

Recall from Chapter 7 that a probability density function (pdf) for a continuous random variable X is a nonnegative-valued function, say $f(x)$, and we determine the probability that a realization of X will occur in $[a, b]$ by calculating $\int_a^b f(x)\,dx$. Because a realization of X must have *some* value, $\int_{-\infty}^{\infty} f(x)\,dx = 1$, and in cases when X is uniformly distributed, the function f is constant. Now that we understand the double integral, we can deal with two continuous random variables that occur together.

▷ Joint probability density functions

In the following example we investigate a scenario in which two continuous random variables occur together, and we introduce mathematical ideas that lead to the concept of a *joint probability density function*. The example has to do with a radio communications network established by a group of autonomous, unmanned aerial vehicles (UAVs). In such networks, each UAV is programmed to announce itself by radio transmission at regular intervals. The announcement, commonly called a HELLO message, can contain information such as the vehicle's identity and other UAVs that it knows are near by. In order for one UAV to recognize a viable communications link with another, it must first send a HELLO message, and then read a receipt of that signal in the next HELLO message of the other vehicle.

> The UAV knows that it can hear the other vehicle because it received the return message, and the receipt indicates that the UAV can be heard by the other vehicle.

Link delays in a mobile wireless network

Example 4.7. Suppose each UAV in a particular network transmits its HELLO message every two seconds, and in order to avoid simultaneous transmissions, the UAVs' timers have been offset. (a) If vehicle $\mathcal{Y}$ sends a HELLO message 1.8 seconds after it comes into communications range with vehicle $\mathcal{X}$, and $\mathcal{X}$ sends a HELLO message 0.1 seconds later, how long after the communications link is physically possible does $\mathcal{X}$ recognize it? (b) If the timers are offset by a random variable that's uniformly distributed over $[0, 2]$, determine the probability that $\mathcal{X}$ takes at least three seconds to recognize a communications link with $\mathcal{Y}$ once they're in range.

> With the random offset and the given two-second interval between HELLO messages, a UAV might send HELLO messages at, for example, times $t = 0.51, 2.51, 4.51, \ldots$ seconds.

Solution: For the sake of simplicity, we're going to assume that there is no delay between sending and receiving signals (the actual delay is extremely small relative to the speed of the vehicles).

(a) Vehicle $\mathcal{X}$ receives a HELLO message 1.8 seconds after $\mathcal{Y}$ comes in range, but $\mathcal{X}$ doesn't know whether its own messages can be heard by the other vehicle. So it has to transmit a HELLO message and wait for the receipt in the next HELLO message from $\mathcal{Y}$, which happens $1.8 + 2 = 3.8$ seconds after the two nodes come into communications range.

(b) At the moment when the UAVs come into communications range, vehicle $\mathcal{X}$ has some time remaining on its timer, say X seconds, before it sends its next HELLO message. When it sends that message, $\mathcal{Y}$ has some time remaining on its timer, say Y seconds, before it responds with its own HELLO message. Using this notation, we're trying to determine the probability that $X + Y \geq 3$.

Due to the initial offset of the timers, both X and Y are continuous random variables that are uniformly distributed over $[0, 2]$, so $X + Y \geq 3$ is the same as calculating the probability that the point (X, Y) lies in the green-shaded triangle that you see in Figure 4.5, which we'll denote by R. In the remaining portion of this solution, you'll see that this probability is

$$P\big(\,(X, Y) \in R\,\big) = \iint_R \frac{1}{4}\,dA. \tag{4.1}$$

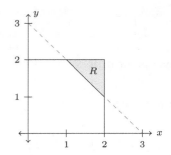

Figure 4.5: Calculating the probability that $X + Y \geq 3$.

To understand why equation (4.1) is correct, suppose we partition R with a regular mesh of n rectangles, $R_1, R_2 \ldots R_n$, each of width Δx and height Δy as in Figure 4.6. Then $P\big((X,Y) \in R \big) \approx P\big((X,Y) \text{ is in } R_1 \text{ or } R_2 \text{ or } \ldots \text{ or } R_n \big)$. This is the same as

$$P\big((X,Y) \in R \big) \approx \sum_{k=1}^{n} P\big((X,Y) \in R_k \big). \qquad (4.2)$$

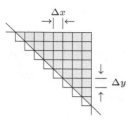

Figure 4.6: A regular mesh over the region R.

Let's talk about the probability that (X,Y) is in an arbitrary rectangle, say R_k, so that $X \in [x_k, x_k + \Delta x]$ and $Y \in [y_k, y_k + \Delta x]$. Because X is uniformly distributed over $[0,2]$, its probability density function has a constant value of 0.5, so the probability that a realization of X lies in $[x_k, x_k + \Delta x]$ is

$$P\big(X \in [x_k, x_k + \Delta x]\big) = \frac{1}{2}\Delta x. \qquad (4.3)$$

Similarly, the probability that $Y \in [y_k, y_k + \Delta y]$ is

$$P\big(Y \in [y_k, y_k + \Delta y]\big) = \frac{1}{2}\Delta y. \qquad (4.4)$$

Now because X and Y are independent, the probability that $(X,Y) \in R_k$ is

$$
\begin{aligned}
P\big((X,Y) \in R_k \big) &= P\big(X \in [x_k, x_k + \Delta x] \text{ and } Y \in [y_k, y_k + \Delta y]\big) \\
&= P\big(X \in [x_k, x_k + \Delta x]\big) \cdot P\big(Y \in [y_k, y_k + \Delta y]\big) \quad (4.5) \\
&= \left(\frac{1}{2}\Delta x\right)\left(\frac{1}{2}\Delta y\right) = \frac{1}{4}\,\Delta x\,\Delta y.
\end{aligned}
$$

So now we can rewrite our approximation in (4.2) as

$$P\big((X,Y) \in R \big) \approx \sum_{k=1}^{n} \frac{1}{4}\,\Delta x\,\Delta y. \qquad (4.6)$$

This approximation becomes equality in the limit as $n \to \infty$ and the Riemann sum becomes a double integral over R. Since R has an area of $1/2$,

$$P\big((X,Y) \in R \big) = \iint_R \frac{1}{4}\,dA = \left(\frac{1}{4}\right)\left(\frac{1}{2}\right) = \frac{1}{8} = 0.125.$$

We conclude that a node will take three seconds or more to establish a communications link 12.5% of the time. ∎

The random variables in Example 4.7 are uniformly distributed, but that's a special case. More generally, if the pdf for X is $f(x)$ and the pdf for Y is $g(y)$, and X and Y are independent random variables, equations (4.3) and (4.4) become

$$P\big(X \in [x_k, x_k + \Delta x]\big) \approx f(x_k^*)\Delta x \quad \text{and} \quad P\big(Y \in [y_k, y_k + \Delta x]\big) \approx g(y_k^*)\Delta x,$$

where (x_k^*, y_k^*) is some point in R_k. Consequently, the analog of equation (4.6) is

$$P\big((X,Y) \in R \big) \approx \sum_{k=1}^{n} f(x_k^*)g(y_k^*)\Delta x\,\Delta y,$$

which leads to

$$P\big((X,Y) \in R \big) = \iint_R f(x)g(y)\,dA. \qquad (4.7)$$

More generally still, the random variables X and Y might not be independent. In this case the integrand of equation (4.7) is replaced with a function $\rho(x,y)$, called

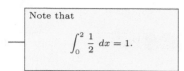

Note that
$$\int_0^2 \frac{1}{2}\,dx = 1.$$

Notice that this probability does not depend on k. It's the same for each rectangle because X and Y are uniformly distributed.

We use independence in equation (4.5).

a *joint probability density function.*

> **Joint PDF:** Suppose X and Y are continuous random variables. We say that a nonnegative-valued function $\rho(x, y)$ is a ***joint probability density function*** (pdf) when the probability that a realization of (X, Y) lies in the region R is
>
> $$P\big((X, Y) \in R \big) = \iint_R \rho(x, y)\, dA.$$

You can think of $\rho(x, y)\, dA$ as the probability that a realization of (X, Y) occurs in a small square of area dA centered at (x, y). If the density ρ has units of probability/area, the product $\rho\, dA$ has units of

$$\left(\frac{\text{probability}}{\text{area}} \right) (\text{area}).$$

Note: Because a realization of (X, Y) must occur *somewhere* in the plane,

$$P\big((X, Y) \in \mathbb{R}^2 \big) = \iint_{\mathbb{R}^2} \rho(x, y)\, dA = \underbrace{\int_{-\infty}^{\infty} \int_{-\infty}^{\infty} \rho(x, y)\, dx\, dy}_{\text{Allows for } (X,Y) \text{ to occur anywhere in the plane.}} = 1.$$

Joint probability density function

Example 4.8. Suppose that the continuous random variables X and Y are distributed according to the joint pdf $\rho(x, y)$, shown below, and R is the triangular region between the x-axis and the line $12y - x = 0$. Determine the probability that a realization of (X, Y) occurs in R.

$$\rho(x, y) = \begin{cases} \frac{2}{3}xy(1 - y) & \text{when } x \in [0, 6] \text{ and } y \in [0, 0.5] \\ 0 & \text{otherwise.} \end{cases}$$

Solution: The probability that a realization of (X, Y) occurs outside the shaded rectangle in Figure 4.7 is 0, so

$$P\big((X, Y) \in R \big) = \int_0^{1/2} \int_{12y}^6 \frac{2}{3}x(y - y^2)\, dx\, dy = \int_0^{1/2} \left[\frac{1}{3}x^2(y - y^2) \right]_{x=12y}^{x=6} dy$$

$$= \int_0^{1/2} \frac{1}{3}(36 - 144y^2)(y - y^2)\, dy = \frac{11}{20}. \qquad \blacksquare$$

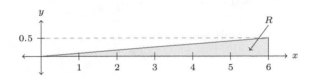

Figure 4.7: The joint pdf for Example 4.8 is 0 outside the rectangle.

▷ Expected Value

In Chapter 7 you saw that a continuous random variable X with a probability density function $f(x)$ has an expected value of

$$\mathcal{E} = \int_{-\infty}^{\infty} \underbrace{x}_{\text{(value)}} \underbrace{f(x)\, dx}_{\times \text{ (probability of that value)}}$$

Intuitively speaking, this integral is calculating a weighted average of the possible values of X, weighting each outcome (x) by the likelihood that it occurs ($f(x)\, dx$).

An analogous definition is used in the current context.

Expected Value: When X and Y are continuous random variables with a joint probability density function $\rho(x, y)$, the **expected value** of X is

$$\mathcal{E}_X = \iint_{\mathbb{R}^2} x\, \rho(x, y)\, dA = \int_{-\infty}^{\infty} \int_{-\infty}^{\infty} x\, \rho(x, y)\, dx\, dy,$$

and the expected value of Y is

$$\mathcal{E}_Y = \iint_{\mathbb{R}^2} y\, \rho(x, y)\, dA = \int_{-\infty}^{\infty} \int_{-\infty}^{\infty} y\, \rho(x, y)\, dx\, dy.$$

Expected Value

Example 4.9. Suppose that X and Y are as in Example 4.8. Determine the expected value of X.

Solution: Since $\rho(x, y) = 0$ outside the rectangle $[0, 6] \times [0, 1/2]$, the expected value of X is

$$\iint_{\mathbb{R}^2} x\, \rho(x, y)\, dA = \int_0^{1/2} \int_0^6 \frac{2}{3} y(1 - y) x^2\, dx\, dy = 48 \int_0^{1/2} y(1 - y)\, dy = 4. \quad \blacksquare$$

Expected Value

Example 4.10. Suppose that X and Y are as in Example 4.8. Determine the expected value of Y.

Answer: $\mathcal{E}_Y = 5/16$ $\blacksquare$

Solution
On-line

The formulas for $\mathcal{E}_X$ and $\mathcal{E}_Y$ are closely related to those for $\bar{x}$ and $\bar{y}$ (the coordinates of a lamina's center of mass). When the mass density is $\rho(x, y)$ in the region R, the total mass of the lamina is

$$m = \iint_R \rho(x, y)\, dA \quad \Rightarrow \quad 1 = \iint_R \frac{\rho(x, y)}{m}\, dA.$$

If you think of $\rho(x, y)\, dA$ as the amount of mass at the point (x, y), the number $\rho(x,y)\, dA / m$ is the fraction of the total mass that's there. The integral adds up all those fractions, which sum to 1 (i.e., 100% of the mass is accounted for).

> Since ρ has units of mass per unit area (e.g., g/cm^2), and dA has units of area (e.g., cm^2), the product $\rho\, dA$ has units of mass.

The fact that $\rho(x,y)\, dA / m$ is a nonnegative-valued function with a total integral of 1 allows us to understand it as a joint pdf of continuous random variables X and Y. When we use it to calculate the expected value of X, for example, we see the weighted average

$$\mathcal{E}_X = \iint_R x\, \underbrace{\frac{\rho(x, y)}{m}}\, dA = \frac{1}{m} \iint_R x\, \rho(x, y)\, dA = \frac{M_y}{m} = \bar{x}.$$

Each value of X...   is weighted by the fraction of the mass that's there

Similarly, we see that $\mathcal{E}_Y = \bar{y}$.

> **You should know**
>
> - the terms *first moment, second moment, joint probability density function (pdf)* and *expected value;*
> - that a joint pdf cannot be negative, and its total integral must be 1;
> - the notation $I_o, I_x, I_y, M_x, M_y, \mathcal{E}_X$ and $\mathcal{E}_Y$.

You should be able to

- determine the units associated with a double integral;
- determine the location of the center of mass of a lamina;
- determine the kinetic energy of a lamina rotating about a fixed axis;
- use a joint probability density function for continuous random variables to calculate probability and expected value;

❖ 14.4 Concept and Application Exercises

1. Suppose length is measured in meters, and R is a plate of metal alloy in which density varies from point to point according to $\rho(x, y)$ kg/m^2. Write an equation that says, "The mass of R is 23.7 kg."   `Quantitative Literacy`

2. Suppose R is a lamina that's rotating about the y-axis at 15 radians per second, and its density varies from point to point according to $\rho(x, y) = 3 + \sin(x^2 - y^2) \frac{\mu g}{mm^2}$. Use the double integral to write an equation that says, "The lamina's rotational kinetic energy is 12 joules."   `Quantitative Literacy`

3. Suppose length is measure in cm, and R is a 12-g lamina in which density varies from point to point according to $\rho(x, y) = 2 + \sin(xy) \frac{g}{cm^2}$. In complete sentences, explain what the equation   `Quantitative Literacy`

$$13 = \frac{1}{12} \iint_R 2x + x\sin(xy) \; dA \quad \text{tells us.}$$

4. Suppose length is measured in meters, and R is a lamina in which the mass density varies from point to point according to $\rho(x, y) = 3 + \sin(x^2 - y^2) \frac{kg}{m^2}$. In complete sentences, explain what the equation   `Quantitative Literacy`

$$523 = \iint_R 3y^2 + \sin(x^2 - y^2)y^2 \; dA \quad \text{tells us.}$$

In #5–10 the density at each point in the region R is $\rho(x, y)$ g/cm^2. Determine the region's mass. Both x and y are measured in cm.   `Mass`

5. $\rho(x, y) = 3x + y$; R is the rectangle $x \in [2, 3]$, $y \in [0, 10]$

6. $\rho(x, y) = 8x + 5y$; R is the rectangle $x \in [6, 8]$, $y \in [1, 7]$

7. $\rho(x, y) = 1 + xy^2$; R is the region between the $y = 0$ and $y = 1/x$ for $x \in [1, 2]$

8. $\rho(x, y) = 1 + x + y$; R is the region between $x = 0$ and $y = \ln x$ for $y \in [0, 1]$

9. $\rho(x, y) = e^{-x^2 - y^2}$; R is the first-quadrant region in which $x^2 + y^2 \leq 1$

10. $\rho(x, y) = 1 + \frac{x}{\sqrt{y^2 + 5}}$; R is the region between $x = 0$ and $y = 3x$ when $y \in [0, 4]$

In #11–18 determine the location of the lamina's center of mass, given that its mass density function is $\rho(x, y)$ g/cm^2. All lengths are measured in centimeters. The regions in #11–14 are rectangular.   `Center of Mass`

11. $\rho(x, y) = 10 - x - y \; \frac{g}{cm^2}$; $x \in [0, 2]$, $y \in [0, 3]$

12. $\rho(x, y) = 1 + 9x^2 + 4y \; \frac{g}{cm^2}$; $x \in [0, 4]$, $y \in [0, 1]$

13. $\rho(x, y) = 1 + xy \; \frac{g}{cm^2}$; $x \in [1, 5]$, $y \in [2, 3]$

14. $\rho(x,y) = 30 - xy \ \frac{\text{g}}{\text{cm}^2}$; $x \in [2,4]$, $y \in [1,6]$

15. $\rho(x,y) = x^2 y + 1 \ \frac{\text{g}}{\text{cm}^2}$; R is the region between $y = 0$ and $y = 1/x$, $x \in [1,7]$

16. $\rho(x,y) = xy^2 + 2 \ \frac{\mu\text{g}}{\text{cm}^2}$; R is the region between $y = 0$ and $y = 1/x^2$, $x \in [3,8]$

17. $\rho(x,y) = 1 + x^2 + y \ \frac{\mu\text{g}}{\text{cm}^2}$; R is bounded by $x = 0$ and $y = \arcsin x$, $y \in [0, \pi/2]$

18. $\rho(x,y) = 1 + \frac{y}{x} \ \frac{\text{kg}}{\text{cm}^2}$; R is the region bounded by $x = 1 + (y-1)^2$ and $x = 2$

19. Suppose R is the region defined by $x \geq 0$, $y = 1 - x$ and $y = -1 + x$, with density $\rho(x,y) = 1 + kx$. Is there a $k > 0$ that results in a center of mass with x-coordinate $1/2$? If so, find it. If not, explain why not.

20. Suppose R is the region defined by $x \geq 0$, $y = 1 - 0.5x$ and $y = -2 + x$, with density $\rho(x,y) = 9 + ky$. Is there a $k > 0$ that results in a center of mass with x-coordinate $1/2$? If so, find it. If not, explain why not.

21. In exercise #51 of Section 14.3 you calculated the annual number of crimes surrounding a police station. Specifically, annual records showed that, on average, police incidents are distributed according to the density function $\rho(r,\theta) = \frac{1}{10\pi}(1 + \cos(\theta))r^2 \frac{\text{crimes}}{\text{mi}^2}$ when $r \in [0,5]$. Based on this information, where should we build a police substation? (Support your answer with reasoning and calculation.)

[City Planning]

22. In exercise #52 of Section 14.3 you worked with socioeconomic data about a community by a lake. The community lives in the upper half of the xy-plane, between a beltway described by $r = 1 + \sin(\theta)$ and an inner loop at $r = 0.25$ (which surrounds the harbor). The annual income of the community is distributed according to $\rho(r,\theta) = (1 + \frac{\theta}{r}) \times 10^6 \frac{\$}{\text{mi}^2}$. Suppose you're planning to open a store in this community. Where is the best place to put it? (Support your answer with reasoning, calculation and/or a transcript from a computer algebra system.)

[Business]

[CAS]

In #23–30 the density at each point in the region R is $\rho(x,y)$ kg/m^2. Determine the region's moment of inertia with respect to the specified axis. Both x and y are measured in meters, and ρ in $\frac{\text{kg}}{\text{m}^2}$.

[Moment of Inertia]

23. R is the rectangle $x \in [3,5]$, $y \in [1,6]$; $\rho(x,y) = 3y + 2xy$; y-axis

24. R is the rectangle $x \in [4,6]$, $y \in [1,2]$; $\rho(x,y) = 4x + 7xy$; y-axis

25. R is the bounded region in the first quadrant defined by the lines $x = 0$ and $y = 0$, and the curve $y = \arccos x$; $\rho(x,y) = 1 + x$; y-axis

26. R is the bounded region in the first quadrant defined by the lines $x = 0$ and $y = 1$, and the curve $y = \arcsin x$; $\rho(x,y) = 1 + y$; y-axis

27. R is the bounded region in the first quadrant defined by the lines $y = 0$ and $x = 1$, and the curve $y = x^2$; $\rho(x,y) = 1 + x - y$; x-axis

28. R is the bounded region in the first quadrant defined by the lines $y = 1$, $y = 2 - x$ and $y = x - 2$; $\rho(x,y) = 2x + \cos \pi y$; x-axis

29. R is the bounded region in the first quadrant between the lines $y = 1$, $7y - x = 0$, and the parabola $x = 2 + 3y^2$; $\rho(x,y) = 13x - 2y$; x-axis.

30. R is the bounded region in the first quadrant between $y = e^x$, $y = \ln x$ and $y = e + 1 - x$; $\rho(x,y) = 1 + x$; x-axis.

31. Suppose R_1 is the disk of radius 1 meter that lies in the xy-plane, centered at the origin, and that it has a uniform density of $\frac{1}{\pi} \frac{\text{kg}}{\text{m}^2}$; and R_2 is the disk of radius 2, also centered at the origin but with a uniform density of $\frac{1}{4\pi} \frac{\text{kg}}{\text{m}^2}$.

    Mechanical Engineering

    (a) Show that R_1 and R_2 have the same mass.

    (b) Calculate the second moment of R_2 with respect to the origin *(Hint: a point at (r, θ) is r units away from the origin.)*

    (c) Calculate the second moment of R_1 with respect to the origin.

    (d) You should have found in parts (b) and (c) that I_o is larger for R_2. What practical significance does this fact have?

32. Suppose R is the disk of radius 1, and that it has a density of $\rho(x, y) = 1 + x^2 + y \frac{\text{kg}}{\text{m}^2}$. (a) Determine the mass of R, and (b) calculate the second moment of R with respect to the origin. *(Hint: a point at (r, θ) is r units away from the origin.)*

    Mechanical Engineering

In #33–34 the function $\rho(x, y)$ is the probability density for the position of an electron in the region R.

    Physics

33. Suppose R is the rectangle $x \in [1, 4]$ and $y \in [3, 4]$, and $\rho(x, y) = (3x^2 + 3y^2)/174$ when $(x, y) \in R$. (a) Show that the electron must be somewhere in R, and (b) calculate the probability that the electron is somewhere in the strip $2 \leq x \leq 3$.

34. Suppose R is the rectangle $0 \leq x \leq 3$ and $4 \leq y \leq 5$, and $\rho(x, y) = y^2 - x^2$ when $(x, y) \in R$.

    (a) Show that $\rho(x, y)$ is *not* a pdf, as written, because $\iint_R \rho(x, y) \, dA > 1$.

    (b) Scale ρ down so that $\iint_R \rho(x, y) \, dA = 1$. Then use the new density function to calculate the probability that the electron is somewhere in the strip $4 \leq y \leq 4.1$.

35. Suppose two vehicles in a mobile network come into range (see Example 4.7), and $F(t)$ is the probability that it takes t seconds or less to recognize a link. If they both have a 2-second HELLO interval, (a) determine a formula for $F(t)$, and (b) graph the function F.

    Mobile Networks

36. Suppose that the vehicles in #35 have an s-second HELLO cycle (where $s > 0$). (a) Determine the probability that it takes t seconds or less to establish a link, $F(s, t)$, and (b) use a graphing utility to render the surface $z = F(s, t)$.

37. Figure 4.8 shows a soccer field that is 60 yards wide. Suppose that $\rho(x, y)$ is the shot-on-goal pdf.

    Sports

    (a) Determine which of $\int_{-22}^{22} \int_0^{18} \rho(x, y) \, dy \, dx$ or $\int_{22}^{30} \int_0^{100} \rho(x, y) \, dy \, dx$ you think is larger, and explain your reasoning in complete sentences.

    (b) Determine the value of $\int_{30}^{40} \int_0^{100} \rho(x, y) \, dy \, dx$.

38. Figure 4.8 shows a baseball diamond. The home plate is the origin, the x-axis is the first-base line, and the y-axis is the third-base line. A batter must hit the ball into the first quadrant in order for it to be in play. Suppose that $\rho(x, y)$ is a joint pdf for the distribution of fielded balls that are hit into play (i.e., the location where a ball in play is first caught or picked up by a fielder).

    Sports

    (a) In complete sentences, explain what the equation $\int_0^{90} \int_0^{90} \rho(x, y) \, dx \, dy = 0.23$ means in practical terms.

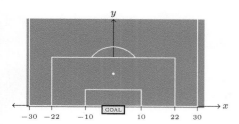

Figure 4.8: A section of a soccer field for #37

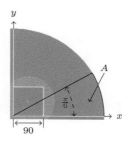

Figure 4.9: The baseball field for #38

(b) Write the iterated integral that you would calculate in order to determine the probability that a ball is fielded in region A beyond the first-to-second-base line (which extends between the points $(90, 0)$ and $(90, 90)$), given that the back fence is uniformly 300 feet away from home plate.

39. A factory is making cylindrical rods. In order to be acceptable, a rod's length must be $\ell \in [99, 101]$ cm, and must have a radius $r \in [10, 12]$ mm. Use a computer algebra system to approximate the probability that a rod from this plant is acceptable if the joint pdf for length and radius is

$$\rho(\ell, r) = \frac{1}{\pi} e^{-0.5(r-11)^2 - 2(\ell-100)^2}.$$

     Quality Control

     CAS

40. A particular grocery store has one checkout lane with a cashier and another that is a self-checkout lane. For any given day, we denote by X the fraction of the store's open hours that the cashier lane is in use, and by Y the fraction of the time that the self-serve lane is in use. Determine the probability that neither checkout lane is used for more than 80% of the open time, given that the joint pdf for X and Y is $\rho(x, y) = 1.5x + 0.5y$.

     Business

41. Suppose airplanes travel straight through the 50-mile transmission range of a ship at sea and the pdf of their velocity distribution is $f(v)$, shown below. If there is no preferred chord across the communications region, the pdf for the length of a transit chord is $\rho(\ell)$, also shown below.

     Aviation

$$f(v) = \begin{cases} \frac{1}{400}(v - 80) & \text{if } v \in [80, 100] \text{ mph} \\ \frac{1}{400}(120 - v) & \text{if } v \in [100, 120] \text{ mph} \\ 0 & \text{otherwise} \end{cases}, \quad \rho(\ell) = \begin{cases} 0.01\ell/\sqrt{10000 - \ell^2} & \text{if } \ell \in [0, 100] \text{ mi} \\ 0 & \text{otherwise} \end{cases}$$

(a) Explain why the probability that $v \in [v_*, v_* + dv]$ and $\ell \in [\ell_*, \ell_* + d\ell]$ is approximately $f(v_*)\rho(\ell_*)\, dv\, d\ell$.

(b) The **dwell time** of an airplane is the length of time that it is within the transmission range of the ship, $t = \frac{\text{distance}}{\text{speed}} = \frac{\ell}{v}$. Determine the probability that a plane's dwell time is 15 minutes or less. (*Hint: the equation $\frac{15}{60} = \frac{\ell}{v}$ defines a line in the $v\ell$-plane. You want to know the probability that the point (v, ℓ) is on or below that line.*)

42. Suppose f and g are continuous functions, and $f(x) > g(x)$ when $x \in [a, b]$. The region R is bounded by the graphs of f and g, and the lines $x = a$ and $x = b$, and has a uniform (constant) density of ρ.

     Center of Mass

(a) Explain how we know that R is y-simple.

(b) Use an iterated integral to show that $M_x = \int_a^b x(f(x) - g(x))\rho\, dx$

(c) Use an iterated integral to show that $M_y = \int_a^b \frac{f(x)+g(x)}{2}(f(x)-g(x))\rho\,dx$.

In #43–46 determine the expected value of the specified random variable.

43. $\mathcal{E}_X$, when $\rho(x,y) = \frac{1}{72}xy^2$ when $x \in [0,4]$ and $y \in [0,3]$, but $\rho(x,y) = 0$ otherwise.

44. $\mathcal{E}_X$, when $\rho(x,y) = \frac{(6x+2y)}{(9+27\sqrt{3})}$ at points in the first quadrant between the x-axis and the the line $y = \sqrt{3}x$ for which $x^2 + 1^2 \leq 9$.

45. $\mathcal{E}_Y$, when $\rho(x,y) = 8e^{-2x-4y}$ when $x \geq 0$ and $y \geq 0$, but $\rho(x,y) = 0$ otherwise.

46. $\mathcal{E}_Y$, when $\rho(x,y) = \frac{1}{\pi}e^{-x^2-(y-3)^2}$

47. Suppose R is a region in the first quadrant of the xy-plane. Prove that the volume of the solid that's generated by revolving R about the y-axis is $2\pi\overline{x}|R|$, where $\overline{x}$ is the x-coordinate of the region's centroid, and $|R|$ is the region's area. This fact is commonly called the **Theorem of Pappus**. (Recall that the centroid is the center of mass when R has a uniform density.)

Mathematics

14.5　The Triple Integral

When mass, charge, energy, or any other quantity is distributed over a volume, we calculate the net total using a *triple integral*. As with all the other integrals in this book, the triple integral is defined as the limit of Riemann sums.

Key Idea(s): *Just as we approximated double integrals by partitioning planar regions into rectangles, we partition three-dimensional regions with a mesh of rectangular boxes.*

Fubini's Theorem continues to apply, although it must be adapted to the three-dimensional context.

❖ The Triple Integral is a Limit of Riemann Sums

The concept of a triple integral is largely the same as that of a double integral. In the discussion below, we quickly recap that concept (the limit of Riemann sums) in the three-dimensional context, and present the standard method of calculation. Suppose $B = [a,b] \times [c,d] \times [p,q]$, by which we mean the collection of points (x,y,z) for which $x \in [a,b]$, $y \in [c,d]$ and $z \in [p,q]$. Such a box is shown in Figure 5.1. To approximate the triple integral of f over B, we use a mesh of smaller rectangular boxes to **partition** B. More specifically, these smaller boxes are defined by partitions of the intervals that define B,

$$a = x_0 < x_1 < \cdots < x_n = b$$
$$c = y_0 < y_1 < \cdots < y_m = d$$
$$p = z_0 < z_1 < \cdots < z_\ell = q.$$

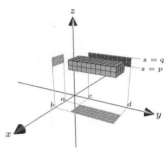

Figure 5.1:　A rectangular region in three dimensions. Its shadow on the xy-plane is the rectangle $[a,b] \times [c,d]$.

When these partitions are all regular, the small rectangular boxes they define are all congruent, and we say that they constitute a **regular** partition of B. In this case, each of the small rectangular boxes has dimensions of

$$\Delta x = \frac{b-a}{n}, \quad \Delta y = \frac{d-c}{m}, \quad \text{and} \quad \Delta z = \frac{p-q}{\ell},$$

and a volume of $\Delta V = \Delta x \Delta y \Delta z$. More generally, the boxes can have different sizes. Let us denote by B_{ijk} the small rectangular box that sits in level k of the mesh, at the intersection of row i and column j. If $(x_{ijk}^*, y_{ijk}^*, z_{ijk}^*)$ denotes an arbitrary point in B_{ijk}, and the box has dimensions of Δx_{ijk}, Δy_{ijk}, and Δz_{ijk},

$$\sum_{i=1}^{m} \sum_{j=1}^{n} \sum_{k=1}^{\ell} f(x_{ijk}^*, y_{ijk}^*, z_{ijk}^*) \, \Delta x_{ijk} \, \Delta y_{ijk} \, \Delta z_{ijk}$$

is a Riemann sum, and as you suspect based on previous discussions, the triple integral is the limit of such Riemann sums. Let us define P to be the collection of the boxes B_{ijk}. Then the **norm** of P is

$$\|P\| = \text{the maximum of all } \Delta x_{ijk}, \Delta y_{ijk} \text{ and } \Delta z_{ijk},$$

and the **triple integral** of f over B is defined to be

$$\iiint_B f(x,y,z) \, dV = \lim_{\|P\| \to 0} \sum_{i=1}^{m} \sum_{j=1}^{n} \sum_{k=1}^{\ell} f(x_i^*, y_j^*, z_k^*) \Delta x_{ijk} \Delta y_{ijk} \Delta z_{ijk} \qquad (5.1)$$

when the limit exists. In such cases, we say that f is **integrable** over B. The differential dV (seen on the left-hand side of the definition) is often called the **volume element**. In the exercises, you'll show that the properties of the triple integral are fundamentally the same as those of the double integral mentioned in Section 14.3.

In the following theorem we include facts about the integrability of continuous functions, and a method of calculating triple integrals.

> **Fubini's Theorem for Rectangular Regions in Three Dimensions:** Suppose $B = [a, b] \times [c, d] \times [p, q]$, and f is continuous over B. Then the triple integral of f over B exists, and
>
> $$\iiint_B f(x, y, z) \, dV = \int_p^q \int_c^d \int_a^b f(x, y, z) \, dx \, dy \, dz.$$
>
> Moreover, we can swap the order of the differentials (e.g., $dy \, dz \, dx$) provided that we reorder the integral signs accordingly.

> That is to say, iterated integrals whose differentials are
>
> $$dx \, dy \, dz$$
> $$dx \, dz \, dy$$
> $$dy \, dx \, dz$$
> $$dy \, dz \, dx$$
> $$dz \, dx \, dy$$
> $$dz \, dy \, dx$$
>
> all lead to the same result.

Using Fubini's Theorem to calculate a triple integral

Example 5.1. Suppose $B = [1, 3] \times [2, 6] \times [4, 5]$, which is shown in Figure 5.2. Determine the value of $\iiint_B xyz \, dV$.

Solution: Writing the triple integral as an iterated integral,

$$\iiint_B xyz \, dV = \int_1^3 \int_2^6 \int_4^5 xyz \, dz \, dy \, dx = \int_1^3 \int_2^6 \left[\frac{1}{2}xyz^2\right]_{z=4}^{z=5} dy \, dx$$

$$= \int_1^3 \int_2^6 \frac{9}{2}xy \, dy \, dx = \int_1^3 \left[\frac{9}{4}xy^2\right]_{y=2}^{y=6} dx = \int_1^3 72x \, dx = 288. \qquad \blacksquare$$

❖ Triple Integrals Over More General Regions

In order to define the triple integral of a function f over a non-rectangular, three-dimensional region we follow the procedure outlined in Section 14.2. If S is the region, we enclose S in a rectangular box and make use of a helper function that's identical to f at every point in the solid, and 0 everywhere else. If B is the box that encloses S, and $\tilde{f}$ is the helper function associated with f, we define

$$\iiint_S f(x, y, z) \, dV = \iiint_B \tilde{f}(x, y, z) \, dV.$$

It can be shown that the right-hand side of this equation exists when the boundary of S is sufficiently nice, even though $\tilde{f}$ is likely to be discontinuous there, and we address several such cases below. Moreover, as you saw with double integrals, Fubini's Theorem can be applied to a non-rectangular region in 3-space, as long as it's ***simple region!simple simple!region***, meaning that it can be characterized as a bundle of parallel line segments that extend from one boundary surface to another.

▷ Regions that are simple in the z-direction

We'll say that a closed and bounded solid is simple in the z-direction, or more concisely that it's z-***simple*** if secant lines parallel to the z-axis intersect its boundary twice (once at the bottom and once at the top, as in the left-hand image of Figure 5.4). In general, a volume is z-simple if it extends between surfaces $z = g(x, y)$ and $z = f(x, y)$, where $g(x, y) \leq f(x, y)$.

Triple integral over a z-simple volume

Example 5.2. Suppose R is the bounded region in the first quadrant between the curves $y = x - x^2$ and $y = 2x - 2x^2$, where length is measured in meters. Denote by S the solid region between R and the graph of $f(x, y) = 4 - x$, (see Figure 5.5). Find the mass of S, supposing that its density is $\rho(x, y, z) = 2z + x + 1$ kg/m^3.

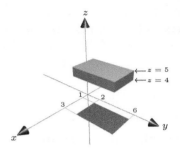

Figure 5.2: The region B for Example 5.1. The projection of the region into the xy-plane is shown in gray.

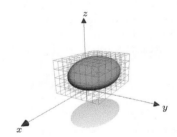

Figure 5.3: Partitioning a solid with rectangular boxes. The shadow of the solid is shown on the xy-plane.

> This implies that there are no voids (e.g., bubbles) in the solid's interior.

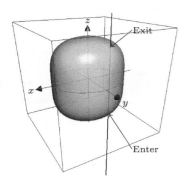
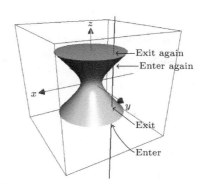

Figure 5.4: (left) An example of a z-simple region; (right) this region is *not* z-simple because a secant line parallel to the z-axis intersects the boundary more than twice (four times, in this case).

Solution: We calculate the mass of this solid with the triple integral

$$\iiint_S \underbrace{\rho(x, y, z)}_{\text{kg/m}^3} \underbrace{dV.}_{\text{m}^3} \leftarrow \text{ product } = \text{kg}$$

Since S is z-simple, we begin the calculation by fixing x and y and integrating in the z-direction, from its "bottom" at $z = 0$ to its "top" at $z = 4 - x$.

$$\iiint_S \rho(x, y, z) \, dV = \iint_R \left(\int_0^{4-x} (2z + x + 1) \, dz \right) dA$$

$$= \iint_R \left[z^2 + (x+1)z \right]_{z=0}^{z=4-x} dA = \iint_R (20 - 5x) \, dA. \quad (5.2)$$

The region R is y-simple (see the left-hand image in Figure 5.5), so we will integrate next in y and then in x. Since the lower and upper boundaries of R are the parabolas $y = x - x^2$ and $y = 2x - 2x^2$ when $0 \le x \le 1$,

$$\iint_R (20 - 5x) \, dA = \int_0^1 \int_{x-x^2}^{2x-2x^2} (20 - 5x) \, dy \, dx = \int_0^1 \left[(20 - 5x)y \right]_{y=x-x^2}^{y=2x-2x^2} dx$$

$$= \int_0^1 (20 - 5x)(x - x^2) \, dx = \frac{35}{12} \text{ kg.} \qquad \blacksquare$$

In Example 5.2 the "base" of the solid was $z = 0$, but it could just as well be the graph of another function, say $g(x, y)$.

Figure 5.5: (left) The region R in Example 5.2; (middle) the region R is the "footprint" of the solid region S; (right) the solid volume in Example 5.2 that lies between R and the graph of f.

Triple Integrals Over z-Simple Volumes: Suppose D is a region in the xy-plane with a simple, piecewise smooth boundary, and S is the 3-dimensional solid over D that lies between the graphs of the continuous functions f and g, where $g(x, y) \leq f(x, y)$ over D. If ρ is a continuous function on S, the triple integral of ρ over S exists, and

$$\iiint_S \rho(x, y, z) \, dV = \iint_D \int_{g(x,y)}^{f(x,y)} \rho(x, y, z) \, dz \, dA, \qquad (5.3)$$

where $dA = dx \, dy$.

> Intuitively speaking, the condition that $g(x, y) \leq f(x, y)$ means that the surface $z = g(x, y)$ is the bottom of V and $z = f(x, y)$ is the top.

Triple integral over a z-simple volume

Example 5.3. Suppose $f(x, y) = 4 + x$, $g(x, y) = 2 - y$, and R is the "dented square" in the first quadrant of the xy-plane bounded by $y = 0$, $y = 1$, $x = 1$ and $x = y(1 - y)$. Denote by S the solid volume between the graphs of f and g over the region R. Calculate $\iiint_S (1 + 4z) \, dV$.

Answer: $\iiint_S (1 + 4z) \, dV = 2361/70.$ ∎

Solution On-line

Note: Look back at the bounds of the iterated integrals in Examples 5.2 and 5.3; each successive integral allows for one less variable in the bounds of integration: 2, then 1, then none (i.e., both bounds are constant).

$$\underbrace{\int_0^1 \int_{x-x^2}^{2x-2x^2} \int_0^{f(x,y)} \cdots \, dz \, dy \, dx}_{\text{from Example 5.2}} \quad \text{and} \quad \underbrace{\int_0^1 \int_{y-y^2}^{1} \int_{g(x,y)}^{f(x,y)} \cdots \, dz \, dx \, dy}_{\text{from Example 5.3}}$$

Notice that the limits of integration don't include x when the differential is dx, nor y when the differential is dy, nor z when the differential is dz.

▷ Regions that are simple in the x-direction

Much as we did in the context of double integrals, we say that a volume is simple in the x direction, or more concisely that it's x-***simple*** if x ranges between the surfaces $x = g(y, z)$ and $x = f(y, z)$. Such a region can be treated as a collection of line segments that are parallel to the x-axis and extend from one boundary surface to another, and we can use an analog of equation (5.3) to calculate triple integrals over it.

> If you topple a z-simple volume by tipping it in the x-direction, you get an x-simple volume.

Triple integrals over x-simple regions

Example 5.4. Suppose R is the bounded region in the yz-plane between the lines $z = 2y$, $z = y$, and $z = 1$. Denote by S the collection of points (x, y, z) for which $(0, y, z)$ is a point in R and $z \leq x \leq 5 - z + y$. Calculate $\iiint_S 12y^2 \, dV$.

Solution: The solid region S is x-simple, and x ranges between the surfaces $x = z$ and $x = 5 - x + y$, so we can write

$$\iiint_S 12y^2 \, dV = \iint_R \int_z^{5-z+y} 12y^2 \, dx \, dA$$
$$= \iint_R \left[12y^2 x \right]_{x=z}^{x=5-z+y} dA = \iint_R \left[12y^3 + 60y^2 - 24y^2 z \right] dA.$$

Because the region R is simple in both the y- and z-directions, we can calculate the remaining double integral with an iterated integral of either the $dy \, dz$ or the $dz \, dy$

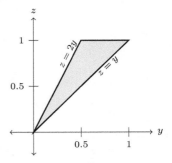

Figure 5.6: The region R for Example 5.4.

form. Our choice is a matter of practicality. If we were to use an iterated integral of the $dz\,dy$ variety we would have to break the region R into two pieces because the maximum value of z occurs at $z = 2y$ in some places, and at $z = 1$ in others (see Figure 5.7). By contrast, the $dy\,dz$ form allows us to use a single iterated integral because the left and right sides of the region are always the same lines, so we choose that option. The values of z range from 0 to 1, and at any particular value of z we see that $z/2 \le y \le z$, so we write the remaining double integral over R as

$$\int_0^1 \int_{z/2}^z \left[12y^3 + 60y^2 - 24y^2z\right] dy\,dz = \int_0^1 \left[\frac{45}{16}z^4 + \frac{35}{2}z^3 - 7z^4\right] dz = \frac{283}{80}. \quad \blacksquare$$

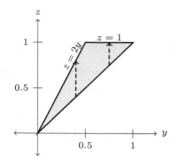

Figure 5.7: If we were to treat R as z-simple, we'd need to compute two separate integrals because the upper bound of integration changes.

Solution On-line

Triple integral over an x-simple region

Example 5.5. Suppose R is the trapezoid in the yz-plane defined by $z = 1 - y$, $z = 0$, $y = 0$, and $y = 0.5$, and S is the solid described by $\sin(yz) \le x \le \cos(yz)$ when $(0, y, z)$ is a point in R. Calculate $\iiint_S (y - 2y^2)\,dV$.

Answer: $\iiint_S (y - 2y^2)\,dV = 3/4 - \cos(1/4) + \sin(1/4)$ $\blacksquare$

▷ Regions that are simple in the y-direction

Much as we did in the context of double integrals, we will say that a solid region is simple in the y-direction, or more concisely that it's **y-simple** when y ranges between the surfaces $y = g(x, z)$ and $y = f(x, z)$. Such a region can be treated as a collection of line segments that are parallel to the y-axis and extend from one boundary surface to another, and we can use an analog of equation (5.3) to calculate triple integrals over it.

> If you topple a z-simple region by tipping it in the y-direction, you get a y-simple region.

Second moment of a y-simple volume

Example 5.6. Suppose R is the triangle in the xz-plane bounded by $x = -1$, $z = -1$, and $z = 1 - x$; and S is the solid over R for which $2 \le y \le 3$. If S has a constant density of 4 kg/m³, determine its second moment with respect to the y-axis. (All lengths measured in m.)

Solution: We calculated second moments of two-dimensional lamina in previous sections, but this is the first time we've done it for a three-dimensional solid. The basic idea is the same as in Section 14.4:

$$\text{second moment} = \iiint_S (\text{distance to axis})^2\,(\text{density})\,dV. \qquad (5.4)$$

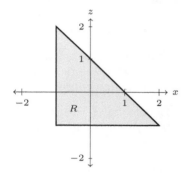

Since the distance from (x, y, z) to the y-axis is $\sqrt{x^2 + z^2}$ m, and the density is always 4 kg/m³, we can write the triple integral over S (which is y-simple) as

$$I_y = \iint_R \int_2^3 4(x^2 + z^2)\,dy\,dA.$$

> The "I" in I_y is for *inertia* (as in "second moment of ..."), and the subscript tells us the axis of revolution.

After sketching R in the xz-plane (see Figure 5.8) we see that z ranges from -1 to $1 - x$ and x varies over $[-1, 2]$, so

$$I_y = \int_{-1}^2 \int_{-1}^{1-x} \int_2^3 4(x^2 + z^2)\,dy\,dz\,dx = 18\,\text{kg-m}^2. \quad \blacksquare$$

> Since density is measured in kg/m³, the product $4\,dV$ has units of kg. When multiplied by (distance)², the outcome is kg-m².

You should know

- the terms *Riemann sum, integrable, volume element, triple integral,* and *simple* (in some direction);

- that all continuous functions are integrable.

You should be able to

- calculate a triple integral by using an iterated integral.

❖ 14.5 Skill Exercises

Calculate each triple integral in #1–6.

1. $\displaystyle\int_0^1 \int_2^3 \int_4^5 \frac{z}{xy} \, dx \, dy \, dz$

2. $\displaystyle\int_3^7 \int_0^1 \int_2^5 (x^2 + zy) \, dy \, dz \, dx$

3. $\displaystyle\int_{-1}^1 \int_{-2}^2 \int_y^z 2x \, dx \, dy \, dz$

4. $\displaystyle\int_0^4 \int_z^{3z} \int_2^5 (xz + y) \, dy \, dx \, dz$

5. $\displaystyle\int_1^8 \int_0^y \int_{x+y}^{xy} (z + 1) \, dz \, dx \, dy$

6. $\displaystyle\int_2^5 \int_0^z \int_{z-2x}^{z+9x} xy \, dy \, dx \, dz$

In #7–10 Write $\iiint_S f(x,y,z) \, dV$ as an iterated integral (or a sum of them) by treating the solid S as (a) x-simple, (b) y-simple, and (c) z-simple.

7. S is in the first octant between the origin and the plane $2x + 3y + z = 7$.

8. S is in the first octant between the cylinder $y = z^2$ and the planes $z = x$ and $y = 1$.

9. S is in the first octant between the cylinder $z = 1/(x+1) - 1/2$, and the planes $z + y = 5$ and $z + x = 4$.

10. S is in the first octant between the plane $z = 0$ and the surface $4 = 2|x - 3| + 3|y - 2| + |z|$.

Exercises #11–14 ask you to integrate over a z-simple volume.

11. Suppose $g(x,y) = -4 - x^2 - 3y^2$, $f(x,y) = 2 + 5x + 8y$, and R is the rectangular region in the xy-plane defined by $-3 \le x \le 0$ and $1 \le y \le 2$. Denote by S the solid volume between the graphs of f and g over R. Calculate $\iiint_S (x + yz) \, dV$.

12. Suppose $f(x,y) = x + y$, $g(x,y) = 4 + 8y - x$, and R is the rectangular region in the xy-plane defined by $1 \le x \le 3$ and $-4 \le y \le -2$. Denote by S the solid volume between the graphs of f and g over R. Calculate $\iiint_S zy^2 \, dV$.

13. Denote by S the region between the graphs of $f(x,y) = 4 + e^{-x} + e^{-y}$, $g(x,y) = x - y$, over the triangle in the first quadrant of the xy-plane bounded by $x = 0$, $y = 0$, and $y = 4 - 2x$. Calculate $\iiint_S (x + 2y)z \, dV$.

14. Suppose $f(x,y) = 2 + xy$, $g(x,y) = 1 - xy$, and R is the first quadrant of the xy-plane bounded by $y = 1$, $y = 2$, $x = 0$ and $y = 1/x$. Denote by S the solid volume between the graphs of f and g over R. Calculate $\iiint_S yz \, dV$.

Exercises #15–18 ask you to integrate over a y-simple volume.

15. Suppose $g(x,z) = 1 - z$, $f(x,z) = 2 + 3x$, and R is the rectangle in the xz-plane in which $2 \le x \le 5$ and $5 \le z \le 6$. Denote by S the region between the surfaces $y = g(x,z)$ and $y = f(x,z)$ when $(x,z) \in R$. Calculate $\iiint_S xy \, dV$.

16. Suppose $g(x,z) = xz^2$, $f(x,z) = 3 + x + z$, and R is the square in the xz-plane in which $0 \le x \le 1$ and $0 \le z \le 1$. Denote by S the solid volume between the surfaces $y = f(x,z)$ and $y = g(x,z)$ when $(x,z) \in R$. Calculate $\iiint_S (z - y) \, dV$.

17. Denote by S the solid region between the surfaces $y = \sqrt{2 + x - z}$ and $y = \sqrt{5 + 3x^2 + 8z}$, where (x, z) is in the triangle in the xz-plane bounded by $x = 1$, $z = 0$, and $z = 3 - x/2$. Calculate $\iiint_S zy\, dV$.

18. Denote by S the solid region between the cylinders $y = 1 + x$ and $y = 5 - x$, where (x, z) is in the bounded region of the xz-plane between the line $z = x$ and the curve $z = -x^2$. Calculate $\iiint_S \sin z\, dV$.

Exercises #19–22 ask you to integrate over an x-simple volume.

19. Suppose $g(y, z) = y + z$, $f(y, z) = \sqrt{3 + 2z + 5y}$, and R is the region in the yz-plane bounded by the curves $z = 1/y$ and $z = 2.25 - 0.5y$. Denote by S the solid volume between the surfaces $x = f(y, z)$ and $x = g(y, z)$ when $(x, z) \in R$. Calculate $\iiint_S 8xy\, dV$.

20. Suppose $g(y, z) = y - z$, $f(y, z) = 5 + z^2$, and R is the region in the yz-plane bounded by $z = y^2$ and $z = 4$. Denote by S the solid volume between the surfaces $x = f(y, z)$ and $x = g(y, z)$ when $(x, z) \in R$. Calculate $\iiint_S 6z^2x\, dV$

21. Suppose $g(y, z) = (yz)^{3/2}$, $f(y, z) = 3 + z$, and R is the bounded region in the first quadrant of the yz-plane that lies between the curves $z = \sqrt{y}$ and $z = y^2$. Denote by S the solid volume between the surfaces $x = f(y, z)$ and $x = g(y, z)$ when $(x, z) \in R$. Calculate $\iiint_S 2yx\, dV$.

22. Suppose $g(y, z) = 1 - 5y - 3z$, $f(y, z) = 3 + 2z + y$, and R is the bounded region in the first quadrant of the yz-plane that lies between the curve $z = y^3$ and the line $z = 4y$. Denote by S the solid volume between the surfaces $x = f(y, z)$ and $x = g(y, z)$ when $(x, z) \in R$. Calculate $\iiint_S (y + x)\, dV$.

Compute the triple integrals in #23–28.

23. The equation $x^2 + z^2 \leq 1$ describes a solid cylinder with the y-axis as the axis of symmetry. Suppose we cut this cylinder with the planes $y = 4$, and $x + y = 0$, and denote the bounded portion (i.e., $-x \leq y \leq 4$) above the xy-plane by S. Calculate $\iiint_S z\, dV$.

24. Determine $\iiint_S y\, dV$ when S is the bounded solid in the first octant bounded by the plane $z = \pi - x - y$ and the cylinder $z = \cos y$.

25. Determine $\iiint_S (3x + 4)\, dV$ when S is the bounded solid in the first octant bounded by the cylinder $x = 1 - y^2$ and the plane $x + y + z = 2$.

26. Determine $\iiint_S (x + z)\, dV$ when S is the solid region bounded by the cylinder $y = 0.5z^2$ and the planes $z = x$, $x = -5$ and $y = 9$.

27. Determine $\iiint_S (2z - 1)\, dV$ when S is the solid region bounded by the cylinder $5 = z + x + y^2$ and the planes $y + z = -1$ and $4 = y - x$.

28. Determine $\iiint_S x\, dV$ when S is the solid region in the first octant bounded by the paraboloid $1 = x^2 + y - z^2$ and the plane $x - y + z = -3$.

29. Suppose S is the solid shown in Figure 5.9. Write $\iiint_S f(x, y, z)\, dV$ as an iterated integral of the form (a) $dy\, dz\, dx$, (b) $dz\, dy\, dx$, and (c) $dx\, dy\, dz$.

30. Suppose S is the solid shown in Figure 5.10. Write $\iiint_S f(x, y, z)\, dV$ as an iterated integral of the form (a) $dz\, dx\, dy$, (b) $dy\, dx\, dz$, and (c) $dx\, dy\, dz$

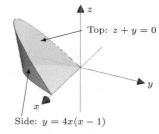

Side: $y = 4x(x - 1)$

Figure 5.9: Solid for #29.

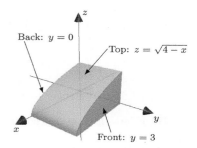

Figure 5.10: Solid for #30.

✧ 14.5 Concept and Application Exercises

In #31–34 determine whether S is x-simple, y-simple, and/or z-simple (it may be all three, or none of them).

31. Suppose R is the unit disk in the xy-plane, and S is the solid volume over R that sits between the paraboloids $z = x^2 + y^2$ and $z = 3x^2 + 5y^2$.

32. Suppose S is the solid ellipsoid $x^2 + 6y^2 + 8z^2 \leq 1$.

33. Suppose S is the spherical shell $1 \leq x^2 + y^2 + z^2 \leq 2$.

34. Suppose S is the volume that sits inside the sphere $x^2 + y^2 + z^2 = 100$ but outside the hyperboloid $z^2 - y^2 + x^2 = 1$.

You know that $\int_a^b 1 \, dx =$ the length of the interval $[a, b]$, and that $\iint_R 1 \, dA =$ the area of the region R. Similarly, the number $\iiint_S 1 \, dV$ is the volume of the solid S. Use this fact in #35–40.

35. Suppose S is the solid in the first octant that lies between the planes $x+y+z = 1$ and $x+y+3z = 5$. Determine the volume of S. (Recall that the first octant is the portion of 3-space above the first quadrant of the xy-plane ($z \geq 0$).)

36. Suppose S is the solid that lies inside the cylinder $z^2 + y^2 \leq 1$, and between the planes $x + 2y + 3z = 0$ and $6x - y + z = 4$. Determine the volume of S.

37. Suppose S is the solid in the first octant that is bounded by the surface $z = \sqrt{xy}$ and the plane $x + y = 9$. Determine the volume of S.

38. Suppose S is the solid in the first octant for which $0 \leq x \leq 1$, $\sqrt{x} \leq y \leq 1$, and $0 \leq z \leq 1 - y$. Determine the volume of S.

39. Suppose S is the smaller of the solid regions that sit between the sphere $x^2 + y^2 + z^2 = 9$ and the plane $y + z = 3$. Write an iterated integral for finding the volume of S.

40. Write an iterated integral for finding the volume of the solid "ice-cream cone" that sits above the xy-plane, bounded by the sphere $x^2 + y^2 + z^2 = 1$ and the cone $z^2 = x^2 + y^2$.

Suppose S is a solid in which the density changes from point to point according to $\rho(x, y, z)$. Then the solid's center of mass is at $(M_{yz}/m, M_{xz}/m, M_{xy}/m)$, where m is the total mass of S, and

$$M_{yz} = \iiint_S x\rho(x, y, z) \, dV \quad \text{is the first moment with respect to the } yz\text{-plane,}$$

$$M_{xz} = \iiint_S y\rho(x, y, z) \, dV \quad \text{is the first moment with respect to the } xz\text{-plane,}$$

$$M_{xy} = \iiint_S z\rho(x, y, z) \, dV \quad \text{is the first moment with respect to the } xy\text{-plane.}$$

Use this fact to answer exercises #41–46.   First Moments

41. If length is measured in meters, and density in $\frac{\text{kg}}{\text{m}^3}$, what are the units of M_{xy}?

42. When length is measured in meters, and density in $\frac{\text{kg}}{\text{m}^3}$, we can write the x-coordinate of the center of mass as

$$\bar{x} = \frac{1}{m} \iiint_V x\rho(x, y, z) \, dV = \iiint_V x \, \frac{\rho(x, y, z) \, dV}{m}.$$

(a) Why is the integral of $x\rho(x, y, z)$ called the moment with respect to the yz-plane? *(Hint: what does x measure?)*

(b) What are the units of $\rho(x, y, z)\ dV$?

(c) What are the units of $\frac{\rho(x,y,z)\ dV}{m}$?

(d) What is the practical *meaning* of $\frac{\rho(x,y,z)\ dV}{m}$?

In #43–46 determine the coordinates of the center of mass. All lengths are measured in millimeters.

                                                      Center of Mass

43. $\rho(x, y, z) = 2 + xyz \ \frac{g}{mm^3}$; S is the solid rectangular block defined by $-1 \le x \le 1$, $-1 \le y \le 2$, and $-1 \le z \le 3$.

44. $\rho(x, y, z) = 25 - xyz \ \frac{g}{mm^3}$; S is the solid rectangular block defined by $-2 \le x \le 2$, $-1 \le y \le 3$, and $-2 \le z \le 4$.

45. $\rho(x, y, z) = 35 - x - y^2 - 0.25z^3 \ \frac{g}{mm^3}$; S is the solid rectangular block defined by $-1 \le x \le 1$, $-4 \le y \le 4$, and $-3 \le z \le 3$.

46. $\rho(x, y, z) = 8 + z \ \frac{g}{mm^3}$; S is the solid between the paraboloid $x = 5 + z^2 + 7y^2$ and the plane $x + y + z = -1$, constrained by $-1 \le y \le 1$ and $-2 \le z \le 1$.

In #47–52 determine the given second moment of S. (See equation (5.4).)

                                                      Moment of Inertia

47. S is the solid from #43; I_x 50. S is the solid from #45; I_y

48. S is the solid from #44; I_x 51. S is the solid from #45; I_z

49. S is the solid from #44; I_y 52. S is the solid from #46; I_z

53. Suppose f, g, and h are continuous functions of a single variable, and S is the solid box defined by $x \in [a, b]$, $y \in [c, d]$ and $z \in [p, q]$. Show that

$$\iiint_S f(x)g(y)h(z)\ dV = \left(\int_a^b f(x)\ dx \right) \left(\int_c^d g(y)\ dy \right) \left(\int_p^q h(z)\ dz \right).$$

Checking the details

In #54–56 we denote by S a solid volume in 3-space. The functions f and g are integrable functions, and k is a scalar.

54. Use equation (5.1) to explain why

$$\iiint_S f(x, y, z)\ dV + \iiint_S g(x, y, z)\ dV = \iiint_S \left[f(x, y, z) + g(x, y, z) \right] dV.$$

55. Use equation (5.1) to explain why $\iiint_S k\, f(x, y, z)\ dV = k \iiint_S f(x, y, z)\ dV$.

56. Suppose S can be separated into disjoint solids, S_1 and S_2. Use equation (5.1) to explain why

$$\iiint_S f(x, y, z)\ dV = \iiint_{S_1} f(x, y, z)\ dV + \iiint_{S_2} f(x, y, z)\ dV.$$

14.6   Integrals in Cylindrical and Spherical Coordinates

The Cartesian coordinate system locates points in 3-space by providing directions from the origin that amount to *over*, *across*, and *up* ($x, y,$ and z). It's a "square" coordinate system, which makes it ill-suited to describe things that are *round* in some sense, such arteries, solenoids, apples, planetary orbits, etc. The coordinate systems introduced below are much better suited to such contexts.

> **Key Idea(s):** *The cylindrical coordinate system is an extension of the polar coordinate system into three dimensions, which is done by including a z-axis.*
>
> *When calculating triple integrals in the cylindrical system, we use $dV = r \, dr \, d\theta \, dz$.*
>
> *The spherical coordinate system uses a pair of angles to "point" at a location. The first is the polar angle, θ, and the second is an angle from the z-axis, written as ϕ.*
>
> *When calculating triple integrals in the spherical system, we use $dV = \rho^2 \sin(\phi) \, d\rho \, d\theta \, d\phi$.*

✧ Cylindrical Coordinates

In short, the **cylindrical** coordinate system is just the polar coordinate system with a z-axis, as depicted in Figure 6.1. We typically denote the coordinates of a point as (r, θ, z), which relates to the Cartesian coordinate system as follows:

$$x = r\cos\theta \tag{6.1}$$
$$y = r\sin\theta \tag{6.2}$$
$$z = z. \tag{6.3}$$

Note: It is common practice to restrict $r \geq 0$ when working in cylindrical coordinates, and we will do so in this book.

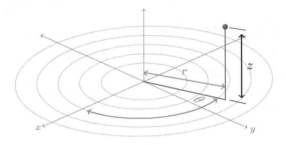

Figure 6.1: The cylindrical coordinate system is just the polar coordinate system with a z-axis.

Transitioning out of cylindrical coordinates

Example 6.1. Suppose P is the point whose cylindrical coordinates are $(2, \pi/2, 7)$. Determine the Cartesian coordinates of P.

Solution: Using equations (6.1)–(6.3), we see that $x = 0$, $y = 2$, and $z = 7$. So the Cartesian coordinates of this points are $(0, 2, 7)$. ∎

Transitioning into cylindrical coordinates

Example 6.2. Suppose P is the point whose Cartesian coordinates are $(-\sqrt{3}, -1, 3)$. Determine the cylindrical coordinates of P.

Solution: Because the Cartesian and cylindrical coordinate systems share the z coordinate, we need only determine r and θ from x and y. Since the point $(-\sqrt{3}, -1, 0)$ is 2 units away from the origin, $r = 2$. And we know that $\tan(\theta) = y/x = 1/\sqrt{3}$, so θ is either $\pi/6$ or $7\pi/6$. The point $(-\sqrt{3}, -1)$ lies in the third quadrant of the xy-plane, so $\theta = 7\pi/6$, and the cylindrical coordinates of this point are $(2, 7\pi/6, 3)$. ∎

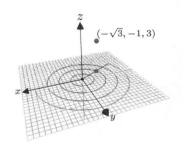

Figure 6.2: The blue, circular arc in the xy-plane subtends $7\pi/6$ radians.

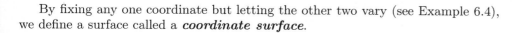

Transitioning between coordinate systems

Example 6.3. The Cartesian coordinates of the point P are $(4, 1, -2)$, and the cylindrical coordinates of the point Q are $(3, \pi/6, 4)$. Determine (a) the cylindrical coordinates of P, and (b) the Cartesian coordinates of Q.

Answer: (a) $(\sqrt{17},\ \tan^{-1}(0.25), -2)$, and (b) $(1.5\sqrt{3}, 1.5, 4)$.　■

Solution On-line

By fixing any one coordinate but letting the other two vary (see Example 6.4), we define a surface called a **coordinate surface**.

Coordinate surfaces

Example 6.4. Describe the surfaces whose equations are (a) $z = 3$, (b) $\theta = \pi/4$, and (c) $r = 2$.

Solution: (a) The equation $z = 3$ determines the altitude of a point, but its distance from the z-axis and the direction you travel to get there are unconstrained, so we get all points with a z-coordinate of 3. That's a plane (see Figure 6.3).

(b) This says that a point's position vector is $\pi/4$ radians removed from the standard x-axis, but neither a point's altitude nor its distance from the z-axis is constrained by this equation. In this case, we get a half-plane ($r \geq 0$).

(c) This equation says that the horizontal distance of a point from z-axis has to be 2, but the height at which we find the point is unconstrained, and there's no mention of its direction from the z-axis. So we get a cylinder whose radius is 2.　■

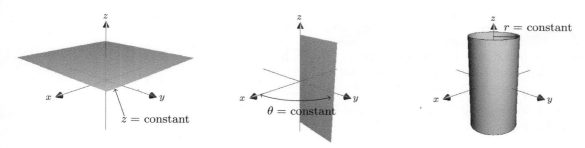

Figure 6.3: Coordinate surfaces in the cylindrical system; (left) constant z; (middle) constant θ; (right) constant r

▷ Triple integrals in cylindrical coordinates

Before we can use iterated integrals in cylindrical coordinates to calculate triple integrals, we need to formulate the volume element in terms of the differentials of r, θ and z. Consider a cylindrical "box" that is Δz tall, with a polar-rectangular base that is Δr wide and subtends an angle of $\Delta\theta$ (see Figure 6.4). In Section 14.3 we showed that the base of such a box has an area of $r\,\Delta r\,\Delta\theta$. Since the box is Δz units tall, its volume is $\Delta V = r\,\Delta r\,\Delta\theta\,\Delta z$. This allows us to approximate the triple integral of f over a three-dimensional region R as

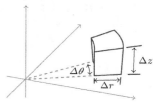

Figure 6.4: A cylindrical "box."

$$\iiint_R f\,dV \approx \sum_{k=1}^{n} f(r_k^*, \theta_k^*, z_k^*)\,\Delta V_k = \sum_{k=1}^{n} f(r_k^*, \theta_k^*, z_k^*)\,r_k\,\Delta r_k\,\Delta\theta_k\,\Delta z_k,$$

where we've partitioned R into n cylindrical boxes, and $(r_k^*, \theta_k^*, z_k^*)$ is some point in the kth box. As you expect by now, when f is continuous this approximation becomes equality in the limit. The important aspect of this calculation is that it shows us the form of the volume element that we'll use to compute the triple integral using an iterated integral: $dV = r\,dr\,d\theta\,dz$. You'll see this product of differentials in the statement below, which combines equations (3.2) and (5.3).

Fubini's Theorem in Cylindrical Coordinates: Suppose R is the region consisting of all points with cylindrical coordinates (r, θ, z) for which $\theta \in [\alpha, \beta]$, $r \in [r_1(\theta), r_2(\theta)]$, and $z \in [z_1(r, \theta), z_2(r, \theta)]$, where $\beta - \alpha \leq 2\pi$. If r_1, r_2, z_1, z_2 and f are continuous,

$$\iiint_R f\ dV = \int_\alpha^\beta \int_{r_1(\theta)}^{r_2(\theta)} \int_{z_1(r,\theta)}^{z_2(r,\theta)} f(r, \theta, z)\ r\ dz\ dr\ d\theta.$$

Integration in cylindrical coordinates

Example 6.5. Suppose S is the solid region between the paraboloid $z = x^2 + y^2$ and the plane $z = 4\pi$ (see Figure 6.5). Calculate $\iiint_S -\sin z\ dV$.

Solution: The plane $z = 4\pi$ meets the paraboloid $z = x^2 + y^2$ when $4\pi = x^2 + y^2 = r^2 \Rightarrow r = 2\sqrt{\pi}$. So the region R stretches between $r = 0$ and $r = 2\sqrt{\pi}$, and it's rotationally symmetric about the z-axis, so $0 \leq \theta \leq 2\pi$. At each r and θ, the value of z varies between $x^2 + y^2 = r^2$ and 4π, so we write $\iiint_S -\sin z\ dV$ as

$$\int_0^{2\pi} \int_0^{2\sqrt{\pi}} \int_{r^2}^{4\pi} -\sin(z)\ r\ dz\ dr\ d\theta = \int_0^{2\pi} \int_0^{2\sqrt{\pi}} \left(1 - \cos r^2\right) r\ dr\ d\theta$$

$$\int_0^{2\pi} \left[\frac{1}{2} r^2 - \frac{1}{2} \sin r^2 \right]_{r=0}^{r=2\sqrt{\pi}} d\theta = \int_0^{2\pi} 2\pi\ d\theta = (2\pi)^2. \qquad \blacksquare$$

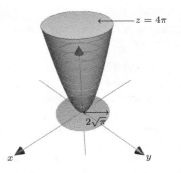

Figure 6.5: The region V in Example 6.5.

Integrating in cylindrical coordinates

Example 6.6. Suppose $\rho > 0$ and $\phi \in (0, \pi/2)$ are constant, and S is the solid region that lies above the cone $z = r \cot \phi$ and inside the sphere $x^2 + y^2 + z^2 = \rho^2$ (see Figures 6.7 and 6.6). Determine the volume of S by calculating $\iiint_S 1\ dV$.

Solution: This z-simple solid sits over a disk in the plane $z = 0$ that's centered at the origin and has a radius of $\rho \sin \phi$.

$$x^2 + y^2 + z^2 = \rho^2$$
$$r^2 + z^2 = \rho^2$$

which we write as $z = \sqrt{\rho^2 - r^2}$ since $z \geq 0$. That is ,

$$\iiint_S 1\ dV = \iint_R \int_{r\cot\phi}^{\sqrt{\rho^2 - r^2}} 1\ dz\ dA = \iint_R \left(\sqrt{\rho^2 - r^2} - r \cot \phi \right) dA$$

$$= \int_0^{2\pi} \int_0^{\rho\sin\phi} \left(\sqrt{\rho^2 - r^2} - r \cot \phi \right) r\ dr\ d\theta$$

$$= \int_0^{2\pi} -\frac{1}{3} \left[(\rho^2 - \rho^2 \sin^2 \phi)^{3/2} - \rho^3 + \rho^3 \sin^3 \phi \cot \phi \right] d\theta.$$

Since the integrand is independent of θ, this is just

$$= -\frac{2\pi}{3} \left[(\rho^2 - \rho^2 \sin^2 \phi)^{3/2} - \rho^3 + \rho^3 \sin^3 \phi \cot \phi \right]$$

$$= -\frac{2\pi}{3} \left[\rho^3 (1 - \sin^2 \phi)^{3/2} - \rho^3 + \rho^3 \sin^3 \phi \cot \phi \right]$$

$$= +\frac{2\pi}{3} \rho^3 \left[\cos^3 \phi - 1 + \sin^2 \phi \cos \phi \right] = \frac{2\pi}{3} \rho^3 \left[1 - \cos \phi \right]. \qquad \blacksquare$$

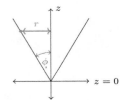

Figure 6.6: Schematic of a circular cone, seen from the side. (The plane $z = 0$ appears as a horizontal line because it's seen edge-on.) Because the edge of this cone is inclined ϕ radians away from the axis of symmetry, each point on the cone (except the origin) has cylindrical coordinates that satisfy the equation $\tan \phi = r/z$, which we write as $z = r \cot \phi$.

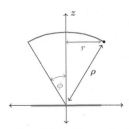

Figure 6.7: The circular cone in Example 6.6 meets the sphere of radius ρ when $r = \rho \sin \phi$.

✧ Spherical Coordinates

The simplest way for you to specify the location of an everyday object is just to point at it. If you're pointing at something above or below you (e.g., birds or bugs) you have to incline your arm, so you're really using three pieces of information: which direction to turn and face, an angle of inclination, and a distance away. That's the *spherical* coordinate system, in a nut shell.

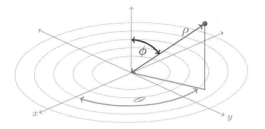
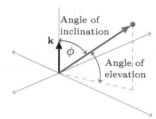

Figure 6.8: (left) The spherical coordinate system "points at" locations using θ and ϕ, and tells you how far away they are with ρ; (right) a point's position vector is inclined away from **k** by an angle of ϕ.

The spherical coordinates of a point are typically written as (ρ, θ, ϕ) where $\rho \geq 0$ is the point's distance from the origin, and as in the polar and cylindrical coordinate systems, the angle θ denotes an angle away from the positive-x axis in the xy-plane (see Figure 6.8). The last coordinate is the angle $\phi \in [0, \pi]$, which measures inclination from the z-axis.

We can convert from spherical coordinates to the other coordinate systems by way of simple trigonometry. In Figure 6.9 you see that a point with spherical coordinates (ρ, θ, ϕ) defines right triangle with a hypotenuse of length of ρ, so $\cos \phi = z/\rho$. Solving this equation for z shows us that

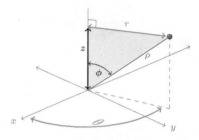

$$z = \rho \cos \phi. \tag{6.4}$$

Figure 6.9: A point's cylindrical and spherical coordinates are related through right-triangle trigonometry.

Similarly, $\sin \phi = r/\rho$ so $r = \rho \sin \phi$. This allows us to use the standard conversion from polar coordinates to find

$$x = r \cos \theta = \rho \sin \phi \cos \theta \tag{6.5}$$
$$y = r \sin \theta = \rho \sin \phi \sin \theta \tag{6.6}$$

Transitioning out of spherical coordinates

Example 6.7. Suppose P is the point with spherical coordinates $(3, \pi/3, \pi/4)$. Determine the Cartesian coordinates of P.

Solution: Using equations (6.4)–(6.6) we see that $x = 3 \sin \frac{\pi}{4} \cos \frac{\pi}{3} = 3\sqrt{6}/4$, $y = 3 \sin \frac{\pi}{4} \sin \frac{\pi}{3} = 3\sqrt{2}/4$ and $z = 3 \cos \frac{\pi}{4} = 3\sqrt{2}/2$. ∎

Transitioning into spherical coordinates

Example 6.8. Suppose P is the point whose Cartesian coordinates are $(1, 5, -4)$. Determine the spherical coordinates of P.

Solution: The distance from P to the origin is $\sqrt{1^2 + (5)^2 + (-4)^2} = \sqrt{42}$, so that's ρ. We know that $\cos \phi = z/\rho = -4/\sqrt{42}$ so $\phi = \arccos(-4/\sqrt{42})$. Lastly, we get θ by looking at the projection of P onto the xy-plane: $(1, 5, 0)$. This sits in the first quadrant, so $\theta = \arctan(5/1)$. So the spherical coordinates of the point P are $(\rho, \theta, \phi) = (\sqrt{42}, \arctan 5, \arccos(-4/\sqrt{42}))$. ∎

Transitioning between coordinate systems

Example 6.9. The Cartesian coordinates of the point P are $(3, -1, 6)$, and the spherical coordinates of the point Q are $(8, \pi/4, \pi/6)$. Determine (a) the spherical coordinates of P, and (b) the Cartesian coordinates of Q.

Answer: (a) $\left(\sqrt{46}, -\tan^{-1}(1/3), \cos^{-1}(6/\sqrt{46})\right)$; (b) $(2\sqrt{2}, 2\sqrt{2}, 4\sqrt{3})$. ∎

Coordinate surfaces

Example 6.10. What surface is described by (a) $\rho = 3$, (b) $\theta = \pi/4$, (c) $\phi = \pi/3$?

Solution: (a) The equation $\rho = 3$ describes all points that are 3 units away from the origin. That's a sphere (see Figure 6.10). (b) This is a half-plane, just as it was in the cylindrical system. (c) This describes all points whose position vectors make an angle of $\pi/4$ with the positive z-axis. This is a cone. ∎

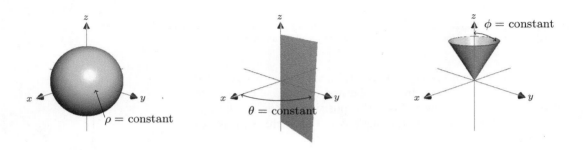

Figure 6.10: Coordinate surfaces: (left) constant ρ; (middle) constant θ; (right) constant ϕ.

In Example 6.10 you saw that a fixed value of ρ corresponds to a sphere. Toward developing a better understanding of the spherical coordinate system, imagine that sphere as the earth, and the z-axis as its axis of revolution. Then each value of θ corresponds to a longitude, and each value of ϕ to a latitude ($\phi = 0$ at the north pole, $\phi = \pi/2$ on the equator, and $\phi = \pi/2$ at the south pole).

▷ Triple integrals in spherical coordinates

In order to express triple integrals as iterated integrals in spherical coordinates, we must write dV in terms of $d\rho, d\theta$ and $d\phi$. Toward this end, we consider a spherical "box" (see Figure 6.11), by which we mean the set of all points for which:

(i) the points' position vectors have magnitudes in $[\rho_1, \rho_2]$

(ii) the points' position vectors are inclined from $\mathbf{k}$ by angles in $[\phi_1, \phi_2]$, and

(iii) the points have polar angles in $[\theta_1, \theta_2]$.

In the End Notes for this chapter, we present a geometric proof that the volume of such a box is $\Delta V = \rho^2 \sin(\phi) \Delta\phi \, \Delta\theta \, \Delta\rho$ where $\Delta\rho = \rho_2 - \rho_1$ (similarly for $\Delta\theta$ and $\Delta\phi$), and the particular values of ρ and ϕ are governed by the Mean Value Theorem; here we opt for an approximation based on a brief intuitive argument. In Figure 6.12 you see that one edge of this box has a length of $\rho\Delta\phi$, and another has a length of $r\Delta\theta = \rho\sin(\phi)\Delta\theta$. The third dimension of this box is $\Delta\rho$, so

$$\Delta V \approx \left(\rho\Delta\phi\right)\left(\rho\sin(\phi)\Delta\theta\right)\Delta\rho = \rho^2\sin(\phi)\Delta\rho\Delta\phi\Delta\phi.$$

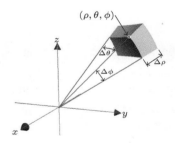

Figure 6.11:   Example of a spherical "box."

> This is an approximation because although one circular arc has a length of $\rho\Delta\phi$, the circular arc on the opposite (back) side of the box is longer.

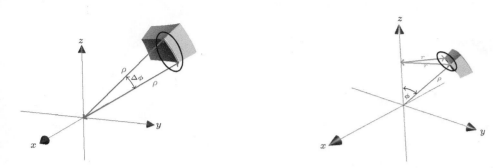

Figure 6.12: (both) Measuring the edges of a spherical box; (left) one edge is a circular arc with a length of $\rho\Delta\phi$; (right) another edge is a circular arc with a length of $r\Delta\theta = \rho\sin(\phi)\Delta\theta$.

Now that we know how to express the volume of a small, spherical box, we can approximate the triple integral of f over a three-dimensional region R as

$$\iiint_R f\, dV \approx \sum_{k=1}^{n} f(\rho_k^*, \theta_k^*, \phi_k^*)\, \Delta V_k = \sum_{k=1}^{n} f(\rho_k^*, \theta_k^*, \phi_k^*)\, (\rho_k^*)^2 \sin(\phi_k^*)\, \Delta\phi_k\, \Delta\rho_k\, \Delta\theta_k,$$

where we've partitioned R into n spherical boxes and $(\rho_k^*, \theta_k^*, \phi_k^*)$ is a point in the kth box. It can be shown that when f is continuous, the approximation becomes equality in the limit. The important aspect of this calculation is that it shows us the form of the volume element that we'll use to compute the triple integral using an iterated integral: $dV = \rho^2 \sin(\phi)\, d\rho\, d\phi\, d\theta$.

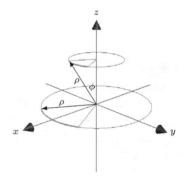

Figure 6.13: Both red arcs subtend $\Delta\theta$ radians. The radius of the upper blue circle is $r = \rho\sin\phi$, and $r = \rho\sin(\pi/2) = \rho$ is the radius of the lower blue circle.

> **Fubini's Theorem in Spherical Coordinates:** Suppose R is the solid region of points with spherical coordinates (ρ, θ, ϕ) for which $\theta \in [\alpha, \beta]$, $\phi \in [\phi_1(\theta), \phi_2(\theta)]$, and $\rho \in [\rho_1(\theta, \phi), \rho_2(\theta, \phi)]$. If the functions $\phi_1, \phi_2, \rho_2, \rho_2$ and f are continuous, the triple integral of f over R exists and
>
> $$\iiint_R f\, dV = \int_\alpha^\beta \int_{\phi_1(\theta)}^{\phi_2(\theta)} \int_{\rho_1(\theta,\phi)}^{\rho_2(\theta,\phi)} f(\rho, \theta, \phi)\, \rho^2 \sin(\phi)\, d\rho\, d\phi\, d\theta.$$

Earlier in this section, we imagined the earth as a sphere of radius ρ that spins about the z-axis. That idea might help you develop an intuitive understanding of the role that $\sin\phi$ plays in the volume element. Points on the equator have $\phi = \pi/2$, and a change in longitude of $\Delta\theta$ corresponds to a circular arc of length $\rho\Delta\theta$. Points near the north pole lie on a circle of radius $\rho\sin\phi$ about the earth's axis, so the same change in longitude corresponds to a circular arc of length $\rho\sin\phi\Delta\theta$ (see Figures 6.13 and 6.14). With this in mind you can think of the volume element as a product of three lengths:

$$dV = \underbrace{(\rho\, d\phi)\, (\rho\sin(\phi)\, d\theta)}_{\substack{\text{These two lengths correspond} \\ \text{to the sides of a "rectangle" on} \\ \text{the surface of a sphere.}}} \underbrace{(d\rho)}_{\substack{\text{This length gives the "rectan-} \\ \text{gle" some "thickness," making} \\ \text{it into a spherical "box."}}}$$

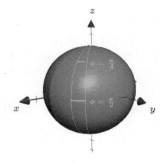

Figure 6.14: The value of ϕ affects the length of a circular arc about the z-axis. Such arcs are longest when $\phi = \pi/2$, near the "equator," and are shorter when $\phi \approx 0$ or $\phi \approx \pi$, near north and south "poles."

Integration in spherical coordinates

Example 6.11. Calculate $\iiint_S xy\, dV$ when S is the set all points with spherical coordinates (ρ, θ, ϕ) where $\rho \in [1, 2]$, $\theta \in [0, \pi/4]$ and $\phi \in [\pi/6, \pi/4]$.

Solution: We begin by rewriting the triple integral as an iterated integral Fubini's Theorem.

$$\iiint_S xy\ dV = \int_{\pi/6}^{\pi/4}\int_0^{\pi/4}\int_1^2 \Big(\rho\sin\phi\cos\theta\Big)\Big(\rho\sin\phi\sin\theta\Big)\ \rho^2\sin\phi\ d\rho\,d\theta\,d\phi$$

$$= \int_{\pi/6}^{\pi/4}\int_0^{\pi/4}\left[\frac{1}{5}\rho^5\sin^3\phi\cos\theta\sin\theta\right]_{\rho=1}^{\rho=2} d\theta\,d\phi$$

$$= \int_{\pi/6}^{\pi/4}\int_0^{\pi/4}\frac{31}{5}\sin^3\phi\cos\theta\sin\theta\ d\theta\,d\phi$$

$$= \int_{\pi/6}^{\pi/4}\left[\frac{31}{10}\sin^3\phi\sin^2\theta\right]_{\theta=0}^{\theta=\pi/4} d\phi = \int_{\pi/6}^{\pi/4}\frac{31}{20}\sin^3\phi\ d\phi.$$

As in Chapter 6, we integrate $\sin^3\phi$ by using the Pythagorean Identity to rewrite it as $(1-\cos^2\phi)\sin\phi$, after which the substitution $u=\cos\phi$, $du=-\sin(\phi)\,d\phi$ brings us to the final answer of

$$-\frac{31}{20}\cos\phi+\frac{31}{60}\cos^3\phi\bigg]_{\phi=\pi/6}^{\phi=\pi/4} = \frac{93}{160}\sqrt{3}-\frac{31}{48}\sqrt{2}. \qquad\blacksquare$$

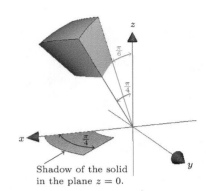

Figure 6.15: The spherical box from Example 6.11.

Calculating mass

Example 6.12. Suppose S is the bounded region above the third quadrant of the xy-plane that lies between the origin and the surface $\rho = 1+\cos\phi$ (see Figure 6.16). If length is measure in mm, determine the volume of S.

Solution: Since this region sits above the third quadrant of the xy-plane, we know that $\theta\in[\pi/2,\pi]$ and $\phi\in[0,\pi/2]$. This allows us to use using Fubini's Theorem to write the volume integral as an iterated integral:

$$\iiint_S 1\ dV = \int_{\pi/2}^{\pi}\int_0^{\pi/2}\int_0^{1+\cos\phi} 1\ \rho^2\sin\phi\ d\rho\,d\phi\,d\theta$$

$$= \int_{\pi/2}^{\pi}\int_0^{\pi/2}\frac{1}{3}(1+\cos\phi)^3\sin\phi\ d\phi\,d\theta = \int_{\pi/2}^{\pi}\frac{15}{12}\ d\theta = \frac{15\pi}{24}.$$

Because length is measured in mm, this volume has units of mm^3. $\qquad\blacksquare$

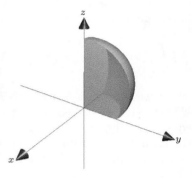

Figure 6.16: The region in Example 6.12

Here use the substitution $u = 1+\cos\phi$, $du = -\sin(\phi)\,d\phi$.

Calculating mass

Example 6.13. Suppose S is the solid region between the surfaces $\rho_1(\theta,\phi) = 3-\sin 6\theta\sin 5\phi$ and $\rho_2(\theta,\phi) = 4+\sin 6\theta\sin 5\phi$ (see Figure 6.17). If the mass density in S is $3\rho^{-2}$ g/cm^3 and length is measured in cm, determine the mass in S.

Solution: Using Fubini's Theorem, we write the triple integral as

$$\iiint_S (\text{mass density})\ dV = \int_0^{\pi}\int_0^{2\pi}\int_{\rho_1(\theta,\phi)}^{\rho_2(\theta,\phi)}\left(\frac{3}{\rho^2}\right)\rho^2\sin\phi\ d\rho\,d\theta\,d\phi$$

$$= \int_0^{\pi}\int_0^{2\pi} 3\big(\rho_2(\theta,\phi)-\rho_1(\theta,\phi)\big)\ \sin\phi\ d\theta\,d\phi$$

After substituting our formulas for $\rho_1(\theta,\phi)$ and $\rho_2(\theta,\phi)$ into this integral, it becomes

$$\int_0^{\pi}\int_0^{2\pi} (3+6\sin 6\theta\sin 5\phi)\sin\phi\ d\theta\,d\phi = \int_0^{\pi}\left[3\theta\sin\phi-\cos 6\theta\sin 5\phi\sin\phi\right]_{\theta=0}^{\theta=2\pi} d\phi$$

$$= \int_0^{\pi} 6\pi\sin(\phi)\ d\phi = 12\pi\ \text{g}. \qquad\blacksquare$$

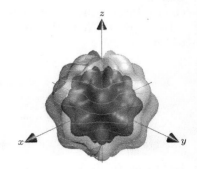

Figure 6.17: Nested "bumpy spheres" as in Example 6.13

Calculating the z-coordinate of a center of mass

Example 6.14. Suppose S is the solid region described in Example 6.11, where all lengths are measured in meters, and that it has a uniform mass density of $2\frac{\text{kg}}{\text{m}^3}$. Calculate the z-coordinate of the region's center of mass.

Answer: $\overline{z} = \frac{45}{112}\left(\sqrt{3} + \sqrt{2}\right)$.   ■

Solution On-line

✦ Common Difficulties

Students sometimes mistake the meaning of ϕ by thinking of it as an angle of elevation off of the xy-plane. In the same way that θ is an angle of separation away from $\mathbf{i}$, the angle ϕ measures the separation from $\mathbf{k}$.

Additionally, it's worth mentioning that there is not a convention across disciplines about whether to use θ or ϕ as the polar angle in the xy-plane (the other denotes the angle of inclination from the z-axis). We have used the mathematicians' convention, which is often employed by graphing calculators and symbolic manipulators.

> **You should know**
>
> - the term *coordinate surface;*
> - that $dV = r\, dr\, d\theta\, dz$ in cylindrical coordinates;
> - that $dV = \rho^2 \sin(\phi)\, d\rho\, d\theta\, d\phi$ in spherical coordinates.

> **You should be able to**
>
> - convert between Cartesian, cylindrical, and spherical coordinates;
> - calculate triple integrals in cylindrical and spherical coordinates.

✦ 14.6 Skill Exercises

1. Determine the cylindrical coordinates for each of the following points, given in Cartesian coordinates: (a) $P = (1, \sqrt{3}, 7)$, (b) $P = (-\sqrt{3}, 1, -4)$, (c) $P = (3, 4, -5)$, (d) $P = (-1, -2, 3)$.

2. Determine the spherical coordinates for each of the following points, given in Cartesian coordinates: (a) $P = (1, \sqrt{3}, 7)$, (b) $P = (-\sqrt{3}, 1, -4)$, (c) $P = (3, 4, -5)$, (d) $P = (-1, -2, 3)$.

3. Determine the spherical coordinates for each of the following points, given in cylindrical coordinates: (a) $P = (4, \pi/6, -4)$, (b) $P = (1/2, 5\pi/3, \sqrt{3}/2)$, (c) $P = (3, 0, 0)$, (d) $P = (0, 0, 1)$.

4. Determine how many different points are listed below, where S denotes spherical coordinates, C denotes cylindrical coordinates, and R denotes rectangular (Cartesian) coordinates.

   (a) $R : (12,\ 5,\ \sqrt{27})$ (b) $C : (11.9,\ \pi/7,\ \sqrt{27})$ (c) $S : (13,\ \pi/7,\ \pi/2.709)$

   (d) $R : (-5,\ 12,\ \sqrt{27})$ (e) $C : (13,\ \pi/8,\ \sqrt{27})$ (f) $S : (13,\ -\pi/8,\ \pi/3)$

Use equations (6.1)–(6.3) to determine what kind of surface is described by the cylindrical equations in exercises #5–16.

5. $2z^2 = 3 - 5r^2$

9. $8z = 7r$

13. $\cos\theta + \sin\theta = 2/r$

6. $-8z^2 = 5 - 9r^2$

10. $z = 5$

14. $\cos\theta + 3\sin\theta = 8/r$

7. $4z = 17r^2$

11. $r = 20$

15. $r\cos(\theta - \frac{\pi}{6}) = -5$

8. $-3z = 11r^2$

12. $-2z = 3r$

16. $r\cos(\theta - \frac{\pi}{3}) + z = 15$

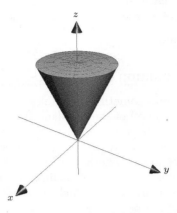

Use equations (6.4)–(6.6) to determine what kind of surface is described by the spherical equations In #17–20.

17. $\rho\sin\phi = 8$

19. $3\rho\tan\phi\sin\theta = 5\sec(\phi) - \rho$

18. $\rho\cos\left(\theta - \frac{\pi}{4}\right) = 9\csc(\phi)$

20. $\rho^2(1 - \cos\phi) = 5$

21. Write the equation for the sphere $\rho = 4$ in cylindrical coordinates.

22. Write the equation for the cylinder $r = 12$ in spherical coordinates.

23. Suppose S is the bounded region between the plane $z = 5$ and a cone, as shown in Figure 6.18. If the point $(0, 2, 5)$ is on the edge where the cone meets the flat top of S, write $\iiint_S f\, dV$ as an iterated integral in (a) cylindrical coordinates, (b) spherical coordinates.

Figure 6.18: The solid $\mathcal{S}$ in exercise #23. The point $(0, 2, 5)$ is on the edge where the flat top meets the conical side.

24. Suppose S is the bounded region between a sphere and a cone, as shown in Figure 6.19. If the point $(1, 2, 4)$ is on the edge where the cone meets the sphere, write $\iiint_S f\, dV$ as an iterated integral in (a) cylindrical coordinates, (b) spherical coordinates.

Use cylindrical coordinates to calculate the triple integrals in #25–30.

25. Suppose S is the cylinder of points (x, y, z) for which $x^2 + y^2 \le 4$ and $0 \le z \le 5$. Calculate $\iiint_S z^2 \sqrt{x^2 + y^2}\, dV$.

26. Suppose S is the solid of points (x, y, z) for which $x^2 + y^2 \le 3$ and $0 \le z \le y^2$. Calculate $\iiint_S (1 + z)\, dV$.

27. Suppose R is the set of points (x, y) in the first quadrant for which $x^2 + y^2 \le 3$, and S is the solid over R for which and $0 \le z \le x$. Calculate $\iiint_S yz^2\, dV$.

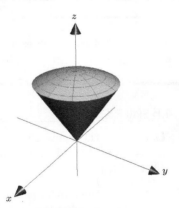

28. Suppose R is the set of points (x, y) in the first quadrant bounded by the curves $y = x$, $y = 0$, and $x^2 + y^2 \le 3$; and S is the solid over R in which $0 \le z \le x + y$. Calculate $\iiint_S (1 + z)\, dV$.

Figure 6.19: The solid $\mathcal{S}$ in exercise #24. The point $(1, 2, 4)$ is on the edge where the conical side meets the spherical cap.

29. Suppose R is the region in the first and second quadrants of the $z = 0$ plane that lies between the spirals $r = 2\theta$ and $r = 5\theta$, and S is the solid over R for which $\cos(\theta) \le z \le 16 + r^2$. Calculate $\iiint_S 8z\, dV$.

30. Suppose R is the planar region that lies between the cardioid $r = 1 + \cos(\theta)$ and the circle $r = 3$ when $\frac{\pi}{4} \le \theta \le \frac{\pi}{2}$, and S is the solid over R for which $-\theta \le z \le \theta + r$. Calculate $\iiint_S \theta z\, dV$.

Use spherical coordinates to calculate the triple integrals in #31–36.

31. Suppose S is the bounded region between the cone $\phi = \frac{\pi}{6}$ and the sphere $\rho = 3$. There are two such regions, in this case, S is the region containing the point $(x, y, z) = (0, 0, -2)$. Determine $\iiint_S x\, dV$.

32. Suppose S is the bounded region in the first octant for which $1 \le x^2 + y^2 + z^2 \le 4$. Calculate $\iiint_S (x^2 + y^2)\, dV$.

33. Suppose S is the bounded region in the first octant for which $x^2 + y^2 + z^2 \leq 2$. Calculate $\iiint_S xyz \, dV$.

34. Suppose S is the bounded region in the first octant for which $1 \leq \rho \leq 2 + \cos\phi$. Calculate $\iiint_S \frac{1}{x^2 + y^2 + z^2} \, dV$.

35. Suppose S is the bounded region between the sphere $x^2 + y^2 + z^2 = 9$ and the surface $\rho = 1 + 0.3 \sin 8\theta$. Determine $\iiint_S 5 \, dV$.

36. Suppose S is the bounded region between the surfaces $\rho = 1 + 0.3 \sin(8\theta)\sin(\phi)$ and $\rho = 4 + \sin(6\theta)\sin(2\phi)$. Determine $\iiint_S \frac{1}{\sqrt{x^2 + y^2 + z^2}} \, dV$.

In #37–42 determine the triple integral using cylindrical or spherical coordinates.

37. $\iiint_S z \, dV$; S is the bounded region enclosed by the cylinder $x^2 + y^2 = 1$, the plane $z = 5$, and the paraboloid $z = 1 - x^2 - y^2$.

38. $\iiint_S x^2 \, dV$; S is the region in which $z^2 \geq x^2 + y^2$ and $x^2 + y^2 + z^2 \leq 4$.

39. $\iiint_S (y^3 + xy^2)x^{-3}) \, dV$; S is the bounded region in the first octant in which $x \geq 1$ and $x^2 + y^2 + z^2 \leq 4$.

40. $\iiint_S y \, dV$; S is the bounded region in the first octant bounded by the cylinder $\sqrt{x^2 + y^2} + x = x^2 + y^2$ and the plane $z + x - y = 3$.

41. $\iiint_S 7z \, dV$; S is the solid region enclosed by $x^2 + y^2 + z^2 - z = 0$.

42. $\iiint_S x \, dV$; S is the solid region in the first octant below the paraboloid $z = 4 - x^2 - y^2$ and above the paraboloid $z = 0.1x^2 + 0.1y^2$.

❖ 14.6 Concept and Application Exercises

43. Suppose S is the test tube-shaped volume that sits above $z = 0.1(x^2 + y^2)^2$ and below $z = 10$, where all lengths are measured in centimeters. If the number density of a particulate in the tube is described by $\rho(x,y,z) = 10^9(1 - 0.1z)\ \frac{\text{particulates}}{\text{cm}^3}$, use an integral in cylindrical coordinates to determine the total number of particulates in the tube.

| Chemistry |

44. Suppose S is the solid region that's above the sphere $x^2 + y^2 + z^2 = 1$ and below the paraboloid $z = 4 - x^2 - y^2$, where all lengths are measured in millimeters. If thermal energy in S has a density of $1 + 0.1z^2\ \frac{\text{J}}{\text{mm}^3}$ use an integral in cylindrical coordinates to determine the total thermal energy in S.

| Physics |

Exercises 45–46 ask you about the *girth* of a surface, by which we mean the circumference of a cross-section at constant z.

| Mechanical Engineering |

45. What's the maximum girth of the surface described by the spherical equation $\rho = \phi^2$.

46. Suppose S is the surface described by $\rho = \phi^n$.

   (a) Show that the maximum girth of S occurs when $\phi = -\frac{1}{n}\tan(\phi)$, where $0 < \phi < \pi$.

   (b) Use the equation from part (a) to derive a formula for $\frac{d\phi}{dn}$ (you'll have to use both the Product Rule and Chain Rule on the right-hand side, since ϕ depends on n).

   (c) Use your formula from part (b) to verify that $\frac{d\phi}{dn} > 0$, and interpret this fact in terms of the surface, S.

Exercises #47–50 ask you to calculate the volume of a region.

Volume

47. Suppose that S is the region inside the sphere $\rho = 3$ and below the cone $\phi = \pi/4$. Determine the volume of S by calculating $\iiint_S 1 \, dV$.

48. Suppose that S is the region between the spheres $\rho = 3$ and $\rho = 10$ that lies above the cone $\phi = \pi/4$ (such points satisfy $z^2 \geq x^2 + y^2$). Determine the volume of S by calculating $\iiint_S 1 \, dV$.

49. Suppose we drill through a spherical ball of material (e.g., wood) with a standard drill. The result is a "bead" that can be strung on a thread. If the diameter of the ball is 1 cm and the drill bit has a diameter of 1 mm, determine the volume of the bead.

50. Suppose the ice cream in a cylindrical tub is 8 inches tall and has a diameter of 10 inches. A scoop is taken from the top of the tub, leaving a gap in the tub of ice cream that's $1/2$ inch deep. If the scooper has a spherical shape with a radius of 1 inch, what volume of ice cream remains in the tub?

Exercises #51–56 ask you to determine the mass of an object.

Mass Density

51. Suppose that length is measured in cm, and S is the cone $8 \geq z^2 \geq x^2 + y^2$ in which the density is $(10 - z)$ g/cm^3. Determine the mass of S.

52. Suppose length is measured in cm, and S is the set of points (ρ, θ, ϕ) for which $1 + 8\sin\phi \geq \rho \geq 5$. If the density at (ρ, θ, ϕ) is ρ^{-1} g/cm^3, determine the mass of S. (Hint: Figure 6.20 shows both the sphere $\rho = 5$ (checkered) and the "apple-shaped" surface $\rho = 1 + 8\sin\phi$. The intersection of the surfaces will determine the bounds in your iterated integral.)

Figure 6.20: The solid for #52.

53. Suppose R is the region of the 1st quadrant between the curve $y = x^2$ and the x-axis, $0 \leq x \leq 2$, where all distances are measured in millimeters; and S is the solid that's generated by revolving R about the x-axis. If the mass density at (x, y, z) is $3 - x \; \frac{\text{g}}{\text{mm}^3}$, use an integral in cylindrical coordinates to determine the mass of S. (Hint: pivot the solid so that its axis of symmetry is the z-axis.)

54. Suppose S is the bounded region between the sphere $\rho = 3$ and the paraboloid $z = -4 + x^2 + y^2$, as shown in Figure 6.21. If S has a uniform density of $2\frac{\text{g}}{\text{cm}^3}$ (and length is measured in cm) determine the mass of S.

55. Suppose S is the bounded region between the paraboloid $z = 4x^2 + y^2$ and the plane $z = 9$, and S has a uniform mass density of 11 g/mm^3.

Figure 6.21: The solid for #54.

    (a) Verify that the mass of S is $\iiint_S 11 \, dV = \iint_R \int_{4x^2+y^2}^{9} 11 \, dz \, dA$, where R is the region bounded by the ellipse $4x^2 + y^2 = 9$.

    (b) You know that $dA = dx \, dy$ in Cartesian coordinates. If $u = 2x$, write dA in terms of du and dy, and write the boundary of R in terms of u and y.

    (c) Calculate the mass of S.

56. Suppose S is the bounded region between the paraboloid $z = x^2 + 9y^2$ and the plane $z = 16$. Use the methods of #55 to determine the mass of S when its mass density is $10 + z$ g/mm^3.

In #57–62 determine the Cartesian coordinates of the object's center of mass. All lengths are measured in centimeters.

Center of Mass

57. Suppose S is the cone in #51.

58. Suppose S is the solid in #54.

59. Suppose R is the region of the xz-plane between the curve $z = x^{1/3}$ and the z-axis where $0 \leq z \leq 2$; and S is the solid that's generated by revolving R about the z-axis in which the mass density is $(3 - z) \, \frac{\text{g}}{\text{cm}^3}$.

60. Suppose R is the region in the xz-plane between the curve $z = 1/(x - 1)$ and the z-axis, $1 \leq z \leq 4$; and S is the solid that's generated by revolving R about the z-axis. The mass density in S is $(1 + x^2) \, \frac{\text{g}}{\text{cm}^3}$.

61. Suppose R is the region in the xy-plane bounded by the cardioid $r = 1 + \cos \theta$, and S is the solid that lies over R and extends between the planes $z = 3$ and $z = x + y$. The mass density in S is $(2 + z) \, \text{g/cm}^3$

62. Suppose S is the region enclosed by $\rho = 2 + \sin(4\theta) \sin(2\phi)$, and its mass density is $(4 + x) \, \text{g/cm}^3$.

In #63–66 determine the solid's moment of inertia with respect to the z-axis. (See equation (5.4).)

Moment of Inertia

63. Suppose S is the cone in # 51.

64. Suppose S is the solid in # 54.

65. Suppose that S is the solid sphere $x^2 + y^2 + z^2 \leq 1$ with a uniform density of $1 \frac{\text{kg}}{\text{m}^3}$, where length is measured in meters.

66. Suppose S is the region enclosed by the surface $0 \leq \rho \leq 2 + \cos(\phi) \sin(\theta)$, length is measured in meters, and S has a uniform mass density $0.5 \, \text{kg/m}^3$.

14.7   Change of Variables

The rectangle in Figure 7.1 (shown twice) has a 1:2 aspect ratio. So if we measure length in centimeters we find that its area is $1 \times 2 = 2$ cm^2; but if we measure length in millimeters, we calculate the area of the same rectangle as $10 \times 20 = 200$ mm^2. Which of these numbers, 2 or 200, is right? Both of them. While there is *a* rectangle, the way we quantify its area depends on how we measure.

> **Key Idea(s):** *You've already seen that certain integral calculations can be simplified by changing into the polar, cylindrical, or spherical coordinate system. Here we extend that technique to other frames of reference, and develop a general theory that tells us how such changes affect our calculation of area and volume.*
>
> *Changing variables can be thought of a changing the way we measure length—e.g., from meters to centimeters, in which case we need to include a scaling factor of m/cm in order to avoid changing our quantification of area.*

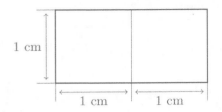 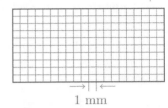

Figure 7.1: The same rectangle, measured differently (e.g., inches or feet, centimeters or meters)

    In this section we introduce a way to simplify the calculation of some integrals by, in essence, changing the way we measure—both the length scale and the orientation of our coordinate system; our goal is to do it without affecting the numerical value of the integrals. The basic ideas and techniques will be established for double integrals, and triple integrals will be addressed at the end of the section.

✥ Changing Variables in Double Integrals

When you learned the substitution technique of integration in Chapter 6, you saw that the substitution $u = 10x$ converts

$$\int_0^9 \sin(10x)\,dx \quad \text{into} \quad \int_0^{90} \sin(u)\,\frac{1}{10}du.$$

You can think of u as measuring length in mm while x measures in cm, so $u = 10$ when $x = 1$, and increasing u by 1 (i.e., $du = 1$) is the same as increasing x by 0.1 (i.e., $dx = {}^1\!/{}_{10}$). This 10:1 ratio in the length scales is stated succinctly by the equation $dx = ({}^1\!/{}_{10})du$. In the following discussion, you'll see a similar relationship between area elements when we change variables in double integrals.

> Note that the units associated with the terms in $dx = ({}^1\!/{}_{10})du$ are
>
> $$\text{cm} = \left(\frac{\text{cm}}{\text{mm}}\right)\text{mm}.$$

▷ Changing Length Scale

Said simply, in order to maintain the value of a double integral when we change the way we measure length, we have to include a factor that scales up (or down) the area element accordingly. This becomes apparent when we include units in our calculations. For example, if f is a function with units of coulombs per square centimeter, and we change our measurement of length from centimeters to inches. Based on the units involved, we see that

$$\underbrace{\iint_R f\,dA_{\text{cm}}}_{\text{units of C}} \quad \text{is not the same as} \quad \underbrace{\iint_R f\,dA_{\text{in}}}_{\text{units of C-in}^2/\text{cm}^2}.$$

> The numbers that you get from these integrals differ by a factor of ${}^4\!/{}_{25}$.

Changing length scales by changing variables

Example 7.1. Suppose R is the rectangle defined by $0 \le x \le \pi/3$ and $0 \le y \le \pi/8$. Calculate $\iint_R \sin(3x)\cos(4y)\,dA$ by making the substitutions $u = 3x$ and $v = 4y$.

Solution: Begin by writing the double integral as an iterated integral:

$$\iint_R \sin(3x)\cos(4y)\,dA = \int_0^{\pi/3}\int_0^{\pi/8} \sin(3x)\cos(4y)\,dy\,dx.$$

Notice that the bounds of integration reflect the size of the rectangle, which has an area of $\left(\frac{\pi}{8}\right)\times\left(\frac{\pi}{3}\right)=\frac{\pi^2}{24}$.

We're instructed to make the substitutions $u=3x$ and $v=4y$, so $du=3\,dx$ and $dv=4\,dy$. Since $dA=dx\,dy$, it follows that

$$\iint_R \sin(3x)\cos(4y)\,dA = \int_0^{\pi}\int_0^{\pi/2} \sin(u)\cos(v)\,\frac{dv}{4}\,\frac{du}{3}. \qquad (7.1)$$

The new bounds of integration reflect the possible values of u and v. Based on these bounds on u and v, the area of the rectangle appears to be $\pi\times\frac{\pi}{2}=\frac{\pi^2}{2}$, which is *12 times larger than the actual area of R!* The factor of $1/12$ in the differentials corrects for the discrepancy.

We finish by calculating the iterated integral on the right-hand side of equation (7.1). Integrating first with respect to v yields

$$\frac{1}{12}\int_0^{\pi}\Big[\sin(u)\sin(v)\Big]_{v=0}^{v=\pi/2}\,du = \frac{1}{12}\int_0^{\pi}\sin(u)\,du = \frac{1}{6}. \qquad \blacksquare$$

variable:	x	u
differential:	dx	$du=3\,dx$
range:	$[0,\pi/3]$	$[0,\pi]$

variable:	y	v
differential:	dy	$dv=4\,dy$
range:	$[0,\pi/8]$	$[0,\pi/2]$

Changing length scales by changing variables

Example 7.2. Suppose R is the rectangle defined by $0\le x\le 5$ and $0\le y\le 2$. Calculate $\iint_R e^{6x-9y}\,dA$ by making the substitutions $u=6x$ and $v=9y$.

Answer: $\iint_R e^{6x-9y}\,dA = \frac{1}{54}(e^{30}-1)(1-e^{-18})$. $\qquad \blacksquare$

Solution On-line

▷ Changing the Frame of Reference

The substitutions in Examples 7.1 and 7.2 affected only the length scale, but when we're working in the plane, changing variables might also involve a rotation of our reference frame. To understand the effect of such a change, the relationship between coordinates and vectors has to be very clear, so let's take a moment to review.

In the familiar Cartesian coordinate system, the coordinates of the point P tell you how to get there from the origin using the displacement vectors $\mathbf{i}$ and $\mathbf{j}$. For example, by saying that the coordinates of P are $(5,14)$, we mean that the position vector $\mathbf{r}=5\mathbf{i}+14\mathbf{j}$ points from the origin to P.

If we use vectors other than $\mathbf{i}$ and $\mathbf{j}$ as the basis of our coordinate notation, the coordinates of P will be different. For example, when we agree to build vectors with $\mathbf{u}=\langle 2,3\rangle$ and $\mathbf{v}=\langle -1.5,1\rangle$ instead of $\mathbf{i}$ and $\mathbf{j}$, the point P that we discussed a moment ago has coordinates $(4,2)$ because

$$4\mathbf{u}+2\mathbf{v} = 4\begin{bmatrix}2\\3\end{bmatrix}+2\begin{bmatrix}-1.5\\1\end{bmatrix}=\begin{bmatrix}5\\14\end{bmatrix}=5\mathbf{i}+14\mathbf{j}\ =\mathbf{r},$$

$\underbrace{\qquad\qquad\qquad\qquad\qquad\qquad\qquad\qquad\qquad\qquad}$

$4\mathbf{u}+2\mathbf{v}$ and $5\mathbf{i}+14\mathbf{j}$ are different ways of building the same position vector.

as seen in Figure 7.2. More generally, when we build vectors by scaling and adding $\mathbf{u}$ and $\mathbf{v}$ instead of $\mathbf{i}$ and $\mathbf{j}$, the position vector $\mathbf{r}=u\mathbf{u}+v\mathbf{v}$ is said to locate the point with coordinates (u,v). The vectors $\mathbf{u}$ and $\mathbf{v}$ *can* have the same length, but they don't have to.

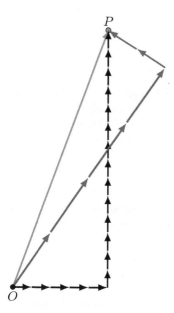

Figure 7.2: The position vector $\mathbf{OP}$ can be written as $5\mathbf{i}+14\mathbf{j}$ or as $4\mathbf{u}+2\mathbf{v}$

Changing reference frame

Example 7.3. Suppose R is the rectangle defined by the position vectors $\mathbf{u} = \langle 2, 3 \rangle$ and $\mathbf{v} = \langle -1.5, 1 \rangle$. Calculate $\iint_R (x + y)\, dA$.

Solution: The position vectors that *define* R seem like natural candidates for a frame of reference in which to perform this calculation. In order to use it, we have to (1) rewrite the integrand in terms of u and v, and (2) understand how the area element is affected by the change. We begin with the integrand.

Step 1 (rewriting the integrand): In the discussion preceding this example, we said that a point has coordinates (u, v) when its position vector is

$$u\mathbf{u} + v\mathbf{v} = u \begin{bmatrix} 2 \\ 3 \end{bmatrix} + v \begin{bmatrix} -1.5 \\ 1 \end{bmatrix} = \begin{bmatrix} 2u - 1.5v \\ 3u + v \end{bmatrix} = (2u - 1.5v)\mathbf{i} + (3u + v)\mathbf{j}.$$

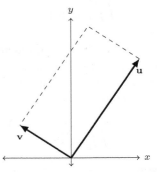

Figure 7.3: The rectangle R for Example 7.3

So the position vector $u\mathbf{u} + v\mathbf{v}$ locates the point with $x = 2u - 1.5v$ and $y = 3u + v$. This allows us to rewrite the integrand as

$$x + y = 2u - \frac{3}{2}v + 3u + v = 5u - \frac{1}{2}v.$$

Step 2 (relating dA to $du\, dv$): We're accustomed to thinking of dA as the product $dx\, dy$, but in order to use our new frame of reference we need to write it in terms of du and dv. This task was easy in Example 7.1 because x and u were related simply by a scale factor, as were y and v. Although the relationship among x, y, u and v is more complicated in this example, the underlying idea is the same, and in the work that follows you'll see that

$$dA = \frac{13}{2} du\, dv. \tag{7.2}$$

> The factor of 13/2 arises from the fact that $\mathbf{u}$ and $\mathbf{v}$ are not unit vectors.

In order to understand why equation (7.2) is true, we need to examine how small changes in u and v affect position. Suppose $\mathbf{r}_0 = u_0\mathbf{u} + v_0\mathbf{v}$ is the position vector for an arbitrary point. A small increase of du in the first component puts us at

$$(u_0 + du)\mathbf{u} + v_0\mathbf{v} = u_0\mathbf{u} + du\ \mathbf{u} + v_0\mathbf{v} = \underbrace{u_0\mathbf{u} + v_0\mathbf{v}}_{\mathbf{r}_0 +} + \underbrace{du\ \mathbf{u}}_{\text{(change in position)}}.$$

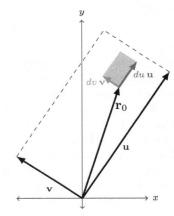

Figure 7.4: Small changes in u and v correspond to changes in x and y

Notice that the resulting change in position has a magnitude of $\|du\ \mathbf{u}\| = du\ \|\mathbf{u}\| = \sqrt{13}\, du$. Similarly, increasing the second component by dv results in a displacement of $\sqrt{13/4}\, dv$ because $\|\mathbf{v}\| = \sqrt{13/4}$ and

$$u_0\mathbf{u} + (v_0 + dv)\mathbf{v} = \underbrace{u_0\mathbf{u} + v_0\mathbf{v}}_{\mathbf{r}_0 +} + \underbrace{dv\ \mathbf{v}}_{\text{(change in position)}}.$$

Since $\mathbf{u}$ and $\mathbf{v}$ are orthogonal, we see that the small rectangle corresponding to these small changes (see Figure 7.4) has an area of

$$dA = \left(\sqrt{13}\, du \right) \left(\sqrt{\frac{13}{4}}\, dv \right) = \frac{13}{2} du\, dv.$$

Now since our rectangle reaches from $u = 0$ to $u = 1$ (i.e., exactly one of $\mathbf{u}$ stretches across the base), and from $v = 0$ to $v = 1$,

$$\iint_R (x + y)\, dA = \int_0^1 \int_0^1 \left(5u - \frac{1}{2}v \right) \frac{13}{2} du\, dv = \frac{117}{8}. \qquad \blacksquare$$

> The bounds of integration make it appear as though R has an area of $1 \times 1 = 1$, but its area in the xy-plane is $13/2$.

Changing reference frame

Example 7.4. Suppose R is the rectangle defined by the position vectors $\mathbf{u} = \langle 1, 7 \rangle$ and $\mathbf{v} = \langle -14, 2 \rangle$. Calculate $\iint_R y^2 \, dA$.

Answer: $\iint_R y^2 \, dA = {}^{7400}/_3$　　　　　　　　　　　　　　　　■

Using a non-orthogonal frame of reference

Example 7.5. Suppose R is the parallelogram with its lower-left corner at the point $(1, 1)$, and edges defined by $\mathbf{u} = \langle 1, 1 \rangle$ and $\mathbf{v} = \langle 1, 3 \rangle$. Determine $\iint_R (x^2 - y) \, dA$.

Solution: The basic calculation strategy remains the same, even though $\mathbf{u}$ and $\mathbf{v}$ are not orthogonal and the region is removed from the origin (see Figure 7.5). In the coordinate system defined by $\mathbf{u}$ and $\mathbf{v}$ we say that a point has coordinates (u, v) when its position vector is $u\mathbf{u} + v\mathbf{v}$. Since we know how to write $\mathbf{u}$ and $\mathbf{v}$ in terms of the standard xy-coordinate system, we see that

$$u\mathbf{u} + v\mathbf{v} = u \begin{bmatrix} 1 \\ 1 \end{bmatrix} + v \begin{bmatrix} 1 \\ 3 \end{bmatrix} = \begin{bmatrix} u + v \\ u + 3v \end{bmatrix},$$

which shows us that $x = u + v$ and $y = u + 3v$. This allows us to rewrite our integrand as $x^2 - y = (u + v)^2 - (u + 3v) = u^2 + 2uv + v^2 - u - 3v$.

Next we relate dA to the product $du \, dv$. As in Examples 7.3 and 7.4, increasing the value of u by du results in a displacement of $du \, \mathbf{u}$, and increasing the value of v by dv results in a displacement of $dv \, \mathbf{v}$; but *unlike* previous examples, the vectors $\mathbf{u}$ and $\mathbf{v}$ are not orthogonal. Rather, the vectors

$$du \, \mathbf{u} = \begin{bmatrix} du \\ du \end{bmatrix} \quad \text{and} \quad dv \, \mathbf{v} = \begin{bmatrix} dv \\ 3 \, dv \end{bmatrix}$$

define a parallelogram with an area of (use the cross product)

$$dA = |\, (du)(3dv) - (dv)(du) \,| = 2 \, du \, dv. \tag{7.3}$$

Lastly, we need to determine the appropriate bounds of integration in u and v, so look again to Figure 7.5. The position vector for P_1 is $\mathbf{u} = 1\mathbf{u} + 0\mathbf{v}$, and the position vector for P_2 is $2\mathbf{u} = 2\mathbf{u} + 0\mathbf{v}$, so we move across the base of the parallelogram as u increases from 1 to 2. The position vector for the point P_4 is $\mathbf{u} + \mathbf{v}$, so we move the length of the parallelogram as v increases from 0 to 1. Therefore,

$$\iint_R (x^2 - y) \, dA = \int_0^1 \int_1^2 (u^2 + 2uv + v^2 - u - 3v) \, 2 \, du \, dv = \frac{7}{3}. \qquad ■$$

Using a non-orthogonal frame of reference

Example 7.6. Suppose the lower-left corner of the parallelogram R is at the point $(0, 18)$, and edges are $\mathbf{u} = \langle 2, 1 \rangle$ and $\mathbf{v} = \langle 1, 5 \rangle$. Determine $\iint_R y \, dA$. *(Hint: the lower-left corner of R has a position vector of $-2\mathbf{u} + 4\mathbf{v}$.)*

Answer: $\iint_R y \, dA = 189$.　　　　　　　　　　　　　　　　■

▷ The Jacobian Matrix

When we are able to express x and y in terms of new coordinates, u and v, the Chain Rule tells us how small changes in u and v manifest as changes in x and y. For example, in Example 7.3 we saw

$$x = 2u - 1.5v \quad \Rightarrow \quad dx = \frac{\partial x}{\partial u} du + \frac{\partial x}{\partial v} dv = 2 \, du - 1.5 \, dv \tag{7.4}$$

Solution On-line

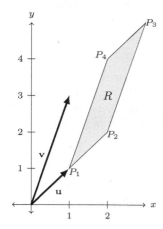

Figure 7.5:　The region R for Example 7.5.

> We use the cross product with the vectors
> $$\langle du, du, 0 \rangle$$
> $$\langle dv, 3 \, dv, 0 \rangle$$
> Note that du and dv *increased* the first and second coordinates, respectively, so they are both positive.

> The bounds of integration make it appear as though the rectangle R has an area of $(1 - 0) \times (3 - 2) = 1$, but its area in the xy-plane is 2.

Solution On-line

and

$$y = 3u + v \quad \Rightarrow \quad dy = \frac{\partial y}{\partial u} du + \frac{\partial y}{\partial v} dv = 3\ du + 1\ dv. \tag{7.5}$$

We can combine these equations into a single statement by using matrix notation to write them as

$$\begin{bmatrix} dx \\ dy \end{bmatrix} = \begin{bmatrix} 1 & -1.5 \\ 3 & 1 \end{bmatrix} \begin{bmatrix} du \\ dv \end{bmatrix}. \tag{7.6}$$

As you can see by comparing equations (7.4)–(7.6), the matrix in equation (7.6) has the form

$$\begin{bmatrix} x_u & x_v \\ y_u & y_v \end{bmatrix}.$$

Such a matrix is called a ***Jacobian matrix***, and its determinant, called simply the ***Jacobian***, plays an important role when changing variables in an integral: the ratio of $dx\,dy$ to $du\,dv$ is the magnitude of the Jacobian (see equations (7.2) and (7.3) for example). When we write the Jacobian as

$$\frac{\partial(x,y)}{\partial(u,v)} = \begin{vmatrix} x_u & x_v \\ y_u & y_v \end{vmatrix} = x_u y_v - y_u x_v,$$

its role in rescaling area can be expressed succinctly as

$$dA_{xy} = \overbrace{\left| \frac{\partial(x,y)}{\partial(u,v)} \right|}^{\text{magnitude of the Jacobian}} dA_{uv} \tag{7.7}$$

$\underbrace{\phantom{dA_{xy}}}_{dx\,dy \text{ in an iterated integral}}$ $\underbrace{\phantom{dA_{uv}}}_{du\,dv \text{ in an iterated integral}}$

> Thinking of x and y as functions of u and v, as in equations (7.4) and (7.5), the Jacobian matrix has the form
> $$\begin{bmatrix} -\!\!-\nabla x-\!\!- \\ -\!\!-\nabla y-\!\!- \end{bmatrix}.$$
> That is, the rows of the Jacobian matrix are the gradients of $x(u,v)$ and $y(u,v)$.

> This notation for the Jacobian indicates that the variables in the numerator (x and y) are differentiated with respect to those in the denominator (u and v).

> Compare with equations (7.2) and (7.3).

The Jacobian for Polar Coordinates

Example 7.7. Use the Jacobian to determine the relationship between dA_{xy} and $dA_{r\theta}$ when $x = r\cos\theta$ and $y = r\sin\theta$.

Solution: In this case r and θ are playing the roles of u and v, so the Jacobian matrix has the form

$$\begin{bmatrix} x_r & x_\theta \\ y_r & y_\theta \end{bmatrix} = \begin{bmatrix} \cos\theta & -r\sin\theta \\ \sin\theta & r\cos\theta \end{bmatrix} \quad \Rightarrow \quad \left| \frac{\partial(x,y)}{\partial(r,\theta)} \right| = r.$$

This tells us that $dA_{xy} = r\,dA_{r\theta}$, which is why $dx\,dy$ becomes $r\ dr\ d\theta$ when we switch into the polar coordinate system to compute a double integral. ∎

> Note that this result agrees with the geometric derivation from Section 14.3.

Calculating the Jacobian

Example 7.8. Calculate (a) the Jacobian matrix from Example 7.4, and (b) the magnitude of the Jacobian.

Answer: (a) $J = \begin{bmatrix} 1 & -14 \\ 7 & 2 \end{bmatrix}$; (b) $\left| \frac{\partial(x,y)}{\partial(u,v)} \right| = 100$. ∎

Solution On-line

In Examples 7.3 and 7.4 the Jacobian was constant because x and y were linear functions of u and v, but equation (7.7) is true even when the Jacobian is non-constant. To state the fact in generality, we need to define some new terms.

In Example 7.5 you saw that the point (x,y) moves across all of R as (u,v) varied over the square $[1,2] \times [0,1]$ in the uv-plane (see Figure 7.6). More generally, suppose R is a region in the xy-plane, and x and y depend on u and v in such a way that the position vector $\mathbf{r} = \langle x(u,v), y(u,v) \rangle$ ranges over R as (u,v) varies across a

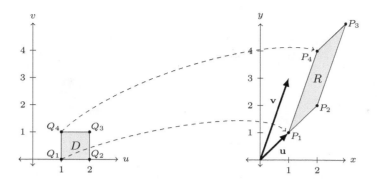

Figure 7.6: The region R is parameterized by u and v as in Example 7.5. The point Q_k is "mapped" to the point P_k with this parameterization.

region D in the uv-plane. Then we say that $\mathbf{r}(u, v)$ is a **parameterization** of R, and refer to D as the **parameter domain**. A parameterization is said to be **one-to-one** when each point in R corresponds to exactly one point in D, and **smooth** when x_u, x_v, y_u and x_v are continuous functions. With this language established, we can state the role of the Jacobian precisely.

Change of Variables in Double Integrals: Suppose f is a continuous function on the region R, and $\mathbf{r}(u, v) = \langle x(u, v), y(u, v) \rangle$ is a smooth, one-to-one parameterization of R over the parameter domain D. Then

$$\iint_R f(x, y) \, dA_{xy} = \iint_D f\big(x(u, v), y(u, v)\big) \left| \frac{\partial(x, y)}{\partial(u, v)} \right| \, dA_{uv}.$$

Compare with equation (7.7).

A non-constant Jacobian from a nonlinear parameterization

Example 7.9. Suppose R is the "curvy wedge" bounded by the hyperbolas $xy = 4$ and $xy = 5$, and the lines $y = 3x$ and $y = 0.5x$ (see Figure 7.7). Calculate $\iint_R x^2 \, dA$ using a change of variables.

Solution: We can describe the hyperbolic parts of the boundary as $v = 4$ and $v = 5$ by setting $v = xy$. Similarly, the lines that bound R are just $u = 0.5$ and $u = 3$ when $u = y/x$. So the parameter domain D is the rectangle $[0.5, 3] \times [4, 5]$.

In order to use the change of variables formula described above, we have to know x and y as functions of u and v. Note that

$$y = ux \;\; \Rightarrow \;\; v = x(ux) \;\; \Rightarrow \;\; \frac{v}{u} = x^2 \;\; \Rightarrow \;\; x = \sqrt{\frac{v}{u}}$$

in the first quadrant. Consequently,

$$y = ux = u\sqrt{\frac{v}{u}} = \sqrt{uv}$$

in the first quadrant. So the Jacobian matrix is

$$\begin{bmatrix} x_u & x_v \\ y_u & y_v \end{bmatrix} = \begin{bmatrix} -0.5v^{1/2}u^{-3/2} & 0.5v^{-1/2}u^{-1/2} \\ 0.5v^{1/2}u^{-1/2} & 0.5v^{-1/2}u^{1/2} \end{bmatrix}, \quad \text{and} \quad \left| \frac{\partial(x, y)}{\partial(u, v)} \right| = \frac{1}{2u}.$$

It follows that

$$\iint_R x^2 \, dx \, dy = \iint_D \left(\sqrt{\frac{v}{u}} \right)^2 \frac{1}{2u} \, du \, dv = \int_4^5 \int_{0.5}^3 \frac{v}{2u^2} \, du \, dv = \frac{15}{4}. \qquad \blacksquare$$

The variable u identifies a line through the origin by telling us its slope.

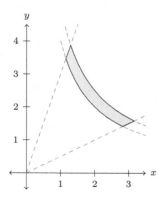

Figure 7.7: The region R in Example 7.9.

Using the Jacobian when integrating

Example 7.10. Suppose R is the wedge described in polar coordinates by $1 \leq r \leq 3$ and $\pi/6 \leq \theta \leq \pi/4$. Calculate $\iint_R (x - y)\, dA$ by using the change of variables $x = r\cos\theta$ and $y = r\sin\theta$.

Solution
On-line

Answer: $\iint_R (x - y)\, dA = \frac{26}{3}\left(\sqrt{2} - \frac{1+\sqrt{3}}{2}\right).$ ∎

❖ Change of Variables in Triple Integrals

The basic ideas, techniques, and notation of changing variables that we established for double integrals extend to triple integrals easily. Suppose the three-dimensional region R is parameterized by $\mathbf{r}(u, v, w) = \langle x(u, v, w),\ y(u, v, w),\ z(u, v, w)\rangle$.

$$\text{the Jacobian is}\quad \frac{\partial(x, y, z)}{\partial(u, v, w)} = \begin{vmatrix} x_u & x_v & x_w \\ y_u & y_v & y_w \\ z_u & z_v & z_w \end{vmatrix},$$

Thinking of x, y and z as functions of u, v and w, the Jacobian matrix has the form

$$\begin{bmatrix} \text{---}\nabla x\text{---} \\ \text{---}\nabla y\text{---} \\ \text{---}\nabla z\text{---} \end{bmatrix}.$$

That is, the rows of the Jacobian matrix are the gradients of the component functions.

and the analog of equation (7.7) is

$$\underbrace{dV_{xyz}}_{dx\ dy\ dz\ \text{in an iterated integral}} = \overbrace{\left|\frac{\partial(x, y, z)}{\partial(u, v, w)}\right|}^{\text{magnitude of the Jacobian}} \underbrace{dV_{uvw}}_{du\ dv\ dw\ \text{in an iterated integral}} \qquad (7.8)$$

> **Change of Variables in Triple Integrals:** Suppose f is a continuous function on the three-dimensional region R, and $\mathbf{r}(u, v, w) = \langle x(u, v, w), y(u, v, w), z(u, v, w)\rangle$ is a smooth, one-to-one parameterization of R over the parameter domain D. Then
> $$\iiint_R f(x, y, z)\, dV_{xyz} = \iiint_D f\big(x(u, v, z), y(u, v, z), z(u, v, w)\big) \left|\frac{\partial(x, y, z)}{\partial(u, v, w)}\right| dV_{uvw}.$$

Here we're using natural extensions of the terms *smooth* and *one-to-one* to this context.

Change of variables for a triple integral

Example 7.11. Calculate $\iiint_R 2z\, dV$ when R is the parallelepiped defined by the position vectors $\mathbf{u} = \langle 6, -3, 2\rangle$, $\mathbf{v} = \langle 4, 8, 0\rangle$ and $\mathbf{w} = \langle 3, 3, 10\rangle$.

Solution: We can establish a uvw-coordinate system with the given vectors by saying that a point has coordinates (u, v, w) if its position vector is

$$u\mathbf{u} + v\mathbf{v} + w\mathbf{w} = u\begin{bmatrix} 6 \\ -3 \\ 2 \end{bmatrix} + v\begin{bmatrix} 4 \\ 8 \\ 0 \end{bmatrix} + w\begin{bmatrix} 3 \\ 3 \\ 10 \end{bmatrix} = \begin{bmatrix} 6u + 4v + 3w \\ -3u + 8v + 3w \\ 2u + 10w \end{bmatrix},$$

which is to say that $x = 6u + 4v + 3w$, $y = -3u + 8v + 3w$, and $z = 2u + 10w$. The Jacobian matrix for this change of variables is

$$\begin{bmatrix} x_u & x_v & x_w \\ y_u & y_v & y_w \\ z_u & z_v & z_w \end{bmatrix} = \begin{bmatrix} 6 & 4 & 3 \\ -3 & 8 & 3 \\ 2 & 0 & 10 \end{bmatrix} \quad \Rightarrow \quad \left|\frac{\partial(x, y, z)}{\partial(u, v, w)}\right| = 576.$$

Now we can calculate

$$\iiint_R 2z\ dV = \int_0^1 \int_0^1 \int_0^1 2(2u + 10w)\ 576\ dw\ du\ dv = 6912.\quad ∎$$

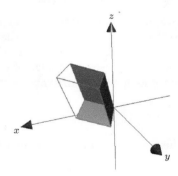

Figure 7.8: The region R in Example 7.11 as seen from above the first quadrant. The faces closer to the origin have been shaded to provide perspective.

Change of variables for a triple integral

Example 7.12. Calculate $\iiint_R 4x \, dV$ when R is the parallelepiped defined by the position vectors $\mathbf{u} = \langle 5, 0, 0 \rangle$, $\mathbf{v} = \langle -1, 3, 0 \rangle$ and $\mathbf{w} = \langle 4, 6, 1 \rangle$.

Answer: $\iiint_R 4x \, dV = 16$.   ∎

Solution On-line

Change of variables with a non-constant Jacobian

Example 7.13. Suppose R is the three-dimensional region parameterized by $\mathbf{r}(u, v, w) = \langle w(2 + 2u), w(1 + v), 6w \rangle$ when $0 \leq u \leq 1$, $0 \leq v \leq 2$ and $0 \leq w \leq 1$. (a) Describe the region R, and (b) determine the mass of R if its density varies according to $\rho(x, y, z) = 1 + x + y + z \, \frac{\text{g}}{\text{cm}^3}$, where x, y and z are measured in cm.

Solution: (a) Notice that each component of the parameterization has a factor of w. This allows us to write

$$\mathbf{r}(u, v, w) = w \begin{bmatrix} 2 + 2u \\ 1 + v \\ 6 \end{bmatrix},$$

from which we see that the variable w simply scales vector $\langle 2 + 2u, 1 + v, 6 \rangle$, pulling it to the origin when $w = 0$ and allowing its full extension when $w = 1$. Let's talk about what happens when $w = 1$. The x-coordinate of $\mathbf{r}(u, v, 1)$ is $2 + 2u$, which ranges over $[2, 4]$ as u varies over $[0, 1]$; for each of those x-coordinates, the y-coordinate of $\mathbf{r}(u, v, 1)$ is $1 + v$, which ranges over $[1, 3]$ as v varies across $[0, 2]$. So when $w = 1$ is fixed but u and v are allowed to vary, $\mathbf{r}(u, v, 1)$ parameterizes the square $[2, 4] \times [1, 3]$ in the plane $z = 6$. This square is shown as the top layer in Figure 7.9, along with squares that correspond to several smaller values of w. As w decreases from 1 to 0 the topmost square is pulled back to the origin, and sweeps out an oblique tetrahedron.

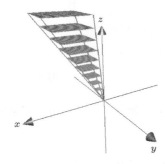

Figure 7.9: Several horizontal slices of the region R in Example 7.13, corresponding to various values of $w \in [0, 1]$.

(b) To calculate the mass of this solid we integrate $\rho(x, y, z)$ over R. When we use the uvw-coordinate system, this triple integral can be calculated with an iterated integral over a rectangular box, but to do it we need to know $\left| \frac{\partial(x,y,z)}{\partial(u,v,w)} \right|$, so we calculate the Jacobian matrix

$$\begin{bmatrix} x_u & x_v & x_w \\ y_u & y_v & y_w \\ z_u & z_v & z_w \end{bmatrix} = \begin{bmatrix} 2w & 0 & (2 + 2u) \\ 0 & w & 1 + v \\ 0 & 0 & 6 \end{bmatrix} \quad \Rightarrow \quad \frac{\partial(x, y, z)}{\partial(u, v, w)} = 12w^2.$$

Figure 7.10: The region R in Example 7.13 is an oblique tetrahedron.

Therefore,

$$\iiint_R \rho(x, y, z) \, dV_{xyz} = \iiint_R \overbrace{(1 + x + y + z)}^{\text{g/cm}^3} \overbrace{dV_{xyz}}^{\text{cm}^3}$$

$$= \iiint_D \Big(1 + (2w + 2wu) + (w + wv) + 6w \Big) 12w^2 \, dV_{uvw}$$

We can rewrite this triple integral as an iterated integral:

$$\int_0^2 \int_0^1 \int_0^1 \Big(12w^2 + (9 + 2u + v)12w^3 \Big) dw \, du \, dv = 74 \text{ g}.$$ ∎

You should know		

- the terms *parameterization*, *parameter domain*, *one-to-one*, *smooth*, *Jacobian matrix*, and *Jacobian*;
- why $dx \, dy = |\det(J)| \, du \, dv$ when x and y are functions of u and v

---

You should be able to

- calculate the Jacobian matrix for a change of variables;
- use the Jacobian to calculate a double integral by changing variables;

❖ 14.7 Skill Exercises

In #1–8 draw the region parameterized by $\mathbf{r}(u, v)$ when $u \in [0, 1]$ and $v \in [0, 1]$.

1. $\mathbf{r} = \langle 2u, 3 + v \rangle$

2. $\mathbf{r} = \langle u - 1, 5v \rangle$

3. $\mathbf{r} = \langle 2 - 7u, -3 + 10v \rangle$

4. $\mathbf{r} = \langle -4 + 2u, -9 + 6v \rangle$

5. $\mathbf{r} = \langle u + v, u - v \rangle$

6. $\mathbf{r} = \langle 2u - 3v, 4u + 5v \rangle$

7. $\mathbf{r} = \langle u \sin^2(0.5\pi v), u \cos^2(0.5\pi v) \rangle$

8. $\mathbf{r} = \langle e^v(1 + u), e^v(3 - u) \rangle$

In #9–14 determine (a) the Jacobian matrix, and (b) the value of $\left| \frac{\partial(x,y)}{\partial(u,v)} \right|$.

9. $x = 3u + 4v$, $y = 2u - 7v$

10. $x = 2u + v$, $y = 9u + 2v$

11. $x = 4u^2 v$, $y = v \sin(uv)$

12. $x = ve^{3u}$, $y = u \ln(v)$

13. $x = u^2 + v^2$, $y = u^2 - v^2$

14. $x = uv$, $y = u/v$

In #15–20 the region R is the trapezoid with one corner at the origin whose edges are the position vectors $\mathbf{u}$ and $\mathbf{v}$. (a) Draw R in the xy-plane, and (b) write $\iint_R f(x, y)\, dA$ as an iterated integral in u and v.

15. $\mathbf{u} = \langle 1, 4 \rangle$, $\mathbf{v} = \langle -8, 2 \rangle$; $f(x, y) = x + y^2$

16. $\mathbf{u} = \langle 2, -5 \rangle$, $\mathbf{v} = \langle 10, 4 \rangle$; $f(x, y) = xy$

17. $\mathbf{u} = \langle 1, 7 \rangle$, $\mathbf{v} = \langle 3, 7 \rangle$; $f(x, y) = xe^y$

18. $\mathbf{u} = \langle -1, -5 \rangle$, $\mathbf{v} = \langle -4, -1 \rangle$; $f(x, y) = \frac{x}{1-x-y}$

19. $\mathbf{u} = \langle 4, 1 \rangle$, $\mathbf{v} = \langle -1, -6 \rangle$; $f(x, y) = \frac{y+x}{37+x^2}$

20. $\mathbf{u} = \langle 3, 2 \rangle$, $\mathbf{v} = \langle -1, 9 \rangle$; $f(x, y) = \sin(2x + y)$

21. Suppose R is the triangular region in the xy-plane with corners at $P_1 = (6, 10)$, $P_2 = (13, 17)$ and $P_3 = (5, 13)$.

    (a) Show that $\mathbf{u} = \langle 7, 7 \rangle$ and $\mathbf{v} = \langle -1, 3 \rangle$ connect vertices of R.

    (b) Show that the uv-coordinates of P_1 are $(u, v) = (1, 1)$.

    (c) Write the equation of the line through P_2 and P_3 in terms of u and v.

    (d) Draw the parameter domain in the uv-plane, D.

    (e) Determine $\iint_R (x + y)\, dA$ by changing into variables u and v and calculating the double integral over D.

22. Suppose R is the triangular region in the xy-plane with corners at $P_1 = (9, 7)$, $P_2 = (11, 10)$ and $P_3 = (14, 8)$.

    (a) Calculate the displacement vectors $\mathbf{u}$, which connects P_1 to P_2, and $\mathbf{v}$, which connects P_1 to P_3.

    (b) Determine the uv-coordinates of P_1.

    (c) Write the equation of the line through P_2 and P_3 in terms of u and v.

    (d) Draw the parameter domain in the uv-plane, D.

    (e) Determine $\iint_R (x - y)\, dA$ by changing into variables u and v and calculating the double integral over D.

23. Use the steps from #22 to compute $\iint_R (x + 3y)\, dA$ when R is the triangular region in the xy-plane with corners at $P_1 = (-9, -2)$, $P_2 = (-10, 5)$ and $P_3 = (-1, 3)$.

24. Use the steps from #22 to determine $\iint_R (2x + y)\, dA$ when R is the triangular region in the xy-plane with corners at $P_1 = (-2, -10)$, $P_2 = (2, -6)$ and $P_3 = (-1, -13)$.

25. Suppose R is the trapezoidal region bounded by $x = 0$, $y = x + 1$, $y = x + 5$, and $y = 8$.

   (a) Draw the region R, and explain why $\iint_R \frac{x+y}{x-y}\, dA$ will be negative.

   (b) Based on the numerator and denominator of the integrand, set $u = x + y$ and $v = x - y$. Solve these equations for x and y in terms of u and v.

   (c) Write equations in terms of u and v that describe the linear boundary segments of R. Then draw those lines in the uv-plane.

   (d) Determine $\left| \frac{\partial(x,y)}{\partial(u,v)} \right|$.

   (e) Write $\iint_R \frac{x+y}{x-y}\, dA$ as an iterated integral in u and v, and calculate its value.

26. Suppose R is the trapezoidal region in the first quadrant bounded by $y = -x + 1$ and $y = -x + 5$, and we want to calculate $\iint_R \sin\left(\frac{x-y}{x+y}\right)\, dA$.

   (a) Draw the region R.

   (b) Based on the argument of the sine, set $u = x + y$ and $v = x - y$. Solve these equations for x and y in terms of u and v.

   (c) Write equations in terms of u and v that describe the linear boundary segments of R. Then draw those lines in the uv-plane.

   (d) Determine $\left| \frac{\partial(x,y)}{\partial(u,v)} \right|$ and write $\iint_R \sin\left(\frac{x-y}{x+y}\right)\, dA$ as an iterated integral in u and v.

   (e) Calculate $\iint_R \sin\left(\frac{x-y}{x+y}\right)\, dA$.

27. Suppose R is the trapezoidal region in the first quadrant between the lines $y = -2x + 3$ and $y = -2x + 8$, and above $y = 2$. Use the change of variable $u = 2x + y$, $v = x - 2y$ to calculate $\iint_R \frac{x-2y}{2x+y}\, dA$.

28. Suppose R is the trapezoidal region in the first quadrant between the lines $y = -3x + 7$ and $y = -3x + 10$, and to the right of $x = 1$. Use the change of variable $u = y + 3x$, $v = y - 8x$ to calculate $\iint_R \frac{6x+2y}{8x-y}\, dA$.

29. The cylindrical coordinate system is related to the Cartesian system by the equations $x = r\cos\theta$, $y = r\sin\theta$, and $z = z$. Determine $\left| \frac{\partial(x,y,z)}{\partial(r,\theta,z)} \right|$.

30. The relationship between the spherical and Cartesian coordinate systems is $x = \rho\sin\phi\cos\theta$, $y = \rho\sin\phi\sin\theta$, and $z = \rho\cos(\phi)$. Determine $\left| \frac{\partial(x,y,z)}{\partial(\rho,\theta,\phi)} \right|$.

In #31–36 the region R is the parallelepiped determined by the position vectors $\mathbf{u}, \mathbf{v}$ and $\mathbf{w}$. Use a change of variables to calculate $\iiint_R f(x,y,z)\, dV$.

31. $\mathbf{u} = \langle 2,2,0 \rangle$, $\mathbf{v} = \langle -1,1,0 \rangle$, $\mathbf{w} = \langle 1,0,4 \rangle$ and $f(x,y,z) = x$

32. $\mathbf{u} = \langle 1,-1,0 \rangle$, $\mathbf{v} = \langle 5,5,0 \rangle$, $\mathbf{w} = \langle -1,0,3 \rangle$ and $f(x,y,z) = y$

33. $\mathbf{u} = \langle -1,-1,1 \rangle$, $\mathbf{v} = \langle -2,3,1 \rangle$, $\mathbf{w} = \langle 2,1,3 \rangle$ and $f(x,y,z) = z$

34. $\mathbf{u} = \langle 1, -1, -1 \rangle, \mathbf{v} = \langle 2, 3, 1 \rangle, \mathbf{w} = \langle 1, 0, 4 \rangle$ and $f(x, y, z) = x$

35. $\mathbf{u} = \langle 5, 1, -1 \rangle, \mathbf{v} = \langle 0, 2, 8 \rangle, \mathbf{w} = \langle 0, 0, -1 \rangle$ and $f(x, y, z) = zy$

36. $\mathbf{u} = \langle 4, -1, -3 \rangle, \mathbf{v} = \langle 2, 3, 0 \rangle, \mathbf{w} = \langle 0, 0, 7 \rangle$ and $f(x, y, z) = y + z$

In #37–40 a parameterization of the three-dimensional region R is given. Calculate the specified triple integral.

37. $\iiint_R (x - y) \, dV$; $x = 3u - 2, y = u(v - 4), z = u(v + 2w)$; $u \in [1, 3]$, $v \in [0, 5]$ and $w \in [0, 4]$

38. $\iiint_R z \, dV$; $x = (2u + 1)(v + 3), y = 2w(v + 3), z = 10(1 - w)$; $u \in [0, 4]$, $v \in [0, 3]$, and $w \in [0, 1]$

39. $\iiint_R xy \, dV$; $x = \sqrt{u}, y = \sqrt{v}, z = \frac{1}{2}(u + v + w)$; $u \in [1, 9]$, $v \in [0, 6]$, and $w \in [0, 2]$

40. $\iiint_R x^2 \, dV$; $x = uv, y = u(v + w), z = 3v - 4w$; $u \in [1, 4]$, $v \in [0, 3]$, and $w \in [0, 2]$

❖ 14.7 Concept and Application Exercises

41. Suppose $x = Au + Bv$ and $y = Cu + Dv$, where A, B, C, D are fixed but arbitrary numbers.

    (a) Calculate the Jacobian of this change of variables.

    (b) What must be true about the vectors $\mathbf{u} = \langle A, C \rangle$ and $\mathbf{v} = \langle B, D \rangle$ in order for the Jacobian to be 0?

42. Suppose $x = 2u + 5v$ and $y = 4u + v$.

    (a) Calculate $\left| \frac{\partial(u,v)}{\partial(x,y)} \right|$.

    (b) Write u and v in terms of x and y, and determine $\left| \frac{\partial(u,v)}{\partial(x,y)} \right|$.

    (c) Compare your answers from parts (a) and (b), and explain your finding in light of the Jacobian's role in scaling area.

43. Suppose R is the region enclosed by the ellipse $\frac{x^2}{a^2} + \frac{y^2}{b^2} = 1$.   `Geometry`

    (a) Write the equation of the ellipse in terms of $u = x/a$ and $v = y/b$.

    (b) Determine $\left| \frac{\partial(x,y)}{\partial(u,v)} \right|$.

    (c) Determine the area of R by using the suggested change of variables to calculate $\iint_R 1 \, dA$.

44. Suppose R is the region enclosed by the ellipse $25x^2 + 4y^2 = 100$, and the   `Mass Density` mass density in R varies according to $\rho(x, y) = 7 + x + y$ g/cm^2, where x and y are measured in cm. Determine the mass of R by using the change of variables suggested in #43 to calculate $\iint_R \rho(x, y) \, dA$.

45. Suppose R is the region in the first quadrant enclosed by the ellipse $4x^2 + y^2 = 36$, and the mass density in R varies according to $\rho(x, y) = 10 - x + y \frac{g}{cm^2}$,   `Center of Mass` where x and y are measured in cm. Determine the region's center of mass by using the change of variables suggested in #43 to calculate the relevant integrals. (Consider using a second change of variables into polar coordinates.)

46. Suppose R is the region in the second quadrant enclosed by the ellipse $5x^2 + 3y^2 = 15$, and the mass density in R is constant $\rho(x,y) = 13\frac{g}{cm^2}$, where x and y are measured in cm. Determine the region's second moment with respect to the y axis by using the change of variables suggested in #43.

> Moment of Inertia

In #47–50 the position vectors $\mathbf{u}$ and $\mathbf{v}$ define a trapezoidal region, R, and density varies with position according to $\rho(x,y)$. (a) Write down the double integrals used to determine the coordinates of the center of mass (see Section 14.1). Then (b) make a change of variables from x and y into the "natural" coordinate frame for the region defined by $\mathbf{u}$ and $\mathbf{v}$, and determine the location of the center of mass.

> Center of Mass

47. $\mathbf{u} = \langle 12, 1 \rangle$, $\mathbf{v} = \langle -1, 12 \rangle$; $\rho(x,y) = 1 + x^2 + y$

48. $\mathbf{u} = \langle 4, -1 \rangle$, $\mathbf{v} = \langle 3, 12 \rangle$; $\rho(x,y) = 40 - x^2 - y$

49. $\mathbf{u} = \langle -1, -1 \rangle$, $\mathbf{v} = \langle -5, 5 \rangle$; $\rho(x,y) = 12 + x^2 - xy$

50. $\mathbf{u} = \langle 1, 1 \rangle$, $\mathbf{v} = \langle -1, 1 \rangle$; $\rho(x,y) = 1 + x^2 + y^2$

51. Suppose R is the rectangle defined by the vectors $\mathbf{u} = \langle 1, 3 \rangle$ and $\mathbf{v} = \langle -6, 2 \rangle$. Calculate the volume between R and the graph of $f(x,y) = 6 - x^2 y$.

> Volume

52. Suppose R is the region in the first quadrant bounded by the hyperbolas $xy = 2$ and $xy = 5$, and the lines $y = 13x$ and $y = 7x$. Calculate the net volume between R and the graph of $f(x,y) = 1 - x^2 + y^2$.

> Net Volume

53. Suppose R is the region in the first quadrant bounded by the curves $xy^3 = 1$, $xy^3 = 2$, $y = 2\sqrt{x}$ and $y = 3\sqrt{x}$. Calculate the volume between R and the graph of $f(x,y) = xy$. (Hint: use the boundary curves to define u and v.)

> Volume

54. Suppose R is the square defined by the position vectors $\mathbf{u} = \langle 1, 1 \rangle$ and $\mathbf{v} = \langle 1, -1 \rangle$, and S is the portion of the surface $z = 0.5x^2 + xy + 0.5y^2$ that lies over R. Calculate the surface area of S.

> Surface Area

You might remember #55 and #56 from Chapter 7. Changing variables allows us to make the relevant calculation with one integral instead of three.

> Hydrostatic Force

55. A trailer detaches during an accident on a bridge and plummets into a lake that's 11 m deep. Miraculously, the trailer comes to rest on the bottom intact and upright. Its back end is held up above the (flat) lake bed by the rear wheels while the front end rests on bottom, so the bed of the trailer is inclined at an angle of 6.75° (see Figure 7.11). Determine the hydrostatic force acting against the long, vertical side of trailer which is 10 meters × 3.5 meters.

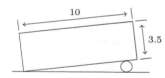

Figure 7.11: The sunken trailer in #55.

56. If the trailer at the bottom of the lake in #55 had dimensions of 17 meters × 3.5 meters and rested on the lake bed at an inclination of 3.6°, determine the hydrostatic force acting against the long, vertical side of trailer.

57. Suppose R is the region enclosed by the ellipsoid $\frac{x^2}{a^2} + \frac{y^2}{b^2} + \frac{z^2}{c^2} = 1$.

> Solid Geometry

    (a) Write the equation of the ellipsoid in terms of $u = \frac{x}{a}$, $v = \frac{y}{b}$ and $w = \frac{z}{c}$.

    (b) Determine the Jacobian of this change of variables, $\frac{\partial(x,y,z)}{\partial(u,v,w)}$.

    (c) Determine the volume of R by using the suggested change of variables to calculate $\iiint_R 1\, dV$.

58. Suppose $x = \frac{1}{2}u + v - w$, $y = \frac{1}{3}v + w$, and $z = 3w$.

    (a) Calculate the Jacobian of this change of variables, $\frac{\partial(x,y,z)}{\partial(u,v,w)}$.

    (b) Write u, v and w in terms of x, y and z, and determine $\frac{\partial(u,v,w)}{\partial(x,y,z)}$.

    (c) Compare your answers from parts (a) and (c), and explain your finding in light of the Jacobian's role in scaling volume.

Chapter 14 Review

❖ True or False

1. The number $\|\Delta A\|$ shrinks when the number of rectangles in a mesh increases.

2. The number of rectangles in a mesh increases when $\|\Delta A\|$ shrinks.

3. All rectangles in a regular mesh are congruent.

4. All continuous functions $f(x, y)$ are integrable over rectangles in the xy-plane.

5. Suppose the center of mass of R is at $(\bar{x}, \bar{y})$, and the average density of R is $\langle \rho \rangle$. Then $\rho(\bar{x}, \bar{y}) = \langle \rho \rangle$.

6. When $f(x, y) > 0$ the number $\iint_R f(x, y) \, dA$ can be interpreted as a volume.

7. Suppose $\iint_R f(x, y) \, dA > 0$. Then the area in R over which $f(x, y) > 0$ is larger than the area in R over which $f(x, y) < 0$.

8. Suppose $\iint_R g(x, y) \, dA < \iint_R f(x, y) \, dA$. Then the graph of g is always below the graph of f.

9. Suppose the graph of g is always below the graph of f, and R has nonzero area. Then $\iint_R g(x, y) \, dA < \iint_R f(x, y) \, dA$.

10. Fubini's Theorem tell us that $\int_a^b \int_c^d f(x, y) \, dx \, dy = \int_b^a \int_d^c f(x, y) \, dx \, dy$.

11. Fubini's Theorem tell us that $\int_a^b \int_c^d f(x, y) \, dx \, dy = \int_c^d \int_a^b f(x, y) \, dx \, dy$.

12. Suppose that $\mathbf{u}$ and $\mathbf{v}$ are orthogonal unit vectors that define a coordinate system. Then $du \, dv = dx \, dy$.

13. $\int_0^1 \int_{\exp(y)}^e f(x, y) \, dx \, dy = \int_1^e \int_0^{\ln(x)} f(x, y) \, dy \, dx$

14. The only solid that's x-simple, y-simple, and z-simple is a rectangular block.

15. The spherical equations $\phi = \pi/4$ and $\theta = \pi/4$ both describe half-planes.

16. Suppose S_1 is the spherical shell between $\rho = 1$ and $\rho = 2$ meters, and that its density is $1/7$ kg/m^3. The spherical shell S_2 lies between $\rho = 10$ and $\rho = 11$ meters, and has a density of $1/331$ kg/m^3. Both S_1 and S_2 have the same moment of inertia with respect to the z-axis.

17. The cylindrical equation $r + z = 1$ describes the plane $x + y + z = 1$.

18. The cylindrical equation $r^2 + 9z = -4$ describes a paraboloid.

❖ Multiple Choice

19. Suppose R is the bounded region in the first quadrant between the curves $x = 4y - y^2$ and $x = \beta y^3$. For what values of β is R y-simple?

    (a) $\beta = 0.5$ (d) $\beta < 0$
    (b) $\beta \geq 0.5$ (e) none of the above
    (c) $0 \leq \beta \leq 0.5$

20. Suppose R is the region $0 \leq x \leq 6$, $0 \leq y \leq 4$, and $f(x, y) = 4 - 2x - 2y$. The volume between the graph of f and the region R is ...

(a) $224/3$ (c) $-192/3$

(b) 0 (d) none of the above

21. The cylindrical coordinates of the point $(x, y, z) = (\sqrt{3}, 1, 8)$ are ...

(a) $(2, \pi/3, 8)$ (d) $(\sqrt{3}, 5\pi/6, 8)$

(b) $(\sqrt{3}, 3\pi/4, 8)$ (e) none of the above

(c) $(2, \pi/6, 8)$

22. The spherical coordinates of the point $(x, y, z) = (3, 3, \sqrt{6})$ are ...

(a) $(\sqrt{24}, \pi/3, \pi/3)$ (d) $(\sqrt{24}, \pi/3, \pi/4)$

(b) $(\sqrt{24}, \pi/4, \pi/4)$ (e) none of the above

(c) $(\sqrt{24}, \pi/4, \pi/3)$

23. When integrating in spherical coordinates, the volume element is ...

(a) $\rho^2 \sin(\phi)\, d\rho\, d\theta\, d\phi$ (d) $\rho \sin^2(\theta)\, d\rho\, d\theta\, d\phi$

(b) $\rho \sin^2(\phi)\, d\rho\, d\theta\, d\phi$ (e) none of the above

(c) $\rho^2 \sin(\theta)\, d\rho\, d\theta\, d\phi$

24. When integrating in cylindrical coordinates, the volume element is ...

(a) $r \sin(\theta)\, dr\, d\theta\, dz$ (d) $z \sin(\theta)\, dr\, d\theta\, dz$

(b) $r \cos(\theta)\, dr\, d\theta\, dz$ (e) none of the above

(c) $z \cos(\theta)\, dr\, d\theta\, dz$

❖ Exercises

25. Suppose R is the region defined by $1 \le x \le 10$ and $2 \le y \le 8$. Calculate $\iint_R 2xy + y\, dA$ as the limit of Riemann sums.

26. Suppose R is the region defined by $-3 \le x \le 1$ and $0 \le y \le 5$. Calculate $\iint_R x - y^2\, dA$ as the limit of Riemann sums.

27. Evaluate $\iint_R e^{x+y}\, dA$, where R is the bounded region defined by $y = 0$, $y = 2x$, and $x = 1$.

28. Calculate the iterated integral $\int_0^1 \int_0^x e^{x^2}\, dy\, dx$.

29. Calculate $\int_0^2 \int_{x/2}^1 \sin(\pi y^2)\, dy\, dx$.

30. Calculate $\int_0^1 \int_{y^2}^1 y \sin(x^2)\, dx\, dy$.

31. Suppose R is the region between $y = x$ and $y = x^2$, where $x \in [0, 1]$. Calculate $\iint_R x + y\, dA$ by treating R as (a) a y-simple region, and (b) an x-simple region.

32. Switch the order of integration in $\int_0^2 \int_{1-\sqrt{1-y}}^{\sqrt[3]{y/2}} \sin(x - y^2)\, dx\, dy$.

33. Determine the volume between R and the surface $z = x^2$ when R is the bounded region in the xy-plane between $y = 5 - x^2$ and $2y - x = 0$.

Volume

34. Determine the volume between R and the graph of $f(x, y) = \sin(\frac{\pi}{8}y^2)$ when R is the triangle in the Cartesian plane bounded by $y = 2$, $x = 0$, and $y = x/2$.

____ Volume

35. Suppose R is the region bounded by $1 + \cos(x) \leq y \leq 10 + \sin(x)$, where $0 \leq x \leq 5\pi$, and the density in R is $\rho(x, y) = x + 2y$. Calculate the x-coordinate of the region's center of mass.

____ Center of Mass

36. Suppose R is the rectangle defined by $0 \leq x \leq 2$ and $2 \leq y \leq 3$. If the mass density in R is described by $\rho(x, y) = x + y$, find the region's center of mass.

____ Center of Mass

37. Suppose the mass density of the I-beam cross section shown in Figure 8.1 is constant ρ kg/m^2. Determine the beam's second moment of inertia with respect to the origin (which affects the beam's stiffness).

____ Civil Engineering

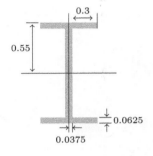

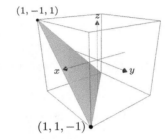

Figure 8.1: For #37. Lengths in meters.   Figure 8.2: The weighted die from #38

38. Suppose the cube in Figure 8.2 has a side length of 1 cm, and is centered at the origin. The die has a density of ρ_1 above the triangle, and a density of ρ_2 below it. Determine the die's center of mass in terms of ρ_1 and ρ_2.

____ Center of Mass

39. Evaluate the integral $\iint_R (x^2 + y^2)^{-1/2} \, dA$, where R is the region that lies inside the cardioid $r = 1 + \sin\theta$, and outside the circle $r = 1$.

40. Find the integral of the function $f(x, y) = y/\sqrt{x^2+y^2}$ over the region that is outside the cardioid $r = 1 + \cos\theta$ and inside the circle of radius $(2 - \sqrt{2})/2$.

41. Find the volume above the cone $z = \sqrt{x^2 + y^2}$ and beneath the sphere $x^2 + y^2 + z^2 = 8$.

42. Suppose R is the region in the third quadrant between the circles of radii 1 and 3 that are centered at the origin. Integrate $f(x, y) = 4x^2 - 3y$ over R.

In #43–44, the region R is the rectangle $0 \leq x \leq 2$, $0 \leq y \leq 1$, and $\rho(x, y) = \frac{1}{4}x + \frac{3}{4}y^2$ is the probability density function that describes the probability of finding an electron in the R. That is, when D is a region within R, the probability of finding the electron in D is

____ Probability

$$\iint_D \rho(x, y) \, dA.$$

43. What's the probability of find the electron in the upper-right quarter of the rectangle?

44. Are we more likely to find the electron in the upper-left quarter of the rectangle, or in the lower half?

45. Calculate $\iint_R e^{\sqrt{x^2+y^2}} \, dA$ when R is the region in the second quadrant bounded by the circle $r = 1$, the spiral $r = \theta$, the x-axis, and the y-axis.

46. Suppose R is the region in the fourth quadrant that's bounded by the lemniscate $r^2 = 2(\cos^2(\theta) - \sin^2(\theta))$, where r is measured in centimeters. If R has a uniform density of 3 g/cm^2, determine its mass.

_____ | Mass |

47. Use a triple integral to find the volume of the region that's described by $1 \leq x \leq 2$, $0 \leq y \leq 1$, and $x + y \leq z \leq 2x - y$.

_____ | Volume |

48. Suppose R is the three-dimensional region that lies between the surfaces $z = y^2 e^x$ and $z = 16$, and is above the triangular region determined by the intersection of the lines $y = 1 - x$, $y = x + 1$, and $x = 1$. Determine $\iiint_R 1/\sqrt{z}\, dV$.

49. Write the equation for the cylinder $r = 3$ in spherical coordinates.

50. Write the equation for the sphere $\rho = 5$ in cylindrical coordinates.

51. Suppose R is the cylindrical region $1 \leq x^2 + y^2 \leq 2$ for which $z^2 \leq 2x^2 + 2y^2$. Calculate the volume of R.

_____ | Volume |

52. Suppose R is the spherical region for which $1 + \cos(\phi) \leq \rho \leq 10$. Calculate the volume of R.

_____ | Volume |

53. Sketch the region parameterized by $\mathbf{r} = \langle 3 + 2u + v, 4 - u - v \rangle$ when $u \in [1, 2]$ and $v \in [-1, 1]$.

54. Sketch the region parameterized by $\mathbf{r} = \langle -1 - u + 3v, 1 - 5u - 2v \rangle$ when $u \in [0, 3]$ and $v \in [1, 4]$.

55. Calculate the Jacobian for the change of coordinates

$$x = \sqrt{\frac{1}{3}u - \frac{1}{3}v}, \quad y = \frac{1}{3}u + \frac{2}{3}v$$

56. Determine the Jacobian matrix $\frac{\partial(x,y,z)}{\partial(u,v,w)}$, corresponding to the change of coordinates

$$x = \frac{1}{2}(u^2 - v^2), \quad y = uv, \quad z = w.$$

The coordinates (u, v, w) are called **parabolic cylindrical coordinates**.

57. Suppose R is the region in the xy plane bounded by the lines $y - 3x = 4$, $y - 3x = 0$, $y - x = 3$, and $y - x = 5$.

   (a) Sketch the region R in the xy-plane.

   (b) Suggest a change of coordinates, $u = \ldots$ and $v = \ldots$ which will simplify the given double integral $\iint_R (y - 3x)e^{y-x}\, dA$.

   (c) Calculate the Jacobian $\frac{\partial(x,y)}{\partial(u,v)}$.

   (d) Use your change of variables to evaluate the integral.

58. Suppose R is the region in the first quadrant bounded by $y - x^2 = 0$, $y - x^2 = 2$, $y + 2x^2 = 3$, and $y + 2x^2 = 2$. (a) Draw a picture of R, and (b) evaluate $\iint_R xy\, dA$. (Hint: Use the change of variables from #55.)

Chapter 14 Projects and Applications

❖ Rolling Times, Moments and Energy

In this project you will compute moments of inertia and use them to predict the length of time it will take for objects to roll down an inclined plane. Then you'll actually roll them, and compare your measurements to your predictions. In preparation, you should get a stopwatch and several objects that (a) can roll, and (b) have either a uniform mass density, or a mass density that changes in a simple and predictable way. For example, you might get a roll of duct tape, a billiard ball or an orange (as spherical as possible), and a can of refried beans (it's important that the contents of the can don't shift when it rolls).

1. Measure the physical dimensions of the items you've collected, and determine the mass of each. What's actually important here is the distribution of the mass. Depending on the objects you collected, it might be reasonable to call the mass density constant. To get more accurate results you might, for example, get two cans of refried beans instead of one. Keep one intact for the rolling experiment that's coming later, and pull the other apart so that you can eat the beans, weigh the end caps, and weigh the cylinder.

2. Use an integral to calculate the moment of inertia of each object with respect to its rolling axis. We'll denote this number by I.

3. Make a stiff, inclined plane; and mark a start line at the top and a finish line at the bottom (see Figure 9.2). Measure the distance between those lines, and measure the plane's angle of elevation, α. The angle α should be small enough that the objects you've collected will roll but not slip down the plane.

4. Explain in detail what the following energy equation means.

$$\frac{1}{2}mv^2 + \frac{1}{2}I\omega^2 = mg\, s\sin(\alpha). \qquad (9.1)$$

5. An object's angular velocity is related to its translational velocity by $\omega = v/R$ when it's rolling and not slipping, where R is the object's outer radius. Use this fact to show that equation (9.1) can be rewritten as

$$\frac{ds}{dt} = C\sqrt{s}, \qquad (9.2)$$

where C is a constant that depends on m, g, R, I and α.

6. Use the techniques from Chapter 10 to solve equation (9.2), and write a formula for $s(t)$.

7. Use your formula from #6 to predict how long it will take each object to roll from the start to the finish line, based on its mass distribution, moment of inertia, radius, and the angle of the plane.

8. Set each object at the starting line and use the stopwatch to determine how long it takes to reach the finish line. Perform several trials for each object, and compare the average time to the prediction you made in #7.

9. Were your predictions from #7 accurate? If not, what do you think went wrong (and what makes you think that)? Can you fix it?

Figure 9.1: Measuring moment of inertia with respect to an axis.

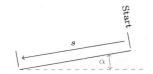

Figure 9.2: The inclined plane.

❖ The Diffusion Equation

Many physical processes are driven by differences in concentration, such as oxygen crossing the alveoli in your lungs, the diffusion of particulates in solution, and in similar fashion, the dissipation of thermal energy. In this project you'll use elementary facts about integration, Fubini's Theorem, and some simple assumptions about diffusion to derive a widely accepted, quantitative description of the phenomenon.

Let's begin by considering dye molecules that are suspended in solution in a linear pathway (imagine a pipet or capillary). When the molecules are unevenly distributed they diffuse from high concentrations to low, so concentration varies from point to point, and also changes over time. For this reason we write the concentration as a function of two variables, $\rho(x, t)$, with units of mass/length.

At any particular moment, we can take a "snapshot" of the concentration by graphing ρ as a function of x. The profile depicted in Figure 9.3, for example, shows that the density of dye molecules is larger to the right of x_1 than to the left, so the molecules near x_1 will tend to exit the interval $[x_1, x_2]$; molecules flow *into* $[x_1, x_2]$ at x_2 for similar reasons, but the in-flow and out-flow of these dye molecules don't happen at the same rate. To understand why, recall that ρ_x tells us the slope of the tangent line to the graph of the concentration profile.

- *When ρ_x is near zero:* If the tangent line is nearly horizontal at some x, the concentration is virtually the same on both sides of x. So there will be roughly as many dye molecules that wander past x headed to the right as there are headed to the left, and although there may be a net gain on one side or the other over time, the rate at which it happens is small.

- *When ρ_x is large:* A steep tangent line indicates that concentration is much higher on one side of x than the other, so many more molecules tend to wander past x in one direction than the other, and the net rate of flow is large.

Figure 9.3: An example profile of concentration at a particular moment, with tangent lines at x_1 and x_2.

Because larger magnitudes of ρ_x correspond to faster diffusion, we model the rate at which molecules diffuse as proportional to ρ_x. More specifically, **Fick's Law** states that molecules cross any particular location at a rate of $\gamma \rho_x$, where γ is a positive constant with units of length^2/time. For example, suppose ρ has units of g/mm and γ has units of mm^2/sec. Then $\gamma \rho_x$ has units of g/sec, and since the total mass of dye in the interval $[x_1, x_2]$ can only change when molecules flow across x_1 or x_2, the total mass of dye in the interval changes at a rate of

$$\overbrace{\gamma \rho_x(x_2)}^{\text{Diffusion of molecules across } x_2} - \overbrace{\gamma \rho_x(x_1)}^{\text{Diffusion of molecules across } x_1}. \tag{9.3}$$

> This is a difference (rather than a sum) because $\rho_x > 0$ corresponds to different physical phenomena at x_1 and x_2: when $\rho_x > 0$ at x_1, molecules diffuse *out of* the interval $[x_1, x_2]$, but $\rho_x > 0$ at x_2 indicates that they're *entering* at x_2. See Figure 9.3.

On the other hand, you also know that

$$\text{the mass between } x_1 \text{ and } x_2 = \int_{x_1}^{x_2} \rho \, dx,$$

so we can say that the total mass of dye in $[x_1, x_2]$ changes at a rate of

$$\frac{\partial}{\partial t} \int_{x_1}^{x_2} \rho \, dx \;=\; \int_{x_1}^{x_2} \frac{\partial \rho}{\partial t} \, dx. \tag{9.4}$$

> WARNING! This equality is colored red because you cannot always pass ∂_t through the integral sign! In order to do it in equation (9.4), we're assuming that ρ is "nice" in a particular sense that you'll learn about in advanced courses. This assumption is standard practice in building mathematical models of diffusion.

Since the expressions in equations (9.3) and (9.4) both describe the same quantity,

$$\int_{x_1}^{x_2} \frac{\partial \rho}{\partial t} \, dx = \gamma \rho_x(x_2) - \gamma \rho_x(x_1). \tag{9.5}$$

The left-hand side of this equation is a definite integral. The right-hand side can also be expressed as an integral:

$$\gamma\rho_x(x_2) - \gamma\rho_x(x_1) = \int_{x_1}^{x_2} \gamma\frac{\partial}{\partial x}(\rho_x)\ dx = \int_{x_1}^{x_2} \gamma\frac{\partial^2\rho}{\partial x^2}\ dx.$$

So equation (9.5) is really

$$\int_{x_1}^{x_2} \frac{\partial\rho}{\partial t}\ dx = \int_{x_1}^{x_2} \gamma\frac{\partial^2\rho}{\partial x^2}\ dx.$$

Said differently, the difference between the two sides is zero:

$$0 = \int_{x_1}^{x_2} \frac{\partial\rho}{\partial t}\ dx - \int_{x_1}^{x_2} \gamma\frac{\partial^2\rho}{\partial x^2}\ dx = \int_{x_1}^{x_2} \frac{\partial\rho}{\partial t} - \gamma\frac{\partial^2\rho}{\partial x^2}\ dx. \qquad (9.6)$$

Since we didn't mention how far x_2 is from x_1, equation (9.6) must be true regardless of how small $[x_1, x_2]$ is. So if the integrand is continuous, we can conclude that $\rho_t - \gamma\rho_{xx}$ must be 0 everywhere. That is,

> The assumption of continuity is not always justified, but is reasonable for many physical phenomena.

$$\frac{\partial\rho}{\partial t} = \gamma\frac{\partial^2\rho}{\partial x^2}. \qquad (9.7)$$

In the following exercises, you'll extend these ideas to diffusion in two-dimensional regions. Suppose the concentration of dye in the xy-plane is $\rho(x, y, t)$ g/cm^2 at time t, and γ has units of cm^2/sec. The time dependence of ρ is suppressed in the first few exercises below (in favor of simplifying our notation), and we take R to be an arbitrary rectangle, say $x \in [a, b]$ and $y \in [c, d]$.

1. Each $y \in [c, d]$ corresponds to a horizontal line segment through R, as seen in Figure 9.4. Instead of a line segment, let's consider a horizontal channel across the rectangle of height dy. Explain why the net rate at which dye is lost (or gained) at the left and right ends of the channel is approximately

$$\left(\gamma\rho_x(b, y) - \gamma\rho_x(a, y)\right) dy = \left(\int_a^b \gamma\rho_{xx}(x, y)\ dx\right) dy. \qquad (9.8)$$

Figure 9.4: Diffusion happens along the vertical boundaries at each y.

2. Explain why the net rate of loss/gain along the vertical sides of R is

$$\int_c^d \left(\int_a^b \gamma\rho_{xx}(x, y)\ dx\right) dy.$$

3. Based on Figure 9.5, explain why the net rate of loss/gain along the horizontal boundaries of the rectangle is

$$\int_a^b \left(\int_c^d \gamma\rho_{yy}(x, y)\ dy\right) dx.$$

Figure 9.5: Diffusion happens along the horizontal boundaries at each x.

4. Using Fubini's Theorem, show that the instantaneous rate of change in the molecular mass of dye in R is

$$\iint_R \gamma\left(\rho_{xx}(x, y) + \rho_{yy}(x, y)\right)\ dA.$$

Since the molecular mass of dye in R is $\iint_R \rho \, dA$ at any given moment, we can also write its rate of change as $\frac{d}{dt} \iint_R \rho \, dA$. Equating this expression for the rate of change in molecular mass with the formula from #4, we see

$$\frac{\partial}{\partial t} \iint_R \rho \, dA = \iint_R \gamma(\rho_{xx} + \rho_{yy}) \, dA.$$

This equation can be simplified further by passing the time derivative through the double integral on the left-hand side (but see the warning on p.1201), and collecting all the terms on one side of the equation:

$$\iint_R \left[\rho_t - \gamma(\rho_{xx} + \rho_{yy})\right] \, dA = 0. \qquad (9.9)$$

Now let's assume that ρ and its partial derivatives are continuous.

5. Explain how equation (9.9) would be violated if $\rho_t - \gamma(\rho_{xx} + \rho_{yy})$ were positive at some point in the plane. (Similarly, the value of $\rho_t - \gamma(\rho_{xx} + \rho_{yy})$ cannot be negative anywhere.)

Based on #5, we can assert that $\rho_t - \gamma(\rho_{xx} + \rho_{yy}) = 0$ everywhere. This fact is typically expressed by repurposing the symbol Δ and writing

$$\rho_t = \gamma \Delta \rho, \qquad (9.10)$$

where $\Delta \rho$ now means $\rho_{xx} + \rho_{yy}$. We refer to Δ, which denotes the sum of the second pure partial derivatives, as the **Laplacian**; and equation (9.10) is called the **2-d diffusion equation**, or the **2-d heat equation**.

> The word *Laplacian* is pronounced "Lah-PLAH-shun," and is derived from the name of Pierre-Simon Laplace (1749–1827).

6. Determine how #1–5 change when we consider diffusion in three dimensions. Take ρ to be a function of x, y, z and t, and let R be an arbitrary rectangular box, $x \in [a, b], y \in [c, d]$ and $z \in [p, q]$.

7. Based on your work in #6, what does $\Delta \rho$ mean when ρ depends on three spacial variables?

Chapter 15
Vector Calculus

In this chapter we focus on *vector fields,* which are often used to represent flows and distributed forces. Integrals will be used to calculate the work required to move against a force, and to determine the rate at which fluid flows through a surface, such as a filter or permeable membrane. At the close of the chapter, we relate such integrals to one another via prominent theorems in vector calculus.

Key Idea(s): *When every point in space is associated with a vector, we refer to the collection of vectors as a vector field.*

Some of the most important vector fields arise as gradients of functions.

Streamlines tell us about the flow through a vector field.

15.1 Vector Fields

Imagine air flowing over a car in a wind tunnel, or water flowing on the surface of an ocean current. Each point in the tunnel or on the water's surface is associated with a vector that tells us the velocity of the fluid. Similarly, each point in the vicinity of a proton is associated with a vector that indicates the electrostatic force that would be experienced by an ion at that location. Regardless of the vectors' physical meaning, when each point in space has an associated vector, we refer to the collection of vectors as a ***vector field***. We often write a vector field as $\mathbf{F}(x, y)$ if the points and vectors lie in the plane, and as $\mathbf{F}(x, y, z)$ if they lie in 3-space, indicating that the vector $\mathbf{F}$ changes with position.

 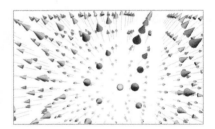

Figure 1.1: (left) A smoke trail shows the path of the air over a car in a wind tunnel; (right) depiction of the electric field generated by a proton (shown as a yellow sphere).

Vector fields

Example 1.1. Discuss qualitative differences among the vector fields (a) $\mathbf{F}(x, y) = \langle 1, 1 \rangle$, and (b) $\mathbf{F}(x, y) = \langle -y/\sqrt{x^2+y^2}\,, x/\sqrt{x^2+y^2} \rangle$, and (c) $\mathbf{F}(x, y) = \langle -y, x \rangle$.

Solution: These vector fields are depicted in Figure 1.2. Vector field (a) is constant, meaning that the vector assigned to each point is always the same. Vector field (b) has a constant magnitude of $\|\mathbf{F}(x, y)\| = 1$ (except at the origin, where it's undefined), but the direction of these vectors changes from point to point. Specifically, $\mathbf{F}(x, y)$ is orthogonal to the position vector $\langle x, y \rangle$. Lastly, vector field (c) is parallel to (b), but both their direction *and* magnitude vary with position. ∎

Don't just read it. Use the dot product to verify the claims about $\mathbf{F}$ in part (b).

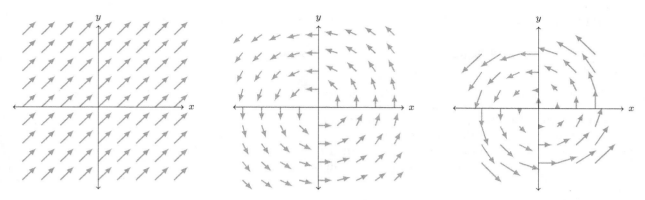

Figure 1.2: (all) Vector fields for Example 1.1; (left) $\mathbf{F}(x, y) = \langle 1, 1 \rangle$; (middle) $\mathbf{F}(x, y) = \langle -y/\sqrt{x^2+y^2}, x/\sqrt{x^2+y^2} \rangle$; (right) $\mathbf{F}(x, y) = \langle -y, x \rangle$. Vectors near the origin have very small magnitudes, so they appear as dots or not at all (but they *are* there).

Analyzing a vector field

Example 1.2. The lines $y = -x$ and $y = -1$ partition the xy-plane into four regions. Discuss qualitative differences in $\mathbf{F}(x, y) = \langle x + y, 1 + y \rangle$ in these regions.

Solution: When $y > -1$ the second component of $\mathbf{F}$ is positive, so the vectors point upward in regions A and B; for similar reasons, the vectors in regions C and D point downward. Since the first component of $\mathbf{F}$ is negative when $x < -y$, but is positive when $x > -y$, the vectors $\mathbf{F}$ point left in regions B and C but point to the right in regions A and D (see Figure 1.3). ∎

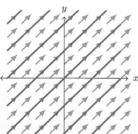

Figure 1.3: The vector field $\mathbf{F}$ for Example 1.2.

A path on which the tangent vector is parallel to the vector field $\mathbf{F}$ at each point is called a ***streamline*** or ***flow line*** of $\mathbf{F}$ (e.g., see Figure 1.1, where the smoke filament follows the velocity vectors in the wind tunnel).

Streamlines

Example 1.3. Determine the streamlines of the vector fields (a) $\mathbf{F}(x, y) = \langle 1, 1 \rangle$, and (b) $\mathbf{F}(x, y) = \langle -y/\sqrt{x^2+y^2}, x/\sqrt{x^2+y^2} \rangle$.

Solution: (a) A streamline is a path along which the tangent vector is parallel to $\mathbf{F}$. So when $\mathbf{r}(t) = \langle x(t), y(t) \rangle$ is a regular parameterization of such a curve, we know that $\mathbf{r}'(t) = \langle x'(t), y'(t) \rangle$ is parallel to $\mathbf{F} = \langle 1, 1 \rangle$. The simplest way for this to happen is arguably for $\mathbf{r}' = \mathbf{F}$, in which case

$$x'(t) = 1 \quad \Rightarrow \quad x(t) = t + C_1$$
$$\text{and}$$
$$y'(t) = 1 \quad \Rightarrow \quad y(t) = t + C_2.$$

Since x and y differ by at most a constant we can write $y = x + C$, so the streamlines are lines. You can see this vector field in Figure 1.2.

(b) When $\mathbf{r}(t)$ parameterizes a stream line In this case, we know that $\mathbf{r}' = \langle x', y' \rangle$ is is orthogonal to the position vector $\langle x, y \rangle$ (because $\mathbf{F}$ is at each point). That is, the velocity vector $\mathbf{r}'(t)$ is always orthogonal to the position vector $\mathbf{r}(t)$. This only happens on a circle centered at the origin, so the streamlines of this vector field are circles (see Figure 1.5). ∎

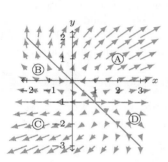

Figure 1.4: $\mathbf{F}$ and streamlines from Example 1.3(a).

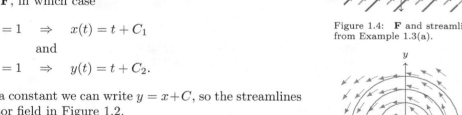

Figure 1.5: $\mathbf{F}$ and streamlines from Example 1.3(b).

Streamlines

Example 1.4. Determine the streamlines of $\mathbf{F}(x, y) = \langle 1, 4x + 1 \rangle$.

Answer: Curves of the form $y = 2x^2 + x + C$.   ∎

Since the components of a vector field can change from point to point, we often write a vector field in the plane as

$$\mathbf{F}(x, y) = \langle P(x, y),\ Q(x, y) \rangle = P(x, y)\mathbf{i} + Q(x, y)\mathbf{j}.$$

The functions P and Q are called the **component functions** of the vector field, and we say that $\mathbf{F}$ is **continuous** (or **differentiable**) when P and Q are continuous (differentiable) functions. Further, we say that $\mathbf{F}$ is **smooth** if the partial derivatives of P and Q are continuous. Similarly for vector fields in three dimensions, $\mathbf{F}(x, y, z) = P(x, y, z)\mathbf{i} + Q(x, y, z)\mathbf{j} + R(x, y, z)\mathbf{k}$.

✤ Gradient Fields and Potentials

In addition to the physical scenarios mentioned above, vector fields arise naturally from real-valued functions via the gradient. When the first partial derivatives of f exist, we can define $\mathbf{F} = \nabla f$. In this case we refer to $\mathbf{F}$ as the **gradient field** of f, and say that f is a **potential** (or potential function) of $\mathbf{F}$.

> The relationship between a *gradient field* and a *potential* is very similar to the relationship between a derivative and an antiderivative in the single-variable setting.

Potentials and gradient fields

Example 1.5. Verify that $f(x, y, z) = C / \sqrt{x^2 + y^2 + z^2}$ is a potential for $\mathbf{F}(x, y, z) = -\frac{C}{\|\mathbf{r}\|^2}\hat{\mathbf{r}}$, where $\mathbf{r} = \langle x, y, z \rangle$ and C is a constant.

Solution: We need to check that $\mathbf{F} = \nabla f$, so let's begin by calculating

$$\frac{\partial f}{\partial x} = -\frac{1}{2} \frac{C}{(x^2 + y^2 + z^2)^{3/2}}\ (2x) = -\frac{C}{(x^2 + y^2 + z^2)^{3/2}}\ (x).$$

The partial derivatives of f with respect to y and z have the same basic structure, but conclude with factors of y and z respectively, so

$$\nabla f(x, y, z) = -\frac{C}{(x^2 + y^2 + z^2)^{3/2}} \begin{bmatrix} x \\ y \\ z \end{bmatrix} = -\frac{C}{x^2 + y^2 + z^2} \frac{1}{\sqrt{x^2 + y^2 + z^2}} \begin{bmatrix} x \\ y \\ z \end{bmatrix}.$$

Since $\|\mathbf{r}\| = \sqrt{x^2 + y^2 + z^2}$ when $\mathbf{r} = \langle x, y, z \rangle$, this equation says $\nabla f = -\frac{C}{\|\mathbf{r}\|^2}\hat{\mathbf{r}}$.   ∎

> The vector $\mathbf{F}(x, y, z)$ in Example 1.5 is exactly the force experienced by an object at (x, y, z) due to the Earth (thinking of Earth's center as the origin) when the constant $C = GMm$, where G is the gravitational constant, M is the mass of the Earth, and m is the mass of some other object. And because the function f has the same units as $\|\mathbf{r}\|\mathbf{F}$, which are (distance)×(force)=(energy), we refer to f as the gravitational potential energy.

Some vector fields are not gradient fields

Example 1.6. Show that $\mathbf{F}(x, y) = \langle 3x + 4y^2,\ 2x^3 + 9x \rangle$ is not a gradient field.

Solution: If $\mathbf{F}$ were a gradient field, there would be a potential function f for which $f_x = 3x + 4y^2$ and $f_y = 2x^3 + 9x$. But then $f_{xy} = 8y$ and $f_{yx} = 6x^2 + 9$, both of which are continuous. You saw Clairaut's Theorem in Section 13.4, which tells us that f_{yx} and f_{xy} must be the same when they are continuous, but $8y$ and $6x^2 + 9$ are clearly not. We conclude that no such function f exists.   ∎

Finding potentials for gradient fields

Example 1.7. Determine a potential for $\mathbf{F}(x, y) = \langle 3x + 4y,\ 4x + 19\cos y \rangle$.

> The wording of this example guarantees that $\mathbf{F}$ is a gradient field.

Solution: Since $\mathbf{F}$ arises from a potential, f, we know that the partial derivative of f with respect to x is $f_x = 3x + 4y$. So in order to recover a formula for f we integrate with respect to x. This leads us to write

$$f(x, y) = \int f_x\ dx = \int 3x + 4y\ dx = \frac{3}{2}x^2 + 4xy + c. \tag{1.1}$$

You're accustomed to seeing capital C as the constant of integration, so the c in equation (1.1) might look like a typo, but it's not. Here we mean that c is constant with respect to x (because it has to become 0 when we differentiate with respect to x) but might depend on y. With this in mind, let's rewrite equation (1.1) as

$$f(x, y) = \frac{3}{2}x^2 + 4xy + c(y).$$

Now we need only determine $c(y)$. On the one hand, we see from $\mathbf{F}$ that $f_y = 4x + 19 \cos y$. On the other, our formula for f tells us that $f_y = 4x + c'(y)$. These must be equal, so $c'(y) = 19 \cos y$. Now a simple integration reveals that

$$c(y) = \int c'(y) \, dy = \int 19 \cos y \, dy = 19 \sin y + C.$$

where C can be any number. (Because C is part of $c(y)$ it cannot depend on x, and it arose from an integration in y, so it cannot depend on y. So this C is a number.) Because we're asked to find a potential function for $\mathbf{F}$, let's choose $C = 0$ for convenience. Then $f(x, y) = \frac{3}{2}x^2 + 4xy + 19 \sin y$. ■

Finding potentials for gradient fields

Solution On-line

Example 1.8. Determine a potential for $\mathbf{F}(x, y) = \langle 2x \cos 5y, \ 36y + 2 - 5x^2 \sin 5y \rangle$.

Answer: $f(x, y) = x^2 \cos 5y + 18y^2 + 2y$. ■

❖ Life in 3D

Our discussion has focused primarily on vector fields in the plane because they're easy to draw and see, and although they are appropriate for certain kinds of problems, we are often confronted with vector fields in 3-space (e.g., see Example 1.5). Like vector fields in the plane, some vector fields in 3-space are gradient fields of potential functions and others aren't.

You should know

- the terms *vector field, streamline, flow line, component functions, continuous, differentiable, smooth, gradient field,* and *potential*;
- that a vector field associates a vector with each location.

You should be able to

- determine the streamlines for a vector field;
- use Clairaut's Theorem to identify vector fields that are not gradient fields;
- determine the potential function for a gradient field.

❖ 15.1 Skill Exercises

In #1–6 determine Cartesian equations that describe the streamlines of $\mathbf{F}$.

1. $\mathbf{F}(x, y) = \langle 2, 7 \rangle$ 3. $\mathbf{F}(x, y) = \langle 1, x \rangle$ 5. $\mathbf{F}(x, y) = \langle x, 1 \rangle$

2. $\mathbf{F}(x, y) = \langle -3, 4 \rangle$ 4. $\mathbf{F}(x, y) = \langle 3, \cos x \rangle$ 6. $\mathbf{F}(x, y) = \langle 5, y \rangle$

In #7–10 write the formula for the gradient vector field of the function f.

7. $f(x, y) = 3x^2 + y \sin x$

8. $f(x, y) = e^{xy} - 7x$

9. $f(x, y, z) = xyz$

10. $f(x, y, z) = 5zy^3 - \ln(z^2 + 1)$

In #11–16 (a) use Clairaut's Theorem to identify the vector fields (if any) that are certainly not gradient fields, as in Example 1.6. The other vector fields (if any) arise from potentials. (b) Use the technique of Example 1.7 to determine potentials for those vector fields that remain after part (a).

11. $\mathbf{F}(x, y) = \langle 8y, 9x \rangle$

12. $\mathbf{F}(x, y) = \langle 2y^2, 13x^4 \rangle$

13. $\mathbf{F}(x, y) = \langle 3x^2, 8 \rangle$

14. $\mathbf{F}(x, y) = \langle 12yx^2, 4x^3 - 2y \rangle$

15. $\mathbf{F}(x, y) = \langle -3 + y \cos xy, 16y + x \cos xy \rangle$

16. $\mathbf{F}(x, y) = \langle \frac{5}{5x+y^2} + 15x^4, \frac{2y}{5x+y^2} \rangle$

❖ 15.1 Concept and Application Exercises

In #17–22 (a) sketch the vectors of $\mathbf{F}$ along the specified lines, and (b) explain in complete sentences how $\mathbf{F}$ changes as we move from one line to the other.

17. $\mathbf{F}(x, y) = \langle y, 1 \rangle$; $y = 1$ and $y = 2$

18. $\mathbf{F}(x, y) = \langle y, y \rangle$; $y = 1$ and $y = 2$

19. $\mathbf{F}(x, y) = \langle 1, x \rangle$; $y = 1$ and $y = 2$

20. $\mathbf{F}(x, y) = \langle x, 1 \rangle$; $y = 1$ and $y = 2$

21. $\mathbf{F}(x, y) = \langle x, y \rangle$; $x = 1$ and $x = 2$

22. $\mathbf{F}(x, y) = \langle y, x \rangle$; $x = 1$ and $x = 2$

In #23–28 determine which of the vector fields in Figure 1.6 (if any) depict $\mathbf{F}$.

23. $\mathbf{F}(x, y) = \langle 3, -1 \rangle$

24. $\mathbf{F}(x, y) = \langle 1, -1 \rangle$

25. $\mathbf{F}(x, y) = \langle x, 0.5x \rangle$

26. $\mathbf{F}(x, y) = \langle y, -1 \rangle$

27. $\mathbf{F}(x, y) = \langle x - y, 3 \rangle$

28. $\mathbf{F}(x, y) = \langle x, x^2 - y^2 \rangle$

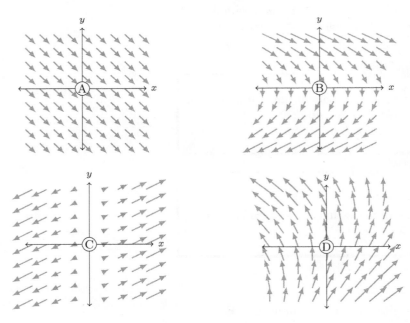

Figure 1.6: Vector fields for exercises #23–28

29. Suppose $\mathbf{F}$ is a vector field for which the streamlines are circles. Explain why $\mathbf{F}$ cannot be the gradient field of a function f.

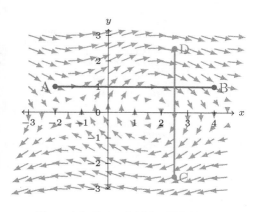

Figure 1.7: Vector field for #31–32   Figure 1.8: Vector field for #33–34

30. If $\mathbf{F} = \nabla f$ is a continuous vector field that's nowhere $\mathbf{0}$, can its streamlines intersect transversely? If not, explain why not. If so, provide an example.

For #31–32, the vector field $\mathbf{F} = \langle P, Q \rangle$ is shown in Figure 1.7.

31. All the points on the line segment from A to B have the same y-coordinate, so the component functions P and Q can be thought of as functions of x. Sketch graphs of P and Q as functions of x between points A and B.

32. All the points on the line segment from C to D have the same x-coordinate, so the component functions P and Q can be thought of as functions of y. Sketch graphs of P and Q as functions of y between points C and D.

In #33–34 , the vector field $\mathbf{F} = \langle P, Q \rangle$ is shown in Figure 1.8.

33. All the points on the line segment from A to B have the same y-coordinate, so the component functions P and Q can be thought of as functions of x. Sketch graphs of P and Q as functions of x between points A and B.

34. All the points on the line segment from C to D have the same x-coordinate, so the component functions P and Q can be thought of as functions of y. Sketch graphs of P and Q as functions of y between points C and D.

35. The map below shows surface winds, which we take to be roughly constant. Suppose a boat sinks at 176° east longitude, 46° north latitude, and the crew fashions a sail on their life raft. (a) Draw the streamline that predicts the path of their raft, and (b) based on your answer to part (a), determine what language they'll need to speak when they finally drift ashore.

Meteorology

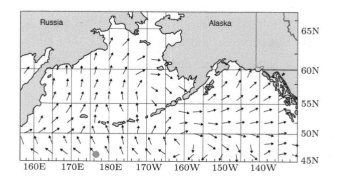

15.2   Line Integrals

In this section we introduce the concept of integrating over a curve, investigate what it might mean, and develop the mathematical tools to do it.

❖ Line Integrals of Scalar-Valued Functions

Figure 2.1 shows the graph of $f(x, y)$ and a curve $\mathcal{C}$ in the xy-plane. By partitioning the curve into small subarcs, we can approximate the net area of the "curtain" between $\mathcal{C}$ and the graph as

$$\text{Area} \approx \sum_{k=1}^{n} \underbrace{f(x_k^*, y_k^*)}_{} \underbrace{\Delta s_k,}_{}$$
$$\text{(height)} \times \text{(length)}$$

where Δs_k is the length of the kth subarc and (x_k^*, y_k^*) is some point in it. Approximation becomes equality in the limit, which exists when f and $\mathcal{C}$ are continuous:

$$\text{Area} = \lim_{\|\Delta s\| \to 0} \sum_{k=1}^{n} f(x_k^*, y_k^*)\, \Delta s_k.$$

This brings us to the following definition.

Definition: Suppose f is a continuous function and $\mathcal{C}$ is a continuous curve. The **line integral** of f over $\mathcal{C}$ with respect to arc length is

$$\int_{\mathcal{C}} f\, ds = \lim_{\|\Delta s\| \to 0} \sum_{k=1}^{n} f(x_k^*, y_k^*)\, \Delta s_k.$$

The basic properties of line integrals follow from their definition as the limit of Riemann sums, just as you saw in Chapter 5 for integrals of the form $\int_a^b f(t)\, dt$.

Properties of Line Integrals (Part 1): Suppose f and g are continuous functions, k is constant, and $\mathcal{C}, \mathcal{C}_1$ and $\mathcal{C}_2$ are continuous curves. Then

1. $\displaystyle \int_{\mathcal{C}} k\, f\, ds = k \int_{\mathcal{C}} f\, ds$

2. $\displaystyle \int_{\mathcal{C}} (f + g)\, ds = \int_{\mathcal{C}} f\, ds + \int_{\mathcal{C}} g\, ds$

3. $\displaystyle \int_{\mathcal{C}_1 + \mathcal{C}_2} f\, ds = \int_{\mathcal{C}_1} f\, ds + \int_{\mathcal{C}_2} f\, ds$

where the notation $\mathcal{C}_1 + \mathcal{C}_2$ means to integrate over the curve $\mathcal{C}_1$ and then over the curve $\mathcal{C}_2$.

▷ Line integrals over parameterized curves

Recall from Section 12.4 that a curve is said to be **smooth** when it can be parameterized by a smooth vector-valued function. When such a parameterization is readily available, we can use it to make calculations. The discussion below shows you how.

Key Idea(s): A line integral is a limit of Riemann sums that calculates the net total of a quantity (e.g. mass or energy) along a line or curve.

We can calculate line integrals of vector fields, or scalar-valued functions.

When calculating the line integral of a vector field, the direction you traverse the curve typically matters.

The term subarc is being used in the same sense as the word subinterval when we first defined Riemann sums. The number of subarcs, n, grows arbitrarily large as $\|\Delta s\| \to 0$.

Perhaps the term curve integral would be more appropriate, but that's not the convention.

Figure 2.1: (left) The surface $z = f(x, y)$ and the curve $\mathcal{C}$ in the xy-plane; (middle) the "curtain" between $\mathcal{C}$ and the graph of f; (right) approximating the area between a curve and the surface $z = f(x, y)$.

Suppose the curve $\mathcal{C}$ is parameterized by the smooth function $\mathbf{r}(t) = \langle x(t),\ y(t) \rangle$ when $t \in [a, b]$, and we partition $[a, b]$ into n subintervals of length Δt, so $a = t_0 < t_1 < t_2 < \cdots < t_n = b$. The corresponding points on $\mathcal{C}$ at $\mathbf{r}(t_0), \mathbf{r}(t_1), \ldots, \mathbf{r}(t_n)$ naturally partition the curve into subarcs of length $\Delta s_1, \Delta s_2, \ldots, \Delta s_n$. When Δt is sufficiently small, we can approximate

$$\underbrace{\Delta s_k}_{\text{distance}} = \underbrace{\|\mathbf{r}'(t_k^*)\|}_{(\text{rate})} \underbrace{\Delta t}_{\times\ (\text{time})}.$$

where t_k^* is some point in the kth subinterval of $[a, b]$. This allows us to write

$$\sum_{k=1}^{n} f(x_k^*,\ y_k^*)\ \Delta s_k \approx \sum_{k=1}^{n} f\big(x(t_k^*),\ y(t_k^*)\big)\ \|\mathbf{r}'(t_k^*)\|\ \Delta t.$$

In the limit, the left-hand side of this equation becomes the line integral over $\mathcal{C}$, and the right-hand side becomes a definite integral over $[a, b]$. This brings us to the following fact.

> You know that distance is (rate)×(time) when moving at a constant rate. The parameterization $\mathbf{r}(t)$ does not necessarily proceed at a constant rate across the kth subarc, but the rate is *almost* constant when the subarc is sufficiently short, which is why we can approximate $\Delta s_k \approx \|\mathbf{r}'(t_k)\|\Delta t$.

Line Integrals of Scalar-Valued Functions Over Parameterized Curves:
Suppose f is a continuous function and $\mathcal{C}$ is parameterized by the smooth function $\mathbf{r}(t) = \langle x(t),\ y(t) \rangle$ over $[a, b]$. Then

$$\int_{\mathcal{C}} f\ ds = \int_a^b f\big(\mathbf{r}(t)\big)\ \|\mathbf{r}'(t)\|\ dt$$

where $f\big(\mathbf{r}(t)\big)$ denotes the value of $\mathbf{f}$ at $\big(x(t),\ y(t)\big)$.

Calculating the line integral of a scalar-valued function

Example 2.1. Suppose $\mathcal{C}$ is the circular arc parameterized by $\mathbf{r}(t) = \langle 2\cos t, 2\sin t \rangle$ over $[0, \pi/3]$, and $f(x, y) = 3x + 5y$. Determine the line integral of f over $\mathcal{C}$.

Solution: With $x = 2\cos t$ and $y = 2\sin t$ we see that $f(x, y) = f(2\cos t, 2\sin t) = 6\cos t + 10\sin t$, and $\mathbf{r}'(t) = \langle -2\sin t, 2\cos t \rangle$ has a constant magnitude of 2. This allows us to write

$$\int_{\mathcal{C}} f\ ds = \int_0^{\pi/3} (6\cos t + 10\sin t)\, 2\, dt = (12\sin t - 20\cos t)\Big|_{t=0}^{t=\pi/3} = 6\sqrt{3} + 10. \quad \blacksquare$$

Calculating the line integral of a scalar-valued function

Example 2.2. Suppose $f(x, y) = x^2 - y$ and $\mathcal{C}$ is the line segment that extends from $(1, 2)$ to $(4, 6)$. Determine whether the graph of f bounds more area above or below $\mathcal{C}$.

Solution: We begin by parameterizing $\mathcal{C}$ with $\mathbf{r}(t) = \langle 1 + 3t, 2 + 4t \rangle$, where $t \in [0, 1]$. Since $\mathbf{r}'(t) = \langle 3, 4 \rangle$, the line integral is

$$\int_0^1 f(1 + 3t, 2 + 4t) \ \|\mathbf{r}'(t)\| \ dt = \int_0^1 \left((1 + 3t)^2 - (2 + 4t) \right) \ 5 \ dt = 15.$$

Since this number is positive, the graph of f captures more area above than below $\mathcal{C}$ (see Figure 2.2). ■

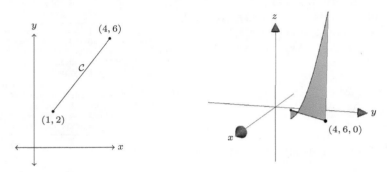

Figure 2.2: For Example 2.2: (left) The line segment $\mathcal{C}$ in the xy-plane; (right) The "curtain" between the graph of f and $\mathcal{C}$.

▷ Application of line integrals: the path of light

The speed of light through a medium is $v = c/n$, where c is its speed in a vacuum, and n is the medium's *index of refraction* ($n = 1$ in a vacuum). So in a region where n is constant, the time it takes light to cross a distance of Δs is

$$\text{Time} = \frac{\text{distance}}{\text{speed}} = \frac{\Delta s}{c/n} = \frac{n}{c} \Delta s. \tag{2.1}$$

When the index of refraction varies along a path, $\mathcal{P}$, equation (2.1) allows us to estimate the time it takes light to traverse it. We begin by approximating $\mathcal{P}$ with a collection of short line segments. If Δs_k is the length of the kth segment, and n_k is the index of refraction at some point on it, the time it takes light to traverse $\mathcal{P}$ is

$$T \approx \sum_k \frac{n_k}{c} \Delta s_k.$$

In the limit as $\|\Delta s\| \to 0$ we get equality. So the time required for light to travel along the path $\mathcal{P}$ is calculated as a line integral:

$$T = \int_{\mathcal{P}} \frac{n}{c} \ ds. \tag{2.2}$$

We would usually write this summation as

$$\sum_{k=1}^{n}$$

where n is the number of segments in the piecewise linear approximation of $\mathcal{P}$, but n denotes the index of refraction in the current context, so instead we're using

$$\sum_k$$

to mean "sum over all of the segments indexed by k."

The time taken by light to travel over a path

Example 2.3. Suppose $\mathcal{P}$ is the circular path in the lower half-plane that extends from $(-1/2, 0)$ to $(1/2, 0)$. How long would it take light to traverse the curve if the index of refraction is $n(x, y) = 1.7 - 0.2x^2 - 0.2y^2$.

Solution: In this case, we can parameterize $\mathcal{P}$ with $\mathbf{r}(\theta) = \langle -0.5\cos\theta, -0.5\sin\theta \rangle$, where $\theta \in [0, \pi]$, which allows us to rewrite equation (2.2) as

$$T = \int_{\mathcal{P}} \frac{n}{c}\, ds = \int_0^\pi \frac{1}{c}\left(1.7 - \frac{1}{5}\left(\frac{\cos\theta}{2}\right)^2 - \frac{1}{5}\left(\frac{\sin\theta}{2}\right)^2\right)\frac{1}{2}\, d\theta$$

which is $^{33\pi}/_{40c}$ seconds (integrate by using half-angle identities). ∎

Said colloquially, *Fermat's Principle* states that light travels along the path of least time. More rigorously, Fermat's Principle says that light travels along the path $\mathcal{P}$ that minimizes the integral in equation (2.2). In the projects of this chapter, you'll see how this principle leads to a better understanding of the way that light travels through a heterogeneous medium.

> In Section 4.7 (exercise #38) you saw Fermat's principle lead to *Snell's Law*, which quantifies the bending of light's trajectory at the interface between two media in which the speed of light differs.

❖ Line Integrals of Vector Fields

Line integrals allow us to characterize the interaction of a vector field and a curve in two ways; one of these describes the extent to which the vector field points (or "flows") along the curve, and the other calculates the extent to which the field crosses it. In this section we will focus on the former.

▷ Intuitive introduction to line integrals of vector fields

Imagine a ball that's falling, and accelerating due to the force of gravity. Said differently, the ball is speeding up because the force of gravity is doing *work* on it, thereby changing its kinetic energy. When you imagined the falling ball a moment ago, was it headed straight down or was it moving sideways as it dropped? In the latter case, some other force is responsible for the side-to-side motion, but gravity has nothing to do with it, so we ignore the side-to-side motion when calculating the work done by gravity.

> You saw this idea in Section 7.4 when we introduced the connection between work and energy.

More generally, when $\mathbf{F}$ is any vector field (of force vectors) and an object moves through it along a curve $\mathcal{C}$, the *work* done by $\mathbf{F}$ on that object depends only on the component of its velocity in the direction of $\mathbf{F}$. You saw this kind of calculation in Section 11.3 when we used the dot product to calculate the work done by a constant force as

$$\text{work} = (\text{force}) \cdot (\text{displacement}).$$

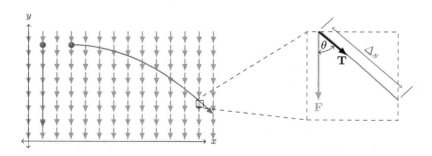

Figure 2.3: An object moving through a vector field. When we zoom in, a segment of the trajectory looks like a linear, which makes it easy to approximate the work done by $\mathbf{F}$ using the dot product.

Now with the line integral, we can extend this idea to forces that vary with position and act on objects that move along curves. In such cases, we think about the trip across the curve $\mathcal{C}$ as the sum of many smaller trips, each across a subarc of length Δs. As shown in Figure 2.3, crossing a subarc corresponds to a displacement of approximately $\mathbf{T}\,\Delta s$, where $\mathbf{T}$ is the curve's unit tangent vector. By treating $\mathbf{F}$ as constant on that small arc, we can approximate the work done by the vector field as the object moves over the subarc:

$$\text{work} \approx \mathbf{F} \cdot \mathbf{T} \, \Delta s.$$

Making this same calculation in each subarc of $\mathcal{C}$, we arrive at an approximation of the work done by the vector field on an object that traverses the entire curve:

$$\text{work} \approx \sum_{k=1}^{n} \mathbf{F}_k \cdot \mathbf{T}_k \, \Delta s,$$

where $\mathbf{F}_k$ is the force vector computed in the kth subarc and $\mathbf{T}_k$ is the unit tangent vector there. This approximation becomes equality in the limit, and we define

$$\text{work} = \lim_{n \to \infty} \sum_{k=1}^{n} \mathbf{F}_k \cdot \mathbf{T}_k \, \Delta s. \qquad (2.3)$$

Although it made this initial discussion a little simpler, it's not mathematically necessary for all the subarcs to have the same length. If the length of the kth arc is Δs_k, we define $\|\Delta s\| = \max\{\Delta s_k\}$ and write the limit in equation (2.3) as

$$\text{work} = \lim_{\|\Delta s\| \to 0} \sum_{k=1}^{n} \mathbf{F}_k \cdot \mathbf{T}_k \, \Delta s_k. \qquad (2.4)$$

> The number of subarcs $n \to \infty$ as $\|\Delta s\| \to 0$.

Since $\mathbf{F}$ and $\mathbf{T}$ depend on s (position along the curve), the right-hand side of equation (2.4) is the limit of Riemann sums. That is, we've defined work as an integral. In the discussion below we generalize this idea, introduce (familiar) properties of this new integral, and demonstrate its calculation is certain cases.

▷ The line integral of a vector field

In order to generalize and formalize the ideas introduced above, we need a new term: a curve is *oriented* when the direction of $\mathbf{T}$ has been specified, so that the curve has an associated direction (e.g., left to right, or top to bottom).

Definition: Suppose $\mathcal{C}$ is a smooth, oriented curve with unit tangent vector $\mathbf{T}$. The *line integral* of $\mathbf{F}$ along $\mathcal{C}$ with respect to arc length is defined to be

$$\int_{\mathcal{C}} \mathbf{F} \cdot \mathbf{T} \, ds = \lim_{\|\Delta s\| \to 0} \sum_{k=1}^{n} \mathbf{F}_k \cdot \mathbf{T}_k \, \Delta s_k,$$

provided that the limit exists.

> Because $\mathcal{C}$ is smooth, we know that $\mathbf{T}$ is continuous (see Section 12.4). If $\mathbf{F}$ is also continuous, the product $\mathbf{F} \cdot \mathbf{T}$ is a continuous function so the line integral will exist.

Work as a line integral

Example 2.4. Suppose $\mathbf{F}$ is the field of force vectors that you see in Figure 2.4, and the curve $\mathcal{C}$ is oriented from left to right. (a) Determine whether $\int_{\mathcal{C}} \mathbf{F} \cdot \mathbf{T} \, ds$ is positive, negative, or 0, and (b) explain what that tells us about the effect of $\mathbf{F}$ on the velocity of an object that traverses $\mathcal{C}$ from left to right.

Solution: (a) Since $\mathcal{C}$ is oriented from left to right, the vector $\mathbf{T}$ always points in a "northeasterly" direction, as does $\mathbf{F}$. Since the angle between $\mathbf{T}$ and $\mathbf{F}$ is always acute, $\mathbf{F} \cdot \mathbf{T} > 0$ on $\mathcal{C}$, so the line integral is positive.

(b) Because $\int_{\mathcal{C}} \mathbf{F} \cdot \mathbf{T} \, ds > 0$, this field of force vectors does positive work on the object, thereby increasing its kinetic energy as it traverses $\mathcal{C}$ from left to right. ∎

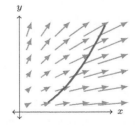

Figure 2.4: The vector field $\mathbf{F}$ and curve $\mathcal{C}$ for Example 2.4.

▷ Line integrals of vector fields over parameterized curves

As we saw earlier in this section, when a parameterization of $\mathcal{C}$ is readily available, we can use it to make calculations. As we did earlier, let's suppose the curve $\mathcal{C}$ is parameterized by the smooth function $\mathbf{r}(t) = \langle x(t), y(t) \rangle$ when $t \in [a, b]$, and we partition $[a, b]$ into n subintervals of length Δt, so $a = t_0 < t_1 < t_2 < \cdots < t_n = b$. The corresponding points on $\mathcal{C}$ at $\mathbf{r}(t_0), \mathbf{r}(t_1), \ldots, \mathbf{r}(t_n)$ naturally partition the curve into subarcs of length $\Delta s_1, \Delta s_2, \ldots, \Delta s_n$. We define $\mathbf{F}_k$ to be $\mathbf{F}$ at the point $\mathbf{r}(t_k)$ and calculate the unit tangent vector by normalizing $\mathbf{r}'(t_k)$, so that

> The definition of *smooth* means that $\mathbf{r}'(t)$ is continuous and never $\mathbf{0}$. This allows us to divide by $\|\mathbf{r}'(t)\|$.

$$\sum_{k=1}^{n} \mathbf{F}_k \cdot \mathbf{T}_k \, \Delta s_k = \sum_{k=1}^{n} \mathbf{F}\big(\mathbf{r}(t_k)\big) \cdot \frac{\mathbf{r}'(t_k)}{\|\mathbf{r}'(t_k)\|} \, \Delta s_k.$$

where $\mathbf{F}\big(\mathbf{r}(t)\big)$ denotes $\mathbf{F}$ at $\big(x(t), y(t)\big)$. Then using $\Delta s \approx \|\mathbf{r}'(t_k)\| \Delta t$ we can approximate the line integral of $\mathbf{F}$ over $\mathcal{C}$ as

$$\sum_{k=1}^{n} \mathbf{F}\big(\mathbf{r}(t_k)\big) \cdot \frac{\mathbf{r}'(t_k)}{\|\mathbf{r}'(t_k)\|} \, \|\mathbf{r}'(t_k)\| \, \Delta t = \sum_{k=1}^{n} \mathbf{F}\big(\mathbf{r}(t_k)\big) \cdot \mathbf{r}'(t_k) \, \Delta t.$$

Because $n \to \infty$ as $\|\Delta s\| \to 0$,

$$\int_{\mathcal{C}} \mathbf{F} \cdot \mathbf{T} \, ds = \lim_{\|\Delta s\| \to 0} \sum_{k=1}^{n} \mathbf{F}_k \cdot \mathbf{T}_k \, \Delta s_k = \lim_{n \to \infty} \sum_{k=1}^{n} \mathbf{F}\big(\mathbf{r}(t_k)\big) \cdot \mathbf{r}'(t_k) \, \Delta t = \int_{a}^{b} \mathbf{F}\big(\mathbf{r}(t)\big) \cdot \mathbf{r}'(t) \, dt.$$

In the same sense that we write $dx = x'(t) \, dt$, we often write $d\mathbf{r} = \mathbf{r}'(t) \, dt$. With this notation, we state our result as follows.

> **Line Integral of a Vector Field Over a Parameterized Curve:** Suppose $\mathbf{r}(t)$ is a smooth parameterization of the oriented curve $\mathcal{C}$, $\mathbf{T}$ is the unit tangent vector to $\mathcal{C}$, and $\mathbf{F}$ is a continuous vector field. Then
> $$\int_{\mathcal{C}} \mathbf{F} \cdot \mathbf{T} \, ds = \int_{\mathcal{C}} \mathbf{F} \cdot d\mathbf{r} = \int_{a}^{b} \mathbf{F}(\mathbf{r}(t)) \cdot \mathbf{r}'(t) \, dt,$$
> where $\mathbf{F}\big(\mathbf{r}(t)\big)$ denotes $\mathbf{F}$ at $\big(x(t), y(t)\big)$.

Calculating line integrals on parameterized curves

Example 2.5. Suppose $\mathbf{F}(x, y) = \langle x - y, y + 2 \rangle$ and $\mathcal{C}$ is the curve parameterized by $\mathbf{r}(t) = \langle t - 1, t^2 \rangle$ when $t \in [1, 2]$. Determine $\int_{\mathcal{C}} \mathbf{F} \cdot d\mathbf{r}$.

Solution: The function $\mathbf{r}(t)$ tells us where we are at each t, and we need to know the value of $\mathbf{F}$ there. Since $x = t - 1$ and $y = t^2$ we can write $\mathbf{F}$ at $\mathbf{r}(t)$ as

$$\mathbf{F} = \langle x - y, \, y + 2 \rangle = \langle t - 1 - t^2, \, t^2 + 2 \rangle.$$

Also from $\mathbf{r}(t)$ we see that $\mathbf{r}'(t) = \langle 1, 2t \rangle$, so

$$\int_{\mathcal{C}} \mathbf{F} \cdot d\mathbf{r} = \int_{1}^{2} \langle t - 1 - t^2, t^2 + 2 \rangle \cdot \langle 1, 2t \rangle \, dt = \int_{1}^{2} (2t^3 - t^2 + 5t - 1) \, dt = \frac{35}{3}. \quad \blacksquare$$

Figure 2.5: $\mathbf{F}$ and $\mathcal{C}$ for Example 2.5. (The vectors have been scaled down for the sake of readability.)

Calculating line integrals on parameterized curves

Example 2.6. Suppose $\mathbf{F}(x, y) = -19.6\mathbf{j}$ and $\mathcal{C}$ is the path parameterized by $\mathbf{r}(t) = \langle t, -\frac{1}{24}(t + 1)^2 + \frac{169}{24} \rangle$ when $t \in [4, 10]$. (a) Show that $\mathcal{C}$ is a parabola with endpoints $(4, 6)$ and $(10, 2)$, and (b) calculate $\int_{\mathcal{C}} \mathbf{F} \cdot d\mathbf{r}$.

Answer: (b) 78.4.   ■

Solution On-line

▷ Properties of line integrals

The properties of line integrals follow from their definition as the limit of Riemann sums, just as you saw in Chapter 5 for integrals of the form $\int_a^b f(t)\,dt$.

Properties of Line Integrals (Part 2): Suppose k is constant, $\mathbf{F}$ and $\mathbf{G}$ are continuous vector fields, and $\mathcal{C}$ is a smooth, oriented curve. Then

$$4.\ \int_{\mathcal{C}} k\mathbf{F}\cdot d\mathbf{r} = k\int_{\mathcal{C}} \mathbf{F}\cdot d\mathbf{r} \qquad\qquad 5.\ \int_{\mathcal{C}}(\mathbf{F}+\mathbf{G})\cdot d\mathbf{r} = \int_{\mathcal{C}}\mathbf{F}\cdot d\mathbf{r} + \int_{\mathcal{C}}\mathbf{G}\cdot d\mathbf{r}.$$

Additionally, in the same way that $\int_a^b f(t)\,dt = -\int_b^a f(t)\,dt$, the line integral of a vector field depends on the orientation of the curve $\mathcal{C}$. In the box below we use a superscripted negative (e.g., $\mathcal{C}^-$) to indicate the reversal of orientation.

Properties of Line Integrals (Part 3): Suppose $\mathbf{F}$ is a continuous vector field, and $\mathcal{C}, \mathcal{C}_1$ and $\mathcal{C}_2$ are smooth, oriented curves. Then

$$6.\ \int_{\mathcal{C}}\mathbf{F}\cdot d\mathbf{r} = -\int_{\mathcal{C}^-}\mathbf{F}\cdot d\mathbf{r} \qquad\qquad 7.\ \int_{\mathcal{C}_1+\mathcal{C}_2}\mathbf{F}\cdot d\mathbf{r} = \int_{\mathcal{C}_1}\mathbf{F}\cdot d\mathbf{r} + \int_{\mathcal{C}_2}\mathbf{F}\cdot d\mathbf{r},$$

where the notation $\mathcal{C}_1 + \mathcal{C}_2$ means to traverse the curve $\mathcal{C}_1$ and then the curve $\mathcal{C}_2$ according to their respective orientations.

The last of these properties is what we have in mind when we integrate over a **piecewise-smooth** curve, meaning one that's composed of smooth curves that have been linked together.

Line integral over a sum of curves

Example 2.7. Suppose $\mathcal{C}$ is the upper half of the unit circle, with its ends connected by the line segment from $(-1,0)$ to $(1,0)$, and $\mathbf{F}(x,y) = \langle x+y, x^2\rangle$. If $\mathcal{C}$ is oriented in the counterclockwise direction, determine $\int_{\mathcal{C}}\mathbf{F}\cdot d\mathbf{r}$.

Solution: In this case we traverse $\mathcal{C}$ by crossing the semicircle, which we'll designate as $\mathcal{C}_1$, and then the horizontal line segment, which we'll call $\mathcal{C}_2$, both oriented according to $\mathcal{C}$ (see Figure 2.6). Then property 4 (above) tells us that the line integral of $\mathbf{F}$ over $\mathcal{C}$ is the sum of $\int_{\mathcal{C}_1}\mathbf{F}\cdot d\mathbf{r}$ and $\int_{\mathcal{C}_2}\mathbf{F}\cdot d\mathbf{r}$, which we calculate separately.

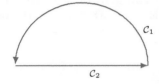

Figure 2.6: Partitioning $\mathcal{C}$ into $\mathcal{C}_1$ and $\mathcal{C}_2$.

Let's parameterize $\mathcal{C}_1$ with $\mathbf{r}(t) = \langle \cos t, \sin t\rangle$ when $t \in [0,\pi]$. Then $\mathbf{F}(\mathbf{r}(t)) = \langle \cos t + \sin t, \cos^2 t\rangle$ and $\mathbf{r}'(t) = \langle -\sin t, \cos t\rangle$ so

$$
\begin{aligned}
\int_{\mathcal{C}_1}\mathbf{F}\cdot d\mathbf{r} &= \int_0^\pi \langle \cos t + \sin t, \cos^2 t\rangle \cdot \langle -\sin t, \cos t\rangle\,dt \\
&= \int_0^\pi (\cos^3 t - \sin t\cos t - \sin^2 t)\,dt = -\frac{\pi}{2}.
\end{aligned}
$$

Now let's parameterize $\mathcal{C}_2$ with $\mathbf{r}(t) = \langle t, 0\rangle$ where $t \in [-1,1]$. Then $\mathbf{F}(\mathbf{r}(t)) = \langle t+0, t^2\rangle$ and $\mathbf{r}'(t) = \langle 1, 0\rangle$ so

$$\int_{\mathcal{C}_2}\mathbf{F}\cdot d\mathbf{r} = \int_{-1}^1 t\,dt = 0,$$

from which we conclude that $\int_{\mathcal{C}}\mathbf{F}\cdot d\mathbf{r} = \int_{\mathcal{C}_1}\mathbf{F}\cdot d\mathbf{r} + \int_{\mathcal{C}_2}\mathbf{F}\cdot d\mathbf{r} = -\frac{\pi}{2} + 0 = -\frac{\pi}{2}$. ∎

Line integral over a sum of curves

Example 2.8. Suppose $\mathbf{F}(x,y) = \langle y^2, 3x-y\rangle$ and $\mathcal{C}$ is the triangle connecting $(1,0), (0,1)$ and $(0,0)$, oriented counterclockwise. Calculate $\int_{\mathcal{C}}\mathbf{F}\cdot d\mathbf{r}$.

Solution
On-line

Answer: $0 + \frac{1}{2} + \frac{2}{3} = \frac{7}{6}$.   ∎

In Examples 2.7 and 2.8 we integrated $\mathbf{F} \cdot \mathbf{T}$ around a curve that started and ended at the same place. Such curves are said to be **closed**, and line integrals of vector fields around them are often called **circulation integrals**.

> We'll study circulation integrals in greater detail in Section 15.5.

▷ Differential Form of the Line Integral

Suppose the vector field $\mathbf{F}(x, y)$ is $\langle P(x,y), Q(x,y) \rangle$, and $\mathcal{C}$ is an oriented curve parameterized by $\mathbf{r}(t) = \langle x(t), y(t) \rangle$ over $[a, b]$. Then $d\mathbf{r} = \langle x'(t), y'(t) \rangle \, dt$, and as done in previous examples, we can write the line integral of $\mathbf{F}$ over $\mathcal{C}$ with respect to arc length as

$$\int_{\mathcal{C}} \mathbf{F} \cdot d\mathbf{r} = \int_a^b \left[P\big(x(t), y(t)\big) \, x'(t) + Q\big(x(t), y(t)\big) \, y'(t) \right] dt.$$

Due to the linearity of the definite integral, this is the same as

$$\int_{\mathcal{C}} \mathbf{F} \cdot d\mathbf{r} = \int_a^b P\big(x(t), y(t)\big) \, x'(t) \, dt + \int_a^b Q\big(x(t), y(t)\big) \, y'(t) \, dt \qquad (2.5)$$

when both integrals on the right-hand side exist independently. Because $x'(t) \, dt = dx$ and $y'(t) \, dt = dy$, the integrals on the right-hand side are often written as

$$\int_{\mathcal{C}} P(x, y) \, dx \quad \text{and} \quad \int_{\mathcal{C}} Q(x, y) \, dy,$$

respectively. Using this notation, equation (2.5) becomes

$$\int_{\mathcal{C}} \mathbf{F} \cdot d\mathbf{r} = \int_{\mathcal{C}} P(x, y) \, dx + \int_{\mathcal{C}} Q(x, y) \, dy,$$

which is commonly written as

$$\int_{\mathcal{C}} \mathbf{F} \cdot d\mathbf{r} = \int_{\mathcal{C}} P(x, y) \, dx + Q(x, y) \, dy. \qquad (2.6)$$

> This is new notation, not a new idea.

As you'll see in the examples below, when y is a function of x along $\mathcal{C}$, we can often write

$$\int_{\mathcal{C}} P(x, y) \, dx = \int_a^b P\big(x(t), \, y(t)\big) \, x'(t) \, dt = \int_{x(a)}^{x(b)} P\big(x, \, y(x)\big) \, dx,$$

which allows us to compute the integral without needing to know the parameterization $\mathbf{r}(t)$. Similarly, if x is a function of y along $\mathcal{C}$,

$$\int_{\mathcal{C}} Q(x, y) \, dy = \int_a^b Q\big(x(t), \, y(t)\big) \, y'(t) \, dt = \int_{y(a)}^{y(b)} Q\big(x(y), \, y\big) \, dy.$$

> Notice that the bounds of integration changed from a and b to $x(a)$ and $x(b)$ when we changed the variable of integration from t to x. In essence, the bounds of the integral in t tell us *when* to start and stop. The corresponding bounds of the integral in x tell us *where* to start and stop.

Using the differential form of a line integral

Example 2.9. Suppose $\mathcal{C}$ is the line segment directed from $(2, 4)$ to $(1, 1)$. Determine $\int_{\mathcal{C}} P(x, y) \, dx + Q(x, y) \, dy$ when $P(x, y) = 2x - y$, and $Q(x, y) = x^2 - 7$.

Solution: Let's begin by establishing a little intuition. This line segment is oriented "downward," and $\mathbf{F} = \langle P, Q \rangle$ points in roughly the same direction. Since the angle between $\mathbf{T}$ and $\mathbf{F}$ is acute, we expect the line integral to be positive. Next, we make the calculation.

Our path of integration lies on the line $y = 3x - 2$, and x decreases from $x = 2$ to $x = 1$. So

$$\int_{\mathcal{C}} P(x,y)\,dx = \int_{\underbrace{2}}^{1} \big(\underbrace{2x - (3x - 2)}\big)\,dx = \int_{2}^{1} (2 - x)\,dx = -\frac{1}{2},$$

$\qquad$ Initial and terminal values of x on $\mathcal{C}$ $\qquad$ $y = 3x - 2$ along $\mathcal{C}$

and because y descends from 4 to 1,

$$\int_{\mathcal{C}} Q(x,y)\,dy = \int_{\underbrace{4}}^{1} \left[\underbrace{\left(\tfrac{y+2}{3}\right)^2 - 7} \right] dy = 14.$$

$\qquad$ Initial and terminal values of y on $\mathcal{C}$ $\qquad$ $x = (y+2)/3$ along $\mathcal{C}$

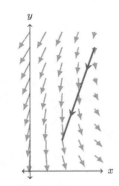

Figure 2.7:　$\mathbf{F}$ and $\mathcal{C}$ for Example 2.9 (vectors not to scale).

Adding these together, we see $\int_{\mathcal{C}} P(x,y)\,dx + Q(x,y)\,dy = -\frac{1}{2} + 14 = \frac{27}{2}.$ ∎

Using the differential form of a line integral

Example 2.10. Determine $\int_{\mathcal{C}} P(x,y)\,dx + Q(x,y)\,dy$ (without parameterizing $\mathcal{C}$) when $\mathcal{C}$ is the curve $y = x^3$ from $(2,8)$ to $(3,27)$, $P(x,y) = x+y$, and $Q(x,y) = {}^x\!/y$.

Answer: ${}^{87}/_4$. ∎

Solution On-line

❖ Life in 3D

Our discussion has focused on line integrals over curves in the plane, but line integrals over curves in space are fundamentally the same. The only practical change to the parameterized form of line integrals is that $\mathbf{F}$ and $\mathbf{T}$ are 3-vectors instead of 2-vectors, and the differential form requires us to account for the contribution of that third component. Specifically, when $\mathcal{C}$ is a smooth, oriented curve parameterized by $\mathbf{r}(t) = \langle x(t), y(t), z(t) \rangle$ over $[a,b]$, the line integral of the continuous vector field $\mathbf{F} = \langle P, Q, R \rangle$ with respect to arc length over $\mathcal{C}$ is

In fact, notice that none of the boxed statements in this section specify that the curve $\mathcal{C}$ is *in the plane.*

$$\int_{\mathcal{C}} \mathbf{F} \cdot \mathbf{T}\,ds = \int_{\mathcal{C}} \mathbf{F} \cdot d\mathbf{r} = \int_{\mathcal{C}} P(x,y,z)\,dx + Q(x,y,z)\,dy + R(x,y,z)\,dz, \qquad (2.7)$$

where the right-hand equality is the natural extension of equation (2.6), with

$$\int_{\mathcal{C}} P(x,y,z)\,dx = \int_{a}^{b} P\big(x(t), y(t), z(t)\big)\,x'(t)\,dt$$

$$\int_{\mathcal{C}} Q(x,y,z)\,dy = \int_{a}^{b} Q\big(x(t), y(t), z(t)\big)\,y'(t)\,dt$$

$$\int_{\mathcal{C}} R(x,y,z)\,dz = \int_{a}^{b} R\big(x(t), y(t), z(t)\big)\,z'(t)\,dt.$$

And similarly, the line integral of the scalar-valued function f over $\mathcal{C}$ is

$$\int_{\mathcal{C}} f(x,y,z)\,ds = \int_{a}^{b} f\big(x(t), y(t), z(t)\big)\,\|\mathbf{r}'(t)\|\,dt.$$

Line integral of a scalar-valued function over a curve in space

Example 2.11. Determine the mass of the straight wire between $(2,0,4)$ and $(3,5,7)$ if length is measured in meters and its density is $\rho(x,y,z) = xz + y \ \frac{\mathrm{g}}{\mathrm{m}}$.

Solution: The displacement vector between $(2,0,4)$ and $(3,5,7)$ is $\langle 1,5,3 \rangle$, so we can parameterize the wire with $\mathbf{r}(t) = \langle 2+t, 0+5t, 4+3t \rangle$ with $t \in [0,1]$. Then $\mathbf{r}'(t) = \langle 1,5,3 \rangle$ has a constant magnitude of $\sqrt{35}$, so the wire's mass is

$$\int_{\mathcal{C}} \overbrace{\rho(x,y,z)}^{\text{g/m}} \overbrace{ds}^{\text{m}} = \int_0^1 \Big((2+t)(4+3t) + 5t \Big) \sqrt{35}\, dt = \frac{33}{2}\sqrt{35} \text{ g.} \qquad \blacksquare$$

In the following example, we use a technique similar to that of Examples 2.9 and 2.10, in which a parameterization is not needed.

Line integral of a vector field over a parameterized curve in space

Example 2.12. Suppose $\mathbf{F}(x,y) = \langle y, x, x+z^2 \rangle$ and $\mathcal{C}$ is the line segment that extends from $(-1,1,6)$ to $(2,5,3)$. Calculate the line integral of $\mathbf{F}$ over $\mathcal{C}$.

Solution: Since x increases from -1 to 2 as y increases from 1 to 5 and z decreases from 6 to 3, we begin by rewriting equation (2.7) as

$$\int_{\mathcal{C}} \mathbf{F} \cdot d\mathbf{r} = \int_{-1}^{2} P(x,y,z)\, dx + \int_{1}^{5} Q(x,y,z)\, dy + \int_{6}^{3} R(x,y,z)\, dz,$$

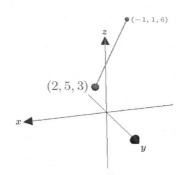

(−1, 1, 6)

(2, 5, 3)

where $P(x,y,z) = y$, $Q(x,y,z) = x$, and $R(x,y,z) = x+z^2$. In order to calculate the first of these integrals, we need to express $P(x,y,z)$ in terms of *only* x, which we accomplish by using the the symmetric equations of the line segment. Specifically, since the displacement vector extending from $(-1,1,6)$ to $(2,5,3)$ is $\langle 3,4,-3 \rangle$, the symmetric equations are

Figure 2.8: The directed line segment $\mathcal{C}$ in Example 2.12.

$$\frac{x+1}{3} = \frac{y-1}{4} = \frac{z-6}{-3}.$$

The first of these equations tells us

$$y = \frac{7}{3} + \frac{4}{3}x, \quad \text{which is the same as} \quad x = \frac{3}{4}y - \frac{7}{4},$$

so that

$$\int_{-1}^{2} P(x,y,z)\, dx = \int_{-1}^{2} \left(\frac{7}{3} + \frac{4}{3}x\right) dx = 9 \quad \text{and} \quad \int_{1}^{5} Q(x,y,z)\, dy = \int_{1}^{5}\left(\frac{3}{4}y - \frac{7}{4}\right) dy = 2.$$

Similarly, by rewriting the equation $\frac{x+1}{3} = \frac{z-6}{-3}$ as $x = 5-z$, we can calculate the remaining integral as

$$\int_{6}^{3} (5 - z + z^2)\, dz = -\frac{129}{2}.$$

Adding this to the previous calculations, we arrive at a final answer of

$$\int_{\mathcal{C}} \mathbf{F} \cdot d\mathbf{r} = 9 + 2 - \frac{129}{2} = -\frac{107}{2}. \qquad \blacksquare$$

Line integral of a vector field over a parameterized curve in space

Example 2.13. Suppose $\mathbf{F}$ and $\mathcal{C}$ are as in Example 2.12. (a) Verify that $\mathcal{C}$ is parameterized by $\mathbf{r}(t) = \langle -1+3t, 1+4t, 6-3t \rangle$ when $t \in [0,1]$, and (b) use the parameterization to calculate $\int_{\mathcal{C}} \mathbf{F} \cdot d\mathbf{r}$.

Solution On-line

Answer: (b) $-107/2$. $\qquad \blacksquare$

> ### You should know
>
> - the terms *smooth, piecewise-smooth, oriented, closed curve,* and *circulation integral;*
> - the definition of the line integral as the limit of Riemann sums;
> - the arithmetic properties of line integrals;
> - the notations $\mathcal{C}^-$, $\mathcal{C}_1 + \mathcal{C}_2$, and $\mathbf{F} \cdot d\mathbf{r}$

> ### You should be able to
>
> - calculate line integrals of vector fields over smooth curves;
> - determine the work done by a vector field on a moving object;
> - determine the net area between the graph of $f(x, y)$ and a curve $\mathcal{C}$.

❖ 15.2 Skill Exercises

In #1–4 use a Riemann sum to approximate $\int_{\mathcal{C}} f(x, y) \, ds$ where $\mathcal{C}$ is the curve that connects points A and B (which is circular in #1 and #2). Numbers beside points on $\mathcal{C}$ indicate the value of f.

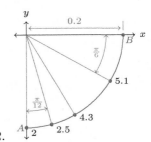

1.

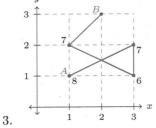

3.

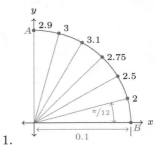

2.

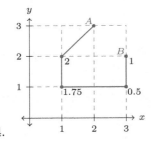

4.

In #5–10 (a) sketch the curve $\mathcal{C}$ parameterized by $\mathbf{r}(t)$, and (b) determine $\int_{\mathcal{C}} \mathbf{F} \cdot d\mathbf{r}$.

5. $\mathbf{r}(t) = \langle 3t + 1, 2t + 4 \rangle$, $t \in [1, 2]$, $\mathbf{F}(x, y) = \langle 8x - y, 3 \rangle$

6. $\mathbf{r}(t) = \langle 2t - 5, t^2 + 1 \rangle$, $t \in [-1, 1]$, $\mathbf{F}(x, y) = \langle 7y, x \rangle$

7. $\mathbf{r}(t) = \langle t, 1/t \rangle$, $t \in [0.25, 5]$, $\mathbf{F}(x, y) = \langle x^2, x \rangle$

8. $\mathbf{r}(t) = \langle \sqrt{t}, t + 4 \rangle$, $t \in [0, 4]$, $\mathbf{F}(x, y) = \langle -1, xy \rangle$

9. $\mathbf{r}(t) = \langle \cos t, \sin t \rangle$, $t \in [0, 2\pi]$, $\mathbf{F}(x, y) = \langle 9x, y \rangle$

10. $\mathbf{r}(t) = \langle 2 \sin t, 2 \cos t \rangle$, $t \in [\pi, 2\pi]$, $\mathbf{F}(x, y) = \langle 9y, x \rangle$

In #11–16 determine the line integral $\int_{\mathcal{C}} P(x, y) \, dx + Q(x, y) \, dy$. The words "from" and "to" indicate the orientation of $\mathcal{C}$.

11. $P(x, y) = 3$, $Q(x, y) = -5$, $\mathcal{C}$ is the linear path from $(0, 2)$ to $(1, 7)$.

12. $P(x, y) = -4$, $Q(x, y) = 7$, $\mathcal{C}$ is the linear path from $(-1, 5)$ to $(2, -1)$.

13. $P(x, y) = -7x$, $Q(x, y) = y^2$, $\mathcal{C}$ is the linear path from $(1, -1)$ to $(-4, -16)$.

14. $P(x, y) = x^2$, $Q(x, y) = 3y$, $\mathcal{C}$ is the linear path from $(-1, 3)$ to $(-2, 4)$.

15. $P(x, y) = x + y$, $Q(x, y) = x - y$, $\mathcal{C}$ is the segment of the parabola $y = x^2$ that extends from $(0, 0)$ to $(2, 4)$.

16. $P(x, y) = yx^2$, $Q(x, y) = 3y$, $\mathcal{C}$ is the segment of $y = \sin x$ that extends from $(\pi/2, 1)$ to $(0, 0)$.

In #17–22 determine $\int_{\mathcal{C}} \mathbf{F} \cdot d\mathbf{r}$ when $\mathcal{C}$ is the specified piecewise smooth curve.

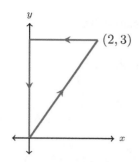

Figure 2.9: The directed path $\mathcal{C}$ for Exercise 17.

17. $\mathbf{F}(x, y) = \langle 1, 5 \rangle$; $\mathcal{C}$ is the triangle shown in Figure 2.9, oriented clockwise.

18. $\mathbf{F}(x, y) = \langle -3, 1 \rangle$; $\mathcal{C}$ is the rectangle shown in Figure 2.10, oriented clockwise.

19. $\mathbf{F}(x, y) = \langle 3y, 2x \rangle$; $\mathcal{C}$ is shown in Figure 2.11. The curved side is $y = x^2$.

20. $\mathbf{F}(x, y) = \langle xy, x + y \rangle$; $\mathcal{C}$ is the upper semi-circle of radius 2 joined with the segment of the x-axis that connects $(-2, 0)$ to $(2, 0)$, oriented counterclockwise.

21. $\mathbf{F}(x, y) = \langle 3x, 4y \rangle$; $\mathcal{C}$ is the curve $y = \sin(x)$ when $x \in [0, \pi]$ and $y = x - \pi$ when $x \in [\pi, 4]$, oriented from left to right.

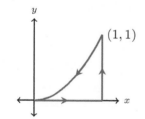

Figure 2.10: The directed path $\mathcal{C}$ for Exercise 18.

22. $\mathbf{F}(x, y) = \langle x, x - y \rangle$; $\mathcal{C}$ is the curve $x = 2 + y(y - 1)$ when $y \in [0, 1]$ and $y = 5x - 9$ when $y \in [1, 2]$, oriented from bottom to top.

In #23–26 determine the line integral of f over the curve $\mathcal{C}$.

23. $f(x, y) = 3x + 4y$; $\mathcal{C}$ is the line segment extending from $(1, 2)$ to $(7, 3)$

24. $f(x, y) = y - 4x$; $\mathcal{C}$ is the line segment extending from $(1, 10)$ to $(2, 15)$

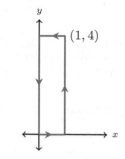

Figure 2.11: The directed path $\mathcal{C}$ for Exercise 19.

25. $f(x, y) = \sqrt{x^2 + 4y^2}$; $\mathcal{C}$ is the part of $y = x^2$ extending from $(0, 0)$ to $(-3, 9)$

26. $f(x, y) = xy$; $\mathcal{C}$ is the part of $y = \sqrt{x}$ that extends from $(1, 1)$ to $(0, 0)$

In #27–32 determine the line integral $\int_{\mathcal{C}} P(x, y, z)\, dx + Q(x, y, z)\, dy + R(x, y, z)\, dz$.

27. $P(x, y, z) = 3x$, $Q(x, y, z) = 4z$, $R(x, y, z) = 7y$; $\mathcal{C}$ is the line segment from $(1, 2, 3)$ to $(2, 5, 7)$.

28. $P(x, y, z) = xy$, $Q(x, y, z) = xz$, $R(x, y, z) = y + 2$; $\mathcal{C}$ is the line segment from $(6, 1, 0)$ to $(4, 3, 3)$.

29. $P(x, y, z) = 13z$, $Q(x, y, z) = x - z$, $R(x, y, z) = y$; $\mathcal{C}$ is the intersection of the plane $y = x$ with the paraboloid $z = x^2 + y^2$, from $x = 0$ to $x = 1$.

30. $P(x, y, z) = z - x$, $Q(x, y, z) = x + z$, $R(x, y, z) = y^2$; $\mathcal{C}$ is the intersection of the plane $y = -3x$ with the paraboloid $z = 5x^2 + y^2$, from $x = 0$ to $x = 1$.

31. $P(x, y, z) = 2y$, $Q(x, y, z) = 3z$, $R(x, y, z) = x^2$; $\mathcal{C}$ is the intersection of the plane $y = 0$ with the ellipsoid $x^2 + 7y^2 + z^2 = 100$, from $(0, 0, 10)$ to $(0, 0, -10)$.

32. $P(x, y, z) = x$, $Q(x, y, z) = 3y$, $R(x, y, z) = z + 8$; $\mathcal{C}$ is the intersection of the plane $y = x$ with the ellipsoid $8x^2 + y^2 + z^2 = 400$, from $(0, 0, -20)$ to $(0, 0, 20)$.

In #33–40 determine $\int_{\mathcal{C}} f\, ds$ when $\mathcal{C}$ is the curve parameterized by $\mathbf{r}(t)$, $t \in [0, 1]$.

33. $f(x, y) = 3x - y^2$;
$\mathbf{r}(t) = \langle 4t - 1, 3t + 7 \rangle$

34. $f(x, y) = xe^y$;
$\mathbf{r}(t) = \langle 5t + 1, 2t - 3 \rangle$

35. $f(x, y) = 3 + x \sin(y)$;
$\mathbf{r}(t) = \langle 1 - t, 0.25\pi t \rangle$

36. $f(x, y) = x - y$;
$\mathbf{r}(t) = \langle 1 - t^2, 3t^2 - 1 \rangle$

37. $f(x, y, z) = x + y/z$;
$\mathbf{r}(t) = \langle 3t, 2t - 1, 8t + 1 \rangle$

38. $f(x, y, z) = x/yz$;
$\mathbf{r}(t) = \langle 2 - t, t + 4, 5t - 3 \rangle$

39. $f(x, y, z) = x + yz$;
$\mathbf{r}(t) = \langle t^3, 5t^3, 2t^3 - 1 \rangle$

40. $f(x, y, z) = xy$;
$\mathbf{r}(t) = \langle 10t, 4, 5t^2 \rangle$

41. Suppose $\mathbf{F}(x, y) = \langle 4y, 7x \rangle$ and $\mathcal{C}$ is a circle of radius r, oriented in the counterclockwise direction. Show that $\int_{\mathcal{C}} \mathbf{F} \cdot d\mathbf{r} = k\pi r^2$ for some constant k.

42. Suppose $\mathbf{F}(x, y) = \langle 5y, 2x \rangle$ and $\mathcal{C}$ is the rectangle with a diagonal that connects the origin to the point (a, b), oriented in the counterclockwise direction. Show that $\int_{\mathcal{C}} \mathbf{F} \cdot d\mathbf{r}$ is directly proportional to the area enclosed by $\mathcal{C}$.

❖ 15.2 Concept and Application Exercises

In #43–46 determine whether the line integrals of the vector field $\mathbf{F}$ (shown in gray) over the oriented curves A, B and C are positive, negative, or zero.

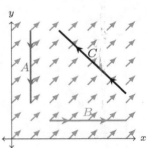

43.

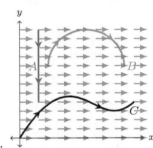

44.

45. See Figure 2.12

46. See Figure 2.13

For #47-50, suppose $\mathbf{F}$ is field of force vectors, and $\mathcal{C}$ is the path described.

47. (a) Sketch $\mathbf{F}(x, y) = \langle y, -x \rangle$ in the xy-plane. (b) Determine whether $\int_{\mathcal{C}} \mathbf{F} \cdot d\mathbf{r}$ is positive, negative, or zero when $\mathcal{C}$ is a circular, clockwise-oriented streamline of $\mathbf{F}$, and (c) explain what that tells us about the field's effect on the kinetic energy of an object that traverses $\mathcal{C}$.

48. (a) Sketch $\mathbf{F}(x, y) = \langle 1, 0 \rangle$ in the xy-plane. (b) Determine whether $\int_{\mathcal{C}} \mathbf{F} \cdot d\mathbf{r}$ is positive, negative, or zero when $\mathcal{C}$ is as shown in Figure 2.14. (c) What will be the field's effect on the kinetic energy of an object that traverses $\mathcal{C}$.

49. $\mathbf{F}(x, y, z) = \langle x, 0, y \rangle$, and $\mathcal{C}$ is parameterized by $\mathbf{r}(t) = \langle 1 + t, t^2, t \rangle$ when $t \in [0, 2]$. (a) Calculate $\int_{\mathcal{C}} \mathbf{F} \cdot d\mathbf{r}$, and (b) explain what that tells us about the field's effect on the kinetic energy of an object that traverses $\mathcal{C}$ from $\mathbf{r}(0)$ to $\mathbf{r}(2)$.

50. $\mathbf{F}(x, y, z) = \langle -x, z, y \rangle$, and $\mathcal{C}$ is parameterized by $\mathbf{r}(t) = \langle t, \cos t, \sin t \rangle$ when $t \in [0, 2\pi]$. (a) Calculate $\int_{\mathcal{C}} \mathbf{F} \cdot d\mathbf{r}$, and (b) explain what that tells us about the field's effect on the kinetic energy of an object that traverses $\mathcal{C}$ from $\mathbf{r}(0)$ to $\mathbf{r}(2\pi)$.

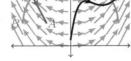

Figure 2.12: For #45.

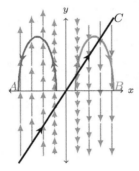

Figure 2.13: For #46.

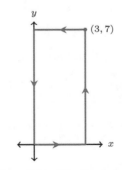

Figure 2.14: The directed path $\mathcal{C}$ for Exercise 48.

In #51–52 the curve $\mathcal{C}$ is the circle $x^2 + y^2 = 1$.

51. Suppose $f(x,y) = 1 + 2x + y$. (a) Based on the graph of f, explain why $\int_{\mathcal{C}} f\, ds$ should be positive, and (b) calculate the integral.

52. Suppose $f(x,y) = 3x - 5y$. (a) Based on the graph of f, explain why $\int_{\mathcal{C}} f\, ds$ should be zero, and (b) calculate the integral.

53. Suppose $f(x,y) = 1 - x^2 + y$ and $\mathcal{C}$ extends from $(2,0)$ to $(0,2)$ along $x^2 + y^2 = 4$. (a) Find a point on $\mathcal{C}$ at which $f > 0$, and another where $f > 0$, and (b) determine whether the graph of f bounds more area above or below $\mathcal{C}$.

54. Suppose $f(x,y) = 1 - x - y$ and $\mathcal{C}$ extends linearly from $(0,-1)$ to $(3,0)$. Determine whether the graph of f bounds more area above or below $\mathcal{C}$.

In #55-58, treat $\mathcal{C}$ as a wire, with x, y, and z in cm; ρ is a density.

55. $\mathcal{C}$ is parameterized by $\mathbf{r}(t) = \langle 3t+1, 5-t^2 \rangle$ when $t \in [0,1]$ and $\rho(x,y) = x^2 + 9y$ g/cm. Determine (a) the units of $\int_{\mathcal{C}} \rho(x,y)\, ds$, and (b) the mass of the wire.

                                                                     `Linear Mass Density`

56. $\mathcal{C}$ is parameterized by $\mathbf{r}(t) = \langle 4+t^2, t^3 \rangle$ when $t \in [1,2]$ and $\rho(x,y) = 1 + (x-4)/y$ g/mm. Determine (a) the units of $\int_{\mathcal{C}} \rho(x,y)\, ds$, and (b) the mass of the wire.

                                                                     `Linear Mass Density`

57. $\mathcal{C}$ is parameterized by $\mathbf{r}(t) = \langle \sqrt{2}\,t, e^t, e^{-t} \rangle$ when $t \in [0,1]$, and $\rho(x,y,z) = 1 + x + yz$ in coulombs/cm. Determine the net charge of the wire.

                                                                     `Linear Charge Density`

58. $\mathcal{C}$ is the linear segment that connects $(1,3,4)$ to $(-1,5,7)$, and $\rho(x,y,z) = 7x^2 + 8yz$ in coulombs/cm. Determine the net charge of the wire.

                                                                     `Linear Charge Density`

In # 59–62 the index of refraction is $n(x,y)$ in the relevant region. Determine how long it would take light to travel across the curve $\mathcal{C}$ (answer in terms of $1/c$).

                                                                     `Optics`

59. $n(x,y) = 1 + 0.1x + 0.2y$; $\mathcal{C}$ extends linearly from $(0,0)$ to $(1,1)$.

60. $n(x,y) = 1 + 0.4x + 0.3y$; $\mathcal{C}$ extends linearly from $(0,1)$ to $(1,1/2)$.

61. $n(x,y) = 1 + 0.5x + 0.1y$; $\mathcal{C}$ extends linearly from $(0,1)$ to $(1,0)$.

62. $n(x,y) = 1 + 0.5x + 0.1y$; $\mathcal{C}$ is the segment of $y = (x-1)^2$ that extends from $(0,1)$ to $(1,0)$.

63. Suppose that the index of refraction is constant. Use Fermat's Principle to show that light will travel along a line.

64. This exercise extends Example 2.3. (a) Determine the time it would take light to cross the line segment that extends between $(-1/2, 0)$ and $(1/2, 0)$. (b) Suppose $\mathcal{C}$ is a segment of the ellipse $4x^2 + (y/b)^2 = 1$ connecting those same points. Show that there is a value of b for which the travel time is less than your answer from part (a). And (c) what does Fermat's Principle say about the path of light through this medium?

15.3   Fundamental Theorem of Line Integrals

In Section 15.2 you learned that when the smooth curve $\mathcal{C}$ is parameterized by $\mathbf{r}(t)$ over $[a, b]$, the line integral of the vector field $\mathbf{F}$ with respect to arc length over $\mathcal{C}$ is

$$\int_{\mathcal{C}} \mathbf{F} \cdot \mathbf{T} \, ds = \int_{\mathcal{C}} \mathbf{F} \cdot d\mathbf{r} = \int_a^b \mathbf{F}(\mathbf{r}(t)) \cdot \mathbf{r}'(t) \, dt. \tag{3.1}$$

In this section, we're going to discuss such integrals in the special case when there is a potential for the vector field, for which $\mathbf{F} = \nabla f$. The potential function plays the same role for line integrals that antiderivatives played in Chapter 5 when evaluating definite integrals (evaluate at the endpoints, and subtract).

> **Key Idea(s):** *When $\mathbf{F} = \nabla f$, we can use f to calculate the line integral of $\mathbf{F}$, much as we used antiderivatives to evaluate definite integrals in single-variable calculus.*
>
> *For certain vector fields, the the particular path along which we integrate $\mathbf{F}$ is irrelevant. All that matters is the location of the endpoints.*

✥ Fundamental Theorem of Line Integrals

Suppose $\mathbf{r}(t) = \langle x(t), y(t) \rangle$ is a smooth parameterization of the curve $\mathcal{C}$. When f is a differentiable function for which $\mathbf{F} = \nabla f$, the Chain Rule tells us that

$$\mathbf{F}(\mathbf{r}(t)) \cdot \mathbf{r}'(t) = \nabla f \cdot \mathbf{r}' = \frac{\partial f}{\partial x} \frac{dx}{dt} + \frac{\partial f}{\partial y} \frac{dy}{dt} = \frac{df}{dt}$$

so the line integral of $\mathbf{F}$ with respect to arc length over $\mathcal{C}$ is

> Similarly for smooth curves in 3-space, when $\mathbf{r}(t) = \langle x(t), y(t), z(t) \rangle$.

$$\int_{\mathcal{C}} \mathbf{F} \cdot d\mathbf{r} = \int_a^b \mathbf{F}(\mathbf{r}(t)) \cdot \mathbf{r}'(t) \, dt = \underbrace{\int_a^b \frac{df}{dt} \, dt = f(x(b), y(b)) - f(x(a), y(a)).}_{\text{From the Fundamental Theorem of Calculus (see Chapter 5).}}$$

We state this fact formally as follows:

> **Fundamental Theorem of Line Integrals:** Suppose $\mathcal{C}$ is a curve that's parameterized by the smooth function $\mathbf{r}(t)$, when $t \in [a, b]$, and f is a differentiable function with continuous partial derivatives. Then
>
> $$\int_{\mathcal{C}} \nabla f \cdot d\mathbf{r} = f(\mathbf{r}(b)) - f(\mathbf{r}(a)),$$
>
> where $f(\mathbf{r}(t))$ denotes $f(x(t), y(t))$.

Intuitively speaking, you're seeing that $\mathbf{F} \cdot \mathbf{r}'(t)$ is the rate at which the value of f changes as we move along $\mathcal{C}$. This allows us to think about the integral of $\mathbf{F} \cdot \mathbf{r}'$ in terms of f. We could, for instance, think about $\mathcal{C}$ crossing the level curves of f to get from point $A = (x_a, y_a)$ to point $B = (x_b, y_b)$ as depicted in Figure 3.1. The integral of $\frac{df}{dt}$ tells us net change in the function value, which depends on the levels curves where we start and stop, but not the path we take from one to the other. Alternatively, we could think about moving along the surface $z = f(x, y)$ from the point $(x_a, y_a, f(x_a, y_a))$ to $(x_b, y_b, f(x_b, y_b))$. In this case, the net change in "altitude" (z) depends only on where you start and stop, not the path you take.

Using the Fundamental Theorem for Line Integrals

Example 3.1. Suppose $\mathbf{F}(x, y) = \langle 3x + 4y, 4x + 19 \cos y \rangle$ and $\mathcal{C}$ is the parabolic arc described by $x = (1 - \frac{y}{\pi})^2 + 5$ when $0 \leq y \leq \pi$, oriented top to bottom. (a) Calculate the line integral of $\mathbf{F}$ with respect to arc length over $\mathcal{C}$, and (b) interpret the result.

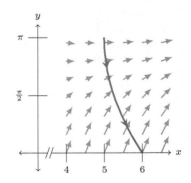

Figure 3.2: $\mathbf{F}$ and $\mathcal{C}$ for Example 3.1. (Vectors not to scale.)

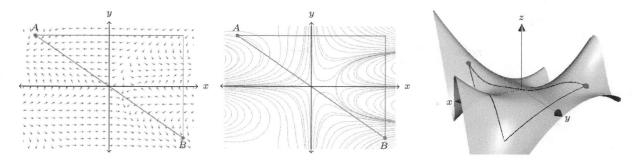

Figure 3.1: (left) Two paths from A to B through a vector field (vectors not to scale) of the form $\mathbf{F} = \nabla f$; (middle) the same paths, seen crossing level curves of f; (right) the graph of f, shown with the two paths projected onto the surface.

Solution: (a) We determined that $f(x,y) = \frac{3}{2}x^2 + 4xy + 19\sin y$ is a potential function for $\mathbf{F}$ in Example 1.7. So the Fundamental Theorem for Line Integrals tells us that when $\mathbf{r}$ is a smooth parameterization of $\mathcal{C}$ that starts at $(5, \pi)$ and ends at $(6, 0)$, which are the endpoints of $\mathcal{C}$,

$$\int_{\mathcal{C}} \nabla f \cdot d\mathbf{r} = f(6, 0) - f(5, \pi) = \frac{33}{2} - 20\pi \approx -46.332.$$

(b) If $\mathbf{F}$ is a force and some object is moving across $\mathcal{C}$ from left to right, this integral is a calculation of the work done by $\mathbf{F}$ on the object. The result tells us that the object's kinetic energy is reduced by ≈ 46.332 joules due to the force of $\mathbf{F}$. ∎

> Other forces (e.g., thrust) might also affect the object's kinetic energy. The net change in its velocity is determined by the net total of the work done by all the forces acting on the object.

Using the Fundamental Theorem for Line Integrals

Example 3.2. Suppose $\mathbf{F}(x,y) = \langle 6x, 8 \rangle$ and $\mathcal{C}$ is the curve described by $1 = x^4 + y^4$ (for which $x \geq 0$ and $y \geq 0$), oriented from right to left. Use the Fundamental Theorem of Line Integrals to calculate the line integral of $\mathbf{F}$ over $\mathcal{C}$.

Answer: 5. ∎

Solution On-line

⚘ Independence of Path

In cases when the line integral of $\mathbf{F}$ depends only on the endpoints of the curve (i.e., the particular curve we use in our calculation is irrelevant), we say that $\mathbf{F}$ is **path independent**. It's common to omit mention of the curve in such circumstances, and simply indicate the initial and terminal points of the line integral. For example,

> It's also common to say that the line integral, itself, is path independent.

$$\int_{A}^{B} \mathbf{F} \cdot d\mathbf{r}.$$

terminal point ⌐

initial point ⌐

We already know from the Fundamental Theorem of Line Integrals that gradient fields are path independent, and this leads us to a question. If we know that a vector field is path independent, *must* it be the gradient of some function? Subject to mild constraints, the answer is yes.

> The terms *open* and *connected* were defined in Chapter 13. As a reminder: a region is *open* when every point is an interior point, and *connected* when any two points can serve as the endpoints of a continuous path that stays in the region.

Theorem: Suppose $\mathbf{F}$ is a continuous vector field in the open, connected region R. Then $\mathbf{F}$ is path independent in R if and only if it has a potential, f.

Proof. Part 1 (potential $\Rightarrow$ path independent): To say that $\mathbf{F}$ has an associated potential function means there is a function f for which $\mathbf{F} = \nabla f$. The continuity of ∇f implies that f is differentiable, and path independence follows immediately

> The differentiability of f (as a consequence of the continuity of ∇f) was discussed in Chapter 13.

from the Fundamental Theorem of Line Integrals.

Part 2 (path independent ⇒ potential): We're going to prove this half of the theorem when R is a region in the plane, and $\mathbf{F} = \langle P, Q \rangle$, but the steps below extend easily to regions and fields in space. Our proof will be done in two steps: (1) use line integrals to define a function f, and (2) show that $\nabla f = \mathbf{F}$ by calculating f_x and f_y as limits of difference quotients.

Step 1 (defining f): We begin by pick an arbitrary point in R, say (x_0, y_0). Every other point in R can be reached from (x_0, y_0) by a path because R is connected, so we can define a function f via the line integral

$$f(x, y) = \int_{(x_0, y_0)}^{(x,y)} \mathbf{F} \cdot d\mathbf{r},$$

by which we mean the line integral over any path in R that extends from (x_0, y_0) to (x, y), because $\mathbf{F}$ is path independent.

Step 2 (calculating f_x and f_y): Suppose $(a, b) \in R$. The partial derivative of f with respect to x at that point is

$$f_x(a, b) = \lim_{\Delta x \to 0} \frac{f(a + \Delta x, b) - f(a, b)}{\Delta x}. \tag{3.2}$$

On a technical note, in order for the difference quotient to make sense, we need to know that $(a + \Delta x, b)$ is a point in R when Δx is sufficiently small (since f is defined in R), and that's why the hypotheses of this theorem require R to be open. When R is open we know there is a small disk centered at (a, b) that's entirely contained in R, so the point $(a + \Delta x, b)$ is also in R when Δx is sufficiently small.

In the work that follows, we're going to show that $f_x(a, b)$ is simply $P(a, b)$, which is the first component of $\mathbf{F}$. To do this, we'll first use the properties of line integrals and the path independence of $\mathbf{F}$ to simplify the numerator of the difference quotient. That will lead us to write the difference quotient as the average value of $P(x, y)$, at which point the Mean Value Theorem will allow us to simplify our expression to the point where evaluating the limit is easy.

Because the line integral of $\mathbf{F}$ in R is path independent, we can calculate $f(a + \Delta x, b)$ by using a path from $\mathbf{r}_0$ to (a, b), and then a horizontal line segment connecting (a, b) to $(a + \Delta x, b)$:

$$f(a + \Delta x, b) = \int_{\mathbf{r}_0}^{(a,b)} \mathbf{F} \cdot d\mathbf{r} + \int_{(a,b)}^{(a+\Delta x, b)} \mathbf{F} \cdot d\mathbf{r} = f(a, b) + \int_{(a,b)}^{(a+\Delta x, b)} \mathbf{F} \cdot d\mathbf{r}.$$

Since $f(a + \Delta x, b)$ can be written as the sum of $f(a, b)$ and a line integral in which the path is a horizontal line segment, the numerator of the difference quotient is

$$f(a + \Delta x, b) - f(a, b) = f(a, b) + \int_{(a,b)}^{(x+\Delta x, b)} \mathbf{F} \cdot d\mathbf{r} - f(a, b) = \int_{(a,b)}^{(a+\Delta x, b)} \mathbf{F} \cdot d\mathbf{r}.$$

At this stage the calculation becomes easier if we write $\mathbf{F}(x, y) = \langle P(x, y), Q(x, y) \rangle$ and use the differential form of the line integral, $\mathbf{F} \cdot d\mathbf{r} = P(x, y)\, dx + Q(x, y)\, dy$. Since $y = b$ is constant along the horizontal line segment over which the remaining integral is calculated, $dy = y'(t)\, dt = 0$, so the difference quotient is

$$\frac{1}{\Delta x} \int_{(a,b)}^{(a+\Delta x, b)} \mathbf{F} \cdot d\mathbf{r} = \frac{1}{\Delta x} \int_{(a,b)}^{(a+\Delta x, b)} \underbrace{P(x, b)\, dx}_{\text{Since } y=b \text{ is constant}} + \underbrace{Q(x, b)\, dy}_{=\,0 \text{ since } y \text{ is constant}} = \frac{1}{\Delta x} \int_{(a,b)}^{(a+\Delta x, b)} P(x, b)\, dx,$$

Recall from Chapter 5 that an integral such as

$$\int_0^x t^2\, dt$$

is a function of x because t is a dummy variable that vanishes in the integration. This definition of f is analogous.

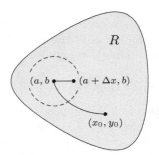

Figure 3.3: Using $f(a, b)$ to calculate $f(a + \Delta x, b)$.

which is the average value of P on the horizontal line segment (see Section 7.7).

Because $\mathbf{F}$ is continuous, the Mean Value Theorem for Integrals guarantees that P achieves its average value at some point on the line segment, say (x^*, b). So we have arrived at the fact that

$$\frac{f(a + \Delta x, b) - f(a, b)}{\Delta x} = \frac{1}{\Delta x} \int_{(a,b)}^{(a+\Delta x, b)} P(x, b) \, dx = P(x^*, b),$$

where (x^*, b) is on the horizontal line segment connecting (a, b) and $(a + \Delta x, b)$. And because P is continuous,

$$f_x(a, b) = \lim_{\Delta x \to 0} \frac{f(a + \Delta x, b) - f(a, b)}{\Delta x} = \lim_{\Delta x \to 0} P(x^*, b) = \lim_{x^* \to a} P(x^*, b) = P(a, b).$$

So we've shown that the first component of $\mathbf{F}$ is the first component of ∇f. A similar argument using the vertical line segment between (a, b) and $(a, b + \Delta y)$ leads us to conclude that

$$f_y(a, b) = \lim_{\Delta y \to 0} \frac{f(a, b + \Delta y) - f(a, b)}{\Delta y} = \lim_{\Delta y \to 0} Q(a, y^*) = \lim_{y^* \to a} Q(a, y^*) = Q(a, b).$$

So we have established that $\langle f_x, f_y \rangle = \langle P, Q \rangle = \mathbf{F}$. Lastly, we note that $f_x = P$ and $f_y = Q$ are continuous in a neighborhood of (a, b), so the function f is differentiable there (see Section 13.5). ∎

The previous theorem tells us that when $\mathbf{F}$ is path independent throughout a region, it has a potential. This fact has an important consequence in the physical sciences, which is discussed in the next example.

Line integrals around closed curves

Example 3.3. Suppose $\mathbf{F}$ is path independent inside the disk of radius 2 that's centered at the origin, and $\mathcal{C}$ is the circle $x^2 + y^2 = 1$. (a) Determine the line integral of $\mathbf{F}$ over $\mathcal{C}$, and (b) interpret the result.

Solution: (a) At first glance it seems that we don't have enough information to make this calculation, but we're told that $\mathbf{F}$ is path independent, so we know that there is a potential of $\mathbf{F}$, say f. If we traverse the unit circle, starting and ending at the same point, say $(1, 0)$, we see that

$$\int_{\mathcal{C}} \mathbf{F} \cdot d\mathbf{r} = \underbrace{f(1, 0)}_{f \text{ at the end of the curve}} - \underbrace{f(1, 0)}_{f \text{ at the start of the curve}} = 0.$$

(b) When $\mathbf{F}$ is a field of force vectors, the work done by $\mathbf{F}$ on an object that travels once around the curve $\mathcal{C}$ is 0, so there's no net change in the object's kinetic energy due to $\mathbf{F}$ (we say that kinetic energy is *conserved*). ∎

Based on part (b) of Example 3.3, we often refer to a vector field as ***conservative*** if it is path independent (i.e., is a gradient field).

| You should know |

- the terms *path independent* and *conservative;*
- the definition of the line integral as the limit of Riemann sums, and how it relates to the calculation of work;

Sidebar notes:

If you have trouble thinking of this as an average value, temporarily suppress all mention of $y = b$ (since it's constant anyway) and write the integral as

$$\frac{1}{\Delta x} \int_a^{a+\Delta x} P(x) \, dx.$$

Because $x^* \in [a, a + \Delta x]$, sending $\Delta x \to 0$ forces $x^* \to a$.

The theorem does not guarantee that we will be able to find a familiar, explicit formula for the potential, only that there *is* a potential.

Note that the direction we travel is irrelevant. We made no mention of orientation.

Whereas the term *path independent* describes $\mathbf{F}$ mathematically, the term *conservative* describes a physical fact about the vector field.

- the Fundamental Theorem of Line Integrals;
- the relationship between path independence and potential functions.

You should be able to

- use the Fundamental Theorem of Line Integrals.

❖ 15.3 Skill Exercises

In #1–2 determine $\int_{\mathcal{C}} \mathbf{F} \cdot d\mathbf{r}$ when $\mathbf{F} = \nabla f$.

1. $f(x, y) = e^{x^2 + \sin(\pi y)}$; $\mathcal{C}$ is a circular arc extending from $(-1, 0)$ to $(0, 1)$.

2. $f(x, y) = \arctan xy + \cos \pi y$; $\mathcal{C}$ is the part of the cardioid $r = 1 - \cos\theta$ in the fourth quadrant that connects $(0, -1)$ to $(0,0)$, oriented from bottom to top.

In #3–8 the given $\mathbf{F}$ is a conservative vector field. (a) Find a potential function, f, and (b) use the Fundamental Theorem of Line Integrals to calculate $\int_{\mathcal{C}} \mathbf{F} \cdot d\mathbf{r}$.

3. $\mathbf{F}(x, y) = \langle 3, -5 \rangle$; $\mathcal{C}$ is the line segment that extends from $(1, 1)$ to $(7, 2)$.

4. $\mathbf{F}(x, y) = \langle 1, -1 \rangle$; $\mathcal{C}$ is the parabolic arc shown in Figure 3.4.

5. $\mathbf{F}(x, y) = \langle y, x + 1 \rangle$; $\mathcal{C}$ is the segment of the ellipse shown in Figure 3.5.

6. $\mathbf{F}(x, y) = \langle 2x - 1, 3y^2 \rangle$; $\mathcal{C}$ is the segment of the cardioid $r = 1 + \sin(\theta)$ in the right half-plane, extending from the origin to the point $(0, 2)$.

7. $\mathbf{F}(x, y) = \langle -\pi y \sin(\pi xy), 4y - \pi x \sin(\pi xy) \rangle$; $\mathcal{C}$ is the arc of the cycloid that's parameterized by $\mathbf{r}(t) = \langle t - \sin t, t - \cos t \rangle$, when $t \in [0, 2\pi]$.

8. $\mathbf{F}(x, y) = \langle 4xy, 2x^2 \rangle$; $\mathcal{C}$ is shown in Figure 3.6.

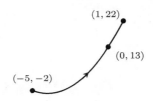

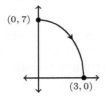

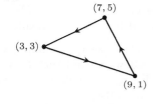

Figure 3.4: The path for exercise #4.

Figure 3.5: The path for exercise #5.

Figure 3.6: Path for the line integrals in #8.

In #9–14 the given $\mathbf{F}$ is a conservative vector field. (a) Find a potential function, f, and (b) use the Fundamental Theorem of Line Integrals to calculate $\int_{\mathcal{C}} \mathbf{F} \cdot d\mathbf{r}$.

9. $\mathbf{F}(x, y) = \langle -5, 7, 10 \rangle$; $\mathcal{C}$ is the line segment extending from $(0, -11, 0)$ to $(1, 9, -1)$.

10. $\mathbf{F}(x, y) = \langle 1, 9, 0 \rangle$; $\mathcal{C}$ is the line segment that extends from $(4, 5, 6)$ to $(4, 5, 9)$.

11. $\mathbf{F}(x, y) = \langle 2x, 4y, 8z \rangle$; $\mathcal{C}$ is a smooth curve extending from $(3, -1, 1)$ to $(-2, 6, 1)$.

12. $\mathbf{F}(x, y) = \langle e^x, \sin y, 2z \rangle$; $\mathcal{C}$ is a smooth curve extending from $(1, 1, 0)$ to $(4, 3, -1)$.

13. $\mathbf{F}(x, y) = \langle yz, xz, xy \rangle$; $\mathcal{C}$ is piecewise linear from $(1, 2, 3)$ to $(2, 0, 5)$ to $(3, 1, 1)$.

14. $\mathbf{F}(x, y) = \langle 2xz, 3y^2, x^2 \rangle$; $\mathcal{C}$ is parameterized by $\mathbf{r}(t) = \langle \cos t, 3t, \sin t \rangle$, $t \in [0, 4\pi]$.

❖ 15.3 Concept and Application Exercises

In exercises #15–16, **F** is conservative. Verify that the line integral of **F** along each of the paths $\mathcal{A}$, $\mathcal{B}$ and $\mathcal{C}$ (shown in the accompanying figures) is the same.

15. $\mathbf{F}(x, y) = \langle 2x, 3y \rangle$ and the paths are shown in Figure 3.7.

16. $\mathbf{F}(x, y) = \langle 4x - y, 3y^2 - x \rangle$ and the paths are shown in Figure 3.8.

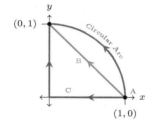

Figure 3.7: Paths for #15.

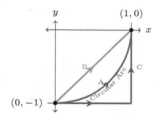

Figure 3.8: Paths for #16.

17. Suppose $\mathcal{C}$ is the path from $(0, 0)$ to $(0, 2)$ that is shown in Figure 3.9, and $\mathbf{F}(x, y) = 4 \sec^2(x/7) \sin(\pi y/4) \mathbf{i} + 7\pi \tan(x/7) \cos(\pi y/4) \mathbf{j}$. Determine $\int_{\mathcal{C}} \mathbf{F} \cdot d\mathbf{r}$.

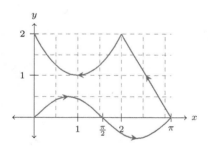

Figure 3.9: In #17 $\mathcal{C}$ is a sine curve, followed by a line segment and a parabolic arc.

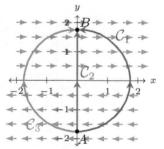

Figure 3.10: The path for #18.

18. Figure 3.10 shows the vector field **F** in gray, and the paths $\mathcal{C}_1$, $\mathcal{C}_2$ and $\mathcal{C}_3$, which extend from point A to point B. (a) Put the line integrals $\int_{\mathcal{C}_1} \mathbf{F} \cdot d\mathbf{r}$, $\int_{\mathcal{C}_2} \mathbf{F} \cdot d\mathbf{r}$ and $\int_{\mathcal{C}_3} \mathbf{F} \cdot d\mathbf{r}$ in order from smallest to largest, and (b) determine whether **F** is a conservative vector field.

19. Selected values of the differentiable function $f(x, y)$ are shown in Table 15.1. Suppose f is a potential for the continuous vector field **F**. Determine the value of $\int_{\mathcal{C}} \mathbf{F} \cdot d\mathbf{r}$ when $\mathcal{C}$ is (a) the line segment that extends from $(2, 5)$ to $(4, 10)$; (b) the line segment that extends from $(4, 9)$ to $(6, 7)$; and (c) the piecewise-linear path from $(2, 5)$ to $(2, 10)$ to $(6, 10)$ to $(2, 5)$.

10	−1	4	11	20	31
9	−2	3	10	19	30
8	−3	2	9	18	29
7	−4	1	8	17	28
6	−5	0	7	16	27
5	−6	−1	6	15	26
y/x	2	3	4	5	6

Table 15.1: Data for #19.

20. Selected values of the differentiable function $f(x, y, z)$ are shown in Table 15.2. Suppose f is a potential for the continuous vector field $\mathbf{F}$. Determine the value of $\int_C \mathbf{F} \cdot d\mathbf{r}$ when C is (a) the line segment that extends from $(9, 6, 1)$ to $(11, 8, 2)$, and (b) the line segment that extends from $(9, 7, 2)$ to $(11, 6, 1)$.

8	-3	2	9
7	-4	1	8
6	-5	0	7
y/x	9	10	11

$z=1$

8	-2	4	10
7	-3	2	11
6	-4	2	9
y/x	9	10	11

$z=2$

Table 15.2: Data for #20

21. Suppose $\mathbf{F}(x, y) = \langle 4x, 2y \rangle$, and C is a line segment of length 5. If one end of C is at $(2, 4)$, where should the other be placed in order to maximize $\int_C \mathbf{F} \cdot d\mathbf{r}$?

22. Suppose $\mathbf{F}(x, y) = \langle -3x, y \rangle$, and C is a line segment with one end at the point $(3, 5)$. Where could the other end of C be if $\int_C \mathbf{F} \cdot d\mathbf{r} = 13$?

In #23–26 determine whether $\mathbf{F}$ appears path independent. (In #23–24 $\mathbf{F} = \mathbf{0}$ on dashed line.)

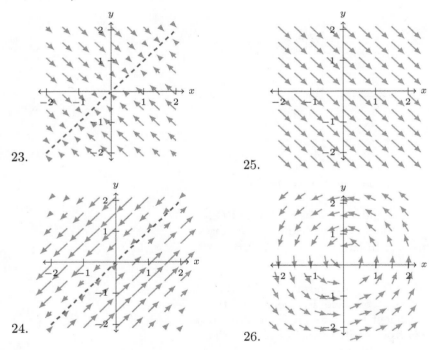

23.

25.

24.

26.

27. Suppose f is a potential of the continuous vector field $\mathbf{F}$, and level curves of f are shown in Figure 3.11. Determine $\int_C \mathbf{F} \cdot d\mathbf{r}$ when C is the linear path that extends from A to B.

28. Suppose $f(x, y) = \arctan\left(\frac{y}{x}\right)$ away from $x = 0$.

   (a) Determine a formula for $\mathbf{F} = \nabla f$.

   (b) Calculate $\int_C \mathbf{F} \cdot d\mathbf{r}$ when C is the counterclockwise-oriented unit circle.

   (c) Explain why your nonzero answer to part (b) does not contradict the Fundamental Theorem of Line Integrals.

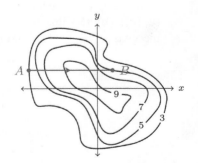

Figure 3.11: Level curves of f in exercise #27. The function value along each curve is shown interrupting the curve.

29. Suppose $\mathbf{F}$ is a conservative vector field for which $\int_{(3,1,4)}^{(0,1,-4)} \mathbf{F} \cdot d\mathbf{r} = 3$ and $\int_{(0,1,-4)}^{(4,8,1)} \mathbf{F} \cdot d\mathbf{r} = 20$. Determine the value of $\int_{(4,8,1)}^{(3,1,4)} \mathbf{F} \cdot d\mathbf{r}$.

30. Suppose $\mathbf{F}$ is a conservative vector field for which $\int_{(1,-1)}^{(0,5)} \mathbf{F} \cdot d\mathbf{r} = -8$, $\int_{(0,5)}^{(9,2)} \mathbf{F} \cdot d\mathbf{r} = 13$, and $\int_{(9,2)}^{(2,7)} \mathbf{F} \cdot d\mathbf{r} = 4$, where each integral is calculated along a line segment that starts at the lower bound of integration and extends to the upper bound. Determine the value of $\int_{(1,-1)}^{(2,7)} \mathbf{F} \cdot d\mathbf{r}$.

In exercises #31-32, $\mathbf{F}$ is a field of force vectors (with units of newtons). (a) Show that $\mathbf{F}$ is conservative, and (b) determine the effect of F on the kinetic energy of an object that moves between the specified points.

31. $\mathbf{F}(x, y) = \langle 3, 4 \rangle$, and the object moves from $(-1, 3)$ to $(1, 3)$.

32. $\mathbf{F}(x, y) = \langle 2xy, x^2 y + \cos y \rangle$, and the object moves from $(-1, 0)$ to $(1, 0.5\pi)$.

In exercises #33–34 the vector field $\mathbf{F}$ is a **central vector field**, meaning that $\mathbf{F}$ is a scaled version of the position vector, $\mathbf{r}$.

33. Suppose $\mathbf{F} = g(\|\mathbf{r}\|)\hat{\mathbf{r}}$, where $\mathbf{r} = \langle x, y \rangle$ and $g(t)$ is continuous except, perhaps, at $t = 0$. Show that
$$f(x, y) = \int_{1}^{\sqrt{x^2+y^2}} g(t)\, dt$$
is a potential function for $\mathbf{F}$ at all points except, perhaps, the origin.

34. Suppose $\mathbf{F} = g(\|\mathbf{r}\|)\hat{\mathbf{r}}$, where $\mathbf{r} = \langle x, y, z \rangle$ and $g(t)$ is continuous except, perhaps, at $t = 0$. Prove that $\mathbf{F}$ is conservative.

35. Suppose that R is a connected, open region in the plane, and $\mathbf{F}$ is a continuous vector field for which $\int_{\mathcal{C}} \mathbf{F} \cdot d\mathbf{r} = 0$ whenever $\mathcal{C}$ is a closed curve. Prove that $\mathbf{F}$ is conservative.

Mathematics

15.4   Green's Theorem (Flux-Divergence Form)

When $\mathbf{F} = \langle P, Q \rangle$ is a vector field and R is a region bounded by the curve $\mathcal{C}$, there are certain cases in which the double integral

$$\iint_R \left(\frac{\partial P}{\partial x} + \frac{\partial Q}{\partial y} \right) dA \quad \text{and the line integral} \quad \int_{\mathcal{C}} P \, dy - Q \, dx$$

have the same value. We'll articulate this fact more precisely later in this section, but first we want to develop some intuition about these integrals, what they tell us, and why we might believe that they're the same.

Key Idea(s):   *We can tell how quickly fluid is produced inside a region by measuring the rate at which it spills across the boundary.*

The flow of a fluid across a curve can be calculated with a line integral.

❖ An Intuitive Introduction

Imagine that the vector field in Figure 4.1 depicts the velocity of traffic on a road, and the rectangular region R is an overpass that prevents you from seeing what's happening on the part of the road beneath it. You observe that traffic is leaving R at a faster rate than it's entering, but that the density of vehicles is the same on both sides. How could that be? (Really, think about it!)

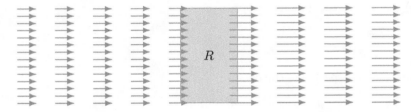

Figure 4.1: A steady-state flow velocity of an incompressible fluid passing through R.

After pondering the traffic problem, perhaps you arrived at the conclusion that traffic must be entering the road at a point beneath the overpass that you cannot see. There must be a "source" of some kind in R. That's an important intuitive idea.

Now let's think of the vector field $\mathbf{F}$ in Figure 4.1 as showing us the velocity of a fluid that flows through R (i.e., although R is pictured as opaque, it is not a solid obstacle). For the sake of discussion, we'll say that the fluid has a uniform density of 1 g/cm^2, and although $\mathbf{F}(x,y)$ depends on location, we'll assume that it's not changing over time (we say it's a *steady state* flow). As we noted earlier, $\|\mathbf{F}\|$ is smaller on the left of R than on the right. For the sake of discussion, suppose that R is 2.6 cm tall, that $\|\mathbf{F}\| = 2$ cm/sec on the left side of R, and $\|\mathbf{F}\| = 3$ cm/sec on the right. Then fluid enters R at a rate of

Amount of fluid, in cm^2/sec

$$\underbrace{2.6}_{\text{cm}} \times \underbrace{2}_{\text{cm/sec}} \times \underbrace{1}_{\text{mass density, in g/cm}^2} = 5.2 \frac{\text{g}}{\text{sec}} \tag{4.1}$$

and fluid exits R at a rate of $2.6 \times 3 \times 1 = 7.8$ grams per second. How could it be that more fluid mass is leaving R than entering every second? After wrestling with the facts that the flow velocity is constant over time, and the fluid density is constant, perhaps you arrived at the conclusion that—as with the traffic flow scenario—there must be a source of fluid inside R augmenting the flow with an additional 2.6 grams of fluid per second. This intuition encapsulates the basic idea that will be expressed

Since this flow is in two dimensions instead of three, we talk about the *area* occupied by the fluid, rather than the volume (e.g., we measure in cm^2 rather than cm^3).

Figure 4.2: A curve that is (left) closed but not simple; (middle-left) simple but not closed; (middle right) neither closed nor simple; (right) simple and closed.

by Green's Theorem later in this section, but in order to articulate the idea mathematically, we'll need to expand our vocabulary and develop some new ideas about calculation with integrals.

We say a curve is **closed** if its initial and terminal points coincide, and that it's **simple** if it never intersects itself (see Figure 4.2). When integrating around a closed curve $\mathcal{C}$, we often denote the line integral with the symbol

$$\oint_{\mathcal{C}} \qquad \text{instead of} \qquad \int_{\mathcal{C}} \qquad \text{although the latter is still correct.}$$

✤ Flux Integrals

In the intuitive introduction above, we calculated the rate at which fluid crossed the boundary of a region R (commonly called the **flux** of the fluid across the boundary). Since $\mathbf{F}$ was constant along the boundary of R and the boundary was composed of line segments, the calculation was done with a simple multiplication in equation (4.1); one factor in that product was the mass density, so our answer had units of grams per second. Henceforth, we assume that the (scalar) density factor is included in the definition of $\mathbf{F}$, so that $\mathbf{F}$ has dimensions of (speed)×(density). Such a vector field is called a **mass velocity** field, or **mass flow**. For instance, a mass flow in two dimensions might have units of

$$(\text{speed}) \times (\text{density}) = \frac{\text{cm}}{\text{sec}} \times \frac{\text{g}}{\text{cm}^2} = \frac{\text{g/sec}}{\text{cm}}.$$

When working in three dimensions, mass flow has units such as

$$\frac{\text{cm}}{\text{sec}} \times \frac{\text{g}}{\text{cm}^3} = \frac{\text{g/sec}}{\text{cm}^2}$$

When the boundary of R is not a collection of line segments, or $\mathbf{F}$ is nonconstant, we use a line integral to calculate the flux of $\mathbf{F}$ across the boundary curve, $\mathcal{C}$. Like all other integrals in this book, this one is the limit of Riemann sums. The basic idea is that, when $\mathcal{C}$ is a piecewise-smooth, simple, closed curve, we can approximate it with a n-sided polygon (see Figure 4.3). Riemann sums arise when we approximate the flux of $\mathbf{F}$ across the line segments of such polygons.

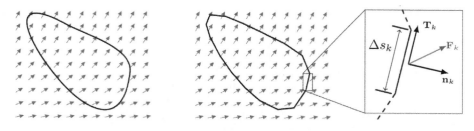

Figure 4.3: (left) A vector field and a smooth curve in the plane; (right) approximating the curve with a polygon (in the cutout, the vectors $\mathbf{F}$, $\mathbf{T}$ and $\mathbf{n}$ have been removed from the line segment in order to avoid overlap with the polygon).

More specifically, suppose $\mathbf{F}_k$ is the flow vector at the midpoint of the kth segment (see Figure 4.3), the unit tangent vector there is $\mathbf{T}_k$, and $\mathbf{n}_k$ is the **outward** *unit normal* vector (which is orthogonal to $\mathbf{T}_k$, points into the unbounded portion of the plane, and has a magnitude of 1). Because flow in the tangential direction does not cross the straight edge of the polygon, only the component of $\mathbf{F}$ in the direction of $\mathbf{n}_k$ contributes to the flux, and we calculate that aspect of $\mathbf{F}$ with the dot product $\mathbf{F}_k \cdot \mathbf{n}_k$.

If the length of the kth segment is Δs_k and $\mathbf{F}$ is continuous, the flow that crosses that segment is approximately $\mathbf{F}_k \cdot \mathbf{n}_k \, \Delta s_k$, so the

$$\text{net flux across } \mathcal{C} \approx \text{net flux across the polygon} \approx \sum_{k=1}^{n} \mathbf{F}_k \cdot \mathbf{n}_k \, \Delta s_k.$$

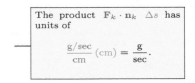

The product $\mathbf{F}_k \cdot \mathbf{n}_k \ \Delta s$ has units of

$$\frac{\text{g/sec}}{\text{cm}} \, (\text{cm}) = \frac{\text{g}}{\text{sec}}.$$

All error vanishes in the limit as $\|\Delta s\| \to 0$ (thereby sending $n \to \infty$), provided that the limit exists, and the Riemann sum becomes the line integral

$$\text{flux} = \oint_{\mathcal{C}} \mathbf{F} \cdot \mathbf{n} \, ds. \tag{4.2}$$

The next example shows that, although equation (4.2) might look new, it's exactly what we did in the introductory example.

Calculating a flux integral

Example 4.1. Suppose $\mathbf{F}$ and R are those from the intuitive discussion at the beginning of the section, as seen in Figure 4.1. Use equation (4.2) to calculate the flux of $\mathbf{F}$ over the boundary of R.

Solution: We're going to calculate

$$\oint_{\mathcal{C}} \mathbf{F} \cdot \mathbf{n} \, ds = \int_{\mathcal{C}_1} \mathbf{F} \cdot \mathbf{n} \, ds + \int_{\mathcal{C}_2} \mathbf{F} \cdot \mathbf{n} \, ds + \int_{\mathcal{C}_3} \mathbf{F} \cdot \mathbf{n} \, ds + \int_{\mathcal{C}_4} \mathbf{F} \cdot \mathbf{n} \, ds$$

where $\mathcal{C}_1$, $\mathcal{C}_2$, $\mathcal{C}_3$ and $\mathcal{C}_4$ are the boundary segments shown in Figure 4.4. On $\mathcal{C}_1$ we know (from the introductory discussion) that $\mathbf{F} = 3\mathbf{i}$, and the outward unit normal vector along $\mathcal{C}_1$ is $\mathbf{n} = \mathbf{i}$, so $\mathbf{F} \cdot \mathbf{n} = 3$. While integrating along $\mathcal{C}_2$ the outward unit normal vector is $\mathbf{n} = \mathbf{j}$, but $\mathbf{F}$ is a horizontal flow so $\mathbf{F} \cdot \mathbf{n} = 0$. During the integration over $\mathcal{C}_3$ the outward unit normal is $\mathbf{n} = -\mathbf{i}$, and $\mathbf{F} = 2\mathbf{i}$, so $\mathbf{F} \cdot \mathbf{n} = -2$. And lastly, the outward unit normal along $\mathcal{C}_4$ is $\mathbf{n} = -\mathbf{j}$, so $\mathbf{F} \cdot \mathbf{n} = 0$ there. So

$$\begin{aligned}
\oint_{\mathcal{C}} \mathbf{F} \cdot \mathbf{n} \, ds &= \int_{\mathcal{C}_1} 3 \, ds + \int_{\mathcal{C}_2} 0 \, ds + \int_{\mathcal{C}_3} -2 \, ds + \int_{\mathcal{C}_4} 0 \, ds \\
&= 3(\text{length of } \mathcal{C}_1) + (-2)(\text{length of } \mathcal{C}_3) \\
&= 3(2.6) - 2(2.6) = 2.6,
\end{aligned}$$

which agrees with our initial calculation. ∎

In Example 4.1 you saw that $\mathbf{F} \cdot \mathbf{n} > 0$ where fluid is leaving R, and $\mathbf{F} \cdot \mathbf{n} < 0$ where fluid is entering. This fact is particularly helpful when interpreting results.

Calculating a flux integral

Example 4.2. Suppose length is measured in cm, $\mathbf{F}(x,y) = \langle x+y, 2 \rangle \frac{\text{g/sec}}{\text{cm}}$, and $\mathcal{C}$ is the triangle shown in Figure 4.5. (a) Use equation (4.2) to calculate the flux of $\mathbf{F}$ over $\mathcal{C}$, and (b) interpret the results.

Solution: (a) As we did in Example 4.1, we're going to calculate the flux along each segment of the boundary:

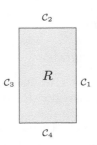

Figure 4.4: The boundary of R is composed of four line segments.

The flow along $\mathcal{C}_2$ skims the edge of R but never enters (or exits). The same happens along $\mathcal{C}_4$.

Note that $\mathbf{F} \cdot \mathbf{n} > 0$ along $\mathcal{C}_1$, indicating outflow, but $\mathbf{F} \cdot \mathbf{n} < 0$ along $\mathcal{C}_3$, indicating that fluid is entering R.

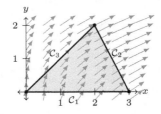

Figure 4.5: The triangle for Example 4.2 (vectors not to scale)

$$\oint_{\mathcal{C}} \mathbf{F} \cdot \mathbf{n}\, ds = \int_{\mathcal{C}_1} \mathbf{F} \cdot \mathbf{n}\, ds + \int_{\mathcal{C}_2} \mathbf{F} \cdot \mathbf{n}\, ds + \int_{\mathcal{C}_3} \mathbf{F} \cdot \mathbf{n}\, ds.$$

Where $\mathcal{C}_1$, $\mathcal{C}_2$ and $\mathcal{C}_3$ are as shown in Figure 4.5. The outward unit normal vector along $\mathcal{C}_1$ is $\mathbf{n} = \langle 0, -1 \rangle$, so $\mathbf{F} \cdot \mathbf{n} = -2$, and

$$\int_{\mathcal{C}_1} \mathbf{F} \cdot \mathbf{n} \underbrace{\, ds\,}_{\text{length element along } \mathcal{C}_1} = \int_0^3 -2 \underbrace{\, dx\,}_{\text{length element along the interval } [0,3]} = -6 \; \frac{\text{g}}{\text{sec}}.$$

> Since $\mathbf{F} \cdot \mathbf{n}$ is interpreted in terms of fluid leaving the region (because $\mathbf{n}$ points outward), a negative value of $\mathbf{F} \cdot \mathbf{n}$ indicates that fluid is *entering* the region.

The second and third integrals are a bit more difficult because $\mathcal{C}_2$ and $\mathcal{C}_3$ are slanted, but we can facilitate our calculation by using parameterizations of the boundary segments. Let's parameterize $\mathcal{C}_2$ with $\mathbf{r}(t) = \langle 3 - t, 2t \rangle$ when $t \in [0, 1]$. Then the unit tangent vector at time t is

$$\mathbf{T} = \frac{\mathbf{r}'}{\|\mathbf{r}'\|} = \left\langle -\frac{1}{\sqrt{5}}, \frac{2}{\sqrt{5}} \right\rangle \quad \Rightarrow \quad \mathbf{n} = \left\langle \frac{2}{\sqrt{5}}, \frac{1}{\sqrt{5}} \right\rangle,$$

> Since $\mathbf{T}$ has a northwesterly direction on $\mathcal{C}_2$ (see Figure 4.5), the vector $\mathbf{n}$ points into the first quadrant. Methods for finding $\mathbf{n}$ from $\mathbf{T}$ were discussed in Chapter 11.

and $\langle x + y, 2 \rangle = \langle (3 - t) + 2t, 2 \rangle = \langle 3 + t, 2 \rangle$, so

$$\mathbf{F} \cdot \mathbf{n} = \langle 3 + t, 2 \rangle \cdot \left\langle \frac{2}{\sqrt{5}}, \frac{1}{\sqrt{5}} \right\rangle = \frac{8 + 2t}{\sqrt{5}} \; \frac{\text{g/sec}}{\text{cm}}.$$

Additionally, note that we travel along $\mathcal{C}_2$ at a rate of $\frac{ds}{dt} = \|\mathbf{r}'(t)\| = \sqrt{5}$ cm/sec, so $ds = \sqrt{5}\, dt$. This allows us to express the integral over $\mathcal{C}_2$ as

$$\int_{\mathcal{C}_2} \mathbf{F} \cdot \mathbf{n}\, ds = \int_0^1 \frac{8 + 2t}{\sqrt{5}} \sqrt{5}\, dt = \int_0^1 (8 + 2t)\, dt = 9 \; \frac{\text{g}}{\text{sec}}.$$

In similar fashion, we parameterize $\mathcal{C}_3$ with $\mathbf{r}(t) = \langle 2 - t, 2 - t \rangle$ when $t \in [0, 2]$. This leads us to write

$$\mathbf{T} = \frac{\mathbf{r}'}{\|\mathbf{r}'\|} = \left\langle -\frac{1}{\sqrt{2}}, -\frac{1}{\sqrt{2}} \right\rangle \quad \Rightarrow \quad \mathbf{n} = \left\langle -\frac{1}{\sqrt{2}}, \frac{1}{\sqrt{2}} \right\rangle,$$

> Intuitively, since $\mathbf{T}$ points in a southwesterly direction on $\mathcal{C}_3$ (see Figure 4.5), the outward normal vector points up and to the left. Methods for finding $\mathbf{n}$ from $\mathbf{T}$ were discussed in Chapter 11.

and $\langle x + y, 2 \rangle = \langle 4 - 2t, 2 \rangle$, so

$$\int_{\mathcal{C}_3} \mathbf{F} \cdot \mathbf{n}\, ds = \int_0^2 \frac{2t - 2}{\sqrt{2}} \sqrt{2}\, dt = 0 \; \frac{\text{g}}{\text{sec}}.$$

This leads us to conclude that the flux of $\mathbf{F}$ across $\mathcal{C}$ is $-6 + 9 + 0 = 3$ g/sec.

(b) Since the flux integral is positive, more fluid is exiting the enclosed region than entering. ∎

Calculating a flux integral

Example 4.3. Determine the flux of $\mathbf{F}$ across $\mathcal{C}$ when $\mathbf{F}(x, y) = \langle x, x^2 + y \rangle$, and $\mathcal{C}$ is the upper half of the unit circle joined with the segment $[-1, 1]$ on the x-axis.

Answer: π. ∎

Solution On-line

In Examples 4.2 and 4.3 we parameterized the boundary curve in order to perform the integration. Generally speaking, if $\mathcal{C}$ is a smooth, simple, closed curve parameterized by $\mathbf{r}(t) = \langle x(t), y(t) \rangle$ when $t \in [a, b]$, and $\|\mathbf{r}'(t)\| = 1$, we have $ds = 1\, dt$ and

$$\mathbf{T} = \langle x', y' \rangle, \quad \Rightarrow \quad \mathbf{n} = \langle y', -x' \rangle.$$

So when we write $\mathbf{F} = \langle P, Q \rangle$, the flux integral becomes

$$\oint_{\mathcal{C}} \mathbf{F} \cdot \mathbf{n} \, ds = \int_a^b \left(Py' - Qx' \right) dt.$$

Since $dx = x'(t) \, dt$ and $dy = y'(t) \, dt$, this integral is often written as

$$\text{flux} = \oint_{\mathcal{C}} \mathbf{F} \cdot \mathbf{n} \, ds = \oint_{\mathcal{C}} P \, dy - Q \, dx \, \frac{\text{g}}{\text{sec}}, \qquad (4.3)$$

which is the first half of the central equation in Green's Theorem. We develop the other half below.

❖ Divergence

We've talked about flux across the boundary of a region, but now let's look inside. When (a, b) is a point inside the open region R, there is a rectangular box of width Δx and height Δy centered there, say $\mathcal{B}$, that is entirely contained inside the region (see Figure 4.6). We're going to calculate the flux of $\mathbf{F} = \langle P, Q \rangle$ through $\mathcal{B}$ in three steps: (1) determine the flux across the horizontal segments of the boundary, and (2) across the vertical segments, then (3) add those quantities together. During this process, we will assume that $\mathbf{F}$ is ***smooth***, by which we mean that the first partial derivatives of its component functions are continuous. (This will guarantee that certain double integrals exist.)

Step 1 (flux across horizontal boundary segments): We'll begin by approximating this quantity with a Riemann sum, and then pass to an exact calculation in the limit. Toward writing our Riemann sum, let's partition the horizontal boundary segments of $\mathcal{B}$ into *microsegments* of length δx, as shown in Figure 4.7, and call two microsegments a *pair* if one is directly over the other. Since $\mathbf{F} = \langle P, Q \rangle$, the flux across the kth pair of microsegments is approximately

$$\begin{aligned} \mathbf{F} \cdot \mathbf{n} \, \delta x &= Q(x_k^*, b + \tfrac{\Delta y}{2}) \, \delta x &&\text{(on the upper segment)} \\ \mathbf{F} \cdot \mathbf{n} \, \delta x &= -Q(x_k^*, b - \tfrac{\Delta y}{2}) \, \delta x &&\text{(on the lower segment)} \end{aligned}$$

where x_k^* is some x-value corresponding to that pair. Their sum is

$$\left[Q(x_k^*, b + \tfrac{\Delta y}{2}) - Q(x_k^*, b - \tfrac{\Delta y}{2}) \right] \delta x.$$

By adding the contributions from all pairs of microsegments we see that

$$\left. \begin{array}{l} \text{flux across horizontal} \\ \text{boundary segments of} \\ \text{the box } \mathcal{B} \end{array} \right\} \approx \sum_{k=1}^{n} \left[Q(x_k^*, b + \tfrac{\Delta y}{2}) - Q(x_k^*, b - \tfrac{\Delta y}{2}) \right] \delta x.$$

Approximation becomes equality in the limit as $n \to \infty$, so

$$\left. \begin{array}{l} \text{flux across horizontal} \\ \text{boundary segments of} \\ \text{the box } \mathcal{B} \end{array} \right\} = \int_{a - \frac{\Delta x}{2}}^{a + \frac{\Delta x}{2}} \left[Q(x, b + \tfrac{\Delta y}{2}) - Q(x, b - \tfrac{\Delta y}{2}) \right] dx. \qquad (4.4)$$

The Fundamental Theorem of Calculus tells us that

$$Q(x, b + \tfrac{\Delta y}{2}) - Q(x, b - \tfrac{\Delta y}{2}) = \int_{b - \frac{\Delta y}{2}}^{b + \frac{\Delta y}{2}} Q_y(x, y) \, dy,$$

In order to make the notation less cumbersome, here we suppress the fact that P and Q might vary with position.

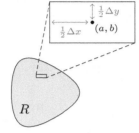

Figure 4.6: Each point inside an open region R can be the center of a rectangular region that's entirely contained in R.

The term *microsegment* is not standard terminology, but is particularly descriptive in the current context.

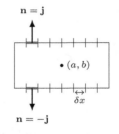

Figure 4.7: Partition the horizontal boundaries into segments of length δx. The blue segments constitute a *pair*.

The bounds of integration are the minimum and maximum values of x.

so equation (4.4) can be written as

$$\left.\begin{array}{l}\text{flux across horizontal}\\\text{boundary segments of}\\\text{the box } \mathcal{B}\end{array}\right\} = \int_{a-\frac{\Delta x}{2}}^{a+\frac{\Delta x}{2}} \int_{b-\frac{\Delta y}{2}}^{b+\frac{\Delta y}{2}} Q_y(x,y)\, dy\, dx = \iint_{\mathcal{B}} Q_y(x,y)\, dA.$$

Step 2 (flux across vertical boundary segments): Using the same ideas, we arrive at the approximation

$$\left.\begin{array}{l}\text{flux across vertical}\\\text{boundary segments}\\\text{of the box } \mathcal{B}\end{array}\right\} \approx \sum_{k=1}^{n} \left[P(a+\tfrac{\Delta x}{2}, y_k^*) - P(a-\tfrac{\Delta x}{2}, y_k^*) \right] \delta y,$$

where δy is the length of the microsegments on the vertical boundary segments of the box $\mathcal{B}$. In the limit we get

$$\left.\begin{array}{l}\text{flux across vertical}\\\text{boundary segments}\\\text{of the box } \mathcal{B}\end{array}\right\} = \int_{b-\frac{\Delta y}{2}}^{b+\frac{\Delta y}{2}} \left[P(a+\tfrac{\Delta x}{2}, y_k^*) - P(a-\tfrac{\Delta x}{2}, y_k^*) \right] dy.$$

Then using the Fundamental Theorem of Calculus, we write our calculation as

$$\left.\begin{array}{l}\text{flux across vertical}\\\text{boundary segments}\\\text{of the box } \mathcal{B}\end{array}\right\} = \int_{b-\frac{\Delta y}{2}}^{b+\frac{\Delta y}{2}} \int_{a-\frac{\Delta x}{2}}^{a+\frac{\Delta x}{2}} P_x(x,y)\, dx\, dy = \iint_{\mathcal{B}} P_x(x,y)\, dA.$$

Step 3 (combining our results): The flux of $\mathbf{F}$ through $\mathcal{B}$ is found by adding the flux across the horizontal and vertical boundary segments:

$$\left.\begin{array}{l}\text{flux across the bound-}\\\text{ary of the rectangle } \mathcal{B}\end{array}\right\} = \iint_{\mathcal{B}} P_x \, dA + \iint_{\mathcal{B}} Q_y \, dA = \iint_{\mathcal{B}} (P_x + Q_y)\, dA. \qquad (4.5)$$

Let's pause to understand the right-hand side of this equation. For the sake of discussion, suppose the integrand $P_x + Q_y > 0$ throughout $\mathcal{B}$. Then the value of this double integral is positive, so the net flux of $\mathbf{F}$ across the boundary of $\mathcal{B}$ is positive, meaning that more fluid mass is exiting than entering. So we conclude that fluid is being injected into the flow by some source inside the rectangle. As we shrink $\mathcal{B}$ to a single point there's only one possible source—the point (a,b)—and the integrand approaches $P_x(a,b) + Q_y(a,b)$, so we often think of $P_x(a,b) + Q_y(a,b)$ as the rate at which fluid is being pushed out of and away from the point (a,b). This is correct in spirit, but needs a slight modification to be accurate.

Since flux is measured in g/sec, those are the units of the integral; the area element has units of cm^2, so $P_x + Q_y$ has units of $\frac{\text{g}}{\text{sec}}$ per cm^2. That is, $P_x + Q_y$ measures the *density* of fluid injection into the flow (a negative value indicates that fluid is being drawn out of the flow). So we refer to $P_x + Q_y$ as the *flux density* or (more commonly) the *divergence* of $\langle P, Q \rangle$.

Definition: Suppose $\mathbf{F} = \langle P, Q \rangle$, where P_x and Q_y exist. The **divergence** of $\mathbf{F}$ (also called its **flux density**) is denoted by $\text{div}(\mathbf{F})$ or $\nabla \cdot \mathbf{F}$, and defined to be

$$\nabla \cdot \mathbf{F} = P_x + Q_y.$$

Note: Formally speaking, the notation $\nabla \cdot \mathbf{F}$ means $P_x + Q_y$ because

$$\frac{\partial P}{\partial x} + \frac{\partial Q}{\partial y} = \frac{\partial}{\partial x} P + \frac{\partial}{\partial y} Q = \left\langle \frac{\partial}{\partial x}, \frac{\partial}{\partial y} \right\rangle \cdot \langle P, Q \rangle = \nabla \cdot \mathbf{F},$$

where ∇ means $\langle \frac{\partial}{\partial x}, \frac{\partial}{\partial y} \rangle$. At this stage in your mathematical education, the symbol $\langle \frac{\partial}{\partial x}, \frac{\partial}{\partial y} \rangle$ should never be by itself in an equation or expression, but always with

Sidebar notes (right margin):

Here we use Fubini's Theorem to write the iterated integral as a double integral over the rectangle $\mathcal{B}$.

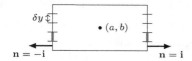

Figure 4.8: Partition the vertical boundaries into segments of length δy. The blue segments constitute a *pair*.

This happens, for example, when P_x and Q_y are continuous functions and $P_x + Q_y > 0$ at (a,b).

By saying that we "shrink" the rectangle to a single point we mean that $\Delta x \to 0$ while the aspect ratio is maintained.

You can also check the units of P and Q, and see that differentiating with respect to length gives you units of g/sec per square cm.

This notational idea also works to give us the gradient of a function. Treating $\langle \frac{\partial}{\partial x}, \frac{\partial}{\partial y} \rangle$ as a vector and $f(x,y)$ as a scalar (it is), we have:

$$\begin{aligned}\nabla f &= \langle \tfrac{\partial}{\partial x}, \tfrac{\partial}{\partial y} \rangle f \\ &= \langle \tfrac{\partial}{\partial x} f, \tfrac{\partial}{\partial y} f \rangle \\ &= \langle f_x, f_y \rangle.\end{aligned}$$

vector field or function. We're just using the dot product notation to write the divergence of a vector field in a conveniently compact form.

The divergence of a vector field

Example 4.4. Suppose $\mathbf{F} = \langle 2x^3 + y, 3y^2 - \sin x \rangle$. (a) Determine where $\mathrm{div}(\mathbf{F}) < 0$, and (b) explain its practical significance.

Solution: (a) The divergence of $\mathbf{F}$ is $\mathrm{div}(\mathbf{F}) = \frac{\partial}{\partial x}(2x^3 + y) + \frac{\partial}{\partial y}(3y^2 - \sin x) = 6x^2 + 6y$, which is negative when $y < -x^2$. (b) In the context of incompressible fluids, fluid is removed from the plane in regions where the divergence is negative. ∎

The divergence of a vector field

Example 4.5. Suppose $\mathbf{F} = \langle 8x + 4y, 13y^2 + e^x \rangle$. Determine a formula for $\nabla \cdot \mathbf{F}$.

Answer: $8 + 26y$. ∎

Solution On-line

When written using the dot product notation, the algebraic properties of $\mathrm{div}(\mathbf{F})$ are reminiscent of the dot product of vectors.

Properties of Divergence: Suppose the first partial derivatives of the vector fields $\mathbf{F}$ and $\mathbf{G}$ exist, as do those of the scalar-valued function f, and k is constant. Then

$$\nabla \cdot (k\mathbf{F}) = k(\nabla \cdot \mathbf{F}) \tag{4.6}$$

$$\nabla \cdot (\mathbf{F} + \mathbf{G}) = (\nabla \cdot \mathbf{F}) + (\nabla \cdot \mathbf{G}) \tag{4.7}$$

$$\nabla \cdot (f\mathbf{F}) = (f)(\nabla \cdot \mathbf{F}) + (\nabla f) \cdot \mathbf{F} \tag{4.8}$$

Note: In the exercise set you'll prove these identities using the Scaling, Sum, and Product Rule of differentiation that you already know.

In the discussion following equation (4.5) we interpreted $P_x(a, b) + Q_y(a, b)$ as the density of fluid injection into the flow $\mathbf{F} = \langle P, Q \rangle$ at the point (a, b). The net contribution to the flow due to all the points in a region can be determined by using the double integral:

$$\text{flux} = \underbrace{\iint_R \underbrace{\nabla \cdot \mathbf{F}}_{\text{g/sec per cm}^2} \underbrace{dA}_{\text{cm}^2}}_{} \; \frac{\text{g}}{\text{sec}}. \tag{4.9}$$

When that net contribution is positive, more fluid will leave the region than enters, so the flux across the boundary will be positive.

❖ Green's Theorem ("Flux-Divergence" or "Normal" Form)

We've talked about flux integrals, and divergence, and now we bring those ideas together. The integrals in equations (4.3) and (4.9) tell us two different ways to calculate the flux of $\mathbf{F} = \langle P, Q \rangle$ across the boundary of a region, so they must have the same value.

Green's Theorem ("Flux-Divergence" or "Normal" Form): Suppose $\mathcal{C}$ is a piecewise-smooth, simple, closed curve in the plane, and R is the bounded region enclosed by $\mathcal{C}$. If $\mathbf{F} = \langle P, Q \rangle$ is a smooth vector field in an open region containing $\mathcal{C}$ and R,

$$\oint_{\mathcal{C}} P\, dy - Q\, dx = \iint_{R} (P_x + Q_y)\, dA,$$

or equivalently

$$\underbrace{\oint_{\mathcal{C}} \mathbf{F} \cdot \mathbf{n}\, ds}_{\text{Net flow across the boundary}} = \underbrace{\iint_{R} \operatorname{div}(\mathbf{F})\, dA.}_{\text{Net contribution to the flow from interior points}}$$

> Hopefully, our intuitive discussion of flowing fluids has made this assertion clear. But if $\mathbf{F}$ does not represent the flow of a fluid, are the integrals still the same? What if $\mathbf{F}$ is an electric field, or a magnetic field? Is the equality of these integrals a particular physical fact, or a general mathematical one? Green's Theorem asserts the latter. We postpone this proof until the conclusion of our discussion in Section 15.5.

Validating Green's Theorem

Example 4.6. Calculate $\iint_{R} \nabla \cdot \mathbf{F}\, dA$ when $\mathbf{F}$ is defined in Example 4.2, and R is the region enclosed by $\mathcal{C}$ in that example.

Solution: When $\mathbf{F} = \langle x + y, 2 \rangle$ we have $\nabla \cdot \mathbf{F} = \partial_x(x + y) + \partial_y(2) = 1 + 0 = 1$, so

$$\iint_{R} \nabla \cdot \mathbf{F}\, dA = \iint_{R} 1\, dA = 1(\text{area of } R) = 3,$$

which agrees with our calculation in in Example 4.2. ∎

Flows of compressible fluids

Example 4.7. Suppose the smooth velocity field of a gas, $\mathbf{F}$, is directed away from the point P. Show that $\nabla \cdot \mathbf{F} \geq 0$ at P.

Solution: Suppose $\mathcal{C}$ is a small circle of radius r around the point P, as seen in Figure 4.9, and R is the disk it encloses. We know that $\mathbf{F} \cdot \mathbf{n} > 0$ at each point on $\mathcal{C}$ because $\mathbf{F}$ points away from P, so Green's Theorem tells us that

$$\iint_{R} \nabla \cdot \mathbf{F}\, dA = \oint_{\mathcal{C}} \mathbf{F} \cdot \mathbf{n}\, ds > 0.$$

The function $\nabla \cdot \mathbf{F}$ is continuous since $\mathbf{F}$ is smooth, so the Mean Value Theorem for Double Integrals guarantees that there is some point in R, say Q, at which

$$\underbrace{\frac{1}{\pi r^2} \iint_{R} \nabla \cdot \mathbf{F}\, dA}_{\text{The average value of } \nabla \cdot \mathbf{F} \text{ over } R \text{ is achieved at } Q.} = \underbrace{\nabla \cdot \mathbf{F}(Q)}.$$

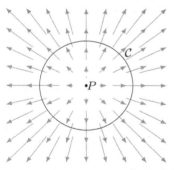

Figure 4.9: The velocity field of a gas that's expanding in the vicinity of P.

Since the left-hand side of this equation is positive, the number $\nabla \cdot \mathbf{F}(Q)$ is too. The point $Q \to P$ as $r \to 0^+$, and the continuity of $\nabla \cdot \mathbf{F}$ guarantees that the limiting value of $\operatorname{div}(\mathbf{F})$ is nonnegative. ∎

Example 4.7 shows another common way of understanding divergence in the context of a compressible medium; the divergence is positive where the medium is expanding, and negative where it's contracting (or being compressed).

❖ Common Difficulties with Green's Theorem

Students sometimes erroneously attempt to apply Green's Theorem to line integrals over curves that are *not* closed. Remember that Green's Theorem relates the line integral over C to the double integral over the region that it encloses. If C is not closed, no region is enclosed, so Green's Theorem does not apply.

You should know

- the terms *mass flow, simple, closed, outward normal, flux, flux density,* and *divergence;*
- the notations $\oint$, $\nabla \cdot \mathbf{F}$, and div($\mathbf{F}$);
- the flux-divergence form of Green's Theorem;
- physical interpretations of positive (or negative) divergence.

You should be able to

- use a line integral to calculate flux of $\mathbf{F}$ across a curve;
- use Green's Theorem to rewrite line integrals over simple, closed curves as double integrals, and vice versa.

❖ 15.4 Skill Exercises

In #1–6 determine a formula for div($\mathbf{F}$).

1. $\mathbf{F} = \langle 8x + y, 9y^2 \rangle$

2. $\mathbf{F} = \langle x^2 - y^2, \cos x \rangle$

3. $\mathbf{F} = \langle \cos(e^{\sin y}), xy^2 + 6x \rangle$

4. $\mathbf{F} = \langle e^{xy}, \ln(x^2 + 1) \rangle$

5. $\mathbf{F} = \langle 8x - 9y, 3x - 8y \rangle$

6. $\mathbf{F} = \langle x + \sin 2x, y \sin^2 x \rangle$

In #7–14 a vector field $\mathbf{F}$ is specified and a curve C is described. Verify Green's Theorem by calculating (a) the line integral $\oint_C \mathbf{F} \cdot \mathbf{n} \, ds$, and (b) the double integral $\iint_R \nabla \cdot \mathbf{F} \, dA$ where R is the region enclosed by C.

7. $\mathbf{F} = \langle y + x, 8 \rangle$; the circle of radius 3 centered at the origin.

8. $\mathbf{F} = \langle x, y \rangle$; the ellipse $25x^2 + 16y^2 = 400$.

9. $\mathbf{F} = \langle x^2, x - y \rangle$; the unit circle at the origin.

10. $\mathbf{F} = \langle 4x, 3y \rangle$; the circle of radius 2 centered at $(3, 4)$.

11. $\mathbf{F} = \langle 1 - x, y + 2 \rangle$; the square with vertices $(3, 1)$, $(5, 1)$, $(5, 3)$ and $(3, 3)$.

12. $\mathbf{F} = \langle 2x+5, 6y-1 \rangle$; the rectangle with vertices $(1, 1)$, $(5, 1)$, $(5, 10)$ and $(1, 10)$.

13. $\mathbf{F} = \langle 4x + 8, 5 - y \rangle$; the triangle with vertices are $(-4, 7)$, $(-1, 4)$, and $(6, 11)$.

14. $\mathbf{F} = \langle 3-2x, 2y+7 \rangle$; the rectangle connecting $(0, 0)$, $(-2, 14)$, $(1, 7)$ and $(5, 15)$.

In #15–20 use a computer algebra system to compute the net flux of the vector field $\mathbf{F}$ across the given curve. In #17, 19–20 the curve is described in polar coordinates.

15. $\mathbf{F} = \langle \cos y, e^{yx^2} \rangle$; C is in Figure 4.10.

16. $\mathbf{F} = \langle e^y, -xe^{y^4} \rangle$; C is in Figure 4.11

17. $\mathbf{F} = \langle \sin y, 7x^2 \rangle$; $r = 1$.

18. $\mathbf{F} = \langle \cos y, -9x^2 \rangle$; $x^2 + 2y^2 = 72$.

19. $\mathbf{F} = \langle e^y, xy \rangle$; $r = 3 + 2\cos\theta$.

20. $\mathbf{F} = \langle e^x, xy^2 \rangle$; $r = 4 + \sin 3\theta$.

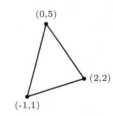

Figure 4.10: C in #15.

CAS

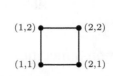

Figure 4.11: C in #16.

❖ 15.4 Concept and Application Exercises

In #21–26 determine whether the specified curve $\mathcal{C}$ is (a) closed, and (b) simple.

21. $\mathcal{C}$ is the parabola $y = x^2$

22. $\mathcal{C}$ is the ellipse $x^2 + 5y^2 = 1$

23. $\mathcal{C}$ is the cardioid $r = 1 + \cos\theta$

24. $\mathcal{C}$ is the limaçon $r = 1 + 1.2\cos\theta$

25. The path $\mathbf{r}(t) = \langle \sin 2t, \cos 3t \rangle$, $t \in [0, 2\pi]$

26. The path $\mathbf{r}(t) = \langle \sin^2 t, 1 + \cos t \rangle$, $t \in [0, \pi]$

27. Suppose $\mathcal{C}$ is the curve described by $\sin(x + y) + x^2 + y^2 = 1$. Use Green's Theorem to show that the flux of $\mathbf{F}_1 = \langle xy, xy \rangle$ over $\mathcal{C}$ is the same as the flux of $\mathbf{F}_2 = \langle 0.5x^2, 0.5y^2 \rangle$ over $\mathcal{C}$.

28. Suppose $\mathcal{C}$ is the curve described by $\cos(x - y) + x^2 + y^2 = 2$. (a) Use a graphing utility to verify that $\mathcal{C}$ is symmetric about the origin, and based on that fact, (b) use Green's Theorem to prove that the flux of $\mathbf{F}_1 = \langle 5x^3, 3y^5 \rangle$ across $\mathcal{C}$ is larger than that of $\mathbf{F}_2 = \langle 2x^4, 3y^6 \rangle$.

29. Suppose a sheet of elastic material is pulled from below (see Figure 4.12) so that, except for the secured top edge of the sheet, each point of the sheet moves. The associated *deformation field* on the original sheet is the set of vectors that describe each point's displacement under the traction.

    (a) Explain what $\nabla \cdot \mathbf{F}(Q) > 0$ tells us about the material at the point Q.

    (b) If a small region of the sheet is much less elastic that the surrounding material, what should be true about $\nabla \cdot \mathbf{F}$ in and around it?

Figure 4.12: A deformation field for an elastic medium under a downward traction.

30. Figure 4.13 shows the vector field associated with a horizontal compression of pixels at the middle of the image. Each vector in the vector field $\mathbf{F}$ indicates the displacement of a pixel in the original image. Based on this vector field, (a) determine whether $\nabla \cdot \mathbf{F}$ is positive, negative, or zero at points A and B, and (b) explain what that means to us, visually.

Image Processing

  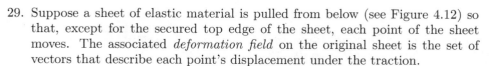

Figure 4.13: (left) The original image; (middle) the distorted image; (right) the associated deformation field (with two points of interest identified).

31. Suppose $\mathbf{F} = \langle x^2, -2xy \rangle$ and $\mathcal{C}_1$ is the portion of the curve $y = 1 + \sin^2(xy)$ that extends from the point $(\pi, 1)$ to $(0, 1)$.

    (a) Suppose $\mathcal{C}_2$ is the line segment from $(0, 1)$ to $(\pi, 1)$. Show that $\mathcal{C}_1 + \mathcal{C}_2$ is a simple, closed curve.

    (b) Use Green's Theorem to show that $\int_{\mathcal{C}_1} \mathbf{F} \cdot \mathbf{n}\, ds = -\int_{\mathcal{C}_2} \mathbf{F} \cdot \mathbf{n}\, ds$.

    (c) Determine the value of $\int_{\mathcal{C}_1} \mathbf{F} \cdot \mathbf{n}\, ds$.

32. Suppose $\mathbf{F} = \langle 1 - x\sin 2y, \sin^2 y \rangle$ and $\mathcal{C}$ is the portion of the curve $x^{2/3} + y^4 = 1$ on which $x \geq 0$. Calculate $\int_{\mathcal{C}} \mathbf{F} \cdot \mathbf{n}\, ds$ using the technique from #31.

33. Suppose length in the xy-plane is measured in cm, and the mass flow of an incompressible fluid is $\mathbf{F} = \langle x + 1, y^2 \rangle$ g/sec per cm. Determine the flux of the fluid across the unit circle by calculating the integral of the flux density over the unit disk. Include proper units in your answer.

Incompressible Fluid Flux

34. Suppose length in the xy-plane is measured in cm, and the mass flow of an incompressible fluid is $\mathbf{F}$ g/sec per cm. The curve $\mathcal{C}$ is an ellipse with a major axis of length 12 and a minor axis of length 7, and R is the region enclosed by $\mathcal{C}$. If $\int_{\mathcal{C}} \mathbf{F} \cdot \mathbf{n} \, ds = 5$, determine the average rate at which fluid is injected into the flow inside of R. Include proper units in your answer.

Incompressible Fluid Flux

In #35–38 the simple, closed, smooth curve $\mathcal{C}$ is the boundary of the region R.

35. Use Green's Theorem to prove **Green's First Identity**, which says that

Mathematics

$$\iint_R f \, \nabla \cdot (\nabla g) \, dA = \oint_{\mathcal{C}} f \, \nabla g \cdot \mathbf{n} \, ds - \iint_R \nabla f \cdot \nabla g \, dA.$$

(Hint: Consider the double integral of $\mathrm{div}(f \nabla g)$ *over R.)*

36. Use Green's First Identity to prove **Green's Second Identity**, which says that $\iint_R f \, \nabla \cdot (\nabla g) - g \, \nabla \cdot (\nabla f) \, dA = \oint_{\mathcal{C}} (f \nabla g - g \nabla f) \cdot \mathbf{n} \, ds$.

Mathematics

37. Suppose f is the potential of the vector field $\mathbf{F}$. Use Green's Theorem to show that the flux of $\mathbf{F}$ across $\mathcal{C}$ is the same as $\iint_R f_{xx} + f_{yy} \, dA$.

38. Suppose that g is a differentiable function, and f is a **harmonic** function, meaning that $f_{xx} + f_{yy} = 0$. Prove that

Mathematics

$$\iint_R \nabla f \cdot \nabla g \, dA = \oint_{\mathcal{C}} g \nabla f \cdot \mathbf{n} \, ds.$$

39. Imagine that you have a black-and-white photo, but some of the pixels in the image have been corrupted (or perhaps there was a smudge on the camera lens) so there's a region, R, that looks wrong. In this exercise, we'll treat the photo as the graph of an "intensity" function, $I(x, y)$, where $I = 1$ at white points in the image, and $I = 0$ black points. Further, we'll suppose that R is an open region with a smooth boundary curve, $\mathcal{C}$, and assume that the restriction of $I(x, y)$ to $\mathcal{C}$ is continuous. The goal of *in painting* is to "fix" the region R by replacing the current values of $I(x, y)$ in R with those of a new function, say $f(x, y)$ that agrees with I on $\mathcal{C}$. (In the exercises below we assume that the functions in question have continuous partial derivatives.)

Image Processing

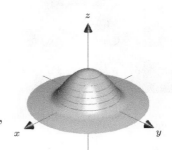

Figure 4.14: An example of a graph of a "bump" function.

    (a) Explain (in terms of the photo) why we might want to minimize $\iint_R \|\nabla f\|^2 \, dA$, which is sometimes called an *energy integral*. (Hint: what would this mean about the pixel intensities in R)?

    (b) Suppose we can find the function f from part (a) that minimizes the energy integral, and that it has continuous second partial derivatives. Explain why any other function that agrees with $I(x, y)$ on $\mathcal{C}$ must have the form $f + g$ where $g(x, y) = 0$ on $\mathcal{C}$.

    (c) With f as the function from part (a), explain why $\iint_R \|\nabla f\|^2 \, dA \leq \iint_R \|\nabla (f + tg)\|^2 \, dA$ for any value of t. *(Hint: check parts (a) and (b).)*

    (d) Show that $\iint_R \|\nabla (f + tg)\|^2 \, dA$ is a differentiable function of t.

    (e) Explain why $\frac{d}{dt} \iint_R \|\nabla (f + tg)\|^2 \, dA$ must be 0 when $t = 0$.

    (f) Determine a formula for $\frac{d}{dt} \iint_R \|\nabla (f + tg)\|^2 \, dA$ at $t = 0$.

(g) By combining Green's Identities (see #35–36) with parts (e) and (f), show that $\iint_R g\Delta f \, dA = 0$, where Δf is defined to be $\nabla \cdot \nabla f = f_{xx} + f_{yy}$.

(h) In part (g) you showed that $\iint_R g\Delta f \, dA = 0$ whenever $g(x, y)$ is a function with continuous partial derivatives. In particular, it's true when the graph of g is a "bump" in the neighborhood of any arbitrary point (a, b) in the interior of R. Explain why $\iint_R g\Delta f \, dA = 0$ implies that f is harmonic throughout R (see #38).

40. In 2002 R. Hughes published a mathematical description of crowds of pedestrians with a common goal at a known location. Intuitively speaking, each pedestrian's path-of-least-time to the goal depends on the distribution of people in the crowd, and that distribution changes as the pedestrians move. Hughes models this situation with a pair of functions: ρ is the pedestrian density, which varies across the crowd, and $\phi(x, y)$ represents the pedestrians' common sense of the task they face in reaching the goal, so that pedestrians at (x_1, y_1) and (x_2, y_2) see no benefit in exchanging places when $\phi(x_1, y_1) = \phi(x_2, y_2)$.

| Crowd Movement |

(a) Suppose we understand $\phi(x, y)$ as the time it would take a pedestrian at (x, y) to reach the goal, given the current distribution of the crowd. Explain why $\frac{d}{dt}\phi(x, y) = -1$.

(b) If the path taken by a pedestrian is parameterized by $\mathbf{r}(t) = \langle x(t), y(t) \rangle$, use part (a) to show that $\mathbf{r}'(t) = -f^2 \nabla \phi$ where $f = 1/\|\nabla \phi\|$.

(c) Based on part (b) describe the relationship between the path of a pedestrian at (x_1, y_1) and the curve $\phi(x, y) = \phi(x_1, y_1)$, and explain why that makes sense in this context.

(d) Based on part (b) show that the speed of a pedestrian's travel is f. Because a pedestrian's speed depends on the density of the crowd near him, we write $f(\rho)$.

(e) Suppose R is a small region with smooth boundary $\mathcal{C}$. Based on our discussion of flux, explain the contextual meaning of the equation

$$\frac{d}{dt} \iint_R \rho \, dA = \oint_{\mathcal{C}} \rho f(\rho)^2 \nabla\phi \cdot \hat{\mathbf{n}} \, ds.$$

(f) Explain how part (e) leads us to write $\frac{\partial \rho}{\partial t} = \nabla \cdot \left(\rho f(\rho)^2 \nabla\phi \right)$.

Checking the details

In #41–43 use $\mathbf{F} = \langle P, Q \rangle$ and $\mathbf{G} = \langle L, M \rangle$.

41. Verify equation (4.6) by using the Scaling Rule for differentiation.

42. Verify equation (4.7) by using the Sum Rule for differentiation.

43. Verify equation (4.8) by using the Product Rule for differentiation.

15.5 Green's Theorem (Circulation Form)

In Section 15.4 we talked about the rate at which a flow $\mathbf{F}$ crosses a curve. In this section we calculate the flow of $\mathbf{F}$ *along* an oriented curve. In this context,

$$\int_{\mathcal{C}} \mathbf{F} \cdot \mathbf{T}\, ds$$

is sometimes called a ***flow integral***, and when $\mathcal{C}$ is a simple closed curve

$$\oint_{\mathcal{C}} \mathbf{F} \cdot \mathbf{T}\, ds$$

is called the ***circulation*** of $\mathbf{F}$ around $\mathcal{C}$.

Like all curves, a simple closed curve can be oriented in two directions. By convention, we refer to the counterclockwise direction as the ***positive orientation***. Said differently, the region enclosed by the curve would remain on your left-hand side if you were to walk along the curve in the positive direction (see Figure 5.1). If you want to include orientation in the integral notation, you can put an arrow on the circle to indicate a clockwise or counterclockwise direction. For example,

$$\oint_{\mathcal{C}} \mathbf{F} \cdot \mathbf{T}\, ds \text{ indicates that } \mathcal{C} \text{ is oriented in the positive direction.}$$

We first calculated the line integral of $\mathbf{F} \cdot \mathbf{T}$ in Section 15.2. As a reminder of the technique, consider the following.

Circulation integral

Example 5.1. Suppose $\mathbf{F} = \langle -xy, 1 \rangle$ and $\mathcal{C}$ is the positively oriented circle of radius 1 that's centered at $(1,0)$. Determine the circulation of $\mathbf{F}$ around $\mathcal{C}$.

Solution: Since $\mathcal{C}$ is a circle, we can easily parameterize it with sine and cosine. Specifically, let's use $\mathbf{r}(t) = \langle 1 + \cos t, \sin t \rangle$. Then $\mathbf{r}'(t) = \langle -\sin t, \cos t \rangle$ is already a unit vector, so $\mathbf{T} = \mathbf{r}'$, and $ds = \|\mathbf{r}'\|\, dt = dt$. Further, at $x = 1 + \cos t$ and $y = \sin t$ we have $\mathbf{F} = \langle -(1 + \cos t) \sin t, 1 \rangle$, so

$$\oint_{\mathcal{C}} \mathbf{F} \cdot \mathbf{T}\, ds = \int_0^{2\pi} \left(\sin^2 t + \sin^2 t \cos t + \cos t \right) dt = \pi. \qquad \blacksquare$$

In Section 15.4 we were able to rewrite the line integral of $\mathbf{F} \cdot \mathbf{n}$ over $\mathcal{C}$ as a double integral of $\operatorname{div}(\mathbf{F})$ over the region enclosed by $\mathcal{C}$. In this section you'll see an analogous result for circulation integrals, but instead of integrating the divergence of $\mathbf{F}$ we integrate a quantity called its *scalar curl*.

❖ Scalar Curl of a Vector Field in the Plane

In the discussion that follows, you'll see that the circulation of the vector field $\mathbf{F}(x, y) = \langle L(x, y), M(x, y) \rangle$ around a rectangle can be calculated as the double integral of $M_x - L_y$ over its interior, and this will lead us to the formal definition of a quantity called the *scalar curl* of a vector field.

Suppose $\mathbf{F}(x, y) = \langle L(x, y), M(x, y) \rangle$ is a smooth vector field, and $\mathcal{C}$ is the positively oriented rectangle centered at (a, b) with opposite corners at the points $\left(a - \frac{\Delta x}{2}, b - \frac{\Delta y}{2} \right)$ and $\left(a + \frac{\Delta x}{2}, b + \frac{\Delta y}{2} \right)$, as depicted in Figure 5.3. Then

$$\oint_{\mathcal{C}} \mathbf{F} \cdot \mathbf{T}\, ds = \int_{\mathcal{C}_1} \mathbf{F} \cdot \mathbf{T}\, ds + \int_{\mathcal{C}_2} \mathbf{F} \cdot \mathbf{T}\, ds + \int_{\mathcal{C}_3} \mathbf{F} \cdot \mathbf{T}\, ds + \int_{\mathcal{C}_4} \mathbf{F} \cdot \mathbf{T}\, ds.$$

Key Idea(s): *The tendency of a fluid to circulate around a region can be quantified with a line integral around its boundary.*

Figure 5.1: A positively oriented curve encloses the bounded region R. You might find it helpful to imagine a pole at the center of the region. As you walk around the curve in the positive direction, you can hold onto the pole with your left hand, your right hand points in the direction that you're traveling, and the vector $\mathbf{k}$ defines "up."

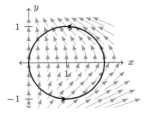

Figure 5.2: The curve and vector field for Example 5.1 (vector field not to scale).

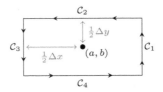

Figure 5.3: The rectangle $\mathcal{C}$.

We're going to calculate this circulation in three steps: (1) calculate the integral of $\mathbf{F} \cdot \mathbf{T}$ over the vertical boundary segments, then (2) over the horizontal segments, and finally (3) add those contributions together.

Step 1 (integrate over the vertical segments): Since $\mathbf{T} = \mathbf{j}$ and $x = a + \frac{\Delta x}{2}$ are constant on $\mathcal{C}_1$, the first integral is

$$\int_{\mathcal{C}_1} \mathbf{F} \cdot \mathbf{T} \; ds = \int_{\mathcal{C}_1} M \; ds = \int_{b-\Delta y/2}^{b+\Delta y/2} M(a + \tfrac{\Delta x}{2}, y) \; dy.$$

On the other vertical leg, $\mathcal{C}_3$, we have $\mathbf{T} = -\mathbf{j}$ and $x = a - \frac{\Delta x}{2}$ so

$$\int_{\mathcal{C}_3} \mathbf{F} \cdot \mathbf{T} \; ds = \int_{b-\Delta y/2}^{b+\Delta y/2} -M(a - \tfrac{\Delta x}{2}, y) \; dy.$$

Adding the contributions from the line integrals over the vertical legs gives us

$$\int_{\mathcal{C}_1} \mathbf{F} \cdot \mathbf{T} \; ds + \int_{\mathcal{C}_3} \mathbf{F} \cdot \mathbf{T} \; ds = \int_{b-\Delta y/2}^{b+\Delta y/2} M(a + \tfrac{\Delta x}{2}, y) \; dy + \int_{b-\Delta y/2}^{b+\Delta y/2} -M(a - \tfrac{\Delta x}{2}, y) \; dy$$

$$= \int_{b-\Delta y/2}^{b+\Delta y} \left[M(a + \tfrac{\Delta x}{2}, y) - M(a - \tfrac{\Delta x}{2}, y) \right] dy. \quad (5.1)$$

The Fundamental Theorem of Calculus tells us that

$$M(a + \tfrac{\Delta x}{2}, y) - M(a - \tfrac{\Delta x}{2}, y) = \int_{a-\Delta x/2}^{a+\Delta x/2} M_x(x, y) \; dx,$$

so equation (5.1) can be written as

$$\int_{b-\Delta y/2}^{b+\Delta y/2} \int_{a-\Delta x/2}^{a+\Delta x/2} M_x(x, y) \; dx \; dy = \iint_R M_x(x, y) \; dA,$$

where R is the rectangular region enclosed by $\mathcal{C}$.

> Here we use Fubini's Theorem to write the iterated integral as a double integral over the rectangle.

Step 2 (integrate over the horizontal segments): Since $\mathbf{T} = \mathbf{i}$ and $y = b - \frac{\Delta y}{2}$ are constant on $\mathcal{C}_4$,

$$\int_{\mathcal{C}_4} \mathbf{F} \cdot \mathbf{T} \; ds = \int_{\mathcal{C}_4} L \; ds = \int_{a-\Delta x/2}^{a+\Delta x/2} L(x, b - \tfrac{\Delta y}{2}) \; dx.$$

On the other horizontal segment, $\mathcal{C}_2$, we have $\mathbf{T} = -\mathbf{i}$ and $y = b + \frac{\Delta y}{2}$ so

$$\int_{\mathcal{C}_2} \mathbf{F} \cdot \mathbf{T} \; ds = \int_{\mathcal{C}_2} -L \; ds = \int_{a-\Delta x/2}^{a+\Delta x/2} -L(x, b + \tfrac{\Delta y}{2}) \; dx.$$

Adding these together, we see that the net contribution to the circulation from the horizontal legs is

$$\int_{\mathcal{C}_2} \mathbf{F} \cdot \mathbf{T} \; ds + \int_{\mathcal{C}_4} \mathbf{F} \cdot \mathbf{T} \; ds = \int_{a-\Delta x/2}^{a+\Delta x/2} -L(x, b + \tfrac{\Delta y}{2}) \; dx + \int_{a-\Delta x/2}^{a+\Delta x/2} L(x, b - \tfrac{\Delta y}{2}) \; dx$$

$$= -\int_{a-\Delta x/2}^{a+\Delta x/2} \left[L(x, b + \tfrac{\Delta y}{2}) - L(x, b - \tfrac{\Delta y}{2}) \right] dx.$$

Using the Fundamental Theorem of Calculus, we can rewrite this as

$$-\int_{a-\Delta x/2}^{a+\Delta x/2} \int_{b-\Delta y/2}^{b+\Delta y/2} L_y(x, y) \; dy \; dx = -\iint_R L_y(x, y) \; dA = \iint_R -L_y(x, y) \; dA.$$

Step 3 (adding results): Based on the calculations we just finished,

$$\oint_{\mathcal{C}} \mathbf{F} \cdot \mathbf{T} \, ds = \int_{\mathcal{C}_1 + \mathcal{C}_3} \mathbf{F} \cdot \mathbf{T} \, ds + \int_{\mathcal{C}_2 + \mathcal{C}_4} \mathbf{F} \cdot \mathbf{T} \, ds = \iint_{R} (M_x - L_y) \, dA.$$

As we indicated at the beginning of the section, the equation

$$\oint_{\mathcal{C}} \mathbf{F} \cdot \mathbf{T} \, ds = \iint_{R} (M_x - L_y) \, dA \tag{5.2}$$

relates the circulation integral to a double integral over the region enclosed by $\mathcal{C}$.

In equation (5.2) you see that the circulation of $\mathbf{F}$ around the rectangle at (a, b) is the same as a double integral of $M_x - L_y$. For this reason, number $M_x(a, b) - L_y(a, b)$ is often understood as quantifying the tendency of the flow to circulate around the point (a, b). This leads us to make the following definition.

Definition: Suppose $\mathbf{F} = \langle L, M \rangle$, where L_y and M_x exist. The ***scalar curl*** of $\mathbf{F}$ is denoted by $\mathrm{curl}(\mathbf{F})$ and defined to be

$$\mathrm{curl}(\mathbf{F}) = M_x - L_y.$$

> The curl of vector fields in space is discussed in Section 15.10.

Scalar curl of a conservative vector field

Example 5.2. Show that $\mathrm{curl}(\mathbf{F}) = 0$ when $\mathbf{F} = \langle L, M \rangle$ is a smooth, conservative vector field.

> The term *conservative* was defined in Section 15.2. It implies that there is a function f for which $\mathbf{F} = \nabla f$.

Solution: Since $\mathbf{F}$ is conservative, let's begin by writing it as $\mathbf{F} = \nabla f = \langle f_x, f_y \rangle$. That is, $L = f_x$ and $M = f_y$. Further, since $\mathbf{F}$ is smooth we know that $L_y = f_{xy}$ and $M_x = f_{yx}$ are continuous. It follows from Clairaut's Theorem (see Section 13.4) that they are equal, so $M_x - L_y = f_{yx} - f_{xy} = 0$. ∎

Calculating scalar curl

Example 5.3. Calculate $\mathrm{curl}(\mathbf{F})$ when $\mathbf{F} = \langle 5xy^2, 9x - \sin y \rangle$.

Answer: $\mathrm{curl}(\mathbf{F}) = 9 - 10xy$. ∎

Solution On-line

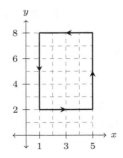

Calculating circulation with a double integral

Example 5.4. Suppose $\mathbf{F} = \langle 3y + 4x, 8x - 19y \rangle$ and $\mathcal{C}$ is the positively oriented rectangle shown in Figure 5.4. Determine the circulation of $\mathbf{F}$ around $\mathcal{C}$.

Solution: We *could* calculate the four line integrals along the four sides of this rectangle, and then add the results, but equation (5.2) gives us an easier way. In this case, $L = 3y + 4x$ and $M = 8x - 19y$, so $M_x - L_y = 8 - 3 = 5$. Since this rectangle is 4 units wide and 6 units tall, its area is 24, so

$$\int_{\mathcal{C}} \mathbf{F} \cdot \mathbf{T} \, ds = \iint_{R} 5 \, dA = (5)(24) = 120.$$

As a brief addendum, we note when length is measured in cm and $\mathbf{F}$ is a mass flow with units of g/sec per cm, the units of $\mathbf{F} \cdot \mathbf{T} \, ds$ are $\frac{\text{g/sec}}{\text{cm}}(\text{cm}) = \frac{\text{g}}{\text{sec}}$. ∎

Figure 5.4: The rectangle $\mathcal{C}$ for Example 5.4.

Scalar curl and circulation with a triangle

Example 5.5. Suppose $\mathcal{C}$ is the positively oriented triangle connecting the points (a, b), $(a + \Delta x, b)$ and $(a, b + \Delta y)$, and $\mathbf{F}$ is a smooth vector field. Show that the circulation of $\mathbf{F}$ around $\mathcal{C}$ is the same as the double integral of $\mathrm{curl}(\mathbf{F})$ over the interior of the triangle.

Solution: The circulation of $\mathbf{F}$ around $\mathcal{C}$ is

$$\oint_{\mathcal{C}} \mathbf{F} \cdot \mathbf{T} \, ds = \int_{\mathcal{C}_1} \mathbf{F} \cdot \mathbf{T} \, ds + \int_{\mathcal{C}_2} \mathbf{F} \cdot \mathbf{T} \, ds + \int_{\mathcal{C}_3} \mathbf{F} \cdot \mathbf{T} \, ds,$$

where $\mathcal{C}_1$, $\mathcal{C}_2$ and $\mathcal{C}_3$ are the boundary segments as shown in Figure 5.5. The first and third of these integrals are relatively easy:

$$\int_{\mathcal{C}_1} \mathbf{F} \cdot \mathbf{T} \, ds = \int_a^{a+\Delta x} L(x, b) \, dx,$$

and because $\mathbf{T} = -\mathbf{j}$ on $\mathcal{C}_3$,

$$\int_{\mathcal{C}_3} \mathbf{F} \cdot \mathbf{T} \, ds = \int_{\mathcal{C}_3} -M \, ds = -\int_b^{b+\Delta y} M(a, y) \, dy.$$

To include the integral over $\mathcal{C}_2$, let's write it as

$$\int_{\mathcal{C}_2} \mathbf{F} \cdot \mathbf{T} \, ds = \int_{\mathcal{C}_2} L \, dx + M \, dy = \int_{\mathcal{C}_2} L \, dx + \int_{\mathcal{C}_2} M \, dy.$$

So the circulation around this triangle is

$$\int_a^{a+\Delta x} L(x, b) \, dx + \int_{\mathcal{C}_2} L \, dx + \int_{\mathcal{C}_2} M \, dy - \int_b^{b+\Delta y} M(a, y) \, dy.$$

In the discussion that follows, we will combine the pair of integrals involving L into a single expression, and do the same for the integrals involving M. Then we'll arrive at the desired result by adding them together.

Step 1 (combining the integrals in L): In order to combine the integrals that involve L, we need to write the second one as a definite integral from a to $a + \Delta x$, but that's a change of orientation (since $\mathcal{C}_2$ runs from right to left), so we begin by writing

$$\int_a^{a+\Delta x} L(x, b) \, dx + \int_{\mathcal{C}_2} L \, dx = \int_a^{a+\Delta x} L(x, b) \, dx - \int_{\mathcal{C}_2^-} L \, dx$$

In order to write the integral over $\mathcal{C}_2^-$ in terms of x (so that we can combine it with the other integral) let's think of $\mathcal{C}_2^-$ as the graph of a function, say $y = f(x)$. Then

$$\int_a^{a+\Delta x} L(x, b) \, dx - \int_{\mathcal{C}_2^-} L \, dx = \int_a^{a+\Delta x} L(x, b) \, dx - \int_a^{a+\Delta x} L(x, f(x)) \, dx = \int_a^{a+\Delta x} \left[L(x, b) - L(x, f(x)) \right] \, dx,$$

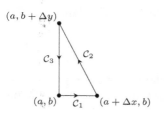

Figure 5.5: The triangle in Example 5.5.

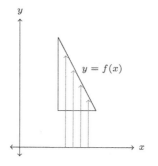
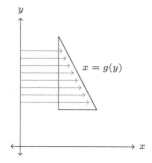

Figure 5.6: Thinking of the hypotenuse as (left) the graph of $y = f(x)$; (right) the graph of $x = g(y)$.

which the Fundamental Theorem of Calculus tells us is

$$\int_a^{a+\Delta x} \int_b^{f(x)} -L_y(x,y)\ dy\ dx = \iint_R -L_y(x,y)\ dA$$

where R is the region enclosed by $\mathcal{C}$ (we used Fubini's Theorem to rewrite the iterated integral as a double integral).

Step 2 (combining the integrals in M): Similarly, in order to combine the integrals involving M, we think of $\mathcal{C}_2$ as the graph of a function, $x = g(y)$, so

$$\int_{\mathcal{C}_2} M\ dy - \int_b^{b+\Delta y} M(a,y)\ dy = \int_b^{b+\Delta y} M(g(y),y)\ dy - \int_b^{b+\Delta y} M(a,y)\ dy = \int_b^{b+\Delta y} \Big[M(g(y),y) - M(a,y) \Big]\ dy,$$

which is the same as

$$\int_b^{b+\Delta y} \int_a^{g(y)} M_x(x,y)\ dx\ dy = \iint_R M_x(x,y)\ dA.$$

> We're using Fubini's Theorem to rewrite the iterated integral as a double integral.

The sum of these integrals is the circulation of $\mathbf{F}$ around $\mathcal{C}$,

$$\oint_{\mathcal{C}} \mathbf{F} \cdot \mathbf{T}\ ds = \iint_R (M_x - L_y)\ dA = \iint_R \text{curl}(\mathbf{F})\ dA. \qquad \blacksquare$$

As we saw with divergence in the previous section, the familiar rules of differentiation result in simply-stated properties of the scalar curl.

Properties of Scalar Curl: Suppose k is a scalar, $\mathbf{F}$ and $\mathbf{G}$ are two-dimensional vector fields, and the first partial derivatives of their component functions exist, as do those of the scalar-valued function $f(x,y)$. Then

$$\text{curl}(k\,\mathbf{F}) = k\,\text{curl}(\mathbf{F}) \qquad (5.3)$$
$$\text{curl}(\mathbf{F} + \mathbf{G}) = \text{curl}(\mathbf{F}) + \text{curl}(\mathbf{G}). \qquad (5.4)$$

And if $\mathbf{F} = \langle L, M \rangle$,

$$\text{curl}(f\mathbf{F}) = (f)\text{curl}(\mathbf{F}) + \nabla f \cdot \langle M, -L \rangle. \qquad (5.5)$$

Note: You'll prove these identities in the exercise set using the Scaling, Sum, and Product Rule of differentiation.

▷ Circulation Density

Suppose $\mathcal{C}$ is a square of side length r centered at the point P, and $\mathbf{F}$ is a smooth vector field. We know from equation (5.2) that

$$\oint_{\mathcal{C}} \mathbf{F} \cdot \mathbf{T}\ ds = \iint_R \text{curl}(\mathbf{F})\ dA,$$

where R is the square region enclosed by $\mathcal{C}$. Since $\text{curl}(\mathbf{F})$ is continuous, the Mean Value Theorem for Double Integrals tells us that there is some point inside the square, say Q, where

> $\text{curl}(\mathbf{F})$ is continuous because $\mathbf{F}$ is smooth

$$\text{curl}(\mathbf{F})\Big|_Q = \frac{1}{|R|} \iint_R \text{curl}(\mathbf{F})\ dA = \frac{\text{circulation of } \mathbf{F}}{\text{area enclosed by } \mathcal{C}}.$$

If length is measured in mm, for example, $\text{curl}(\mathbf{F})$ has units of "circulation" per mm^2, so $\text{curl}(\mathbf{F})$ is sometimes called the ***circulation density*** of $\mathbf{F}$.

❖ Green's Theorem ("Circulation" or "Tangential" Form)

You've seen that the circulation of **F** around a rectangle or triangle is the same as the double integral of curl(**F**) over the enclosed region. We can prove that this holds true in more general regions by using a limit.

Green's Theorem ("Circulation" or "Tangential" Form): Suppose $\mathcal{C}$ is a piecewise-smooth, simple, closed curve in the plane that's oriented in the positive direction, and R is the bounded region enclosed by $\mathcal{C}$. If $\mathbf{F} = \langle L, M \rangle$ is a smooth vector field in an open region containing $\mathcal{C}$ and R,

$$\oint_{\mathcal{C}} L\,dx + M\,dy = \iint_R (M_x - L_y)\,dA,$$

or equivalently

$$\underbrace{\oint_{\mathcal{C}} \mathbf{F} \cdot \mathbf{T}\,ds}_{\text{Circulation around the boundary}} = \underbrace{\iint_R \operatorname{curl}(\mathbf{F})\,dA.}_{\substack{\text{Accumulation of circulation density} \\ \text{throughout the enclosed region}}}$$

Proof. As indicated by Figure 5.7, our strategy will be to fill R with a finite collection of small rectangles and triangles, to the best of our ability. We'll call these rectangles and triangles denoted by $T_1, T_2, \ldots T_n$, and we'll write the positively-oriented boundary of the kth tile as $\mathcal{C}_k$.

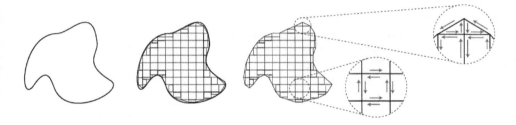

Figure 5.7: (left) The curve $\mathcal{C}$ encloses the region R; (middle) approximating R with a mesh of rectangles and triangles; (right) the net circulation along interior edges of the mesh is 0 because we integrate along each interior edge both "up" and "down," or both "right" and "left".

The circulation around the boundary of the kth tile is

$$\oint_{\mathcal{C}_k} \mathbf{F} \cdot \mathbf{T}\,ds = \iint_{T_k} (M_x - L_y)\,dA.$$

Adding these together yields

$$\sum_{k=1}^{n} \oint_{\mathcal{C}_k} \mathbf{F} \cdot \mathbf{T}\,ds = \sum_{k=1}^{n} \iint_{T_k} (M_x - L_y)\,dA \approx \iint_R (M_x - L_y)\,dA. \qquad (5.6)$$

In Figure 5.7 you see that this sum requires us to integrate over each edge of an interior tile in both directions, so the net contribution of $\mathbf{F} \cdot \mathbf{T}$ along such edges is 0. The remaining segments closely approximate $\mathcal{C}$, and $\mathbf{F}$ is continuous, so

$$\oint_{\mathcal{C}} \mathbf{F} \cdot \mathbf{T}\,ds \approx \sum_{k=1}^{n} \oint_{\mathcal{C}_k} \mathbf{F} \cdot \mathbf{T}\,ds. \qquad (5.7)$$

Comparing equations (5.6) and (5.7), and then taking a limit we see that

$$\oint_{\mathcal{C}} \mathbf{F} \cdot \mathbf{T} \, ds = \iint_{R} (M_x - L_y) \, dA.$$

We conclude by noting that the *flux-divergence* form of Green's theorem follows from the circulation form by setting $P = M$ and $Q = -L$. ∎

> We've suppressed some important facts about the limit-taking process. Proving equality in the limit relies on the curve $\mathcal{C}$ being "nice" in a certain sense, the details of which are discussed in advanced courses. Our statement that $\mathcal{C}$ is piecewise-smooth suffices.

Confirming Green's Theorem

Example 5.6. Suppose $\mathbf{F}$ and $\mathcal{C}$ are as in Example 5.1, and R is the disk bounded by $\mathcal{C}$. Calculate $\iint_{R} \text{curl}(\mathbf{F}) \, dA$ and compare it to the calculation in Example 5.1.

Solution: The scalar curl of $\mathbf{F}$ is $\text{curl}(\mathbf{F}) = \partial_x(1) - \partial_y(-xy) = x$. We'll integrate this function over the disk by using polar coordinates, taking r to be the distance between a point and the center of the disk, and θ to mean the angle that separates the point from the x-axis (see Figure 5.8). Using these variables, the x-coordinate of a point in the disk has the form $x = 1 + r\cos\theta$. Therefore,

$$\iint_{R} \text{curl}(\mathbf{F}) \, dA = \iint_{R} x \, dA = \int_{0}^{2\pi} \int_{0}^{1} (1 + r\cos\theta)\, r \, dr \, d\theta$$

$$= \int_{0}^{2\pi} \left[\frac{1}{2}r^2 + \frac{1}{3}r^3 \cos\theta \right]_{r=0}^{r=1} d\theta = \int_{0}^{2\pi} \left[\frac{1}{2} + \frac{1}{3}\cos\theta \right] d\theta = \pi,$$

which is the value of the circulation integral we calculated in Example 5.1. ∎

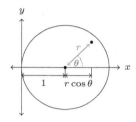

Figure 5.8: The disk for Example 5.6

Using Green's Theorem to facilitate calculations

Example 5.7. Calculate $\int_{\mathcal{C}_1} \mathbf{F} \cdot d\mathbf{r}$ when $\mathbf{F} = \langle 2xy - y^2, x^2 + y \rangle$ and $\mathcal{C}_1$ is the segment of $x = \sin(\pi y^2)$ that extends from the origin to the point $(0, 1)$.

Solution: We could parameterize this curve and use the technique introduced in Section 15.2, but Green's Theorem provides us with an easier way. Let's denote by $\mathcal{C}_2$ the line segment from $(0, 1)$ to the origin, oriented from top to bottom. If we append $\mathcal{C}_2$ to $\mathcal{C}_1$, we make a closed, piecewise smooth curve $\mathcal{C} = \mathcal{C}_1 + \mathcal{C}_2$ that's oriented positively with respect to the enclosed region R (see Figure 5.10). Since $\mathbf{F}$ is a smooth vector field,

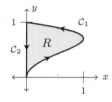

Figure 5.9: The curve $\mathcal{C}_1$ for Example 5.7.

$$\iint_{R} \text{curl}(\mathbf{F}) \, dA = \int_{\mathcal{C}_1 + \mathcal{C}_2} \mathbf{F} \cdot d\mathbf{r} = \int_{\mathcal{C}_1} \mathbf{F} \cdot d\mathbf{r} + \int_{\mathcal{C}_2} \mathbf{F} \cdot d\mathbf{r},$$

This allows us to calculate the desired line integral as

$$\int_{\mathcal{C}_1} \mathbf{F} \cdot d\mathbf{r} = \iint_{R} \text{curl}(\mathbf{F}) \, dA - \int_{\mathcal{C}_2} \mathbf{F} \cdot d\mathbf{r}. \tag{5.8}$$

Since R is x-simple, and $\text{curl}(\mathbf{F}) = 2x - (2x - 2y) = 2y$ we write

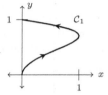

Figure 5.10: The curve $\mathcal{C}$ and region R for Example 5.7.

$$\int_{R} \text{curl}(\mathbf{F}) \, dA = \int_{0}^{1} \int_{0}^{\sin(\pi y^2)} 2y \, dx \, dy = \int_{0}^{1} 2y \sin(\pi y^2) \, dy = \frac{2}{\pi}.$$

And when we parameterize $\mathcal{C}_2$ with $\mathbf{r}(t) = \langle 0, 1 - t \rangle$, we see that

$$\int_{\mathcal{C}_2} \mathbf{F} \cdot d\mathbf{r} = \int_{0}^{1} \langle -(1-t)^2, 1-t \rangle \cdot \langle 0, -1 \rangle \, dt = \int_{0}^{1} (t - 1) \, dt = -\frac{1}{2}.$$

By using this values in equation (5.8) we arrive at

$$\int_{\mathcal{C}_1} \mathbf{F} \cdot d\mathbf{r} = \frac{2}{\pi} + \frac{1}{2}.$$ ∎

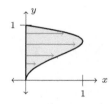

Figure 5.11: Treating R as x-simple, each horizontal line segment extends from $x = 0$ to $x = \sin(\pi y^2)$.

The hypotheses of Green's Theorem are important

Example 5.8. Suppose $\mathbf{F} = \langle -y/(x^2+y^2), x/(x^2+y^2) \rangle$ away from the origin. (a) Determine curl($\mathbf{F}$), (b) calculate the circulation of $\mathbf{F}$ around the positively-oriented unit circle, and (c) explain why this example doesn't contradict Green's Theorem.

Solution: (a) This vector field is defined with $L = -\frac{y}{x^2+y^2}$ and $M = \frac{x}{x^2+y^2}$, so

$$M_x = \frac{1}{x^2+y^2} - \frac{2x^2}{(x^2+y^2)^2}, \qquad L_y = -\frac{1}{x^2+y^2} + \frac{2y^2}{(x^2+y^2)^2},$$

> Using the Product Rule and the Chain Rule.

and curl($\mathbf{F}$) $= M_x - L_y = \frac{2}{x^2+y^2} - \frac{2x^2+2y^2}{(x^2+y^2)^2} = 0$ away from the origin.

(b) Let's use $\mathbf{r}(t) = \langle \cos t, \sin t \rangle$ to parameterize the unit circle. Then $\mathbf{T} = \langle -\sin t, \cos t \rangle$ and $\mathbf{F} = \langle -\sin t, \cos t \rangle$, so $\mathbf{F} \cdot \mathbf{T} = 1$, from which it follows that

$$\oint_{\mathcal{C}} \mathbf{F} \cdot \mathbf{T} \, ds = \int_0^{2\pi} 1 \, dt = 2\pi.$$

(c) Green's Theorem implies that the circulation of $\mathbf{F}$ around any simple, closed curve is 0 when curl($\mathbf{F}$) $= 0$ everywhere, but the theorem doesn't apply in this case because $\mathbf{F}$ is not smooth throughout the enclosed disk (the domain of $\mathbf{F}$ doesn't include the origin). ∎

▷ Regions with holes

The regions we've been discussing have been enclosed by simple, closed curves. Such regions have no holes and are said to be *simply connected*. More generally, a planar region R is **simply connected** when every simple, closed curve in R encloses only points that are in R. By contrast, the region R in the top image of Figure 5.12 is *not* simply connected because the dashed-line curve encloses points that are not in R. But suppose we separate R into regions R_1 and R_2, each of which is simply connected. Then

$$\oint_{B_1} \mathbf{F} \cdot \mathbf{T} \, ds = \iint_{R_1} \text{curl}(\mathbf{F}) \, dA \quad \text{and} \quad \oint_{B_2} \mathbf{F} \cdot \mathbf{T} \, ds = \iint_{R_2} \text{curl}(\mathbf{F}) \, dA,$$

where B_1 and B_2 are the positively oriented boundaries of R_1 and R_2, respectively. Upon sliding R_1 and R_2 back together, we see that our line integrals have crossed each vertical boundary segment in both directions, so the net contribution to the total is 0. This leaves us with

$$\oint_{\mathcal{C}_1} \mathbf{F} \cdot \mathbf{T} \, ds + \oint_{\mathcal{C}_2} \mathbf{F} \cdot \mathbf{T} \, ds = \iint_{R_1} \text{curl}(\mathbf{F}) \, dA + \iint_{R_2} \text{curl}(\mathbf{F}) \, dA = \iint_{R} \text{curl}(\mathbf{F}) \, dA,$$

where $\mathcal{C}_1$ and $\mathcal{C}_2$ are the positively oriented boundary curves of R, meaning that each is oriented so that the region R remains on the left as we traverse it.

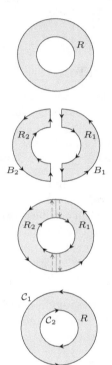

Figure 5.12: (top) A region that is not simply connected; (middle-top) separating the region into two simply connected regions so that we can work with each, independently; (middle-bottom) bringing the simply connected regions back together; (bottom) the boundary curves of R are oriented so that R remains on the left as we traverse them.

Using a hole to facilitate calculations

Example 5.9. Suppose $\mathbf{F}$ is the vector field from Example 5.8, and $\mathcal{C}_1$ is the positively oriented curve described by $(2 + \sin x)y^2 + (2 + \cos y)x^2 = 6$, which is shown in Figure 5.13. Determine the circulation of $\mathbf{F}$ around $\mathcal{C}_1$.

Solution: The curve $\mathcal{C}_1$ is sufficiently complicated that direct integration of $\mathbf{F} \cdot \mathbf{T}$ is impossible, but in Example 5.8 we showed that curl($\mathbf{F}$) $= 0$ away from the origin. We can use this to our advantage by considering the unit circle about the origin, which we'll call $\mathcal{C}_2$, oriented in the *clockwise* direction. Together with $\mathcal{C}_1$, this new curve constitutes the boundary of a region R in which $\mathrm{curl}(\mathbf{F}) = 0$, so

$$0 = \iint_R \mathrm{curl}(\mathbf{F})\,dA.$$

Green's Theorem allows us to write this equation as

$$0 = \int_{\mathcal{C}_1+\mathcal{C}_2} \mathbf{F}\cdot\mathbf{T}\,ds = \int_{\mathcal{C}_1} \mathbf{F}\cdot\mathbf{T}\,ds + \int_{\mathcal{C}_2} \mathbf{F}\cdot\mathbf{T}\,ds,$$

from which we conclude that the line integrals of $\mathcal{C}_1$ and $\mathcal{C}_2$ are opposites. That is

$$\int_{\mathcal{C}_1} \mathbf{F}\cdot\mathbf{T}\,ds = -\int_{\mathcal{C}_2} \mathbf{F}\cdot\mathbf{T}\,ds = \int_{\mathcal{C}_2^-} \mathbf{F}\cdot\mathbf{T}\,ds.$$

Since $\mathcal{C}_2^-$ is the unit circle with a *counterclockwise* orientation, we know from Example 5.8 that the right-hand side of this equation is 2π. Thus we conclude that

$$\int_{\mathcal{C}_1} \mathbf{F}\cdot\mathbf{T}\,ds = 2\pi. \qquad \blacksquare$$

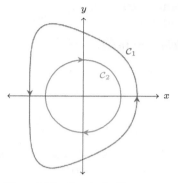

Figure 5.13: Curves for Example 5.9.

❖ The Curl Test

In Example 5.2 we showed that the scalar curl of a conservative vector field is 0. Green's Theorem is the key to proving the converse.

> **Curl Test:** Suppose $\mathbf{F} = \langle L, M \rangle$ is smooth in the simply connected region R, and $\mathrm{curl}(\mathbf{F}) = 0$ throughout. Then $\mathbf{F}$ is conservative.

Proof. We're going to show that line integrals of $\mathbf{F}$ are path independent in R, from which the result follows (see Section 15.2). Begin by choosing any two points in R, say A and B. Then pick two piecewise-smooth curves from A to B that remain in R, say $\mathcal{C}_1$ and $\mathcal{C}_2$. Then $\mathcal{C} = \mathcal{C}_1 + \mathcal{C}_2^-$ is a piecewise-smooth, closed curve. If $\mathcal{C}$ is simple, Green's Theorem tells us that

$$\oint_{\mathcal{C}} \mathbf{F}\cdot\mathbf{T}\,ds = \int_{\mathcal{R}} \mathrm{curl}(\mathbf{F})\,dA = \int_{\mathcal{R}} 0\,dA = 0,$$

where $\mathcal{R}$ is the region enclosed by $\mathcal{C}$. If $\mathcal{C}$ is not simple, its self-intersections form small loops, and the integral around each is 0 because $\mathrm{curl}(\mathbf{F}) = 0$ in the region enclosed by each. Now

$$\int_{\mathcal{C}_1} \mathbf{F}\cdot\mathbf{T}\,ds + \int_{\mathcal{C}_2^-} \mathbf{F}\cdot\mathbf{T}\,ds = 0 \quad \Rightarrow \quad \int_{\mathcal{C}_1} \mathbf{F}\cdot\mathbf{T}\,ds = \int_{\mathcal{C}_2} \mathbf{F}\cdot\mathbf{T}\,ds. \qquad \blacksquare$$

Consider the statement, "If it's raining, there are clouds." That's certainly true. Its converse is the statement, "If there are clouds, it's raining," which is not true. Similarly, we know that, "If a smooth vector field is conservative, its scalar curl is 0." Here we prove the converse, "If the scalar curl of a smooth vector field is 0, it's conservative."

Using the Curl Test

Example 5.10. Use the Curl Test to determine whether $\mathbf{F} = \langle 4xy+1, 2x^2 + \cos y \rangle$ is conservative in the first quadrant of the xy-plane.

Solution: The vector field $\mathbf{F}$ is smooth in the first quadrant of the xy-plane, and $\mathrm{curl}(\mathbf{F}) = M_x - L_y = (4x) - (4x) = 0$, so the field is conservative. Using the technique of Example 1.6, we can determine that the potential for this vector field is $f(x, y) = 2x^2 y + x + \sin y$, which you can check by verifying that $\nabla f = \mathbf{F}$. $\qquad \blacksquare$

Using the Curl Test

Example 5.11. Use the Curl Test to determine whether $\mathbf{F} = \langle 8x+y, 4x+\sin y \rangle$ is conservative in the xy-plane.

Answer: It's not. $\qquad \blacksquare$

Solution On-line

❖ Life in 3D

This section has focused on curves that bound regions in the plane. In Section 15.10 we'll extend the discussion to curves that bound surfaces in 3-space.

You should know

- the terms *circulation, curl,* and *circulation density;*
- the notation curl($\mathbf{F}$);
- the circulation form of Green's Theorem.

You should be able to

- use a line integral to calculate the circulation of $\mathbf{F}$ along a curve;
- use Green's Theorem to rewrite line integrals over simple, closed curves as double integrals, and vice versa;
- use the Curl Test to determine whether a vector field is conservative.

❖ 15.5 Skill Exercises

In #1–6 determine curl($\mathbf{F}$).

1. $\mathbf{F}(x,y) = \langle x, y \rangle$

2. $\mathbf{F}(x,y) = \langle y, x \rangle$

3. $\mathbf{F}(x,y) = \langle -y, x \rangle$

4. $\mathbf{F}(x,y) = \langle x+y, y-3x \rangle$

5. $\mathbf{F}(x,y) = \langle e^{\cos x} + xy^2, x^7 \cos y \rangle$

6. $\mathbf{F}(x,y) = \langle 8xe^y, \ln(\cos(y^2)+2) \rangle$

In #7–18 verify Green's Theorem by calculating the circulation of $\mathbf{F}$ around the positively oriented curve $\mathcal{C}$ that's described. Use (a) the line integral of $\mathbf{F} \cdot \mathbf{T}$ around $\mathcal{C}$, and (b) the double integral of curl($\mathbf{F}$) over the region enclosed by $\mathcal{C}$.

7. $\mathbf{F}(x,y) = \langle 3, 1 \rangle$; parameterized by $\mathbf{r}(t) = \langle 5\cos t, 5\sin t \rangle$ when $t \in [0, 2\pi]$

8. $\mathbf{F}(x,y) = \langle 5, 7 \rangle$; parameterized by $\mathbf{r}(t) = \langle 3\cos \pi t, 9\sin \pi t \rangle$ when $t \in [0, 2]$

9. $\mathbf{F}(x,y) = \langle 4, -5 \rangle$; the square with vertices at $(1,5), (2,5), (2,6)$ and $(1,6)$

Figure 5.14: $\mathcal{C}$ for #17.

10. $\mathbf{F}(x,y) = \langle -8x, 18y \rangle$; the ellipse $9x^2 + 4y^2 = 36$

11. $\mathbf{F}(x,y) = \langle -y, 10x \rangle$; the rectangle with vertices $(5,6), (9,7), (8,11)$ and $(4,10)$

12. $\mathbf{F}(x,y) = \langle 7x, 5-9y \rangle$; the rectangle defined by the points $(0,0), (14,2), (15,-5)$ and $(1,-7)$

13. $\mathbf{F}(x,y) = \langle 8x^2 y, 13x - y^2 \rangle$; the rectangle defined by the points $(0,3), (7,3), (7,4)$ and $(0,4)$

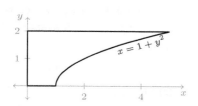

Figure 5.15: $\mathcal{C}$ for #18.

14. $\mathbf{F}(x,y) = \langle x^2 - xy, 2y^4 \rangle$; the rectangle defined by the points $(-1,0), (0,0), (0,6)$ and $(-1,6)$

15. $\mathbf{F}(x,y) = \langle 5x - 2y, 3x + y^2 \rangle$; the rectangle in #11

16. $\mathbf{F}(x,y) = \langle 9x^2 - 3y, 10y - 5x^2 \rangle$; the rectangle in #12

17. $\mathbf{F}(x,y) = \langle 0, y \rangle$; $\mathcal{C}$ in Figure 5.14

18. $\mathbf{F}(x,y) = \langle 4x, -3y \rangle$; $\mathcal{C}$ in Figure 5.15

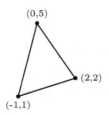

Figure 5.16: $\mathcal{C}$ in #19.

In #19–24 use a computer algebra system to calculate the circulation of $\mathbf{F}$ around the curve $\mathcal{C}$. In #21, 23–24 the curve is described in polar coordinates.

19. $\mathbf{F}(x,y) = \langle \cos y, e^{yx^2} \rangle$; $\mathcal{C}$ is in Figure 5.16.

20. $\mathbf{F}(x,y) = \langle e^y, -xe^{y^4} \rangle$; $\mathcal{C}$ is in Figure 5.17

21. $\mathbf{F}(x,y) = \langle \sin y, 7x^2 \rangle$; $r = 1$.

22. $\mathbf{F}(x,y) = \langle \cos y, -9x^2 \rangle$; $x^2 + 2y^2 = 72$.

23. $\mathbf{F}(x,y) = \langle e^y, xy \rangle$; $r = 3 + 2\cos\theta$.

24. $\mathbf{F}(x,y) = \langle e^x, xy^2 \rangle$; $r = 4 + \sin 3\theta$.

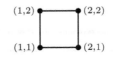

Figure 5.17: $\mathcal{C}$ in #20.

❖ 15.5 Concept and Application Exercises
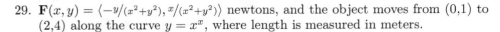

In #25–26, the vector field $\mathbf{F}$ is smooth and f is a scalar-valued, differentiable, function of two variables. Determine which of the expressions are meaningless and explain in complete sentences what's wrong with them.

25. (a) $\text{curl}(\nabla f \cdot \mathbf{F})$; (b) $\text{curl}(\text{div}(\mathbf{F}))$; (c) $\mathbf{F} \cdot \text{curl}(\nabla f)$

26. (a) $\text{div}(\nabla f \cdot \text{curl}(\mathbf{F}))$; (b) $f(\text{curl}(\mathbf{F}), \nabla f \cdot \mathbf{F})$; (c) $\text{curl}(f)$

Exercises #27–28 refer to Figure 5.18, in which the region R extends between circles $\mathcal{C}_1$ (radius $1/2$), $\mathcal{C}_2$ (radius $3/4$) and $\mathcal{C}_3$ (radius 2).

27. Determine $\oint_{\mathcal{C}_3} \mathbf{F} \cdot \mathbf{T}\, ds$ based on the following:

$$\text{curl}(\mathbf{F}) = 0 \text{ in } R, \qquad \oint_{\mathcal{C}_1} \mathbf{F} \cdot \mathbf{T}\, ds = 4\pi, \quad \text{and} \quad \oint_{\mathcal{C}_2} \mathbf{F} \cdot \mathbf{T}\, ds = 8\pi.$$

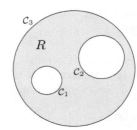

Figure 5.18:   The region R for #27–28.

28. If $\text{curl}(\mathbf{F})$ is constant in R, determine its value based on the following information:

$$\oint_{\mathcal{C}_1} \mathbf{F} \cdot \mathbf{T}\, ds = 3.5 \qquad \oint_{\mathcal{C}_2} \mathbf{F} \cdot \mathbf{T}\, ds = 3.125 \quad \text{and} \quad \oint_{\mathcal{C}_3} \mathbf{F} \cdot \mathbf{T}\, ds = 13$$

In Section 15.2 we interpreted the line integral $\int_{\mathcal{C}} \mathbf{F} \cdot \mathbf{T}\, ds$ as the work done by the vector field $\mathbf{F}$ on an object that travels along the oriented curve $\mathcal{C}$. In exercises #29–32 use Green's Theorem to expedite such calculations.

29. $\mathbf{F}(x,y) = \langle -y/(x^2+y^2), x/(x^2+y^2) \rangle$ newtons, and the object moves from $(0,1)$ to $(2,4)$ along the curve $y = x^x$, where length is measured in meters.

```
____ Work [        ]
```

30. $\mathbf{F}(x,y) = \langle 8x + 7, 2.5x^2 + e^y \rangle$ newtons, and the object moves from $(0,0)$ to $(1,0)$ along the curve $y = x\sin(\pi x^2)$, where length is measured in meters.

```
____ Work [        ]
```

31. Suppose $\mathcal{C}_1$ is the half of the cardioid $r = 1 + \sin\theta$ on which $x \geq 0$, oriented so that it extends from the origin to the point $(0,2)$, and $\mathcal{C}_2$ is the line segment that extends from $(0,2)$ to $(0,0)$. Length is measured in meters.

```
____ Work [        ]
```

(a) Calculate the work done by the vector field $\mathbf{F}(x,y) = \langle 2x + 1, y - 4 \rangle$ N on an object that moves from $(0,2)$ to the origin along $\mathcal{C}_2$.

(b) Verify that $\mathcal{C} = \mathcal{C}_1 + \mathcal{C}_2$ is a simple, closed curve.

(c) Calculate $\iint_R \text{curl}(\mathbf{F})\, dA$, where R is the region enclosed by $\mathcal{C}$.

(d) Use your answers from parts (a) and (c) to determine the work done by $\mathbf{F}$ when an object moves from $(0,0)$ to $(0,2)$ along $\mathcal{C}_1$.

32. Suppose $\mathcal{C}_1$ is the portion of the rose $r = \cos 4\theta$ for which $0 \le \theta \le \pi/4$, oriented from $(1,0)$ to the origin, and $\mathcal{C}_2$ is the line segment that extends from $(0,0)$ to $(1,0)$. Length is measured in meters. ____| Work |

    (a) Calculate the work done by the vector field $\mathbf{F}(x,y) = \langle 9x - 17y, 3 \rangle$ N on an object that moves from the origin to the point $(1,0)$ along $\mathcal{C}_2$.

    (b) Verify that $\mathcal{C} = \mathcal{C}_1 + \mathcal{C}_2$ is a simple, closed curve.

    (c) Calculate $\iint_R \operatorname{curl}(\mathbf{F})\, dA$, where R is the region enclosed by $\mathcal{C}$.

    (d) Use your answers from parts (a) and (c) to determine the work done by $\mathbf{F}$ on an object that moves from $(1,0)$ to $(0,0)$ along $\mathcal{C}_1$.

33. Suppose $\mathcal{C}$ is a piecewise-smooth, simple, closed curve and R is the region it encloses. Show that $\oint x\, dy - y\, dx$ is twice the area of R. ____| Geometry |

34. In this exercise we use the result of #33 to determine the area of a polygon. ____| Geometry |

    (a) Suppose $\mathcal{C}_1$ is the line segment that extends from (a,b) to the point (c,d). Show that $\int_{\mathcal{C}_1} x\, dy - y\, dx = ad - bc$.

    (b) Suppose $\mathcal{C}$ is the positively oriented rectangle with vertices at $(2,3), (4,3)$, $(4,7)$ and $(2,7)$. Use part (a) to calculate the circulation of the vector field $\mathbf{F}(x,y) = \langle -y, x \rangle$ around $\mathcal{C}$ and compare your answer to the result in #33.

    (c) Suppose $\mathcal{C}$ is the polygon with vertices at $(-1,-4), (-2,3), (0,7), (8,4)$ and $(1,-2)$. Use part (a) to calculate the area enclosed by $\mathcal{C}$.

In #35–36 you'll establish new formulas for the center of mass, and first moments of a region R that's enclosed by a piecewise-smooth, simple, closed curve $\mathcal{C}$.

35. Suppose R is a lamina with constant density, ρ. Use Green's Theorem to show that its center of mass (see Section 14.4) has coordinates ____| Center of Mass |

$$\bar{x} = \frac{1}{2|R|} \oint_{\mathcal{C}} x^2\, dy \quad \text{and} \quad \bar{y} = \frac{1}{2|R|} \oint_{\mathcal{C}} y^2\, dx$$

where $|R|$ denotes the area of R. (Recall that the center of mass is called the *centroid* when the mass density is constant.)

36. Suppose R is a lamina with constant density, ρ. Use Green's Theorem to show that its second moments of R (see Section 14.4) are ____| Moment of Inertia |

$$I_x = -\frac{\rho}{3} \oint_{\mathcal{C}} y^3\, dx \quad \text{and} \quad I_y = \frac{\rho}{3} \oint_{\mathcal{C}} x^3\, dy.$$

37. Suppose R is the portion of the disk $x^2 + y^2 \le 1$ for which $x \ge 0$ and $y \ge 0$, where length is measured in cm, and the density in R is $\rho = 6\frac{\text{g}}{\text{cm}^2}$. Determine the center of mass of R by (a) using the result of #35, and (b) calculating the double integral developed in Section 14.4. ____| Center of Mass |

38. Suppose length is measured in mm, and R is the rectangular region for which $0 \le x \le 3$ and $0 \le y \le 1$. If the density in R is $\rho = 0.5$ g/mm^2, determine the center of mass of R by (a) using the result of #35, and (b) calculating the double integral developed in Section 14.4. ____| Center of Mass |

39. Suppose length is measured in cm, and R is the portion of the disk $x^2 + y^2 \leq 1$ for which $x \geq 0$ and $y \geq 0$. If the density in R is $\rho = 3$ g/cm^2, calculate the second moments of R with respect to the x- and the y-axis by using (a) the result of #36, and (b) the double integral developed in Section 14.4.

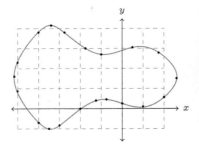

_____ Moments of Inertia

40. Suppose length is measured in mm, and R is the rectangular region for which $0 \leq x \leq 3$ and $0 \leq y \leq 1$. If the density in R is $\rho = 0.125$ kg/mm^2, calculate the second moments of R with respect to the x- and the y-axis by using (a) the result of #36, and (b) the double integral developed in Section 14.4.

_____ Moments of Inertia

41. Suppose the curve in Figure 5.19, $\mathcal{C}$, is the boundary of a decorative pond.

   (a) Use Green's Theorem to show that the area of the pond's surface is $\oint_{\mathcal{C}} x \, dy$.

   (b) The following table lists the approximate locations of several points on $\mathcal{C}$, where length is measured in meters. Use it with part (a) to approximate the area of the pond's surface. (The topmost point is listed first. Proceed left-to-right across the rows to move around $\mathcal{C}$ in the positive direction.)

$(-3.4, 4.15)$	$(-4, 3.8)$	$(-5, 2.3)$	$(-5.16, 1.6)$	$(-5, 0.87)$
$(-4, -0.7)$	$(-3.5, -1)$	$(-3, -0.83)$	$(-2, 0)$	$(-1.25, 0.4)$
$(-0.75, 0.45)$	$(0, 0.25)$	$(1, 0.1)$	$(2, 0.56)$	$(2.6, 1.5)$
$(1.75, 2.78)$	$(0.5, 3.05)$	$(-1, 2.7)$	$(-1.75, 3)$	$(-2.75, 3.8)$

Figure 5.19:   The curve $\mathcal{C}$ in exercise #41.

42. Suppose an electrical current of I amps flows up the z-axis, through the xy-plane. This current induces a magnetic field $\mathbf{B}$ that circulates around the line as depicted in Figure 5.20), and it follows from the _Law of Biot and Savart_ that its magnitude r meters away from the current-carrying line is $\|\mathbf{B}\| = \mu_0 I / 2\pi r$, where $\mu_0 = 4\pi \times 10^{-7}$ is called the _permeability of free space_.

   (a) Write a formula for $\mathbf{B}(x, y)$ and show that its scalar curl is 0 away from the wire.

   (b) If $\mathcal{C}$ is a circle of radius r that's centered on the wire, use a line integral to show that the circulation of $\mathbf{B}$ around $\mathcal{C}$ is independent of r.

   (c) Suppose $\mathcal{C}$ is a piecewise-smooth, simple, closed planar curve (e.g., see Figure 5.20). Use Green's Theorem to show that the circulation of $\mathbf{B}$ around $\mathcal{C}$ is $\mu_0 I$ if the curve encloses the wire, and is 0 otherwise. This fact is known as _Ampère's Law_.

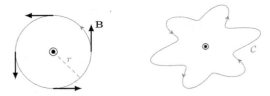

Figure 5.20: For #42 (left) the **B**-field; (right) a smooth curve enclosing the wire.

Checking the details

In #43–45 use $\mathbf{F} = \langle P, Q \rangle$ and $\mathbf{G} = \langle L, M \rangle$.

43. Verify equation (10.7) by using the Scaling Rule.

44. Verify equation (10.8) by using the Sum Rule for differentiation.

45. Verify equation (10.9) by using the Product Rule for differentiation.

15.6   Flux Through Simple Surfaces in Space: Graphs, Cylinders, and Spheres

In Section 15.4 we introduced the flux of vector fields across curves. Now we extend that idea to the flux of three-dimensional vector fields through simple surfaces. The intuitive idea that pervades this section is that the rate at which fluid passes through a region of space (e.g., measured in grams per second) depends on how quickly the fluid is moving, and the cross-sectional area of the flow. The section begins with simple examples of uniform flow through flat surfaces, and then moves toward more complicated examples in which the velocity field of the flow is non-constant, and the surface through which it's flowing is not flat. The ideas and calculation techniques developed here are presented in more generality in Section 15.8.

> **Key Idea(s):** *Some aspects of fluid flow happen* along *a surface, and one component of the velocity (which is quantified using a dot product) tells us how quickly the fluid is flowing* through *a surface.*
>
> *The flux of a fluid across a surface is computed with a double integral.*

❖ Flux Through a Flat Surface

Suppose $R = [a, b] \times [c, d]$ is a rectangular region in the xy-plane, where length is measured in cm, and an incompressible fluid is flowing through R with a uniform velocity of $\mathbf{v} = \langle 0, 0, 3 \rangle$ cm/sec, as depicted in Figure 6.1.

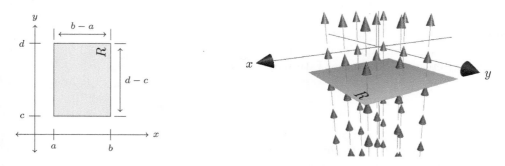

Figure 6.1: (left) A rectangular region in the xy-plane; (right) fluid flow through R.

If the fluid has a uniform density of ρ g/cm^3, the fluid passes through R at a rate of

$$\underbrace{\underbrace{3}_{\text{cm/sec}} \times \overbrace{\underbrace{(b-a) \times (d-c)}_{\text{area of } R \text{ in cm}^2}}^{\text{volume of fluid per second}} \times \overbrace{\rho}^{\text{density in g/cm}^3}}_{} = \iint_R 3\rho \; dA \quad \frac{\text{g}}{\text{sec}}.$$

If we define $\mathbf{F}$ to be the mass-flow of the fluid, $\mathbf{F} = \rho\mathbf{v} = \langle 0, 0, 3\rho \rangle$, we can write this flow rate as

$$\text{flux of } \mathbf{F} \text{ through } R \; = \; \iint_R \mathbf{F} \cdot \mathbf{k} \; dA \quad \frac{\text{g}}{\text{sec}}. \tag{6.1}$$

Equation (6.1) applies even when the flow is not solely in the $\mathbf{k}$-direction because flow in the $\mathbf{i}$- and $\mathbf{j}$-directions carries fluid *along* R, not *through* it. Only the vertical component of the flow is responsible for passing fluid through R, and the dot product isolates that component of the flow for us. Figure 6.2 shows such a scenario: a column of fluid is passing through the plane $z = 0$, and moving with a constant velocity of $\mathbf{v}$ cm/sec. If this column's intersection with the plane has an area of ΔA cm^2, the mass of fluid that passes through the plane in Δt seconds is

$$\text{(density) (height) (base area)} = \rho \, (\mathbf{v} \cdot \mathbf{k}) \Delta t \, \Delta A = (\mathbf{F} \cdot \mathbf{k}) \Delta t \, \Delta A \text{ g,}$$

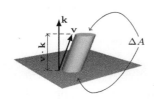

Figure 6.2:   A fluid with velocity $\mathbf{v}$ cm/sec flows through a plane.

where $\mathbf{F} = \rho\mathbf{v}$ is the mass flow of the fluid. So this fluid passes through the plane at a rate of $(\mathbf{F} \cdot \mathbf{k})\,\Delta A$ g/sec. When $\mathbf{F}$ is not constant, but varies over a region R in the plane, we approximate the flux through R by partitioning the region with many small "tiles." By treating $\mathbf{F}$ as constant in each one, we see that

$$\text{flux of } \mathbf{F} \text{ through } R \approx \sum_j (\mathbf{F}_j \cdot \mathbf{k})\,\Delta A_j \; \frac{\text{g}}{\text{sec}} \qquad (6.2)$$

> We intend this summation to mean "sum over all tiles indexed by j."

where ΔA_j is the area of the jth tile, and $\mathbf{F}_j$ is the mass flow at some point in it. In the limit at $\|\Delta A\| \to 0$, we arrive at equation (6.1).

Flux through a rectangle in the xy-plane

Example 6.1. Suppose $\mathbf{F}(x,y,z) = \langle z^2, xyz, x+y+z^2 \rangle \; \frac{\text{g/sec}}{\text{cm}^2}$, and $R = [1,3] \times [2,7]$ is a rectangle in the xy-plane, where length is measured in cm. Determine the flux of $\mathbf{F}$ through R in the direction of $\mathbf{k}$.

Solution: Since $\mathbf{F} \cdot \mathbf{k} = x + y + z^2$ and $z = 0$ in R, the flux of $\mathbf{F}$ through R is

$$\iint_R (x+y)\,dA = \int_2^7 \int_1^3 (x+y)\,dx\,dy = 65\frac{\text{g}}{\text{sec}}. \qquad \blacksquare$$

Flux through a rectangle above the xy-plane

Example 6.2. Suppose $\mathbf{F}$ and R are as defined in Example 6.1, and $\mathcal{M}$ is the portion of the plane $z = 2$ that sits over R. Determine the flux of $\mathbf{F}$ through $\mathcal{M}$ in the direction of $\mathbf{k}$.

Answer: 105 g/sec. $\qquad \blacksquare$

Solution On-line

Next we address the case when $\mathbf{F}$ is continuous, but the plane through which it passes is not horizontal. In order to adapt equation (6.1) to this situation, we'll need to specify the normal to the plane. Generally speaking, there are always two choices, and by designating one as the ***orientation*** of the surface, we provide a specific (directional) meaning to the number we calculate.

> Both $\mathbf{k}$ and $-\mathbf{k}$ are normal to the plane $z = 0$

Suppose $\mathcal{M}$ is a planar surface oriented according to the unit normal vector $\mathbf{n}$, and that $\mathcal{M}$ sits over a region R in the xy-plane. When we partition R with a regular mesh of n rectangles of width Δx and length Δy, the part of $\mathcal{M}$ that sits directly over the kth rectangle will be called the kth ***patch*** of $\mathcal{M}$ (see Figure 6.3). By treating $\mathbf{F}$ as constant on each patch of $\mathcal{M}$ we produce an analog of approximation (6.2):

$$\text{the flux of } \mathbf{F} \text{ through } \mathcal{M} \approx \sum_{k=1}^n (\mathbf{F}_k \cdot \mathbf{n})\,\Delta S_k, \qquad (6.3)$$

where ΔS_k is the area of the kth patch of $\mathcal{M}$, and $\mathbf{F}_k$ is the value of $\mathbf{F}$ at some point in it. The exact value is obtained in the limit, which is a double integral:

$$\text{the flux of } \mathbf{F} \text{ through } \mathcal{M} = \iint_{\mathcal{M}} \mathbf{F} \cdot \mathbf{n}\,dS, \qquad (6.4)$$

where dS denotes the area element on the surface $\mathcal{M}$ (see Example 6.3).

Flux through a tilted plane

Example 6.3. Suppose length is measured in cm, and R is the region in the xy-plane in which $x \in [1,6]$ and $y \in [2,5]$, and $\mathcal{M}$ is the portion of the plane $0x + 1y + 1z = 8$ directly above R (see Figure 6.3), oriented in the direction of $\mathbf{n} = \langle 0, 1, 1 \rangle$. Further, suppose $\mathbf{F}(x,y,z) = \langle z, \; 2x, \; z - 4x \rangle \; \frac{\text{g/sec}}{\text{cm}^2}$ is the mass-flow of a fluid. Determine the flux of $\mathbf{F}$ through $\mathcal{M}$.

Solution: In order to demonstrate the use of equation (6.4) we begin by developing a practical formula for ΔS_k in approximation (6.3). After rewriting the equation of $\mathcal{M}$ as $z = 8 - y$ we see that

$$\frac{\partial z}{\partial x} = 0 \quad \Rightarrow \quad \langle 1, 0, 0 \rangle \text{ lies in the plane } z = 8 - y.$$

Similarly,

$$\frac{\partial z}{\partial y} = -1 \quad \Rightarrow \quad \langle 0, 1, -1 \rangle \text{ lies in the plane } z = 8 - y.$$

So if the kth rectangle in the mesh of R has edges defined by the vectors

$$\Delta x \langle 1, 0, 0 \rangle \qquad \text{and} \qquad \Delta y \langle 0, 1, 0 \rangle,$$

as seen in Figure 6.3, the kth patch on $\mathcal{M}$ is defined by the vectors

$$\mathbf{u}_k = \Delta x \langle 1, 0, 0 \rangle \qquad \text{and} \qquad \mathbf{v}_k = \Delta y \langle 0, 1, -1 \rangle.$$

Therefore, the kth patch has an area of $\Delta S_k = \|\mathbf{u}_k \times \mathbf{v}_k\| = \sqrt{2}\Delta x \Delta y$.

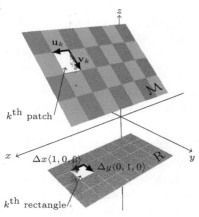

Next we determine a formula for $\mathbf{F}_k$. Pick a point in the kth rectangle of the mesh of R, say (x_k, y_k). Because $z = 8 - y$ on $\mathcal{M}$, we know that the corresponding point on $\mathcal{M}$ is $(x_k, y_k, 8 - y_k)$, and that's where we calculate $\mathbf{F}_k$. That is,

$$\mathbf{F}_k = \langle z_k, \ 2x_k, \ z_k - 4x_k \rangle = \langle 8 - y_k, \ 2x_k, \ 8 - y_k - 4x_k \rangle.$$

Figure 6.3: Vectors $\mathbf{u}_k$ and $\mathbf{v}_k$ define the kth patch of $\mathcal{M}$.

These formulas allow us to write the approximation in (6.3) as

$$\text{flux} \approx \sum_{k=1}^{n} (\mathbf{F}_k \cdot \mathbf{n}) \, \Delta S_k = \sum_{k=1}^{n} \overbrace{\left(\frac{8 - y_k - 2x_k}{\sqrt{2}} \right)}^{\frac{\text{g/sec}}{\text{cm}^2}} \overbrace{\sqrt{2}\Delta x \Delta y}^{\text{cm}^2} = \sum_{k=1}^{n} (8 - y_k - 2x_k)\Delta x \Delta y \ \frac{\text{g}}{\text{sec}}.$$

This approximation becomes equality in the limit as $n \to \infty$. That is,

$$\text{flux of } \mathbf{F} \text{ through } \mathcal{M} = \underbrace{\iint_{\mathcal{M}} \mathbf{F} \cdot \mathbf{n} \, dS}_{} = \underbrace{\iint_{R} (8 - y - 2x) \, dA}_{} \ \frac{\text{g}}{\text{sec}}, \qquad (6.5)$$

This integral displays the central concept: the dot product calculates the component of $\mathbf{F}$ that passes directly through $\mathcal{M}$. The differential, dS, is the area element on the surface.

This integral tells us explicitly what calculation we're going to make. The differential, dA, is the area element in the xy-plane.

Fubini's Theorem allows us to rewrite the double integral over R as

$$\text{flux of } \mathbf{F} \text{ through } \mathcal{M} = \int_{1}^{6} \int_{2}^{5} (8 - y - 2x) \, dy \, dx = -\frac{75}{2} \ \frac{\text{g}}{\text{sec}}.$$

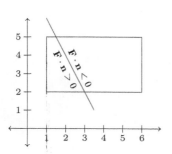

Figure 6.4: The line $\mathbf{F} \cdot \mathbf{n} = 0$ cuts the region R into two pieces—one where $\mathbf{F} \cdot \mathbf{n}$ is positive, and the other where its negative.

There's no such thing as negative mass, of course, but remember that we were calculating flux *in a given direction*. The mass flow is crossing $\mathcal{M}$ in the direction of $\mathbf{n}$ at points where $\mathbf{F} \cdot \mathbf{n} > 0$, and in the opposite direction where $\mathbf{F} \cdot \mathbf{n} < 0$. Figure 6.4 shows the region R with the line where $\mathbf{F} \cdot \mathbf{n} = 0$. You can see that there is much more area in which $\mathbf{F}$ is flowing across $\mathcal{M}$ in the direction opposite $\mathbf{n}$. This alone is insufficient to make the integral negative (the *rate* of flow is important too), but it gives you a sense of what our negative answer means. ∎

Let's pause to note that the right-hand side of equation (6.5) includes the term

$$(8 - y - 2x) \, dA = \mathbf{F} \cdot \langle 0, 1, 1 \rangle \, dA,$$

which is similar to terms in equation (6.1). You'll see this again in the following example.

Flux through a tilted plane

Example 6.4. Suppose $\mathbf{F} = \langle x+z,\ 7y,\ 10y-z \rangle\ \frac{\text{g/sec}}{\text{cm}^2}$, and $\mathcal{M}$ is the portion of the plane $3x + 2y + 5z = 1$ that's directly above the rectangle in the xy-plane where $x \in [-1, 2]$ and $y \in [-4, 4]$. If $\mathcal{M}$ is oriented according to the normal vector $\langle 3, 2, 5 \rangle$, (a) determine the flux of $\mathbf{F}$ through $\mathcal{M}$ and (b) interpret the result.

Answer: (a) 8.16 grams per second, (b) more fluid passes through $\mathcal{M}$ in the direction of $\mathbf{n}$ than $-\mathbf{n}$ each second. ■

Solution On-line

✤ Flux Through the Graph of a Function

Now we adapt our calculation technique to graphs of differentiable functions. As in our previous discussion, R will denote a region in the xy-plane, and $\mathcal{M}$ will be the portion of the surface $z = f(x, y)$ that sits directly over it. Imagine zooming in on the smooth surface. Now get even closer. If you get close enough, the surface seems flat (because f is differentiable), and we know how to calculate the flux through a flat surface. This leads us to approximate $\mathcal{M}$ as a collection of planar "facets," much in the same way that the flat facets of a disco ball approximate a sphere (compare Figures 6.5 and 6.6).

Figure 6.5: The facets of a disco ball approximate a sphere.

More specifically, suppose we partition the domain R with a regular mesh of n rectangles of width Δx and length Δy. The part of $\mathcal{M}$ that sits directly over the kth rectangle will be called the kth patch of $\mathcal{M}$. When $\mathbf{F}$ is a continuous vector field,

$$\text{the flux of } \mathbf{F} \text{ through } \mathcal{M} \approx \sum_{k=1}^{n} (\mathbf{F}_k \cdot \mathbf{n}_k)\Delta S_k, \qquad (6.6)$$

> Compare this to the approximation in (6.3).

where ΔS_k is the area of the kth patch, $\mathbf{F}_k$ denotes $\mathbf{F}$ at a point $(x_k, y_k, f(x_k, y_k))$ in the patch, and $\mathbf{n}_k$ is the unit normal vector to $\mathcal{M}$ there. As we mentioned above, although $\mathcal{M}$ is not flat, it's well approximated by the tangent plane at $(x_k, y_k, f(x_k, y_k))$ because f is differentiable. The portion of this tangent plane that sits over the kth rectangle of the mesh will be called the kth **_facet_** of $\mathcal{M}$. In the work that follows, we'll use the area of the kth facet to approximate ΔS_k.

> The term *facet* is not common. We're using it here because of the imagery it evokes.

Figure 6.6: (left) The graph of a differentiable function; (right) a coarse approximation of the surface with planar facets.

The area of the kth facet of $\mathcal{M}$ can be calculated using the cross product if we can determine the vectors that define its edges (as in Example 6.3). Recall that

$$\frac{\partial z}{\partial x} = f_x \quad \Rightarrow \quad \text{the vector } \langle 1, 0, f_x \rangle \text{ lies in the tangent plane,}$$

and the width of the kth rectangle in the mesh is Δx, so $\mathbf{u}_k = \Delta x \langle 1, 0, f_x(x_k, y_k) \rangle$ runs along one edge of the kth facet (much as you see in Figure 6.3). Similarly,

$$\frac{\partial z}{\partial y} = f_y \quad \Rightarrow \quad \text{the vector } \langle 0, 1, f_y \rangle \text{ lies in the tangent plane,}$$

and the length of the kth rectangle in the mesh is Δy, so $\mathbf{v}_k = \Delta y \langle 0, 1, f_y(x_k, y_k) \rangle$ also lies along an edge of the kth facet. Because $\mathbf{u}_k$ and $\mathbf{v}_k$ define the parallelogram that is the kth facet, its area is $\|\mathbf{u}_k \times \mathbf{v}_k\|$. So when the mesh size is small we have

$$\Delta S_k \approx \|\mathbf{u}_k \times \mathbf{v}_k\|.$$

Additionally, the vector $\mathbf{u}_k \times \mathbf{v}_k$ is normal to the kth facet, so

$$\mathbf{n}_k = \frac{\mathbf{u}_k \times \mathbf{v}_k}{\|\mathbf{u}_k \times \mathbf{v}_k\|}.$$

Now we can rewrite the approximation (6.6) as

$$\text{flux of } \mathbf{F} \text{ through } \mathcal{M} \approx \sum_{k=1}^{n} \left(\mathbf{F}_k \cdot \frac{\mathbf{u}_k \times \mathbf{v}_k}{\|\mathbf{u}_k \times \mathbf{v}_k\|} \right) \|\mathbf{u}_k \times \mathbf{v}_k\| = \sum_{k=1}^{n} \mathbf{F}_k \cdot (\mathbf{u}_k \times \mathbf{v}_k).$$

After determining that $\mathbf{u}_k \times \mathbf{v}_k = \langle -f_x(x_k, y_k), -f_y(x_k, y_k), 1 \rangle \Delta x \Delta y$, our approximation becomes

$$\text{flux of } \mathbf{F} \text{ through } \mathcal{M} \approx \sum_{k=1}^{n} \mathbf{F}_k \cdot \langle -f_x(x_k, y_k), -f_y(x_k, y_k), 1 \rangle \, \Delta x \Delta y.$$

Don't just read it. Check the vector $\mathbf{u}_k \times \mathbf{v}_k$ for yourself!

All error vanishes in the limit and the Riemann sum becomes a double integral:

$$\text{flux of } \mathbf{F} \text{ through } \mathcal{M} = \iint_{\mathcal{M}} \mathbf{F} \cdot \mathbf{n} \, dS = \iint_R \mathbf{F}\big(x, y, f(x,y)\big) \cdot \langle -f_x(x,y), -f_y(x,y), 1 \rangle \, dA.$$

This integral displays the central concept: the dot product calculates the component of $\mathbf{F}$ that passes directly through $\mathcal{M}$, and the double integral adds up the contributions from all the points on $\mathcal{M}$. The differential, dS, is the area element on the surface.

This is the integral that we actually calculate. The differential, dA, is the area element in the xy-plane. In practice, we'll typically reduce this double integral to an iterated integral.

It's common to compress the right-hand side of this equality by suppressing the dependence of $\mathbf{F}$ on x and y—i.e., writing $\mathbf{F}$ instead of $\mathbf{F}\big(x, y, f(x,y)\big)$—and by defining the ***area vector*** as $d\mathbf{A} = \langle -f_x(x,y), -f_y(x,y), 1 \rangle \, dA$. This notation will be used in the summary statement below. However, before making that statement we need additional vocabulary: we will say that $\mathcal{M}$ has a ***positive orientation*** when $\mathbf{n}$ points in the direction of $\langle -f_x, -f_y, 1 \rangle$, as in the derivation above.

Remember that all planes have two unit normal vectors (which point in opposite directions).

> **Flux Through the Graph of a Function:** Suppose R is a region in the xy-plane, f is a differentiable function with continuous partial derivatives, and $\mathcal{M}$ is the portion of the surface $z = f(x,y)$ that lies over R. If $\mathcal{M}$ has a positive orientation, and $\mathbf{F}$ is a continuous vector field on $\mathcal{M}$,
>
> $$\text{the flux of } \mathbf{F} \text{ through } \mathcal{M} = \iint_R \mathbf{F} \cdot d\mathbf{A},$$
>
> where $d\mathbf{A} = \langle -f_x(x,y), -f_y(x,y), 1 \rangle \, dA$.

Flux through the graph of a nonlinear function

Example 6.5. Suppose length is measured in cm, and $\mathcal{M}$ is the positively oriented graph of $f(x,y) = x^2 - y^2$ over the disk $x^2 + y^2 \leq 1$ (see Figure 6.5), and $\mathbf{F}(x,y,z) = \langle x, y, x^2 + y^2 \rangle \frac{\text{g/sec}}{\text{cm}^2}$. Determine the flux of $\mathbf{F}$ through $\mathcal{M}$.

Solution: The area vector for this surface is $d\mathbf{A} = \langle -2x, 2y, 1 \rangle \, dA$, so the flux integral is

$$\iint_R \mathbf{F} \cdot d\mathbf{A} = \iint_R (3y^2 - x^2) \, dA,$$

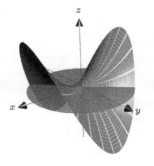

Figure 6.7: The graph of f over the disk in Example 6.5.

where R is the unit disk. Because R is rotationally symmetric, let's calculate this double integral in polar coordinates: $x = r\cos\theta$, $y = r\sin\theta$, and $dA = r \, dr \, d\theta$.

$$\text{flux of } \mathbf{F} \text{ through } \mathcal{M} = \int_0^{2\pi} \int_0^1 (3r^2 \sin^2\theta - r^2 \cos^2\theta) \, r \, dr \, d\theta = \frac{\pi}{2} \, \frac{\text{g}}{\text{sec}}. \quad \blacksquare$$

Flux through the graph of a nonlinear function

Solution On-line

Example 6.6. Suppose R is the bounded region between $y = x^2$ and $y = 2x + 3$, where x and y are measured in cm. Determine the flux of $\mathbf{F}(x,y,z) = \langle 1, -x, x - y \rangle \, \frac{\text{g/sec}}{\text{cm}^2}$ through the positively oriented graph of $f(x,y) = -x^2 + 6y$ over R.

Answer: $896/15$ grams per second $\blacksquare$

✢ Flux Through a Cylinder

As with planes and graphs of functions, when $\mathcal{M}$ is a cylinder our calculation of flux begins with approximation (6.6). For the sake of discussion, suppose $\mathcal{M}$ is a cylinder of radius r about the z-axis on which $a \le z \le b$ (the circular end caps are not included). When we partition $[a, b]$ into subintervals of length Δz, and partition the angular interval $[0, 2\pi]$ into subintervals of length $\Delta\theta$, we produce a regular grid of patches on $\mathcal{M}$, each with an area of $\Delta S_k = r \, \Delta\theta \, \Delta z$.

As you see in Figure 6.8, we intend $\mathbf{n}_k$ to point away from the cylinder's central axis, and we'll refer to this choice as the ***positive orientation*** of the cylinder. So at the point $(r\cos\theta_k, r\sin\theta_k, z_k)$ in the kth patch of the cylinder, the normal vector is $\mathbf{n}_k = \langle \cos\theta_k, \sin\theta_k, 0 \rangle$. When we insert these expressions for ΔS_k and $\mathbf{n}_k$ into approximation (6.6), we see that

$$\text{the flux of } \mathbf{F} \text{ through } \mathcal{M} \approx \sum_{k=1}^n \mathbf{F}_k \cdot \langle \cos\theta_k, \sin\theta_k, 0 \rangle \, r \, \Delta\theta \, \Delta z.$$

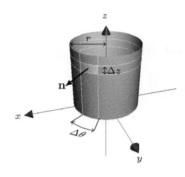

Figure 6.8: A regular mesh on a cylindrical surface of radius r consists of patches of area $r\Delta\theta \, \Delta z$.

Approximation becomes equality in the limit and this Riemann sum becomes a double integral, which we write here as an iterated integral:

$$\text{the flux of } \mathbf{F} \text{ through } \mathcal{M} = \int_a^b \int_0^{2\pi} \mathbf{F}(r, \theta, z) \cdot \langle \cos\theta, \sin\theta, 0 \rangle \, r \, d\theta \, dz.$$

As before, it's common to simplify this formulation by defining the ***area vector*** $d\mathbf{A} = \langle \cos\theta, \sin\theta, 0 \rangle \, r \, d\theta \, dz$.

Flux Through a Cylinder: Suppose $\mathcal{M}$ is the positively oriented, open-ended cylinder of radius r about the z-axis, and $a \le z \le b$. If $\mathbf{F}$ is a continuous vector field, the

$$\text{flux of } \mathbf{F} \text{ through } \mathcal{M} = \int_a^b \int_0^{2\pi} \mathbf{F} \cdot d\mathbf{A},$$

where $d\mathbf{A} = \langle \cos\theta, \sin\theta, 0 \rangle \, r \, d\theta \, dz$. If $\mathcal{M}$ is a slice of a cylinder, $\theta \in [\theta_1, \theta_2]$, the lower and upper bounds of integration in θ are θ_1 and θ_2 respectively.

> If the cylinder includes its end caps, they must be dealt with separately.

Flux through a cylinder

Example 6.7. Suppose length is measured in cm, $\mathcal{M}$ is the portion of the positively oriented cylinder of radius 2 (centered at the origin) that sits over the first and fourth quadrants, where $1 \le z \le 5$ (see Figure 6.9). Determine the flux of $\mathbf{F}$ through $\mathcal{M}$ when $\mathbf{F}(x,y,z) = 3x\mathbf{i} \, \frac{\text{g/sec}}{\text{cm}^2}$.

Solution: Since this cylindrical surface sits over the first and fourth quadrants, we take $\theta \in [-\pi/2, \pi/2]$. And since $x = 2\cos\theta$ on this cylinder, $\mathbf{F} = \langle 6\cos\theta, 0, 0 \rangle \frac{\text{g/sec}}{\text{cm}^2}$, its flux through $\mathcal{M}$ is

$$\int_1^5 \int_{-\pi/2}^{\pi/2} \langle 6\cos\theta, 0, 0 \rangle \cdot d\mathbf{A} = \int_1^5 \int_{-\pi/2}^{\pi/2} \langle 6\cos\theta, 0, 0 \rangle \cdot \langle \cos\theta, \sin\theta, 0 \rangle \, 2 \, d\theta \, dz$$

$$= \int_1^5 \int_{-\pi/2}^{\pi/2} 12\cos^2(\theta) \, d\theta \, dz = \int_1^5 3\pi \, dz = 24\pi \, \frac{\text{g}}{\text{sec}}. \blacksquare$$

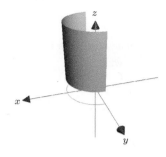

Figure 6.9:   The cylindrical surface in Example 6.7 sits over a circular arc of radius 1.

Flux through a cylinder

Example 6.8. Suppose length is measured in meters, $\mathcal{M}$ is the surface of the cylinder of radius 3 that sits over the first and second quadrants, $2 \leq z \leq 4$, and $\mathbf{F}(x, y, z) = 5z\mathbf{j} + \mathbf{k}\frac{\text{kg/sec}}{\text{m}^2}$. Determine the flux of $\mathbf{F}$ through $\mathcal{M}$.

Answer: $180 \, \frac{\text{kg}}{\text{sec}}$. $\blacksquare$

Solution On-line

❖ Flux Through a Sphere

As we've done previously, our calculation of flux through a spherical surface begins with approximation (6.6). For the sake of discussion, suppose $\mathcal{M}$ is a sphere of radius ρ about the origin, and we lay down a mesh of n spherical "rectangles" (see Figure 6.10), each of which extends across $\Delta\phi$ radians of "latitude" and $\Delta\theta$ radians of "longitude." These rectangles will serve as patches on $\mathcal{M}$, and based on our discussion in Section 14.6 we know that the kth patch has an area of $\Delta S_k = \rho^2 \sin(\phi_k)\Delta\theta\Delta\phi$. Now suppose that $\mathbf{r}_k = \rho\langle \cos\theta_k \sin\phi_k, \sin\theta_k \sin\phi_k, \cos\phi_k \rangle$ is a position vector for a point in the kth rectangle, and $\mathbf{F}_k$ is the value of $\mathbf{F}$ there. The outward-pointing unit normal vector at $\mathbf{r}_k$ is

$$\mathbf{n}_k = \frac{\mathbf{r}_k}{\|\mathbf{r}_k\|} = \langle \cos\theta_k \sin\phi_k, \ \sin\theta_k \sin\phi_k, \ \cos\phi_k \rangle,$$

so we can write approximation (6.6) as

$$\text{flux} \approx \sum_{k=1}^n (\mathbf{F}_k \cdot \mathbf{n}_k) \, \Delta S_k = \sum_{k=1}^n \left(\mathbf{F}_k \cdot \langle \cos\theta_k \sin\phi_k, \sin\theta_k \sin\phi_k, \cos\phi_k \rangle \right) \rho^2 \sin(\phi_k)\Delta\theta\Delta\phi.$$

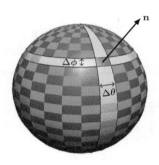

Figure 6.10:   A mesh on a sphere of radius ρ in which each "patch" extends across $\Delta\phi$ radians of "latitude" and $\Delta\theta$ radians of "longitude."

Approximation becomes equality in the limit as the mesh size tends to 0 (so $n \to \infty$), and we arrive at the following result, in which the term ***positively oriented*** means that $\mathbf{n}$ is an outward-pointing vector.

Flux Through a Sphere: Suppose $\mathcal{M}$ is the positively oriented sphere of radius ρ. If $\mathbf{F}$ is a vector field that's continuous in the vicinity of $\mathcal{M}$,

$$\text{the flux of } \mathbf{F} \text{ through } \mathcal{M} = \int_0^\pi \int_0^{2\pi} \mathbf{F} \cdot d\mathbf{A},$$

where

$$d\mathbf{A} = \langle \cos\theta \sin\phi, \sin\theta \sin\phi, \cos\phi \rangle \, \rho^2 \sin(\phi) \, d\theta \, d\phi.$$

If $\mathcal{M}$ is a slice of the sphere for which $\theta \in [\theta_1, \theta_2]$ and $\phi \in [\phi_1, \phi_2]$, the bounds of integration should reflect the ranges of θ and ϕ respectively.

Coulomb's Law, and Gauss's Law for a sphere

Example 6.9. According to Coulomb's Law, a charge of q coulombs at the origin induces an electric field $\mathbf{E} = \frac{1}{4\pi\varepsilon_0} \frac{q}{\|\mathbf{r}\|^2} \hat{\mathbf{r}}$ where $\mathbf{r} = \langle x, y, z \rangle$ and ε_0 is a constant called the *permittivity* of free space. Calculate the flux of $\mathbf{E}$ through the sphere of radius ρ.

Solution: Because this is a sphere of radius ρ, the vector $\mathbf{n} = \hat{\mathbf{r}} = \frac{1}{\|\mathbf{r}\|}\mathbf{r}$ and $\|\mathbf{r}\| = \rho$. So we can write

$$\text{flux} = \int_0^\pi \int_0^{2\pi} \mathbf{E} \cdot \mathbf{n}\, \rho^2 \sin(\phi)\, d\theta\, d\phi = \int_0^\pi \int_0^{2\pi} \frac{1}{4\pi\varepsilon_0} \frac{q}{\|\mathbf{r}\|^2} \hat{\mathbf{r}} \cdot \hat{\mathbf{r}}\, \rho^2 \sin(\phi)\, d\theta\, d\phi$$

$$= \int_0^\pi \int_0^{2\pi} \frac{q}{4\pi\varepsilon_0} \sin(\phi)\, d\theta\, d\phi = \int_0^\pi \frac{q}{2\varepsilon_0} \sin(\phi)\, d\phi = \frac{q}{\varepsilon_0}.$$

Notice our answer is independent of ρ. The fact that the flux of an electric field through a sphere is directly proportional to the amount of charge that's enclosed is known as **Gauss's Law**. ∎

> Using techniques in Section 15.9 you will be able to show that Gauss's Law applies to any continuous deformation of the sphere.

You should know

- the terms *positive orientation, area vector* and *Gauss's Law;*
- that $\mathbf{F} \cdot \mathbf{n}$ is the component of $\mathbf{F}$ that's traveling directly *through* a surface.

You should be able to

- calculate the flux of a vector field through the graph of a function, a cylinder, and a sphere.

❖ 15.6 Skill Exercises

In #1–8 calculate the flux of $\mathbf{F}$ through the planar surface.

1. $\mathbf{F}(x, y, z) = 3\mathbf{i} + 4\mathbf{j} - 2\mathbf{k}$; the plane $z = 0$ where $x \in [1, 3]$, $y \in [7, 10]$; $\mathbf{n} = \mathbf{k}$.

2. $\mathbf{F}(x, y, z) = 2\mathbf{i} + 7\mathbf{j} - \mathbf{k}$; the plane $x = 0$ where $y \in [-1, 1]$, $z \in [0, 5]$; $\mathbf{n} = \mathbf{i}$

3. $\mathbf{F}(x, y, z) = 3xy\mathbf{i} + 7y\mathbf{j} + 8z\mathbf{k}$; the plane $y = 2$ where $x \in [3, 5]$, $z \in [1, 9]$; $\mathbf{n} = \mathbf{j}$.

4. $\mathbf{F}(x, y, z) = x^2\mathbf{i} + 9z\mathbf{j} + y^6\mathbf{k}$; the plane $x = 4$ where $y \in [-1, 0]$, $z \in [1, 6]$; $\mathbf{n} = \mathbf{i}$.

5. $\mathbf{F}(x, y, z) = \langle 3x, 5, xy \rangle$; the plane $z = 0$ where $x \in [2, 3]$, $y \in [4, 7]$; $\mathbf{n} = -\mathbf{k}$.

6. $\mathbf{F}(x, y, z) = \langle 3 + x, 9x, e^{2y} \rangle$; the plane $z = 0$ where $x \in [12, 13]$, $y \in [0, 1]$; $\mathbf{n} = -\mathbf{k}$.

7. $\mathbf{F}(x, y, z) = \langle 3 - x, x - y, 15 \rangle$; the plane $y = -1$ where $x \in [0, 4]$, $z \in [1, 6]$; $\mathbf{n} = -\mathbf{j}$.

8. $\mathbf{F}(x, y, z) = \langle x^3yz, 19x\sin y, e^{2xy} \rangle$; the plane $x = -4$ where $y \in [-1, 3]$, $z \in [1, 2]$; $\mathbf{n} = -\mathbf{i}$.

In #9–16 determine $\iint_{\mathcal{M}} \mathbf{F} \cdot \mathbf{n}\, dS$, where $\mathcal{M}$ is the specified portion of the positively oriented graph of the given linear function.

9. $f(x, y) = 3x + 9y$ where $x \in [0, 1]$ and $y \in [1, 3]$; $\mathbf{F}(x, y, z) = \langle 1, -4, 5 \rangle$

10. $f(x, y) = 8x - 19y$ where $x \in [-1, 2]$ and $y \in [0, 4]$; $\mathbf{F}(x, y, z) = \langle -2, 7, -1 \rangle$

11. $f(x, y) = x + 2y$ where $x \in [0, 1]$ and $y \in [1, 3]$; $\mathbf{F}(x, y, z) = \langle 8x + y, 10y^2 - x, xy \rangle$

12. $f(x, y) = -6x - 2y$ where $x \in [0, 2]$ and $y \in [-1, 5]$; $\mathbf{F}(x, y, z) = \langle 8 + y^2, 12y + x, z \rangle$

13. $f(x, y) = -2x + y$ where (x, y) is a point in the bounded region between the curves $y = 4 - 4x^2$ and $y = \cos(0.5\pi x)$; $\mathbf{F}(x, y, z) = \langle 7 + y, 12y + x, 1 \rangle$

14. $f(x, y) = x + 7y$ where (x, y) is a point in the bounded region between the line $y = x$ and the parabola $y = x^2 + 2x - 20$; $\mathbf{F}(x, y, z) = \langle z + y, x, y \rangle$

15. $f(x, y) = 2 + x - 9y$ where $x^2 + y^2 \leq 4$; $\mathbf{F}(x, y, z) = \langle 1 - x, 2y + x, z \rangle$

16. $f(x, y) = 2y - x/3$ where $x^2 + y^2 \leq 9$; $\mathbf{F}(x, y, z) = \langle 6x + 9, y, z^2 \rangle$

In #17–22 determine $\iint_{\mathcal{M}} \mathbf{F} \cdot \mathbf{n} \, dS$, where $\mathcal{M}$ is the specified portion of the positively oriented graph of f.

17. $f(x, y) = 2x^2 + \frac{1}{4}y^2$ where $x \in [0, 2]$ and $y \in [1, 3]$; $\mathbf{F}(x, y, z) = \langle 2, -1, 5 \rangle$

18. $f(x, y) = x^2 - \frac{1}{3}y^2$ where $x \in [0, 2]$ and $y \in [1, 3]$; $\mathbf{F}(x, y, z) = \langle 1, 1, -2 \rangle$

19. $f(x, y) = xy$ where (x, y) is in the first quadrant between the lines $y = 9 - x$ and $y = 4.5 - 0.5x$; $\mathbf{F}(x, y, z) = \langle 1, 3, -3 \rangle$

20. $f(x, y) = x - \sin y$ where $\sin y \leq x \leq 2$ and $0 \leq y \leq \pi$; $\mathbf{F}(x, y, z) = \langle 4, 1, 4 \rangle$

21. $f(x, y) = 5xy + y^2$ where (x, y) is in the first quadrant between the parabolas $x = 1 - y^2$ and $x = 2 + y^2$ with $y \in [0, 1]$; $\mathbf{F}(x, y, z) = \langle x, y, -2z \rangle$

22. $f(x, y) = 8xy + x^3$ where (x, y) is in the first quadrant between the curves $y = \sin(1.5\pi x)$ and $y = 4 + 2x - x^2$ with $x \in [0, 2]$; $\mathbf{F}(x, y, z) = \langle x, -0.375x, x \rangle$

In #23–28 determine $\iint_{\mathcal{M}} \mathbf{F} \cdot \mathbf{n} \, dS$, where $\mathcal{M}$ is the specified positively oriented, open-ended cylindrical surface.

23. $r = 3$, $\theta \in [0, \pi/2]$, $z \in [3, 5]$; $\mathbf{F}(x, y, z) = \langle 3x, y + z, 5 \rangle$

24. $r = 2$, $\theta \in [\pi/4, 2\pi/3]$, $z \in [1, 3]$; $\mathbf{F}(x, y, z) = \langle z, 2y - x, x \rangle$

25. $r = 1$, $\theta \in [0, 2\pi]$, $z \in [-1, 4]$; $\mathbf{F}(x, y, z) = \langle 3, 1, z \rangle$

26. $r = 4$, $\theta \in [0, 2\pi]$, $z \in [-1, 4]$; $\mathbf{F}(x, y, z) = \langle z, 2x + y, z^2 \rangle$

27. $r = 2$, $\theta \in [0, \pi]$, $0 \leq z \leq \theta$; $\mathbf{F}(x, y, z) = \langle 1, 4z, xy \rangle$

28. $r = 1$, $\theta \in [\pi, 2\pi]$, $-1 + \cos\theta \leq z \leq 8 + 2\sin 2\theta$; $\mathbf{F}(x, y, z) = \langle 5z, 1, x - y \rangle$

In #29–32 determine $\iint_{\mathcal{M}} \mathbf{F} \cdot \mathbf{n} \, dS$, where $\mathcal{M}$ is the specified positively oriented, spherical surface.

29. $\rho = 2$, $\theta \in [0, \pi/2]$, $\phi \in [0, \pi/4]$; $\mathbf{F} = \langle x, y, z \rangle$

30. $\rho = 3$, $\theta \in [0, \pi]$, $\phi \in [\pi/4, \pi/2]$; $\mathbf{F} = \langle x^{-1}, y^{-1}, z \rangle$

31. $\rho = 5$, $\theta \in [\pi/2, 5\pi/6]$, $\phi \in [0, \pi/3]$; $\mathbf{F} = \langle z, 0, 1 \rangle$

32. $\rho = 1$, $\theta \in [5\pi/6, \pi]$, $\phi \in [\pi/3, \pi/2]$; $\mathbf{F} = \langle z, z, 1 \rangle$

In #33–38 use a computer algebra system to determine $\iint_{\mathcal{M}} \mathbf{F} \cdot \mathbf{n} \, dS$, where $\mathcal{M}$ is the specified positively oriented surface.

CAS

33. $\mathcal{M}$ is the graph of $f(x, y) = \sin x - \sin y$ over the bounded region between the curves $y = \ln(1 + \cos x)$ and $y = x^2 - 4x + 3$; $\mathbf{F}(x, y, z) = \langle 4x, -2z, e^y \rangle$.

34. $\mathcal{M}$ is the graph of $f(x, y) = x^2 + x - 5y$ over the region between the circle $x^2 + y^2 = 1$ and the ellipse $6x^2 + 4\sqrt{3}xy + 10y^2 = 4$; $\mathbf{F}(x, y, z) = \langle 4x, z, 1 \rangle$.

35. $\mathcal{M}$ is the cylindrical surface with $r = 2$, and $0 \leq z \leq \theta^2$ when $\theta \in [-\pi, \pi]$; $\mathbf{F}(x, y, z) = \langle z, x, x - y \rangle$.

36. $\mathcal{M}$ is the cylindrical surface with $r = 7$, and $\sin\theta \leq z \leq \cos\theta$ when $\theta \in [0, \pi/4]$; $\mathbf{F}(x, y, z) = \langle x, z, e^y \rangle$.

37. $\mathcal{M}$ is the spherical surface $\rho = 1.5$, $0 \leq \phi \leq \theta$, $\theta \in [0, \pi/2]$; $\mathbf{F}(x, y, z) = \langle x, -2z, 5y \rangle$.

38. $\mathcal{M}$ is the spherical surface $\rho = 2.3$, $\phi \in [\theta/2, 2\theta]$, $\theta \in [\pi/6, \pi/4]$; $\mathbf{F}(x, y, z) = \langle 1, -x, zy \rangle$.

❖ 15.6 Concept and Application Exercises

In #39–40 two constant vector fields are provided, and the surface $\mathcal{M}$ is the positively oriented graph of $f(x, y) = x + 0.5y$ over the rectangle $[0, 2] \times [0, 2]$ in the xy-plane. Calculate the flux through $\mathcal{M}$ for each field, and explain in complete sentences what aspects of the fields and/or $f(x, y)$ cause the differences in the flux value.

39. Compare the flux of

    (a) $\mathbf{F}_1 = \langle 3, 0, 0 \rangle$ and $\mathbf{F}_2 = \langle 0, 0, 3 \rangle$
    (b) $\mathbf{F}_1 = \langle 2, 2, 1 \rangle$ and $\mathbf{F}_2 = \langle 2, 1, 2 \rangle$

40. Compare the flux of

    (a) $\mathbf{F}_1 = \langle 3, 0, 0 \rangle$ and $\mathbf{F}_2 = \langle 0, 3, 0 \rangle$
    (b) $\mathbf{F}_1 = \langle 2, 2, 1 \rangle$ and $\mathbf{F}_2 = \langle 1, 2, 2 \rangle$

41. Suppose $\mathbf{F} = \mathbf{k}$ and $t > 0$, and $\mathcal{M}$ is the positively oriented portion of the plane $x + 2y + tz = 0$ that sits over the rectangle $[1, 4] \times [2, 6]$ in the xy-plane. (a) Explain how $\mathcal{M}$ changes as t increases. (b) Suppose $f(t)$ is the flux of $\mathbf{F}$ through $\mathcal{M}$. Graph f.

42. Suppose $\mathbf{F} = \mathbf{k}$ and $t > 0$, and $\mathcal{M}$ is the positively oriented portion of the plane $tx + 2y + z = 0$ that sits over the rectangle $[1, 4] \times [2, 6]$ in the xy-plane. (a) Explain how $\mathcal{M}$ changes as t increases. (b) Suppose $f(t)$ is the flux of $\mathbf{F}$ through $\mathcal{M}$. Graph f.

43. Suppose $\mathbf{F} = \mathbf{j}$ and $t > 0$, and $\mathcal{M}$ is the positively oriented portion of the plane $2x + 3y + tz = 0$ that sits over the rectangle $x \in [1, 4]$, $y \in [2, s]$, where $s \geq 2$. (a) Determine a formula for the flux of $\mathbf{F}$ through $\mathcal{M}$, which we'll denote here by $f(s, t)$, (b) show that $f_s > f_t$, and (c) explain why part (b) makes sense from a geometric point of view.

44. Suppose $\mathbf{F} = \mathbf{k}$, and $\mathcal{M}$ is the positively oriented portion of the surface $z = x^2 + 3y^2$ over the rectangle $[0, t] \times [0, s]$ in the xy-plane, where t and s are both positive. Further, we'll define $f(s, t)$ to be the flux of $\mathbf{F}$ through $\mathcal{M}$. Determine whether f_t or f_x is greater when $t = s$, and explain why that makes sense in simple, geometric terms.

45. Suppose $\mathbf{F} = \frac{1}{\|\mathbf{r}\|^k} \mathbf{r}$, where $\mathbf{r} = \langle x, y, z \rangle$, and $\mathcal{M}$ is the positively oriented portion of the sphere $\rho = t$ for which $\theta \in [0, \pi/2]$ and $\phi \in [0, \pi/2]$. If $f(t)$ is the flux of $\mathbf{F}$ through $\mathcal{M}$, determine the value(s) of k for which $f(t)$ is decreasing.

46. Suppose $\mathbf{F}$ is a constant vector field, and $\mathcal{M}$ is the positively oriented portion of the cylinder of radius r for which $\theta \in [0, \pi]$ and $z \in [0, t]$, where $t > 0$. If $f(t)$ is the flux of $\mathbf{F}$ through $\mathcal{M}$, determine a formula for $f'(t)$.

47. Suppose R is the region in the first quadrant of the xy-plane that lies between the unit circle and the parabola $x = 1 - y^2$, and $\mathcal{M}$ is the positively oriented portion of $3x + y + z = 2$ that sits over R. If length is measured in cm, and $\mathbf{F}(x, y, z) = \langle x, y + z, 2 \rangle \frac{\text{g/sec}}{\text{cm}^2}$ is the mass flow of an incompressible fluid, determine the flux of $\mathbf{F}$ through $\mathcal{M}$. Include correct units in your answer.

$\underline{\hspace{1cm}}$ Mass Flow

48. Suppose R is the triangular region in the yz-plane defined by the points $(y, z) = (0, 1), (1, 0)$, and $(2, 0)$, and $\mathcal{M}$ is the positively oriented portion of the plane $-x + 2y + 5z = 1$ for which $(y, z) \in R$. If length is measured in

$\underline{\hspace{1cm}}$ Mass Flow

m, and $\mathbf{F}(x, y, z) = \langle 2, x, z\rangle \frac{\text{kg/min}}{\text{m}^2}$ is the mass flow of an incompressible fluid, determine the flux of $\mathbf{F}$ through $\mathcal{M}$. Include correct units in your answer.

49. Suppose the z-axis is a wire with a linear charge density of λ coulombs per meter. The induced electric field at the point (x, y, z) is $\mathbf{E} = \frac{\lambda}{2\pi\varepsilon_0 r}\hat{\mathbf{r}}$, where ε_0 is a number called the *permittivity constant*; the vector $\hat{\mathbf{r}}$ is the unit vector in the direction of $\langle x, y, 0\rangle$, and $r = \|\langle x, y, 0\rangle\|$. Show that the flux of $\mathbf{E}$ through an open-ended cylinder of radius R that extends from $z = 0$ to $z = L$ depends on L but not R.

_____ Electric Fields

50. Suppose length is measured in meters, and the line segment connecting the points $(0, 0, -L)$ and $(0, 0, L)$ has a linear charge density of λ coulombs per meter. Then the electric field at the point (r, θ, z) is

_____ Electric Fields

$$\mathbf{E}(x, y, z) = \frac{\lambda}{4\pi\varepsilon_0 r}\left(\frac{L+z}{\sqrt{r^2 + (L+z)^2}} + \frac{L-z}{\sqrt{r^2 + (L-z)^2}}\right)\hat{\mathbf{r}} +$$

$$\frac{\lambda}{4\pi\varepsilon_0}\left(\frac{1}{\sqrt{r^2 + (z-L)^2}} - \frac{1}{\sqrt{r^2 + (z+L)^2}}\right)\mathbf{k},$$

where $\hat{\mathbf{r}}$ is the unit vector that points in the direction of increasing r, and ε_0 is a number called the *permittivity constant*. Imagine that the segment is contained in a closed cylinder of radius $R > 0$ that extends from $z = -L - \varepsilon$ to $z = L + \varepsilon$ (where $\varepsilon > 0$ is an arbitrary but fixed constant). In this exercise you'll use surface integrals to calculate the flux of $\mathbf{E}$ through the cylinder.

(a) Determine the flux of $\mathbf{E}$ through the side of the cylinder.

(b) Determine the flux of $\mathbf{E}$ through the top end cap of the cylinder.

(c) Determine the flux of $\mathbf{E}$ through the bottom end cap of the cylinder.

(d) Explain how the net flux of $\mathbf{E}$ through the cylinder is related to the total charge inside, and compare this result to Example 6.9.

In #51–54 a current of I amps flows along the z-axis in the $\mathbf{k}$ direction (positive charges head in the direction of $\mathbf{k}$, or equivalently, negative charges flow in the direction of $-\mathbf{k}$). The magnetic field induced by this current is

$$\mathbf{B}(x, y, z) = \frac{\mu_0 I}{2\pi(x^2 + y^2)}\langle -y, x, 0\rangle,$$

where $\mu_0 = 4\pi \times 10^7$ is called the *permeability of free space*. The *magnetic flux* of $\mathbf{B}$ through an oriented surface $\mathcal{M}$ is

$$\Phi_M = \iint_{\mathcal{M}} \mathbf{B} \cdot \mathbf{n}\, dS, \tag{6.7}$$

where dS is the area element on S. In #51–54 determine Φ_M.

51. $\mathcal{M}$ is the rectangular region with vertices $(0.2, 0.1, 0)$, $(0.5, 0.1, 0)$, $(0.5, 0.1, 1)$ and $(0.2, 0.1, 1)$, with $\mathbf{n} = \mathbf{j}$.

_____ Magnetic Fields

52. $\mathcal{M}$ is the rectangular region with vertices $(0.06, 0.03, -0.1)$, $(0.06, 0.03, 0.2)$, $(0.08, 0.05, 0.2)$ and $(0.08, 0.05, -0.1)$, with $\mathbf{n} = \langle -1, 1, 0\rangle/\sqrt{2}$.

_____ Magnetic Fields

53. $\mathcal{M}$ is the positively oriented triangle with vertices $(1, 1, -1)$, $(6, 1, 3)$ and $(4, 3, 0)$.

_____ Magnetic Fields

54. $\mathcal{M}$ is the positively oriented graph of $f(x, y) = 0.1x^2 + y^2$ over the region of the xy-plane in which $0 \le x \le 0.5$ and $0.25 \le y \le 0.4$.

_____ Magnetic Fields

Faraday's Law states the relationship between the flux of a magnetic field through a surface and the induced *electromotive force* (emf), here denoted by $\mathcal{E}$, which causes current to flow along the boundary curve of the surface. Specifically, when the piecewise-smooth, simple, closed curve $\mathcal{C}$ is the boundary of the surface $\mathcal{M}$,

$$\mathcal{E} = -\frac{d}{dt}\Phi_M,$$

where Φ_M is the magnetic flux defined in equation (6.7). In #55–58 a current of I amps flows along the z-axis, as it did in #51–54 above, but now the current varies with time. Determine a formula for the resulting emf.

55. $I(t) = \cos(\pi t)$ amps, and $\mathcal{M}$ is the rectangle with vertices $(0.01, 0.02, 0)$, $(0.01, 0.07, 0)$, $(0.01, 0.07, 0.5)$ and $(0.01, 0.02, 0.5)$, oriented with $\mathbf{n} = \mathbf{i}$.

  ___ | Induced EMF |

56. $I(t) = 10e^{-0.1t}$ amps, and $\mathcal{M}$ is the positively oriented triangle with vertices $(-0.2, 0.1, 0.4)$, $(0, 0.1, 0.4)$ and $(0.3, 0.6, 0.7)$.

  ___ | Induced EMF |

57. $I(t) = 10\sin(3\pi t)e^{-0.02t}$ amps, and $\mathcal{M}$ is the positively oriented spherical surface for which $\rho = 2$, $\pi/6 \leq \phi \leq \pi/3$, and $0 \leq \theta \leq \pi/4$.

  ___ | Induced EMF |

58. $I(t) = 1/(1+t^2)$ amps, and $\mathcal{M}$ is the positively oriented graph of $f(x, y) = 3 + y\sin x$ that sits over the rectangle in the xy-plane in which $\pi/6 \leq x \leq \pi/4$ and $0 \leq y \leq 1$.

  ___ | Induced EMF |

15.7   Parameterized Surfaces and Their Areas

In Section 15.6 you learned about the flux of vector fields through graphs of functions, cylinders, and spheres. This section is intended to equip you with the basic ideas and skills needed to generalize that theory (which will happen in Sections 15.8–15.10) by introducing a general way of talking about surfaces, their tangent planes and area.

> **Key Idea(s):** *A parameterized surface in $\mathbb{R}^3$ is one that can be described by two independent variables (the surface $z = f(x, y)$ is a familiar example—location on the surface depends on the two variables x and y).*
>
> *We can approximate area on the surface by using parallelograms whose sides are tangent vectors to the surface.*

❖ Parameterized Surfaces

In Chapter 9 you saw that the curve $y = f(x)$ can be parameterized by $\mathbf{r}(t) = \langle t, f(t) \rangle$, although we didn't use vector notation at the time. Similarly, points on the surface $z = f(x, y)$ can be located with $\mathbf{r}(s, t) = \langle s, t, f(s, t) \rangle$. More generally, a **parameterized surface** in 3-space is one that's described by two independent variables. Such surfaces can be more complicated than graphs of functions, as exemplified by the **toroid** in Figure 7.1, but we'll begin with something more familiar as we develop the important ideas (a region in the xy-plane between the graphs of two functions).

Suppose R is the region bounded above by the curve $y = f(x)$ and below by $y = g(x)$, as in Figure 7.2. If we parameterize these curves with $\mathbf{r}_1(s) = \langle s, f(s) \rangle$ and $\mathbf{r}_2(s) = \langle s, g(s) \rangle$, each value of s corresponds to a pair of points, one on the graph of f and the other (directly below it) on the graph of g. In the discussion that follows, we will focus on the vertical line segment that extends between them, through R. Its length is $L = f(s) - g(s)$, so its midpoint has a y-coordinate of

Figure 7.1: A parameterized surface called a toroid.

$$g(s) + \frac{1}{2}L = g(s) + \frac{1}{2}\big(f(s) - g(s)\big) = \frac{1}{2}g(s) + \frac{1}{2}f(s)$$

> Note that the coefficients sum to 1. This is an average of $f(s)$ and $g(s)$.

Similarly, the point with a y coordinate of

$$g(s) + \frac{1}{4}L = g(s) + \frac{1}{4}\big(f(s) - g(s)\big) = \frac{3}{4}g(s) + \frac{1}{4}f(s)$$

> These coefficients are positive and sum to 1. This is a weighted average of $f(s)$ and $g(s)$.

is on the segment, but it's closer to the lower endpoint. More generally, each point between $\big(s, f(s)\big)$ and $\big(s, g(s)\big)$ has a y-coordinate of the form

$$g(s) + tL = g(s) + t\big(f(s) - g(s)\big) = (1 - t)\,g(s) + t\,f(s)$$

> Since t and $(1 - t)$ are positive numbers that sum to 1, this is a weighted average of $f(s)$ and $g(s)$.

for some $t \in [0, 1]$, so its position vector has the form

$$\begin{bmatrix} s \\ (1-t)\,g(s) + t\,f(s) \end{bmatrix} = (1 - t)\begin{bmatrix} s \\ g(s) \end{bmatrix} + t\begin{bmatrix} s \\ f(s) \end{bmatrix} = (1 - t)\mathbf{r}_1(s) + t\,\mathbf{r}_2(s),$$

> Since $t \in [0, 1]$ and $t + (1 - t) = 1$, this is a weighted average of $\mathbf{r}_1$ and $\mathbf{r}_2$.

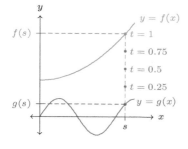 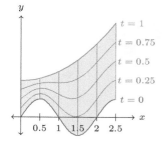 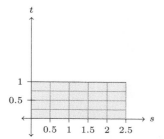

Figure 7.2: (left) The number t determines height on the vertical line segment between $(s, g(s))$ and $(s, f(s))$; (middle) the region between the curves, including lines of constant s and curves of constant t; (right) when characterized in terms of s and t, the region is simply a rectangle.

which we write at $\mathbf{r}(s,t)$. We can shift the head of this position vector left or right by adjusting the parameter s, and changing t moves the head up or down. Every point in R is associated with a unique s and t, so we say that $\mathbf{r}(s,t)$ parameterizes R. The benefit of creating such a parameterization is two-fold; whereas the region looks "curvy" from when we describe it in terms of x and y, describing position in terms of s and t allows us to understand R as a much simpler shape (in this case, a rectangle). Secondly, the parameterization provides us with a "map" of the region (compare the right-hand image of Figure 7.2 to the middle image, paying special attention to the grid). Both of these facts are very useful when working with surfaces in space. In the discussion that follows, we introduce parameterizations of familiar surfaces.

The same "weighted average" technique often allows us to describe simple surfaces in 3-space that extend between curves. For instance, $\mathbf{r}_1(\theta) = \langle 2\cos\theta, 2\sin\theta, 0 \rangle$ parameterizes a circle of radius 2 in the xy-plane, and $\mathbf{r}_2(\theta) = \langle 2\cos\theta, 2\sin\theta, 1 \rangle$ parameterizes a circle of radius 2 directly above it, in the plane $z = 1$. By employing t as a means of moving from one curve to the other, we get

$$\mathbf{r}(\theta, t) = t\mathbf{r}_1(\theta) + (1-t)\,\mathbf{r}_2(\theta)$$
$$= \langle \underbrace{2\cos\theta,\ 2\sin\theta,}\ \underbrace{t}\ \rangle, \tag{7.1}$$

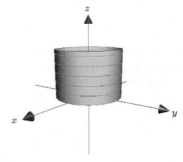

Figure 7.3: A parameterized cylinder.

This part parameterizes a circle of radius 2   This part controls the height

which parameterizes a *cylinder* of radius 2 and height 1 when we restrict $t \in [0,1]$, shown in Figure 7.3. Although we originally thought of t as being some number in $[0,1]$—a weight in our weighted average—in the final formula we see that it simply controls altitude. So we can change the vertical extension of the cylinder by adjusting the interval over which we allow t to vary. For example, Figure 7.4 shows a cylinder of radius 2 that extends from $z = -2$ to $z = 3$, which is accomplished by letting t vary over $[-2, 3]$.

The parameters θ and t occur in separate components of $\mathbf{r}$ in equation (7.1), but they don't have to. For example, the cone in Figure 7.5 is parameterized by

$$\mathbf{r}(\theta, t) = \langle \underbrace{t\cos\theta,\ t\sin\theta,}\ \underbrace{t}\ \rangle,$$

This part parameterizes a circle of radius t This part controls the height

where $\theta \in [0, 2\pi)$ and $t \in [0, 3]$. As you've seen in these examples, each parameter of $\mathbf{r}$ moves the position vector in a direction, and those directions are often orthogonal on simple surfaces.

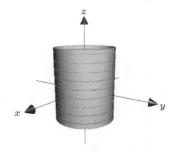

Figure 7.4: A parameterized cylinder

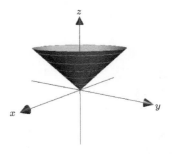

Figure 7.5: A parameterized cone.

Parameterizing a paraboloid

Example 7.1. Parameterize the paraboloid $x = y^2 + 0.5z^2$ for $x \in [0, 4]$.

Solution: This paraboloid opens along the x-axis, as you see in Figure 7.6. In keeping with our usage of t above, we begin by writing our parameterization as $\langle t, \ , \ \rangle$, where we've left the latter components empty because they're currently undetermined. Because this surface is an elliptic paraboloid, each $t > 0$ corresponds to an ellipse in the y- and z-directions:

$$t = y^2 + \frac{1}{2}z^2.$$

The maximum value of y allowed by this equation is $y = \sqrt{t}$, and the maximum value of z is $\sqrt{2t}$, so we can move around the ellipse by setting

$$y = \sqrt{t}\cos\theta \quad \text{and} \quad z = \sqrt{2t}\sin\theta.$$

Inserting this into our position vector, we see

$$\mathbf{r}(\theta, t) = \langle t, \sqrt{t}\cos\theta, \sqrt{2t}\sin\theta\rangle, \text{ where } \theta \in [0, 2\pi) \text{ and } t \in [0, 4]. \quad \blacksquare$$

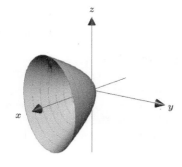

Figure 7.6: A parameterized paraboloid.

It doesn't matter which of y or z is paired with the cosine. That affects the direction of travel around the ellipse, and where we start, but we're still traveling along the same ellipse.

Solution On-line

Parameterizing a paraboloid

Example 7.2. Parameterize the paraboloid $y = -3x^2 - 5z^2$ for $y \in [-7, 0]$.

Answer: $\mathbf{r}(\theta, t) = \langle \sqrt{-t/3}\cos\theta, t, \sqrt{-t/5}\sin\theta\rangle$ where $\theta \in [0, 2\pi)$ and $t \in [-7, 0]$. $\quad \blacksquare$

It's common to talk about parameterized surfaces using parametric equations rather than position vectors. For instance, in the previous examples we could write

$$\underbrace{\begin{aligned} x(\theta, t) &= t \\ y(\theta, t) &= \sqrt{t}\cos\theta \\ z(\theta, t) &= \sqrt{2t}\sin\theta \end{aligned}}_{\text{Example 7.1}} \qquad \underbrace{\begin{aligned} x(\theta, t) &= \sqrt{-t/3}\cos\theta \\ y(\theta, t) &= t \\ z(\theta, t) &= \sqrt{-t/5}\sin\theta \end{aligned}}_{\text{Example 7.2}}$$

Although we used θ and t as the parameters in those examples, we can of course denote the two independent variables with any letters we choose; we'll often use s and t as parameters. The collection of (s, t) pairs corresponding to points on a surface is called the ***parameter domain***. The parameter domain has been a rectangle in all of the examples so far, but it doesn't have to be.

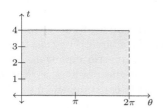

Figure 7.7: The domain for the parameterization in Example 7.1.

Parameter domain

Example 7.3. Determine the parameter domain if we parameterize the paraboloid in Example 7.1 with $\mathbf{r}(s, t) = \langle s^2 + 0.5t^2, s, t\rangle$.

Solution: In order to keep $x \in [0, 4]$ we need $s^2 + 0.5t^2 \le 4$, which is the region bounded by an ellipse in the st-plane. $\quad \blacksquare$

The parameterizations in Examples 7.1 and 7.3 amount to two different ways of thinking about and describing the same surface. The former makes use of the paraboloid's central axis and the familiar geometry of its cross sections, while the latter makes use of the fact that x is a function of y and z on the paraboloid. This contrast can be seen in the corresponding *grid curves* of the parameterizations, which we discuss next.

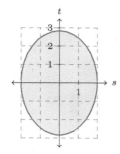

Figure 7.8: The parameter domain for Example 7.3.

▷ Grid curves of a parameterization

Figure 7.9 shows a cylinder parameterized by equation (7.1), and its parameter domain. Each constant value of t corresponds to a circle at a specific height on the cylinder (shown), and each value of θ corresponds to a vertical line that runs up the cylinder's side (not shown). In general, fixing one of the independent variables and letting the other vary produces a curve on the surface. Such curves are called *grid curves*.

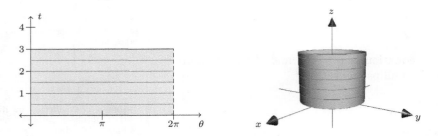

Figure 7.9: A cylinder and its parameter domain. Each horizontal line in the parameter domain corresponds to a circle on the cylinder.

Grid curves

Example 7.4. Suppose $\mathcal{M}$ is the surface parameterized by $x(s,t) = \cos s \cos t$, $y(s,t) = \cos s \sin t$, and $z(s,t) = \sin s$ where $s \in [0, \pi]$ and $t \in [\pi/6, \pi/3]$. Describe (a) the surface $\mathcal{M}$, (b) its grid curves, and (c) its parameter domain.

Solution: (a) These parametric equations describe a sector of a unit sphere (shown in Figure 7.11) which you can verify by showing that $x^2 + y^2 + z^2 = 1$.

(b) The grid curves on $\mathcal{M}$ are generated by fixing one of the independent variables at a time. For example, choosing any particular value of s effectively reduces the parametric equations to functions of a single variable, t, so as t varies over $[\pi/6, \pi/3]$ the point at $\mathbf{r}(t) = \langle x(s,t), y(s,t), z(s,t) \rangle$ traverses a curve. Specifically, since z is constant when s is held fixed, $\mathbf{r}(t)$ parameterizes a circular arc of constant "latitude." Similarly, Figure 7.11 shows that when t is held fixed and s is allowed to vary from $\pi/6$ to $\pi/3$, the parametric equations trace out a circular arc of constant "longitude," from the "top" to the "bottom" of $\mathcal{M}$.

(c) Since s is allowed to vary over $[0, \pi]$ regardless of t, and t varies over $[\pi/6, \pi/3]$ regardless of s, we can understand the parameter domain as a rectangle in the st-plane, as shown in Figure 7.10.   ∎

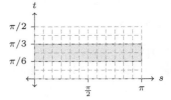

Figure 7.10:   A grid on the parameter domain for Example 7.4.

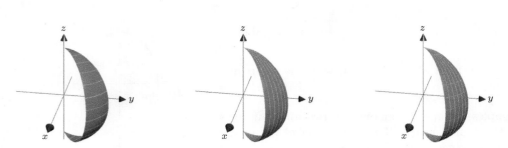

Figure 7.11: (all) The surface $\mathcal{M}$ from Example 7.4; (left) Grid curves at different values of s; (middle) grid curves at different values of t; (right) grid curves form a mesh on $\mathcal{M}$.

Grid curves on a parameterized plane

Example 7.5. Suppose $\mathcal{M}$ is the planar surface that passes through the point $(3, 1, 4)$ and includes the vectors $\mathbf{u} = \langle -4, 6, 1 \rangle$ and $\mathbf{v} = \langle -1, -1, 1 \rangle$. (a) Determine a parameterization for $\mathcal{M}$, and (b) use a computer to graph $\mathcal{M}$ with grid lines of your parameterization.

Solution: (a) We can get from the origin to any point on $\mathcal{M}$ by first heading to the point $(3, 1, 4)$, then traveling in the direction of $\pm\mathbf{u}$, and then moving some distance in the direction of $\pm\mathbf{v}$. For this reason, we write

$$\mathbf{r}(s,t) = \langle 3, 1, 4 \rangle + s\mathbf{u} + t\mathbf{v} = \langle 3 - 4s - t, 1 + 6s - t, 4 + 1s + t \rangle.$$

Figure 7.12:   The plane in Example 7.5 with grid curves (lines in this case).

(b) Figure 7.12 shows the graph of $\mathcal{M}$ with several of its grid lines, where s is restricted to $[-1, 1]$ and $t \in [-2, 2]$.   ∎

Grid curves

Example 7.6. Compare and contrast the grid curves from the parameterizations in Examples 7.1 and 7.3.

Answer: See on-line solution.   ∎

Solution On-line

✤ Tangent Planes to Parameterized Surfaces

Suppose the surface $\mathcal{M}$ is parameterized by $\mathbf{r}(s,t) = \langle x(s,t), y(s,t), z(s,t) \rangle$. By holding t constant, we effectively reduce $\mathbf{r}$ to a function of a single variable, s, so it parameterizes a grid curve on $\mathcal{M}$. Where the vector

$$\mathbf{r}_s = \left\langle \frac{\partial x}{\partial s}, \frac{\partial y}{\partial s}, \frac{\partial z}{\partial s} \right\rangle$$

is nonzero, it's tangent to that grid curve, and so tangent to $\mathcal{M}$. Similarly, each fixed value of s defines a grid curve on $\mathcal{M}$, and

$$\mathbf{r}_t = \left\langle \frac{\partial x}{\partial t}, \frac{\partial y}{\partial t}, \frac{\partial z}{\partial t} \right\rangle$$

is tangent to $\mathcal{M}$ (where the vector is nonzero). Since $\mathbf{r}_s$ and $\mathbf{r}_t$ are tangent to $\mathcal{M}$, they lie in the tangent plane, so $\mathbf{r}_s \times \mathbf{r}_t$ is normal to the tangent plane, provided that it's nonzero. This leads us to make the following definition: the parameterization $\mathbf{r}(s,t)$ is said to be ***regular*** if $\mathbf{r}_s \times \mathbf{r}_t$ is never zero in the interior of the parameter domain. Further, we'll say that a regular parameterization $\mathbf{r}$ is ***smooth*** if $\mathbf{r}_s$ and $\mathbf{r}_t$ are continuous.

Figure 7.13:   Diagram of grid curves on a surface, (top) t is fixed along "horizontal" curves, and s is constant along "vertical" curves; (bottom) tangent vectors at the point where $s = a$ and $t = c$.

Tangent plane to a parameterized surface

Example 7.7. Suppose the surface $\mathcal{M}$ is parameterized by $\mathbf{r}$ (see below) when $s \in [0, 1]$ and $t \in [0, 1]$. (a) Verify that $\mathbf{r}$ is a regular parameterization, and (b) determine the tangent plane to $\mathcal{M}$ at the point $\mathbf{r}(1/3, 1/4)$.

$$\mathbf{r}(s,t) = s \begin{bmatrix} t \\ -1 \\ t^2 \end{bmatrix} + (1 - s) \begin{bmatrix} t \\ 1 \\ \sin \pi t \end{bmatrix}.$$

Solution: Let's take a moment to understand how $\mathbf{r}$ parameterizes $\mathcal{M}$. The grid curve associated with $s = 1$ is parameterized by $\mathbf{r}(1, t) = \langle t, -1, t^2 \rangle$, in which $y = -1$ is constant and z is a quadratic function of x. So this grid curve is a parabola that lies in the vertical plane $y = -1$ (see Figure 7.14). Similarly, when we fix $s = 0$ we

Figure 7.14: For Example 7.7 (left) a parabolic arc in the plane $y = -1$, and a sinusoidal arc in the plane $y = 1$; (right) the surface extends between those curves.

have $\mathbf{r}(0,t) = \langle t, 1, \sin \pi t \rangle$, which is the curve $z = \sin \pi x$ in the vertical plane $y = 1$. As s increases from 0 to 1, the parameterization $\mathbf{r}(s,t)$ traverses a line in the plane $x = t$ from the parabola to the sine curve.

> This idea (using a parameter to drive a point from one curve to another) can help you parameterize many simple surfaces.

(a) In order to more easily determine $\mathbf{r}_s$ and $\mathbf{r}_t$ let's add the constituent vectors of $\mathbf{r}$ and rewrite the parameterization as

$$\mathbf{r}(s,t) = \langle t, \ 1 - 2s, \ st^2 + (1-s)\sin \pi t \rangle.$$

Then it's easy to determine that

$$\mathbf{r}_s(s,t) = \langle 0, -2, t^2 - \sin \pi t \rangle$$
$$\mathbf{r}_t(s,t) = \langle 1, 0, 2st + (1-s)\pi \cos \pi t \rangle.$$

The cross product of these two vectors is

$$\left[\mathbf{r}_s \times \mathbf{r}_t \right](s,t) = -(4st + 2\pi(1-s)\cos \pi t)\mathbf{i} + (t^2 - \sin \pi t)\mathbf{j} + 2\mathbf{k}. \qquad (7.2)$$

Because the third component of $\mathbf{r}_s \times \mathbf{r}_t$ is always 2, this vector is never $\mathbf{0}$, so $\mathbf{r}$ is a regular parameterization.

(b) To determine the equation of the tangent plane, we need to know $\mathbf{r}\left(1/3, 1/4 \right) = \left\langle 1/3, \ 1/2, \ (1+16\sqrt{2})/48 \right\rangle$, and a normal direction,

$$\left[\mathbf{r}_s \times \mathbf{r}_t \right](1/3, 1/4) = \left\langle -\frac{1 + 2\pi\sqrt{2}}{3}, \ \frac{1 - 8\sqrt{2}}{16}, \ 2 \right\rangle.$$

Now with a point and a normal direction, we can write the equation of the tangent plane as

$$0 = -\frac{1 + 2\pi\sqrt{2}}{3}\left(x - \frac{1}{3} \right) + \frac{1 - 8\sqrt{2}}{16}\left(y - \frac{1}{2} \right) + \frac{1 - 8\sqrt{2}}{16}\left(z - \frac{1 + 16\sqrt{2}}{48} \right). \qquad \blacksquare$$

Tangent plane to a parameterized surface

Example 7.8. Suppose $\mathcal{M}$ is parameterized by $\mathbf{r}(s,t) = \langle s - t, s + t\cos \pi s, s + \sin \pi t \rangle$, where $s \in [0, 10]$ and $t \in [-1, 1]$. Determine (a) whether $\mathbf{r}$ is a regular parameterization, and (b) the equation of the tangent plane to $\mathcal{M}$ at $\mathbf{r}(1, 1/2)$.

Answer: (a) It's not regular; (b) $1x - 1y + 0z = 0$. $\qquad \blacksquare$

Solution On-line

✥ Area of a Parameterized Surface

Suppose $\mathbf{r}$ is a smooth parameterization of $\mathcal{M}$, and (s_0, t_0) is a point in the interior of the parameter domain. When we hold $s = s_0$ fixed, the vector-valued function $\mathbf{r}(s_0, t)$ moves across the surface with a velocity of $\mathbf{r}_t$, so moving from t_0 to $t_0 + \Delta t$ in the parameter domain corresponds to a displacement of

$$\underbrace{\Delta \mathbf{r}}_{\text{displacement}} \approx \underbrace{\mathbf{r}_t(s_0, t_0)}_{\text{(velocity)}} \underbrace{\Delta t}_{\text{(time)}}$$

on the surface (see Figure 7.15). Similarly, a short span of Δs in the parameter domain corresponds to a displacement of approximately $\mathbf{r}_s(s_0, t_0)\Delta s$ on $\mathcal{M}$. So a rectangle that is Δs wide and Δt tall in the parameter domain corresponds to a patch on $\mathcal{M}$ with an area of $\Delta S \approx \|\mathbf{r}_s \, \Delta s \times \mathbf{r}_t \, \Delta t\| = \|\mathbf{r}_s \times \mathbf{r}_t\| \Delta s \Delta t$.

So if $\mathbf{r}$ is a **one-to-one** parameterization of $\mathcal{M}$, meaning that each point on the surface corresponds to a single point in the parameter domain, we can partition the parameter domain with a mesh of n rectangles and approximate

$$\text{the area of } \mathcal{M} \approx \sum_{k=1}^{n} \|\mathbf{r}_s(s_k, t_k) \times \mathbf{r}_t(s_k, t_k)\| \; \Delta s_k \Delta t_k,$$

where Δs_k and Δt_k are the length and width of the kth rectangle of the mesh, and (s_k, t_k) is some point in it. This yields the following result in the limit.

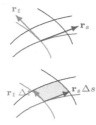

Figure 7.15: Diagram of grid curves on a surface, (top) from Figure 7.13; (bottom) the area of the parallelogram defined by $\mathbf{r}_s \, \Delta s$ and $\mathbf{r}_t \, \Delta t$ closely approximates the area of a patch on the surface.

Area of a Parameterized Surface: Suppose $\mathbf{r}(s, t)$ is a smooth, one-to-one parameterization of the surface $\mathcal{M}$ over the parameter domain R. Then the **surface area** of $\mathcal{M}$ is

$$\text{area of } \mathcal{M} = \iint_R \|\mathbf{r}_s \times \mathbf{r}_t\| \, dA \qquad (7.3)$$

Surface area of a parameterized sphere

Example 7.9. Use equation (7.3) to determine the area of the unit sphere.

Solution: Based on the standard conversion from spherical to Cartesian coordinates, let's parameterize the sphere with $\mathbf{r}(s, t) = \langle x(s,t), y(s,t), z(s,t) \rangle$ where

$$x(s, t) = \sin s \cos t, \quad y(s, t) = \sin s \sin t \quad \text{and} \quad z(s, t) = \cos s,$$

Then

$$\mathbf{r}_s(s, t) = \langle \cos s \cos t, \; \cos s \sin t, \; -\sin s \rangle$$
$$\mathbf{r}_t(s, t) = \langle -\sin s \sin t, \sin s \cos t, 0 \rangle$$
$$[\mathbf{r}_s \times \mathbf{r}_t](s, t) = \langle -\cos^2 s \cos t, -\cos^2 s \sin t, -\cos s \sin s \rangle.$$

A quick calculation shows us that $\|\mathbf{r}_s \times \mathbf{r}_t\| = \sin s$, and because we're talking about the entire sphere, we know that $s \in [0, \pi]$ and $t \in [0, 2\pi]$. So we calculate the area of the sphere as

$$\iint_R \|\mathbf{n}(s, t)\| \, dA = \int_0^\pi \int_0^{2\pi} \sin(s) \, dt \, ds = 2\pi \int_0^\pi \sin(s) \, ds = 4\pi. \qquad \blacksquare$$

Don't just read it. Verify that $\|\mathbf{n}(s, t)\| = \sin s$.

Surface area of a parameterized paraboloid

Example 7.10. Use equation (7.3) to determine the surface area of the paraboloid $y = 2x^2 + 2z^2$ for which $0 \leq y \leq 6$.

Answer: $57\pi/4$. $\blacksquare$

Solution On-line

❖ Connections to Previous Topics

We conclude this section by noting two connections to previous topics: change of variables, and the surface area of the graph of a function.

▷ Surface Area of the Graph of a Function

Suppose the surface $\mathcal{M}$ is the graph of a function, say $f(x, y)$, over a region R. Then $\mathcal{M}$ is naturally parameterized by $\mathbf{r}(x, y) = \langle x, y, f(x, y) \rangle$, whence $\mathbf{r}_x = \langle 1, 0, f_x \rangle$ and $\mathbf{r}_y = \langle 0, 1, f_y \rangle$. So the ideas from this section tell us the surface area of $\mathcal{M}$ is

$$\iint_R \|\mathbf{r}_x \times \mathbf{r}_y\| \, dA = \iint_R \sqrt{\left(f_x(x, y)\right)^2 + \left(f_y(x, y)\right)^2 + 1} \, dA,$$

which agrees with our formula from Section 14.1.

▷ Change of Variables

Suppose the region R is parameterized by $\mathbf{r}(u, v) = \langle x(u, v), y(u, v), 0 \rangle$ when (u, v) ranges over the parameter domain D. Then R is a surface that lies in the xy-plane, and the area element in R is

$$dA_{xy} = \|\mathbf{r}_u \times \mathbf{r}_v\| \, du \, dv = \left| x_u y_v - x_v y_u \right| du \, dv = \left| \frac{\partial(x, y)}{\partial(u, v)} \right| du \, dv = \left| \frac{\partial(x, y)}{\partial(u, v)} \right| dA_{uv},$$

which is the relationship that we first saw in Section 14.7.

You should know

- the terms *parameterized surface*, *parameter domain*, *grid curves*, *regular* and *smooth*.

You should be able to

- formulate parameterizations of simple surfaces;
- determine whether a parameterization is regular;
- use a parameterization to determine a normal direction to a surface;
- find the equation of the tangent plane to a parameterized surface at a point;
- use a smooth parameterization to determine the area of a surface.

❖ 15.7 Skill Exercises

In #1–4 parameterize the given plane.

1. Through the point $(-1, 4, -7)$, including the directions $\langle 8, 1, -3 \rangle$ and $\langle 1, 14, 9 \rangle$.
2. Through the point $(12, 3, 8)$, including the directions $\langle 5, -1, 2 \rangle$ and $\langle 1, 1, 6 \rangle$.
3. Through the point $(2, 1, 0)$ with normal vector $\langle 3, 5, 1 \rangle$.
4. Through the points $(1, 0, 2)$, $(0, 3, 1)$ and $(5, 5, -8)$.

In #5–10 determine a parameterization of the given surface and describe the parameter domain.

5. $3x^2 + 16y^2 = 1$, $|z| \leq 7$ 6. $12 - \frac{3}{4}z^2 = 9x^2$, $|y| \leq 3$

7. The cone about the z-axis with its tip at the origin, opening in the direction of $\mathbf{k}$, whose edge makes an angle of $\pi/6$ radians with the xy-plane.

15.8   Surface Integrals

In previous sections we've talked about the meaning and method of calculating integrals over regions in the plane, and here we extend that discussion to integration over surfaces in space. We begin with the integration of scalar-valued functions, and then move to the calculation of flux through a surface.

> **Key Idea(s):** *Like double integrals are approximated by Riemann sums of the form $f\,dA$, the integral of some quantity over a parameterized surface is approximated by Riemann sums of the form $f\,dS$, where dS is the area element on the parameterized surface.*

❖ Integrating a Scalar-Valued Function Over a Parameterized Surface

Imagine a surface as the snapshot of a billowing sheet, and suppose the mass density at each point on the sheet is $f(x, y, z)$ g/cm^2, where x, y and z are all measured in cm. If the surface were an *actual* sheet we could determine its mass by folding it and putting it on a scale, but it's not. So how can we use this information about density to calculate the mass of the "sheet?" More generally, how can we determine the cumulative total of *any* quantity (not just mass but, e.g., charge or thermal energy) that's distributed over the surface? We use an integral, of course.

Figure 8.1: A surface in space is like a snapshot of a billowing sheet.

As you've seen in previous sections, we can form a Riemann sum for a function f over a surface $\mathcal{M}$ if we can partition $\mathcal{M}$ into patches. By evaluating f at a point in each patch, we form the Riemann sum

$$\sum_{k=1}^{n} f(x_k, y_k, z_k)\, \Delta S_k,$$

where ΔS_k is the area of the kth patch, and (x_k, y_k, z_k) is some point in it. Roughly said, the **surface integral** of f over $\mathcal{M}$, which is denoted by $\iint_{\mathcal{M}} f\, dS$, is the limit of this sum as the size of the patches grows arbitrarily small and their number grows arbitrarily large. As always, we must be concerned about whether that limit converges, but as you suspect by now, it does when f is continuous and $\mathcal{M}$ is a reasonably nice surface. In Section 15.7 we developed the tools to make this statement precise in the case of a parameterized surface. When $\mathbf{r}(s, t)$ is a smooth parameterization of $\mathcal{M}$, a small rectangle of width Δs and height Δt in the parameter domain corresponds to a patch of area $\Delta S \approx \|\mathbf{r}_s \times \mathbf{r}_t\| \Delta s \Delta t$ on the surface. So we can write our Riemann sum as

$$\sum_{k=1}^{n} f(x_k, y_k, z_k)\, \Delta S_k \approx \sum_{k=1}^{n} f\big(\mathbf{r}(s_k, t_k)\big)\, \underbrace{\|\mathbf{r}_s \times \mathbf{r}_t\|}_{\text{Evaluated at } (s_k, t_k)}\, \Delta s_k \Delta t_k,$$

where (s_k, t_k) is some point in the kth rectangle of the mesh, which has a width of Δs_k and a height of Δt_k. When f is continuous, approximation becomes equality in the limit as the mesh size tends to zero, and the Riemann sum converges to a double integral. This fact is summarized below.

Suppose $\mathbf{r}(s, t)$ is a smooth, one-to-one parameterization of the surface $\mathcal{M}$ over the parameter domain R, and f is continuous on $\mathcal{M}$. Then the surface integral of f over $\mathcal{M}$ is

$$\iint_{\mathcal{M}} f\, dS = \iint_{R} f(\mathbf{r}(s, t))\, \|\mathbf{r}_s \times \mathbf{r}_t\|\, dA. \tag{8.1}$$

Surface integral of a scalar-valued function

Example 8.1. Determine $\iint_{\mathcal{M}} x^2 z\, dS$ when $\mathcal{M}$ is the upper half of the unit sphere.

Solution: We need a parameterization of $\mathcal{M}$ in order to perform this integral. In Example 7.9 we parameterized the unit sphere with $\mathbf{r}(s,t) = \langle \sin s \cos t, \sin s \sin t, \cos s \rangle$ so let's use that again. In this case we have only half of a sphere, so $s \in [0, \pi/2]$ and $t \in [0, 2\pi]$, which means that R is a rectangle in the st-plane. Since $\|\mathbf{r}_s \times \mathbf{r}_t\| = \sin s$ (see Example 7.9), this surface integral is

$$\iint_{\mathcal{M}} x^2 z \, dS = \iint_R \sin^2(s) \cos^2(t) \cos(s) \sin(s) \, dA$$

Now using Fubini's Theorem we can rewrite this double integral in the parameter domain as an iterated integral,

$$\iint_R (\sin^3 s \cos s \cos^2 t) \, dA = \int_0^{2\pi} \int_0^{\pi/2} (\sin^3 s \cos s \cos^2 t) \, ds \, dt$$

$$= \int_0^{2\pi} \left[\frac{1}{4} \cos^2 t \sin^4 s \right]_{s=0}^{s=\pi/2} dt = \int_0^{2\pi} \frac{1}{4} \cos^2(t) \, dt = \frac{\pi}{4}. \qquad \blacksquare$$

Surface integral of a scalar-valued function

Example 8.2. Suppose R is the triangular region in the Cartesian plane with vertices at the points $(0,0)$, $(3,0)$ and $(0,7)$. Determine $\iint_{\mathcal{M}} (1-z) \, dS$ when $\mathcal{M}$ is the portion of the plane $2x + 3y + z = 1$ that sits over R.

Solution: This surface is actually the graph of the function $f(x,y) = 1 - 2x - 3y$, which is clear when we write its defining equation as $z = 1 - 2x - 3y$. So we can parameterize it as $\mathbf{r}(x,y) = \langle x, y, f(x,y) \rangle$. This parameterization gives us

$$[\mathbf{r}_x \times \mathbf{r}_y](x,y) = \langle -f_x, -f_y, 1 \rangle = \langle 2, 3, 1 \rangle,$$

which has a magnitude of $\sqrt{14}$, so our surface integral is

$$\iint_{\mathcal{M}} (1-z) \, dS = \iint_R (2x + 3y) \sqrt{14} \, dA = \sqrt{14} \iint_R (2x + 3y) \, dA.$$

The region R is enclosed by a right triangle, the hypotenuse of which lies along the line $y = 7 - 7x/3$ (see Figure 8.2), so we can use Fubini's Theorem to rewrite our double integral as

$$\sqrt{14} \int_0^3 \int_0^{7-(7x/3)} (2x + 3y) \, dy \, dx = \sqrt{14} \int_0^3 \left[2xy + \frac{3}{2}y^2 \right]_{y=0}^{y=7-(7x/3)} dx$$

$$= \sqrt{14} \int_0^3 \left[\frac{147}{2} + \frac{7}{2}x^2 - 35x \right] dx = \frac{189}{2}. \qquad \blacksquare$$

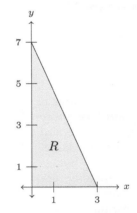

Figure 8.2: The region R for Example 8.2.

Surface integral

Example 8.3. Determine $\iint_{\mathcal{M}} (xz + y) \, dS$ when $\mathcal{M}$ is the surface parameterized by $\mathbf{r}(s,t) = \langle s + 2t, 4s - t, s + t \rangle$, and the parameter domain is the region in the st-plane between the s-axis and the parabola $t = 1 - s^2$, where $-1 \le s \le 1$.

Answer: $\frac{12}{35} \sqrt{107}$. $\blacksquare$

Solution On-line

❖ Flux Through a Parameterized Surface

In Section 15.6 we talked about the flux of an incompressible fluid through uncomplicated surfaces such as cylinders and spheres. Now we generalize that discussion to flows through parameterized surfaces by combining the ideas of Section 15.6 with the integration techniques developed above. As a preliminary step, we need to define the *orientation* of a parameterized surface.

▷ Orientation

Generally speaking, a surface is said to be **orientable** if there is a consistent, continuous way to define the unit normal vector to the surface at each point. Typically, there are two such options, each of which is called an **orientation**. For example, in Section 15.6 we chose to work with the outward-pointing normal vector to spheres and cylinders, and called that choice the *positive orientation*.

Of course, if all surfaces were *orientable* there'd be no need for us to define the word. One of the most famous non-orientable surfaces is the **Möbius strip**, an example of which is shown in Figure 8.3. You can make a facsimile of a Möbius strip for yourself by cutting a long, thin band of paper and connecting the ends after making a half-twist. To see why the surface is non-orientable, imagine that you could shrink yourself small enough to walk along the strip, as if it were a road. Use a pencil to mark your starting place on the strip, note which direction is "up" from your point of view, and then stroll down the "road" (trace the path with your finger). Eventually, you return to the starting point but on the *other* side of the strip. So by moving continuously over the strip, you've come back to the starting point but "up" is not the same direction as it was initially. This lack of consistency is what makes the Möbius strip non-orientable.

> **Note:** We referred to the half-twisted paper strip as a *facsimile* of a Möbius strip. That's because the paper has some physical thickness to it but the Möbius strip does not. So when your twisting promenade returns you to the starting point on the Möbius strip, it's not on the other side of the paper—it really is the same point.

▷ Flux Integrals

Much as you saw in Section 15.6, the flux of a vector field $\mathbf{F}$ through an oriented surface $\mathcal{M}$ is the surface integral of $\mathbf{F} \cdot \mathbf{n}$ over $\mathcal{M}$, where $\mathbf{n}$ is the unit normal to the surface. That is,

$$\text{the flux of } \mathbf{F} \text{ through } \mathcal{M} = \iint_{\mathcal{M}} \mathbf{F} \cdot \mathbf{n} \, dS$$

When $\mathbf{r}$ is a smooth parameterization of $\mathcal{M}$, we know that $\mathbf{r}_s \times \mathbf{r}_t$ is normal to the tangent plane at $\mathbf{r}(s,t)$, so we can write

$$\mathbf{n} = \pm \frac{\mathbf{r}_s \times \mathbf{r}_t}{\|\mathbf{r}_s \times \mathbf{r}_t\|},$$

where the choice of $\pm$ is determined by the orientation of $\mathcal{M}$. Unless otherwise specified, we'll always assume that $\mathbf{n}$ is defined as the positive. Now with the help of equation (8.1) we can write the flux of $\mathbf{F}$ through $\mathcal{M}$ as

$$\iint_{\mathcal{M}} \mathbf{F} \cdot \mathbf{n} \, dS = \iint_{R} \mathbf{F} \cdot \frac{\mathbf{r}_s \times \mathbf{r}_t}{\|\mathbf{r}_s \times \mathbf{r}_t\|} \, \|\mathbf{r}_s \times \mathbf{r}_t\| \, dA = \iint_{R} \mathbf{F} \cdot (\mathbf{r}_s \times \mathbf{r}_t) \, dA.$$

This equation is often expressed in terms of $\mathbf{n} \, dS$ and $d\mathbf{A} = \mathbf{r}_s(s,t) \times \mathbf{r}_t(s,t) \, dA$, which are called **area vectors**.

Flux Through a Parameterized Surface: Suppose $\mathcal{M}$ is an oriented surface, and $\mathbf{r}$ is a smooth, one-to-one parameterization of $\mathcal{M}$ over the parameter domain R. Further, suppose $\mathbf{F}$ is a continuous vector field on $\mathcal{M}$. Then the flux of $\mathbf{F}$ through $\mathcal{M}$ is

$$\iint_{\mathcal{M}} \mathbf{F} \cdot d\mathbf{S} = \iint_{R} \mathbf{F} \cdot d\mathbf{A},$$

where $d\mathbf{S} = \mathbf{n} \, dS$ and $d\mathbf{A} = \mathbf{r}_s(s,t) \times \mathbf{r}_t(s,t) \, dA$.

> The normal vector defines the direction "up," off of the surface. The surface of the Earth is orientable because, although the direction that you call "up" is not the same as that used by people on the other side of the planet, the direction "up" would change continuously if you were to move from here to there; and when you returned to your current position, the direction of "up" would be the same for you then as it is now.

Figure 8.3: An example of a Möbius strip.

> A point in space is not a physical object that occupies volume or has sides. It's just a location. The Möbius strip is a set of points on which there is no consistent way to define the direction of "up."

> The vector $\mathbf{r}_s \times \mathbf{r}_t$ is nonzero because $\mathbf{r}$ is regular

> In order to express the relevant ideas succinctly, we've suppressed the dependence of $\mathbf{F}$ on the parameters. So on the right-hand side of the equation, the notation $\mathbf{F}$ is shorthand for $\mathbf{F}(\mathbf{r}(s,t))$.

> This statement summarizes all of Section 15.6.

Flux integral through a parameterized surface

Example 8.4. Suppose R is the bounded region between the line $t = 4 - s$ and the curve $st = 3$ (see Figure 8.4), and $\mathcal{M}$ is parameterized by $\mathbf{r}(s,t) = \langle s^2, st, t^2 \rangle$ when $(s,t) \in R$. If x, y and z are measured in cm, determine the flux of the mass flow $\mathbf{F}(x,y,z) = \langle 3z, 2x, -4y \rangle \frac{\mathrm{g/sec}}{\mathrm{cm}^2}$ through $\mathcal{M}$.

Solution: As noted above, we are assuming that the vector $\mathbf{n}$ points in the direction of $\mathbf{r}_s \times \mathbf{r}_t$, so we begin by calculating $\mathbf{r}_s(s,t) = \langle 2s, t, 0 \rangle$ and $\mathbf{r}_t(s,t) = \langle 0, s, t^2 \rangle$. Then

$$\left[\mathbf{r}_s \times \mathbf{r}_t \right](s,t) = \langle t^3, -2st^2, 2s^2 \rangle,$$

so $d\mathbf{A} = \langle t^3, -2st^2, 2s^2 \rangle \, dA$. And since $x = s^2$, $y = st$ and $z = t^2$, the vector field $\mathbf{F}$ is $\langle 3t^2, 2s^2, -4st \rangle$. So the flux of $\mathbf{F}$ through $\mathcal{M}$ is

$$\iint_{\mathcal{M}} \mathbf{F} \cdot d\mathbf{S} = \iint_R \mathbf{F} \cdot d\mathbf{A} = \iint_R \langle 3t^2, 2s^2, -4st \rangle \cdot \langle t^3, -2st^2, 2s^2 \rangle \, dA$$

$$= \iint_R (3t^5 - 4s^3t^2 - 8s^3t) \, dA.$$

Since $\mathbf{F}$ has units of $\frac{\mathrm{g/sec}}{\mathrm{cm}^2}$ and $d\mathbf{S} = \mathbf{n} \, dS$ has units of cm^2 (dS is the area element), this integral has units of g/sec. Fubini's Theorem allows us to rewrite it as

$$\int_1^3 \int_{3/s}^{4-s} (3t^5 - 4s^3t^2 - 8s^3t) \, dt \, ds = -\frac{5356}{105} \frac{\mathrm{g}}{\mathrm{sec}}. \qquad \blacksquare$$

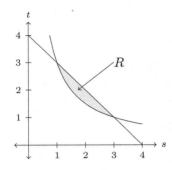

Figure 8.4:   The region R in Example 8.4.

As in previous sections, we understand the negative as indicating that $\mathbf{F}$ tends to flow through $\mathcal{M}$ in the direction opposite $\mathbf{n} = \mathbf{r}_s \times \mathbf{r}_t$.

Flux integral through a parameterized surface

Example 8.5. Suppose R is the bounded region between $t = 2s$ and $t = (s-4)^2$, and $\mathcal{M}$ is parameterized by $\mathbf{r}(s,t) = \langle s+1, s-t, s+3t \rangle$ over R. If x, y and z are measured in cm, determine the flux of $\mathbf{F}(x,y,z) = \langle 2z, -x, y \rangle \frac{\mathrm{g/sec}}{\mathrm{cm}^2}$ through $\mathcal{M}$.

Answer: $\iint_R (10s + 25t + 3) \, dA = 7668 \frac{\mathrm{g}}{\mathrm{sec}}$. $\blacksquare$

Solution On-line

You should know

- the term *orientable;*
- that the Möbius strip is an example of a non-orientable surface.

You should be able to

- calculate the integral of a scalar-valued function over a parameterized surface;
- calculate the flux of a vector field through a parameterized surface.

❖ **15.8 Skill Exercises**

In #1–4 compute the integral of f over the specified surface $\mathcal{M}$.

1. $f(x,y,z) = z \sin(x+y)$; $\mathcal{M}$ is the surface described by $z = 2\cos(x+y)$ over the bounded region in the xy-plane between the lines $y = -x$ and $y = \frac{\pi}{2} - x$ when $y \in [6, 10]$.

2. $f(x, y, z) = xy$; $\mathcal{M}$ is the surface described by $z = 5y^2 - x + 4$ over the triangular region in the xy-plane with vertices at $(0,0), (10, -2)$, and $(10, 5)$.

3. $f(x, y, z) = y + z$; $\mathcal{M}$ is the paraboloid $z = 4 - x^2 - y^2$ for $z \in [0, 4]$

4. $f(x, y, z) = xy$; $\mathcal{M}$ is the graph of $z = \ln(x) + y$ over the region in the xy-plane in which $x \in [1, e]$ and $0 \le y \le \sqrt{x}$. *(Hint: parameterize the surface using $x = e^t$ and $y = s$.)*

In #5–8 Compute the flux of $\mathbf{F}$ through the specified surface $\mathcal{M}$, which is oriented in the direction of $\mathbf{r}_s \times \mathbf{r}_t$.

5. $\mathbf{F}(x, y, z) = \langle -yz, -xz, -xy \rangle$; $\mathcal{M}$ is parameterized by $\mathbf{r}(s, t) = \langle s + 3t, s - t, 2t - s \rangle$ where the parameter domain is the bounded region in the third quadrant of the st-plane that lies between the curves $t - s^3 = 0$ and $t + s^{2/3} = 0$.

6. $\mathbf{F}(x, y, z) = \langle (3z - x - 20)e^{2x - z}, -21, 10 \rangle$; $\mathcal{M}$ is parameterized by $\mathbf{r}(s, t) = \langle 3s + 2t, 9s - t, s + 4t \rangle$ where the parameter domain is the bounded region in the second quadrant of the st-plane that lies between the curve $s = t^2 - 4t + 3$ and the line $s = 0$.

7. $\mathbf{F}(x, y, z) = \langle x, 4, 3 \rangle$; $\mathcal{M}$ is parameterized by $\mathbf{r}(s, t) = \langle e^{2t - s}, 8t + 1, 2 - 3s \rangle$ where the parameter domain is the triangle in the st-plane that lies between the lines $t = -1$, $t + s = 0$ and $t + 2s = 0$.

8. $\mathbf{F}(x, y, z) = \langle y, 0, y/z \rangle$; $\mathcal{M}$ is parameterized by $\mathbf{r}(s, t) = \langle t \ln(t) - t, \sqrt{1 + s^2}, ts \rangle$ where the parameter domain is the region in the first quadrant of the st-plane that lies between the curve $t^2 - s = 1$ and the line $t = 3$.

In #9–12 Use a computer algebra system to compute the integral of f over the specified surface $\mathcal{M}$.

CAS

9. $f(x, y, z) = x$; $\mathcal{M}$ is the elliptic paraboloid $z = x^2 + 3y^2$ over the triangle in the first quadrant bounded by the lines $y - x = 0$ and $x = 3$.

10. $f(x, y, z) = z$; $\mathcal{M}$ is the hyperbolic paraboloid $z = 4x^2 - y^2$ over the bounded region in the first quadrant that lies between the lines $y - x = 0$ and $4y - x = 0$, and the hyperbola $xy = 1$.

11. $f(x, y, z) = (2x - z)^2 + z + 4y^2$; $\mathcal{M}$ is parameterized by $\mathbf{r}(s, t) = \langle \sin(\pi s) + 2t, \cos(\pi s), 4t \rangle$, where the parameter domain is the bounded region in the st-plane that lies between $t = 1$ and $t = s^2 - 12$.

12. $f(x, y, z) = (z - 1)(y + 3)$; $\mathcal{M}$ is parameterized by $\mathbf{r}(s, t) = \langle \ln(st), 9t - 3, 4s + 1 \rangle$, where the parameter domain is the bounded region in the st-plane that lies between the curves $t = (s - 2)^2 + 1$ and $t = (s - 2)^3 + 1$.

In #13–16 Use a computer algebra system to compute the flux of $\mathbf{F}$ through the specified surface $\mathcal{M}$, which is oriented in the direction of $\mathbf{r}_s \times \mathbf{r}_t$.

CAS

13. $\mathbf{F}(x, y, z) = \langle (x - y)^{1/3}, z, 2 \rangle$; $\mathcal{M}$ is parameterized by $\mathbf{r}(s, t) = \langle 2t + s, t + s, 3s - 4t \rangle$ where the parameter domain is the bounded region in the third quadrant of the st-plane that lies between the curves $t = s^3$ and $t = s^5$.

14. $\mathbf{F}(x, y, z) = (10 + x + y)\mathbf{i}$; $\mathcal{M}$ is parameterized by $\mathbf{r}(s, t) = \langle 8s - t, 2s + t, s + t \rangle$ where the parameter domain is the bounded region in the first quadrant of the st-plane that lies between the curve $t = s^2 + 9$ and the line $t = 6s$.

15. $\mathbf{F}(x, y, z) = \mathbf{k}$; $\mathcal{M}$ is parameterized by $\mathbf{r}(s, t) = \langle e^s, te^t, s \rangle$ where the parameter domain is the bounded region in the upper half of the st-plane that lies between the circle $s^2 + t^2 = 1$ and the s-axis.

16. $\mathbf{F}(x, y, z) = \langle y, x, 4xyz\rangle$; $\mathcal{M}$ is parameterized by $\mathbf{r}(s, t) = \langle \sqrt{t}, \sqrt{s}, s + 4t\rangle$ where the parameter domain is the bounded region in the fourth quadrant of the st-plane that lies between the hyperbola $st = -1$ and the line $s - 5t = 6$.

❖ 15.8 Concept and Application Exercises

17. Suppose $\mathcal{M}$ is the surface parameterized by $\mathbf{r}(s, t) = \langle t - \sin 3t, 1 - \cos 3t, s\rangle$ where $s \in [0, 1]$ and $t \in [0, \pi]$. (a) Use a graphing utility to render $\mathcal{M}$, and (b) explain why it's a non-orientable surface.

18. The **Roman surface** is parameterized by $\mathbf{r}(\theta, \phi) = (\cos\theta\cos\phi\sin\phi)\mathbf{i} + (\sin\theta\cos\phi\sin\phi)\mathbf{j} + (\cos\theta\sin\theta\cos^2\phi)\mathbf{k}$. (a) Use a graphing utility to render this surface, and (b) explain why it's non-orientable. *(Hint: examine the surface near the x-axis.)*

19. The surface $\mathcal{M}$ is parameterized by $\mathbf{r}(s, t)$, where the parameter domain is the rectangle in which $s \in [2, 5]$ and $t \in [1, 3]$. Figure 8.5 shows a mesh of this rectangle. The value of $\|\mathbf{r}_s \times \mathbf{r}_t\|$ at one point in each sub-rectangle is shown in red (left), and the value of $f(\mathbf{r}(s, t))$ at that point is shown in blue (right). Use this information to approximate $\iint_{\mathcal{M}} f \, dS$.

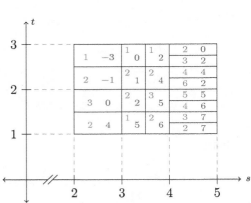

Figure 8.5: Parameter domain and data for #19.

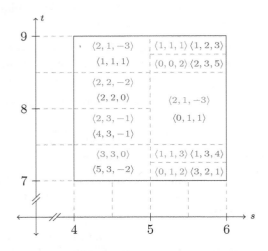

Figure 8.6: Parameter domain and data for #20.

20. The surface $\mathcal{M}$ is parameterized by $\mathbf{r}(s, t)$ and oriented according to $\mathbf{r}_s \times \mathbf{r}_t$, when $s \in [4, 6]$ and $t \in [7, 9]$. Figure 8.6 shows a mesh of this rectangle. The vector $\mathbf{r}_s \times \mathbf{r}_t$ at one point in each sub-rectangle is shown in red, and the vector $\mathbf{F}(\mathbf{r}(s, t))$ at that point is shown in blue. Use this information to approximate $\iint_{\mathcal{M}} \mathbf{F} \cdot d\mathbf{S}$.

21. Suppose x, y and z are measured in centimeters, and $\mathcal{M}$ is the graph of $f(x, y) = x^2 + 0.1y^2$, where $x \in [1, 2]$ and $y \in [1, 3]$. Determine the mass of $\mathcal{M}$ if the mass density on the surface is $\rho(x, y, z) = xy$ g/cm^2.

_____ | Mass Density |

22. Suppose x, y and z are measured in meters, and $\mathcal{M}$ is the surface $x = y^2 - 2z^2$, where $y \in [2, 5]$ and $z \in [1, 7]$. Determine the mass of $\mathcal{M}$ if the mass density on the surface is $\rho(x, y, z) = zy^3$ kg/m^2.

_____ | Mass Density |

23. Suppose x y and z in meters, and $\mathcal{M}$ is the surface parameterized by $\mathbf{r}(s, t) = \langle e^t + e^s, e^t - e^s, e^t - e^s\rangle$, where $t \in [1, 1.5]$ and $s \in [0, 1]$. Determine the net charge on $\mathcal{M}$ if the charge density at $\mathbf{r}(s, t)$ is e^{-t} coulombs per square meter.

_____ | Charge Density |

24. Suppose x, y and z are in mm, and $\mathcal{M}$ is the surface parameterized by $\mathbf{r}(s,t) = \langle 3s - t, t - 3s, st \rangle$, where the parameter domain is the triangle in the st-plane bounded by the lines $t = -s$, $t = 1$, and $s = 0$. Determine the net charge on $\mathcal{M}$ if the charge density at $\mathbf{r}(s,t)$ is $(s - t) \times 10^{-7}$ C/mm^2.

| Charge Density |

25. Suppose length is measured in centimeters, and $\mathcal{M}$ is the surface parameterized by $\mathbf{r}(s,t) = \langle 9s + t, 7s + t, 2s + 2t \rangle$, where the parameter domain is the bounded region in the st-plane enclosed by the lines $t - 7s = 0$ and $t + 14s = 21$, and the parabola $t = s^2 - 30$. Determine the total thermal energy in $\mathcal{M}$ if the energy density on the surface is $\rho(x,y,z) = 1 + x - y$ J/cm^2.

| Energy Density |

26. Suppose length is measured in millimeters and $\mathcal{M}$ is the surface parameterized by $\mathbf{r}(s,t) = \langle 4s + t, 5s - t, t^2 \rangle$, where the parameter domain is the bounded region in the first quadrant of the st-plane between the hyperbola $st = 5$ and the line $s + t = 6$. Determine the total thermal energy in $\mathcal{M}$ if the energy density on the surface is $\rho(x,y,z) = 4z$ J/mm^2.

| Energy Density |

The surfaces in #27–30 are oriented in the direction of $\mathbf{n} = \mathbf{r}_s \times \mathbf{r}_t$, and length on the surface is measured in centimeters.

27. Suppose $\mathcal{M}$ is the surface parameterized by $\mathbf{r}(s,t) = \langle st, e^t, s^2 \rangle$, where the parameter domain is the triangle in the st-plane bounded by the lines $t = 1$, $t - s = 0$ and $2t - s = 0$. If the mass flow of a fluid is $\mathbf{F}(x,y,z) = \langle \frac{x}{\sqrt{z}}, \ln y, 2\sqrt{z} \rangle \frac{\text{g/sec}}{\text{cm}^2}$, determine its flux through $\mathcal{M}$. Include correct units in your answer.

| Mass Flow |

28. Suppose $\mathcal{M}$ is parameterized by $\mathbf{r}(s,t) = \langle t + s, t - s, \ln(t/s) \rangle$, where the parameter domain is the bounded region between the lines $t = 8$ and $t - 2s = 0$, and the parabola $t = 8 - s^2$. If the mass flow of a fluid is $\mathbf{F}(x,y,z) = \langle 1, 1, xy \rangle \frac{\text{g/sec}}{\text{cm}^2}$, determine its flux through $\mathcal{M}$. Include correct units in your answer.

| Mass Flow |

29. Suppose $\mathcal{M}$ is the surface parameterized by $\mathbf{r}(s,t) = \langle s^t, t, e^s \rangle$, where $1 \le s \le 2$ and $0 \le t \le 3$. If the ambient electric field is $\mathbf{E}(x,y,z) = y\mathbf{k}$ newtons per coulomb, determine the flux of $\mathbf{E}$ through $\mathcal{M}$.

| Electric Field Flux |

30. Suppose $\mathcal{M}$ is the surface parameterized by $\mathbf{r}(s,t) = \langle s^2 + t^2, s^2 t, t^2 s \rangle$, where the parameter domain is the bounded region in the st-plane between the curves $t = \ln(s)$ and $st = e$, and the line $s = 1$. If a magnetic field is $\mathbf{B} = 8\mathbf{i} \, \frac{\text{V-sec}}{\text{cm}^2}$, determine the flux of $\mathbf{B}$ through $\mathcal{M}$.

| Magnetic Field Flux |

15.9   The Divergence Theorem

In Section 15.4 we discussed the flux of a vector field $\mathbf{F}$ across a simple, closed curve $\mathcal{C}$. The culmination of our discussion was Green's Theorem, which says

$$\oint_{\mathcal{C}} \mathbf{F} \cdot \mathbf{n} \, ds = \iint_{R} \operatorname{div}(\mathbf{F}) \, dA, \tag{9.1}$$

where R is the region enclosed by $\mathcal{C}$. The aim of this section is to develop an analog of equation (9.1) that applies to vector fields and surfaces in 3-space.

> **Key Idea(s):**   *The Divergence Theorem is an extension of the flux-divergence form of Green's Theorem. It relates the flux of a vector field across a surface in 3-space to the triple integral of the field's divergence over the region bounded by that surface.*
>
> *We can determine the rate at which fluid is produced in a region by measuring the rate at which it spills across the boundary.*

❖ Preliminary Ideas

In order to extend the flux-divergence form of Green's Theorem into 3-space, we need to understand what divergence means for vector fields in three dimensions, and we need to define the analog of a closed curve, which we'll call a *closed surface*.

▷ Divergence of a vector field in space

In Section 15.4 we defined the divergence of $\mathbf{F} = \langle L, M \rangle$ to be $\operatorname{div}(\mathbf{F}) = \nabla \cdot \mathbf{F} = L_x + M_y$. Similarly, here we define the **divergence** of $\mathbf{F} = \langle L, M, N \rangle$ to be

$$\operatorname{div}(\mathbf{F}) = \nabla \cdot \mathbf{F} = L_x + M_y + N_z$$

when L_x, M_y and N_z exist.

Divergence of a vector field

Example 9.1. Determine a formula for the divergence of $\mathbf{F} = \langle x^2, 8yz, 9yz^3 \rangle$.

Solution: The divergence of $\mathbf{F}$ is

$$\nabla \cdot \mathbf{F} = \langle \partial_x, \partial_y, \partial_z \rangle \cdot \langle x^2, 8yz, 9yz^3 \rangle$$

$$= \frac{\partial}{\partial x}(x^2) + \frac{\partial}{\partial y}(8yz) + \frac{\partial}{\partial z}(9yz^3) = 2x + 8z + 27yz^2. \qquad \blacksquare$$

The algebraic properties of the divergence that you learned in in Section 15.4 are the same for vector fields in 3-space (the proofs differ only in the presence of a third component).

Properties of Divergence: Suppose k is a scalar, and the first partial derivatives of the vector fields $\mathbf{F}$ and $\mathbf{G}$ exist, as do those of the scalar-valued function f. Then

$$\nabla \cdot (k\mathbf{F}) = k(\nabla \cdot \mathbf{F}) \tag{9.2}$$

$$\nabla \cdot (\mathbf{F} + \mathbf{G}) = (\nabla \cdot \mathbf{F}) + (\nabla \cdot \mathbf{G}) \tag{9.3}$$

$$\nabla \cdot (f\mathbf{F}) = (f)(\nabla \cdot \mathbf{F}) + (\nabla f) \cdot \mathbf{F} \tag{9.4}$$

▷ Closed surfaces

Consider the surface of a solid ball, or a solid cube, or a solid cylinder. These surfaces do not have boundary curves that delimit them, and they effectively separate 3-space into two regions (one enclosed by the surface, and the other outside it). Such surfaces are said to be **closed**, and we say that a closed surface has a **positive orientation** if its unit normal points into the unbounded part of 3-space (i.e., away from the enclosed solid) at all points where it's defined.

Closed surfaces need not be smooth, but most of the surfaces that arise in applications are **piecewise-smooth**, by which we mean that the surface is composed of smooth surfaces that have been joined at their boundaries (see Figure 9.1).

❖ The Divergence Theorem

Now that we understand the idea of a closed surface, and the notation $\nabla \cdot \mathbf{F}$, we can state our extension of the flux-divergence form of Green's Theorem (a proof is included in the End Notes).

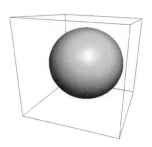

> **Divergence Theorem:** Suppose $\mathcal{M}$ is a positively oriented, piecewise-smooth, closed surface that encloses a solid region E, and $\mathbf{F}$ is a smooth vector field in an open region that contains E. Then
>
> $$\iint_{\mathcal{M}} \mathbf{F} \cdot \mathbf{n} \, dS = \iiint_{E} \operatorname{div}(\mathbf{F}) \, dV, \qquad (9.5)$$
>
> where $\mathbf{n}$ is the outward-pointing, unit normal vector to $\mathcal{M}$.

Equation (9.5) is often expressed in terms of the area vector $d\mathbf{S} = \mathbf{n} \, dS$,

$$\iint_{\mathcal{M}} \mathbf{F} \cdot d\mathbf{S} = \iiint_{E} \nabla \cdot \mathbf{F} \, dV.$$

Verifying the Divergence Theorem

Example 9.2. Verify the Divergence Theorem when $\mathbf{F} = \langle x^2, 2y^5, 3z \rangle$ and E is the cube in the first octant in which x, y and z vary between 0 and 1.

Solution: We begin by calculating the flux density, $\mathbf{F} \cdot \mathbf{n}$, on each face of the cube:

$x = 0$, the flux density is $\mathbf{F} \cdot (-\mathbf{i}) = 0$; $x = 1$, the flux density is $\mathbf{F} \cdot \mathbf{i} = 1$;

$y = 0$, the flux density is $\mathbf{F} \cdot (-\mathbf{j}) = 0$; $y = 1$, the flux density is $\mathbf{F} \cdot \mathbf{j} = 2$;

$z = 0$, the flux density is $\mathbf{F} \cdot (-\mathbf{k}) = 0$; $z = 1$, the flux density is $\mathbf{F} \cdot \mathbf{k} = 3$.

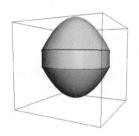

Figure 9.1: (top) A sphere is a closed surface; (middle) this parabolic surface is not closed, and you can see its boundary; (bottom) a piecewise-smooth, closed surface made by joining two paraboloids with a cylindrical ring.

Each of these faces has an area of 1 square unit , so

$$\iint_{\mathcal{M}} \mathbf{F} \cdot \mathbf{n} \, dS = \iint_{x=1} \mathbf{F} \cdot \mathbf{n} \, dS + \iint_{y=1} \mathbf{F} \cdot \mathbf{n} \, dS + \iint_{z=1} \mathbf{F} \cdot \mathbf{n} \, dS$$
$$= 1 \, (1) + 2 \, (1) + 3 \, (1) = 6.$$

On the other hand, we see that

$$\iiint_{E} \operatorname{div}(\mathbf{F}) \, dV = \int_{0}^{1} \int_{0}^{1} \int_{0}^{1} (2x + 10y^4 + 3) \, dx \, dy \, dz = 6. \qquad \blacksquare$$

Using the Divergence Theorem

Example 9.3. Determine the flux of $\mathbf{F} = \langle 3x, 8z, 17y \rangle$ across the sphere $\rho = 5$.

Solution: If E is the solid ball enclosed by the sphere, $\mathcal{M}$, the Divergence Theorem tells us that the flux of $\mathbf{F}$ across $\mathcal{M}$ is

> We could calculate this integral using the methods of Section 15.6, but the Divergence Theorem is easier!

$$\iint_{\mathcal{M}} \mathbf{F} \cdot d\mathbf{S} = \iiint_{E} \nabla \cdot \mathbf{F} \, dV = \iiint_{E} \left(\frac{\partial}{\partial x}(3x) + \frac{\partial}{\partial y}(8z) + \frac{\partial}{\partial z}(17y) \right) dV$$

$$= \iiint_{E} \left(3 + 0 + 0 \right) dV = \iiint_{E} 3 \, dV = 500\pi. \qquad \blacksquare$$

Using the Divergence Theorem

Example 9.4. Suppose E is the bounded region shown in Figure 9.2, which is enclosed by the planes $z = 0$, $z = 1$ and the cylinder of radius 1 about the z-axis, and $\mathcal{M}$ is the boundary of E. Determine whether the net flux of $\mathbf{F} = \langle -3y, 2x^5, 1 + z^2 \rangle$ across $\mathcal{M}$ is positive or negative.

Solution: We could calculate $\iint_{\mathcal{M}} \mathbf{F} \cdot d\mathbf{S}$ by separating $\mathcal{M}$ into three surfaces (the base, the cylindrical wall, and the top) and calculating the flux across each, but there's no need. The Divergence Theorem tells us that

$$\iint_{\mathcal{M}} \mathbf{F} \cdot \mathbf{n} \, dS = \iiint_E \operatorname{div}(\mathbf{F}) \, dV = \iiint_E 2z \, dV,$$

which is positive since $z \geq 0$ in E.   ∎

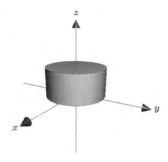

Figure 9.2: The region E for Example 9.4.

▷ Applications of the Divergence Theorem

As in Section 15.4, when $\mathbf{F}$ is the mass flow of an incompressible fluid, its divergence can be understood as measuring the rate at which fluid is absorbed or injected into the flow at a point (per unit of volume). For example, if length is measured in centimeters, and the mass flow $\mathbf{F}$ has units of $\frac{\text{g}}{\text{sec}}$ per square centimeter,

$$\text{the units of } \nabla \cdot \mathbf{F} \text{ are } \left(\frac{1}{\text{cm}} \right) \left(\frac{\text{g/sec}}{\text{cm}^2} \right) = \frac{\text{g/sec}}{\text{cm}^3}. \quad \begin{array}{l} \leftarrow \text{ rate of fluid injection} \\ \leftarrow \text{ per unit volume} \end{array}$$

In this context, the left-hand side of equation (9.5) is the net rate at which the fluid mass exits E. If that's positive, there must be a source inside E that's injecting fluid into the flow. The right-hand side calculates the rate at which that happens. So equation (9.5) says that the excess flow across the boundary is exactly the amount that was injected by the source.

By contrast, when $\mathbf{F}$ is the velocity field of a compressible fluid, like a gas, the flux across a closed surface could be positive not because gas is being produced but because it's expanding. This is how we interpret $\nabla \cdot \mathbf{F} > 0$ in a region. Similarly, we understand the gas to be contracting where $\nabla \cdot \mathbf{F}$ is negative.

Flow of a compressible fluid

Example 9.5. Suppose the velocity field of a gas is $\mathbf{F} = \langle z, -z, 0 \rangle$. Calculate $\nabla \cdot \mathbf{F}$ and interpret the result.

Solution: The divergence of $\mathbf{F}$ is $\nabla \cdot \mathbf{F} = \partial_x(z) + \partial_y(-z) + \partial_z(0) = 0$. The Divergence Theorem tells us that for any small sphere E, with boundary $\mathcal{M}$,

$$\iint_{\mathcal{M}} F \cdot d\mathbf{S} = \iiint_E \nabla \cdot F \, dV = \iiint_E 0 \, dV = 0.$$

Because the left-hand side is the net flow of the gas out of E, which can be arbitrarily small, this equation says the gas is neither expanding nor contracting at any point. This makes sense since $\mathbf{F}$ is a laminar flow in which the gas at each value of z is all moving in the same direction at the same speed (see Figure 9.3).   ∎

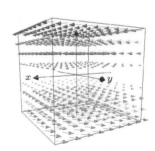

Figure 9.3: The laminar velocity field in Example 9.5.

The equation $\nabla \cdot \nabla f = 0$ arises in the mathematical description of diffusion (see the projects in Chapter 14). Functions f for which $\nabla \cdot \nabla f = 0$ are said to be **harmonic**, and in the next example we use the Divergence Theorem to show that they are uniquely determined by their value on closed and bounded surfaces.

Uniqueness of the solution to $\nabla \cdot \nabla f = 0$

Example 9.6. Suppose $h(x, y, z)$ is defined on the piecewise-smooth, closed surface $\mathcal{M}$. Show that if there's a function that's harmonic throughout the enclosed region E and that equals h on $\mathcal{M}$, there's *only* one.

Solution: Suppose there were two such functions, f and g. Our job is to show that althou... ...mulas of f and g might *appear* to be different, the functions would actuall... ...gy is to show that their difference is constant in E, wh... ...$-g) = \mathbf{0}$ throughout E. Then because the differ- ence i... ...uous, the difference must be 0 throughout all of E.

T... ...roughout E, we're going to combine two equations. First,...

$$V = \iiint_E \|\nabla f - \nabla g\|^2 \, dV$$
$$= \iiint_E (\nabla f - \nabla g) \cdot (\nabla f - \nabla g) \, dV. \qquad (9.6)$$

Se... ...that divergence obeys the Product Rule, so

$$\iiint_E \nabla \cdot \left[(f-g)(\nabla f - \nabla g)\right] dV = \iiint_E \left[(f-g) \, \nabla \cdot (\nabla f - \nabla g) + \nabla(f-g) \cdot (\nabla f - \nabla g)\right] dV$$

$$= \iiint_E \left[(f-g) \, (\nabla \cdot (\nabla f) - \nabla \cdot (\nabla g)) + (\nabla f - \nabla g) \cdot (\nabla f - \nabla g)\right] dV$$

Because $\nabla \cdot (\nabla f) = 0$ and $\nabla \cdot (\nabla g) = 0$, this reduces to

$$\iiint_E \nabla \cdot \left[(f-g)(\nabla f - \nabla g)\right] dV = \iiint_E (\nabla f - \nabla g) \cdot (\nabla f - \nabla g) \, dV \qquad (9.7)$$

Notice that the right-hand sides of equations (9.6) and (9.7) are the same. That means their left-hand sides are too, so

$$\iiint_E \nabla \cdot \left[(f-g)(\nabla f - \nabla g)\right] dV = \iiint_E \|\nabla(f-g)\|^2 \, dV.$$

The Divergence Theorem allows us to rewrite the left-hand side as an integral over $\mathcal{M}$, after which the equation becomes

$$\iint_\mathcal{M} (f-g) \, \nabla(f-g) \cdot d\mathbf{S} = \iiint_E \|\nabla(f-g)\|^2 \, dV.$$

The left-hand side is zero since $(f-g) = (h-h) = 0$ on $\mathcal{M}$, so now we know that

$$0 = \iiint_E \|\nabla(f-g)\|^2 \, dV.$$

Since $\|\nabla(f-g)\|^2$ is continuous and non-negative, it must be 0 throughout E. ∎

▷ The Divergence Theorem and the Fundamental Theorem of Calculus

Let's define the 1-dimensional vector field $\mathbf{F} = f(x)\mathbf{i}$ along the x-axis and apply the Divergence Theorem on the interval $[a, b]$. The outward normal vector at $x = b$ is $\mathbf{n} = \mathbf{i}$, and at $x = a$ is $\mathbf{n} = -\mathbf{i}$, so the flux of $\mathbf{F}$ across the boundary of $[a, b]$ is

$$\mathbf{F} \cdot \mathbf{n}(b) + \mathbf{F} \cdot \mathbf{n}(a) = f(b) - f(a).$$

It follows from the Divergence Theorem that

$$\mathbf{F} \cdot \mathbf{n}(b) + \mathbf{F} \cdot \mathbf{n}(a) = \int_a^b \nabla \cdot \mathbf{F} \, dx$$

$$f(b) - f(a) = \int_a^b f'(x) \, dx,$$

which you'll recognize as the Fundamental Theorem of Calculus from Chapter 5.

You should know

- the terms *closed surface, piecewise-smooth surface, positive orientation (of a closed surface),* and *divergence;*
- the notation $\nabla \cdot \mathbf{F}$ and $\text{div}(\mathbf{F})$;
- that the Divergence Theorem is an extension of Green's Theorem (flux-divergence form) to regions in 3-space;
- the algebraic properties of divergence.

You should be able to

- determine the divergence of a vector field $\mathbf{F}$
- interpret $\text{div}(\mathbf{F})$ when $\mathbf{F}$ describes a fluid flow;
- use the Divergence Theorem to rewrite surface integrals of vector fields as triple integrals.

❖ 15.9 Skill Exercises

Calculate the specified divergence in #1–6 using $\mathbf{F}(x,y,z) = \langle xz, ye^x, z - y \rangle$ and $\mathbf{G}(x,y,z) = \langle y - 3z, x\sin(y), x^2 - z^2 \rangle$

1. $\nabla \cdot \mathbf{F}$ 3. $\nabla \cdot (-3\mathbf{G})$ 5. $\nabla \cdot (2\mathbf{F} - 3\mathbf{G})$

2. $\nabla \cdot \mathbf{G}$ 4. $\nabla \cdot (0.5\mathbf{F})$ 6. $\nabla \cdot (5\mathbf{F} + 2\mathbf{G})$

Exercises #7 –12 refer to $f(x,y,z) = z^2 - y$, $g(x,y,z) = x - yz$ and $h(x,y,z) = x$, and $\mathbf{F}$ and $\mathbf{G}$ as defined for #1–6. Determine a formula for the divergence.

7. $\nabla \cdot f\mathbf{F}$ 9. $\nabla \cdot (f(\mathbf{F} - \mathbf{G}))$ 11. $\nabla \cdot ((h - g)\mathbf{F})$

8. $\nabla \cdot g\mathbf{G}$ 10. $\nabla \cdot (g(\mathbf{F} + \mathbf{G}))$ 12. $\nabla \cdot ((h + g)\mathbf{G})$

In #13–18 calculate the net flux through the given surface by using (a) the surface integral of $\mathbf{F} \cdot d\mathbf{S}$, and (b) using the Divergence Theorem. In #13–16, $\mathcal{M}$ is the surface of the specified rectangular box.

13. $\mathbf{F}(x,y,z) = \langle 3x, 7y, 2z \rangle$; $x, y, z \in [0,1]$.

14. $\mathbf{F}(x,y,z) = \langle -4x, y, 9z \rangle$; $x \in [0,2], y \in [0,5]$ and $z \in [0,3]$

15. $\mathbf{F}(x,y,z) = \langle x^2 + 3y, 8xy, 3z^2y \rangle$; $x \in [1,5]$, $y \in [2,3]$ and $z \in [4,6]$.

16. $\mathbf{F}(x,y,z) = \langle 4xy, -xy^2, yz^3 - 5xy \rangle$; $x \in [2,3]$, $y \in [1,3]$ and $z \in [0,4]$.

17. $\mathbf{F}(x,y,z) = \langle 3 + 8x, 2xz, 4 + z^2 \rangle$; $\mathcal{M}$ is the surface of the tetrahedron in the first octant defined by the plane $x + y + z = 1$.

18. $\mathbf{F}(x, y, z) = \langle yx^3 + y, 4y - 7z, y + x \rangle$; $\mathcal{M}$ is the surface of the tetrahedron with vertices at $(0, 0, 0)$, $(1, 0, 0)$, $(0, -1, 0)$ and $(0, 0, -1)$.

In #19–24 the surface $\mathcal{M}$ is the boundary of the specified region V. Determine the net flux of $\mathbf{F}$ through $\mathcal{M}$ by using the Divergence Theorem.

19. $\mathbf{F}(x, y, z) = \langle 3x + z^2, 4x^2 y, 9z + xy \rangle$; R is the bounded region in Figure 9.4; V is the volume over R that extends between $z = 2$ and $z = 18$.

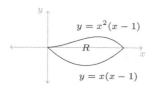
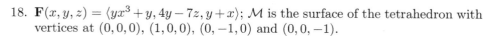

20. $\mathbf{F}(x, y, z) = \langle 7yz, 8x^2, 9xz \rangle$; R is the bounded region in Figure 9.5; V is the volume over R that extends between $z = 2$ and $z = 18$

Figure 9.4: The region for R #19 lies between the curves.

21. $\mathbf{F}(x, y, z) = \langle x + 1, 3y, 9z + 2 \rangle$; R is the disk of radius 1 about the origin in the yz-plane; V is the volume over R between $x = 1 - y^2 - z^2$ and $x = 0.5(3 - y)(4 - z)$

22. $\mathbf{F}(x, y, z) = \langle 7xy + 2, xyz, z - yz \rangle$; R is the triangle in the xz-plane connecting $(0, 0, 0)$, $(1, 0, 0)$ and $(0, 0, 1)$; V is the volume over R between $y = 2 + x$ and $y = 1 - 4z^2$

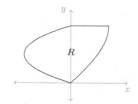

23. $\mathbf{F}(x, y, z) = \langle x^3, y^3, z^3 \rangle$; V is the bounded volume between the cone $z^2 = 4x^2 + 4y^2$ and the paraboloid $z = 3 - x^2 - y^2$

24. $\mathbf{F}(x, y, z) = \langle 1 - x^3, 3y + x^5, 4x - z^3 \rangle$; V is the bounded volume between the cone $y = -3\sqrt{x^2 + z^2}$ and the sphere of radius 3 centered at the origin

Figure 9.5: The region R for #20 is bounded by $y = \pi/2$, $x = y(2y - \pi)$ and $x = \arcsin y$.

❖ 15.9 Concept and Application Exercises

25. Suppose $\mathcal{M}_1$ is the sphere of radius 1 that's centered at the origin; $\mathcal{M}_2$ is the surface of the $1 \times 1 \times 1$ cube centered at the point $(1, 3, 2)$; $\mathcal{M}_3$ is the surface of the bounded region between the plane $z = -1$ and the paraboloid $z = -4 + x^2 + 3y^2$. All three surfaces are positively oriented. If $\mathbf{F} = \langle 4y, 2z + x, x - z^2 \rangle$, put the following flux integrals in order from least to greatest:

$$\iint_{\mathcal{M}_1} \mathbf{F} \cdot d\mathbf{S}, \quad \iint_{\mathcal{M}_2} \mathbf{F} \cdot d\mathbf{S}, \quad \iint_{\mathcal{M}_3} \mathbf{F} \cdot d\mathbf{S}.$$

26. Suppose $\mathcal{M}_1$ is the positively oriented half of the sphere $\rho = 1$ for which $z \geq 0$, and S_2 is the disk $x^2 + y^2 \leq 1$ ($z = 0$) with $\mathbf{n} = -\mathbf{k}$. If $\mathbf{F} = \langle a, b, c \rangle$ is constant and $\iint_{\mathcal{M}_2} \mathbf{F} \cdot d\mathbf{S} = 7.2$, determine the value of $\iint_{\mathcal{M}_1} \mathbf{F} \cdot d\mathbf{S}$.

27. Suppose $\mathbf{F}$ is a smooth vector field and $\nabla \cdot \mathbf{F} = 2$ at the origin. If $f(s)$ is the flux of $\mathbf{F}$ through the positively oriented surface of the $s \times s \times s$ cube centered at the origin, sketch an approximation of the graph of f for small values of s.

28. Suppose that $\mathbf{F}(x, y, z) = f(r)\langle -y, x, 0 \rangle$ where $r = \sqrt{x^2 + y^2}$.

   (a) Describe the level surfaces of $f(r)$ in $\mathbb{R}^3$.
   (b) Describe the orientation of ∇f and its relationship to $\langle -y, x, 0 \rangle$.
   (c) Use property (9.4) and part (b) to show that $\nabla \cdot \mathbf{F} = 0$.

29. When a current of I amps flows along the z-axis in the $\mathbf{k}$ direction (positive charges head in the direction of $\mathbf{k}$, or equivalently, negative charges flow in the direction of $-\mathbf{k}$) it induces a magnetic field:

$$\mathbf{B}(x, y, z) = \frac{\mu_0 I}{2\pi (x^2 + y^2)} \langle -y, x, 0 \rangle,$$

where $\mu_0 = 4\pi \times 10^7$ is called the *permeability of free space*. Suppose the closed, piecewise-smooth, surface $\mathcal{M}$ does not intersect the z-axis. Prove that the magnetic flux through $\mathcal{M}$ is 0.

| Induced Magnetic Field |

30. In Example 6.9 of Section 15.6 we proved **Gauss's Law** for spheres. Suppose $\mathbf{E} = \frac{1}{4\pi\varepsilon_0}\frac{q}{\|\mathbf{r}\|^2}\hat{\mathbf{r}}$, as in that example.

| Electric Field Flux |

   (a) Prove that $\nabla \cdot \mathbf{E} = 0$ away from the origin.

   (b) Prove that the flux of $\mathbf{E}$ through any piecewise-smooth, simple, closed surface is q/ε_0.

31. Suppose you take a typical kitchen sponge and lay it on the counter top, then cover it with your hand and push gently so that the sponge is compressed to 75% of its original thickness. Now suppose that $\mathbf{F}$ is a vector field in the original, uncompressed sponge that shows the displacement of each point under the applied pressure. In complete sentences, explain what you expect to be true of $\nabla \cdot \mathbf{F}$, and why.

| Everyday Divergence |

32. Suppose the density of a fluid changes with position, and because the fluid is flowing, with time, we have $\rho(x, y, z, t)$. In this exercise we'll denote the velocity field of the fluid by $\mathbf{v}$, and the divergence operator "∇" will refer only to differentiation in the spacial variables.

| Fluid Flow |

   (a) Use the Chain Rule to show that the density at P_0 changes at a rate of $\frac{d\rho}{dt} = \rho_t + \nabla\rho \cdot \mathbf{v}$.

   (b) Use the properties of divergence to show that the formula in part (a) is the same as $\frac{d\rho}{dt} = \rho_t + \nabla \cdot (\rho\mathbf{v}) - \rho\nabla \cdot \mathbf{v}$.

   (c) Suppose R is a region through which fluid is passing. Use the Divergence Theorem to explain why $\iiint_R \nabla \cdot (\rho\mathbf{v})\, dV$ describes the rate at which the mass of fluid in R is changing due to the flow of the fluid.

   (d) Based on part (c), explain the equation

$$\frac{d}{dt}\iiint_R \rho\, dV = -\iiint_R \nabla \cdot (\rho\mathbf{v})\, dV$$

   paying special attention to the negative sign on the right-hand side.

   (e) When we pass the time derivative through the triple-integral on the left-hand side of the previous equation (which is legitimate in certain cases), it becomes

$$\iiint_R \rho_t\, dV = -\iiint_R \nabla \cdot (\rho\mathbf{v})\, dV.$$

   Use this fact to explain why, when both integrands are continuous, this leads to the equation $\rho_t = -\nabla \cdot (\rho\mathbf{v})$.

   (f) Use parts (b) and (e) to verify that $\rho\nabla \cdot \mathbf{v} + \frac{d\rho}{dt} = 0$.

33. Suppose $\mathbf{F}(x, y, z) = \langle x, y, z \rangle$ and R is an open region in $\mathbb{R}^3$ with a smooth boundary surface $\mathcal{M}$. Show that the volume of R is $\iint_{\mathcal{M}} \mathbf{F} \cdot d\mathbf{S}$.

34. Suppose that $\mathcal{M}$ is a piecewise-smooth, closed surface and $f_{xx} + f_{yy} + f_{zz} = 0$. Show that the flux of ∇f across $\mathcal{M}$ is 0.

| Mathematics |

35. The symbol Δ is often used to denote the **Laplacian** operator, which acts on functions as follows: $\Delta f = f_{xx} + f_{yy} + f_{zz}$. Show that $\Delta f = \nabla \cdot \nabla f$.

| Mathematics |

15.10   Stokes' Theorem

Key Idea(s):   *Stokes' Theorem is an extension of Green's Theorem, and relates the circulation of a vector field around a curve to the double integral of its curl over the bounded surface.*

In Section 15.5 we discussed the circulation of $\mathbf{F} = \langle L, M \rangle$ around a positively oriented, simple, closed curve $\mathcal{C}$ that encloses a region R. The culmination of our discussion was Green's Theorem, which says

$$\oint_{\mathcal{C}} \mathbf{F} \cdot \mathbf{T} = \iint_{R} (M_x - L_y) \, dA. \tag{10.1}$$

In this section we develop an analog of equation (10.1) that applies to curves in 3-space and the surfaces they delimit. To do it, we'll extend our understanding of scalar curl to a vector that we'll call the *curl.*

❖ The Curl of a Vector Field in Space

When we first discussed equation (10.1) in Section 15.5, we thought of $\mathbf{F}$ as a field of 2-vectors, $L\mathbf{i} + M\mathbf{j}$. Now let's consider $\mathbf{F} = L\mathbf{i} + M\mathbf{j} + N\mathbf{k}$. Because $\mathcal{C}$ lies in the xy-plane, the vector $\mathbf{T}$ is orthogonal to $\mathbf{k}$, so $\mathbf{F} \cdot \mathbf{T}$ involves only L and M, just as before. And the equality of the line integral to the double integral follows in the same fashion as before. In short, nothing changes.

See the discussion that accompanies Figure 5.3 in Section 15.5.

Now consider the circulation of $\mathbf{F}$ around a positively oriented curve in the yz-plane, as shown in the right-hand image of Figure 10.1. In that case, the value of $\mathbf{F} \cdot \mathbf{T}$ depends on only M and N, and the spacial variables are y and z, so the analog of equation (10.1) is

$$\oint_{\mathcal{C}} \mathbf{F} \cdot \mathbf{T} \, ds = \iint_{R} (N_y - M_z) \, dA. \tag{10.2}$$

The analog of equation (10.1) is slightly different in the xz-plane. Instead of integrating $N_x - L_z$ over R, we find that

$$\oint_{\mathcal{C}} \mathbf{F} \cdot d\mathbf{r} = \iint_{R} (L_z - N_x) \, dA. \tag{10.3}$$

The reasons for this modification are subtle, but perhaps you can get an intuitive understanding based on Figure 10.2, in which the left-hand image shows a curve and a vector field in the xz-plane, as seen from a vantage point with a positive y-coordinate. Notice that the positive x-axis points "left" instead of "right," as if the coordinate system is a mirror image of what we expect to see. The right-hand image of Figure 10.2 shows a reflection of the plane in which the positive x-axis extends to the right, as usual, but notice that the curve now has a *negative* orientation relative

The images in Figure 10.1 are seen from a positive x-coordinate, and a positive y-coordinate respectively.

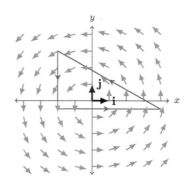
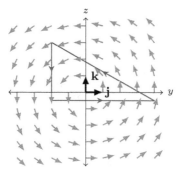

Figure 10.1: Circulation around a positively orientated curve (left) in the xy-plane as seen from a vantage point with a positive z-coordinate; (right) in the yz-plane as seen from a vantage point with a positive x-coordinate.

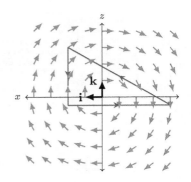 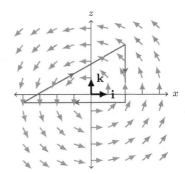

Figure 10.2: (left) Seen from a vantage point with a positive y-coordinate, the blue triangle has a positive orientation relative to the enclosed region, but the positive direction of the x-axis is unusual; (right) the same vector field and triangle but seen from a vantage point with a negative y-coordinate.

to the region it bounds. In short, this leads to a double integrand that's the *opposite* of what you might expect.

The integrands of the double integrals in equations (10.1)–(10.3) are often sorted according to the normal vector of the associated plane, and collected in a single vector called the ***curl*** of $\mathbf{F}$. Specifically, the curl of $\mathbf{F} = \langle L, M, N \rangle$ is

$$\text{curl}(\mathbf{F}) = \begin{bmatrix} N_y - M_z \\ L_z - N_x \\ M_x - L_y \end{bmatrix} \begin{matrix} \leftarrow \text{from eq. (10.2); } \mathbf{i} \text{ is normal to the } yz\text{-plane} \\ \leftarrow \text{from eq. (10.3); } \mathbf{j} \text{ is normal to the } xz\text{-plane} \\ \leftarrow \text{from eq. (10.1); } \mathbf{k} \text{ is normal to the } xy\text{-plane} \end{matrix} \qquad (10.4)$$

> Note that the third component of curl($\mathbf{F}$) is the scalar curl from Section 15.5.

At a symbolic level, when ∂_x is understood as an instruction to differentiate with respect to x (likewise for ∂_y and ∂_z), and we treat $\nabla = \langle \partial_x, \partial_y, \partial_z \rangle$ as a vector, we find that

$$\nabla \times \mathbf{F} = \begin{vmatrix} \mathbf{i} & \mathbf{j} & \mathbf{k} \\ \partial_x & \partial_y & \partial_z \\ L & M & N \end{vmatrix} = \begin{bmatrix} N_y - M_z \\ L_z - N_x \\ M_x - L_y \end{bmatrix} = \text{curl}(\mathbf{F}), \qquad (10.5)$$

> Alternatively, you can use the matrix-action method to calculate $\nabla \times \mathbf{F}$, by letting
>
> $$\begin{bmatrix} 0 & -\partial_z & \partial_y \\ \partial_z & 0 & -\partial_x \\ -\partial_y & \partial_x & 0 \end{bmatrix}$$
>
> act on the vector $\langle L, M, N \rangle$.

which many people find easier to remember than equation (10.4). The vector curl($\mathbf{F}$) allows us to consolidate equations (10.1)–(10.3) into a single statement.

> Stokes' Theorem, which you'll see later in this section, extends this result to non-planar curves.

Suppose $\mathbf{F} = \langle L, M, N \rangle$ is a smooth vector field, and $\mathcal{C}$ is a positively oriented, piecewise-smooth, simple, closed curve in either the xy-, yz-, or xz-plane. Then

$$\oint_{\mathcal{C}} \mathbf{F} \cdot d\mathbf{r} = \iint_R \text{curl}(\mathbf{F}) \cdot \mathbf{n} \, dA, \qquad (10.6)$$

where R is the planar region enclosed by $\mathcal{C}$ and $\mathbf{n}$ is one of $\mathbf{i}, \mathbf{j}$ or $\mathbf{k}$, as appropriate.

Calculating a curl vector

Example 10.1. Determine curl($\mathbf{F}$) when $\mathbf{F} = \langle 3x + y^2, 4y + z^8, 2z + x^3 \rangle$.

Solution: Equation (10.4) tells us that

$$\text{curl}(\mathbf{F}) = \begin{bmatrix} \partial_y(2z + x^3) - \partial_z(4y + z^8) \\ \partial_z(3x + y^2) - \partial_x(2z + x^3) \\ \partial_x(4y + z^8) - \partial_y(3x + y^2) \end{bmatrix} = \begin{bmatrix} -8z^7 \\ -3x^2 \\ -2y \end{bmatrix}. \qquad \blacksquare$$

The curl of a gradient field is $\mathbf{0}$

Example 10.2. Suppose second partial derivatives of $f(x, y, z)$ are continuous. Show that curl(∇f) = $\mathbf{0}$.

Solution: Using equation (10.5), we see

$$\nabla \times (\nabla f) = \begin{vmatrix} \mathbf{i} & \mathbf{j} & \mathbf{k} \\ \partial_x & \partial_y & \partial_z \\ f_x & f_y & f_z \end{vmatrix} = \left(\frac{\partial f_z}{\partial y} - \frac{\partial f_y}{\partial z} \right) \mathbf{i} - \left(\frac{\partial f_z}{\partial x} - \frac{\partial f_x}{\partial z} \right) \mathbf{j} + \left(\frac{\partial f_y}{\partial x} - \frac{\partial f_x}{\partial y} \right) \mathbf{k}.$$

Since the second partial derivatives of f are continuous, Clairaut's Theorem (see Section 13.4) guarantees that $f_{zy} = f_{yz}$. So the difference $f_{zy} - f_{zy} = 0$. Likewise for $f_{zx} - f_{xz}$ and $f_{yx} - f_{xy}$, so $\text{curl}(\nabla f) = 0\mathbf{i} + 0\mathbf{j} + 0\mathbf{k} = \mathbf{0}$. ∎

When $\text{curl}(\mathbf{F})$ is $\mathbf{0}$ everywhere, as you saw in Example 10.2, we say that the vector field $\mathbf{F}$ is *irrotational* or *curl-free*.

Calculating a curl vector

Solution On-line

Example 10.3. Determine whether $\mathbf{F} = \langle 2y + 4z, 8x + 9z, 2y + 4x \rangle$ is irrotational.

Answer: It's not. The vector $\text{curl}(\mathbf{F})$ is constant but not zero. ∎

When written using the cross-product notation, the algebraic properties of $\text{curl}(\mathbf{F})$ are reminiscent of the vector cross product.

Properties of the Curl: Suppose the first partial derivatives of the vector fields $\mathbf{F}$ and $\mathbf{G}$ exist, as do those of the real-valued function f, and k is a scalar. Then

$$\nabla \times (k\mathbf{F}) = k(\nabla \times \mathbf{F}) \tag{10.7}$$
$$\nabla \times (\mathbf{F} + \mathbf{G}) = (\nabla \times \mathbf{F}) + (\nabla \times \mathbf{G}) \tag{10.8}$$
$$\nabla \times (f\mathbf{F}) = (f)(\nabla \times \mathbf{F}) + (\nabla f) \times \mathbf{F} \tag{10.9}$$

Additionally, if the second partial derivatives of $\mathbf{F}$ are continuous

$$\text{div}(\text{curl}(\mathbf{F})) = \nabla \cdot (\nabla \times \mathbf{F}) = 0. \tag{10.10}$$

Note: You'll prove these facts in the exercise set using the rules of differentiation that you already know.

✛ Stokes' Theorem

In its simplest form, Stokes' Theorem asserts that equation (10.6) is true whenever the curve $\mathcal{C}$ lies entirely in *any* plane. More generally, it extends equation (10.6) to cases when $\mathcal{C}$ bounds a non-planar, oriented surface $\mathcal{M}$. In preparation for that generalization, let's rewrite equation (10.6) as

$$\oint_{\mathcal{C}} \mathbf{F} \cdot \mathbf{T} \, ds = \iint_{\mathcal{M}} \text{curl}(\mathbf{F}) \cdot \mathbf{n} \, dS, \tag{10.11}$$

where $\mathbf{n}$ is unit normal vector on $\mathcal{M}$, and $\mathcal{C}$ is the positively oriented boundary of $\mathcal{M}$, meaning that when "up" is determined by $\mathbf{n}$, the surface remains on your left as you traverse the curve $\mathcal{C}$, as depicted in Figure 10.3.

Circulation around a curve in a tilted plane

Example 10.4. Suppose R is the region in the xy-plane for which $1 \le x \le 3$ and $1 \le y \le 2$, and $\mathcal{M}$ is the positively oriented portion of the plane $z = 3x + 2y + 1$ that lies directly above R. Verify equation (10.11) when $\mathbf{F}(x, y, z) = \langle -y, z, 2 \rangle$ and $\mathcal{C}$ is the positively oriented boundary of $\mathcal{M}$, which lies directly above the boundary or R.

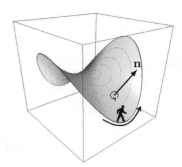 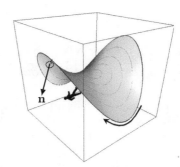

Figure 10.3: A surface naturally has two sides, and intuitively speaking, the vector **n** defines the direction that we agree to call "up." We say that you are walking around a curve in the positive direction if the surface it delimits remains on your left as you traverse the curve.

Solution: Let's begin by calculating the right-hand side of equation (10.11). First we determine that $\text{curl}(\mathbf{F}) = \nabla \times \mathbf{F} = \langle -1, 0, 1 \rangle$. Then because $\mathcal{M}$ is a planar surface, we can use the methods of Section 15.6 to write the surface integral as

$$\iint_{\mathcal{M}} \text{curl}(\mathbf{F}) \cdot \mathbf{n} \ dS = \iint_{R} \langle -1, 0, 1 \rangle \cdot \langle -3, -2, 1 \rangle \ dA = \iint_{R} 4 \ dA = 8.$$

In order to calculate the left-hand side of equation (10.11) we parameterize the four linear segments of $\mathcal{C}$ (see Figure 10.4) and calculate the flow of $\mathbf{F}$ along each.

Alternatively, we could have parameterized $\mathcal{M}$ with $\mathbf{r}(x, y) = \langle x, y, 3x + 2y + 1 \rangle$ and used the methods of Section 15.8.

1. Since $\mathcal{C}_1$ lies in the plane $y = 1$, we know that $z = 3x + 2y + 1$ on $\mathcal{C}_1$. This allows us to parameterize the curve with

$$\mathbf{r}(t) = \langle \underbrace{1 + t, \ 1,} \ 3(1 + t) + 2(1) + 1 \rangle = \langle 1 + t, \ 1, \ 6 + 3t \rangle$$

x increases from 1 to 3 while $y = 1$ remains constant

as t increases from 0 to 2. We're working with $\mathbf{F}(x, y, z) = \langle -y, z, 2 \rangle$ which is $\langle -1, 6 + 3t, 2 \rangle$ at such points. So the flow of $\mathbf{F}$ along $\mathcal{C}_1$ is

$$\int_{\mathcal{C}_1} \mathbf{F} \cdot d\mathbf{r} = \int_0^2 \langle -1, 6 + 3t, 2 \rangle \cdot \mathbf{r}'(t) \ dt$$
$$= \int_0^2 \langle -1, 6 + 3t, 2 \rangle \cdot \langle 1, 0, 3 \rangle \ dt = \int_0^2 5 \ dt = 10.$$

2. Similarly, since $\mathcal{C}_2$ lies in the plane $x = 3$ we can parameterize it with $\mathbf{r}(t) = \langle 3, 1 + t, 12 + 2t \rangle$ as t rises from 0 to 1. The vector field $\mathbf{F}$ has the form $\langle -1 - t, 12 + 2t, 2 \rangle$ at such points, so

$$\int_{\mathcal{C}_2} \mathbf{F} \cdot d\mathbf{r} = \int_0^1 \langle -1 - t, 12 + 2t, 2 \rangle \cdot \mathbf{r}'(t) \ dt = \int_0^1 (2t + 16) \ dt = 17.$$

3. The line segment $\mathcal{C}_3$ can be parameterized with $\mathbf{r}(t) = \langle 3 - t, 2, 14 - 3t \rangle$ as t varies from 0 to 2, and $\mathbf{F}$ has the form $\langle -2, 14 - 3t, 2 \rangle$ at such points, so

$$\int_{\mathcal{C}_3} \mathbf{F} \cdot d\mathbf{r} = \int_0^2 \langle -2, 14 - 3t, 2 \rangle \cdot \mathbf{r}'(t) \ dt = \int_0^2 -4 \ dt = -8.$$

4. The line segment $\mathcal{C}_4$ can be parameterized with $\mathbf{r}(t) = \langle 1, 2 - t, 8 - 2t \rangle$ for $t \in [0, 1]$. The vector field $\mathbf{F}$ has the form $\langle t - 2, 8 - 2t, 2 \rangle$ at such points, so

$$\int_{\mathcal{C}_4} \mathbf{F} \cdot d\mathbf{r} = \int_0^1 \langle t - 2, 8 - 2t, 2 \rangle \cdot \mathbf{r}'(t) \ dt = \int_0^1 (2t - 12) \ dt = -11.$$

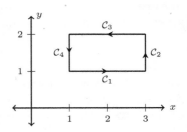

Figure 10.4: Looking "down" on $\mathcal{M}$ from a vantage point with large z-coordinate. The boundary of $\mathcal{M}$ is partitioned into four segments.

So we have

$$\int_{\mathcal{C}} \mathbf{F} \cdot d\mathbf{r} = \int_{\mathcal{C}_1} \mathbf{F} \cdot d\mathbf{r} + \int_{\mathcal{C}_2} \mathbf{F} \cdot d\mathbf{r} + \int_{\mathcal{C}_3} \mathbf{F} \cdot d\mathbf{r} + \int_{\mathcal{C}_4} \mathbf{F} \cdot d\mathbf{r} = 8 \qquad \blacksquare$$

Circulation around a curve in a tilted plane

Example 10.5. Suppose R is the triangular region in the xy-plane with vertices $(1,2)$, $(1,7)$ and $(5,2)$, and $\mathcal{M}$ is the positively oriented portion of $x + y + z = 10$ directly above R. Verify equation (10.11) when $\mathbf{F}(x,y,z) = \langle z, x-y, x-z \rangle$ and $\mathcal{C}$ is the positively oriented boundary of $\mathcal{M}$, which lies directly above the boundary or R.

Solution On-line

Answer: Both sides are 10. $\blacksquare$

    As we indicated earlier, Stokes' Theorem asserts that equation (10.11) is true even when $\mathcal{C}$ is the boundary curve of a nonplanar surface, $\mathcal{M}$.

Stokes' Theorem: Suppose $\mathcal{M}$ is a smooth, oriented surface that is bounded by a simple, closed, piecewise-smooth curve $\mathcal{C}$ that has a positive orientation with respect to $\mathcal{M}$. If $\mathbf{F}$ is a vector field whose first partial derivatives are continuous in an open region containing $\mathcal{M}$, the circulation of $\mathbf{F}$ around $\mathcal{C}$ is

$$\oint_{\mathcal{C}} \mathbf{F} \cdot d\mathbf{r} = \iint_{\mathcal{M}} \text{curl}(\mathbf{F}) \cdot \mathbf{n} \, dS$$

where $\mathbf{n}$ is the unit normal on $\mathcal{M}$.

Proof. Here we address the special case when $\mathcal{M}$ is composed of rectangular and triangular facets (a more general proof is included in the End Notes). As you saw in Examples 10.4 and 10.5, equation (10.11) applies to each of them. So if the facets of $\mathcal{M}$ are labeled as $T_1, T_2, \ldots, T_n$, we can write

$$\iint_{\mathcal{M}} \text{curl}(\mathbf{F}) \, dS = \sum_{k=1}^{n} \iint_{T_k} \text{curl}(\mathbf{F}) \, dS = \sum_{k=1}^{n} \oint_{\mathcal{C}_k} \mathbf{F} \cdot d\mathbf{r}.$$

As you saw in the proof of Green's Theorem in Section 15.5, the positive orientation of our integration leads us to integrate over the interior edges in both directions. The sum of these integrations is zero, so we are left with a line integral along the outer edges of $\mathcal{M}$, the collection of which constitutes $\mathcal{C}$. $\blacksquare$

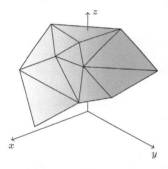

Figure 10.5: A surface composed of triangular facets. We integrate both ways over interior edges of the faceted surface, so the net contribution from those edges is zero.

The surface integral of curl(F) depends on the boundary curve

Example 10.6. The spherical equation $\rho = 3 + \sin 3\theta \sin 5\phi$ describes the bumpy surface depicted in Figure 10.6. Suppose $\mathcal{M}$ is the portion of that surface above the plane $6x + y + 7z = 0$, and $\mathbf{F}(x,y,z) = \langle 2y + 4z, 8x + 9z, 2y + 4x \rangle$. Determine the surface integral of curl($\mathbf{F}$) over $\mathcal{M}$.

Solution: The boundary of $\mathcal{M}$ is the smooth curve $\mathcal{C}$ where it meets the plane, as seen in Figure 10.6. So Stokes' Theorem tells us that

$$\iint_{\mathcal{M}} \text{curl}(\mathbf{F}) \cdot \mathbf{n} \, dS = \oint_{\mathcal{C}} \mathbf{F} \cdot d\mathbf{r}.$$

Making this calculation by parameterizing $\mathcal{C}$ is impractical, but note that $\mathcal{C}$ is also the boundary of the region it encloses on the plane $6x + y + 7z = 0$. We'll denote that planar region by $\mathcal{R}$. In Example 10.3 you showed that curl($\mathbf{F}$) $= \langle -7, 0, 6 \rangle$,

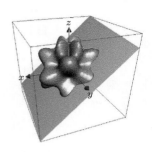
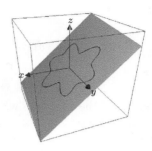

Figure 10.6: (left) The surface $\mathcal{M}$ in Example 10.6, and the plane $6x + y + 7z = 0$; (right) the intersection forms a curve.

and the unit normal vector to the plane is $\mathbf{n} = \langle 6, 1, 7 \rangle / \sqrt{86}$, so Stokes' Theorem tells us that

$$\oint_{\mathcal{C}} \mathbf{F} \cdot d\mathbf{r} = \iint_{\mathcal{R}} \frac{\langle -7, 0, 6 \rangle \cdot \langle 6, 1, 7 \rangle}{\sqrt{86}}\, dA = \iint_{\mathcal{R}} 0\, dA = 0. \qquad \blacksquare$$

A surface with two boundary curves

Example 10.7. Suppose $\mathbf{F}(x, y, z) = \langle x + y^2, x - z, z \rangle$ and $\mathcal{M}$ is the surface of the positively oriented cylinder described by the polar equation $r = 1$ that stretches between the planes $z = -1$ and $z = 1$. Use Stokes' Theorem to determine $\iint_{\mathcal{M}} \operatorname{curl}(\mathbf{F}) \cdot d\mathbf{S}$.

Solution: This surface poses a technical challenge in the application of Stokes' Theorem because, as shown in Figure 10.7, its boundary is not a single curve. Figure 10.8 shows how we'll deal with this issue. We begin by omitting a thin, vertical slice of the cylinder of width ε. This results in a smooth surface, $\mathcal{M}_\varepsilon$, with a piecewise smooth boundary, $\mathcal{C}_\varepsilon$, so Stokes' Theorem tells us that

$$\oint_{\mathcal{C}_\varepsilon} \mathbf{F} \cdot d\mathbf{r} = \iint_{\mathcal{M}_\varepsilon} \operatorname{curl}(\mathbf{F}) \cdot \mathbf{n}\, dS.$$

The surface $\mathcal{M}_\varepsilon$ includes more of $\mathcal{M}$ as ε decreases, and in the limit the integral on the right-hand side of this equation converges to surface integral in which we're interested:

$$\lim_{\varepsilon \to 0^+} \iint_{\mathcal{M}_\varepsilon} \operatorname{curl}(\mathbf{F}) \cdot \mathbf{n}\, dS = \iint_{\mathcal{M}} \operatorname{curl}(\mathbf{F}) \cdot \mathbf{n}\, dS.$$

Also in the limit, the line integral proceeds across a vertical line segment in both directions, so that

$$\lim_{\varepsilon \to 0^+} \oint_{\mathcal{C}_\varepsilon} \mathbf{F} \cdot d\mathbf{r} = \oint_{\mathcal{C}_1} \mathbf{F} \cdot d\mathbf{r} + \oint_{\mathcal{C}_2} \mathbf{F} \cdot d\mathbf{r},$$

where $\mathcal{C}_1$ and $\mathcal{C}_2$ are the circles on the top and bottom of the cylinder, both oriented in the positive direction with respect to $\mathcal{M}$. To calculate these integrals, we parameterize the oriented circles with

$$\underbrace{\mathbf{r}_1(t) = \langle \cos t, -\sin t, 1 \rangle}_{\text{Proceeds clockwise around the circle}} \quad \text{and} \quad \underbrace{\mathbf{r}_2(t) = \langle \cos t, \sin t, -1 \rangle.}_{\text{Proceeds counterclockwise around the circle}}$$

At the point $\mathbf{r}_1(t)$ we see that $\mathbf{F}$ has the form $\langle \cos t + \sin^2 t, \cos(t) - 1, 1 \rangle$, so

$$\oint_{\mathcal{C}_1} \mathbf{F} \cdot d\mathbf{r} = \int_0^{2\pi} \mathbf{F} \cdot \mathbf{r}_1'\, dt = \int_0^{2\pi} \left(\cos t - \sin^3 t - \cos^2 t - \sin t \cos t \right) dt = -\pi.$$

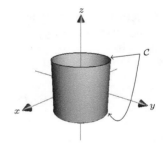

Figure 10.7: The boundary of the cylinder consists of two separate curves.

We're relying on the continuity of $\mathbf{F}$ in this argument.

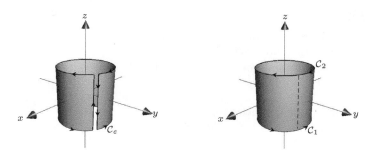

Figure 10.8: (left) The curve $\mathcal{C}_\varepsilon$ is the boundary of the surface $\mathcal{M}_\varepsilon$; (right) we recover $\mathcal{M}$ in the limit.

Similarly,

$$\oint_{\mathcal{C}_2} \mathbf{F} \cdot d\mathbf{r} = \int_0^{2\pi} \mathbf{F} \cdot \mathbf{r}_2' \, dt = \int_0^{2\pi} \left(\cos^2 t + \cos t - \cos t \sin t - \sin^3 t \right) dt = \pi.$$

So we arrive at the conclusion that

$$\iint_{\mathcal{M}} \text{curl}(\mathbf{F}) \cdot d\mathbf{S} = \oint_{\mathcal{C}_1} \mathbf{F} \cdot d\mathbf{r} + \oint_{\mathcal{C}_2} \mathbf{F} \cdot d\mathbf{r} = 0. \qquad \blacksquare$$

Confirming the result of Stokes' Theorem

Example 10.8. Confirm the result of Example 10.7 by calculating $\iint_{\mathcal{M}} \text{curl}(\mathbf{F}) \cdot d\mathbf{S}$ directly, using the techniques of Section 15.6.

Answer: See on-line solution. $\qquad \blacksquare$

▷ Surfaces with holes

As we saw with Green's Theorem in Section 15.5, Stokes' Theorem can be applied to oriented surfaces with holes, provided that their boundaries are positively oriented with respect to the surface. The solution to Example 10.7 suggests the basic technique:

$$\iint_{\mathcal{M}} \text{curl}(\mathbf{F}) \, dS = \sum_k \oint_{\mathcal{C}_k} \mathbf{F} \cdot d\mathbf{r}.$$

▷ Circulation Density

In Section 15.5 we talked about curl(**F**) as the circulation density of **F** in the xy-plane. Stokes' Theorem allows us to generalize that discussion by including the idea of direction. Specifically, suppose $\mathcal{C}$ is a circle of radius r that's centered at P and lies in a plane; we denote by **n** the unit normal vector to the plane, and by $\mathcal{M}$ the planar disk enclosed by $\mathcal{C}$. Because curl(**F**) $\cdot$ **n** is continuous over $\mathcal{M}$ when **F** is a smooth vector field, the Mean Value Theorem for Double Integrals tells us that there is some point on $\mathcal{M}$, say Q, where

$$\text{curl}(\mathbf{F}) \cdot \mathbf{n}\Big|_Q = \underbrace{\frac{1}{\pi r^2} \iint_{\mathcal{M}} \text{curl}(\mathbf{F}) \cdot \mathbf{n} \, dA}_{\text{The average value of curl}(\mathbf{F}) \cdot \mathbf{n}} = \frac{1}{\pi r^2} \oint_{\mathcal{C}} \mathbf{F} \cdot d\mathbf{r} = \frac{\text{circulation of } \mathbf{F} \text{ around } \mathcal{C}}{\text{area enclosed by } \mathcal{C}}.$$

The point $Q \to P$ as $r \to 0^+$, so we understand curl(**F**) $\cdot$ **n**$|_P$ as the circulation density of **F** at P *in the plane orthogonal to* **n**.

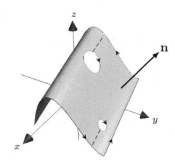

Figure 10.9: A surface with holes. Each boundary curve is positively oriented.

✢ The Curl Test for Vector Fields in Space

In Section 15.5 we showed that a smooth vector field $\mathbf{F}$ in the plane is conservative if and only if $\mathrm{curl}(\mathbf{F}) = 0$. Here we extend that result to vector fields in 3-space, and regions V that are **convex**, meaning that every pair of points in V is connected by a line segment that lies entirely inside of V.

Curl Test: Suppose $\mathbf{F}$ is a smooth vector field in an open, convex region V in 3-space. Then there is a function f (called a *potential*) for which $\mathbf{F} = \nabla f$ if and only if $\mathrm{curl}(\mathbf{F}) = \mathbf{0}$.

Proof. In Example 10.2 we showed that $\mathrm{curl}(\mathbf{F}) = \mathbf{0}$ when $\mathbf{F} = \nabla f$ is a smooth vector field, so here we need only prove the converse—that there must be such a function f whenever $\mathrm{curl}(\mathbf{F}) = \mathbf{0}$.

> We performed a similar proof in Section 15.2, but there we knew that $\mathbf{F}$ was path independent.

Pick a point in V at random, say P. Every other point in V can be reached from P by a line segment because V is convex, so we define f as the line integral

$$f(a,b,c) = \int_P^{(a,b,c)} \mathbf{F} \cdot d\mathbf{r},$$

where the line integral is calculated along the line segment connecting the point at P to the point at (a,b,c). Our claim is that $\nabla f = \mathbf{F}$, and we prove it much as we did in Section 15.2. Because V is open, there is a small sphere about the point (a,b,c) that encloses only points in V. So when Δx is small, we know the point $(a+\Delta x, b, c)$ is in V. Therefore, we can calculate the difference quotient

$$\frac{\Delta f}{\Delta x} = \frac{1}{\Delta x}\Big(f(a+\Delta x, b, c) - f(a,b,c)\Big).$$

In a moment we'll use Stokes' Theorem to show that

$$f(a+\Delta x, b, c) = \int_P^{(a,b,c)} \mathbf{F} \cdot d\mathbf{r} + \int_{(a,b,c)}^{(a+\Delta x,b,c)} \mathbf{F} \cdot d\mathbf{r}, \qquad (10.12)$$

where the second integral is performed along the horizontal line segment connecting (a,b,c) to $(a+\Delta x, b, c)$. It follows that

$$\frac{\Delta f}{\Delta x} = \frac{1}{\Delta x}\Big(f(a+\Delta x, b, c) - f(a,b,c)\Big)$$
$$= \frac{1}{\Delta x}\left(\int_P^{(a,b,c)} \mathbf{F} \cdot d\mathbf{r} + \int_{(a,b,c)}^{(a+\Delta x,b,c)} \mathbf{F} \cdot d\mathbf{r} - \int_P^{(a,b,c)} \mathbf{F} \cdot d\mathbf{r}\right) = \frac{1}{\Delta x}\int_{(a,b,c)}^{(a+\Delta x,b,c)} \mathbf{F} \cdot d\mathbf{r}.$$

The remaining line integral is done over a horizontal line segment along which $\mathbf{T} = \mathbf{i}$, so if we write $\mathbf{F} = \langle L, M, N \rangle$ the integral becomes

$$\frac{\Delta f}{\Delta x} = \frac{1}{\Delta x}\int_{(a,b,c)}^{(a+\Delta x,b,c)} L(x,b,c)\, dx.$$

Since L is continuous, the Mean Value Theorem for Integrals tells us that this is the same as $L(x^*, b, c)$ for some $x^* \in [a, a+\Delta x]$. Furthermore, the continuity of L guarantees that

$$L(a,b,c) = \lim_{\Delta x \to 0} L(x^*, b, c) = \lim_{\Delta x \to 0} \frac{\Delta f}{\Delta x} = \frac{\partial f}{\partial x}.$$

Similarly, $f_y = M$ and $f_z = N$ at (a,b,c), so $\nabla f = \mathbf{F}$.

We finish our proof by verifying equation (10.12). Since the point $(a + \Delta x, b, c)$ is in V, there is a line segment that connects it to P. We'll refer to this line segment as $\mathcal{C}_3$. The line segment connecting P to (a, b, c) will be called $\mathcal{C}_1$, and the horizontal line segment connecting (a, b, c) to $(a + \Delta x, b, c)$ will be denoted by $\mathcal{C}_2$. When taken together, these line segments join to make a simple closed curve, $\mathcal{C} = \mathcal{C}_1 + \mathcal{C}_2 + \mathcal{C}_3^{-}$, that bounds a planar triangle, $\mathcal{M}$. Stokes' Theorem tells us that

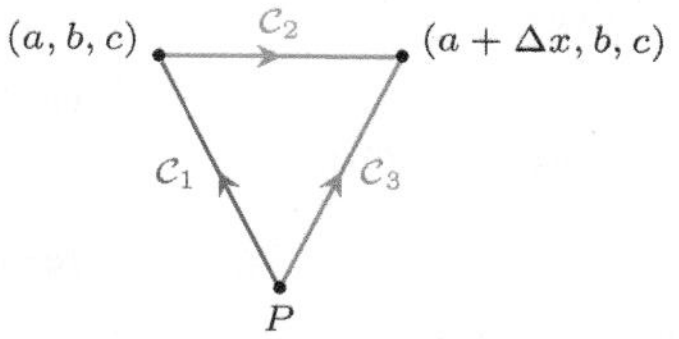

$$\int_{\mathcal{C}} \mathbf{F} \cdot d\mathbf{r} = \int_{\mathcal{M}} \text{curl}(\mathbf{F}) \cdot \mathbf{n} \, dA = \int_{\mathcal{M}} 0 \, dA = 0$$

Figure 10.10: The three points determine a triangle in V.

since $\text{curl}(\mathbf{F}) = \mathbf{0}$. Now

$$0 = \int_{\mathcal{C}} \mathbf{F} \cdot d\mathbf{r} = \int_{\mathcal{C}_1 + \mathcal{C}_2} \mathbf{F} \cdot d\mathbf{r} - \int_{\mathcal{C}_3} \mathbf{F} \cdot d\mathbf{r}$$

implies that

$$f(a + \Delta x, b, c) = \int_{\mathcal{C}_3} \mathbf{F} \cdot d\mathbf{r} = \int_{\mathcal{C}_1 + \mathcal{C}_2} \mathbf{F} \cdot d\mathbf{r} = \int_{\mathcal{C}_1} \mathbf{F} \cdot d\mathbf{r} + \int_{\mathcal{C}_2} \mathbf{F} \cdot d\mathbf{r},$$

which is equation (10.12).   ∎

You should know

- the terms *curl, irrotational, curl free, convex,* and *circulation density;*
- the notation $\nabla \times \mathbf{F}$ and $\text{curl}(\mathbf{F})$;
- the algebraic properties of $\text{curl}(\mathbf{F})$;
- that under mild constraints, $\nabla \times \mathbf{F} = \mathbf{0} \Rightarrow \mathbf{F}$ is the gradient of a potential function;
- that Stokes' Theorem is an extension of Green's Theorem (circulation form) to surfaces in 3-space.

You should be able to

- determine the curl of a vector field;
- interpret the meaning of $\text{curl}(\mathbf{F})$ when $\mathbf{F}$ describes the flow of a fluid;
- use Stokes' Theorem to convert a line integral of $\mathbf{F}$ around a closed curve into a surface integral of $\text{curl}(\mathbf{F})$.

❖ 15.10 Skill Exercises

In #1–6 determine the curl of the given vector field.

1. $\mathbf{F}(x, y, z) = \langle 8z, 3x, 4y \rangle$

2. $\mathbf{F}(x, y, z) = \langle 3x, 4y, 8z \rangle$

3. $\mathbf{F}(x, y, z) = \langle z^2, 3xz, -4yx \rangle$

4. $\mathbf{F}(x, y, z) = \langle 7y^4 z, -x^2 y, 3yz \rangle$

5. $\mathbf{F}(x, y, z) = \cos(z)\mathbf{i} + e^y \mathbf{j} + x^2 \mathbf{k}$

6. $\mathbf{F}(x, y, z) = \ln(xz)\mathbf{i} + \arctan(z)\mathbf{j} + \frac{x}{y}\mathbf{k}$

In #7–10 use equation (10.9) to determine the curl of $f\mathbf{F}$.

7. $f(x, y, z) = 3x + 4y + 10z, \ \mathbf{F}(x, y, z) = \langle 2y, 3z, 4x \rangle$

8. $f(x, y, z) = 2x - 7y - z, \ \mathbf{F}(x, y, z) = \langle z, -4x, 6y \rangle$

9. $f(x, y, z) = ye^x, \ \mathbf{F}(x, y, z) = \langle 6y, 5z^2, x \rangle$

10. $f(x, y, z) = x \sin(z)$, $\mathbf{F}(x, y, z) = \langle x^2, yz + x, -yz \rangle$

In #11–14 calculate the circulation of $\mathbf{F}$ around the given curve (a) directly with a line integral, and (b) using Stokes' Theorem.

11. $\mathbf{F}(x, y, z) = \langle 3x, -7, z \rangle$; $\mathcal{C}$ is the triangle connecting the points $(1, 0, 4)$, $(3, 0, 1)$, and $(5, 0, 2)$, in that order.

12. $\mathbf{F}(x, y, z) = \langle 2y, 4y^2, 3xy \rangle$; $\mathcal{C}$ is the triangle connecting the points $(3, 1, -1)$, $(0, 1, 2)$, and $(4, 1, 3)$, in that order.

13. $\mathbf{F}(x, y, z) = \langle 2z, \cos y, 3x \rangle$; $\mathcal{C} = \mathcal{C}_1 + \mathcal{C}_2$, where $\mathcal{C}_1$ is the line segment that extends from $(-1, 0, 0)$ to $(1, 0, 0)$ and $\mathcal{C}_2$ is the portion of the circle $x^2 + z^2 = 1$ in the plane $y = 0$ for which $z \leq 0$, and $\mathcal{C}$ is traversed in the counterclockwise direction when viewed from the point $(0, 1, 0)$.

14. $\mathbf{F}(x, y, z) = \langle 5x^3 z, 14y + z, 3x - 9z \rangle$; $\mathcal{C} = \mathcal{C}_1 + \mathcal{C}_2$, where $\mathcal{C}_1$ is the line segment that extends from $(2, 0, -1)$ to $(2, 0, 1)$ and $\mathcal{C}_2$ is the portion of the circle $y^2 + z^2 = 9$ in the plane $x = 2$ for which $y \geq 0$, and $\mathcal{C}$ is traversed in the counterclockwise direction when viewed from the origin.

In exercises #15–18 the curve $\mathcal{C}$ is the circle of radius 1 that's centered at the point $(2, 3, -1)$ and lies in the plane with normal vector $\mathbf{n}$. Determine the circulation of $\mathbf{F}$ around $\mathcal{C}$ when the circle is oriented in the positive direction with respect to $\mathbf{n}$ (meaning that the region enclosed by $\mathcal{C}$ would be on your left if you were to walk around $\mathcal{C}$ with "up" defined to be in the direction of $\mathbf{n}$).

15. $\mathbf{F}(x, y, z) = 3x\mathbf{i} + y\mathbf{j} - 2z\mathbf{k}$; $\mathbf{n} = \langle 4, 9, 1 \rangle$

16. $\mathbf{F}(x, y, z) = 7z\mathbf{i} - x\mathbf{j} + 5z\mathbf{k}$; $\mathbf{n} = \langle 1, 0, 1 \rangle$

17. $\mathbf{F}(x, y, z) = -y\mathbf{i} + 5z\mathbf{j} + 7x\mathbf{k}$; $\mathbf{n} = \langle 1, 1, 18 \rangle$

18. $\mathbf{F}(x, y, z) = 2x\mathbf{i} + 8z\mathbf{j} + 5y\mathbf{k}$; $\mathbf{n} = \langle 3, 3, 3 \rangle$

In #19–22 determine all values of k for which the circulation density of $\mathbf{F}$ in the given direction is 1.

19. $\mathbf{F}(x, y, z) = \langle -z, 2y - 4z, 8x + ky \rangle$; $\mathbf{n} = \langle 2, -3, -1 \rangle$

20. $\mathbf{F}(x, y, z) = \langle 8y, x + y, 2x - y \rangle$; $\mathbf{n} = \langle 2, k, -1 \rangle$

21. $\mathbf{F}(x, y, z) = \langle z - 2y, 5x + y, 6x + ky \rangle$; $\mathbf{n} = \langle k, 1, k \rangle$

22. $\mathbf{F}(x, y, z) = \langle y - 2z, 3x - y, x + 2y \rangle$; $\mathbf{n} = \langle 5, 2, \ln k \rangle$

In #23–26 use the curl test to determine whether the given vector field is conservative.

23. $\mathbf{F}(x, y, z) = (x^2 + y^2 + z^2)\langle x, y, z \rangle$

24. $\mathbf{F}(x, y, z) = \frac{1}{\ln(2 + x^2 + y^2 + z^2)}\langle x, y, z \rangle$

25. $\mathbf{F}(x, y, z) = (z + y^2 x^2)\langle x, y, z \rangle$

26. $\mathbf{F}(x, y, z) = xyz\langle x, y, z \rangle$

❖ 15.10 Concept and Application Exercises

In #27–28, the vector field $\mathbf{F}$ is smooth and f is a scalar-valued, differentiable, function of three variables. Determine which of the expressions are meaningless and explain what's wrong with them in complete sentences.

27. (a) $\nabla \times \nabla \cdot \mathbf{F}$; (b) $\nabla f \cdot \nabla \times \mathbf{F}$; (c) $\nabla \cdot \nabla \times f$; (d) $f(\mathbf{i} \cdot \nabla \times \mathbf{F}, \mathbf{j} \cdot \nabla \times \mathbf{F}, \mathbf{k} \cdot \nabla \times \mathbf{F})$

28. (a) $\nabla \times \nabla \times \mathbf{F}$; (b) $\nabla \cdot \nabla \times \mathbf{F}$; (c) $\nabla \cdot \nabla \cdot \mathbf{F}$; (d) $\mathbf{F} \times \nabla \cdot f$

29. Suppose $\mathbf{F}$ is a smooth vector field and $\mathcal{M}$ is a smooth, oriented, closed surface. Prove that $\iint_{\mathcal{M}} \mathrm{curl}(\mathbf{F}) \cdot d\mathbf{S} = 0$. *(Hint: slice $\mathcal{M}$ into two pieces, each of which has a boundary.)*

30. We say that $\mathbf{G}$ is a **vector potential** of $\mathbf{F}$ when $\mathbf{F} = \mathrm{curl}(\mathbf{G})$.

    (a) Suppose $\mathbf{G}_1$ is a vector potential of $\mathbf{F}$, and $\mathbf{G}_2 = \mathbf{G}_1 + \mathbf{C}$, where $\mathbf{C}$ is a constant vector field. Show that $\mathbf{G}_2$ is also a vector potential of $\mathbf{F}$.

    (b) Use Stokes' Theorem to prove that $\iint_{\mathcal{M}} \mathbf{F} \cdot d\mathbf{S}$ depends only on the boundary of $\mathcal{M}$ when $\mathbf{G}$ is a vector potential of $\mathbf{F}$, not on the surface itself.

31. Suppose a current of I amps flows along the z-axis in the $\mathbf{k}$ direction (positive charges head in the direction of $\mathbf{k}$, or equivalently, negative charges flow in the direction of $-\mathbf{k}$). The magnetic field induced by this current is depicted in Figure 10.11, and its magnitude r meters away from the current-carrying line is $\|\mathbf{B}(r)\| = \mu_0 I / (2\pi r)$, where $\mu_0 = 4\pi \times 10^7$ is called the *permeability of free space*. In exercise #42 of Section 15.5 you showed that the circulation of $\mathbf{B}$ around a circle that encloses the current-carrying line is $\mu_0 I$ when that circle is in a plane that's perpendicular to the current. Now prove that the fact remains true when the plane of the circle is *not* perpendicular to the wire.

32. A magnetic field can be generated by running current through a coil of wire called a **solenoid**. Figure 10.12 depicts a solenoid of radius R that coils around the z-axis. When the length of the solenoid is much larger than its radius, the magnetic field is nearly uniform inside the coils and nearly vanishes outside. In this exercise we idealize this phenomenon by characterizing the solenoid's magnetic field as $\mathbf{0}$ outside the coils, and $\mathbf{B} = \beta \mathbf{k}$ inside, where β is a number that depends on the current (which we take to be steady) and the number of turns in the coil per unit of length on the z-axis.

    (a) Prove that the following vector field is a vector potential for $\mathbf{B}$ (see #30):

$$\mathbf{G}(x, y, z) = \begin{cases} \frac{\beta}{2}\langle -y, x, 0 \rangle & \text{if } r \in [0, R] \\ \frac{\beta R^2}{2r^2}\langle -y, x, 0 \rangle & \text{if } r > R \end{cases}, \quad \text{where } r = \sqrt{x^2 + y^2}.$$

    (b) Graph $\|\mathbf{G}\|$ as a function of r.

33. Suppose $\mathbf{F} = f(\|\mathbf{r}\|)\mathbf{r}$ where $\mathbf{r} = \langle x, y, z \rangle$, and f is a differentiable, real-valued function of a single variable.

    (a) Thinking of $f(\|\mathbf{r}\|)$ as a function of three variables, what do the level surfaces of $f(\|\mathbf{r}\|)$ look like?

    (b) Thinking of $f(\|\mathbf{r}\|)$ as a function of three variables, describe the orientation of ∇f and $\mathbf{F}$.

    (c) Use curl property (10.9) to prove that $\mathbf{F}$ is conservative.

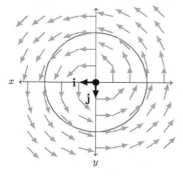

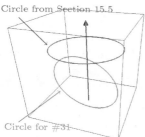

Figure 10.11: (top) The current-carrying wire (heading out of the page) and the associated $\mathbf{B}$ field (not to scale) with the circle from #42 of Section 15.5; (bottom) the circles for #31.

Solenoids

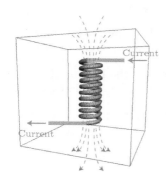

Figure 10.12: Current through a solenoid generates a magnetic field.

34. Use curl property (10.9) to prove property (10.7).

35. In the exercises of Section 15.6 we introduced **Faraday's Law**, which relates changes in the flux of a magnetic field through a surface to the induced electromotive force along its boundary. This relationship is often written as

$$\mathcal{E} = -\iint_{\mathcal{M}} \partial_t \mathbf{B} \cdot d\mathbf{S},$$

where $\mathcal{M}$ is a smooth, simple surface, $\mathbf{B}$ is the magnetic field in question, and $\mathcal{E}$ is the electromotive force along the boundary of $\mathcal{M}$. In the same way that *voltage* is the line integral of an *electric field*, we can write the electromotive force as the line integral of the *induced electric field*, $\mathbf{E}$, along the boundary of $\mathcal{M}$. Specifically, if the boundary of $\mathcal{M}$ is the piecewise smooth, simple closed curve $\mathcal{C}$,

$$\oint_{\mathcal{C}} \mathbf{E} \cdot d\mathbf{r} = \mathcal{E}.$$

Based on these equations, write the relationship between the changing magnetic field $\mathbf{B}$ and the induced electric field, $\mathbf{E}$.

| Induced Magnetic Field |

Checking the details

36. In this exercise you'll verify that equations (h.39) and (h.40) are the same. This relies on the Chain Rule, which tells us that

$$\frac{\partial L}{\partial s} = \frac{\partial L}{\partial x}\frac{\partial x}{\partial s} + \frac{\partial L}{\partial y}\frac{\partial y}{\partial s} + \frac{\partial L}{\partial z}\frac{\partial z}{\partial s}.$$

   (a) Use the Chain Rule to write the formula for calculating $\frac{\partial L}{\partial t}$.

   (b) Use the Chain Rule to expand $(\frac{\partial L}{\partial s})x_t - (\frac{\partial L}{\partial t})x_s$.

   (c) Perform the dot product on the right-hand side of equation (h.39) and collect the terms including L. Compare to part (b).

   (d) Use a similar technique to account for the terms including M, and those including N.

37. Use the Scaling Rule of differentiation to prove property (10.7) by examining each component of the curl.

38. Use the Sum Rule of differentiation to prove property (10.8) by examining each component of the curl.

39. Use the Product Rule of differentiation to prove property (10.9) by examining each component of the curl.

40. Prove curl property (10.10).

15.11　Summary

The theorems presented in this chapter are all multivariable extensions of the Fundamental Theorem of Calculus that you learned in Chapter 5. Here we provide a brief list of the results (without hypotheses) for your reference.

❖ Fundamental Theorems (Sections 5.4 and 15.3)

Fundamental Theorem of Calculus

$$\int_a^b f'(x)\,dx = f(b) - f(a)$$

Fundamental Theorem of Line Integrals

$$\int_{\mathcal{C}} \nabla f \cdot d\mathbf{r} = f(\mathbf{r}(a)) - f(\mathbf{r}(b))$$

❖ Flux-Divergence Theorems (Sections 15.4 and 15.9)

Green's Theorem (flux-divergence form)

$$\iint_R \operatorname{div}(\mathbf{F})\,dA = \oint_{\mathcal{C}} \mathbf{F} \cdot \mathbf{n}\,ds$$

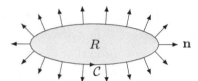

Divergence Theorem

$$\iiint_E \nabla \cdot \mathbf{F}\,dV = \iint_{\mathcal{M}} \mathbf{F} \cdot d\mathbf{S}$$

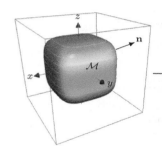

Recall that $\nabla \cdot \mathbf{F} = \operatorname{div}(\mathbf{F})$, and $d\mathbf{S} = \mathbf{n}\,dS$. Both of these theorems relate the flux of $\mathbf{F}$ through a region's boundary to the cumulative total of its divergence in the region's interior.

❖ Circulation Theorems (Sections 15.5 and 15.10)

Green's Theorem (circulation form)

$$\iint_R \operatorname{curl}(\mathbf{F})\,dA = \int_{\mathcal{C}} \mathbf{F} \cdot d\mathbf{r}$$

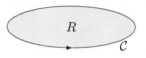

Stokes' Theorem

$$\iint_{\mathcal{M}} (\nabla \times \mathbf{F}) \cdot d\mathbf{S} = \int_{\mathcal{C}} \mathbf{F} \cdot d\mathbf{r}$$

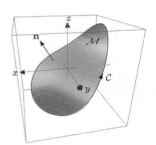

Recall that $\nabla \times \mathbf{F} = \operatorname{curl}(\mathbf{F})$, and $d\mathbf{S} = \mathbf{n}\,dS$. Both of these theorems relate the circulation of $\mathbf{F}$ on a region's boundary to the cumulative total of its curl in the region's interior.

Chapter 15 Review

❖ True or False

1. The streamlines of ∇f are the level curves of f.

2. $f(x, y, z) = 2x^6 - 4y + z$ is a potential function for $\mathbf{F}(x, y, z) = \langle 2x^6, -4y, z \rangle$.

3. The notations $\mathbf{F} \cdot \mathbf{T}\, ds$ and $\mathbf{F} \cdot d\mathbf{r}$ mean the same thing for line integrals.

4. If $\mathcal{C}$ is a closed curve oriented in the positive direction, the line integral of $\mathbf{F}$ over $\mathcal{C}$ is positive.

5. Suppose $\int_{\mathcal{C}} \mathbf{F} \cdot d\mathbf{r} = \int_{\mathcal{C}^-} \mathbf{F} \cdot d\mathbf{r}$. Then $\mathcal{C}$ is a closed curve.

6. Suppose $\mathcal{C}$ is a closed curve. Then $\int_{\mathcal{C}} \mathbf{F} \cdot d\mathbf{r} = \int_{\mathcal{C}^-} \mathbf{F} \cdot d\mathbf{r}$.

7. $\oint_{\mathcal{C}} \mathbf{F} \cdot d\mathbf{r} = 0$ if $\mathcal{C}$ is a simple closed curve in a region where $\mathrm{curl}(\mathbf{F}) = \mathbf{0}$.

8. The parameterization $\mathbf{r}(s, t) = \langle 3s, 8st, t^2 \rangle$ is regular when the parameter domain is the disk of radius 1 centered at the origin of the st-plane.

9. Suppose $\mathbf{r}(s, t)$ parameterizes the surface $\mathcal{M}$. A grid line is a curve on $\mathcal{M}$ made by holding either s or t fixed and letting the other parameter vary.

10. The notations $\mathbf{F} \cdot d\mathbf{S}$ and $\mathbf{F} \cdot \mathbf{n}\, dS$ mean the same thing for surface integrals.

11. A sphere is an orientable surface but the graph of a function is not.

12. A sphere is a closed surface but the graph of a function is not.

13. Divergence can be understood as flux density.

14. The expression $\nabla \cdot \mathbf{F}$ denotes the curl of the vector field $\mathbf{F}$.

15. $\nabla \times \nabla f = \mathbf{0}$ when f is a function with continuous second partial derivatives.

16. $\nabla \cdot (\nabla \times \mathbf{F}) = 0$ when the component functions of $\mathbf{F}$ have continuous second partial derivatives.

17. The vector field $\nabla \times \mathbf{F}$ is orthogonal to $\mathbf{F}$ at each point.

18. Suppose $\mathbf{F}$ is a smooth and $\nabla \times \mathbf{F} = \mathbf{0}$ in all 3-space. Then $\mathbf{F}$ is conservative.

❖ Multiple Choice

19. Suppose the differentiable function f is a potential for the vector field $\mathbf{F}$ in an open region, R. Then . . .

   (a) $\mathbf{F} = \nabla f$
   (b) f can be used to calculate line integrals of $\mathbf{F}$
   (c) $\mathbf{F} = \mathbf{0}$ at extrema of f in R
   (d) all of the above
   (e) none of the above

20. Suppose f is a potential for the smooth vector field $\mathbf{F}$ in an open region of the xy-plane, R. Then . . .

   (a) $\mathrm{div}(\mathbf{F}) < 0$ at local maxima of f in R
   (b) $\mathrm{div}(\mathbf{F}) > 0$ at local maxima of f in R
   (c) $\mathrm{div}(\mathbf{F}) = 0$ at local maxima of f in R
   (d) $\mathrm{curl}(\mathbf{F}) < \mathbf{0}$ at local maxima of f in R
   (e) none of the above

21. The flux-divergence form of Green's Theorem says that . . .

   (a) $\iint_{R}(P_x + Q_y)\, dA = \oint_{\mathcal{C}} Q\, dy - P\, dx$
   (b) $\iint_{R}(P_x + Q_y)\, dA = \oint_{\mathcal{C}} Q\, dx - P\, dy$
   (c) $\iint_{R}(P_x + Q_y)\, dA = \oint_{\mathcal{C}} P\, dx - Q\, dy$
   (d) $\iint_{R}(P_x + Q_y)\, dA = \oint_{\mathcal{C}} P\, dy - Q\, dx$
   (e) none of the above

22. The circulation form of Green's Theorem says that ...

(a) $\iint_R (M_x - L_y)\, dA = \oint_C L\, dx + M\, dy$ (d) $\iint_R (L_x - M_y)\, dA = \oint_C L\, dy - M\, dx$

(b) $\iint_R (L_x - M_y)\, dA = \oint_C L\, dx + M\, dy$ (e) none of the above

(c) $\iint_R (M_x + L_y)\, dA = \oint_C L\, dy + M\, dx$

23. The expression $\nabla \cdot \nabla \times \mathbf{F}$ ...

(a) is nonsensical   (c) is a vector   (e) none of the above

(b) is a scalar   (d) is the same as $\nabla \times \nabla \cdot \mathbf{F}$

24. When f is differentiable, saying that the surface $z = f(x, y)$ has a positive orientation means ...

(a) that its normal vector makes an acute angle with $\mathbf{k}$

(b) that its normal vector makes an obtuse angle with $\mathbf{k}$

(c) that its normal vector is never $\mathbf{n} = \mathbf{0}$

(d) that $f(x, y)$ is always positive

(e) none of the above

25. The area vector on a positively oriented sphere of radius ρ (using the standard parameterization with spherical coordinates) is ...

(a) $d\mathbf{S} = \langle \sin\phi \cos\theta, \sin\phi \sin\theta, \sin\phi \rangle\, \rho \cos\phi\, d\phi\, d\theta$ (d) $d\mathbf{S} = \langle \cos\phi \cos\theta, \cos\phi \sin\theta, \sin\phi \rangle\, \rho^2 \cos\phi\, d\phi\, d\theta$

(b) $d\mathbf{S} = \langle \sin\phi \cos\theta, \sin\phi \sin\theta, \sin\phi \rangle\, \rho \sin\phi\, d\phi\, d\theta$ (e) $d\mathbf{S} = \langle \cos\phi \sin\theta, \sin\phi \cos\theta, \cos\phi \rangle\, \rho^3 \cos\phi\, d\phi\, d\theta$

(c) $d\mathbf{S} = \langle \cos\phi \cos\theta, \cos\phi \sin\theta, \sin\phi \rangle\, \rho^2 \sin\phi\, d\phi\, d\theta$ (f) none of the above

26. Suppose $\mathbf{F} = \langle a, b, c \rangle$ is a constant vector field. Then ...

(a) $\operatorname{div}(\mathbf{F}) = 0$ (c) the flux of $\mathbf{F}$ across any   (d) all of the above

(b) $\operatorname{curl}(\mathbf{F}) = \mathbf{0}$ closed surface is 0   (e) none of the above

27. The Divergence Theorem says that ...

(a) $\iint_{\mathcal{M}} \nabla \cdot \mathbf{F}\, dS = \iiint_E \mathbf{F}\, dV$ (d) $\iint_{\mathcal{M}} \mathbf{F} \cdot d\mathbf{S} = \iiint_E \nabla \cdot \mathbf{F}\, dV$

(b) $\iint_{\mathcal{M}} \nabla \times \mathbf{F}\, dS = \iiint_E \mathbf{F}\, dV$ (e) none of the above

(c) $\iint_{\mathcal{M}} \mathbf{F} \cdot d\mathbf{S} = \iiint_E \nabla \times \mathbf{F}\, dV$

28. Stokes' Theorem is an extension of ...

(a) the Divergence Theorem   (d) the Fundamental Theorem of Calculus

(b) Green's Theorem (flux-divergence form)   (e) none of the above

(c) Green's Theorem (circulation form)

❖ Exercises

29. Determine whether $\mathbf{F}(x, y) = \langle xy + 4, 8x^2 - 4y \rangle$ is a conservative vector field.

30. Determine a potential function for $\mathbf{F}(x, y) = \langle 4x + 8y^2, 3 + 16xy \rangle$.

31. Suppose $\mathbf{F}(x, y) = \langle 2x, 7x + y \rangle$ and $\mathcal{C}$ is the parabolic arc that extends from $(0, 0)$ to $(1, 1)$, oriented from left to right. Determine $\int_{\mathcal{C}} \mathbf{F} \cdot d\mathbf{r}$.

32. Suppose $f(x, y) = xy$ and $\mathcal{C}$ is the parabolic arc that extends from $(0, 0)$ to $(2, 4)$, oriented from left to right. Determine $\int_{\mathcal{C}} f\, ds$.

33. Suppose $\mathbf{F}(x, y) = \langle 4 - y^2, 0 \rangle$ is a field of force vectors. (a) Use a line integral to calculate the amount of work done by $\mathbf{F}$ on an object that moves along a line segment from the point $(10, 0)$ to the point $(0, 1)$, and (b) explain what that means in terms of the object's kinetic energy.

____ Work and Kinetic Energy

34. Suppose $\mathbf{F}(x, y, z) = \langle -x, y, 5 - z \rangle$ is a field of force vectors. (a) Use a line integral to calculate the amount of work done by $\mathbf{F}$ on an object that moves from the origin to the point $(1, 1, 1)$ along the path parameterized by $\mathbf{r}(t) = \langle t, t^2, \sqrt{t} \rangle$ and (b) explain what that means in terms of the object's kinetic energy.

____ Work and Kinetic Energy

35. Suppose $\mathcal{C}$ is the portion of the curve $y \sin^2(x) = x \cos(\pi y)$ that extends from $(0, 0.5)$ to $(\pi, 0.5)$, oriented from left to right. (a) Verify that $f(x, y) = 15x^2 + 2 + 3.5y^2$ is a potential for $\mathbf{F}(x, y) = \langle 3x, 7y \rangle$, and (b) calculate $\int_{\mathcal{C}} \mathbf{F} \cdot d\mathbf{r}$.

36. Suppose $\mathbf{F} = \langle L, M \rangle$ is shown in Figure 12.1. At the point P determine the sign of (a) M_x, (b) L_y, and (c) curl$(\mathbf{F})$.

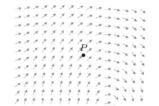

Figure 12.1: The vector field for #36.

37. Suppose R is the bounded region in Figure 12.2. Use Green's Theorem to determine $\oint_{\mathcal{C}} \mathbf{F} \cdot d\mathbf{r}$ when $\mathcal{C}$ is the positively oriented boundary of R, and $\mathbf{F}(x, y) = \langle 7\sqrt{x} - 4xy, 8x + \cos y \rangle$.

38. Suppose $\mathbf{F}(x, y) = \langle -2(x + 2y)^{1.5}, 3y\sqrt{x + 2y} \rangle$ and R is the bounded region enclosed by $y = 0$, $y = \sqrt{x}$ and $x = 1 + (y - 1)^2$. Use Green's Theorem to determine $\oint_{\mathcal{C}} \mathbf{F} \cdot \mathbf{n} \, ds$ when $\mathcal{C}$ is the positively oriented boundary of R.

39. Suppose the diagonal of the positively oriented rectangle $\mathcal{C}$ extends from the origin to the point $(b, 4)$, and $\mathbf{F}$ is a vector field for which curl$(\mathbf{F}) = 2$. Determine a value of b for which $\oint_{\mathcal{C}} \mathbf{F} \cdot d\mathbf{r} = 13$.

40. Suppose div$(\mathbf{F}) = 7$, and the diagonal of the rectangle $\mathcal{C}$ extends from $(0, 0)$ to $(3, b)$. Determine a value of b for which $\oint_{\mathcal{C}} \mathbf{F} \cdot \mathbf{n} \, ds = 100$.

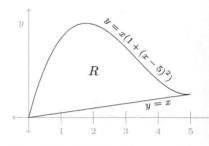

Figure 12.2: For #37. The y axis is not to scale.

In #41–44 determine the specified formula using $f(x, y, z) = z^2 - y$, $g(x, y, z) = x - y$, $\mathbf{F}(x, y, z) = \langle z, e^x, 1 \rangle$ and $\mathbf{G}(x, y, z) = \langle y - 3z, x \sin(y), x^2 - z^2 \rangle$.

41. $\nabla \cdot (f\mathbf{G})$ 42. $\nabla \cdot (\mathbf{F} + \mathbf{G})$ 43. $\nabla \times (g\mathbf{F})$ 44. $\nabla \times (\mathbf{G} - \mathbf{F})$

45. Suppose length is measured in cm, R is the triangle in the xy-plane with vertices $(-1, -3)$, $(2, 6)$ and $(2, -3)$, and $\mathcal{M}$ is the positively oriented portion of $x + 3y - z = 4$ over R. If $\mathbf{F} = 3\mathbf{i} + x\mathbf{j} + \mathbf{k} \, \frac{\text{g/sec}}{\text{cm}^2}$ is the mass flow of a fluid, determine the rate at which fluid passes through $\mathcal{M}$ and in which direction.

____ Fluid Flux

46. Consider the positively-oriented cylinder of radius 3 that's symmetric about the z-axis and extends between $z = 1$ and $z = 2$, where length is measured in millimeters. If $\mathcal{M}$ is the half of that cylinder for which $x \geq 0$ and $\mathbf{F}(x, y, z) = \langle 1, y, xy \rangle \frac{\text{g/sec}}{\text{mm}^2}$ is the mass flow of a fluid, determine the rate at which fluid passes through $\mathcal{M}$ and in which direction.

____ Fluid Flux

47. Suppose $\mathcal{M}$ is the positively oriented surface for which $\rho = 5$, $\theta \in [\pi/4, \pi/2]$ and $\phi \in [\pi/3, 2\pi/3]$. Calculate the flux of the electric field $\mathbf{E} = \mathbf{i} \, \frac{\text{N}}{\text{C}}$ through $\mathcal{M}$.

____ Electric Field Flux

48. Suppose R is the parallelogram in the xy-plane defined by the position vectors $\mathbf{u} = \langle 4, 1 \rangle$ and $\mathbf{v} = \langle 1, 3 \rangle$, and $\mathcal{M}$ is the portion of the positively oriented graph of $f(x, y) = x^2 - y$ that sits over R. Calculate the flux of the vector field $\mathbf{F} = \mathbf{i} + 2x\mathbf{j} + y\mathbf{k}$ through $\mathcal{M}$.

49. Show that div$(\mathbf{F} \times \mathbf{G}) = $ curl$(\mathbf{F}) \cdot \mathbf{G} - \mathbf{F} \cdot $ curl$(\mathbf{G})$.

50. Suppose $\mathbf{F}(x,y) = f(x^2 + y^2)\langle x, y\rangle$ where f is a differentiable function of a single variable. Verify that $\mathbf{F}$ is irrotational.

51. Determine the unit normal vector of the plane in which the curl density of $\mathbf{F}(x,y,z) = \langle 3x + zy, 4x^2 - 8zy, 5xz^3\rangle$ is greatest at the point $(1, -1, 2)$.

52. Suppose $\mathbf{F} = \langle L, M, N\rangle$ is smooth, and its components are nonzero. Show

$$\mathbf{F} \cdot \nabla \times \mathbf{F} = \|\mathbf{F}\|^2 \left\{ \left(\frac{N}{\|\mathbf{F}\|}\right)^2 \left(\frac{M}{N}\right)_x + \left(\frac{L}{\|\mathbf{F}\|}\right)^2 \left(\frac{N}{L}\right)_y + \left(\frac{M}{\|\mathbf{F}\|}\right)^2 \left(\frac{L}{M}\right)_z \right\}$$

53. An object of M kilograms at the origin induces a gravitational field of $\mathbf{F} = GM\mathbf{r}/\|\mathbf{r}\|^3$, where $\mathbf{r} = \langle x, y, z\rangle$ and G is the gravitational constant. $\qquad$ Gravitational Field

   (a) Use a surface integral to find the flux of $\mathbf{F}$ through the sphere $\rho = R$.

   (b) Show that $\nabla \cdot \mathbf{F} = 0$ away from the origin.

   (c) Suppose $\mathcal{M}$ is a piecewise-smooth, closed surface that encloses the origin. Use parts (a) and (b) to determine the flux of $\mathbf{F}$ through $\mathcal{M}$.

   (d) Suppose the object is at the point $(0,0,1)$ instead of the origin, and $\mathcal{M}$ is the sphere $\rho = 3$. Determine the flux of $\mathbf{F}$ through $\mathcal{M}$.

   (e) Suppose there are three objects inside the sphere of radius 7: mass M_1 is at the point $(1,0,0)$, M_2 is at $(0,1,0)$, and mass M_3 is at $(0,0,1)$. Compare the flux of their combined gravitational field through the sphere to that of a single object at the origin with mass $M = M_1 + M_2 + M_3$.

54. The **_Maxwell-Faraday Law of Electromagnetism_** says that changes in a magnetic field induce an electric field. Specifically, change in the magnetic field $\mathbf{B}$ induces an electric field $\mathbf{E}$ for which $-\mathbf{B}_t = \nabla \times \mathbf{E}$. $\qquad$ Electromagnetic Theory

   (a) Assuming that the components of $\mathbf{B}$ have continuous second partial derivatives, use Clairaut's Theorem in conjunction with the equation $-\mathbf{B}_t = \nabla \times \mathbf{E}$ to prove that $\nabla \cdot \mathbf{B}$ is constant.

   (b) Assuming that $\mathbf{B}(0) = \mathbf{0}$, use part (a) to prove that $\nabla \cdot \mathbf{B} = 0$. This fact is known as **_Gauss' Law of Magnetism_**.

55. A vector field $\mathbf{F}$ is said to be **_incompressible_** (or **_solenoidal_**) if $\nabla \cdot \mathbf{F} = 0$. Show that the cross product of two irrotational vector fields is incompressible.

56. Suppose $\mathbf{F} = \|\mathbf{r}\|^{-4}\mathbf{r}$ away from the origin, where $\mathbf{r} = \langle x, y, z\rangle$.

   (a) Determine the flux of $\mathbf{F}$ through the sphere of radius 10.

   (b) Show that $\operatorname{div}(\mathbf{F}) < 0$ at each point away from the origin.

   (c) Suppose that $\mathcal{M}_1$ is the positively oriented "bumpy sphere" described by $\rho = 5 + \sin 5\theta \sin 3\phi$. Use the Divergence Theorem to determine whether the flux of $\mathbf{F}$ through $\mathcal{M}_1$ is greater than or less than the number you calculated in part (a).

57. Suppose $\mathbf{F}(x,y,z) = \langle 5x, y, -6z\rangle$, and $\mathcal{M}$ is the positively oriented surface of the cube in which $x, y, z \in [0, 2]$.

   (a) Use surface integrals to determine the flux of $\mathbf{F}$ across the $\mathcal{M}$.

   (b) Calculate $\iiint_E \operatorname{div}(\mathbf{F})\, dV$ where E is the region enclosed by $\mathcal{M}$.

58. Suppose $\mathcal{C}$ is the intersection of the cylinder $x^2 + y^2 = 1$ with the plane $x + y + z = 0$, and $\mathcal{C}$ is positively oriented with respect to the normal of the plane, $\mathbf{n} = \langle 1, 1, 1\rangle$. Use Stokes' Theorem to calculate $\oint_{\mathcal{C}} \mathbf{F} \cdot d\mathbf{r}$ when $\mathbf{F} = xyz\langle 1, -1, 1\rangle$.

Chapter 15 Projects and Applications

✣ Fermat's Principle and the Index of Refraction

In Section 15.2 we said that the time required for light to travel along the path $\mathcal{P}$ is calculated as a line integral:

$$T = \int_{\mathcal{P}} \frac{n}{c}\, ds. \tag{13.1}$$

where n is the index of refraction, and c is the speed of light. This allowed us to restate Fermat's Principle quantitatively: when light travels from point A to point B, it travels along a path $\mathcal{P}$ that minimizes the value of the line integral in equation (13.1). This path is a line when the index of refraction is constant, but the shape of $\mathcal{P}$ is less obvious when the index of refraction varies with position. In the work that follows we assume that $n = n(x, y)$ has continuous partial derivatives, and proceed to formulate equations (called the *Euler-Lagrange* equations) that describe the path that light follows through such a medium.

▷ Euler-Lagrange equations

Suppose $\mathcal{P}$ is a path in the xy-plane that connects the points A and B, and that $\mathcal{P}$ is parameterized by the smooth function $\mathbf{r}(\tau) = r_1(\tau)\mathbf{i} + r_2(\tau)\mathbf{j}$ when $\tau \in [0, 1]$, so $\mathbf{r}(0)$ and $\mathbf{r}(1)$ are the position vectors for the points A and B respectively. Then $ds = \|d\mathbf{r}/d\tau\|\, d\tau$, so the time it takes light to travel over $\mathcal{P}$ is

> We're using τ instead of t in order to avoid confusing the parameter, which acts like time for the parameterization, with actual time.

$$\int_{\mathcal{P}} \frac{n}{c}\, ds = \frac{1}{c} \int_0^1 n\big(r_1(\tau), r_2(\tau)\big) \left\| \frac{d\mathbf{r}}{d\tau} \right\| d\tau.$$

Any other smooth path from A to B can be thought of as a deviation from $\mathcal{P}$, and so parameterized by a vector-valued function of the form $\mathbf{r}(\tau) + \varepsilon\mathbf{p}(\tau)$, where $\mathbf{p}(\tau) = \langle p_1(\tau), p_2(\tau)\rangle$ is a smooth vector-valued function, and ε is a scalar.

> The function $\varepsilon\mathbf{p}(\tau)$ accounts for the deviation between this other path and $\mathcal{P}$.

1. Explain why $p_1(0), p_1(1), p_2(0)$, and $p_2(1)$ are all 0.

The time it takes light to traverse such a path is

$$\frac{1}{c} \int_0^1 n\big(x(\tau), y(\tau)\big) \left\| \frac{d\mathbf{r}}{d\tau} + \varepsilon \frac{d\mathbf{p}}{d\tau} \right\| d\tau,$$

where $x(\tau) = r_1(\tau) + \varepsilon p_1(\tau)$ and $y(\tau) = r_2(\tau) + \varepsilon p_2(\tau)$. If the light were traveling in a vacuum, this amount of time would correspond to a distance of

$$S = \int_0^1 n\big(\underbrace{r_1(\tau) + \varepsilon p_1(\tau)}_{= x(\tau)}, \underbrace{r_2(\tau) + \varepsilon p_2(\tau)}_{= y(\tau)}\big) \left\| \frac{d\mathbf{r}}{d\tau} + \varepsilon \frac{d\mathbf{p}}{d\tau} \right\| d\tau, \tag{13.2}$$

which is called the *optical path length*. Note that S is a function of ε. If $\mathcal{P}$ is the path of least time, the function $S(\varepsilon)$ has a minimum at $\varepsilon = 0$, which means that $dS/d\varepsilon = 0$ at $\varepsilon = 0$.

2. By passing $d/d\varepsilon$ through the integral sign in (13.2), show that

$$\left. \frac{dS}{d\varepsilon} \right|_{\varepsilon=0} = \int_0^1 \left[\|\mathbf{r}'\| \nabla n \cdot \mathbf{p} + \frac{n}{\|\mathbf{r}'\|} \mathbf{r}' \cdot \mathbf{p}' \right] d\tau \tag{13.3}$$

where $\mathbf{r}'$ and $\mathbf{p}'$ denote $d\mathbf{r}/d\tau$ and $d\mathbf{p}/d\tau$ respectively, n is the index of refraction at $\big(x(\tau), y(\tau)\big)$, and $\nabla n = \langle n_x, n_y\rangle$ is its gradient.

3. Integrate by parts and use what you know of $\mathbf{p}(0)$ and $\mathbf{p}(1)$ to show that

$$\int_0^1 \frac{n}{\|\mathbf{r}'\|}\mathbf{r}' \cdot \mathbf{p}' \, d\tau = -\int_0^1 \frac{d}{d\tau}\left(\frac{n}{\|\mathbf{r}'\|}\mathbf{r}'\right) \cdot \mathbf{p} \, d\tau$$

The result from #3 allows us to rewrite equation (13.3) as

$$\left.\frac{dS}{d\varepsilon}\right|_{\varepsilon=0} = \int_0^1 \left[\|\mathbf{r}'\|\nabla n - \frac{d}{d\tau}\left(\frac{n}{\|\mathbf{r}'\|}\mathbf{r}'\right)\right] \cdot \mathbf{p} \, d\tau.$$

This integral looks complicated, but we can write it as

$$\int_0^1 \mathbf{u}(\tau) \cdot \mathbf{p}(\tau) \, d\tau \quad \text{where} \quad \mathbf{u} = \|\mathbf{r}'\|\nabla n - \frac{d}{d\tau}\left(\frac{n}{\|\mathbf{r}'\|}\mathbf{r}'\right).$$

The formula above defines $\mathbf{u}$ in terms of $\mathbf{r}$, but recall that we don't yet know the path $\mathcal{P}$, so although the function $\mathbf{r}$ exists in principle, we don't have an explicit formula for it. Consequently, we don't have an explicit formula for $\mathbf{u}$, but because we know that the integral must be 0 for every smooth $\mathbf{p}(\tau)$ with $\mathbf{p}(0) = \mathbf{0} = \mathbf{p}(1)$, we can say something important about $\mathbf{u}(\tau)$.

4. Suppose we write $\mathbf{u} = \langle u_1(\tau), u_2(\tau)\rangle$. If the continuous function $u_1(\tau)$ were nonzero at some $\tau_1 \in (0,1)$, it would remain nonzero in some small interval, say $(\tau_1 - \delta, \tau_1 + \delta) \subset (0,1)$. So if $\mathbf{p}(\tau) = \langle p_1(\tau), 0\rangle$ where $p_1(\tau)$ is a continuous function that's positive in $(\tau_1 - \delta, \tau_1 + \delta)$ but vanishes outside that interval, the integral $\int_0^1 \mathbf{u} \cdot \mathbf{p} \, d\tau > 0$. Explain why this cannot happen.

> $\mathbf{u}(\tau)$ is continuous because $\mathbf{r}$ is smooth and n has continuous partial derivatives.

5. Based on #4, explain why

$$\|\mathbf{r}'\|\nabla n = \frac{d}{d\tau}\left(\frac{n}{\|\mathbf{r}'\|}\mathbf{r}'\right) \quad \text{when} \quad \tau \in (0,1). \tag{13.4}$$

We could write equation (13.4) as a pair of equations (one for each component of the vectors). Those equations are called the **Euler-Lagrange** equations.

▷ "F=ma" optics

In 1986 J. Evans and M. Rosenquist proposed a clever re-parameterization of $\mathcal{P}$ that makes equation (13.4) tractable in some simple but important cases. Specifically, they suggest using a parameter a for which

$$\left\|\frac{d\mathbf{r}}{da}\right\| = n.$$

Then from the Chain Rule, we see that

$$n = \left\|\frac{d\mathbf{r}}{da}\right\| = \left\|\frac{d\tau}{da}\frac{d\mathbf{r}}{d\tau}\right\| = \|\mathbf{r}'\|\left|\frac{d\tau}{da}\right|, \tag{13.5}$$

and for any differentiable function f,

$$\frac{df}{d\tau} = \frac{d\tau}{da}\frac{df}{da}. \tag{13.6}$$

6. Use equations (13.5) and (13.6) to verify that the Euler-Lagrange equations can be written as

$$n\nabla n = \frac{d^2\mathbf{r}}{da^2}. \tag{13.7}$$

▷ Snell's Law

In Section 4.7 (exercise #38) you saw Fermat's Principle lead to *Snell's Law*, which quantifies the bending of light's trajectory at the interface between two media in which the speed of light differs. Snell's Law is a direct consequence of equation (13.7). Suppose $n_2 > n_1$ and

$$n(x,y) = \begin{cases} n_1 & \text{if } y \geq 0 \\ n_2 & \text{if } y < 0 \end{cases}$$

7. Use equation (13.7) to show that $\mathbf{r}$ is a piecewise-linear function of a.

8. Use equation (13.7) to show that, because $n_x = 0$ at all points along the light path parameterized by $\mathbf{r} = \langle x(a), y(a) \rangle$, it must be that $\frac{dx}{da}$ is constant.

9. Using a subscript of 1 to denote $y \geq 0$ and a subscript of 2 to denote $y < 0$, the result from #8 can be written as $\left(\frac{dx}{da}\right)_1 = \left(\frac{dx}{da}\right)_2$. Use this fact in conjunction with Figure 13.1 to prove that $n_1 \sin\theta_1 = n_2 \sin\theta_2$, which is Snell's Law.

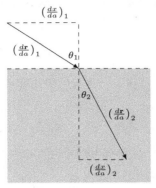

Figure 13.1: Diagram of Snell's Law.

▷ Gradient index optics

Instead of bending a light path via the interface between two regions of different but constant indices, we can design a lens that bends light by continuously varying the material's index of refraction. Such a lens is called a *gradient index (GRIN) lens*. For example, consider a lens that appears to be an ordinary glass rod, but in which the index of refraction varies according to

$$n(x,y) = n_0\left(1 - \frac{1}{2}By^2\right).$$

where x is measured along the axis of the cylinder, y is a radial variable, and n_0 and B are positive constants.

10. Determine the vector $n\nabla n$.

11. Use #10 and equation (13.7) to show that $\frac{dx}{da}$ is constant, say $\frac{dx}{da} = k$.

In the following steps, we'll assume that $k > 0$ so that we traverse the light path from left to right as the parameter a increases.

12. Use #10 and #11 to show that

$$\frac{d^2y}{dx^2} = -\left(\frac{n_0}{k}\right)^2 By\left(1 - \frac{1}{2}By^2\right). \tag{13.8}$$

Provided that $By^2 \ll 1$ equation (13.8) leads us to approximate the relationship between y'' and y as

$$\frac{d^2y}{dx^2} = -\left(\frac{n_0}{k}\right)^2 By, \tag{13.9}$$

from which we conclude that the light proceeds through the lens along a sinusoidal path:

$$y(x) = A_1 \sin\omega x + A_2 \cos\omega x.$$

13. Suppose a light ray enters the lens at $x = 0$, parallel to its axis, with $y = R$ (see Figure 13.3). Determine the values of A_1 and A_2.

14. Based on equation (13.9), determine how ω depends on n_0, B, and k.

Figure 13.2: A cylindrical lens

> We're using y for radius instead of r because we've already used the letter $\mathbf{r}$ to denote the parameterization of the light path.

> Here we're using the prime notation to denote differentiation with respect to x.

Figure 13.3: A light ray entering the lens.

While n_0 and B are design parameters of a particular lens, in order to determine the period of the light path, we need to determine the number k. Figure 13.4 shows a segment of a light path. Because $\|d\mathbf{r}\| = \sqrt{dx^2 + dy^2}$, we can write

$$k = \frac{dx}{da} = \frac{\|d\mathbf{r}\|}{da} \frac{dx}{\sqrt{dx^2 + dy^2}} = \frac{n}{\sqrt{1 + (dy/dx)^2}}. \tag{13.10}$$

Figure 13.4: An infinitesimal segment of the light path.

15. Use equation (13.10) to determine the period of the sinusoidal path from #13.

16. Show that if $BR^2 \ll 1$ (which is consistent with the hypothesis of our approximation above) all the light rays that enter this lens parallel to its axis are focused to a single point.

Appendix A

Trigonometry

This appendix assumes that you've already been exposed to trigonometry and know many of the basic facts (e.g., the interior angles of a triangle in the plane sum to 180°), but that you would either like a brief review, are looking for some mnemonics, or want to see the subject from a different point of view.

❖ The Pythagorean Theorem

While we expect that you already know the Pythagorean Theorem, it's extremely important, and this review of trigonometry would be decidedly lacking without it.

> **Pythagorean Theorem:** Suppose the legs of a right triangle have lengths a and b, and the length of the hypotenuse is c. Then
> $$a^2 + b^2 = c^2.$$

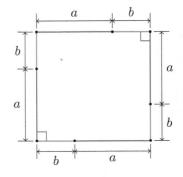

Figure A.1: A square of side length $a + b$

Proof. Consider taking a pole of length a and joining it to another of length b, making one long pole of length $a + b$. In fact, suppose you do that four times, and then lay the poles in the shape of a square, as seen in Figure A.1 (notice that the poles are always oriented in the same direction as you walk around the square).

By connecting the points on adjacent sides of this square where the short and long poles are joined, as in the left-hand image of Figure A.2, we subdivide the original square into four right triangles and a smaller square. We'll denote by c the side length of that interior square, and now we're ready to prove the theorem. Our proof rests on two facts: (1) the four triangles are all congruent, with legs of

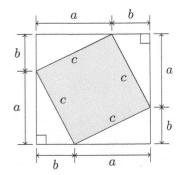 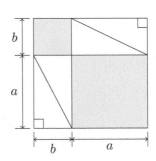

Figure A.2: (left) Subdividing the square into four triangles, and an interior square of side length c; (right) rearranging the triangles to see the area differently.

length a and b, and (2) shifting and rotating the triangles does not change their area. Because of these facts, the area of the shaded regions in both images of Figure A.2 is the same; the shaded square on the left has an area of c^2, and on the right the shaded squares have areas of a^2 and b^2. That is, $c^2 = a^2 + b^2$.   ■

Calculating the side lengths of a $45°, 45°, 90°$ triangle

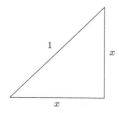

Figure A.3: A right triangle whose legs are the same length.

Example A.1. Consider the right triangle that's made by cutting a square along its diagonal (so the interior angles of the triangle are $45°, 45°, 90°$). If the diagonal has a length of 1, what are the lengths of the legs of this right triangle?

Solution: Since we cut a square across its diagonal, the legs of this right triangle have the same length. Let's call it x (see Figure A.3). Then the Pythagorean Theorem tells us that

$$1^2 = x^2 + x^2 \quad \Rightarrow \quad 1 = 2x^2 \quad \Rightarrow \quad x = \frac{1}{\sqrt{2}},$$

which is often rewritten as $x = \sqrt{2}/2$.   ■

Calculating the side lengths of a $30°, 60°, 90°$ triangle

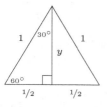

Example A.2. Consider the right triangle that's made by dropping an altitude from one vertex of an equilateral triangle (so the interior angles of our triangle are $30°, 60°, 90°$). If the equilateral triangle has a side length of 1, what are the lengths of the legs of this right triangle?

Solution: Since this triangle is equilateral, the altitude bisects the angle at the vertex from which it originates, and also bisects the opposite side (see Figure A.4), resulting in a pair of triangles whose interior angles are $30°, 60°, 90°$. The only unknown length is that of the altitude, but we can calculate it using the Pythagorean Theorem:

Figure A.4: Dropping an altitude from one vertex of the triangle creates a pair of triangles whose interior angles are $30°, 60°, 90°$.

$$\left(\frac{1}{2}\right)^2 + y^2 = 1^2 \quad \Rightarrow \quad y^2 = \frac{3}{4} \quad \Rightarrow \quad y = \frac{\sqrt{3}}{2}.$$
     ■

✧ The Trigonometric Functions

Suppose you draw a circle in the sand, and to provide an orientation for our discussion, you also draw a pair of perpendicular lines through the center—one traveling from north to south, and the other from east to west. We're going to talk about lengths in a moment so we need a unit of some kind, and since the circle cuts the orientation lines so nicely, it seems natural to use those segments somehow. In the larger scheme of things, it's irrelevant whether we define our unit length using the radius or the diameter of the circle, so we'll just choose the radius of the circle as our unit. By virtue of this choice, the radius of the circle is 1.

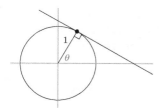

Figure A.5: The unit circle, with north-south and east-west lines providing orientation.

With that said, suppose you draw a line that intersects the circle at exactly one point, somewhere in the northeast quadrant of the circle, as seen in Figure A.5. Such a line is called a *tangent line,* and is perpendicular to the line segment that joins the point of its intersection to the center of the circle. This right angle can be understood as part of a right triangle whose hypotenuse is the east-west axis, as seen in Figure A.6. The lengths of the legs and hypotenuse of this triangle depend on exactly where the tangent line intersects the circle. We'll keep track of that location using the interior angle of our triangle at the origin, which we'll denote by the Greek letter θ.

- The length of this triangle's altitude is called the **sine** of θ, and is denoted by $\sin\theta$.

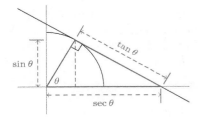

Figure A.6: The lengths of the triangle's legs and hypotenuse depend on the angle θ.

- One leg of our right triangle (which extends from the circle's center to the point where the tangent line intersects the circle) has a length of 1.

- The other leg of this right triangle lies along the tangent line. Its length is called the **tangent** of θ, and is denoted by $\tan\theta$.

- The hypotenuse of this right triangle is on a line that cuts through the circle (such a line is called secant line). Its length is called the **secant** of θ, and is denoted by $\sec\theta$.

- According to the Pythagorean Theorem $\left(\tan\theta\right)^2 + 1 = \left(\sec\theta\right)^2$, which is usually written as
$$\tan^2\theta + 1 = \sec^2\theta.$$

You might wonder why we made a triangle with a hypotenuse on the east-west axis, rather than one with its hypotenuse on the north-south axis. Couldn't we measure the corresponding lengths of that other—let us say "co"-triangle? Yes. See Figure A.7.

- The length of this co-triangle's altitude is called the **cosine** of θ, and is denoted by $\cos\theta$.

- One leg of the co-triangle has a length of 1.

- The other leg of the co-triangle sits on the tangent line. Its length is called the **cotangent** of θ, and is denoted by $\cot\theta$.

- The hypotenuse of the co-triangle is on a line that cuts through the circle (such a line is called secant line). Its length is called the **cosecant** of θ, and is denoted by $\csc\theta$.

- According to the Pythagorean Theorem $\left(\cot\theta\right)^2 + 1 = \left(\csc\theta\right)^2$, which is usually written as
$$\cot^2\theta + 1 = \csc^2\theta.$$

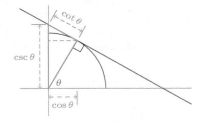

Figure A.7: The lengths of the "co"-triangle's legs and hypotenuse depend on the angle θ.

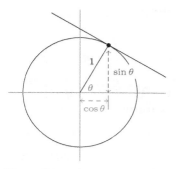

When we combine the information in the left and right images of Figure A.6, we see that $\cos\theta$ and $\sin\theta$ are the side lengths of a right triangle whose hypotenuse has a length of 1 (see Figure A.8), so the Pythagorean Theorem tells us that

$$\big(\cos\theta\big)^2 + \big(\sin\theta\big)^2 = 1,$$

which is usually written as

$$\cos^2\theta + \sin^2\theta = 1.$$

Lastly, because the ratio of side lengths is the same in similar triangles, we find that

$$\frac{\tan\theta}{1} = \frac{\sin\theta}{\cos\theta} \tag{a.1}$$

$$\frac{\sec\theta}{1} = \frac{1}{\cos\theta} \tag{a.2}$$

$$\frac{\csc\theta}{1} = \frac{1}{\sin\theta}. \tag{a.3}$$

Figure A.8: A triangle with legs of length $\sin\theta$ and $\cos\theta$.

Many people have trouble remembering whether these equations say that secant is the reciprocal of the sine or the cosine. It might help to note that when you read equations (a.2) and (a.3) you hear the phoneme "co" exactly one time.

✢ Radian Measure

Have you ever wondered why there are 360° in a circle? We inherited this way of measuring angle from the ancient Babylonians, who used a sexagesimal instead of a decimal number system (i.e., base 60 instead of base 10). We could measure angle in other ways, too, and the one that we use in calculus is called *radian* measure. This way of measuring angle, which we'll discuss in a moment, has the practical benefit of simplifying discussions about the rate at which the sine and cosine change as the angle θ varies. (This discussion happens in Chapter 3.)

Imagine that you're a Babylonian astronomer, and you want to communicate the location of stars. So you divide the arc of the sky into three equal segments: one directly overhead, one to the west, and one to the east. Then you use the number system—i.e., base 60—to refine the segments. You have now divided the semi-circle into $3 \times 60 = 180$ equal parts.

So what are radians? On p. 1317 we drew a circle, and used its radius as our unit of length. Figure A.9 shows the portion of the circle's circumference that you'd cross were you to start at the easternmost point and walk 1, 2, or 3 units around it. If you walk 1 unit around the edge of this circle, we say that the angle subtended by your path is $\theta = 1$ **radian**. If you walk 2 units around it, we say that the angle subtended by your path is $\theta = 2$ radians, and an angle of $\theta = 3$ radians means that you walked 3 units around the edge of the circle.

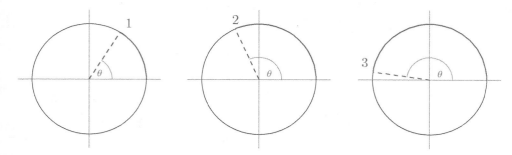

Figure A.9: (left to right) The bold blue arc shows how much of the circumference you would cover by walking 1, 2, or 3 units around the edge of the circle of radius is 1.

You can see from Figure A.9 that the upper half of the unit circle is a little more than 3 units long. In fact, its length is the irrational number $\pi \approx 3.14159\ldots$ so we say that the upper semicircle subtends an angle of π radians, and there are 2π radians of angle in the whole circle. We can use this fact to convert back and forth between radians and degrees.

Converting degrees to radians

Example A.3. Convert the angles $30°, 60°$ and $90°$ into radians.

Solution: There are $360°$ of angle in a circle, so an angle of $30°$ corresponds to

$$\frac{30°}{360°} = \frac{1}{12} \quad \text{of the the total angle in the circle.}$$

Therefore, that same angle is $\frac{1}{12}(2\pi) = \frac{\pi}{6}$ radians. Similarly, we can determine the radian measure of $60°$ by calculating

$$2\pi \left(\frac{60°}{360°} \right) = 2\pi \left(\frac{1}{6} \right) = \frac{\pi}{3}.$$

And the radian measure of $90°$ is

$$2\pi \left(\frac{90°}{360°} \right) = 2\pi \left(\frac{1}{4} \right) = \frac{\pi}{2}. \qquad \blacksquare$$

Converting degrees to radians

Example A.4. Convert the angles (a) $45°$, and (b) $120°$ into radians.

Answer: (a) $\pi/4$, (b) $2\pi/3$. $\qquad \blacksquare$

Solution
On-line

Converting radians to degrees

Example A.5. Convert the angles (a) $\frac{3\pi}{4}$ and (b) $\frac{7\pi}{6}$ to degree measure.

Solution: (a) Since there are π radians of angle in the upper semicircle, a radian measure of $\frac{3\pi}{4} = \frac{3}{4}\pi$ corresponds to $\frac{3}{4}$ of the angle in a semicircle. Since there are $180°$ degrees in a semicircle, we conclude that

$$\frac{3\pi}{4} \text{ radians is the same angle as } \frac{3}{4}(180°) = 135°.$$

> Most people have to think for a moment before realizing that $135°$ corresponds to $3/4$ of a semicircle, but that fact appears explicitly in the radian measure of the angle.

(b) Since $\frac{7\pi}{6} > \pi$, this angle sweeps over the upper semicircle and then some. Specifically, since $\frac{7\pi}{6} = \frac{7}{6}\pi = \pi + \frac{1}{6}\pi$, we know that it sweeps across the upper semicircle and then, starting from the westernmost point of the circle, $\frac{1}{6}$ of the lower semicircle. Since each semicircle corresponds to $180°$,

$$\frac{7\pi}{6} \text{ radians is the same angle as } 180° + \frac{1}{6}(180°) = 210°. \qquad \blacksquare$$

Converting radians to degrees

Example A.6. Convert the angles (a) $\frac{5\pi}{4}$, (b) $\frac{11\pi}{6}$ and (c) $\frac{3\pi}{2}$ to degree measure.

Answer: (a) $225°$, (b) $330°$, (c) $270°$. $\qquad \blacksquare$

Solution
On-line

❖ Trigonometric Functions and the Cartesian Plane

The perpendicular axes and circle that we've drawn can be used to define a Cartesian plane: the center of the circle will be the reference point to which we relate all locations (i.e., the origin), the radius of the circle will be what we call the unit of length (as it has been heretofore), and we'll say that a point has coordinates (x, y) if you can arrive there from the origin by walking x units east and y units north ($x < 0$ means to travel west, and $y < 0$ means to travel south). For example, the easternmost point on the unit circle has coordinates $(1, 0)$; and the northernmost point has coordinates $(0, 1)$.

Now suppose P is some point on the northeast part of the unit circle, and it's separated from $(1, 0)$ by θ units of length along the circle. Based on our work so far, the coordinates of P are the cosine and sine, as depicted in Figure A.10:

$$x = \cos\theta$$
$$y = \sin\theta.$$

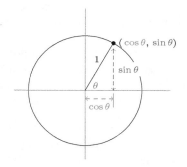

Figure A.10: From Figure A.8 we see that the cosine tells us the x-coordinate of a point on the unit circle, and the sine tells us its y-coordinate.

Values of the trigonometric functions at standard reference angles

Example A.7. Determine the values of sine and cosine at the standard reference angles, $\theta = 0, \frac{\pi}{6}, \frac{\pi}{4}, \frac{\pi}{3}, \frac{\pi}{2}$.

Solution: We discussed the side lengths of some particular right triangles in Examples A.1 and A.2. In the latter, we saw that the legs have lengths $\frac{\sqrt{3}}{2}$ and $\frac{1}{2}$.

- If we lay that triangle with one vertex at the origin and its long side on the x-axis, as shown in the left-hand image of Figure A.11, the hypotenuse reaches to the point $(\frac{\sqrt{3}}{2}, \frac{1}{2})$ and makes a $\pi/6$ angle with the horizontal. So $\cos\left(\frac{\pi}{6}\right) = \frac{\sqrt{3}}{2}$ and $\sin\left(\frac{\pi}{6}\right) = \frac{1}{2}$.

- If we flip the triangle so that its short side is on the x-axis, as shown in the right-hand image of Figure A.11, the hypotenuse reaches to the point $(\frac{1}{2}, \frac{\sqrt{3}}{2})$ and makes a $\pi/3$ angle with the horizontal. So $\cos\left(\frac{\pi}{3}\right) = \frac{1}{2}$ and $\sin\left(\frac{\pi}{3}\right) = \frac{\sqrt{3}}{2}$.

Similarly, if we lay the triangle from Examples A.1 on the plane with one vertex at the origin and one leg on the x-axis (see the middle image of Figure A.11), the hypotenuse reaches to the point $(\frac{\sqrt{2}}{2}, \frac{\sqrt{2}}{2})$ and makes a $\pi/4$ angle with the horizontal. So $\cos\left(\frac{\pi}{4}\right) = \frac{\sqrt{2}}{2}$ and $\sin\left(\frac{\pi}{4}\right) = \frac{\sqrt{2}}{2}$.

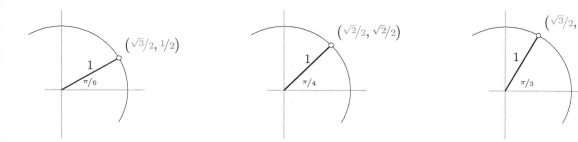

Figure A.11: (left to right) Using familiar triangles to determine the sine and cosine of $\pi/6$, $\pi/4$ and $\pi/3$.

As seen in Figure A.12, an angle of $\theta = 0$ means that we've not moved from the easternmost point at all, whose coordinates are $(1, 0)$. So thinking of the cosine and sine as x- and y-coordinates of that point, respectively, we say that $\cos(0) = 1$ and $\sin(0) = 0$.

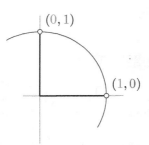

And lastly, an angle of $\theta = \frac{\pi}{2}$ corresponds to the northernmost point of the circle, whose coordinates are $(0, 1)$. So thinking of the cosine and sine as x- and y-coordinates of that point, respectively, we say $\cos\left(\frac{\pi}{2}\right) = 0$ and $\sin\left(\frac{\pi}{2}\right) = 1$. ∎

Figure A.12: Angles of 0 and $\pi/2$ correspond to the easternmost and northern-most points of the circle, whose coordinates we already know.

When we combine the information from Example A.7 into a single diagram, we see Figure A.13. We've written 1 as $\frac{\sqrt{4}}{2}$, and 0 as $\frac{\sqrt{0}}{2}$ in that figure because it makes a pattern in the numbers particularly clear. As we move counterclockwise around the circle, increasing θ from zero to $\frac{\pi}{2}$ we see that ...

- the y-coordinate increases. Specifically, the y-coordinate (the sine) at the standard reference angles is $\frac{\sqrt{0}}{2}, \frac{\sqrt{1}}{2}, \frac{\sqrt{2}}{2}, \frac{\sqrt{3}}{2}, \frac{\sqrt{4}}{2}$, in which the number under the radical increments by 1 each time we increase θ from one of the standard reference angles to the next.

- the x-coordinate decreases. Specifically, the x-coordinate (the cosine) at the standard reference angles is $\frac{\sqrt{4}}{2}, \frac{\sqrt{3}}{2}, \frac{\sqrt{2}}{2}, \frac{\sqrt{1}}{2}, \frac{\sqrt{0}}{2}$, in which the number under the radical is reduced by 1 each time we increase θ from one of the standard reference angles to the next.

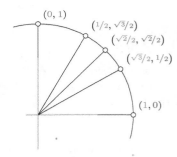

Figure A.13: Combining the information from Example A.7 into a single diagram.

Alternatively, it might help you to remember the values of the sine and cosine if you note that they can only produce the numbers $1, \frac{\sqrt{3}}{2}, \frac{\sqrt{2}}{2}, \frac{1}{2}, 0$ at the standard reference angles. If you think of this list as a numerical teeter-totter whose fulcrum is the number $\frac{\sqrt{2}}{2}$, the numbers $\cos\theta$ and $\sin\theta$ always "balance."

▷ Negative values of sine and cosine

When we introduced the sine and cosine, we said that they were lengths. While that motivation is true to their geometric origin, at this time we want to extend the idea that $(\cos\theta, \sin\theta)$ are the coordinates of a point on the unit circle by addressing points that do not lie in the northeast quadrant of our Cartesian plane.

- When a point on the unit circle is in the left half-plane, its x-coordinate (the cosine) will be negative (see Figure A.14).

- When a point on the unit circle is in the lower half-plane, its y-coordinate (the sine) will be negative (see Figure A.14).

Negative values of sine and/or cosine

Example A.8. Determine the sine and cosine of (a) the angle $\theta = \pi$, (b) the angle $\theta = \frac{5\pi}{6}$, and (c) the angle $\theta = \frac{5\pi}{4}$.

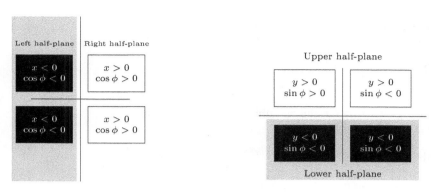

Figure A.14: (left) $\cos\theta < 0$ when the angle θ identifies a point on the unit circle that's in the left half-plane; (right) $\sin\theta < 0$ when the angle θ identifies a point on the unit circle that's in the lower half-plane.

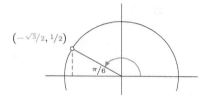

Figure A.15: The cosine is negative in part (b) of Example A.8 because the corresponding point on the unit circle is in the left half-plane.

Solution: (a) The radian angle $\theta = \pi$ corresponds to the westernmost point of the circle, whose coordinates are $(-1, 0)$. So we say that $\cos(\pi) = -1$ and $\sin(\pi) = 0$.

(b) As mentioned in part (a), the westernmost point of the circle is found when $\theta = \pi$, so the point on the unit circle corresponding to $\theta = \frac{5}{6}\pi$ is just shy of that— i.e., it's in the northwest (second) quadrant. We can locate it precisely by laying the long leg of the triangle from Example A.2 (whose interior angles are $\pi/6, \pi/3$ and $\pi/2$) on the negative-x axis, as seen in Figure A.15. Since we know the lengths of that triangle's legs, we know that the point's coordinates are $(-\frac{\sqrt{3}}{2}, \frac{1}{2})$. That is, $\cos\left(\frac{5\pi}{6}\right) = -\frac{\sqrt{3}}{2}$ and $\sin\left(\frac{5\pi}{6}\right) = \frac{1}{2}$.

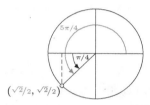

Figure A.16: The cosine is negative in part (c) of Example A.8 because the corresponding point on the unit circle is in the left half-plane, and the sine is negative because it lies in the lower half-plane.

(c) Similarly, since $\frac{5}{4}\pi = \pi + \frac{1}{4}\pi$, we have to traverse more than just the upper semicircle in order to locate the point on the unit circle corresponding to an angle of $\theta = \frac{5\pi}{4}$. It's found in the southwest (third) quadrant. We can locate it precisely by laying a leg edge of the triangle from Example A.1 along the negative-x axis, as seen in Figure A.16. Since we know that both lengths of that triangle have a length of $\frac{\sqrt{2}}{2}$, we know that the point's coordinates are $(-\frac{\sqrt{2}}{2}, -\frac{\sqrt{2}}{2})$. That is, $\cos\left(\frac{5\pi}{4}\right) = -\frac{\sqrt{2}}{2}$ and $\sin\left(\frac{5\pi}{4}\right) = -\frac{\sqrt{2}}{2}$. ∎

Negative values of sine and/or cosine

Example A.9. Determine the sine and cosine of (a) the angle $\theta = 2\pi$, (b) the angle $\theta = \frac{4\pi}{3}$ and (c) the angle $\theta = \frac{5\pi}{3}$.

Answer: (a) $(1, 0)$, (b) $\left(-\frac{1}{2}, -\frac{\sqrt{3}}{2}\right)$, (c) $\left(\frac{1}{2}, -\frac{\sqrt{3}}{2}\right)$. ∎

Solution On-line

✣ Radian Angles Beyond $[0, 2\pi]$

When a radian angle is negative, it simply means to start at $(1, 0)$ and proceed *clockwise* around the circle, rather than counterclockwise, and radian angles larger than 2π mean simply that you have to complete more that one full circuit of the circle in order to find the corresponding point on the circle. For example, the radian angles of $-\pi/6$, $11\pi/6$ and $23\pi/6$ all locate the same point on the circle. Since the x-coordinate of the point is always the same, regardless of how we arrived at it, we have

$$\cos\left(-\frac{\pi}{6}\right) = \cos\left(\frac{11\pi}{6}\right) = \cos\left(\frac{23\pi}{6}\right).$$

Similarly, since the y-coordinate of the point is always the same, regardless of how we arrived at it, we have

$$\sin\left(-\frac{\pi}{6}\right) = \sin\left(\frac{11\pi}{6}\right) = \sin\left(\frac{23\pi}{6}\right)$$

More generally, since moving from a point to itself by traversing the unit circle any number of times will always leave us with the same x and y coordinates, we see that

$$\sin\theta = \sin(\theta + 2\pi m) \quad \text{and} \quad \cos\theta = \cos(\theta + 2\pi m)$$

for any integer m. For this reason, we say that the sine and cosine are ***periodic*** functions and that their period is 2π. This periodicity is explicitly apparent in the graphs of sine and cosine (as functions of θ) shown in Figure A.17. Beginners sometimes have difficulty remembering which graph corresponds to which function. You can pin it down by remembering that $\sin 0 = 0$, so its graph will pass through the origin.

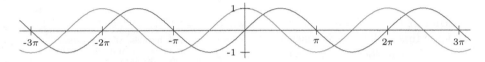

Figure A.17: The periodicity of cosine and sine is seen in the curves $y = \cos x$ and $y = \sin x$.

❖ Area and Circumference

We said earlier that the upper half of the circle has a length of π units (where "unit" means the length of the radius). Amazingly, the area enclosed by the unit circle is also π. To see why, suppose we slice the circle into many equal sectors—much like cutting a pizza for a large group of friends who are all equally hungry. If we line up those slices, alternating "tip up" and "tip down" (as in Figure A.18) we see an almost rectangular region. As we make the slices thinner, their cumulative area is always the same, but the sides of the "rectangle" become more vertical while its top and bottom become less bumpy—i.e., it becomes more and more like a rectangle. So as we use more and more slices, we're led to the fact that

$$\text{the area of the unit circle } = (1)\pi = \pi.$$

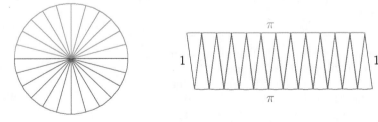

Figure A.18: By reorienting the slices of a circle, we see a rectangular shape, which allows us to relate circumference to area.

✤ When the Radius is Not 1

Earlier in this appendix, we began our discussion of the trigonometric functions by imagining a circle in the sand. We declared the radius of the circle to be our "unit," meaning that all lengths have been expressed in terms of it. Now suppose a friend comes along with a tape measure, and tells you that your radius is actually ...

- 5 feet. Since you know that the circumference is 2π lengths of radius, and each radius is 5 feet, the circumference of the circle is $2\pi \times 5$ feet long.

- 60 inches. Since you know that the circumference is 2π lengths of radius, and each radius is 60 inches, the circumference of the circle is $2\pi \times 60$ inches long.

- 152.4 centimeters. Since you know that the circumference is 2π lengths of radius, and each radius is 152.4 centimeters, the circumference of the circle is $2\pi \times 152.4$ centimeters long.

In short, if the length of the radius is r, the circumference of the circle is $2\pi r$. And if some arc of the circle subtends an angle of θ radians, its length is θr, which you can think of as

$$\theta r = (\text{number of lengths of radius}) \times (\underbrace{\text{units per radius}}_{\text{ft, in, cm} \ldots})$$

or as

$$\theta r = \left(\frac{\theta}{2\pi}\right)(2\pi r) = \begin{pmatrix} \text{fraction of the cir-} \\ \text{cle's total angle sub-} \\ \text{tended by the arc} \end{pmatrix} \times (\text{circumference}).$$

Changing scale affects our measurement of area, much in the same way that it affected our calculation of circumference. Since each half of the circle has a length of πr, and the radius has a length of r, the technique of slicing the circle into wedges and making a "rectangle" (as seen in Figure A.18) leads directly to the conclusion that the area of the circle is $(\pi r) \times r = \pi r^2$.

Similarly, we've said that a point on the unit circle that's separated from $(1,0)$ by θ radians has an x-coordinate of $\cos\theta$ and a y-coordinate of $\sin\theta$. That is, its horizontal displacement from the origin is $\cos\theta$ units, and its vertical displacement is $\sin\theta$ units. If 1 "unit" is actually ...

- 5 feet, the horizontal displacement is $5\cos\theta$ feet.

- 60 inches, the vertical displacement is $60\sin\theta$ inches.

In general, when the radius of the circle is r, the point has coordinates

$$\begin{aligned} x &= r\cos\theta \\ y &= r\sin\theta, \end{aligned}$$

whose consequences we'll study in greater detail when we discuss *polar coordinates* in Chapter 9. For now let's note that, when x and y are nonnegative, the first of these equations allows us to express

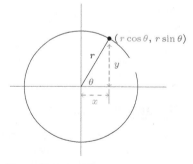

Figure A.19: A point on the circle of radius r.

$$\cos\theta = \frac{x}{r} = \frac{\text{length of leg adjacent to } \theta}{\text{length of hypotenuse}}, \quad \text{or in brief} \quad \cos\theta = \frac{\text{adjacent}}{\text{hypotenuse}}.$$

Similarly,

$$\sin\theta = \frac{y}{r} = \frac{\text{length of leg opposite from } \theta}{\text{length of hypotenuse}}, \quad \text{or in brief} \quad \sin\theta = \frac{\text{opposite}}{\text{hypotenuse}}.$$

� Dimensional Analysis

The idea that θ radians is a *number of lengths* of radius is helpful when using dimensional analysis to check that an equation makes sense. For example, a moment ago we said that the circumference of a circle is

$$\underbrace{C}_{\text{measured in, e.g., centimeters}} = 2\pi \underbrace{r}_{\text{measured in the same unit, e.g., centimeters}}.$$

In order for both sides of this equation to have units of *length*, the number 2π must not affect the dimensions (i.e., the *kind* of quantity being described) on the right-hand side. More generally, when an arc of the circle subtends an angle of θ radians, we said that its length, L is

$$\underbrace{L}_{\text{length of arc}} = \theta \underbrace{r}_{\text{length of radius}}.$$

Here you see that θ is acting as a constant of proportionality which, in order for this statement to make sense, must have units of "length of arc length *per* length of radius." That is, the dimensions of θ are

$$\frac{\text{length of arc}}{\text{length of radius}}.$$

You can see this at work in Figure A.20, which shows several circular arcs that all subtend an angle of $\pi/6$ radians. Each time the radius is incremented by 1, the circular arc gets longer by θ units. Because θ has units of "(length)/(length)," we say that radians are a **dimensionless** quantity.

> An equation that says mass = length is nonsensical. Mass and length are entirely different characteristics of an object. Similarly, an equation that says time = color is meaningless. In order for an equation to make sense, both sides must quantify the same *kind* of thing.

> For a more detailed discussion of what's meant by the words "dimensions" and "units," see Appendix E.

> For a more detailed discussion of *dimensionless* quantities, see Appendix E.

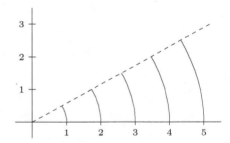

radius of circle	angle subtended	length of arc
1	$\pi/6$	$\pi/6$
2	$\pi/6$	$2(\pi/6)$
3	$\pi/6$	$3(\pi/6)$
4	$\pi/6$	$4(\pi/6)$
5	$\pi/6$	$5(\pi/6)$

Figure A.20: The length of a circular arc that subtends θ radians is proportional to the radius of the circle.

✳ Law of Cosines

The Law of Cosines is an extension of the Pythagorean Theorem that allows us to address non-right triangles. For example, an acute triangle with side lengths A, B and C is depicted in the left-hand image of Figure A.21.

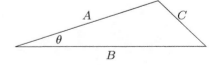 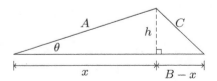

Figure A.21: (left) An acute triangle; (right) introducing "helper" variables x and h.

Since we know a lot about right triangles, let's introduce them into the diagram by drawing an altitude of the triangle, as indicated by the right-hand image of Figure A.21. We'll refer to the length of the altitude as h, and say that it separates the horizontal leg of the triangle into segments of length x and $B - x$. Now using the Pythagorean Theorem on these right triangles, we find

$$h^2 + x^2 = A^2 \quad \text{and} \quad h^2 + (B - x)^2 = C^2.$$

Solving both equations for h^2 leads us to write

$$
\begin{aligned}
C^2 - (B - x)^2 &= A^2 - x^2 \\
C^2 - (B^2 - 2Bx + x^2) &= A^2 - x^2 \\
C^2 &= A^2 + B^2 - 2Bx.
\end{aligned}
$$

If we think of our triangle as sitting in the plane, with its left corner at the origin, the topmost point of the altitude has coordinates (x, h) and is A units away from the origin, so $x = A \cos \theta$. Therefore,

$$C^2 = A^2 + B^2 - 2AB \cos \theta, \tag{a.4}$$

which is called the **Law of Cosines**. Note that equation (a.4) reduces to the Pythagorean Theorem when $\theta = \pi/2$ because $\cos(\pi/2) = 0$.

❖ Sum Formulas for Sine and Cosine

Suppose P and Q are points on the unit circle at $(\cos \phi, \sin \phi)$ and $(\cos \theta, \sin \theta)$ respectively, as shown in the left-hand image of Figure A.22. Then the distance between them is

$$\sqrt{(\cos \theta - \cos \phi)^2 + (\sin \theta - \sin \phi)^2}.$$

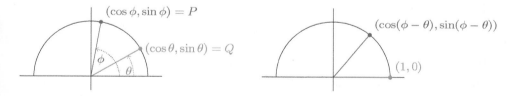

Figure A.22: (left) A pair of points on the unit circle; (right) the same pair of points after rotating the circle.

If we rotate the circle clockwise by θ radians, the point Q arrives at $(1, 0)$, and the point P ends up at $(\cos(\phi - \theta), \sin(\phi - \theta))$, as seen in the right-hand image of Figure A.22. The distance between them is

$$\sqrt{(1 - \cos(\phi - \theta))^2 + (0 - \sin(\phi - \theta))^2}.$$

Since rotating the circle changes the position of our points but not the distance between them, these numbers are the same:

$$\sqrt{(1 - \cos(\phi - \theta))^2 + (0 - \sin(\phi - \theta))^2} = \sqrt{(\cos \theta - \cos \phi)^2 + (\sin \theta - \sin \phi)^2}.$$

In the following steps, we'll solve this equation for $\cos(\phi - \theta)$. We begin by squaring both sides:

$$(1 - \cos(\phi - \theta))^2 + (0 - \sin(\phi - \theta))^2 = (\cos\theta - \cos\phi)^2 + (\sin\theta - \sin\phi)^2. \qquad (a.5)$$

When we expand the left-hand side of this equation, we see

$$1 - 2\cos(\phi - \theta) + \underbrace{\cos^2(\phi - \theta) + \sin^2(\phi - \theta)}_{=1 \text{ (Pythagorean Thereom)}} = 2 - 2\cos(\phi - \theta).$$

The right-hand side of equation (a.5) is

$$\begin{aligned}
(\cos\theta - \cos\phi)^2 + (\sin\theta - \sin\phi)^2 &= \cos^2\theta - 2\cos\theta\cos\phi + \cos^2\phi \\
&\quad + \sin^2\theta - 2\sin\theta\sin\phi + \sin^2\phi \\
&= 2 - 2\cos\phi\cos\theta - 2\sin\phi\sin\theta.
\end{aligned}$$

> This equation also relies on the Pythagorean Theorem.

Using these expansions, we rewrite equation (a.5) as

$$2 - 2\cos(\phi - \theta) = 2 - 2\cos\phi\cos\theta - 2\sin\phi\sin\theta,$$

after which it's easy to see that

$$\cos(\phi - \theta) = \cos\phi\cos\theta + \sin\phi\sin\theta, \qquad (a.6)$$

which is called the ***difference formula*** for the cosine. When $\theta = -\beta$ it becomes

$$\cos(\phi + \beta) = \cos\phi\cos(-\beta) + \sin\phi\sin(-\beta).$$

Since $\cos(-\beta) = \cos(\beta)$ and $\sin(-\beta) = -\sin(\beta)$, which follow from their interpretations as x and y-coordinates (also see Figure A.17), we can rewrite this as

$$\cos(\phi + \beta) = \cos\phi\cos\beta - \sin\phi\sin\beta, \qquad (a.7)$$

which is called the ***sum formula*** for the cosine. Similarly, when we have $\theta = -\phi$ in equation (a.6), we see

$$\cos(2\phi) = \cos^2\phi - \sin^2\phi, \qquad (a.8)$$

which is called the ***double angle*** formula for the cosine. When we use the Pythagorean Theorem to write $\sin^2\phi = 1 - \cos^2\phi$, we can rearrange the equation to read

$$\cos^2\phi = \frac{1}{2} + \frac{1}{2}\cos(2\phi),$$

which is sometimes called the ***half-angle formula*** for the cosine. Similarly, when we use the Pythagorean Theorem to write $\cos^2\phi = 1 - \sin^2\phi$, equation (a.8) can be rewritten as

$$\sin^2\phi = \frac{1}{2} - \frac{1}{2}\cos(2\phi),$$

which is called the ***half-angle formula*** for the sine. Both of these formulas are particularly helpful in certain techniques of integral calculus.

> Note that adding the half-angle formulas for sine and cosine returns us to the Pythagorean Theorem:
> $$\cos^2\phi + \sin^2\phi = 1.$$

For the sake of completeness, we note that when $\theta = \beta - \frac{\pi}{2}$, the difference formula for the cosine becomes

$$\cos\left(\phi - \beta + \frac{\pi}{2}\right) = \cos\phi\cos\left(\beta - \frac{\pi}{2}\right) + \sin\phi\sin\left(\beta - \frac{\pi}{2}\right). \qquad (a.9)$$

Since for all angles ω it's true that

$$\begin{aligned}
\cos\left(\omega + \frac{\pi}{2}\right) &= -\sin(\omega) \\
\cos\left(\omega - \frac{\pi}{2}\right) &= \sin(\omega) \\
\sin\left(\omega + \frac{\pi}{2}\right) &= \cos(\omega),
\end{aligned}$$

> You can convince yourself of this fact by understanding the sine and cosine as coordinates, or by looking at their graphs in Figure A.17.

equation (a.9) reduces to

$$\sin(\phi - \beta) = \cos \phi \sin(\beta) - \sin \phi \cos(\beta),$$

which is called the **difference formula** for the sine. When $\beta = -\theta$ this relationship becomes

$$\sin(\phi + \theta) = \cos \phi \sin(\theta) + \sin \phi \cos(\theta),$$

> We're using the fact that $\sin(-\theta) = -\sin(\theta)$.

which is called the **sum formula** for the sine. When $\theta = \phi$, this becomes the **double angle** formula for the sine:

$$\sin(2\phi) = 2 \sin \phi \cos \phi.$$

❖ Exercises

In exercises #1–4 the lengths of a right triangle's legs are given. Use the Pythagorean Theorem to determine the length of the hypotenuse.

1. $a = 3, b = 4$ 2. $a = 5, b = 12$ 3. $a = 2, b = 7$ 4. $a = 3, b = x$

In exercises #5–8 the length of a right triangle's hypotenuse and the length of one of its legs are given. Use the Pythagorean Theorem to determine the length of the remaining leg.

5. $a = 1, c = 4$ 6. $a = 2, c = 15$ 7. $a = 3, c = 8$ 8. $a = 4, c = x$

In exercises #9–12 convert the given angle from degrees to radians.

9. $240°$ 10. $120°$ 11. $300°$ 12. $350°$

In exercises #13–16 convert the given angle from radians to degrees.

13. $4\pi/3$ 14. $8\pi/3$ 15. $3\pi/2$ 16. $11\pi/6$

In exercises #17–24 locate the point on the unit circle whose coordinates are $(\cos \theta, \sin \theta)$.

17. $\theta = 2\pi/3$ 19. $\theta = -3\pi/2$ 21. $\theta = 15\pi/4$ 23. $\theta = -34\pi/6$

18. $\theta = 4\pi/3$ 20. $\theta = -7\pi/6$ 22. $\theta = 25\pi/3$ 24. $\theta = -41\pi/2$

Answer #25–28 based on the geometric discussion of the trigonometric functions on p. 1317.

25. Explain what happens to the number $\tan \theta$ as θ increases toward $\pi/2$.

26. Explain what happens to the number $\cot \theta$ as θ decreases toward 0.

27. Explain what happens to the number $\cos \theta$ as θ increases from $\theta = -1$ to $\theta = 1$.

28. Explain what happens to the number $\sin \theta$ as θ increases from $\theta = 1.4\pi$ to $\theta = 1.6\pi$.

Appendix B

Review of Algebraic Techniques

In this appendix we review some algebraic techniques that often come in handy.

❖ Completing the Square

The term *completing the square* means answering questions such as, "What constant would I append to the expression $x^2 + 2x$ in order to make it a perfect square?" In this case we would append "+1" to make a perfect square since $x^2 + 2x + 1 = (t+1)^2$. Similarly, appending "+9" to the end of the expression $x^2 + 6x$ makes a perfect square since $x^2 + 6x + 9 = (x+3)^2$. It's more difficult to figure out what we should append to expressions such as $x^2 + \sqrt{7}\, x$, so let's look at the general structure of a perfect square:

$$(x+b)^2 = x^2 + 2bx + b^2. \tag{b.1}$$

What we're talking about are cases in which we know the first two terms, $x^2 + 2bx$, but have to figure out the third. Consider the two examples that we've discussed above. Comparing to equation (b.1), we see

$$x^2 + 2x \quad \Rightarrow \quad 2b = 2 \quad \Rightarrow \quad b = 1,$$

so we append "+1^2" to make a perfect square (which is what we did). Similarly,

$$x^2 + 6x \quad \Rightarrow \quad 2b = 6 \quad \Rightarrow \quad b = 3,$$

so we append "+3^2" to make a perfect square (which is what we did).

Completing the square

Example B.1. Determine the constant that would you append to $x^2 + \sqrt{7}\, x$ in order to make it a perfect square.

Solution: In this case we have $2b = \sqrt{7}$, so $b = \frac{\sqrt{7}}{2}$. That means we should append $+\left(\frac{\sqrt{7}}{2}\right)^2$ to the end of the expression in order to make it a perfect square. We can check by expanding

$$\left(x + \frac{\sqrt{7}}{2}\right)^2 = x^2 + 2\left(\frac{\sqrt{7}}{2}\right)x + \left(\frac{\sqrt{7}}{2}\right)^2 = x^2 + \sqrt{7}\, t + \frac{7}{4}. \qquad \blacksquare$$

We often complete the square in order to rewrite expressions in simpler or more compact form, but we want to avoid actually changing them.

Completing the square without changing a quantity

Example B.2. Rewrite the expression $x^2 + 14x + 3$ in the form $(x+b)^2 + c$.

Solution: Start by looking at the quadratic and linear terms, as we had above. With $x^2 + 14x$ we have $2b = 14 \Rightarrow b = 7$, so we should append "$+7^2$" to this expression in order to make it a perfect square. Now that we know what we would like to see, we insert it by adding zero ...

$$\begin{aligned} x^2 + 14x + 3 &= x^2 + 14x + 49 - 49 + 3 \\ &= (x^2 + 14x + 49) - 49 + 3 = (x+7)^2 - 46. \end{aligned}$$

So $b = 7$ and $c = -46$. ∎

Now consider the perfect square in which you see a difference, rather than a sum:

$$(x - b)^2 = x^2 - 2bx + b^2. \tag{b.2}$$

Comparing this to equation (b.1), see that a positive linear term in the expression indicates a *sum* in the perfect square, and a negative linear term indicates a difference.

Completing the square without changing a quantity

Example B.3. Rewrite the expression $x^2 - 3x + 10$ in the form $(x-b)^2 + c$.

Solution: As before, we begin by focusing on the quadratic and linear terms. With $x^2 - 3x$ we have $2b = 3 \Rightarrow b = \frac{3}{2}$, so we should append "$+\left(\frac{3}{2}\right)^2$" to this expression in order to make a perfect square. So let's write

$$x^2 - 3x + 10 = x^2 - 3x + \frac{9}{4} - \frac{9}{4} + 10 = \left(x - \frac{3}{2}\right)^2 + \frac{31}{4}.$$

So $b = 3/2$ and $c = 31/4$. ∎

Lastly, note that both equations (b.1) and (b.2) address quadratic expressions whose leading coefficient is 1. If that's not true, you have to begin by factoring our the leading coefficient.

Completing the square without changing a quantity

Example B.4. Rewrite the expression $5t^2 - 3t + 20$ in the form $a(t-b)^2 + c$.

Solution: We begin by factoring out the 5:

$$5t^2 - 3t + 20 = 5\left(t^2 - \frac{3}{5}t + 4\right).$$

Now let's work with the expression in parentheses, in which $2b = 3/5$, so $b = 3/10$ and we can make a perfect square by adding $9/100$:

$$\begin{aligned} 5\left(t^2 - \frac{3}{5}t + 4\right) &= 5\left(t^2 - \frac{3}{5}t + \frac{9}{100} - \frac{9}{100} + 4\right) \\ &= 5\left(\left(t - \frac{3}{10}\right)^2 + \frac{391}{400}\right). \end{aligned}$$

Lastly, we redistribute the factor of 5 to arrive at the desired form:

$$5\left(t - \frac{3}{10}\right)^2 + \frac{391}{80},$$

Now we see that $a = 5$, $b = -3/10$ and $c = 391/80$. ∎

❖ Polynomial Division

The key to understanding polynomial division is the division algorithm that you learned in elementary school. It's been a while since most people have thought about it any detail, so we're going to begin by using an example to review. Simple as it might seem, read Example B.5 carefully because it presents the first principles on which the entire method is based.

Principles that are central to the division algorithm

Example B.5. Use the division algorithm to calculate $\frac{852}{4}$.

Solution: The first important fact to recognize is that $4\left(\frac{852}{4}\right) = 852$. So we're looking for a number that we can multiply by 4 to get 852. The key to finding it is *place value*. Recall that

$$852 = 800 + 50 + 2 = 8(10^2) + 5(10^1) + 2.$$

Similarly, the number we're calculating could include hundreds, tens and units. So let's write

$$8(10^2) + 5(10^1) + 2 \;=\; 4\Big(a(10^2) + b(10^1) + c \Big) \qquad \text{(b.3)}$$
$$=\; 4a(10^2) + 4b(10^1) + 4c.$$

Since the two sides of this equation are the same, they have the same number of hundreds in them. That is, $8 = 4a$, from which we gather that $a = 2$. So

$$852 = 800 + 4b(10^1) + 4c.$$

By designating $a = 2$ we have "built" 800 of the 852, so $4b(10^1) + 4c$ must account for the remaining 52. Written as an equation,

$$52 = 4b(10^1) + 4c.$$

Now recall that we're only dealing with integers. If $b = 2$, the right-hand side would have 8 tens, but the left-hand side has only 5. So let's try $b = 1$. In that case, our equation reduces to

$$52 = 40 + 4c.$$

By designating $b = 1$, we've accounted for 40 of the 52, so $4c$ must account for the remaining 12. Written as an equation,

$$12 = 4c \quad \Rightarrow \quad c = 3.$$

Now that we know a, b and c, we can rewrite equation (b.3) as

$$852 = 4\big(2(10^2) + 1(10^1) + 3\big) = 4(213).$$

Dividing both sides of the equation by 4 brings us to the answer: $\frac{852}{4} = 213$.   ∎

In essence, the process demonstrated above deconstructs a number by using the idea of *place value*—the 8 in 852 means 8 hundreds, and the 5 means 5 tens. The technique is often done in a shorthand notation. Most recently, it was encoded using the $\overline{}$ symbol, which we use to organize the relevant information by putting the divisor on the left, the dividend "inside," and the quotient "atop." For example, writing

$$\frac{852}{4} = 213 \quad \text{is the same as writing} \quad 4\,\overline{\big)\,852}^{\;213}$$

The same ideas and notation are used in the division of polynomials. Because understanding the notation is important to using it, Example B.6 will show the calculation of 852/4 using the $\overline{\rceil }$ shorthand. It's important to note that the steps we perform below are exactly the ones we discussed above, and the $\overline{\rceil }$ notation is acting solely as a bookkeeping device.

Principles that are central to the division algorithm

Example B.6. Use the division algorithm to calculate $\frac{852}{4}$.

Solution: Before beginning, let's use the idea of place value to rewrite

$$4\,\overline{\smash{\big)}\,852} \quad \text{as} \quad 4\,\overline{\smash{\big)}\,8(10^2) + 5(10^1) + 2}\,.$$

Now we're ready to begin the process. First, since the quotient can have 2 hundreds in it but no more, we place a 2 in the hundreds column:

$$
\begin{array}{r}
2(10^2) \\
\hline
4\,\overline{\smash{\big)}\,8(10^2) \;+\; 5(10^1) \;+\; 2(10^1)}
\end{array}
$$

Since $4 \times 2(10^2) = 8(10^2)$, we have "built" 800 of the 852. To find out how much remains unaccounted for, we subtract 800 from 852:

$$
\begin{array}{r}
2(10^2) \\
4\,\overline{\smash{\big)}\,8(10^2) \;+\; 5(10^1) \;+\; 2(10^1)} \\
-8(10)^2 \\
\hline
5(10^1) \;+\; 2(10^1)
\end{array}
$$

So we have to "build" an additional $5(10^1) + 2(10^1) = 52$. Since the remaining 52 units can accommodate 4 tens but not 8, we add 10 onto our quotient and account for its contribution by writing

$$
\begin{array}{r}
2(10^2) \;+\; 1(10^1) \\
4\,\overline{\smash{\big)}\,8(10^2) \;+\; 5(10^1) \;+\; 2(10^1)} \\
-8(10)^2 \\
\hline
5(10^1) \;+\; 2(10^1) \\
-4(10^1) \\
\hline
1(10^1) \;+\; 2(10^1)
\end{array}
$$

$4 \times 1(10^1) = 4(10^1)$

meaning that we have accounted for all but $1(10^1)+2(10^1) = 12$ of the original 852. At this point, we've already added hundreds and tens into our quotient, so all that remains is units. Since $(4)(3) = 12$, we add 3 units onto our quotient and see ...

$$
\begin{array}{r}
2(10^2) \;+\; 1(10^1) \;+\; 3 \\
4\,\overline{\smash{\big)}\,8(10^2) \;+\; 5(10^1) \;+\; 2(10^1)} \\
-8(10)^2 \\
\hline
5(10^1) \;+\; 2(10^1) \\
-4(10^1) \\
\hline
1(10^1) \;+\; 2(10^1) \\
-(1(10^1) \;+\; 2(10^1)) \\
\hline
0
\end{array}
$$

This is often written in a more compact form as
$$\begin{array}{r} 213 \\ 4\,\overline{\smash{\big)}\,852} \\ -800 \\ \hline 52 \\ -52 \\ \hline 0 \end{array}$$
We're using the verbose form because our actual goal is to prepare for polynomial division.

The zero at the bottom of our calculation indicates that we have successfully divided 852 into 4, with no remainder, and we see in our notation that the quotient is

$$2(10^2) + 1(10^1) + 3 = 213.$$

∎

Practice with the division algorithm

Example B.7. Use the division algorithm to calculate $3225/75$.

Solution: Since $3225 = 3(10^3) + 2(10^2) + 2(10^1) + 5$ and $75 = 7(10^1) + 5$, let's begin by writing

$$7(10^1) + 5 \,\big)\,\overline{3(10^3) \quad + \quad 2(10^2) \quad + \quad 2(10^1) \quad + \quad 5}$$

It might seem strange to write 75 as $7(10^1) + 5$, but remember that our real objective to prepare for polynomial division, in which the divisor might have the form $7x + 5$.

We know the quotient cannot have any thousands since $75 \times 1000 = 75000$, which is far greater than 3225. Similarly, the quotient cannot have any hundreds since $75 \times 100 = 7500$, which is larger than 3225. However, it can have tens. Since $75 \times 50 = 3750$ (which is too large) but $75 \times 40 = 3(10^3)$, let's add 4 tens into our quotient and account for their contribution by writing

$$
\begin{array}{r}
4(10^1) \\
7(10^1) + 5 \,\big)\,\overline{3(10^3) \quad + \quad 2(10^2) \quad + \quad 2(10^1) \quad + \quad 5} \\
\underline{-3(10^3)} \\
2(10^2) \quad + \quad 2(10^1) \quad + \quad 5
\end{array}
$$

which means that we still have to account for $2(10^2) + 2(10^1) + 5 = 225$ of the original 3225. Since $75 \times 3 = 225$, we add 3 units onto the quotient and write

$$
\begin{array}{r}
4(10^1) \quad + \quad 3 \\
7(10^1) + 5 \,\big)\,\overline{3(10^3) \quad + \quad 2(10^2) \quad + \quad 2(10^1) \quad + \quad 5} \\
\underline{-3(10^3)} \\
2(10^2) \quad + \quad 2(10^1) \quad + \quad 5 \\
\underline{-(\,2(10^2) \quad + \quad 2(10^1) \quad + \quad 5\,)} \\
0
\end{array}
$$

This tells us that $3225 = 75 \times (4(10^1) + 3)$, so $\frac{3225}{75} = 4(10^1) + 3 = 43$. ∎

Practice with the division algorithm

Example B.8. Use the division algorithm to calculate $3228/75$.

Solution: In Example B.7 we established that 3225 is a multiple of 75, so we know that 3228 is not. In this division we will have a remainder of of 3. This is seen in the last step of the algorithm ...

$$
\begin{array}{r}
4(10^1) \quad + \quad 3 \\
7(10^1) + 5 \,\big)\,\overline{3(10^3) \quad + \quad 2(10^2) \quad + \quad 2(10^1) \quad + \quad 8} \\
\underline{-3(10^3)} \\
2(10^2) \quad + \quad 2(10^1) \quad + \quad 8 \\
\underline{-(\,2(10^2) \quad + \quad 2(10^1) \quad + \quad 5\,)} \\
3
\end{array}
$$

We conclude from this calculation that $3228 = (75)(43) + 3$, so $\frac{3228}{75} = 43 + \frac{3}{75}$. ∎

　　The point of spending so much time on elementary arithmetic and notation is that the factors of 10 were entirely inert in our calculation. All that mattered to us during the calculations was that, for example, $(10^2) \times (10^1) = 10^3$, but that's a matter of exponents and has nothing to do with the fact that the base is 10. It might as well have been 8, or 18, or ... you guessed it, x.

Polynomial division with no remainder

Example B.9. Determine $(6x^3 + 30x^2 + 38x + 4)/(2x + 4)$.

Solution: The process for polynomial division is *exactly* the same as what you saw with integer division a moment ago. We begin by writing

$$2x + 4 \,\big|\, \overline{6x^3 \quad + \quad 30x^2 \quad + \quad 38x \quad + \quad 4}$$

The quotient cannot have any x^3 terms, since $(2x + 4)(x^3) = 2x^4 + 4x^3$ and our dividend has no powers of x^4. However, the quotient *can* include quadratic factors. Specifically, since

$$(2x + 4)(3x^2) = 6x^3 + 12x^2$$

has the same leading term as $6x^3 + 30x^2 + 38x + 4$, we begin our quotient with $3x^2$. Note that $6x^3 + 12x^2$ differs from our dividend by $18x^2 + 38x + 4$, which we'll account for in later steps of the algorithm using lower-degree terms in the quotient. Written in the notation of the division algorithm,

We chose *three* x^2 precisely because its product with $2x + 4$ yields the first term in the dividend.

$$
\begin{array}{r}
3x^2 \\
2x + 4 \,\big|\, \overline{6x^3 \quad + \quad 30x^2 \quad + \quad 38x \quad + \quad 4} \\
\underline{-(6x^3 \quad + \quad 12x^2)} \\
18x^2 \quad + \quad 38x \quad + \quad 4
\end{array}
$$

We can produce the $18x^2$ of the remaining polynomial by adding $9x$ onto the quotient. Specifically,

$$(2x + 4)(3x^2 + 9x) = 6x^3 + 12x^2 + 18x^2 + 36x = 6x^3 + 30x^2 + 36x,$$

which is another step closer to $6x^3 + 30x^2 + 38x + 4$. In fact, our product now differs from $6x^3 + 30x^2 + 38x + 4$ by exactly $2x + 4$. Written in the notation of the division algorithm,

$$
\begin{array}{r}
3x^2 \quad + \quad 9x \\
2x + 4 \,\big|\, \overline{6x^3 \quad + \quad 30x^2 \quad + \quad 38x \quad + \quad 4} \\
\underline{-(6x^3 \quad + \quad 12x^2)} \\
18x^2 \quad + \quad 38x \quad + \quad 4 \\
\underline{-(18x^2 \quad + \quad 36x)} \\
2x \quad + \quad 4
\end{array}
$$

Now adding 1 onto the quotient, we arrive at the conclusion of the division algorithm:

$$
\begin{array}{r}
3x^2 \quad + \quad 9x \quad + \quad 1 \\
2x + 4 \,\big|\, \overline{6x^3 \quad + \quad 30x^2 \quad + \quad 38x \quad + \quad 4} \\
\underline{-(6x^3 \quad + \quad 12x^2)} \\
18x^2 \quad + \quad 38x \quad + \quad 4 \\
\underline{-(18x^2 \quad + \quad 36x)} \\
2x \quad + \quad 4 \\
\underline{-(2x \quad + \quad 4\,)} \\
0
\end{array}
$$

This tells us that (check!)

$$6x^3 + 30x^2 + 38x + 4 = (2x + 4)(3x^2 + 9x + 1).$$

Now dividing both sides by $2x + 4$ yields our answer:

$$\frac{6x^3 + 30x^2 + 38x + 4}{2x + 4} = 3x^2 + 9x + 1.$$ ∎

Polynomial division when there's a remainder

Example B.10. Calculate $(5x^3 + 2x^2 + 4x + 1)/(8x + 2)$ using the division algorithm.

Solution: We begin by writing

$$8x + 2 \overline{\smash{)}\,5x^3 \quad + \quad 2x^2 \quad + \quad 4x \quad + \quad 1}$$

The quotient cannot have any x^3 terms, since $(8x + 2)(x^3) = 8x^4 + 2x^3$, and our dividend has no x^4 terms in it. However, the quotient can include quadratic terms. Specifically, since

$$(8x + 2)\left(\frac{5}{8}x^2\right) = 5x^3 + \frac{5}{4}x^2,$$

which has the same leading term as $5x^3 + 2x^2 + 4x + 1$, we begin our quotient with $\frac{5}{8}x^2$. Note that $5x^3 + \frac{5}{4}x^2$ differs from our dividend by $\frac{3}{4}x^2 + 4x + 1$. Written in the notation of the division algorithm,

$$
\begin{array}{r}
\frac{5}{8}x^2 \qquad\qquad\qquad\quad \\
8x + 2 \overline{\smash{)}\,5x^3 \quad + \quad 2x^2 \quad + \quad 4x \quad + \quad 1} \\
-(8x^3 \quad + \quad \frac{5}{4}x^2) \qquad\qquad\qquad \\
\hline
\frac{3}{4}x^2 \quad + \quad 4x \quad + \quad 1
\end{array}
$$

> We chose a coefficient of $\frac{5}{8}$ precisely so that this product would yield the leading term of the dividend.

Next we add linear terms into the quotient. Specifically, since we need an additional $\frac{3}{4}$ of an x^2, we'll add $\frac{3}{32}x$ onto the quotient. Then we have

$$(8x + 2)\left(\frac{5}{8}x^2 + \frac{3}{32}x\right) = 5x^3 + \frac{5}{4}x^2 + \frac{3}{4}x^2 + \frac{3}{16}x = 5x^3 + 2x^2 + \frac{3}{16}x,$$

whose first and second terms are the same as $5x^3 + 2x^2 + 4x + 1$. Note that $5x^3 + 2x^2 + \frac{3}{16}x$ differs from our dividend by $\frac{61}{16}x + 1$. Written in the notation of the division algorithm,

$$
\begin{array}{r}
\frac{5}{8}x^2 \quad + \quad \frac{3}{32}x \qquad\qquad\qquad \\
8x + 2 \overline{\smash{)}\,5x^3 \quad + \quad 2x^2 \quad + \quad 4x \quad + \quad 1} \\
-(8x^3 \quad + \quad \frac{5}{4}x^2) \qquad\qquad\qquad \\
\hline
\frac{3}{4}x^2 \quad + \quad 4x \quad + \quad 1 \\
-(\frac{3}{4}x^2 \quad + \quad \frac{3}{16}x \quad) \\
\hline
\frac{61}{16}x \quad + \quad 1
\end{array}
$$

Next we add constant terms into the quotient. Specifically, since we need an additional $\frac{61}{16}$ of an x, we'll add $\frac{61}{128}$ onto the quotient. Then we have

$$(8x+2)\left(\frac{5}{8}x^2 + \frac{3}{32}x + \frac{61}{128}\right) = 5x^3 + \frac{5}{4}x^2 + \frac{3}{4}x^2 + \frac{3}{16}x + \frac{61}{16}x + \frac{61}{64} = 5x^3 + 2x^2 + 4x + \frac{61}{64}.$$

This differs from $5x^3 + 2x^2 + 4x + 1$ by only $\frac{3}{64}$. Written in the notation of the division algorithm,

$$
\begin{array}{r}
\frac{5}{8}x^2 \quad + \quad \frac{3}{32}x \quad + \quad \frac{61}{128} \\[2pt]
8x+2\ \overline{\big)\ 5x^3 \quad + \quad 2x^2 \quad + \quad 4x \quad + \quad 1 } \\
-(8x^3 \quad + \quad \frac{5}{4}x^2) \\ \hline
\frac{3}{4}x^2 \quad + \quad 4x \quad + \quad 1 \\
-(\frac{3}{4}x^2 \quad + \quad \frac{3}{16}x\ ) \\ \hline
\frac{61}{16}x \quad + \quad 1 \\
-(\frac{61}{16}x \quad + \quad \frac{61}{64}) \\ \hline
\frac{3}{64}
\end{array}
$$

The algorithm stops at this point, just like it would in the case of elementary arithmetic, and we write

$$5x^3 + 2x^2 + 4x + 1 = (8x+2)\left(\frac{5}{8}x^2 + \frac{3}{32}x + \frac{61}{128}\right) + \frac{3}{64}.$$

After dividing both sides of this equation by $8x+2$ we have our answer:

$$\frac{5x^3 + 2x^2 + 4x + 1}{8x+2} = \frac{5}{8}x^2 + \frac{3}{32}x + \frac{61}{128} + \frac{3/64}{8x+2}. \qquad \blacksquare$$

The division algorithm can be expedited by modifications in special cases, but all of them come back to the same basic ideas shown here.

> For example, the technique called *synthetic division* is particularly handy when the divisor has the form $x-a$, where a is any number.

❖ Exercises

In #1–16 rewrite the expression in the form $a(t+b)^2 + c$ (b and c might be negative).

1. $t^2 + 12t + 100$
2. $t^2 + 20t + 321$
3. $t^2 + 18t + 70$
4. $t^2 + 16t + 50$

5. $t^2 - 8t + 22$
6. $t^2 - 60t + 1$
7. $t^2 - 7t + 10$
8. $t^2 + 9t + 13$

9. $2t^2 + 12t + 100$
10. $4t^2 + 20t + 88$
11. $5t^2 + 18t + 70$
12. $7t^2 + 16t + 50$

13. $2t^2 - 8t + 22$
14. $3t^2 - 60t + 12$
15. $3t^2 - 7t + 10$
16. $5t^2 + 9t + 13$

In #17–24 use polynomial division to write the quotient as $q(x) + r(x)$ where $q(x)$ is a polynomial and r is a rational function whose numerator has a lower degree than its denominator (we say that such a rational function is in *lowest terms*).

17. $\frac{3x^2 + 4x + 7}{x+2}$
18. $\frac{5x^2 + 8x + 17}{x+5}$

19. $\frac{16x^2 + 7x + 9}{2x+1}$
20. $\frac{10x^2 + 6x + 2}{3x+5}$

21. $\frac{7x^3 + 5x^2 - x + 19}{x^2 + 1}$
22. $\frac{2x^3 + 15x^2 + 2x + 1}{x^2 - 3}$

23. $\frac{4x^5 + 8x + 1}{7x^2 + 10}$
24. $\frac{8x^4 + 3x^3 + x}{2x^2 + 7x + 1}$

In #25–26 suppose that $p(x)$ is a polynomial whose degree is 2 or more.

25. Explain why the remainder of $\frac{p(x)}{x-a}$ must be constant.

26. Based on #25 we know that $p(x)$ can be written as $q(x)(x-a) + r$ where q is a polynomial function and r is a constant. Explain why $r = 0$ if and *only if* a is a root of p.

In #27–30 use the result of #26 to check whether $x - a$ is a factor of $p(x)$ by calculating $p(a)$.

27. $p(x) = 7x^4 + 2x^2 + x - 10$, $a = 1$

28. $p(x) = 13x^4 - x^2 + 3x - 9$, $a = -1$

29. $p(x) = x^5 - x^4 + 8x - 30$, $a = 2$

30. $p(x) = 2x^4 - 15x^2 - 14x + 3$, $a = -2$

In Chapter 6 you'll see a technique called *partial fractions decomposition.* The presentation there focuses on its usage in *integration,* but doesn't push far into the algebra that underlies the general formulation. In exercises #31–34 we use polynomial division to provide you with a motivation for the general form that you see in Chapter 6.

31. In this exercise you're going to use polynomial division as a tool to rewrite

$$\frac{3x^5 + 9x^4 + 8x^3 + 17x^2 + 6x + 15}{(x^2 + 1)^3}$$

as the sum of three simpler fractions.

(a) Use polynomial division to verify that

$$\frac{3x^5 + 9x^4 + 8x^3 + 17x^2 + 6x + 15}{x^2 + 1} = 3x^3 + 9x^2 + 5x + 8 + \frac{x + 7}{x^2 + 1}.$$

(b) Use polynomial division to verify that

$$\frac{3x^3 + 9x^2 + 5x + 8}{x^2 + 1} = 3x + 9 + \frac{2x - 1}{x^2 + 1}.$$

(c) Combine parts (a) and (b) to verify that

$$\frac{3x^5 + 9x^4 + 8x^3 + 17x^2 + 6x + 15}{(x^2 + 1)^2} = 3x + 9 + \frac{2x - 1}{x^2 + 1} + \frac{x + 7}{(x^2 + 1)^2}.$$

(d) Based on part (c), verify that

$$\frac{3x^5 + 9x^4 + 8x^3 + 17x^2 + 6x + 15}{(x^2 + 1)^3} = \frac{3x + 9}{x^2 + 1} + \frac{2x - 1}{(x^2 + 1)^2} + \frac{x + 7}{(x^2 + 1)^3}.$$

(e) Based on the method used above, explain why all the numerators are linear (it's not coincidence).

By following the procedure demonstrated in #31 rewrite the following rational functions as the sum of simpler fractions.

32. $\dfrac{2\,x^5 + 3\,x^4 + 21\,x^3 + 25\,x^2 + 56\,x}{(x^2 + 4)^3}$

33. $\dfrac{x^5 + 3\,x^4 + 19\,x^3 + 25\,x^2 + 67\,x + 14}{(x^2 + x + 5)^3}$

34. $\dfrac{x^5 + 12\,x^4 + 47\,x^3 + 153\,x^2 + 233\,x + 304}{(x^2 + 2x + 6)^3}$

Appendix C

Binomial Coefficients

The **binomial coefficients** are numbers that arise when we expand expressions of the form $(a+b)^n$, but they are also extremely useful in a variety of other situations. It's easiest to get a feel for them by looking at an example, so consider

$$(a+b)^3 = (a+b)(a+b)(a+b) \tag{c.1}$$
$$= (aa+ab+ba+bb)(a+b)$$
$$= aaa + aba + baa + bba + aab + abb + bab + bbb. \tag{c.2}$$

The prefix "bi" means 2, as in America's *bi*cameral legislature, or your *bi*weekly paycheck. The expression $(a+b)$ is called a binomial because it has 2 parts, a and b (*nomos* is the Greek word for *part*).

When we collect terms according to how many factors of a and b they include, we get the standard equation

$$(a+b)^3 = a^3 + 3a^2b + 3ab^2 + b^3. \tag{c.3}$$

There are two important points to notice here:

- We've written $(a+b)^3$ as (blue)(green)(red) on the right-hand side of (c.1), and each summand on the right-hand side of (c.2) has one blue, one red, and one green factor. This allows us to see that each factor of $(a+b)$ in $(a+b)^3$ contributes either an a or a b (but not both) to each term on the right-hand side of (c.2).

- The coefficients in equation (c.3) *count the number of ways* to get each combination of a and b. For example, *aba*, *baa*, and *aab* are all equal to a^2b, so the coefficient of a^2b is 3. Similarly, there are three ways to get ab^2, but there's only one way to get a^3 (all a), and only one way to get b^3 (all b).

When we combine these ideas, we get a powerful tool for making calculations. For example, suppose we want to know the coefficient of a^6b^4 in $(a+b)^{10}$. If we printed each of the 10 factors of $(a+b)$ with a different color, much as we did on the right-hand side of (c.1), each summand in the expanded form of $(a+b)^{10}$ would have 10 *differently colored* factors, much as you see on the right-hand side of (c.2). We're interested in finding out how many of them have exactly four factors of b, so let's ask ourselves, "How many ways can four different colors (indicating which factors are b) be selected from a group of 10 distinct colors?"

We're *really* selecting which specific copies of $(a+b)$ contribute a factor of b to the product.

1. Without knowing the particular colors that are used or the order in which they appears, let's just say that the first factor of b could be any of the 10 colors.

2. For each of those possibilities, there are 9 possibilities for the color of the second factor of b.

3. For each of *those* possibilities, there are 8 possibilities for the color of the third factor of b.

4. For each of *those* possibilities, there are only 7 possibilities for the color of the fourth factor of b.

So our initial estimate is that there are $10 \cdot 9 \cdot 8 \cdot 7 = 5040$ ways to chose four distinct colors from a group of 10. That's a good beginning, but it's not right because we've overcounted. We said, "There are 10 possibilities for making the first choice, and for each of those ..." so we've counted $bbbba^6$ as being different from $bbbba^6$; but the summand whose factors of b are blue, green, red, and black occurs only once in the expanded form of $(a + b)^{10}$.

So how many times did we overcount it? To answer, think about using blue, green, red and black to color the factors of b in $bbbba^6$. How many ways can we color the first factor? Four, since there are four colors. How many ways can we color the second? Three, since only three colors remain to be used. The third factor? Two, then the color that goes in the last slot is determined. There are $4 \cdot 3 \cdot 2 \cdot 1 = 24$ ways to order the four colors, so we've counted the summand $bbbba^6$ a total of 24 times. To fix the overcounting problem, we divide our original answer by 24, and conclude that the total number of ways to choose four colors from 10 is $5040/24 = 210$. Therefore, the coefficient of $a^6 b^4$ is 210. We refer to this binomial coefficient as ***10 choose 4*** and write it as $\binom{10}{4}$.

In calculating $\binom{10}{4}$ we saw products of consecutive decreasing integers: $10 \cdot 9 \cdot 8 \cdot 7$ and $4 \cdot 3 \cdot 2 \cdot 1$. When that decreasing string of integers is allowed to decrease all the way to 1, we refer to the product as a ***factorial*** and denote it with an exclamation mark. For example,

$$4! = 4 \cdot 3 \cdot 2 \cdot 1$$
$$5! = 5 \cdot 4 \cdot 3 \cdot 2 \cdot 1$$
$$6! = 6 \cdot 5 \cdot 4 \cdot 3 \cdot 2 \cdot 1.$$

Notice that

$$\binom{10}{4} = \frac{10 \cdot 9 \cdot 8 \cdot 7}{4!} = \frac{(10 \cdot 9 \cdot 8 \cdot 7)6!}{6!4!} = \frac{10!}{6!4!}.$$

More generally, after expanding $(a + b)^n$ and collecting like terms, the coefficient of $a^{n-k} b^k$ is

k consecutive integers in the numerator, starting at n and decreasing

$$\binom{n}{k} = \frac{n \cdot (n - 1) \cdot (n - (k - 1))}{k!} = \frac{(n \cdot (n - 1) \cdot (n - (k - 1)))(n - k)!}{(n - k)!k!} = \frac{n!}{(n - k)!k!}.$$

This formula is reminiscent of the color discussion above, but ...

... *this* formulation is often easier for people to remember because of its symmetry.

Note that, after expanding $(a + b)^n$ and collecting like terms, the coefficient of a^n is 1, and so is the coefficient of b^n. That's one way to remember that

$$\binom{n}{n} = 1 \quad \text{and} \quad \binom{n}{0} = 1.$$

Alternatively, you can apply the general formula if you remember that $0!$ is the number 1. (You can think of $0! = 1$ as a convention for now, but it comes from the relationship between the factorial and something called the *Gamma function* which is defined by way of a *improper integral* in Chapter 6.)

> Just as the summand whose factors of b are blue and green occurs only once on the right-hand side of (c.2).

Calculating binomial coeffiecients

Example C.1. Calculate $\binom{7}{4}$, $\binom{7}{3}$, and $\binom{5}{0}$.

Solution: Using the formula above, we see that

$$\binom{7}{4} = \frac{7!}{4!3!} = 35, \quad \binom{7}{3} = \frac{7!}{3!4!} = 35, \quad \text{and} \quad \binom{5}{0} = \frac{5!}{0!5!} = \frac{5!}{(1)(5!)} = 1. \quad \blacksquare$$

Expanding a binomial

Example C.2. Verify that $(a+b)^3 = \binom{3}{0}a^3b^0 + \binom{3}{1}a^2b^1 + \binom{3}{2}a^1b^2 + \binom{3}{3}a^0b^3$.

Solution: Using the formula $\binom{3}{k} = \frac{3!}{k!(3-k)!}$ we calculate

$$\binom{3}{0} = 1, \quad \binom{3}{1} = 3, \quad \binom{3}{2} = 3, \quad \text{and} \quad \binom{3}{3} = 1,$$

so the coefficients are exactly what we see in equation (c.3). $\quad \blacksquare$

In summary, when n is a positive integer ...

$$(a+b)^n = \sum_{k=0}^{n} \binom{n}{k} a^{n-k} b^k. \tag{c.4}$$

Note: This formula is extended to non-integer n in Chapter 8.

Expanding a binomial

Example C.3. Use equation (c.4) to expand $(1+u)^5$.

Solution: When $a = 1$ and $b = u$, equation (c.4) tells us that

> Notice the symmetry in the pattern of coefficients.

$$(1+u)^5 = \binom{5}{0}1^5u^0 + \binom{5}{1}1^4u^1 + \binom{5}{2}1^3u^2 + \binom{5}{3}1^2u^3 + \binom{5}{4}1^1u^4 + \binom{5}{5}1^0u^5$$

$$= 1 + 5u + 10u^2 + 10u^3 + 5u^4 + u^5. \quad \blacksquare$$

❖ Binomial coefficients and counting

We've introduced the binomial coefficients as numbers that occur in the expansion of a binomial, but they are also extremely useful in other ways, some of which are introduced in the following examples.

Using binomial coefficients for quick counting

Example C.4. You walk up to a fruit tray at a friend's wedding, but all that's left is 1 strawberry, 1 chunk of pineapple, 1 slice of mango, 1 chunk of watermelon, and 1 slice of a strange green fruit that you've never seen before. How many different ways are there for you to select three of them?

Solution: You might put (in order) the strawberry, the pineapple, and the strange green fruit on your plate. On the other hand, you might put (in order) the pineapple, the strange green fruit, and the pineapple chunk on your plate. Either way, you have the same selection of fruit on your plate when you leave. *The order in which you choose them doesn't matter,* and that's the kind of counting the binomial coefficients are good for. So we can say that the number of ways is "five choose three," or $\binom{5}{3} = 10$. Alternatively, since choosing three is the same as leaving two, we could also say that the answer is "five choose two" (where we're choosing which fruits to leave), or $\binom{5}{2} = 10$. ∎

In Example C.4 we said that choosing 3 of the 5 fruit slices is the same as leaving 2 of them, and verified that $\binom{5}{3} = \binom{5}{2}$ by calculating both numbers independently. And in Example C.1, you saw that $\binom{7}{4} = \binom{7}{3}$, which makes sense in the context of expanding $(a+b)^7$. Much as we saw in equation (c.2) on p. 1339, each summand of the expanded $(a+b)^7$ comprises 7 factors. Choosing 4 of them to be b is the same as choosing 3 of them to be a. More generally,

$$\binom{n}{k} = \binom{n}{n-k}.$$

> If n things are available, selecting k of them is mathematically equivalent to excluding $n-k$ of them.

Using binomial coefficients for quick counting

Example C.5. Suppose that five cars exit the turnpike and head toward three toll booths, numbered 1 through 3. From the point of view of the workers in the booths, the cars are identical (it doesn't matter *which* cars line up at your booth, only the number of them). Determine the number of ways the cars could line up at the booths.

Solution: It's tempting to start by setting the cars into different configurations (one of which is depicted in Figure C.1). That would work *eventually,* but it involves a lot of bookkeeping and takes a lot of time. Instead, let's draw 8 slots, from left to right, and place either a car or a booth into each slot. We'll place the booths in order, so that the leftmost is #1 and the rightmost is #3. If a car is at booth #j, it is placed to the *right* of booth #j in our diagram. For example, the configuration that you see in Figure C.1 is depicted in Figure C.2.

Each car is at *some* booth, so it must be to the *right* of some booth. Therefore, the leftmost slot in our diagram will never be a car. It will always be booth #1. The other 7 slots are up for grabs. The number of ways to choose 2 of the 7 slots (selecting them for the booths) is $\binom{7}{2} = 21$, so that's the number of different ways that the cars could line up at the booths. ∎

Figure C.1: One way that 5 cars could line up at 3 booths.

Figure C.2: Determining the number of ways that 5 identical cars can line up at 3 distinct toll booths.

Each particular way that the cars could line up at the booths in Example C.5 is called a *microstate* of the system. For example, the particular configuration depicted in Figure C.1 is a microstate. Another microstate would be 5 cars at booth #1 and no cars at the other booths. We found that there are 21 different microstates when there are 5 cars and 3 booths. Of course, that number would change if there were a different number of cars or booths. The particular numbers of cars and booths is called a *macrostate* of the system.

The terms *microstate* and *macrostate* are used in thermal physics to describe the distribution of identical energy packets across a body with n atoms (the energy packets are like the cars, and the atoms are like the booths). The number of atoms in a given object is fixed, so the macrostate tells us the number of energy packets that are in the object. A microstate tells us the particular fashion in which those energy packets are distributed across the atoms. In the exercises at the end of this appendix, you'll use the technique that was demonstrated in Example C.5 to show that the number of ways that q identical packets of energy can arrange themselves across n atoms, denoted by $\Omega(q)$, is

$$\Omega(q) = \binom{q+n-1}{q}.$$

When you have q packets and n atoms, the number of different microstates is Ω.

Now suppose there are *two* bodies that share the q packets of thermal energy, the first with n_1 atoms, and the second with n_2 atoms. There could be 0 in the first and q in the second, or 1 in the first and $q-1$ in the second, or 2 in the first and $q-2$ in the second, ... or q in the first and 0 in the second. Let's consider the case when there are k packets of energy in the first body and $q-k$ in the second. The number of possible microstates in the first body is $\Omega_1(k) = \binom{k+n_1-1}{k}$, and for each of those arrangements the packets in the second body have $\Omega_2(q-k) = \binom{q-k+n_2-1}{q_2}$ ways to distribute themselves, so the total number of ways that the packets of energy could arrange themselves in this configuration is

$$\Omega_1(k)\Omega_2(q-k) = \binom{k+n_1-1}{k}\binom{q-k+n_2-1}{q-k},$$

which we denote by $\Omega(k, q-k)$. In virtually any situation that concerns us, from cells to cell phones, the number of atoms involved is *astonishingly large*, so the number Ω is larger than you could possibly comprehend. We cut it down to a manageable, but still amazingly big number by asking how many powers of e are in it. Specifically, we define the *thermal entropy* of the system to be $S = k_B \ln(\Omega)$. With this vocabulary we can state ...

The function ln, called the *natural logarithm*, is introduced in Chapter 1.

The number k_B is Boltzmann's constant. Its value is $1.3806503 \times 10^{-23}$, and carries units of joules per kelvin.

The numbers Ω and $\ln(\Omega)$ are pure numbers, so entropy has units of J/K (i.e., the units associated with k_B).

> **The Second Law of Thermodynamics:** Any spontaneous change in the distribution of thermal energy will increase the entropy of a system.

Because Ω (and so S) counts the number of ways to rearrange energy packets, the Second Law of Thermodynamics says that Nature makes spontaneous changes in order to provide more thermodynamic flexibility.

❖ Pascal's Triangle

A famous array of numbers known as ***Pascal's triangle*** is commonly described as follows: the so-called 0th row contains only the number 1. The nth row $(n \geq 1)$ begins and ends with the number 1, and comprises a total of $n+1$ numbers. Each "interior" entry is the sum of the entries that are found in the previous row, to its upper left and upper right. The first few rows of Pascal's triangle are shown below:

```
n = 0 .........................................  1
n = 1 ...................................   1    1
n = 2 ...............................   1    2    1
n = 3 ..........................   1    3    3    1
n = 4 .....................  1    4    6    4    1
n = 5 ................  1    5   10   10    5    1
                    .·     ⋮    ⋮    ⋮    ⋮    ⋮    ·.
```

Notice that the numbers $\binom{3}{k}$ compose the third row. Similarly, the numbers $\binom{5}{k}$ compose the fifth row. This happens in general: the nth row of Pascal's triangle contains the numbers $\binom{n}{k}$, and so gives us the coefficients in the expanded form of $(a + b)^n$.

This happens because the binomial coefficients satisfy the same recursion relationship that defines Pascal's triangle. Specifically:

> Suppose n and k are positive integers. Then
> $$\binom{n}{k} = \binom{n-1}{k} + \binom{n-1}{k-1}. \qquad (\text{c.5})$$

The number $\binom{n}{k}$ is in the nth row of Pascal's triangle. The numbers $\binom{n-1}{k}$ and $\binom{n-1}{k-1}$ are in row $(n - 1)$. Because the columns are slightly offset from row to row, columns k and $k-1$ of row $n-1$ are on the right and left of column k in row n.

Proof. Imagine that we have a collection of n items, and want to know how many different groups of k items can be made by selecting from it. The key to understanding equation (c.5) is recognizing that any such group must either (a) *exclude* the first item in the collection or (b) *include* the first item in the collection.

(a) How many groups of k items (selected from our set of n) *exclude* the first item of the collection? In this case, we have k choices to make, but there are only $n-1$ items to choose from (since we cannot choose item #1). Therefore, there are a total of $\binom{n-1}{k}$ groups of k items (selected from a set of n) that exclude item #1.

(b) How many groups of k items (selected from our set of n) *include* the first item of the collection? Since item #1 *has* to be in the group of k, each group is completed by making $k - 1$ other choices. None of those choices can be item #1 (since it has already been selected), so there are $n - 1$ items to choose from. Therefore, there are a total of $\binom{n-1}{k-1}$ groups of k items (selected from our set of n) that include item #1.

Adding these numbers together gives us (c.5). ∎

✤ Exercises

1. How many ways are there to choose 0 items from a group of 9?

2. How many ways are there to choose 9 items from a group of 9?

3. In complete sentences, using the ideas of "choosing" and "leaving," explain why it *should* be true that $\binom{n}{k} = \binom{n}{n-k}$. Then verify that the two numbers are the same by using the formula for $\binom{n}{k}$ that's provided on p. 1340.

4. Suppose there are five (different) DVDs next to your computer. How many ways are there for you to choose three of them?

5. Suppose there are 360 (different) mp3's on your computer. How many ways can you make a playlist of 10 songs? (Suppose your iPod is set to shuffle the playlist, so the order in which you select the songs is irrelevant.)

In #6–8 write the expanded form of the given expression.

6. $(1 + x)^7$ 7. $(2 + x)^5$ 8. $(2x + 4)^6$ 9. $(3x + 2)^5$

10. Suppose that 14 cars exit the turnpike and head toward five toll booths, numbered 1 through 5. From the point of view of the workers in the booths, the cars are identical (it doesn't matter *which* cars line up at your booth, only the number of them). How many different ways could the cars could line up at the booths?

11. Suppose that, at the same time the cars are exiting the turnpike in #10, there are four cars that are about to *enter* the turnpike, and are approaching another set of five booths. How many different ways are there for the 18 cars to line up at the 10 booths, given the division of the cars and booths? *(For each way that the entering cars could line up at the booths, how many ways are there for the exiting cars to line up?)*

12. Suppose that q identical "packets" of thermal energy are in a body with n atoms, numbered 1 through n. By mimicking the reasoning in Example C.5, show that there are $\binom{q+n-1}{q}$ different ways that the packets of energy could distribute themselves across the atoms.

13. Suppose there are q packets of energy shared between two bodies. Then there might be 0 in the first and q in the second, or 1 in the first and $q-1$ in the second, or 2 in the the first and $q-2$ in the second .... When there are k in the first and $q-k$ in the second, the number of microstates is $\Omega(k, q-k)$, so the total number of microstates is

$$\Omega_T = \sum_{k=0}^{q} \Omega(k, q-k). \tag{c.6}$$

The Σ-notation for summation is introduced at the beginning of Chapter 5.

    (a) Find the total number of microstates when $n_1 = 10$, $n_2 = 8$, and $q = 20$.

    (b) When all microstates are equally likely, the probability of seeing $q_1 = k$ and $q_2 = 20 - k$ is

$$P(k) = \frac{\Omega(k, 20-k)}{\Omega_T}.$$

        Calculate $P(k)$ for each k between 0 and 20.

    (c) Explain why we expect $\sum_{j=0}^{20} P(k) = 1$, then verify that it's true.

    (d) Plot these probabilities as a function of k (i.e., plot the points $(k, P(k))$).

    (e) What is the most likely macrostate (what are q_1 and q_2)?

    (f) How does your answer from part (e) correspond to the values of n_1 and n_2?

    (g) Complete parts (a)–(f) with $n_1 = 30$, $n_2 = 50$ and $q = 100$.

14. The **Laguerre polynomials** help us determine the *radial wave functions* for an electron in a hydrogen atom. They are defined as follows:

The name *Laguerre* is pronounced "Log-AIR."

$$L_0(x) \;=\; 1 \tag{c.7}$$
$$L_1(x) \;=\; 1 - x \tag{c.8}$$
$$L_2(x) \;=\; 1 - 2x + \frac{1}{2}x^2. \tag{c.9}$$

In general,

$$L_n(x) = \sum_{k=0}^{n} (-1)^k \binom{n}{k} \frac{x^k}{k!}. \tag{c.10}$$

    (a) Verify that $L_1(x)$ and $L_2(x)$ are described by (c.10).

    (b) Use (c.10) to write down formulas for $L_3(x)$ and $L_4(x)$ like those you see in (c.7)–(c.9).

Appendix D

Conic Sections

We refer to parabolas, ellipses, and hyperbolas as conic sections because they can be formed by intersecting a plane with a cone, as seen in Figure D.1.

Figure D.1: (all) Intersecting a plane with a cone generates the conic sections; (left) the intersection of the cone with a plane that's parallel to its edge but offset from its tip creates a parabola; (middle) the intersection of the cone with a plane that's parallel to its central axis creates a hyperbola; (right) planes at other angles create ellipses (or circles) when intersected with the cone.

The conic sections can also be described in terms of distances, which is how we proceed below. As with our presentation of trigonometry on p. 1316, we assume that this appendix is review material, not presented to you for the first time, but used as a refresher.

✤ Ellipses

Suppose you want to send a signal from one radio tower to another. Because transmission occurs in all directions, some of the signal can hit the ground between the towers and reflect to the receiver; but since such signals have to travel a larger distance than the direct signal, they arrive later. The net effect is that the receiver hears many copies of the same message but time-delayed and overlapped. This makes it difficult to read the signal at the receiving end.

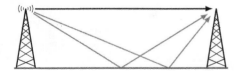

Figure D.2: Sending from one tower to another; reflections from the ground cause interference.

In the discussion below we'll show that when the curve of the ground is an ellipse rather than a line, all of the reflected signals travel the same distance, and so arrive at the receiver simultaneously. So rather than having multiple overlapping signals, the receiver hears only two.

Suppose the transceivers at the top of the radio towers are at $(\pm c, 0)$ in the Cartesian plane, where $c > 0$ (i.e., the x-axis of the plane runs through the transceivers). Then all the points on the y-axis are equidistant from them. For example, the origin is c units from both, and the point $(0, -2)$ is $\sqrt{4 + c^2}$ from both (using the Pythagorean Theorem). More generally, the point $(0, -b)$ is $\sqrt{b^2 + c^2}$ from each transceiver. We'll call this distance a, as depicted in Figure D.3. That is,

$$a^2 = b^2 + c^2. \tag{d.1}$$

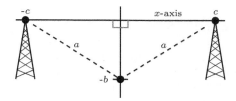

Figure D.3: Points on the y-axis are equidistant from $(\pm c, 0)$.

If (x, y) is any other point of reflection for which the signal travels a path of length $2a$,

$$\underbrace{\sqrt{(x + c)^2 + (y - 0)^2}}_{\text{distance from } (-c, 0) \text{ to } (x, y)} + \underbrace{\sqrt{(x - c)^2 + (y - 0)^2}}_{\text{distance from } (x, y) \text{ to } (c, 0)} = 2a.$$

We can remove the roots from this equation by isolating one radical at a time and then squaring both sides, which takes two steps. Step 1 is to write the equation as

$$\sqrt{(x + c)^2 + y^2} = 2a - \sqrt{(x - c)^2 + y^2}$$

and square both sides. This yields

$$(x + c)^2 + y^2 = (2a)^2 - 2(2a)\sqrt{(x - c)^2 + y^2} + (x - c)^2 + y^2,$$

which simplifies to

$$a\sqrt{(x - c)^2 + y^2} = a^2 - xc.$$

We eliminate the remaining radical by squaring again, thereby arriving at

$$a^2\left((x - c)^2 + y^2\right) = a^4 - 2a^2cx + c^2x^2,$$

which reduces to

$$(a^2 - c^2)x^2 + a^2y^2 = a^2(a^2 - c^2).$$

Looking back to equation (d.1) we see that $a^2 - c^2 = b^2$, so we can rewrite this equation as

$$b^2x^2 + a^2y^2 = a^2b^2,$$

or after dividing by a^2b^2,

$$\frac{x^2}{a^2} + \frac{y^2}{b^2} = 1, \quad \text{where} \quad a \geq b > 0. \tag{d.2}$$

The curve described by equation (d.2) is an ***ellipse***. Notice that $|y|$ cannot exceed b since the left-hand side sums to 1 and x^2/a^2 cannot be negative, and the points $(0, \pm b)$ are on the curve. Similarly, $|x|$ cannot exceed a, and the points $(\pm a, 0)$ are on the ellipse. We say that $(\pm c, 0)$ are the ***foci*** of the ellipse, and we refer to $(\pm a, 0)$ as its ***vertices***. (Some people also refer to $(0, \pm b)$ as vertices of the ellipse.)

The word foci (pronounced "FOE-sigh") is the plural of *focus,* and the word vertices (pronounced "VUR-tuh-sees") is the plural of the word *vertex.*

If the foci had been at $(0, \pm c)$ instead, the same work would have resulted in the equation

$$\frac{x^2}{b^2} + \frac{y^2}{a^2} = 1 \quad \text{where} \quad a \geq b > 0, \tag{d.3}$$

and a and b are related to c by equation (d.1). In this case, the vertices are the points $(0, \pm a)$.

You can tell whether the foci are displaced vertically or horizontally from the ellipse's center by the denominators of (d.2) and (d.3)—horizontal if the denominator associated with x^2 is larger, and vertical otherwise. In either case, the line that passes through the foci is called the ***focal axis*** of the ellipse, and the segment of it that connects the vertices is called the ***major axis*** of the ellipse. The ***conjugate axis*** is the line that passes through the center of the ellipse and is perpendicular to the focal axis, and the ***minor axis*** of the ellipse is the segment of the conjugate axis enclosed by the ellipse. We often use the prefix *semi-* to mean *half,* so a ***semi-major axis*** is half of the major axis (starting at the center and heading toward a vertex), and a ***semi-minor axis*** is half of the minor axis (starting at the center and heading toward the edge of the ellipse).

Major axes, vertices and foci of an ellipse

Example D.1. Determine (a) the major axis, (b) the location of the vertices, and (c) the location of the foci for the ellipse $8x^2 + 6y^2 = 48$.

Solution: (a) If we divide both sides of this equation by 48, it becomes

$$\frac{x^2}{6} + \frac{y^2}{8} = 1.$$

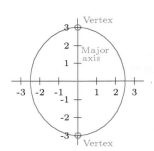

Figure D.4: The ellipse in Example D.1.

This equation allows $|y|$ to get as large as $\sqrt{8}$, but $|x|$ can only grow to $\sqrt{6}$, so this ellipse is taller than it is wide. That is, the vertical axis of this ellipse is its major axis. (b) Since the major axis is vertical, and $|y|$ can get as large as $\sqrt{8}$, the vertices are at $(0, \pm\sqrt{8})$. (c) Our equation indicates that $a^2 = 8$ and $b^2 = 6$ (a^2 is always the larger denominator), so $c^2 = 8 - 6 = 2$. That is, the foci are located $c = \sqrt{2}$ units from the origin. Since they're on the major axis, their coordinates are $(0 \pm \sqrt{2})$. ∎

Major axes, vertices and foci of an ellipse

Example D.2. Determine (a) the major axis, (b) the location of the vertices, and (c) the location of the foci for the ellipse $7x^2 + 13y^2 = 91$.

Answer: (a) the segment $[-\sqrt{13}, \sqrt{13}]$ on the x-axis, (b) the points $(\pm\sqrt{13}, 0)$, and (c) at $(\sqrt{6}, 0)$. ∎

Solution On-line

A slight modification changes the center of the ellipse, but not its width or height. Specifically, consider the equation

$$\frac{(x-h)^2}{a^2} + \frac{(y-k)^2}{b^2} = 1 \tag{d.4}$$

where $a, b > 0$. This equation requires $|x - h| \le a$, so $h - a \le x \le h + a$. Similarly, $|y - k| \le b$ means that $k - b \le y \le k + b$, so this ellipse is centered at (h, k).

An ellipse that's not at the origin

Example D.3. Determine (a) the center, (b) the location of the vertices, and (c) the location of the foci for the ellipse $8x^2 + 16x + 10y^2 - 60y = 0$.

Solution: We begin by completing the square in both x and y, writing

$$8(x^2 + 2x) + 10(y^2 - 6y) = 0$$
$$8(x^2 + 2x + 1) + 10(y^2 - 6y + 9) = 0 + 8 + 90$$
$$8(x + 1)^2 + 10(y - 3)^2 = 98.$$

Dividing both sides by 98 yields

$$\frac{4(x + 1)^2}{49} + \frac{5(y - 3)^2}{49} = 1,$$

which is the same as

$$\frac{(x + 1)^2}{\frac{49}{4}} + \frac{(y - 3)^2}{\frac{49}{5}} = 1.$$

Note that $49/4 > 49/5$, so this is a version of equation (d.4) with $a^2 = 49/4$, $b^2 = 49/5$, $h = -1$ and $k = 3$. Now we can read off our answers: (a) The center of the ellipse is at $(-1, 3)$. (b) Since this ellipse is wider than it is tall, its vertices are found by starting at the center and moving $a = 7/2$ units to the left or right. That is, the vertices are at $(-1 \pm 7/2, 3)$. (c) To locate the vertices, we need to know c, which we find by calculating

$$c^2 = a^2 - b^2 = \frac{49}{4} - \frac{49}{5} = \frac{49}{20} \quad \Rightarrow \quad c = \frac{7\sqrt{5}}{10}.$$

Since this ellipse is wider than it is tall, the foci are found by starting at the center and moving c units to the left or right. That is, the foci are at $(-1 \pm 0.7\sqrt{5}, 3)$. ∎

An ellipse not at the origin

Example D.4. Determine (a) the center, (b) the location of the vertices, and (c) the location of the foci for the ellipse $4x^2 - 80x + 5y^2 + 30y = 0$.

Answer: (a) center at $(10, -3)$, (b) vertices at $(-0.5475, -3)$ and $(20.5475, -3)$, and (c) foci at $(5.283, -3)$ and $(14.717, -3)$. ∎

Solution
On-line

As we saw in equation (d.3), when the numbers a^2 and b^2 in equation (d.4) are swapped, the ellipse that's described is taller than it is wide. In summary:

Suppose $a > b > 0$. Then the equation

$$\frac{(x - h)^2}{a^2} + \frac{(y - k)^2}{b^2} = 1 \qquad (d.5)$$

describes an ellipse centered at the point (h, k) whose vertices are at $(h \pm a, k)$. The foci of the ellipse are at $(h \pm c, k)$, where $c^2 = a^2 - b^2$. Similarly, the equation

$$\frac{(x - h)^2}{b^2} + \frac{(y - k)^2}{a^2} = 1 \qquad (d.6)$$

describes an ellipse centered at the point (h, k) whose vertices are at $(h, k \pm a)$. The foci of the ellipse are at $(h, k \pm c)$, where $c^2 = a^2 - b^2$.

▷ Eccentricity of an ellipse

When the foci of an ellipse are closer to its center than to its vertices, the curve appears almost circular. By contrast, when the foci are closer to the vertices than to the center, the ellipse is more elongated (see Figure D.5). We quantify this structural characteristic with a number called the *eccentricity*. Specifically, the eccentricity of an ellipse described by (d.5) or (d.6) is

$$\varepsilon = \frac{c}{a}. \tag{d.7}$$

Since the semi-major axis has a length of a, the number ε tells us how far out the semi-major axis (as a fraction of its total length) we find the foci.

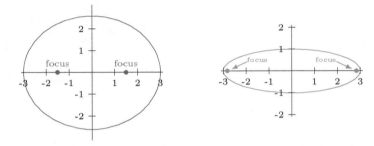

Figure D.5: (left) An ellipse whose eccentricity is $\varepsilon \approx 0.5$; (right) an ellipse whose eccentricity is near 1.

Calculating eccentricity of an ellipse

Example D.5. Determine the eccentricity of the ellipse $x^2 + 9y^2 = 9$, which is shown in the right-hand image of Figure D.5.

Solution: When we divide this equation by 9, we see

$$\frac{x^2}{9} + \frac{y^2}{1} = 1,$$

from which we conclude that $a = 3$ and $b = 1$. Therefore, $c = \sqrt{8}$, and $\varepsilon = c/a = 0.94$. That is, the foci can be found by traveling 94% of a semi-major axis away from the center of the ellipse. ∎

Calculating eccentricity of an ellipse

Example D.6. Determine the eccentricity of the ellipse $x^2 + 9y^2 = 9$, which is shown in the left-hand image of Figure D.5.

Answer: $\varepsilon = 47/100$. ∎

Solution
On-line

The relationship between eccentricity and the shape of an ellipse becomes apparent when we consider the fact that $c^2 = a^2 - b^2$, which allows us to see that

$$\varepsilon^2 = \left(\frac{c}{a}\right)^2 = \frac{a^2 - b^2}{a^2} = 1 - \left(\frac{b}{a}\right)^2 \quad \Rightarrow \quad \varepsilon = \sqrt{1 - \left(\frac{b}{a}\right)^2}.$$

An almost-circular ellipse has $b \approx a$, so that $\varepsilon \approx 0$. Looking back to equation (d.7), we conclude that the foci are very close to the center. Similarly, the number a is much larger than b in a very elongated ellipse, so $b/a \approx 0 \Rightarrow \varepsilon \approx 1$. Looking back to equation (d.7), we conclude that the foci are very close to the vertices.

✤ Hyperbolas

Suppose you touch the surface of still water at two points, called *touchpoints,* one after the other, and the leading edge of each disturbance travels at the same speed. The wavefronts will eventually meet, and after that time the point of intersection will proceed away from both touchpoints (see Figure D.6).

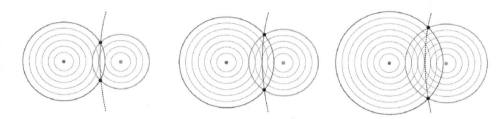

Figure D.6: When the wavefronts travel at the same speed, they meet on the edge of a hyperbolic curve (the first touchpoint is marked with ●, and the second with ◉).

Let's denote the point were the wavefronts meet by P, and the touchpoints by F_1 and F_2. Since the wavefronts are traveling at the same speed, the lengths $|PF_1|$ and $|PF_2|$ are increasing at the same rate. Consequently, their difference is constant. That is,

$$|PF_1| - |PF_2| = \text{constant}.$$

This equation describes a hyperbola, and as we did with ellipses, we can rewrite it in Cartesian coordinates. Suppose the touchpoints are at $(\pm c, 0)$, and the wavefronts first meet at $(a, 0)$, so $0 < a < c$. If P is at (x, y),

$$\underbrace{\sqrt{(x+c)^2 + (y-0)^2}}_{\text{distance from } (-c,0) \text{ to } (x,y)} - \underbrace{\sqrt{(x-c)^2 + (y-0)^2}}_{\text{distance from } (x,y) \text{ to } (c,0)} = 2a.$$

> The point $(a, 0)$ is $a + c$ units away from one touchpoint, and $c - a$ units away from the other. The difference of these distances is
>
> $$(a + c) - (c - a) = 2a.$$

By using the same "isolate-and-square" technique as we did with the ellipse, we arrive at the following:

$$\frac{x^2}{a^2} - \frac{y^2}{b^2} = 1, \quad \text{where} \quad b^2 = c^2 - a^2. \tag{d.8}$$

As with the ellipse, we can derive a similar equation when the touchpoints—called the **foci** of the hyperbola—are at $(0, \pm c)$, and when the whole enterprise is re-centered on (h, k). The first point where the wavefronts meet, $(a, 0)$ in our discussion above, and its reflection across the center of the hyperbola are called the **vertices** of the hyperbola.

Suppose $a, b > 0$. Then the equation

$$\frac{(x - h)^2}{a^2} - \frac{(y - k)^2}{b^2} = 1 \tag{d.9}$$

describes a hyperbola whose vertices are at $(h \pm a, k)$ and whose foci are at $(h \pm c, k)$ where $c^2 = a^2 + b^2$. Similarly, the equation

$$\frac{(y - k)^2}{a^2} - \frac{(x - h)^2}{b^2} = 1 \tag{d.10}$$

describes a hyperbola whose vertices are at $(h, k \pm a)$ and whose foci are at $(h, k \pm c)$ where $c^2 = a^2 + b^2$.

> Equation (d.9) prohibits $x = h$, so the hyperbola has two *branches,* one on each side of that vertical line.
>
> Similarly, equation (d.10) prohibits $y = h$, so the hyperbola has two branches that are separated by that horizontal line.

As with ellipses, the line connecting the foci of a hyperbola is called its *focal axis*, and the perpendicular line through the center is called the *conjugate axis.*

Locating the center, vertices, and foci of a hyperbola

Example D.7. Determine the location of (a) the center, (b) the vertices, and (c) the foci of the hyperbola $4x^2 + 24x - 3y^2 + 12y = 0$.

Solution: As in Example D.3, we begin by completing the square in both x and y, writing our equation as

$$4(x^2 + 6x) - 3(y^2 - 4y) = 0$$
$$4(x + 3)^2 - 3(y - 2)^2 = 24.$$

Dividing both sides by 24 yields

$$\frac{(x + 3)^2}{6} - \frac{(y - 2)^2}{8} = 1.$$

This is a version of equation (d.9) in which $h = -3$, $k = 2$, $a = \sqrt{6}$ and $b = \sqrt{8}$. Now we can answer the questions: (a) the center is at $(-3, 2)$, (b) the vertices are at $(-3 \pm \sqrt{6}, 2)$, and (c) the number $c = \sqrt{14}$ so the foci are at $(-3 \pm \sqrt{14}, 2)$. These facts are shown in Figure D.7. ∎

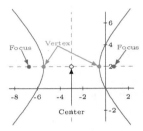

Figure D.7: The hyperbola in Example D.7.

Locating the center, vertices, and foci of a hyperbola

Example D.8. Determine the location of (a) the center, (b) the vertices, and (c) the foci of the hyperbola $3y^2 + 24y - 7x^2 + 28x = 0$.

Answer: (a) The center is at $(2, -4)$, (b) the vertices are at $\left(2, -4 \pm \frac{2\sqrt{15}}{3}\right)$, (c) the foci are at $\left(2, -4 \pm \frac{10\sqrt{42}}{21}\right)$. ∎

Solution On-line

▷ Asymptotes of a Hyperbola

We can rewrite equation (d.8) as

$$y^2 = \frac{b^2}{a^2}x^2 - b^2 \quad \Rightarrow \quad y = \pm\sqrt{\frac{b^2}{a^2}x^2 - b^2}.$$

After factoring x^2 out of the radicand, this becomes

$$y = \pm\sqrt{\left(\frac{b^2}{a^2} - \frac{b^2}{x^2}\right)x^2} = \pm\sqrt{\frac{b^2}{a^2} - \frac{b^2}{x^2}}\; x.$$

When x is much larger than b, the number $(b/x)^2 \approx 0$ and this reduces to

$$y = \pm\frac{b}{a}x.$$

That is, points on a hyperbola described by equation (d.8) approach the lines $y = \pm\frac{b}{a}x$ when x is large. We say that these lines are *asymptotes* of the hyperbola. More generally:

> Suppose $a, b > 0$. Then the asymptotes of the hyperbola described by equation (d.9) are $y - k = \pm\frac{b}{a}(x - h)$.
>
> Similarly, the asymptotes of the hyperbola described by equation (d.10) are $y - k = \pm\frac{a}{b}(x - h)$.

This information is often used to make quick sketches of hyperbolas.

Asymptotes of a hyperbola

Example D.9. Determine the center, vertices, and asymptotes of the hyperbola $x^2 - 7y^2 = 21$, and sketch a graph of it.

Solution: After dividing both sides of this equation by 21, it becomes

$$\frac{x^2}{21} - \frac{y^2}{3} = 1.$$

This is an example of equation (d.9) where $h = 0$, $k = 0$, $a = \sqrt{21}$ and $b = \sqrt{3}$. So this hyperbola is centered at the origin, and its vertices are at $(\pm\sqrt{21}, 0)$. Based on our work above, we know that the asymptotes are the lines $y = \pm\sqrt{\frac{3}{21}}\, x$. After plotting these points and asymptotes (which we draw dashed to indicate their role as guidelines), we can sketch a graph of the hyperbola by passing a curve through the vertices that's curved away from the center, and approaches the asymptotes as $|x|$ grows (see Figure D.8). ∎

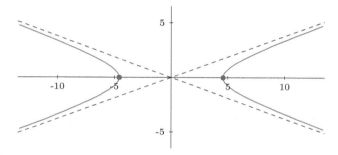

Figure D.8: The hyperbola for Example D.9.

Asymptotes of a hyperbola

Example D.10. Determine the center, vertices, and asymptotes of the hyperbola $3y^2 + 48y - 2x^2 = 0$, and sketch a graph of it.

Answer: The center is at $(0, -8)$, the vertices at $(0, 0)$ and $(0, -16)$, and the asymptotes are $y + 8 = \pm\frac{8}{9}x$. ∎

Solution
On-line

▷ Eccentricity of a hyperbola

As with an ellipse, we define the **_eccentricity_** of a hyperbola to be

$$\varepsilon = \frac{c}{a} = \frac{\text{distance between the foci}}{\text{distance between the vertices}}.$$

Note: Since $c > a$, the eccentricity of a hyperbola is always > 1.

Eccentricity of a hyperbola

Example D.11. Determine the eccentricity of the hyperbola described by $(x + 3)^2 - 6(y - 2)^2 = 6$.

Solution: Dividing both sides of this equation by 6 yields

$$\frac{(x+3)^2}{6} - \frac{(y-2)^2}{1} = 1,$$

from which we conclude that $c^2 = a^2 + b^2 = 6 + 1 = 7 \Rightarrow c = \sqrt{7}$. Therefore, the eccentricity is $\varepsilon = c/a = \sqrt{7}/6$.   ∎

Solution On-line

Eccentricity of a hyperbola

Example D.12. Determine the eccentricity of the hyperbola in Example D.8.

Answer: $\varepsilon = \sqrt{10/7}$.   ∎

The hyperbolas in Examples D.11 and D.7 are closely related. They have the same center and vertices, but the eccentricity of the hyperbola in Example D.7 is larger ($\varepsilon = \sqrt{14}/6$). The pair of hyperbolas are graphed in Figure D.9, where you can see that an eccentricity closer to 1 results in greater curvature at the vertices.

As before, we can understand this by using the fact that $c^2 = a^2 + b^2$ to write

$$\varepsilon^2 = \frac{c^2}{a^2} = \frac{a^2 + b^2}{a^2} = 1 + \left(\frac{b}{a}\right)^2 \quad \Rightarrow \quad \varepsilon = \sqrt{1 + \left(\frac{b}{a}\right)^2}.$$

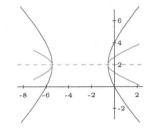

When the focal axis of a hyperbola is horizontal, the slopes of its asymptotes are $\pm b/a$. When ε is near 1, that number must be small, so the angle between the asymptotes is small. Consequently, there is greater curvature at the vertices.

Figure D.9: The hyperbolas from Example D.11 and Example D.7.

✛ Parabolas

Unlike hyperbolas and ellipses, in which points are related to a pair of foci, a parabola is the set of points that are equidistant from a specified point, called its *focus*, and a given line, called its *directrix*. For example, if the focus is at $(0, c)$ and the directrix is the line $y = -c$, the origin is on the parabola because it's c units from both. More generally, the point at (x, y) is on the parabola if

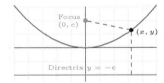

Figure D.10: Example of a parabola.

$$\underbrace{\sqrt{(x-0)^2 + (y-c)^2}}_{\text{distance from } (x,y) \text{ to the focus at } (0,c)} = \underbrace{y + c.}_{\text{distance from } (x,y) \text{ to the directrix } y = -c.}$$

Squaring both sides of this equation and solving the resulting expression for y yields

$$y = \frac{1}{4c}x^2.$$

Similarly, when the focus is at $(c, 0)$ and the directrix at $x = -c$, as seen in Figure D.11, points on the parabola are described by

$$\sqrt{(x-c)^2 + y^2} = x + c \quad \Rightarrow \quad x = \frac{1}{4c}y^2.$$

While we have drawn $c > 0$ in Figures D.10 and D.11, the mathematics is the same when $c < 0$. The sign of c determine whether the parabola cups up or down, right or left. In any event, the line through the focus that's perpendicular to the directrix is called the *axis* of the parabola, and its *vertex* is the point of the parabola on its axis (half way between the focus and the directrix). As before, a slight change in the formula shifts the vertex of the parabola.

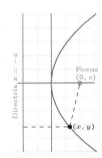

Figure D.11: Example of a parabola.

Suppose $c \neq 0$. The equation

$$y = k + \frac{1}{4c}(x - h)^2 \tag{d.11}$$

describes a parabola whose focus is the point $(h, k + c)$, and whose directrix is the horizontal line $y = k - c$. The parabola's vertex is at (h, k), it opens upward when $c > 0$, and it opens downward when $c < 0$. Similarly, the equation

$$x = h + \frac{1}{4c}(y - k)^2 \tag{d.12}$$

describes a parabola whose focus is the point $(h + c, k)$, and whose directrix is the vertical line $x = h - c$. The parabola's vertex is at (h, k), it opens to the right when $c > 0$, and it opens to the left when $c < 0$.

> No matter the value of x, the number $(x - h)^2 > 0$. So when $c > 0$, this equation says that $y = k$+more, allowing y to be any number $\geq k$. That's one way to understand why $c > 0$ makes the parabola open up.

> No matter the value of y, the number $(y - k)^2 > 0$. So when $c > 0$, this equation says that $x = h$+more, so x cannot be less than h. That's one way to understand why $c > 0$ makes the parabola open to the right.

Determining a parabola

Example D.13. Determine the focus, directrix, and vertex of the parabola $13x + 26y^2 = 7$.

Solution: When we solve this equation for the linear variable, we see

$$x = \frac{7}{13} - 2y^2.$$

Since x cannot be larger than $7/13$, this parabola opens to the left. Its vertex is its rightmost point, which is $(7/13, 0)$. Comparing this with equation (d.12) yields

$$\frac{1}{4c} = -2 \quad \Rightarrow \quad c = -\frac{1}{8},$$

which means the focus and directrix are $1/8$ of a unit away from the focus. Since this parabola opens to the left, the focus is left of the vertex and the directrix is to the right. Specifically, the directrix is the line $x = \frac{7}{13} + \frac{1}{8} = \frac{57}{104}$, and the focus is the point $\left(\frac{55}{104}, 0\right)$. ∎

Determining a parabola

Example D.14. Determine (a) the focus, (b) the directrix, and (c) the vertex of the parabola $3x^2 - 5y = 2$.

Answer: (a) The point $\left(0, \frac{1}{60}\right)$, (b) the line $y = -\frac{49}{60}$, (c) the point $\left(0, -\frac{2}{5}\right)$. ∎

Solution On-line

▷ Eccentricity of a Parabola

Earlier in our discussion, eccentricity told us the extent to which an ellipse was elongated rather than nearly circular, and whether the two sides of a hyperbola raced away from each other or lazily meandered apart. Whereas ellipses have eccentricity $\varepsilon < 1$, and hyperbolas have $\varepsilon > 1$, the eccentricity of a parabola is always $\varepsilon = 1$, so we cannot use it to quantify structure. However, the number c tells us how close the focus is to the vertex, which is at the heart of the idea. Small values of c indicate that the focus and vertex are very close, and the result is greater curvature at the vertex. By contrast, larger values of c result parabolas that appear more flat (see Figure D.12).

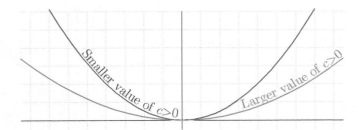

Figure D.12: Larger values of c mean the vertex and focus are farther apart, so the parabola appears "flatter."

❖ Reflective Properties of Conic Sections

We started this discussion by showing that signals that are emitted from one focus of an ellipse and arrive at the other after reflecting off the curve all travel the same distance, but we didn't show that a reflected signal is actually reflected toward that second focus. That can be done by showing that the line segments PF_1 and PF_2 make equal angles with the tangent line at each point P on the ellipse (see Figure D.13), and calculus allows us to determine the slope of the tangent line at P.

In a similar fashion, a parabola reflects signals to its focus that arrive on trajectories parallel to its axis. This fact, which is widely used with parabolic dishes, can be shown by calculating the slope of the tangent line and relevant angles.

Lastly, the tangent line to a hyperbola at the point P bisects the angle $F_1 P F_2$, so a signal directed toward F_2 will reflect off the hyperbola and head toward F_1. This fact is used, for example, in the construction of Cassegrain reflecting telescopes.

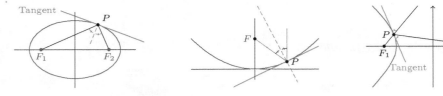

Figure D.13: Reflective properties of (left) ellipses; (middle) hyperbolas; (right) parabolas.

❖ Skill Exercises

For questions #1-4, determine (a) the length of the major axis, (b) the location of the vertices, and (c) the location of the foci of the given ellipse.

1. $4x^2 + 9y^2 = 36$ 3. $16x^2 + 9y^2 = 144$

2. $6x^2 + 10y^2 = 30$ 4. $5^2 + 8y^2 = 12$

For questions #5-8, determine (a) the center, (b) the location of the vertices, and (c) the location of the foci of the given ellipse.

5. $x^2 + 4x + 8y^2 = 1$

7. $3x^2 + 2y^2 = 8x - 4y$

6. $2x^2 + 12x + y^2 - 6y = 0$

8. $9x^2 - 4x = 7y - 3y^2$

For questions #9-12 (a) determine the eccentricity of the given ellipse, and (b) sketch the ellipse.

9. $x^2 + 5y^2 = 1$

11. $x^2 + 4x + y^2 + 2y = 0$

10. $8x^2 + 3y^2 = 1$

12. $2x^2 + 12x = 4y^2 + 9y$

For questions #13-16 determine the equation of the ellipse.

13. Centered at the origin with a major axis of 4 units and an eccentricity of $1/2$.

14. Centered at $(2, 4)$ with an eccentricity of 0.3 and a semi-minor axis of 6 units.

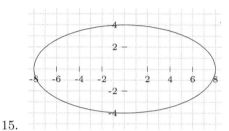

15.

16.

For questions #17-20 determine (a) the vertices, (b) the foci, and (c) the equations of the asymptotes of the hyperbola.

17. $4x^2 - 9y^2 = 36$

19. $5y^2 - 9x^2 = 45$

18. $25x^2 - 4y^2 = 100$

20. $10y^2 - 6x^2 = 12$

For questions #21-24 determine (a) the vertices, (b) the foci, and (c) the equations of the asymptotes of the hyperbola.

21. $x^2 - y^2 + 6y = 0$

23. $6x^2 + 2x = y^2 + 8y$

22. $2x^2 - 8x + 18y - 9y^2 = 0$

24. $10x^2 - 6y^2 = 40x - 30y$

For questions #25-28 (a) determine the eccentricity, and (b) sketch the hyperbola.

25. $x^2 - 8y^2 = 48$

27. $2x^2 - 10y^2 = 4y + 3x$

26. $9x^2 - 4y^2 = 72$

28. $8x^2 + 6x = 7y^2 - 11y$

For questions #29-34 use the foci F, vertices V, point P on the curve, or eccentricity E to find the equation of the hyperbola.

29. F: $(\pm 10, 0)$, V: $(\pm 4, 0)$

31. V: $(\pm 2, 0)$, P: $(6, 4)$

33. F: $(2, 3)$ and $(5, 3)$, E: $3/2$

30. F: $(0, \pm 6)$, V: $(0, \pm 5)$

32. V: $(0, \pm 1)$, P: $(-2, 3)$

34. F: $(-1, 2)$ and $(-1, -8)$, E: 4

For questions #35-42 (a) find the vertex, focus and directrix of the parabola, then (b) sketch its graph, showing the focus and directrix.

35. $7y = x^2$

36. $4x = 3y^2$

37. $8x = -5y^2$

38. $10y = -x^2$

39. $3 = x^2 + y$

40. $y = 4 + 7x - 3x^2$

41. $y^2 + 2y = 3x$

42. $6x + 4 = 3 - 8y^2$

For questions #43-50 use the focus F, directrix D, vertex V, point P, or orientation O to find the equation of the parabola that satisfies the given conditions.

43. F: $(4, 0)$, $D : x = 1$

44. F: $(2, 3)$, D: $x = 8$

45. F: $(0, 6)$, D: $y = 1$

46. F: $(-2, 5)$, D: $y = 5$

47. V: $(1, 0)$, D: $x = -1$

48. V: $(4, -3)$, D: $x = -8$

49. V: $(0, 10)$, D: $y = 1$

50. V: $(-2, -5)$, D: $y = 3/2$

51. V: $(7, 0)$, P: $(8, 2)$, O: horizontal

52. V: $(2, 9)$, P: $(1, 1)$, O: horizontal

53. V: $(0, -5)$, P: $(-2, -8)$, O: vertical

54. V: $(4, 12)$, P: $(2, 13)$, O: vertical

❖ Concept and Application Exercises

55. The moon's orbit about the earth is elliptical with an eccentricity of 0.0549 and a major axis of 769496 km. The earth is located at one of the foci, which we'll take as the origin of the Cartesian plane. Determine (a) the equation of the ellipse describing the moon's orbit, and (b) the maximum and minimum distance between the moon the earth.

56. Lithotripsy is a procedure used to break up kidney stones using the reflective properties of the ellipse. High-energy waves are generated at one focus of an elliptical reflector (called a *lithotripter*), which directs them to the second focus (see Figure D.14). With careful positioning, the second focus is centered on the kidney stone. A standard lithotripter has a semi-major axis of 13.8 cm and a minor axis of 15.5 cm. (a) Determine the equation of the ellipse described by the lithotripter dimensions. (b) If the kidney stone is 140 mm below the skin, how far from the body should the lithotripter's vertex be located?

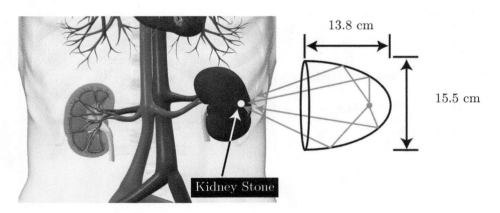

Figure D.14: Diagram of a lithotripter in action (not to scale).

57. On an ellipse, the line segment perpendicular to the major axis, through one of the foci, and with endpoints on the ellipse is called a **focal chord.** Show that the length of an ellipse's focal chord is $2b^2/a$.

58. In the LORAN navigation system, synchronized radio signals from three navigation stations (whose locations are known) are detected by ships. Since the signals travel at the same speed, the difference in their arrival time allows us to calculate the difference in the distances they have traveled.

    Suppose three navigation stations are situated along a coastline so that Station 1 is six kilometers due west of Station 2 and Station 3 is eight kilometers further east (see Figure D.15). As a ship approaches from the west, it detects signals from each of the stations and determines that the signal from Station 2 traveled four kilometers farther than the signal from Station 1, and the signal from Station 3 traveled six kilometers farther than the signal from Station 2. (a) Place Station 2 at the origin, and then determine the equation for the hyperbola whose foci are at Stations 1 and 2 and for which $2a = 2$ (i.e. the difference in the distance their signals traveled). (b) Keeping Station 2 at the origin, determine the equation for the hyperbola whose foci are at Stations 2 and 3, and for which $2a = 6$. (c) Determine the exact location of the ship, which sits on both hyperbolas from parts (a) and (b).

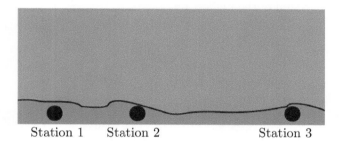

Station 1   Station 2   Station 3

Figure D.15: The distribution of LORAN stations for #58.

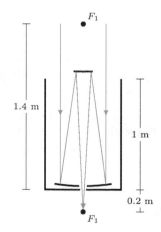

Figure D.16: Diagram of light rays in a Cassegrain reflecting telescope.

59. The Cassegrain reflecting telescope uses a double-mirror system such as the one shown in Figure D.16. The primary mirror is parabolic and reflects the incoming light rays up towards the parabola's focus, F_1. The secondary mirror is hyperbolic and one of its foci is also at F_1. It reflects light rays downwards to the hyperbola's second focus at F_2.

    Consider the Cassegrain reflecting telescope in Figure D.16. It has a tube length of 1 meter and a primary focal length of 1.4 meters. Determine the equation of the hyperbola describing the secondary mirror.

60. What kind of curve is represented by

$$\frac{x^2}{p} + \frac{y^2}{p-9} = 1$$

for (a) $p > 9$, (b) $0 < p < 9$, and (c) $p < 0$?

61. The Photon Energy Transformation and Astrophysics Laboratory (PETAL) in Sede Boqer, Israel is one of the world's largest solar energy concentrators.

It is a parabolic dish that is 24 m across and has a focal length (the distance from the vertex to the focus) of approximately 13 m (see Figure D.17). (a) Determine the equation of the parabola that runs from edge to edge through the center, and (b) determine the depth, d, of the dish.

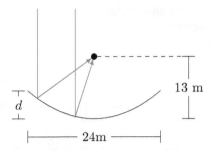

Figure D.17: Diagram of the parabolic reflector for #61.

62. A bridge spanning a two-lane highway is designed with a parabolic arch. The standard width for a two-lane highway is 36 feet (including both lanes and the shoulders). Each lane is 12 feet wide and the the parabolic arch must be 14 feet high on the outside edge of the lanes to accommodate tractor-trailers (see Figure D.18). Determine the height above ground of the highest point of the arch.

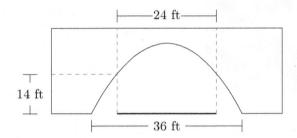

Figure D.18: Diagram of the bridge for #62.

63. Consider the parabola $y = \frac{1}{4p}x^2$, where $p > 0$. An ellipse shares the focus at $(0, p)$, and the endpoints of its minor axis lie on the parabola. Which curve has a vertex closest to the shared focus?

64. Consider the ellipse with a fixed focus at $(0, c)$ and centered at $(0, c + k)$. Show that as k grows without bound the equation of the ellipse reduces to the parabola $x^2 = 4cy$.

Appendix E

The World We Live In

The vast majority of your life experience has involved something we call *contact force*. When you *flip* open the cover of a book, *push* on the keys of a computer, *pull* up your covers at night, *turn* the steering wheel of your car, *twist* a door knob, *tug* open a refrigerator door, *kick* a soccer ball, or *lift* your backpack, you act on another object by making contact with it. This is the kind of force that Newton, Hooke, Halley and the others had experienced in their lives, too, so the suggestion that the sun could exert a force on the planets even though it doesn't touch them seemed very strange. Newton called the idea "action at a distance," and he was uncomfortable with it.

Since we've grown up knowing about gravity, electricity, and magnetism, it's hard for many people to empathize with Newton, but here's a modern example that elicits the same intellectual discomfort in many people: When NASA wants to send a probe into the outer reaches of the solar system, it uses the planets to "slingshot" the vehicle forward along its trajectory. In short, when the probe gets "close enough" to the planet, the probe and planet exchange something called *momentum,* which is discussed below, and the result is roughly equivalent to a fast-swung bat (the planet) colliding with a golf ball (the probe). On the one hand, that's pretty cool. On the other, it's also a little spooky. How was momentum or anything else exchanged since, unlike the bat and ball, the probe and the planet were never in contact?

After a few minutes thinking about that example, or about gravity, or about electrostatics—all of which involve "action at a distance," you might begin to wonder whether the word "force" is being used to gloss over things that we don't fully comprehend, but in today's world we have a very good understanding of force. The essence of that understanding is encapsulated in Newton's Laws of Motion, which focus on the quantity called *momentum.*

> Electrostatic force and magnetic force were not well understood in 1684, when Newton and his peers were struggling with the idea of gravity, so Newton couldn't look to those forces as other examples of "action at a distance."

> In fact, it wasn't until 1733 that Charles François du Fay discovered that electricity comes in two kinds, which he called resinous(-) and vitreous (+); and it wasn't until 1750 that John Michell discovered that the two poles of a magnet are equal in strength and that the force associated with an individual pole obeys an inverse square law.

> You might guess that the probe picks up speed because it falls into the planet's gravity well, but it also has to climb *out* of the well! What's happening is a bit more complicated.

✤ Momentum

Informally, you might think of an object's *momentum,* which is often denoted by p, as quantifying how much it will hurt when it hits you. Objects that are more massive will hurt more, as will objects that are traveling faster. From that standpoint, **momentum** should be (and is) defined as $p = mv$, where v is the object's velocity.

Technically speaking, an object's velocity has both a magnitude (speed) and a direction, so we call it a *vector.* Consequently momentum (which inherits the directional information included in the object's velocity) is also a vector. Vectors are typically denoted by bold characters, so we write $\mathbf{p} = m\mathbf{v}$. Note that the units associated with momentum are $(\text{kg})\left(\frac{\text{m}}{\text{sec}}\right)$.

> The formula $p = m + v$ also describes the basic idea of momentum communicated here, but what should be true about an object's momentum if it has mass but no speed (it's still), or silly as it sounds, speed but no mass? Compare the formulas $p = mv$ and $p = m + v$ in these cases.

> See Chapter 11 for a discussion of vectors.

✤ Newton's Laws of Motion

In short, Newton's Laws describe the relationship between momentum and force. We've already talked a little bit about momentum, but what's force? That's a fair question, but it's also the wrong one to ask—at least inititally. The first job of the physical sciences is to say what things *do*, not what they are. So let's address action instead of essence, and ask, "What does a force *do?*" Newton's answer is that force changes an object's momentum. In fact, Newton's First Law of motion tells us that force is the *only* thing that changes an object's momentum.

> **Newton's First Law of Motion:** Consider a body that's free of external forces. If the body is in motion, it will stay in motion (maintaining both its direction and speed). If the body is at rest, it will stay at rest.

But what about a body that's *not* free of external forces? How does its momentum change? In order to simplify the answer, let's restrict our discussion to cases in which the object's mass is constant (unlike a jet or rocket, which is throwing fuel out the back end). When m is constant, momentum can only change when there's a change in velocity, which we call an *acceleration* and often denote by **a**. Of course, you know from experience that when you apply the same force to different objects, those with more mass experience less acceleration (smaller Δp). This is the essence of Newton's Second Law of motion.

> Notice that the word *acceleration* is not used only when an object "speeds up." It means only that there is a *change* in velocity. That could mean that the object speeds up, slows down, or changes direction.

> **Newton's Second Law of Motion:** When a force, **F**, acts on a body whose mass is m kilograms (constant), the body's velocity changes by $\mathbf{a} = \mathbf{F}/m$ meters per second each second.

If we multiply that equation by m, we have the famous formula

$$\mathbf{F} = m\mathbf{a}. \tag{e.1}$$

Since mass is measured in kilograms (kg), and acceleration is measured as $\frac{\text{m/sec}}{\text{sec}}$, which we often write at $\frac{\text{m}}{\text{sec}^2}$, equation (e.1) leads us to say that force has units of $\frac{\text{kg m}}{\text{sec}^2}$. The term *kilogram-meters-per-second-squared* is cumbersome, so we just say that force has units of **newtons**, which we denote by N.

> When we read (e.1) aloud, we read the equals sign as the word "is," so (e.1) says that force is the product of mass and acceleration. Many people find the equation $a = F/m$ to be more closely in line with their intuition.

Now let's return to the question that we posed initially, "What *is* a force?" Newton's answer was that force is an *interaction between two objects*. This is an extremely important idea, so let's spend a moment with it.

Consider the following simple question: when you jump, do you push on the planet or does the planet push on you? Based on symmetry, you might be tempted to answer, "both," and that's exactly right. It's not that one object acts on another but, rather, that two objects act on *each other*.

> You may have heard it said that "forces come in pairs," which expresses the spirit of the Third Law of Motion.

> **Newton's Third Law of Motion:** Suppose that Object #1 acts on Object #2 with a force of **F**. Then simultaneously, Object #2 acts on Object #1 with a force of $-\mathbf{F}$.

> The negative sign indicates an opposite *direction* of force.

For example, when a Hummer hits a Mini Cooper, delivering a force **F**, the Mini Cooper delivers the same amount of force to the Hummer, but in the opposite direction. That assertion is often met with some degree of sarcasm. "*Sure* it does. Why don't we test that out? *I'll* drive the Hummer, and *you* sit in the Mini Cooper." Of course the driver of the Mini will be much worse off in a collision, but that's because the Mini experiences a much greater acceleration than the Hummer, not a greater force.

Figure E.1: A Hummer is much more massive than a Mini Cooper.

When we look at Newton's Second Law, we see

$$\mathbf{a}_{\text{hummer}} = \frac{\mathbf{F}}{m_{\text{hummer}}} \quad \text{and} \quad \mathbf{a}_{\text{mini}} = -\frac{\mathbf{F}}{m_{\text{mini}}}.$$

> The negative sign in a_{mini} indicates an opposite *direction*.

Since m_{hummer} is so much larger than m_{mini}, the Hummer experiences much less acceleration. The same kind of thing happens in the example of jumping. You apply a force to the Earth, and the Earth applies the same amount of force to you. Since the Earth is so much more massive than you, the acceleration it experiences because of this force is much, *much* smaller than the acceleration you experience.

In Summary: You can understand Newton's Laws of Motion as telling us three things: (1) *without* external force, momentum is constant, (2) *with* external force, momentum changes, and (3) forces occur in pairs.

The ideas of momentum and force, and the way they relate (according to Newton's Laws of Motion), are extremely helpful as we try to understand the world we live in, but they don't tell us everything. The next section introduces an important concept—*energy*—that allows us to understand and predict a much wider variety of phenomena.

✥ Energy

When you slow your car by applying the brakes, you generate a lot of heat from friction, and afterwards you're traveling more slowly. So the statement that

(initial momentum) − (heat from brakes) = (final momentum)

might appeal to you. While the spirit of this equation is right, it doesn't actually make sense. To see why, rewrite it as

−(heat from brakes) = (final momentum) − (initial momentum)

On the right-hand side you see the difference in the car's momentum, $\Delta \mathbf{p}$, which accounts for changes in both direction and magnitude, but heat is described only in terms of magnitude. That is, on the right-hand side we see a *vector* quantity, but on the left-hand side we see a *scalar* quantity, so our statement equates two quantities that are fundamentally different, much as if we had equated mass and color, or length and time.

> We talk about how much heat is generated, but you never hear someone say, "Wow, that stove has a lot of westerly heat!" Though heat can be carried by a flow, heat itself does not have a direction.

This is not to say that heat and motion are unrelated in our example, just that the equation we wrote is nonsensical at a technical level. We fix this problem by relating both heat and momentum to something called **energy,** which then allows us to relate them to each other:

$$-\begin{pmatrix} \text{the energy generated} \\ \text{from the friction of} \\ \text{the brakes} \end{pmatrix} = \begin{pmatrix} \text{the final energy} \\ \text{associated with} \\ \text{motion} \end{pmatrix} - \begin{pmatrix} \text{the initial en-} \\ \text{ergy associated} \\ \text{with motion} \end{pmatrix}. \qquad (\text{e.2})$$

The energy associated with motion is called **kinetic energy**, and is often denoted by K. In Chapter 7 you'll see kinetic energy arise naturally from Newton's Second Law by way of something called the *definite integral*. For now, let's just cite the conclusions that are developed there: when a body has a mass of m and a velocity of $\mathbf{v}$, its kinetic energy is $K = 0.5m\|\mathbf{v}\|^2$, where $\|\mathbf{v}\|$ denotes the object's speed. Therefore, the units of kinetic energy are

$$\text{(kg)} \left(\frac{\text{m}}{\text{sec}}\right)^2 = \underbrace{\left(\frac{\text{kg m}}{\text{sec}^2}\right)}_{\substack{\text{remember that we} \\ \text{call this a newton}}} \text{(m)} = Nm,$$

which we read as **newton-meters**. This unit is also called a **joule**, and is denoted by J. In fact, the joule is used not only for *kinetic* energy, but for *all* kinds of energy.

> The notation $\|\mathbf{v}\|$ is used to mean the magnitude of the vector $\mathbf{v}$, much as $|t|$ means the magnitude of the number t.

The idea of energy and its consequences are quite a bit more slippery than the idea of force. The physicist Richard Feynman once remarked, "... in physics today, we have no knowledge of what energy *is*. We do not have a picture that energy comes in little blobs of a definite amount. It is not that way. [And yet there is a quantity, which we call *energy,* that] does not change when something happens. It is not a description of a mechanism, or anything concrete; it is just a strange fact that we can calculate some number and when we finish watching nature go through her tricks and calculate the number again, it is the same." This fact is called the **Conservation of Energy** and it's one of the most important things that we know about the world we live in.

Another extremely important fact about energy is that it can change forms. For example, when you jump, your body converts stored *chemical* energy into *kinetic* energy (you move), which is then converted into *potential* energy (you rise). When all of the kinetic energy has been converted into potential energy, you stop rising. As you fall back to Earth, the potential energy is converted back into kinetic energy, which (when you land) is converted into *thermal* energy. So while the total amount of energy doesn't change, the place that we find it—the way we experience it—the *form* it takes does change.

In closing we should mention that, aside from kinetic energy, the most important form of energy is called **potential energy,** which is often denoted by U. Potential energy is important because, when mechanical systems change spontaneously, they do so in a way that reduces potential energy.

> In Chapter 7, you'll see simple cases in which the Conservation of Energy can be seen in the equations.

> You'll see potential energy arise naturally from Newton's Second Law in Chapter 7.

❖ Dimensions and Units

In the physical sciences, the word **dimension** refers to the *kind* of thing being measured, and the word **unit** refers to the *way* we measure. For example, the physical characteristic of *length* is a dimension, and it can be measured in units of *inches, meters, miles,* etc. Similarly, *time, mass, temperature, velocity, force,* and *energy* are physical dimensions that are measured in units of *seconds, kilograms, kelvins, meters per second, newtons,* and *joules.*

Other settings make use of different dimensions, depending on what's important. For example, *money* is a dimension in business and economics, and can be measured in units of *dollars, cents, euros,* or *yen.* And *population* is a dimension in the social and biological sciences that's measured in units of *cells, individuals,* or *family groups* as appropriate.

A basic principle of applied mathematics is that an equation can only be meaningful if both sides have the same dimensions. For example, an equation that says

> There are seven *base dimensions* in the SI system of measurement, including *time, mass* and *length.* Dimensions such as *velocity, force* and energy are called *derived dimensions* because, as you might guess, they are derived from the base dimensions. For example, velocity is calculated as length per unit time. Force and energy are also derived dimensions.

length = mass is nonsensical because length and mass are fundamentally different characteristics—i.e., different physical *dimensions* of an object—so cannot be equated. The technique of using quantities' units to check that an equation makes sense is called **dimensional analysis**.

Dimensional analysis

Example E.1. Suppose that if you travel for t minutes, you cross x meters, where $x = 3t$. Determine the dimensions of the "3."

Solution: Since the left-hand side of $x = 3t$ has dimensions of *length,* the right-hand side must also. The variable t has dimensions of *time,* so in order for the equation to make sense, the coefficient of 3 must have dimensions of *length per time.* Dimensionally speaking, the equation

$$x = 3t \quad \text{looks like} \quad (\text{length}) = \left(\frac{\text{length}}{\text{time}}\right)(\text{time}).$$

More specifically, since x is measured in meters and t is measured in seconds,

$$x = 3t \quad \text{looks like} \quad (\text{meters}) = \left(\frac{\text{meters}}{\text{second}}\right)(\text{second}),$$

in which the units of seconds on the right-hand side appear to cancel, like common factors in a fraction, leaving us with (meters) = (meters). ∎

Here we should also mention **dimensionless** quantities, which often occur as ratios of other quantities that each have associated dimensions. Dimensionless quantities often act as scale factors in equations where the two sides have—at least at first glance—the same dimensions but different units.

Dimensionless quantities

Example E.2. When converting from miles, m, to yards, y, we have $y = 1760m$. Show that 1760 is a dimensionless quantity.

Solution: In order for the equation $y = 1760m$ to make sense, both sides must have the same dimensions. Since y has dimensions of length, the quantity $1760m$ must also have dimensions of length—and m already does—so 1760 cannot have dimensions.

This is not to say that 1760 is without *units,* and that's often where people get confused so let's take a moment to look closer. Since m has units of "miles," and y has units of "yards," the number 1760 must have (and *does* have) units of "yards per mile." Written as a fraction, the units of of the scale factor are

$$\frac{1760}{1} \frac{\text{yards}}{\text{mile}}.$$

So dimensionally speaking, the equation

$$y = 1760m \quad \text{looks like} \quad (\text{length}) = \left(\frac{\text{length}}{\text{length}}\right)(\text{length})$$

in which the dimensions of (length) on the right-hand side appear to cancel, like common factors in a fraction.

Because the scale factor has dimensions of length per length, it doesn't change the *kind* of thing on the right-hand side of $y = 1760m$. *This is the sense in which 1760 is dimensionless.* ∎

Dimensional analysis

Example E.3. Suppose you invest P dollars in an account that pays $r\%$ APR, compounded continually. If you leave the account alone for t years, the amount of money in the account, A, is related to the initial investment by the equation $A = Pe^{rt}$. Perform a dimensional analysis of this equation.

Solution: In order for $A = Pe^{rt}$ to be meaningful, both sides must have the same dimensions. Since the left-hand side has dimensions of *money*, the quantity Pe^{rt} must also—and P already does—so the factor e^{rt} must be dimensionless. ∎

Dimensional analysis

Example E.4. Suppose the altitude of an oscillating mass (in centimeters) is $y = \sin(\omega t)$, where ω is constant and t is measured in seconds. Perform a dimensional analysis of this equation.

Solution: The argument of a trigonometric function, in this case ωt, should be in radians. Since t is measured in seconds, the number ω must have units of radians per second. Note that the left-hand side of this equation is measured in centimeters, but the output of a trigonometric function is dimensionless. That might make you think that the equation is dimensionally inconsistent. However, remember that we often neglect to write a coefficient of 1, and that's what has happened here. The equation is actually $y = 1\sin(\omega t)$, and the "1" has units of centimeters. ∎

> Recall from Appendix A that the sine is a ratio of lengths: (opposite length)/(hypotenuse length). Since its dimensions are length/length, it's dimensionless.

> We typically omit a coefficient of 1, and write $y = x + 4$ rather than $y = 1x + 4$.

We close by remarking that, at least for the purposes of this book, the most important dimensionless quantity is the *radian*, which is discussed in Appendix A.

Appendix F

Introduction to Matrices

A *matrix* is just a table of numbers. The number of columns and rows can be different, but our discussion will tend to focus on matrices in which they are the same, such as

$$\begin{bmatrix} 1 & 2 \\ 3 & 4 \end{bmatrix} \quad \text{and} \quad \begin{bmatrix} 3 & 6 & -2 \\ -5 & 1 & 8 \\ 4 & -3 & 7 \end{bmatrix}.$$

Further, in this book we will tend to treat matrices as a kind of function for which the input and output are vectors. Specifically, we determine the output by calculating the dot products of the matrix rows (as if they are vectors) with the input vector:

$$\begin{bmatrix} 1 & 2 \\ 3 & 4 \end{bmatrix} \mathbf{u} = \begin{bmatrix} \langle 1, 2 \rangle \cdot \mathbf{u} \\ \langle 3, 4 \rangle \cdot \mathbf{u} \end{bmatrix}, \tag{f.1}$$

and

$$\begin{bmatrix} 3 & 6 & -2 \\ -5 & 1 & 8 \\ 4 & -3 & 7 \end{bmatrix} \mathbf{v} = \begin{bmatrix} \langle 3, 6, -2 \rangle \cdot \mathbf{v} \\ \langle -5, 1, 8 \rangle \cdot \mathbf{v} \\ \langle 4, -3, 7 \rangle \cdot \mathbf{v} \end{bmatrix}. \tag{f.2}$$

> This way of thinking about and working with matrices comes from a study of linear functions of several variables, which you'll see in a course called *linear algebra*.

A matrix as a function

Example F.1. Determine the vector $A\mathbf{u}$ when $\mathbf{u} = \langle 1, 3, 2 \rangle$ and

$$A = \begin{bmatrix} 1 & 1 & 0 \\ 0 & 2 & 3 \\ 4 & 0 & 7 \end{bmatrix}.$$

Solution: Following the pattern displayed in equation (f.2), we see

$$\begin{bmatrix} 1 & 1 & 0 \\ 0 & 2 & 3 \\ 4 & 0 & 7 \end{bmatrix} \begin{bmatrix} 1 \\ 3 \\ 2 \end{bmatrix} = \begin{bmatrix} \langle 1, 1, 0 \rangle \cdot \langle 1, 3, 2 \rangle \\ \langle 0, 2, 3 \rangle \cdot \langle 1, 3, 2 \rangle \\ \langle 4, 0, 7 \rangle \cdot \langle 1, 3, 2 \rangle \end{bmatrix} = \begin{bmatrix} 4 \\ 12 \\ 18 \end{bmatrix} \qquad \blacksquare$$

Based on the process we use to calculate output, vectors in the domain of a matrix must have exactly as many components as the matrix has columns. The output of a matrix will have as many components as the matrix has rows (because that's how many dot products we're computing).

Calculating the action of a matrix on a vector

Example F.2. Suppose A and B are the matrices shown below, and $\mathbf{v} = \langle 2, 9 \rangle$. (a) Calculate $A\mathbf{v}$, and (b) calculate $A(B\mathbf{v})$.

$$A = \begin{bmatrix} 5 & 7 \\ 2 & 3 \end{bmatrix}, \quad B = \begin{bmatrix} 3 & -7 \\ -2 & 5 \end{bmatrix}.$$

Solution On-line

Answer: (a) $\langle 73, 31 \rangle$, and (b) $\langle 2, 9 \rangle$ (which is **v**). ∎

Because matrices act on vectors using the dot product, their action inherits some of the algebraic properties of the dot product. For instance, the following example demonstrates that matrices distribute over sums.

Matrices distribute over sums of vectors

Example F.3. Suppose $\mathbf{u} = \langle 3, 4 \rangle$ and $\mathbf{v} = \langle 2, -1 \rangle$. Show that

$$A(\mathbf{u} + \mathbf{v}) = A\mathbf{u} + A\mathbf{v} \quad \text{when} \quad A = \begin{bmatrix} 6 & 1 \\ 2 & 3 \end{bmatrix}.$$

Solution: We verify this fact by direct calculation. On the one hand,

$$A\mathbf{u} = \begin{bmatrix} 6 & 1 \\ 2 & 3 \end{bmatrix} \begin{bmatrix} 3 \\ 4 \end{bmatrix} = \begin{bmatrix} \langle 6, 1 \rangle \cdot \langle 3, 4 \rangle \\ \langle 2, 3 \rangle \cdot \langle 3, 4 \rangle \end{bmatrix} = \begin{bmatrix} 22 \\ 18 \end{bmatrix}$$

and

$$A\mathbf{v} = \begin{bmatrix} 6 & 1 \\ 2 & 3 \end{bmatrix} \begin{bmatrix} 2 \\ -1 \end{bmatrix} = \begin{bmatrix} \langle 6, 1 \rangle \cdot \langle 2, -1 \rangle \\ \langle 2, 3 \rangle \cdot \langle 2, -1 \rangle \end{bmatrix} = \begin{bmatrix} 11 \\ 1 \end{bmatrix}$$

so

$$A\mathbf{u} + A\mathbf{v} = \begin{bmatrix} 22 \\ 18 \end{bmatrix} + \begin{bmatrix} 11 \\ 1 \end{bmatrix} = \begin{bmatrix} 33 \\ 19 \end{bmatrix}.$$

On the other hand, if we begin by calculating $\mathbf{u} + \mathbf{v} = \langle 5, 3 \rangle$, we can write

$$A(\mathbf{u} + \mathbf{v}) = \begin{bmatrix} 6 & 1 \\ 2 & 3 \end{bmatrix} \begin{bmatrix} 5 \\ 3 \end{bmatrix} = \begin{bmatrix} \langle 6, 1 \rangle \cdot \langle 5, 3 \rangle \\ \langle 2, 3 \rangle \cdot \langle 5, 3 \rangle \end{bmatrix} = \begin{bmatrix} 33 \\ 19 \end{bmatrix}. \quad ∎$$

In the previous example you saw a 2×2 matrix distribute over the sum of vectors. This is characteristic of *all* matrices, and is tied to the distributive property of the dot product. The following generalization of this fact also relies on the fact that the dot product scales (see Section 11.3).

Matrices as Functions: Suppose β is a scalar, A is a matrix, and **u** and **v** are vectors with the same number of components as A has columns. Then

$$A(\mathbf{u} + \mathbf{v}) = A\mathbf{u} + A\mathbf{v}$$
$$A(\beta\mathbf{u}) = \beta A\mathbf{u}$$

We communicate the fact that $A(\mathbf{u} + \mathbf{v}) = A\mathbf{u} + A\mathbf{v}$ by saying that matrices are *additive*, and that $A(\beta\mathbf{u}) = \beta\,A\mathbf{u}$ by saying that matrices are **homogeneous**.

The word *homogeneous* is pronounced "homo-JEEN-ee-us."

▷ Adding matrices

Like the functions to which you're accustomed, we can add matrix functions. Remember that adding *functions* is done by adding their outputs:

$$(f + g)(x) \stackrel{\text{def}}{=} f(x) + g(x).$$

This leads us directly to a way of adding matrices. Suppose

$$A = \begin{bmatrix} 4 & 14 \\ 5 & 8 \end{bmatrix}, \quad B = \begin{bmatrix} -1 & -2 \\ 7 & 3 \end{bmatrix} \quad \text{and} \quad \mathbf{v} = \begin{bmatrix} v_1 \\ v_2 \end{bmatrix}.$$

Then

$$A\mathbf{v} = \begin{bmatrix} 4 & 14 \\ 5 & 8 \end{bmatrix} \begin{bmatrix} v_1 \\ v_2 \end{bmatrix} = \begin{bmatrix} 4v_1 + 14v_2 \\ 5v_1 + 8v_2 \end{bmatrix}$$

$$B\mathbf{v} = \begin{bmatrix} -1 & -2 \\ 7 & 3 \end{bmatrix} \begin{bmatrix} v_1 \\ v_2 \end{bmatrix} = \begin{bmatrix} -1v_1 - 2v_2 \\ 7v_1 + 3v_2 \end{bmatrix}.$$

The sum of these vectors is

$$A\mathbf{v} + B\mathbf{v} = \begin{bmatrix} (4v_1 + 14v_2) + (-1v_1 - 2v_2) \\ (5v_1 + 8v_3) + (7v_1 + 3v_3) \end{bmatrix} = \begin{bmatrix} 3v_1 + 12v_2 \\ 12v_1 + 11v_2 \end{bmatrix} = \underbrace{\begin{bmatrix} 3 & 12 \\ 12 & 11 \end{bmatrix}}_{=C} \mathbf{v}.$$

A quick examination of A, B, and C reveals that the matrix C is an element-by-element addition of A and B. For example, focussing on the upper left-hand corner, $3 = 4 + (-1)$; and in the lower right-hand corner, $11 = 8 + 3$. This leads us to write

$$\underbrace{\begin{bmatrix} -1 & -2 \\ 7 & 3 \end{bmatrix}}_{A} + \underbrace{\begin{bmatrix} 4 & 14 \\ 5 & 8 \end{bmatrix}}_{B} = \underbrace{\begin{bmatrix} 3 & 12 \\ 12 & 11 \end{bmatrix}}_{A+B}$$

Because the sum of vectors is calculated component by component in 3-dimensions (and higher), the same kind of thing happens when working with larger matrices. The statement below generalizes what we've seen for 2×2 matrices.

Adding Matrices: Suppose A and B are matrices with the same number of rows and the same number of columns. Denote by A_{ij} the number in the ith row and j^{th} column of the matrix A, and similarly for the matrix B. Then the numbers in the sum matrix $(A + B)$ are

$$(A + B)_{ij} = A_{ij} + B_{ij}.$$

Adding matrices

Example F.4. Find the sum of matrices

$$A = \begin{bmatrix} 6 & 2 & 7 \\ 1 & 0 & 8 \\ 2 & 3 & 4 \end{bmatrix} \quad \text{and} \quad B = \begin{bmatrix} 1 & 5 & 4 \\ 9 & -1 & -2 \\ 3 & 7 & 9 \end{bmatrix}$$

Solution: Done in a term-by-term fashion,

$$A + B = \begin{bmatrix} 6+1 & 2+5 & 7+3 \\ 1+9 & 0+(-1) & 8+7 \\ 2+3 & 3+7 & 4+9 \end{bmatrix} = \begin{bmatrix} 7 & 7 & 10 \\ 10 & -1 & 15 \\ 5 & 10 & 13 \end{bmatrix}. \qquad \blacksquare$$

▷ Multiplying matrices

In Example F.2 you calculated the action of the matrix B act on the vector $\mathbf{v}$, and then let the matrix A act on that output. In essence, that's a composition of functions, and it leads us to a way of defining what we mean by the multiplication of matrices. For example, suppose $\mathbf{v} = \langle 7, 8 \rangle$,

$$A = \begin{bmatrix} a_1 & a_2 \\ a_3 & a_4 \end{bmatrix} \quad \text{and} \quad B = \begin{bmatrix} b_1 & b_2 \\ b_3 & b_4 \end{bmatrix}.$$

When we let B act on $\mathbf{v}$, and then let A act on the result, here's what happens:

$$Bv = \left[\begin{array}{cc} b_1 & b_2 \\ b_3 & b_4 \end{array}\right] \left[\begin{array}{c} 7 \\ 8 \end{array}\right] = \left[\begin{array}{c} 7b_1 + 8b_2 \\ 7b_3 + 8b_4 \end{array}\right],$$

and

$$A(Bv) = \left[\begin{array}{cc} a_1 & a_2 \\ a_3 & a_4 \end{array}\right] \left[\begin{array}{c} 7b_1 + 8b_2 \\ 7b_3 + 8b_4 \end{array}\right] = \left[\begin{array}{c} a_1(7b_1 + 8b_2) + a_2(7b_3 + 8b_4) \\ a_3(7b_1 + 8b_2) + a_4(7b_3 + 8b_4) \end{array}\right].$$

This looks complicated at first glance, but it simplifies nicely. If we gather the 7s and the 8s in each row, we see that

$$A(Bv) = \left[\begin{array}{c} 7(a_1b_1 + a_2b_3) + 8(a_1b_2 + a_2b_4) \\ 7(a_3b_1 + a_4b_3) + 8(a_3b_2 + a_4b_4) \end{array}\right] = \left[\begin{array}{cc} a_1b_1 + a_2b_3 & a_1b_2 + a_2b_4 \\ a_3b_1 + a_4b_3 & a_3b_2 + a_4b_4 \end{array}\right] \left[\begin{array}{c} 7 \\ 8 \end{array}\right]$$

That is,

$$\left[\begin{array}{cc} a_1 & a_2 \\ a_3 & a_4 \end{array}\right] \left[\begin{array}{cc} b_1 & b_2 \\ b_3 & b_4 \end{array}\right] \mathbf{v} = \left[\begin{array}{cc} a_1b_1 + a_2b_3 & a_1b_2 + a_2b_4 \\ a_3b_1 + a_4b_3 & a_3b_2 + a_4b_4 \end{array}\right] \mathbf{v}.$$

The particular vector $\mathbf{v}$ that we used in this calculation is irrelevant. The same algebra works for all 2-vectors. This leads us to define the product of AB as

$$\left[\begin{array}{cc} a_1 & a_2 \\ a_3 & a_4 \end{array}\right] \left[\begin{array}{cc} b_1 & b_2 \\ b_3 & b_4 \end{array}\right] = \left[\begin{array}{cc} a_1b_1 + a_2b_3 & a_1b_2 + a_2b_4 \\ a_3b_1 + a_4b_3 & a_3b_2 + a_4b_4 \end{array}\right]. \tag{f.3}$$

If you look closely, you'll see a simple pattern for finding the entries of the product matrix: *calculate the dot product of rows of A with columns of B.* More specifically:

Multiplying Matrices: Suppose A and B are square matrices of the same size. If the rows of the matrix A are denoted by A_i, and the columns of the matrix B are denoted by B_j, the number in the ith row and j^{th} column of the product matrix AB, denoted by $(AB)_{ij}$, is

$$(AB)_{ij} = A_i \cdot B_j.$$

We can define the product AB even when A and B are not square, but the sizes of the matrices have to align so that the range of B is in the domain of A.

Multiplying matrices

Example F.5. Suppose that A and B are the matrices shown below. Find AB.

$$A = \left[\begin{array}{cc} 2 & 7 \\ 3 & -1 \end{array}\right] \qquad B = \left[\begin{array}{cc} 12 & -3 \\ 1 & 7 \end{array}\right]$$

Solution: Using (f.3), we calculate the dot products to find

$$\left[\begin{array}{cc} (2)(12) + (7)(1) & (2)(-3) + (7)(7) \\ (3)(12) + (-1)(1) & (3)(-3) + (-1)(7) \end{array}\right] = \left[\begin{array}{cc} 31 & 43 \\ 35 & -16 \end{array}\right]. \qquad \blacksquare$$

Multiplying Matrices

Example F.6. Determine AB when A and B are the matrices from Example F.2.

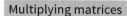

Solution
On-line

Answer: $\begin{bmatrix} 1 & 0 \\ 0 & 1 \end{bmatrix}$. ∎

Multiplying matrices

Example F.7. Suppose that A and B are the matrices shown below. Find AB.

$$A = \begin{bmatrix} 2 & 7 & 1 \\ 3 & -1 & -2 \\ 1 & 0 & 5 \end{bmatrix} \qquad B = \begin{bmatrix} 12 & -3 & 0 \\ 1 & 7 & 8 \\ 0 & 1 & 3 \end{bmatrix}$$

Solution: To determine the numbers in the ith row of the product matrix, AB, we dot the ith row of A with the columns of B. This yields

$$\begin{bmatrix} (2)(12)+(7)(1)+(1)(0) & (2)(-3)+(7)(7)+(1)(1) & (2)(0)+(7)(8)+(1)(3) \\ (3)(12)+(-1)(1)+(-2)(0) & (3)(-3)+(-1)(7)+(-2)(1) & (3)(0)+(-1)(8)+(-2)(3) \\ (1)(12)+(0)(1)+(5)(0) & (1)(-3)+(0)(7)+(5)(1) & (1)(0)+(0)(8)+(5)(3) \end{bmatrix}$$

That is,

$$AB = \begin{bmatrix} 31 & 44 & 59 \\ 35 & -18 & -14 \\ 12 & 2 & 15 \end{bmatrix}.$$ ∎

▷ Inverse Matrices and Determinants

In Example F.2 you saw that the actions of matrices B and A seemed to "undo" one another—we started with $\mathbf{v} = \langle 2, 9 \rangle$, used A, used B, and found ourselves with the vector $\langle 2, 9 \rangle$ again. This didn't happen because the vector $\langle 2, 9 \rangle$ is special, but because of the relationship between the matrices. When $\mathbf{v} = \langle x, y \rangle$,

$$A\mathbf{v} = \begin{bmatrix} 5 & 7 \\ 2 & 3 \end{bmatrix} \begin{bmatrix} x \\ y \end{bmatrix} = \begin{bmatrix} 5x + 7y \\ 2x + 3y \end{bmatrix},$$

so that

$$B(A\mathbf{v}) = \begin{bmatrix} 3 & -7 \\ -2 & 5 \end{bmatrix} \begin{bmatrix} 5x + 7y \\ 2x + 3y \end{bmatrix} = \begin{bmatrix} 3(5x + 7y) - 7(2x + 3y) \\ -2(5x + 7y) + 5(2x + 3y) \end{bmatrix} = \begin{bmatrix} x \\ y \end{bmatrix}.$$

For this reason, we say that B is the **inverse** of A (as in "inverse function"), and typically name it A^{-1}. In general, the inverse of

$$A = \begin{bmatrix} a & b \\ c & d \end{bmatrix} \quad \text{is the matrix} \quad A^{-1} = \begin{bmatrix} \frac{d}{ad-bc} & \frac{-b}{ad-bc} \\ \frac{-c}{ad-bc} & \frac{a}{ad-bc} \end{bmatrix} \qquad \text{(f.4)}$$

when $ad - bc \neq 0$, and the matrix inverse doesn't exist when $ad - bc = 0$. In Section 11.4 we named this important number, $ad - bc$, the **determinant** of the 2×2 matrix A. It is commonly denoted by either $\det(A)$ or $|A|$.

$$A = \begin{bmatrix} a & b \\ c & d \end{bmatrix} \quad \Rightarrow \quad |A| = \det(A) = ad - bc. \qquad \text{(f.5)}$$

> $\det(A)$ and $|A|$ are two different notations for the same number. It's called the *determinant* because we can determine whether an inverse matrix exists by checking it.

Finding the determinant of a 2×2 matrix

Example F.8. Calculate the determinant, $|A|$, of the matrix

$$A = \begin{bmatrix} 4 & 2 \\ 8 & 1 \end{bmatrix}.$$

Solution: Using equation (f.5), we calculate $|A| = (4)(1) - (2)(8) = -12$. It might seem strange that $|A|$ is negative, but remember that $|A|$ means "determinant of A," *not* "absolute value of A." ∎

Also in Section 11.4 we defined the ***determinant*** of a 3×3 matrix A, similarly denoted by $\det(A)$ or by $|A|$, to be the number

$$\begin{vmatrix} a_1 & a_2 & a_3 \\ b_1 & b_2 & b_3 \\ c_1 & c_2 & c_3 \end{vmatrix} \overset{\text{def}}{=} a_1 \begin{vmatrix} b_2 & b_3 \\ c_2 & c_3 \end{vmatrix} - a_2 \begin{vmatrix} b_1 & b_3 \\ c_1 & c_3 \end{vmatrix} + a_3 \begin{vmatrix} b_1 & b_2 \\ c_1 & c_2 \end{vmatrix}.$$

In the context of Section 11.4 we interpreted the magnitude of this number as the volume of a parallelepiped. When it is nonzero, the three vectors that constitute the matrix rows point in three independent directions (meaning that the shape has nonzero length, width, and height), which is the fundamental idea on which the following theorem rests.

> **Theorem (Invertibility of Matrices):** The square matrix A is invertible if and only if $\det(A) \neq 0$.

The proof of this theorem is beyond the scope of this book, as are methods for determining A^{-1} when A is a 3×3 or larger matrix.

❖ Skill Exercises

Several of the exercises below will make use of the following matrices:

$$A = \begin{bmatrix} 2 & 7 \\ 3 & 5 \end{bmatrix} \qquad B = \begin{bmatrix} 1 & -1 & 1 \\ 2 & 5 & 0 \\ 8 & -1 & 0 \end{bmatrix} \qquad C = \begin{bmatrix} 1 & 0 \\ 3 & 3 \\ 2 & 8 \end{bmatrix} \qquad I_2 = \begin{bmatrix} 1 & 0 \\ 0 & 1 \end{bmatrix}$$

$$D = \begin{bmatrix} 8 & 2 \\ 4 & 1 \end{bmatrix} \qquad E = \begin{bmatrix} -1 & 1 & -1 \\ 8 & 0 & 3 \\ 3 & 7 & 1 \end{bmatrix} \qquad F = \begin{bmatrix} 3 & 10 \\ 4 & 31 \\ 6 & 18 \end{bmatrix} \qquad I_3 = \begin{bmatrix} 1 & 0 & 0 \\ 0 & 1 & 0 \\ 0 & 0 & 1 \end{bmatrix}$$

In #1–6, calculate the specified product.

1. $A\mathbf{v}$, where $\mathbf{v} = \langle 1, 2 \rangle$
2. $A\mathbf{v}$, where $\mathbf{v} = \langle 3, 7 \rangle$
3. $D\mathbf{v}$, where $\mathbf{v} = \langle 1, -4 \rangle$
4. $D\mathbf{v}$, where $\mathbf{v} = \langle -3, 2 \rangle$

5. $B\mathbf{v}$, where $\mathbf{v} = \langle -1, 6, 1 \rangle$
6. $B\mathbf{v}$, where $\mathbf{v} = \langle 1, 2, 3 \rangle$
7. $E\mathbf{v}$, where $\mathbf{v} = \langle 0, 4, 1 \rangle$
8. $E\mathbf{v}$, where $\mathbf{v} = \langle 8, 0, 2 \rangle$

9. $C\mathbf{v}$, where $\mathbf{v} = \langle 2, 4 \rangle$
10. $C\mathbf{v}$, where $\mathbf{v} = \langle 4, -5, 8 \rangle$
11. $F\mathbf{v}$, where $\mathbf{v} = \langle 3, -3 \rangle$
12. $F\mathbf{v}$, where $\mathbf{v} = \langle -4, 1 \rangle$

13. Determine $I_2\mathbf{v}$ where $\mathbf{v} = \langle 2, 9 \rangle$.
14. Determine $I_2\mathbf{v}$ where $\mathbf{v} = \langle v_1, v_2 \rangle$.

15. Determine $I_3\mathbf{v}$ where $\mathbf{v} = \langle 1, 2, 3 \rangle$.
16. Determine $I_3\mathbf{v}$ where $\mathbf{v} = \langle v_1, v_2, v_3 \rangle$.

In #17–20 calculate the determinant of the given matrix, A, and if it's nonzero, find the associated inverse matrix.

17. $A = \begin{bmatrix} 2 & 7 \\ 3 & 11 \end{bmatrix}$
18. $A = \begin{bmatrix} 3 & -7 \\ 2 & 0 \end{bmatrix}$
19. $A = \begin{bmatrix} 9 & 0 \\ 12 & 10 \end{bmatrix}$
20. $A = \begin{bmatrix} 7 & 2 \\ 5 & -1 \end{bmatrix}$

In exercises #21–26 calculate the determinant of the given matrix.

21. $\begin{bmatrix} 2 & 7 & 0 \\ 3 & 11.5 & 0 \\ 0 & 0 & 1 \end{bmatrix}$

23. $\begin{bmatrix} -2 & 3 & 9 \\ 8 & 1 & -1 \\ 1 & 0 & 9 \end{bmatrix}$

25. $\begin{bmatrix} 1 & 1 & 1 \\ 1 & 1 & 1 \\ 1 & 1 & 1 \end{bmatrix}$

22. $\begin{bmatrix} 3 & -7 & 0 \\ 2 & 0 & 0 \\ 0 & 0 & 1 \end{bmatrix}$

24. $\begin{bmatrix} 3 & 0 & 0 \\ 0 & 2 & 0 \\ 0 & 0 & 4 \end{bmatrix}$

26. $\begin{bmatrix} 4 & 5 & 1 \\ 3 & 5 & 11 \\ 10 & -1 & 1 \end{bmatrix}$

❖ Concept and Application Exercises

27. Suppose $\mathbf{u} = \langle 2, 3 \rangle$, $\mathbf{v} = \langle 8, -2 \rangle$, and A is the matrix below. Check that $A(\mathbf{u} + \mathbf{v}) = A\mathbf{u} + A\mathbf{v}$ by calculating both sides of the equation independently, and then verifying that they are equal.

$$A = \begin{bmatrix} 2 & 5 \\ 7 & 1 \end{bmatrix}$$

28. Suppose that $\mathbf{v} = \langle 3, 4 \rangle$ and A is the matrix from #27.

    (a) Determine the component representation of $8\mathbf{v}$.

    (b) Use your answer from part (a) to calculate $A(8\mathbf{v})$.

    (c) Separately, calculate $A\mathbf{v}$, and then $8(A\mathbf{v})$.

    (d) Your results in parts (b) and (d) should be the same. In full sentences, explain what happens when a matrix acts on a scaled vector.

29. Using t, b, and g to represent numbers of TV's, Blu-ray players, and gaming systems, a major electronics retailer is tracking sales at three local stores with   ── Business

$$Q = \begin{bmatrix} t_1 & b_1 & g_1 \\ t_2 & b_2 & g_2 \\ t_3 & b_3 & g_3 \end{bmatrix} \quad \text{and} \quad \mathbf{p} = \langle p_t, p_b, p_g \rangle,$$

    where the components of the vector, p_t, p_b, and p_g, tell us the revenue generated by the sale of a TV, Blu-ray player, or gaming systems (respectively). The subscripts on the matrix entries indicate the store at which the items were sold (Store 1, Store 2 or Store 3).

    (a) In complete sentences, describe what the t_1, b_2, and g_3 entries of the Q matrix tell us.

    (b) How do we interpret the sum of the entries in the third *column* of Q?

    (c) Calculate the vector $\mathbf{r} = Q\mathbb{1}$, where $\mathbb{1} = \langle 1, 1, 1 \rangle$. What information do the components of $\mathbf{r}$ convey?

    (d) What does the number $\mathbb{1} \cdot \mathbf{r}$ tell us?

    (e) What do the components of the vector $Q\mathbf{p}$ tell us?

30. Continuing exercise #29, suppose the company keeps track of the quantities   ── Business
    sold at each of the three local area stores for the months of January (Q_J) and
    February (Q_F):

$$Q_J = \begin{bmatrix} 35 & 64 & 400 \\ 30 & 70 & 650 \\ 30 & 60 & 600 \end{bmatrix} \qquad Q_F = \begin{bmatrix} 41 & 75 & 700 \\ 25 & 80 & 750 \\ 38 & 51 & 800 \end{bmatrix}$$

(a) Determine the numbers of TV's, Blu-ray players and gaming systems (respectively) that were sold in Store 1 during the two-month period.

(b) Calculate the same three numbers for stores 2 and 3.

(c) Based on parts (a) and (b), write a 3×3 matrix that summarizes the sales data in all three stores across the two-month period, Q. Keep the basic format of Q_J and Q_F, in which the first row contains sales data from Store 1.

(d) Determine $Q\mathbb{1}$, where $\mathbb{1} = \langle 1, 1, 1 \rangle$, and explain the practical meaning of the components in the resulting vector.

(e) Sum the entries in the first column of the matrix Q and interpret the resulting number.

(f) Use the following prices for the entries in the price vector $\mathbf{p}$: the TVs sell for \$1500 each, Blu-ray players for \$320 each, and the gaming systems for \$250 each. Use the matrix Q and the vector $\mathbf{p}$ to determine the revenue earned from the sale of each item individually over the two months.

31. In this exercise use the matrix A from the beginning of the Skill Exercises.

Linear Combination of Columns

(a) Show that $A\mathbf{i}$ gives you the first column of A.

(b) Show that $A\mathbf{j}$ gives you the second column of A.

(c) Use the fact thats $A(\mathbf{i} + \mathbf{j}) = A\mathbf{i} + A\mathbf{j}$ and $A(b\mathbf{j}) = b(A\mathbf{j})$ to show that

$$A \begin{bmatrix} a \\ b \end{bmatrix} = a \begin{bmatrix} 2 \\ 3 \end{bmatrix} + b \begin{bmatrix} 7 \\ 5 \end{bmatrix}. \qquad (f.6)$$

(Hint: recall that $\langle a, b \rangle$ is really a shorthand for $a\mathbf{i} + b\mathbf{j}$.)

(d) Based on equation (f.6) we can understand the equation $A\mathbf{u} = \mathbf{b}$ as asking whether the vector $\mathbf{b}$ can be constructed by scaling and adding the columns of A, and if so, how? Answer that question for $\mathbf{b} = \langle 9, 8 \rangle$.

32. This exercise introduces the idea that matrices affect area. Use the matrix A from the beginning of the Skill Exercises.

Determinants and Area

(a) Find the area of the rectangle defined by $2\mathbf{i}$ and $3\mathbf{j}$.

(b) Calculate the vectors $A(2\mathbf{i})$ and $A(3\mathbf{j})$, and determine a vector $\mathbf{u}$ that's orthogonal to $A(3\mathbf{j})$.

(c) The vectors you calculated in part (b) define a parallelogram, as shown in Figure F.1. The area of this parallelogram is the product of its length and width, which we calculate next by using the dot product. If we use $\|A(3\mathbf{j})\|$ as the length of the parallelogram, the shape's width is found by calculating the component of $A(2\mathbf{i})$ in the direction of $\mathbf{u}$. Do this, and determine the area of the parallelogram.

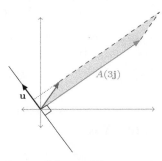

Figure F.1: The vectors $A(2\mathbf{i})$, $A(3\mathbf{j})$, and $\mathbf{u}$, the last of which is orthogonal to $A(3\mathbf{j})$.

(d) In part (c) you should have found that the area of the parallelogram is 11 times greater than the area you calculated in part (a). Repeat parts (b) and (c), but this time using the matrix $\begin{bmatrix} a & b \\ c & d \end{bmatrix}$, and show that area is scaled by $|ad - bc|$.

(e) Based on part (d), show that the matrix $A = \begin{bmatrix} 6 & 2 \\ 36 & 12 \end{bmatrix}$ will crush area to zero by calculating its determinant. Then explain *why* this happens, in light of the results from parts (a) and (b) of #31.

(f) Verify that $A\mathbf{v} = A\mathbf{u}$ when $\mathbf{v} = \langle 7, -2 \rangle$ and $\mathbf{u} = \langle 8, -5 \rangle$.

(g) In light of part (f), explain why no inverse function could possibly exist.

33. Suppose R is a matrix. You know from #31 that $R\mathbf{i}$ tells you the first column of the matrix R, and that $R\mathbf{j}$ tells you the second column. We can use this information to build a matrix that rotates vectors in the plane.

Rotation Matrices

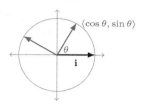

(a) If the matrix R rotates the plane by θ radians, it rotates the vector $\langle 1, 0 \rangle$ to $\langle \cos\theta, \sin\theta \rangle$. Use this fact to determine the first column of R.

(b) Use the congruent triangles in Figure F.2 to determine the component representation of the vector to which $\langle 0, 1 \rangle$ is rotated.

(c) Use your answer from part (b) to determine the second column of R.

Figure F.2:   For #33.

(d) Based on what you've found in parts (a)–(c), write the matrix that rotates the plane by $\pi/2$ radians.

(e) Based on what you've found in parts (a)–(c), write the matrix that rotates the plane by $-\pi/2$ radians.

34. Suppose R is the matrix shown below. By calculating $R\mathbf{u}$, where $\mathbf{u} = \langle x, y, z \rangle$, show that R rotates the "horizontal" part of a vector (the xy-components) but leaves the "height" of a vector, z, unchanged.

Rotation Matrices

$$R = \begin{bmatrix} \cos\theta & -\sin\theta & 0 \\ \sin\theta & \cos\theta & 0 \\ 0 & 0 & 1 \end{bmatrix}$$

35. Based on what you saw in #34, make a conjecture about the effect of the matrix R (below) on vectors, and then show that you're right.

Rotation Matrices

$$R = \begin{bmatrix} 1 & 0 & 0 \\ 0 & \cos\theta & -\sin\theta \\ 0 & \sin\theta & \cos\theta \end{bmatrix}$$

36. Suppose we rotate the parabola $y = x^2 - 4$ by ϕ radians (counter-clockwise) about the origin, and $\langle x, y \rangle$ is a position vector that picks out a point on that rotated parabola. If we rotate $\langle x, y \rangle$ by $-\phi$ radians (i.e., in the *clockwise* direction), it will pick out a point on the original, unrotated parabola. Use this idea to derive the equation for the rotated version of $y = x^2 - 4$.

Rotation Matrices

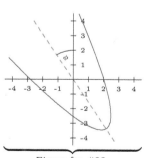

Figure for #36

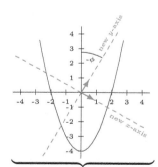

Figure for #37

37. In #36 we left our frame of reference fixed and rotated a parabola by ϕ radians. Equivalently, we could leave the parabola fixed and rotate the reference frame by $-\phi$ radians, and sometimes that makes calculations a lot easier.

Rotation Matrices

(a) Show that rotating $\mathbf{i}$ by $-\phi$ radians gives the vector $\langle \cos\phi, -\sin\phi \rangle$.

(b) We make a new "x-axis" by scaling $\langle \cos\phi, -\sin\phi \rangle$. That is, the new axis consists of all points whose position vectors are $k\langle \cos\phi, -\sin\phi \rangle$, where $k \in \mathbb{R}$ can be either positive or negative. Find the values of k at which the parabola $y = x^2 - 4$ intersects this new axis (your answer will depend on ϕ, which we'll assume to lie between 0 and $\pi/2$).

(c) You found two numbers in part (b). Where do these two numbers appear in the figure for #36?

Appendix G

End Notes

In this appendix we support some assertions that were made in the body of the text but were not central to our discussion (e.g., Torricelli's Law, and the rate at which the human body metabolizes medicine), and we provide rigorous proofs of some important theorems. We begin by establishing some important facts about the set of real numbers.

✢ Important Facts About the Real Numbers

Let's begin by establishing vocabulary for expressing basic ideas about sets. When a set S contains at least one number we say that it's **nonempty**, and such a set is said to be **bounded below** when there is a number m that's less than or equal to every $x \in S$; the number m is called a **lower bound** of S. Similarly, we say that a nonempty set S is **bounded above** when there is a number M that is larger than or equal to every $x \in S$; the number M is called an **upper bound** of S. If S is both bounded above and below, we say that it's **bounded**.

Consider the set $(0,1)$, for example. This set is bounded, the number -6 is a lower bound, and the numbers 31 and 2.4 are upper bounds. The number 1 is also an upper bound for the set, but no smaller number is an upper bound. For this reason we say that 1 is the *least* upper bound. More generally, suppose that S is a nonempty set of numbers that's bounded above by M, and any number smaller than M is *not* an upper bound for S. Then we say that M is the **least upper bound** of S. The least upper bound is also called the **supremum** of S.

Perhaps the most important property of the real numbers is that every nonempty set with an upper bound also has a supremum. This fact has to do with the *completeness* of the real numbers. The proof is beyond the scope of this book, but here we state the result.

> **Theorem (Supremum Property):** Suppose S is a nonempty set of real numbers that is bounded above. Then S has a supremum.

A consequence of the Supremum Property is that any infinite, bounded set of numbers gives rise to a convergent sequence (sequences are discussed in Chapter 8). The language of the following theorem, and ideas expressed in its proof are best understood after reading Section 8.1.

> **Bolzano-Weierstrass Theorem:** Suppose S is an infinite set of numbers in $[m, M]$. Then S contains a convergent sequence of distinct numbers.

Proof. The midpoint of the interval $[m, M]$ is at $x = 0.5(m + M)$. Because S is an infinite collection of points, there is either an infinite set of points from S in the interval $[m, 0.5(m + M)]$ or in the interval $[0.5(m + M), M]$. Whichever it is, define

A set can be "empty" in the same sense that a bag can have nothing in it.

This might seem obvious at first, but there's something subtle here; the rational numbers don't have this property. For example, suppose S is the set of all rational numbers x for which $x^2 < 2$. Then $1 \in S$, so the set is nonempty, and S is bounded above by 2, and 1.5, and 1.42, and.... But because $\sqrt{2}$ is not a rational number, it's not available to serve as the least upper bound of the set. So when we restrict ourselves to rational numbers, this set S has no supremum; but if we extend our scope to the real numbers, it does, and so does every other bounded set.

The supremum of S might be in S, but might not. For example, the number 1 is the least upper bound for the intervals $(0, 1]$ and $(0, 1)$.

that subinterval to be I_1. In similar fashion, use the midpoint of I_1 to separate it into two closed subintervals, at least one of which includes an infinite number of points from S. Choose that subinterval to be I_2. We communicate the fact that I_2 is fully contained inside I_1 by writing $I_1 \supset I_2$.

Continuing in this way, bisecting a closed interval and selecting the closed subinterval with an infinite number of points from S, we generate a collection of nested intervals $I_1 \supset I_2 \supset I_3 \supset \cdots$. Let's denote the left and right endpoints of I_k by a_k and b_k respectively. Then because the sets I_k are nested,

$$a_k \le a_{k+m} < b_{k+m} \le b_k$$

for every pair of positive integers k and m. Since each b_k is an upper bound for the sequence $\{a_k\}$, the sequence has a supremum, which we'll denote by c. It follows from the definition of a supremum that

$$a_k \le c \le b_k \quad \text{for each positive integer } k.$$

Now we use the intervals I_k to produce a sequence of distinct points in S that converges to c. The interval (a_1, b_1) has an infinite set of points from S; choose one and denote it by x_1. The interval (a_2, b_2) has an infinite set of points from S; choose one that's not x_1 and denote it by x_2. For each $k \ge 3$, do the same: pick a point from S in (a_k, b_k) that is neither x_1 nor $x_2 \ldots$ nor x_{k-1}, and call it x_k. Because x_k and c are both in I_k, which is an interval of length $2^{-k}(M - m)$, we know that

$$|x_k - c| \le \frac{1}{2^k}(M - m),$$

which converges to 0 as $k \to \infty$. ∎

Whereas the Bolzano-Weierstrass Theorem makes an assertion about an infinite collection of points in the closed interval $[m, M]$, the following theorem makes an assertion about an infinite collection of open intervals that **covers** it, meaning that each $x \in [m, M]$ is contained in (at least) one of the open intervals.

> **Heine-Borel Theorem:** Suppose $\mathcal{O}$ is an infinite collection of open intervals that covers the interval $[m, M]$. Then there is a finite collection of open intervals from $\mathcal{O}$ that covers $[m, M]$.

Proof. We prove this by contradiction. Suppose that no finite collection of open intervals from $\mathcal{O}$ covers $[m, M]$. Then either $[m, 0.5(m + M)]$ or $[0.5(m + M), M]$ cannot be covered by any finite collection of the open intervals in $\mathcal{O}$. Denote that subinterval by I_1 (if both subintervals have the property, it doesn't matter which we choose). In similar fashion, use the midpoint of I_1 to separate it into two closed subintervals. At least one of these cannot be covered by a finite collection of the intervals in $\mathcal{O}$. Denote that interval by I_2. Continuing like this, we generate nested closed intervals $I_1 \supset I_2 \supset I_3 \supset \cdots$.

As in the proof of the Bolzano-Weierstrass Theorem, we write $I_k = [a_k, b_k]$ and denote by c the supremum of the sequence $\{a_k\}$. Recall that c is in every I_k. We also know that c is in some open interval from $\mathcal{O}$, say (a^*, b^*). One of the endpoints is probably closer to c than the other, so let's define ε to be the smaller of $c - a^*$ and $b^* - c$. Next we use c and ε to arrive at a contradiction.

The length of I_k is $2^{-k}(M - m)$, which converges to 0 in the limit, so there is some N for which $2^{-N}(M - m) < \varepsilon$. But then I_N is covered by (a^*, b^*). That is, there is a single open interval from $\mathcal{O}$ that covers I_N, which contradicts the fact that I_N cannot be covered by a finite collection of intervals from $\mathcal{O}$. This contradiction indicates that the original assumption is incorrect, so there is a finite collection of open intervals from $\mathcal{O}$ that covers $[m, M]$. ∎

Margin notes:

If both intervals have an infinite number of points from S, the choice of which to call I_1 is irrelevant.

The fact that c is an upper bound for the set $\{a_k\}$ gives us that $a_k \le c$; and $c \le b_k$ comes from the fact that b_k is also an upper bound (but c is the *least* upper bound).

If we could cover each of $[m, 0.5(m + M)]$ and $[0.5(m + M), M]$ with a finite collection of intervals from $\mathcal{O}$, the union of those finite collections would cover $[m, M]$, which we're assuming cannot be done.

✥ End Notes for Chapter 1

In Chapter 1 we asserted that Koopman's Sighting Law could be derived from some simple geometry, though we didn't show it at the time. This section is where we take care of that omission.

▷ Koopman's sighting formula

In the mid-1940s Bernard Koopman developed the modern theory of sighting based the experiences of fighter pilots searching for ships in the open ocean. His basic premise was simple: you're more likely to see something if it takes up a larger fraction of your field of vision. More specifically, he said that the likelihood of seeing an object is directly proportional to the *solid angle* it subtends. The term *solid angle* refers to the product of the angles α and β that are shown in the left-hand image of Figure G.1.

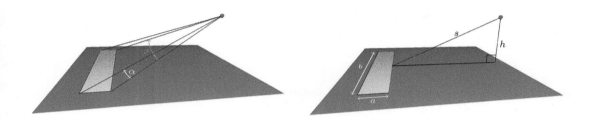

Figure G.1: (both) The point denotes a plane that's searching the water, and the rectangle approximates the object that's in the water.

By using a little geometry, we can rephrase Koopman's idea in terms of distance, altitude, and area rather than solid angle. Consider the right-hand image of Figure G.1, in which the altitude of a plane is h, the object in the ocean is approximated by a rectangle of width a and length b, and the distance between them is s. Figure G.2 depicts the same situation, but from a vantage point far above the water and the plane. There you see that the width of the object is about equal to the length of a circular arc. When β is measured in radians, that arc has a length of $\beta s \approx b$, from which we conclude that $\beta \approx b/s$.

Deriving a formula for α takes a little more work, but relies on the same ideas. Figure G.3 depicts our scenario as seen from the side, and Figure G.4 zooms in on the object in the water.

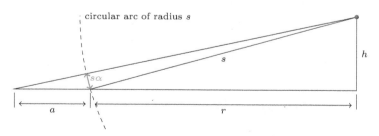

circular arc of radius s

Figure G.3: The altitude of an aircraft is h, its direct distance from the object is s, the across-the-water distance between the plane and the object in the water is r, and the width of the object is a.

The leg of a right triangle has been superimposed on Figure G.4, and you can see that its length is very close to αs (the length of the circular arc) when

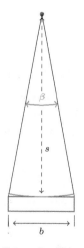

Figure G.2: Looking at the right-hand image of Figure G.1 from above.

the width of the object is much smaller than its distance to the pilot. Using the Pythagorean Theorem, we can approximate the length of this right triangle's other leg as $\sqrt{a^2 - (s\alpha)^2}$, so that the large right triangle in Figure G.3 has a hypotenuse of length

$$s + \sqrt{a^2 - (s\alpha)^2}.$$

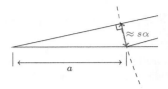

Figure G.4: Zooming in on the lower-left portion of Figure G.3; note that the circular arc nearly forms a right triangle when α is small.

With real objects in real oceans, the number a is much smaller than s, and $\sqrt{a^2 - (s\alpha)^2}$ is even smaller than that. So let's approximate further by writing

$$s + \sqrt{a^2 - (s\alpha)^2} \approx s + 0.$$

What this approximation loses in accuracy it makes up for in simplicity. Now using the similarity of the large right triangle in Figure G.3 and the small right triangle shown in Figure G.4, we have

$$\frac{\alpha s}{a} \approx \frac{h}{s} \quad \Rightarrow \quad \alpha \approx \frac{ha}{s^2}.$$

Now recall our premise: the likelihood of sighting the object in the ocean, which we'll denote by L, is proportional the $\alpha\beta$. If the constant of proportionality is k, we can write this as

$$L = k \ \alpha\beta = kh\frac{ab}{s^3}.$$

Note how this formula, called *Koopman's inverse cube law of sighting,* includes the altitude of the plane, the area of the object that's in the water, and the distance between them. By using the Pythagorean Theorem to write $s = \sqrt{h^2 + r^2}$, where r is the across-the-water distance between the plane and the object (see Figure G.3), we can rewrite this formula as

$$L = kh \ \frac{A}{(h^2 + r^2)^{3/2}}.$$

❖ End Notes for Chapter 2

We had not yet developed the technical definition of the limit when we first presented the Limit Laws, so we had to make an intuitive argument. In Section 2.4 we made the notion of a limit precise, and with that definition firmly in hand we are now able to prove the basic limit laws that were presented in Section 2.2.

▷ Proofs of the Limit laws

In the discussion that follows, we assume that $\lim_{x \to c} f(x) = L$ and $\lim_{x \to c} g(x) = M$.

Limit Law 4: $\lim_{x \to c} \big(f(x) + g(x) \big) = L + M$

Proof. We have to show that for every $\varepsilon > 0$ there is an associated $\delta > 0$ so that

$$\left| \big(f(x) + g(x) \big) - (L + M) \right| < \varepsilon \quad \text{whenever} \quad 0 < |x - c| < \delta.$$

Suppose $\varepsilon > 0$. Because $\lim_{x \to c} f(x) = L$, there is a $\delta_1 > 0$ so that $|f(x) - L| < \varepsilon/2$ whenever $0 < |x - c| < \delta_1$. Similarly, because $\lim_{x \to c} g(x) = M$ there is a $\delta_2 > 0$ so that $|g(x) - M| < \varepsilon/2$ whenever $0 < |x - c| < \delta_2$. Set δ to be the smaller of δ_1 and δ_2. Then whenever $0 < |x - c| < \delta$ we have

We pass from (g.1) to (g.2) using the Triangle Inequality, which says that $|a+b| \le |a|+|b|$

$$|f(x) + g(x) - (L + M)| = |f(x) - L + g(x) - M| \qquad \text{(g.1)}$$
$$\leq |f(x) - L| + |g(x) - M| < \frac{\varepsilon}{2} + \frac{\varepsilon}{2} = \varepsilon, \qquad \text{(g.2)}$$

which completes the proof. ∎

Limit Law 5: $\lim_{x \to c} f(x)g(x) = LM$

Proof. We have to show that for every $\varepsilon > 0$ there is an associated $\delta > 0$ so that

$$|f(x)g(x) - LM| < \varepsilon \quad \text{whenever} \quad 0 < |x - c| < \delta.$$

So let $\varepsilon > 0$. We begin by stating some facts about the limits that we already know. Because $\lim_{x \to c} f(x) = L$, there is a $\delta_1 > 0$ so that

$$|f(x) - L| < 1 \quad \text{whenever} \quad 0 < |x - c| < \delta_1, \qquad \text{(g.3)}$$

and there is a $\delta_2 > 0$ so that

$$|f(x) - L| < \frac{\varepsilon}{2(|M| + 1)} \quad \text{whenever} \quad 0 < |x - c| < \delta_2. \qquad \text{(g.4)}$$

Similarly, because $\lim_{x \to c} g(x) = M$ there is a $\delta_3 > 0$ so that

$$|g(x) - M| < \frac{\varepsilon}{2(|L| + 1)} \quad \text{whenever} \quad 0 < |x - c| < \delta_3. \qquad \text{(g.5)}$$

> This is true regardless of whether $L = 0$.

Choose δ to be the minimum of δ_1, δ_2 and δ_3. It follows from (g.3) that

$$|f(x)| < |L| + 1 \quad \text{whenever} \quad 0 < |x - c| < \delta, \qquad \text{(g.6)}$$

so that

$$|f(x)g(x) - LM| = |f(x)g(x) - f(x)M + f(x)M - LM| \qquad \text{(g.7)}$$
$$\leq |f(x)g(x) - f(x)M| + |f(x)M - LM| \qquad \text{(g.8)}$$
$$= |f(x)(g(x) - M)| + |(f(x) - L)M|$$
$$= |f(x)| \, |g(x) - M| + |f(x) - L| \, |M| \qquad \text{(g.9)}$$
$$< (|L| + 1)|g(x) - M| + |f(x) - L||M|. \qquad \text{(g.10)}$$

> We pass from (g.7) to (g.8) using the Triangle Inequality, which says that $|a + b| \leq |a| + |b|$

> We pass from (g.9) to (g.10) using (g.6).

In light of (g.4) and (g.5) we know that the right-hand side of (g.10), is less than

$$(|L| + 1)\frac{\varepsilon}{2(|L| + 1)} + \frac{\varepsilon}{2(|M| + 1)}|M| \leq \varepsilon \quad \text{whenever} \quad 0 < |x - c| < \delta.$$

Limit Law 3: $\lim_{x \to c} kf(x) = kL$

Proof. This follows immediately from Limit Law 5 by taking g to be the constant function $g(x) = k$. ∎

Limit Law 6: $\lim_{x \to c} \frac{f(x)}{g(x)} = \frac{L}{M}$ when $M \neq 0$

Proof. The strategy for establishing this limit law is to prove that $\lim_{x \to c} 1/g(x) = 1/M$. Then it follows from Limit Law 5 that

$$\lim_{x \to c} \left(\frac{f(x)}{g(x)} \right) = \lim_{x \to c} \left(f(x) \frac{1}{g(x)} \right) = \left(\lim_{x \to c} f(x) \right) \left(\lim_{x \to c} \frac{1}{g(x)} \right) = L\frac{1}{M} = \frac{L}{M}.$$

To prove that $\lim_{x \to c} 1/g(x) = 1/M$ we must show that for each $\varepsilon > 0$ there is a $\delta > 0$ such that

$$\left| \frac{1}{g(x)} - \frac{1}{M} \right| < \varepsilon \quad \text{whenever} \quad 0 < |x - c| < \delta.$$

Without loss of generality, we're going to work under the assumption that $\varepsilon \in (0, |M|)$. Because $\lim_{x \to c} g(x) = M$, there is a $\delta_1 > 0$ such that

$$|g(x) - M| < \varepsilon \quad \text{whenever} \quad 0 < |x - c| < \delta_1.$$

When the value of $g(x)$ is within ε of M, its magnitude is within ε of $|M|$. It follows that $|g(x)|$ is positive when $0 < |x - c| < \delta_1$ because

$$|g(x)| > \underbrace{|M| - \varepsilon}_{\text{Positive since } \varepsilon \in (0, |M|)} \quad \text{whenever} \quad 0 < |x - c| < \delta_1. \tag{g.11}$$

Similarly, there is a $\delta_2 > 0$ so that

$$|g(x) - M| < \underbrace{(|M| - \varepsilon)}_{\text{positive since } \varepsilon \in (0, |M|)} |M| \varepsilon \quad \text{whenever} \quad 0 < |x - c| < \delta_2. \tag{g.12}$$

Choose δ to be the minimum of δ_1 and δ_2. Then

$$\left| \frac{1}{g(x)} - \frac{1}{M} \right| = \frac{|M - g(x)|}{|g(x)M|} \underset{\underset{\text{from (g.11)}}{\uparrow}}{<} \frac{|M - g(x)|}{(|M| - \varepsilon)|M|} \underset{\underset{\text{from (g.12)}}{\uparrow}}{<} \frac{(|M| - \varepsilon)|M|\varepsilon}{(|M| - \varepsilon)|M|} = \varepsilon$$

whenever $0 < |x - c| < \delta$. ∎

Limit Law 8: Limits preserve inequalities.

Proof. Here we are assuming that $f(x) \leq g(x)$ in some open interval containing $x = c$, except perhaps at c itself, and want to prove that $L \leq M$. We do this by showing that the supposition $L > M$ leads to a logical contradiction. Indeed, because $\lim_{x \to c} f(x) = L$, there is a $\delta_1 > 0$ such that

$$\left| f(x) - L \right| < \frac{L - M}{2} \quad \text{whenever} \quad 0 < |x - c| < \delta_1 \tag{g.13}$$

and a $\delta_2 > 0$ such that

$$\left| g(x) - M \right| < \frac{L - M}{2} \quad \text{whenever} \quad 0 < |x - c| < \delta_2. \tag{g.14}$$

Choose δ to be the smaller of δ_1 and δ_2. It follows from (g.13) that

$$f(x) > L - \frac{L - M}{2} = \frac{L + M}{2} \quad \text{whenever} \quad 0 < |x - c| < \delta,$$

Equation (g.13) tells us that $f(x)$ is within $(L-M)/2$ of L when $0 < |x - c| < \delta$.

and it follows from (g.14) that

$$g(x) < M + \frac{L - M}{2} = \frac{L + M}{2} \quad \text{whenever} \quad 0 < |x - c| < \delta.$$

Equation (g.14) tells us that $g(x)$ is within $(L-M)/2$ of M when $0 < |x - c| < \delta$.

But then $g(x) < f(x)$ whenever $0 < |x - c| < \delta$, which contradicts the hypothesis. So it cannot be true that $L > M$. ∎

Limit laws 1 and 2 follow immediately from the definition of the limit, and the proof of Limit Law 7 is beyond the scope of this book, but is included in more advanced texts.

▷ Proof of the Squeeze Theorem

Here we prove that if $\lim_{x \to c} f(x) = L$, $\lim_{x \to c} h(x) = L$ and $f(x) \leq g(x) \leq h(x)$ when x is near c, it must be true that $\lim_{x \to c} g(x) = L$. That is, for each $\varepsilon > 0$ there is a $\delta > 0$ such that

$$|g(x) - L| < \varepsilon \quad \text{whenever} \quad 0 < |x - c| < \delta.$$

Suppose $\varepsilon > 0$. Then because $\lim_{x \to c} f(x) = L$ there is a $\delta_1 > 0$ so that

$$|f(x) - L| < \varepsilon \quad \text{whenever} \quad 0 < |x - c| < \delta_1. \tag{g.15}$$

Similarly, because $\lim_{x \to c} h(x) = L$ there is a $\delta_2 > 0$ so that

$$|h(x) - L| < \varepsilon \quad \text{whenever} \quad 0 < |x - c| < \delta_2. \tag{g.16}$$

Choose δ to be the smaller of δ_1 and δ_2. Then both $f(x)$ and $h(x)$ are within ε of L when $0 < |x - c| < \delta$. Since $g(x)$ is between $f(x)$ and $h(x)$, it follows that

$$\underbrace{L - \varepsilon < f(x)}_{\text{From (g.15)}} \leq g(x) \leq \underbrace{h(x) < L + \varepsilon}_{\text{From (g.16)}} \quad \text{whenever} \quad 0 < |x - c| < \delta. \qquad ■$$

▷ Proof of the Intermediate Value Theorem

In the statement of the Intermediate Value Theorem, we require that f is continuous over $[a, b]$ and $f(a) \neq f(b)$. Here we treat the case when $f(a) < f(b)$. Suppose L is some number between $f(a)$ and $f(b)$. We want to prove that f achieves the value of L at some point in (a, b).

Denote by S the set of points in $[a, b]$ for which $f(x) < L$. This set is nonempty since $f(a) < L$, and it's bounded above since b is not in the set. Therefore, the set S has a supremum, which we'll denote by c. The strategy of our proof is to use the continuity of f to show that $f(c) \neq L$ would contradict the fact that c is the least upper bound of S (so it must be that $f(c) = L$).

> Note that $a \leq c \leq b$.

Let's begin by talking about the continuity of f. If it were true that $f(c) \neq L$, the number $\varepsilon = 0.5|f(c) - L|$ would be positive. Then because f is continuous on $[a, b]$, there would be an associated $\delta > 0$ so that

$$\left| f(x) - f(c) \right| < \varepsilon \quad \text{whenever} \quad x \in [a, b] \text{ and } |x - c| < \delta. \tag{g.17}$$

Without loss of generality, we assume that $\delta < c - a$. Our proof proceeds in two steps, first proving that $f(c)$ cannot be less than L, and then proving that it cannot be larger.

Case 1: If it were true that $f(c) < L$, we would know that $c \neq b$. Then we could choose $x \in (c, b)$ within δ of c, and the continuity of f (see (g.17)) would guarantee that $f(x)$ is within ε units of $f(c)$. Consequently,

> In this case, the above definition of ε becomes $\varepsilon = 0.5(L - f(c))$.

$$\underbrace{f(x) < f(c) + \varepsilon =}_{\text{By virtue of (g.17)}} f(c) + 0.5(L - f(c)) = \underbrace{\frac{1}{2}(L + f(c)) < L.}_{\text{Since } L \text{ is larger than } f(c)}$$

> The statement that $f(c) < L$ means that $c \in S$. That alone is not a contradiction (e.g., 1 is the supremum of $[0, 1]$), but here we're using the continuity of f to show that there must be other $x > c$ at which $f(x) < L$.

This shows that x is in S, but that cannot be true because $c < x$ and c is an upper bound of S. Therefore, it cannot be true that $f(c) < L$.

Case 2: If it were true that $f(c) > L$, we could choose $x \in (c - \delta, c)$, and the

> In this case, the above definition of ε becomes $\varepsilon = 0.5(f(c) - L)$.

continuity of f would guarantees that $f(x)$ is within ε units of $f(c)$. Consequently,

$$f(x) > f(c) - \varepsilon = f(c) - \frac{1}{2}(f(c) - L) = \underbrace{\frac{1}{2}(f(c) + L)}_{\text{Since } f(c) > L} > L.$$

So x is not in S when $x \in (c - \delta, c)$. We also know that c is not in S (since $f(c) > L$), and no numbers in S can be larger than c because c is an upper bound of S. So the set S must be contained in the interval $[a, c-\delta]$. This means $c - \delta/2$ is an upper bound for S, but that cannot be true because c is the *least* upper bound of S.

Since $f(c)$ is in the range of f, but $f(c)$ can be neither greater than nor less than L, it must be true that $f(c) = L$.   ∎

▷ Proof of the Extreme Value Theorem

The Extreme Value Theorem tells us that a continuous function over a closed, bounded interval achieves a maximum (and minimum) value somewhere in the interval. Suppose the function is f, and the interval is $[a, b]$. Our proof proceeds in two steps. First we show that $f(x)$ cannot grow arbitrarily large on $[a, b]$, which allows us to conclude that the range of f has an upper bound. In the second step of the proof we show that the least upper bound of the range is achieved by f at some point in $[a, b]$.

Step 1 (show that the range of a continuous function is bounded): Our strategy will be to assume—contrary to the assertion of the theorem—that the continuous function f grows arbitrarily large in $[a, b]$, and to show that this assumption leads us to contradict the continuity of f.

Suppose that f grows arbitrarily large on $[a, b]$. Then for each positive integer k there is a $c_k \in [a, b]$ at which $f(c_k) > k$. Because the set of numbers $\{c_k\}$ is infinite and is contained in a closed and bounded interval, the Bolzano-Weierstrass Theorem guarantees that it contains a convergent sequence of distinct numbers $c_{k_1}, c_{k_2}, c_{k_3}, c_{k_4} \ldots$. Let's define $c = \lim_{n \to \infty} c_{k_n}$, which is in $[a, b]$ since the interval is closed.

> The indices $k_1, k_2, k_3 \ldots$ might not be consecutive, or even in order. For example, the sequence of points that converges to c might be $c_{921}, c_5, c_{16}, c_{11}, \ldots$, in which case $k_1 = 921, k_2 = 5, k_3 = 16, k_4 = 11$, and so on.

Because f is continuous on $[a, b]$ there is a $\delta > 0$ so that

$$\left| f(x) - f(c) \right| < 1 \quad \text{whenever} \quad x \in [a, b] \text{ and } |x - c| < \delta.$$

And because $c_{k_n} \to c$ as $n \to \infty$, there is an index M such that $|c_{k_n} - c| < \delta$ when $n > M$. Because c_{k_n} is less than δ units away from c when $n > M$, the number $f(c_{k_n})$ is less than 1 unit away from $f(c)$. It follows that

$$1 + f(c) > f(c_{k_n}) \tag{g.18}$$

when $n > M$. Recall that $f(c_{k_n}) > k_n$ (because of how we found the c_k earlier), so the inequality in (g.18) leads directly to

$$1 + f(c) > k_n,$$

but that cannot be true because $k_n \to \infty$ as $n \to \infty$. To understand why, recall that the numbers in our convergent sequence are distinct, so the indices k_n are too. Consequently, at most ten of the indices k_n can be less than 11 (each k_n is a positive integer). More generally, for each positive integer N, there can be at most N occurrences of $k_n \le N$, after which the remaining $k_n > N$. Therefore, the numbers k_n eventually grow larger than each positive integer N.

> The numbers $k_1, k_2, k_7, k_8, k_9, k_{31}, k_{58}, k_{1121}, k_{1970}, k_{1972}$, and k_{2012} might be the ten numbers that are less than 11. The k_n that are smaller than 11 might not be consecutive terms in the sequence $\{k_n\}$, but there are at most ten of them. If the ten terms mentioned above are all less than 11, we know that $k_n \ge 11$ when $n \ge 2012$.

The assumption that f is continuous but grows arbitrarily large in $[a, b]$ has led to two assertions that cannot be true simultaneously: $1 + f(c) > k_n$, and $k_n \to \infty$. Therefore, the assumption must be wrong. The value of f cannot grow arbitrarily large on $[a, b]$. This means its range is bounded above, and we conclude that there is a least upper bound, say M.

Step 2 (showing that the least upper bound is achieved): Since M is the least upper bound of the range of f, the number $M - 1/k$ is *not* an upper bound when k is any positive integer. That is, there is some point $c_k \in [a, b]$ at which $f(c_k) \geq M - 1/k$. If it happens that $f(c_k) = M$ for some k, we're done. Otherwise, the set $\{c_k\}$ is infinite and is contained in a closed and bounded interval, so the Bolzano-Weierstrass Theorem guarantees that $\{c_k\}$ contains a convergent sequence of distinct numbers, say $\{c_{k_n}\}$.

Define $c = \lim_{n \to \infty} c_{k_n}$, which is in $[a, b]$ since the interval is closed. We know that $f(c) \leq M$ since M is an upper bound for the range of f. In the remainder of the proof, we use the continuity of f to show that $f(c) < M$ contradicts the fact that M is the *least* upper bound. Then, knowing that $f(c)$ can be neither greater nor less than M, we'll be able to conclude that $f(c) = M$.

If $f(c)$ were less than M, the number $\varepsilon = 0.5(M - f(c))$ would be positive. Then because f is continuous on $[a, b]$, there would be a $\delta > 0$ so that

$$|f(x) - f(c)| < \varepsilon \quad \text{whenever} \quad x \in [a, b] \text{ and } |x - c| < \delta.$$

Further, since $c_{k_n} \to c$ as $n \to \infty$, there is a positive number N such that $|c_{k_n} - c| < \delta$ whenever $n \geq N$. Since c_{k_n} is less than δ units from c when $n \geq N$, the number $f(c_{k_n})$ is less than ε units from $f(c)$ when $n \geq N$. It follows that, when $n \geq N$,

$$f(c_{k_n}) < f(c) + \varepsilon = f(c) + \frac{1}{2}(M - f(c)) = \frac{f(c) + M}{2}.$$

Since $(f(c)+M)/2 < M$, the above inequality prevents the numbers $f(c_{k_n})$ from becoming arbitrarily close to M. This cannot be true because of the way that the c_k were originally generated (and because $k_n \to \infty$ as $n \to \infty$, just as in Step 1 of this proof). So it cannot be true that $f(c) < M$.

> Since $f(c) < M$, the mean of $f(c)$ and M is less than M.

Now because $f(c) \geq M$, but M is an upper bound for the range of f, we know that $f(c) = M$. So the least upper bound is achieved as a function value.

Lastly, to prove that f achieves its minimum value, note that the minimum value of f is the maximum value of $-f(x)$. Because $-f(x)$ is also a continuous function on $[a, b]$, it achieves its maximum value. ∎

▷ Uniform continuity

Suppose $f(x)$ is continuous at $x = c$. Then for each $\varepsilon > 0$ there is a $\delta > 0$ so that

$$|f(x) - f(c)| < \varepsilon \quad \text{whenever} \quad |x - c| < \delta.$$

When the graph of f is a line, the number δ is the same for all values of c, which we communicate by saying that f is **uniformly continuous**. When the graph of f is not a line, we typically think of δ as being smaller at points where the graph is steeper, but the following theorem says that every continuous function is uniformly continuous when restricted to a closed interval.

> If $f'(c)$ exists and $f'(c) \neq 0$ the number $\delta \approx \varepsilon/|f'(c)|$.

Theorem (Uniform Continuity of Continuous Functions on a Closed Interval): Suppose f is continuous on $[a,b]$. Then for each $\varepsilon > 0$ there is a $\delta > 0$ such that, for every $c \in [a,b]$,

$$|f(x) - f(c)| < \varepsilon \quad \text{whenever} \quad x \in [a,b] \text{ and } |x - c| < \delta$$

Note that the same δ works for all $c \in [a,b]$.

Proof. Choose $\varepsilon > 0$. Because f is continuous on $[a,b]$, at each $c \in [a,b]$ there is a $\delta_c > 0$ such that

$$|f(x) - f(c)| < \frac{\varepsilon}{4} \quad \text{whenever} \quad x \in [a,b] \text{ and } |x - c| < \delta_c.$$

The open intervals $(c - \delta_c, c + \delta_c)$ cover $[a,b]$, so the Heine-Borel Theorem guarantees that there is a finite set of them that covers $[a,b]$. Denote these by $U_1, U_2, U_3, \ldots, U_m$, centered at c_k and with radius δ_k respectively. That is, $U_k = (c_k - \delta_k, c_k + \delta_k)$ when $k = 1, 2, 3, \ldots, m$.

Now choose an arbitrary $c \in [a,b]$. In what follows we prove that

$$|f(x) - f(c)| < \varepsilon \quad \text{whenever} \quad x \in [a,b] \text{ and } 0 < |x - c| < \delta,$$

where δ is the smallest of the δ_k. There are two cases for us to consider:

1. the interval $(c - \delta, c + \delta)$ is entirely contained in one of the open intervals, say U_1;

2. the interval $(c - \delta, c + \delta)$ contains points from two (or more) overlapping open intervals, say U_1 and U_2.

Case 1: In this case, each $x \in (c - \delta, c + \delta)$ is within δ_1 of c_1, so $f(x)$ is within $\varepsilon/4$ of $f(c_1)$. The same is true of $f(c)$ since c is within δ_1 of c_1. It follows that

$$\bigl|f(x) - f(c)\bigr| = \bigl|f(x) - f(c_1) + f(c_1) - f(c)\bigr| \tag{g.19}$$

$$\leq \bigl|f(x) - f(c_1)\bigr| + \bigl|f(c_1) - f(c)\bigr| < \frac{\varepsilon}{4} + \frac{\varepsilon}{4} < \frac{\varepsilon}{2}, \tag{g.20}$$

We pass from (g.19) to (g.20) using the Triangle Inequality.

which is less than ε.

Case 2: In this case it can happen that $x \in (c - \delta, c + \delta)$, but $c \in U_1$ while $x \in U_2$. If so, choose a point in the intersection of the open intervals U_1 and U_2, say c^*. Because c and c^* are both in U_1, we know from Case 1 that $|f(c) - f(c^*)| < \varepsilon/2$. Similarly, since x and c^* are both in U_2 we know that $|f(c^*) - f(x)| < \varepsilon/2$. Therefore,

$$\bigl|f(x) - f(c)\bigr| = \bigl|f(x) - f(c^*) + f(c^*) - f(c)\bigr|$$

$$\leq \bigl|f(x) - f(c^*)\bigr| + \bigl|f(c^*) - f(c)\bigr| < \frac{\varepsilon}{2} + \frac{\varepsilon}{2} = \varepsilon. \qquad \blacksquare$$

❖ End Notes for Chapter 3

In Chapter 3 we asserted that pressure decays exponentially with altitude, and promised a rigorous proof that the inverse of a differentiable, one-to-one function is also differentiable.

▷ Exponential decay of atmospheric pressure

For the purposes of this discussion, we will treat the atmosphere as an isothermal ideal gas. Also, we will assume that the air in any given column experiences a net vertical acceleration of 0. Consider a thin "slab" of the atmosphere, say a cylinder with circular faces of area A on top and bottom, and a thickness of Δz (see Figure G.5). If the average mass of an air molecule is m, and the density of the air is ρ molecules per cubic meter, the number of particles in this slab is $\rho A \Delta z$, so its mass is $m \rho A \Delta z$, and the force it experiences due to gravity is $F_{\text{gravity}} = -gm\rho A \Delta z$, where g is the acceleration due to gravity (negative because gravity pulls "downward"). There are two other forces acting on the this slab: pressure from below, and pressure from above. If the bottom circular face is at an altitude of z, where the pressure is $P(z)$, it experiences a force of $F_{\text{bottom}} = P(z)A$. Similarly, the top circular face is at an altitude of $z + \Delta z$, so it experiences a force of $F_{\text{top}} = -P(z + \Delta z)A$. Since the net acceleration on the slab is 0, Newton's Second Law tells us that

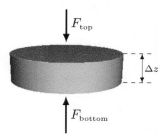

Figure G.5: A short cylinder of air.

$$0 = F_{\text{gravity}} + F_{\text{bottom}} + F_{\text{top}} = -gm\rho A \Delta z + P(z)A - P(z + \Delta z)A.$$

Dividing this equation by $A\Delta z$ and rearranging terms bring us to

$$\frac{P(z + \Delta z) - P(z)}{\Delta z} = -gm\rho. \tag{g.21}$$

The Ideal Gas Law tells us that $PV = Nk_BT$ where k_B is Boltzmann's constant, N is the number of atoms of a gas, V is the volume in which the gas resides, P is its pressure, and T is its temperature (which we're taking to be fixed). Written differently, this becomes

$$\frac{P}{k_BT} = \frac{N}{V} = \rho.$$

which allows us to rewrite equation (g.21) as

$$\frac{P(z + \Delta z) - P(z)}{\Delta z} = -\frac{mg}{k_BT}P.$$

In the limit as $\Delta z \to 0$ this equation says that $P'(z) = -\frac{mg}{k_BT}P$. That is, P' is a scaled version of P. In Section 4.5 we'll prove that only scaled exponential functions have this property, so it must be that $P(z) = P_0 e^{-mgz/k_bT}$. In Chapter 3 we've set P_0 equal to the air pressure at sea level, and rewritten the exponent as $-\ln(1/2)z/5.6$.

▷ Differentiability of an inverse function (proof)

We're going to prove the differentiability of f^{-1} in the common case when f is a continuous function, and in order to reduce notational clutter we'll denote f^{-1} by g, so $f(g(y)) = y$ and $g(f(x)) = x$. This proof has two steps. The first is proving that g is continuous. In the second step we use the continuity of g to show that difference quotients of g converge in the limit, thereby proving both the differentiability of g and its relationship to f'.

Step 1 (continuity of the inverse function): Suppose $f(c) = k$. Then $g(k) = c$, and we must show that for each $\varepsilon > 0$ there is a $\delta > 0$ such that

$$\left| g(y) - c \right| < \varepsilon \quad \text{when} \quad |y - k| < \delta. \tag{g.22}$$

This is due to the continuity of f, because of which each interval $[c - \varepsilon/2, c + \varepsilon/2]$ on the x-axis corresponds to an interval on the y-axis, say $[k - \delta_1, k + \delta_2]$. Equation (g.22) is established by setting $\delta = 0.5 \min\{\delta_1, \delta_2\}$.

The fact that intervals in x correspond to intervals in y is obvious when the graph of f is relatively simple. Mathematically speaking, we have to worry about whether it's true even for the functions whose graphs we don't think to draw. This is something that's often done in introductory courses in topology.

Step 2 (differentiability of the inverse function): We know that $g(k) = c$. Let's write $g(k + \Delta y) = c + \Delta x$, so $f(c + \Delta x) = k + \Delta y$, which is the same as writing

$$\Delta y = f(c + \Delta x) - k.$$

Further, we know that $\Delta x \to 0$ as $\Delta y \to 0$ because g is continuous. It follows that

$$\lim_{\Delta y \to 0} \frac{g(k + \Delta y) - g(k)}{\Delta y} = \lim_{\Delta x \to 0} \frac{(c + \Delta x) - c}{f(c + \Delta x) - k} = \lim_{\Delta x \to 0} \frac{\Delta x}{f(c + \Delta x) - k}.$$

Because $k = f(c)$ and f is differentiable, we can write this as

$$\lim_{\Delta y \to 0} \frac{g(k + \Delta y) - g(k)}{\Delta y} = \frac{1}{\lim_{\Delta x \to 0} \frac{f(c + \Delta x) - f(c)}{\Delta x}} = \frac{1}{f'(c)},$$

provided that $f'(c) \neq 0$. Note that we've both proven the differentiability of g and demonstrated the formula for calculating the derivative!

❖ End Notes for Chapter 5

In Chapter 5 we claimed that all continuous functions are integrable over a closed interval, but we postponed the proof because of its technical detail. Now we take the opportunity to present that proof.

▷ Continuous functions are integrable over closed, bounded intervals

Suppose P is a partition of the interval $[a, b]$, say $a = x_0 < x_1 < x_2 < \cdots < x_{n-1} < x_n = b$. The Extreme Value Theorem tells us that the continuous function f achieves a minimum and a maximum value on each $[x_{k-1}, x_k]$, which we denote by m_k and M_k respectively. We say that

$$\sum_{k=1}^{n} m_k(x_k - x_{k-1}) \text{ is a } \textbf{lower sum} \text{ of } f, \text{ and we denote it by } L(f, P).$$

Similarly, we say that

$$\sum_{k=1}^{n} M_k(x_k - x_{k-1}) \text{ is an } \textbf{upper sum} \text{ of } f, \text{ and we denote it by } U(f, P).$$

Any scheme for sampling f in the subintervals $[x_k, x_{k+1}]$ produces a Riemann sum with a value between $L(f, P)$ and $U(f, P)$.

Next we establish a way of comparing Riemann sums from different partitions. We say that the partition P^* is a **refinement** of P if every partition point in P is also a partition point in P^*, but P^* includes additional partition points (at least one) that are not in P. In the following discussion you'll see that refining a partition increases the lower sum and decreases the upper sum, bringing them closer together. For the sake of discussion, suppose we refine P by adding a single partition point, say $c \in (x_0, x_1)$. We'll refer to this refinement as P^*. We don't know whether the maximum of f over $[x_0, x_1]$ occurs in $[x_0, c]$ or in $[c, x_1]$, so

$$M_1 = \max_{[x_0, x_1]} f(x) \geq \max_{[x_0, c]} f(x), \text{ which we denote by } M_{1A}^*$$

and

$$M_1 = \max_{[x_0, x_1]} f(x) \geq \max_{[c, x_1]} f(x), \text{ which we denote by } M_{1B}^*.$$

Since all of the other subintervals are the same,

$$U(f, P) = M_1(x_1 - x_0) + \sum_{k=2}^{n} M_k(x_k - x_{k-1})$$

$$\geq M_{1A}^*(c - x_0) + M_{1B}^*(x_1 - c) + \sum_{k=2}^{n} M_k(x_k - x_{k-1}) = U(f, P^*).$$

Similarly, the minimum of f over $[x_0, x_1]$ occurs in either $[x_0, c]$ or in $[c, x_1]$, or perhaps at c. So

$$m_1 = \min_{[x_0, x_1]} f(x) \leq \min_{[x_0, c]} f(x) \quad \text{and} \quad m_1 = \min_{[x_0, x_1]} f(x) \leq \min_{[c, x_1]} f(x),$$

from which it follows that $L(f, P) \leq L(f, P^*)$.

Now suppose that P_1 and P_2 are two partitions of $[a, b]$. Each time we refine P_1 by adding a point from P_2, we increase its lower sum and decrease its upper sum. Denote by P^* the partition that results from adding all of the points of P_2 into P_1 one at a time. We could also get P^* by adding all the points of P_1 into P_2 one at a time, which would have the same effect on lower and upper sums. So

> Because we're adding *all* of the points from one partition into the other, the order in which we do it is irrelevant.

$$L(f, P_1) \leq L(f, P^*) \leq U(f, P^*) \leq U(f, P_1) \tag{g.23}$$

$$L(f, P_2) \leq L(f, P^*) \leq U(f, P^*) \leq U(f, P_2). \tag{g.24}$$

By comparing (g.23) and (g.24) we see that $L(f, P_1) \leq U(f, P_2)$ and $L(f, P_2) \leq U(f, P_2)$. Because we can compare any two partitions in this manner, we have established that each upper sum is an upper bound for the collection of lower sums. Denote the least upper bound of the lower sums by I. Then for each partition P,

$$L(f, P) \leq I \leq U(f, P). \tag{g.25}$$

We finish our proof by showing that the lower sums and upper sums converge to I as $\|P\| \to 0$. This happens because a continuous function is uniformly continuous on a closed interval. Suppose $\varepsilon > 0$. Then there is a $\delta > 0$ so that

> By $\|P\|$ we mean the *norm* of the partition, which was defined in Section 5.2.

$$\left| f(x) - f(t) \right| < \frac{\varepsilon}{b - a} \quad \text{whenever} \quad x, t \in [a, b] \text{ and } 0 < |x - t| < \delta.$$

Since $\|P\| \to 0$, it eventually happens that $\|P\| < \delta$, which means that all the points in a subinterval are within δ of each other. It follows that $M_k - m_k < \varepsilon/(b-a)$, so

$$U(f, P) - L(f, P) = \sum_{k=1}^{n} (M_k - m_k)(x_k - x_{k-1})$$

$$< \sum_{k=1}^{n} \frac{\varepsilon}{b - a}(x_k - x_{k-1}) = \frac{\varepsilon}{b - a} \sum_{k=1}^{n}(x_k - x_{k-1}) = \varepsilon.$$

Because $L(f, P)$ and $U(f, P)$ are within ε of each other, it follows from (g.25) that they are both within ε of I. Since this happens for all $\varepsilon > 0$, we have established that

$$\lim_{\|P\| \to 0} L(f, P) = I \quad \text{and} \quad \lim_{\|P\| \to 0} U(f, P) = I.$$

Lastly, note that all other sampling schemes give us Riemann sums with values between the lower and upper sums. So the Squeeze Theorem allows us to conclude that all Riemann sums converge to the same value in the limit as $\|P\| \to 0$. ∎

❖ End Notes for Chapter 8

At the beginning of Chapter 8 we said that the length of time required by the body to metabolize half of a dose of medicine is always the same, regardless of how much is present initially. Here we take a moment to support that claim. Additionally, there are some facts about the real numbers that are best stated using the vocabulary of Chapter 8, but which support results from previous chapters. We present those results here for reference.

▷ Metabolizing medicine at therapeutic levels

At therapeutic levels, the rate at which the body metabolizes the drug is proportional to how much is present. Using $a(t)$ to denote amount of some drug in the body at time t, that statement of proportionality is expressed mathematically with the equation

$$a'(t) = -k\, a(t), \tag{g.26}$$

where $k > 0$ is a constant that depends on the particular drug and patient. On p. 296 we established that only exponential functions (and scaled versions of them) are described by equation (g.26), so

$$a(t) = Ae^{-kt}, \tag{g.27}$$

where A is the initial amount of the drug that's present. So half of the original amount is gone when

$$\frac{1}{2}A = Ae^{-kt} \quad \Rightarrow \quad \frac{1}{2} = e^{-kt} \quad \Rightarrow \quad t = \frac{1}{k}\ln(2).$$

Notice that A doesn't appear in the final result.

▷ Proof of the Bounded Monotone Convergence Theorem

The Bounded Monotone Convergence Theorem guarantees that a monotonic sequence $\{a_k\}$ contained in some closed and bounded interval, say $[m, M]$, must converge. If the terms of the sequence include only a finite set of distinct numbers, monotonicity requires that the largest (or the smallest) is eventually reached and then repeated thereafter, so the sequence converges. In the case that the sequence includes an infinite set of distinct numbers, we prove convergence by employing the Bolzano-Weierstass Theorem.

Suppose that $\{a_k\}$ is monotonically increasing. Since $\{a_k\}$ is an infinite set of numbers that's bounded above by M, the Bolzano-Weierstass Theorem guarantees that it gives rise to a convergent sequence of distinct numbers, say $\{a_{k_n}\}$. Set $L = \lim_{n\to\infty} a_{k_n}$. If any term of the original sequence were larger than L, say $a_N > L$, it would be true (since the sequence is monotonically increasing) that $a_{k_n} \geq a_N > L$ when $k_n > N$. That would prevent $a_{k_n} \to L$ as $n \to \infty$, so it cannot happen. We conclude that the number L is an upper bound for the sequence $\{a_k\}$. Further, the definition of the limit tells us that for each positive ε there is an integer N so that

$$|a_{k_n} - L| < \varepsilon \quad \text{whenever} \quad n \geq N.$$

That is,

$$L - \varepsilon < a_{k_n} \leq L \quad \text{whenever} \quad n \geq N.$$

But then because the sequence $\{a_k\}$ is increasing, we know that

$$L - \varepsilon < a_k \leq L \quad \text{whenever} \quad k > k_N.$$

Because this happens for every $\varepsilon > 0$, have established that $\lim_{k\to\infty} a_k = L$. ∎

▷ Intervals of Convergence for Power Series

In Section 8.6 we said that the set of x at which $\sum a_k(x-c)^k$ converges is always an interval that's symmetric about $x = c$ (perhaps with a radius that's infinite or 0).

Theorem: For the series $\sum a_k(x-c)^k$ there are only three possibilities:

1. There is a positive number R such that the series converges absolutely when $|x - c| < R$ and diverges when $|x - c| > R$.

2. The power series converges for all x.

3. The power series converges only at c.

Proof. Suppose that neither (2.) nor (3.) is true. Then there is a number $b \neq c$ at which the series converges, and a number d at which it diverges.

Because $\sum a_k(b-c)^k$ converges, we know that $\lim_{k \to \infty} a_k(b-c)^k = 0$. Consequently, there is an index N beyond which $|a_k(b-c)^k| < 1$, which plays an important role in the next step of our proof: establishing that the series converges absolutely at all x that are closer to c than is b. Let us suppose that $|x - c| < |b - c|$. Then

$$\sum_{k=N}^{\infty} |a_k(x-c)^k| = \sum_{k=N}^{\infty} |a_k(b-c)^k| \left| \frac{x-c}{b-c} \right|^k \leq \sum_{k=N}^{\infty} \left| \frac{x-c}{b-c} \right|^k.$$

Since $|x - c| < |b - c|$, the series on the right-hand side of this inequality is a convergent geometric series. It follows from the Direct Comparison Test that the series on the left converges. Since the first N terms of a series do not affect whether it converges, this establishes that $\sum a_k(x-c)^k$ converges absolutely when $|x - c| < |b - c|$.

Now let us define S to be the set of x at which $\sum a_k(x-c)^k$ converges. The set is non-empty since $b \in S$, and in light of our previous work, it includes all x for which $|x - c| < |b - c|$. Since S does not include d, we know that S is bounded above, and by virtue of the supremum property of the real numbers, that S has a least upper bound. Let us define $R > 0$ as the distance between c and the supremum of S, so that the supremum is at $c + R$. If $|x - c| > R$ we know that $\sum a_k(x-c)^k$ diverges, for otherwise $c + R$ would not be an upper bound of the set. When $|x - c| < R$ there is a number $b_1 \in (c, c + R)$ that's farther from c than is x. Since $c + R$ is the least upper bound, we know that $b_1 \in S$. And because $|x - c| < |b_1 - c|$, we know that the series converges absolutely at x. ∎

> What matters here is the *distance* between x to c, regardless of whether x is larger or smaller than c. In this sense, we've established some symmetry about c.

❖ End Notes for Chapter 10

In various places through the book we cite Torricelli's Law for fluid flow, and in Chapter 10 we use it extensively. Here we provide a brief derivation of the law based on the ideas of force, work, and energy from Chapter 7.

▷ Torricelli's Law

Suppose a small hole forms in the side of a large tank, and the liquid it holds begins to drain. For the sake of discussion, let's assume the hole is circular, and consider a small "coin" of water next to the hole that's pushed out because of the pressure in the tank (see Figure G.6). Let's denote by A the area of coin's face, and denote the coin's thickness by Δx.

We know from Chapter 7 that when there are y meters of liquid above the hole, the hydrostatic pressure next to the hole is $P = g\rho y$, where g is the acceleration due

> We're assuming that the hole is small enough, relative to the size of the tank, that it's reasonable to approximate by saying that every point of the hole has the same amount of water above it.

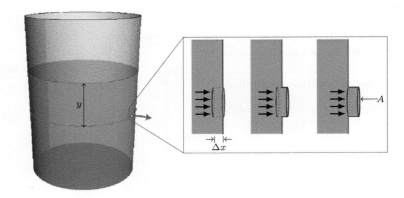

Figure G.6: A small "coin" of water is pushed out of a hole due to pressure in the tank.

to gravity and ρ is the density of the liquid. So the force that acts to push the coin through the hole is $F = PA = g\rho y A$. Because the coin of water has a thickness of Δx, the hydrostatic force moves it a distance of Δx in order to expel it from the tank. We know from Chapter 7 that (force)×(distance)=(work), and that work changes kinetic energy. Assuming that the coin of water had no horizontal velocity before it was expelled, we get

$$ \underbrace{F\Delta x}_{\text{work}} = \underbrace{\frac{1}{2}mv^2 - 0}_{\Delta K} $$

where m is the mass of the "coin." Since $m =$(density)×(volume)$= \rho A \Delta x$, we can rewrite this equation as

$$ g\rho y A \Delta x = \frac{1}{2}\rho A \Delta x \, v^2 \quad \Rightarrow \quad v = \sqrt{2gy}. $$

❖ End Notes for Chapter 11

We postponed the proof that the cross product is distributive because it requires an understanding of planes. Now having read Section 11.5, you're ready to see it.

▷ Proof of the Distributive Property for the Cross Product

In Section 11.4 we postponed the proof that the cross product is distributive because it relies on an elementary understanding of planes in 3-space. Now we take up the task of proving that fact. We'll assume that neither $\mathbf{u}$ nor $\mathbf{v}$ nor $\mathbf{w}$ is the vector $\mathbf{0}$, since the result is trivial in that case, and our proof will proceed in two steps. First, we'll show that $\mathbf{w} \times (\mathbf{u} + \mathbf{v}) = \mathbf{w} \times \mathbf{u} + \mathbf{w} \times \mathbf{v}$ in the special case when $\mathbf{u}$ and $\mathbf{v}$ are both orthogonal to $\mathbf{w}$. Then we'll extend the result to all vectors by showing that $\mathbf{w} \times \mathbf{u} = \mathbf{w} \times \mathbf{u}_\perp$ where, loosely said, $\mathbf{u}_\perp$ is the part of $\mathbf{u}$ that's orthogonal to $\mathbf{w}$.

Step 1 (when $\mathbf{u}$ and $\mathbf{v}$ are orthogonal to $\mathbf{w}$): The collection of vectors that are orthogonal to $\mathbf{w}$ all lie in a plane, $\mathcal{P}$. This collection includes $\mathbf{u}$ by assumption, but also $\mathbf{w} \times \mathbf{u}$ by virtue of the geometric definition of the cross product. Since $\mathbf{w} \times \mathbf{u}$ lies in $\mathcal{P}$ and is orthogonal to $\mathbf{u}$ (again, by virtue of the geometric definition), its direction is found by rotating $\mathbf{u}$ through $\pi/2$ radians in the plane $\mathcal{P}$. The direction of the rotation is determined by the right-hand rule (see the left-hand image of Figure

G.7). The vector $\mathbf{u}$ is not special in this regard; the effect of crossing $\mathbf{w}$ with *any* vector in $\mathcal{P}$ is to rotate the vector by $\pi/2$ radians. The right-hand image of Figure G.7 shows this relationship for $\mathbf{u}$ and $\mathbf{w} \times \mathbf{u}$, for $\mathbf{v}$ and $\mathbf{w} \times \mathbf{v}$, and for $\mathbf{u} + \mathbf{v}$ and $\mathbf{w} \times (\mathbf{u} + \mathbf{v})$. Note that the direction of the rotation is always in the same direction (counter-clockwise, according to the right-hand rule) because $\mathbf{w}$ is fixed.

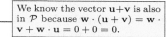

We know the vector $\mathbf{u}+\mathbf{v}$ is also in $\mathcal{P}$ because $\mathbf{w} \cdot (\mathbf{u} + \mathbf{v}) = \mathbf{w} \cdot \mathbf{v} + \mathbf{w} \cdot \mathbf{u} = 0 + 0 = 0$.

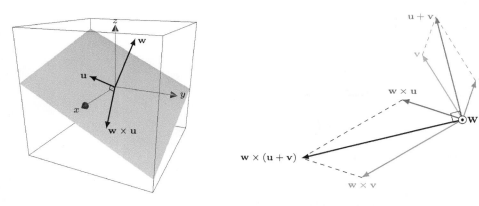

Figure G.7: (both) The plane $\mathcal{P}$; (left) as seen in standard orientation. To use the right hand rule, lay your right-hand along $\mathbf{w}$ and curl your fingers toward $\mathbf{u}$. Your thumb points in the direction of $\mathbf{w} \times \mathbf{u}$. (right) As seen from directly above the vector $\mathbf{w}$, which is pointing out of the page.

Additionally, it follows (from orthogonality) that

$$\|\mathbf{w} \times \mathbf{u}\| = \|\mathbf{w}\| \, \|\mathbf{u}\| \sin(\pi/2) = \|\mathbf{w}\| \, \|\mathbf{u}\|$$
$$\|\mathbf{w} \times \mathbf{v}\| = \|\mathbf{w}\| \, \|\mathbf{v}\| \sin(\pi/2) = \|\mathbf{w}\| \, \|\mathbf{v}\|$$
$$\|\mathbf{w} \times (\mathbf{u} + \mathbf{v})\| = \|\mathbf{w}\| \, \|(\mathbf{u} + \mathbf{v})\| \sin(\pi/2) = \|\mathbf{w}\| \, \|(\mathbf{u} + \mathbf{v})\|.$$

So the cross product of $\mathbf{w}$ with a vector in $\mathcal{P}$ both rotates it by $\pi/2$ radians and scales it by a factor of $\|\mathbf{w}\|$, which is the key to completing Step 1. When the vectors $\mathbf{u}$, $\mathbf{v}$ and $(\mathbf{u} + \mathbf{v})$ are all scaled by $\|\mathbf{w}\|$, the additive relationship among them is preserved. And when the scaled vectors are all rotated by $\pi/2$ radians, again the additive relationship among them is preserved. That is,

$$\underbrace{\mathbf{w} \times (\mathbf{u} + \mathbf{v})}_{} = \underbrace{\mathbf{w} \times \mathbf{u} + \mathbf{w} \times \mathbf{v}}_{} \qquad \text{(g.28)}$$

Scaling and rotating a sum **is the same as** adding scaled and rotated vectors .

when $\mathbf{u}$ and $\mathbf{v}$ are orthogonal to $\mathbf{w}$.

Step 2 (extending Step 1 to a general result): Now we address the case when $\mathbf{u}$ is not necessarily orthogonal to $\mathbf{w}$. Let's begin by using the vector projection to isolate the part of the vector $\mathbf{u}$ that *is* orthogonal to $\mathbf{w}$ since we already know what happens in that case. Intuitively speaking, the vector projection $\text{proj}_{\mathbf{w}}\mathbf{u} = (\mathbf{u} \cdot \hat{\mathbf{w}})\hat{\mathbf{w}}$ is the portion of $\mathbf{u}$ that points in the direction of $\mathbf{w}$, so if we subtract it away from $\mathbf{u}$, what remains *should* be orthogonal to $\mathbf{w}$. Let's check. If we define $\mathbf{u}_\perp$ to be this difference, $\mathbf{u}_\perp = \mathbf{u} - \text{proj}_{\mathbf{w}}\mathbf{u}$, we see that

$$\mathbf{u}_\perp \cdot \mathbf{w} = (\mathbf{u} - \text{proj}_{\mathbf{w}}\mathbf{u}) \cdot \mathbf{w} = (\mathbf{u} - (\mathbf{u} \cdot \hat{w})\hat{w}) \cdot \mathbf{w} = \mathbf{u} \cdot \mathbf{w} - (\mathbf{u} \cdot \hat{w})(\hat{w} \cdot \mathbf{w})$$

$$= \mathbf{u} \cdot \mathbf{w} - \left(\frac{\mathbf{u} \cdot \mathbf{w}}{\|\mathbf{w}\|}\right)\left(\frac{\mathbf{w} \cdot \mathbf{w}}{\|\mathbf{w}\|}\right) = \mathbf{u} \cdot \mathbf{w} - \frac{\mathbf{u} \cdot \mathbf{w}}{\|\mathbf{w}\|}\frac{\|\mathbf{w}\|^2}{\|\mathbf{w}\|} = \mathbf{u} \cdot \mathbf{w} - \mathbf{u} \cdot \mathbf{w} = 0.$$

The vector $\mathbf{u}_\perp$ is important to our extension of Step 1 because, as we'll show in just a moment,

$$\mathbf{w} \times \mathbf{u} = \mathbf{w} \times \mathbf{u}_\perp. \qquad \text{(g.29)}$$

To prove equation (g.29) we're going to show that the vectors on the left-hand and right-hand sides have the same direction and magnitude. Toward establishing that they have the same direction, note that the vectors $\mathbf{u}$ and $\mathbf{w}$ lie in a plane. The vector $\text{proj}_\mathbf{w}\mathbf{u}$ also lies in that plane (since it's parallel to $\mathbf{w}$), so $\mathbf{u}_\perp = \mathbf{u} - \text{proj}_\mathbf{w}\mathbf{u}$ does too. Due to the right hand rule, the vectors $\mathbf{w} \times \mathbf{u}_\perp$ and $\mathbf{w} \times \mathbf{u}$ point in the same direction (e.g., into the page, in Figure G.8).

> Any pair of nonzero vectors in 3-space share *some* plane.
>
> If $\mathbf{u}$ is a scaled version of $\mathbf{w}$ we know that $\mathbf{w} \times \mathbf{u} = \mathbf{0}$, and you can check that $\mathbf{u}_\perp = \mathbf{0}$, so
>
> $$\mathbf{w} \times \mathbf{u}_\perp = \mathbf{0} = \mathbf{w} \times \mathbf{u}.$$

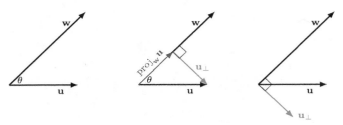

Figure G.8: (left) Vectors $\mathbf{u}$ and $\mathbf{w}$; (middle) $\mathbf{u} = \text{proj}_\mathbf{w}\mathbf{v} + \mathbf{u}_\perp$ where $\mathbf{u}_\perp$ is orthogonal to $\mathbf{w}$; (right) $\mathbf{u}_\perp \times \mathbf{w}$ points in the same direction as $\mathbf{u} \times \mathbf{w}$ due to the right-hand rule.

Now let's talk about magnitude. Because $\|\mathbf{u}_\perp\| = \|\mathbf{u}\| \sin\theta$, where θ is the angle between $\mathbf{u}$ and $\mathbf{w}$, we have

$$\|\mathbf{w} \times \mathbf{u}\| = \|\mathbf{w}\| \ \|\mathbf{u}\| \sin\theta = \|\mathbf{w}\| \ \|\mathbf{u}_\perp\| = \underbrace{\|\mathbf{w}\| \ \|\mathbf{u}_\perp\| \sin(\pi/2)}_{\text{Because } \mathbf{u}_\perp \text{ is orthogonal to } \mathbf{w}} = \|\mathbf{w} \times \mathbf{u}_\perp\|.$$

Since the vectors $\mathbf{w} \times \mathbf{u}_\perp$ and $\mathbf{w} \times \mathbf{u}$ have the same direction and magnitude, they are equal, which is what equation (g.29) asserts.

To conclude our discussion of $\mathbf{u}_\perp$, we note that

$$(\mathbf{u}+\mathbf{v})_\perp = (\mathbf{u}+\mathbf{v}) - \text{proj}_\mathbf{w}(\mathbf{u}+\mathbf{v})$$
$$= (\mathbf{u}+\mathbf{v}) - \left((\mathbf{u}+\mathbf{v}) \cdot \hat{\mathbf{w}}\right)\hat{\mathbf{w}}$$
$$= \mathbf{u}+\mathbf{v} - (\mathbf{u}\cdot\hat{\mathbf{w}} + \mathbf{v}\cdot\hat{\mathbf{w}})\hat{\mathbf{w}}$$
$$= \mathbf{u}+\mathbf{v} - (\mathbf{u}\cdot\hat{\mathbf{w}})\hat{\mathbf{w}} - (\mathbf{v}\cdot\hat{\mathbf{w}})\hat{\mathbf{w}}$$
$$= \left(\mathbf{u} - (\mathbf{u}\cdot\hat{\mathbf{w}})\hat{\mathbf{w}}\right) + \left(\mathbf{v} - (\mathbf{v}\cdot\hat{\mathbf{w}})\hat{\mathbf{w}}\right) = \mathbf{u}_\perp + \mathbf{v}_\perp.$$

Together with equation (g.29), this gives us

$$\mathbf{w} \times (\mathbf{u}+\mathbf{v}) = \mathbf{w} \times (\mathbf{u}+\mathbf{v})_\perp = \mathbf{w} \times (\mathbf{u}_\perp + \mathbf{v}_\perp). \qquad (\text{g.30})$$

Now since $\mathbf{u}_\perp$ and $\mathbf{v}_\perp$ lie in the plane $\mathcal{P}$, equation (g.28) allows us to distribute $\mathbf{w}$ on the right-hand side of (g.30) and rewrite it as

$$\mathbf{w} \times (\mathbf{u}+\mathbf{v}) = \mathbf{w} \times \mathbf{u}_\perp + \mathbf{w} \times \mathbf{v}_\perp = \mathbf{w} \times \mathbf{u} + \mathbf{w} \times \mathbf{v}.$$

So we've proved that cross products distribute "to the right." And since $\mathbf{w} \times \mathbf{u} = -(\mathbf{u} \times \mathbf{w})$, we can show that cross products distribute "to the left" by writing

$$(\mathbf{u}+\mathbf{v}) \times \mathbf{w} = -\left(\mathbf{w} \times (\mathbf{u}+\mathbf{v})\right) = -\left(\mathbf{w} \times \mathbf{u} + \mathbf{w} \times \mathbf{v}\right)$$
$$= -(\mathbf{w} \times \mathbf{u}) - (\mathbf{w} \times \mathbf{v}) = \mathbf{u} \times \mathbf{w} + \mathbf{v} \times \mathbf{w}.$$

▷ Pseudovectors

In Section 11.1 we introduced angular velocity by defining the vector's direction and magnitude. Here we take a moment to remark on a subtlety that distinguishes it from vectors such as displacement, velocity and force.

Imagine a disk in the familiar xy-plane. If the disk is spinning, its angular velocity vector points up (or down) off of the disk, rather than somewhere in the plane. This is different than displacement and velocity vectors, which point in the direction of motion, and force vectors, which point in the direction of an action or effect. Further, in defining the angular velocity vector, *we made a choice* to define its direction using the right hand rather than the left hand. Because of this choice, the angular velocity vector behaves differently in some situations than do vectors such as position and velocity. For instance, the spinning tops in Figure 1.11 are mirror reflections of each other, but the associated angular velocity vectors are not (the mirror reflection of one is the opposite of the other). Physicists refer to such vector quantities as *pseudovectors*, and although an in-depth discussion of their subtleties lies beyond the scope of this book, you'll see them emerge again when we talk about a vector operation called the *cross product*.

As a final remark on this topic, we note that *angular momentum* is another pseudovector, and that it plays an important role in our understanding of the physical world. Whereas the angular velocity vector tells us a spinning object's axis of rotation, direction and rate of spin, the angular momentum vector also accounts for the way that an object's mass is distributed.

❖ End Notes for Chapter 13

In Section 13.5 we pointed out that the existence of partial derivatives does not imply the differentiability of a function of several variables, but their continuity does. Here we prove that assertion for functions of two variables.

▷ Proof that Continuity of Partial Derivatives Implies Differentiability

The difference between the value of f and its linear approximation (computed at the point (a, b)) is

$$\mathcal{D} = f(x, y) - \Big(f(a, b) + f_x(a, b)(x - a) + f_y(a, b)(y - b) \Big).$$

When we write $x - a$ as Δx, and $y - b$ as Δy, this becomes

$$
\begin{aligned}
\mathcal{D} &= f(a + \Delta x, b + \Delta y) - \Big(f(a, b) + f_x(a, b)\Delta x + f_y(a, b)\Delta y \Big) \\
&= \underbrace{f(a + \Delta x, b + \Delta y) - f(a, b)}_{=\Delta f} \underbrace{- f_x(a, b)\Delta x - f_y(a, b)\Delta y}_{=-df} . \quad\quad \text{(g.31)}
\end{aligned}
$$

We want to show that $\mathcal{D}$ vanishes faster than $\|\langle \Delta x, \Delta y \rangle\|$. Note that the difference in the first two terms is the change in function value that happens when we move from (a, b) to $(a + \Delta x, b + \Delta y)$. The key idea in our proof is that this move can be accomplished in two steps instead of one, as depicted in Figure G.9: first move from (a, b) to $(a + \Delta x, b)$, and then move from there to $(a + \Delta x, b + \Delta y)$. (This has the benefit of changing only one variable at a time.) That is, the difference in function value is

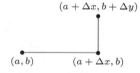

Figure G.9: Moving from (a, b) to $(a + \Delta x, b + \Delta y)$ can be done in two steps instead of one.

$$\Delta f = \underbrace{f(a + \Delta x, b + \Delta y) - f(a + \Delta x, b)}_{\text{change in } f \text{ from the second step}} + \underbrace{f(a + \Delta x, b) - f(a, b)}_{\text{change in } f \text{ from the first step}}.$$

The variable y is constant during the first step, and only x is changing. Since f is a differentiable function of x, the Mean Value Theorem tells us that

$$\underbrace{f(a + \Delta x, b) - f(a, b)}_{\text{change in } f \text{ from the first step}} = f_x(x^*, b)\Delta x$$

for some x^* between a and $a + \Delta x$. Similarly, the variable x is constant in the second step and f is a differentiable function of y, so the Mean Value Theorem tells us that

$$\underbrace{f(a + \Delta x, b + \Delta y) - f(a + \Delta x, b)}_{\text{change in } f \text{ from the second step}} = f_y(a + \Delta x, y^*)\Delta y$$

for some y^* between b and $b + \Delta y$. Putting these together, we have

$$\Delta f = \underbrace{f_x(x^*, b)\Delta x}_{\text{change in } f \text{ from the first step}} + \underbrace{f_y(a + \Delta x, y^*)\Delta y}_{\text{change in } f \text{ from the second step}}$$

so that equation (g.31) reads

$$\mathcal{D} = f_x(x^*, b)\Delta x + f_y(a + \Delta x, y^*)\Delta y - f_x(a, b)\Delta x - f_x(a, b)\Delta x$$

Collecting like terms (those with Δx, and those with Δy), we see

$$\begin{aligned} \mathcal{D} &= \Big(f_x(x^*, b) - f_x(a, b)\Big)\Delta x + \Big(f_y(a + \Delta x, y^*) - f_y(a, b)\Big)\Delta y \\ &= \Big\langle f_x(x^*, b) - f_x(a, b), f_y(a + \Delta x, y^*) - f_y(a, b)\Big\rangle \cdot \langle \Delta x, \Delta y\rangle. \end{aligned}$$

Recall that in general $|\mathbf{u} \cdot \mathbf{v}| \leq \|\mathbf{u}\|\,\|\mathbf{v}\|$ because $\mathbf{u} \cdot \mathbf{v} = \|\mathbf{u}\|\,\|\mathbf{v}\|\cos(\theta)$ and $|\cos(\theta)|$ cannot exceed 1. It follows that

$$|\mathcal{D}| \leq \left\|\Big\langle f_x(x^*, b) - f_x(a, b), f_y(a + \Delta x, y^*) - f_y(a, b)\Big\rangle\right\| \, \|\langle\Delta x, \Delta y\rangle\|.$$

Now as $\Delta x \to 0$, the number x^* is pushed to a. Since f_x is continuous, it follows that $f_x(x^*, b) - f_y(a, b) \to 0$ as $\|\langle\Delta x, \Delta y\rangle\| \to 0$; and since f_y is also continuous, the difference $f_y(a + \Delta x, y^*) - f_y(a, b)$ tends to 0 simultaneously, so

$$\left\|\Big\langle f_x(x^*, b) - f_x(a, b), f_y(a + \Delta x, y^*) - f_y(a, b)\Big\rangle\right\| \to 0$$

as $\|\langle\Delta x, \Delta y\rangle\| \to 0$. This tells you that the difference between the function and its linear approximation, $\mathcal{D}$, vanishes faster than $\|\langle\Delta x, \Delta y\rangle\|$ alone, which is exactly the definition of differentiability. ∎

▷ Proof of the Second Derivative Test

The Second Derivative Test was introduced in Section 13.8. Here we prove the first part of the theorem (the second part is an exercise in Section 13.8). Our strategy for establishing ($\star$) is to show that the graph of f has the same concavity in all directions when the determinant of the Hessian matrix is positive.

In order to avoid being bogged down by notation, let's adopt the convention that f_{xx}, f_{yy}, f_{xy} and f_{yx} will always refer to the second derivatives at the point (a, b). Additionally, let's write the unit vector $\langle \alpha, \beta\rangle$ from equation (8.4) as $\langle\cos\theta, \sin\theta\rangle$ so that we can talk about the sign of the directional derivative as a function of θ.

Since the second partial derivatives are continuous near (a, b), Clairaut's Theorem tells us that $f_{xy} = f_{yx}$, so we can rewrite equation (8.3) as

$$\frac{d^2 f}{dt^2} = \cos^2(\theta)f_{xx} + 2\cos(\theta)\sin(\theta)f_{xy} + \sin^2(\theta)f_{yy}. \qquad \text{(g.32)}$$

Equation (g.32) characterizes d^2f/dt^2 as a continuous function of θ, so its sign can change only at a value of θ for which

$$\cos^2(\theta)f_{xx} + 2\cos(\theta)\sin(\theta)f_{xy} + \sin^2(\theta)f_{yy} = 0. \qquad \text{(g.33)}$$

> Remember that f_{xx}, f_{xy} and f_{yy} are particular numbers.

The remainder of the proof is devoted to showing that there is no such angle when determinant of the Hessian matrix is positive. When you read equation (g.33) from left to right, you see that the first term has a cosine *squared,* the second has cosine *to the first power,* and the last has no cosine at all. That is, the equation has the form

$$A\big(\cos\theta\big)^2 + B\cos\theta + C = 0, \tag{g.34}$$

where $A = f_{xx}$, $B = 2\sin(\theta)f_{xy}$, and $C = \sin^2(\theta)f_{yy}$. This quadratic equation has real solutions only when its discriminant is nonnegative, so we check

$$
\begin{aligned}
B^2 - 4AC &= 4\sin^2(\theta)(f_{xy})^2 - 4(f_{xx})\sin^2(\theta)f_{yy} \\
&= -4\sin^2(\theta)\big(f_{xx}f_{yy} - (f_{xy})^2\big) = -4\sin^2(\theta)\det(H),
\end{aligned}
$$

where $\det(H)$ is the determinant of the Hessian matrix. Since $\det(H)$ is positive, this expression only nonnegative when $\sin\theta = 0$. In this case, the numbers B and C are both 0, and $\cos^2\theta = 1$, so equation (g.34) becomes $A = 0$. That is, $f_{xx} = 0$, but in the Section 13.8 exercises you'll show that this cannot happen when $\det(H) > 0$, so there is no angle at which equation (g.33) is true. Since the second directional derivative is a continuous function of θ that cannot be zero, it's either always positive, or always negative. ∎

> This proof is *much* easier once you know about the *eigenvalues* and *eigenvectors* of a symmetric matrix. You'll learn about them in a course called *Linear Algebra.*

✤ End Notes for Chapter 14

In Section 14.6 we presented an intuitive argument for the volume of a spherical box, and promised to present a rigorous geometric argument in the End Notes, so that's what we will do next. A spherical box can be made by slicing parts away from a spherical wedge. Specifically, we will (1) use a sphere to slice off the tip of the spherical wedge, (2) cut out the core of what remains to make a "ring," and (3) take a segment of the ring as our "box."

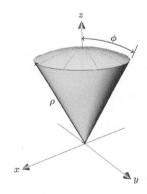

Figure G.10: A spherical wedge of radius ρ with an angle of ϕ radians between its central axis and its side.

- *Step 1 (slicing off the tip of the wedge):* In Example 6.6 we showed that the volume of a spherical wedge of radius ρ is $\frac{2\pi}{3}\rho^3[1 - \cos\phi]$ when the angle between its side and central axis is ϕ radians. Consider the solid that's made by starting with a spherical wedge of radius ρ_2, and slicing away a similar but smaller spherical wedge of radius ρ_1 (including the tip). What remains looks like a cupcake with a spherical bottom (see Figure G.11), and has a volume of

$$\underbrace{\frac{2\pi}{3}\rho_2^3[1 - \cos\phi]}_{}-\underbrace{\frac{2\pi}{3}\rho_1^3[1 - \cos\phi]}_{} = \frac{2\pi}{3}(\rho_2^3 - \rho_1^3)(1 - \cos\phi).$$

$$\big(\text{Volume of the larger wedge}\big) - \big(\text{Volume of the smaller wedge}\big)$$

The Mean Value Theorem, applied to the function ρ^3 on the interval $[\rho_1, \rho_2]$, guarantees that there is some $\rho \in [\rho_1, \rho_2]$ at which $\rho_2^3 - \rho_1^3 = 3\rho^2\Delta\rho$, where $\Delta\rho = \rho_2 - \rho_1$, so we can rewrite the volume of this "cupcake" as $2\pi\rho^2[1 - \cos\phi]\Delta\rho$.

- *Step 2 (cutting out the core of the "cupcake" to make a "ring"):* Now consider starting with a cupcake-like solid on which the side and central axis are separated by ϕ_2 radians. We can make a "ring" by cutting out a smaller cupcake-like solid that shares the same top, bottom and central axis, but has ϕ_1 radians between its side and central axis (where $\phi_1 < \phi_2$). The result is a "ring" (see Figure G.12) that has a volume of

$$\underbrace{2\pi\rho^2[1 - \cos\phi_2]\Delta\rho}_{} - \underbrace{2\pi\rho^2[1 - \cos\phi_1]\Delta\rho}_{} = 2\pi\rho^2[\cos\phi_1 - \cos\phi_2]\Delta\rho.$$

$$\big(\text{Volume of the bigger "cupcake"}\big) - \big(\text{Volume of the smaller "cupcake"}\big)$$

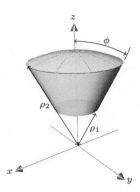

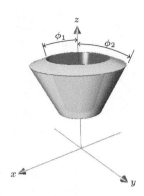

Figure G.11: Removing a smaller spherical wedge from a larger one results in a volume that looks like a "cupcake."

Figure G.12: The result of removing a smaller "cupcake" that shares the same top, bottom, and central axis.

The Mean Value Theorem, applied to the function $\cos\phi$ on the interval $[\phi_1, \phi_2]$, guarantees that there is some $\phi \in [\phi_1, \phi_2]$ at which $\cos\phi_1 - \cos\phi_2 = \sin(\phi)\,\Delta\phi$, where $\Delta\phi = \phi_2 - \phi_1$. So the volume of our solid can be written as $2\pi\rho^2\sin(\phi)\,\Delta\phi\,\Delta\rho$.

- *Step 3 (taking a segment of the "ring"):* Lastly, we make our spherical "box" by keeping only the portion of the ring in which $\theta \in [\theta_1, \theta_2]$. If we write $\Delta\theta = \theta_2 - \theta_1$, the fraction of the ring that we're selecting is $\Delta\theta/2\pi$, so its volume is

$$\left(2\pi\rho^2\sin(\phi)\,\Delta\phi\,\Delta\rho\right)\frac{\Delta\theta}{2\pi} = \rho^2\sin(\phi)\,\Delta\phi\,\Delta\rho\,\Delta\theta.$$

❖ End Notes for Chapter 15

In Section 15.9 we stated the Divergence Theorem, and in Section 15.10 you saw Stokes' Theorem. Here we prove provide proofs of those theorems in special (but common) cases.

▷ Proof of the Divergence Theorem

Since dot products distribute over sums, the surface integral

$$\iint_{\mathcal{S}} \mathbf{F} \cdot d\mathbf{S} = \iint_{\mathcal{S}} (L\mathbf{i} + M\mathbf{j} + N\mathbf{k}) \cdot \mathbf{n}\, dS$$

$$= \iint_{\mathcal{S}} L\mathbf{i}\cdot\mathbf{n} + M\mathbf{j}\cdot\mathbf{n} + N\mathbf{k}\cdot\mathbf{n}\, dS$$

$$= \iint_{\mathcal{S}} L\mathbf{i}\cdot\mathbf{n}\, dS + \iint_{\mathcal{S}} M\mathbf{j}\cdot\mathbf{n}\, dS + \iint_{\mathcal{S}} N\mathbf{k}\cdot\mathbf{n}\, dS. \qquad \text{(g.35)}$$

Similarly, we can write the triple integral as a sum of three integrals,

$$\iiint_{E} \nabla \cdot \mathbf{F}\, dV = \iiint_{E} L_x + M_y + N_z\, dV$$

$$= \iiint_{E} L_x\, dV + \iiint_{E} M_y\, dV + \iiint_{E} N_z\, dV, \qquad \text{(g.36)}$$

so we can prove the theorem by establishing that the corresponding integrals in equations (g.35) and (g.36) are equal. We'll begin by showing that

$$\int_{\mathcal{S}} N\mathbf{k}\cdot\mathbf{n}\, dS = \iiint_{E} N_z\, dV \qquad \text{(g.37)}$$

in the special case when E is a simple solid, by which we mean it's x-simple, and y-simple, *and* z-simple (see Figure G.13). The bounding surface of such a solid can be decomposed into three pieces: $\mathcal{S}_1$ is the graph of a function over a region R in the xy-plane, say $z = f(x, y)$, $\mathcal{S}_2$ is also the graph of a function over the same region R, say $z = g(x, y)$, and $\mathcal{S}_3$ is the vertical face that connects $\mathcal{S}_1$ and $\mathcal{S}_2$ (if there is one). Then

$$\iint_{\mathcal{S}} N\mathbf{k} \cdot \mathbf{n} \, dS = \iint_{\mathcal{S}_1} N\mathbf{k} \cdot \mathbf{n} \, dS + \iint_{\mathcal{S}_2} N\mathbf{k} \cdot \mathbf{n} \, dS + \iint_{\mathcal{S}_3} N\mathbf{k} \cdot \mathbf{n} \, dS$$

$$= \iint_{\mathcal{S}_1} N\mathbf{k} \cdot \mathbf{n} \, dS + \iint_{\mathcal{S}_2} N\mathbf{k} \cdot \mathbf{n} \, dS + 0 \qquad \text{(g.38)}$$

since $\mathbf{n}$ is orthogonal to $\mathbf{k}$ on the vertical surface $\mathcal{S}_3$. Without loss of generality, let's suppose that $f(x, y) \geq g(x, y)$ so that $\mathcal{S}_1$ is above $\mathcal{S}_2$. In Section 15.6 we saw that the flux of a vector field (in this case, $N\mathbf{k}$) through the positively oriented graph of a f is

$$\iint_{\mathcal{S}_1} N\mathbf{k} \cdot \mathbf{n} \, dS = \iint_R N(x, y, f(x, y))\mathbf{k} \cdot \frac{\mathbf{n}}{\|\mathbf{n}\|} \, \|\mathbf{n}\| \, dA$$

where $\mathbf{n} = \langle -f_x(x, y), -f_y(x, y), 1 \rangle$. The dot product of $\mathbf{n}$ with $\mathbf{k}$ reduces this integral to

$$\iint_{\mathcal{S}_1} N\mathbf{k} \cdot \mathbf{n} \, dS = \iint_R N(x, y, f(x, y)) \, dA.$$

Because $\mathcal{S}_2$ has a positive orientation with respect to the solid E, its normal vector points in a downward direction, $\mathbf{n} = \langle g_x(x, y), g_y(x, y), -1 \rangle$, so

$$\iint_{\mathcal{S}_2} N\mathbf{k} \cdot \mathbf{n} \, dS = \iint_R N(x, y, g(x, y))\mathbf{k} \cdot \frac{\mathbf{n}}{\|\mathbf{n}\|} \, \|\mathbf{n}\| \, dA = \iint_R -N(x, y, g(x, y)) \, dA.$$

So we can write equation (g.38) as

$$\iint_{\mathcal{S}} N\mathbf{k} \cdot \mathbf{n} \, dS = \iint_R N(x, y, f(x, y)) \, dA + \iint_R -N(x, y, g(x, y)) \, dA$$

$$= \iint_R N(x, y, f(x, y)) - N(x, y, g(x, y)) \, dA = \iint_R \int_{g(x,y)}^{f(x,y)} N_z \, dz \, dA.$$

Fubini's Theorem tells us that the iterated integral on the right-hand side of this equation is the same as the triple integral over E, so we have

$$\iint_{\mathcal{S}} N\mathbf{k} \cdot \mathbf{n} \, dS = \iiint_E N_z \, dV.$$

Because E is a simple solid, the equations

$$\int_{\mathcal{S}} L\mathbf{i} \cdot \mathbf{n} \, dS = \iiint_E L_x \, dV \quad \text{and} \quad \int_{\mathcal{S}} M\mathbf{j} \cdot \mathbf{n} \, dS = \iiint_E M_y \, dV$$

can be established in similar fashion (separating $\mathcal{S}$ into surfaces along which one variable is a function of the other two). This proves the result for solids such as cubes, tetrahedra, pyramids and the like. Moreover, the vast majority of solid regions that arise in applications can be sliced into simple regions, $E_1, E_2, \ldots, E_n$, and

$$\iiint_{E_k} \nabla \cdot \mathbf{F} \, dV = \iint_{\partial E_k} \mathbf{F} \cdot d\mathbf{S}$$

where ∂E_k denotes the boundary of E_k. Because the normal vectors on the surfaces of adjacent simple regions are antiparallel (see Figure G.14), the flux integrals across shared boundary faces sum to zero, leaving only the flux across $\mathcal{S}$. That is,

$$\iiint_E \nabla \cdot \mathbf{F} \, dV = \sum_{k=1}^{n} \iiint_{E_k} \nabla \cdot \mathbf{F} \, dV = \sum_{k=1}^{n} \iint_{\partial E_k} \mathbf{F} \cdot d\mathbf{S} = \iint_{\mathcal{S}} \mathbf{F} \cdot d\mathbf{S}. \qquad \blacksquare$$

The terms x-simple, y-simple, and z-simple were defined in Section 14.5.

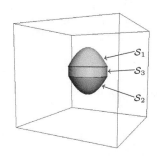

Figure G.13: The surface of a simple region. In this case, $\mathcal{S}_1$ and $\mathcal{S}_2$ are reflections of one another (both are elliptic paraboloids), but that's not necessary.

Figure G.14: Imagine these blocks as adjacent (touching, face-to-face). Because their normal vectors point in opposite directions on the shared face, the net flux across that boundary is 0.

▷ Proof of Stokes' Theorem

Stokes' Theorem!proof We prove Stokes' Theorem in the case when $\langle x(s,t),\, y(s,t),\, z(s,t)\rangle$ is a one-to-one, regular parameterization of $\mathcal{S}$ with continuous second partial derivatives on its parameter domain, R, which is a simply connected domain to which Green's Theorem applies.

We begin by examining the surface integral of $\mathrm{curl}(\mathbf{F}) \cdot d\mathbf{S}$ over $\mathcal{S}$. When $\mathbf{F} = \langle L, M, N\rangle$ we have $\mathrm{curl}(\mathbf{F}) = \langle N_y - M_z, L_z - N_x, M_x - L_y\rangle$, and $d\mathbf{S} = \mathbf{n}\, dS$, where

$$\mathbf{n} = \langle x_s, y_s, z_s\rangle \times \langle x_t, y_t, z_t\rangle = \langle z_t y_s - y_t z_s,\ x_t z_s - z_t x_s,\ y_t x_s - s_t y_s\rangle.$$

These facts allow us to write $\iint_{\mathcal{S}} \mathrm{curl}(\mathbf{F}) \cdot d\mathbf{S}$ as

$$\iint_{\mathcal{S}} \mathrm{curl}(\mathbf{F}) \cdot d\mathbf{S} = \iint_{R} \begin{bmatrix} N_y - M_z \\ L_z - N_x \\ M_x - L_y \end{bmatrix} \cdot \begin{bmatrix} z_t y_s - y_t z_s \\ x_t z_s - z_t x_s \\ y_t x_s - x_t y_s \end{bmatrix} dA. \tag{g.39}$$

Here we pause to clarify notation. The components of $\mathbf{F}$ (and their partial derivatives) depend on x, y, and z, which depend on s and t, so the term $N_y - M_z$ that you see in equation (g.39) is really

$$N_y\Big(x(s,t), y(s,t), z(s,t)\Big) - M_z\Big(x(s,t), y(s,t), z(s,t)\Big).$$

We have suppressed this chain of dependence in order to avoid notational clutter, and will continue to do so. In the exercise set you'll use the Chain Rule to show that the integral on the right-hand side of equation (g.39) reduces to

$$\iint_{R} \left[\frac{\partial L}{\partial s}\frac{\partial x}{\partial t} - \frac{\partial L}{\partial t}\frac{\partial x}{\partial s} + \frac{\partial M}{\partial s}\frac{\partial y}{\partial t} - \frac{\partial M}{\partial t}\frac{\partial y}{\partial s} + \frac{\partial N}{\partial s}\frac{\partial z}{\partial t} - \frac{\partial N}{\partial t}\frac{\partial z}{\partial s} \right] dA, \tag{g.40}$$

which we write as

$$\iint_{R} \left[\frac{\partial L}{\partial s}\frac{\partial x}{\partial t} - \frac{\partial L}{\partial t}\frac{\partial x}{\partial s} \right] dA + \iint_{R} \left[\frac{\partial M}{\partial s}\frac{\partial y}{\partial t} - \frac{\partial M}{\partial t}\frac{\partial y}{\partial s} \right] dA + \iint_{R} \left[\frac{\partial N}{\partial s}\frac{\partial z}{\partial t} - \frac{\partial N}{\partial t}\frac{\partial z}{\partial s} \right] dA.$$

Because the second partial derivatives of $x(s,t)$ are continuous, we know that $x_{st} = x_{ts}$, so the first of these double integrals is

$$\iint_{R} \left[\frac{\partial}{\partial s}\left(L\, \frac{\partial x}{\partial t} \right) - \frac{\partial}{\partial t}\left(L\, \frac{\partial x}{\partial s} \right) \right] dA.$$

> Use the Product Rule to calculate the derivatives.

According to Green's Theorem, this is the same as the line integral around the boundary of R,

$$\oint_{\partial R} \langle Lx_s, Lx_t\rangle \cdot \mathbf{T}\, d\ell,$$

where ∂R denotes the positively oriented boundary of R and $d\ell$ is the length element along it. Similarly,

> When we first saw the circulation form of Green's Theorem, we wrote the length element as ds. We're using $d\ell$ in this proof because the letter s is already serving as one of our parameters.

$$\iint_{R} \left[\frac{\partial M}{\partial s}\frac{\partial y}{\partial t} - \frac{\partial M}{\partial t}\frac{\partial y}{\partial s} \right] dA = \oint_{\partial R} \langle My_s, My_t\rangle \cdot \mathbf{T}\, d\ell$$

and

$$\iint_{R} \left[\frac{\partial N}{\partial s}\frac{\partial z}{\partial t} - \frac{\partial N}{\partial t}\frac{\partial z}{\partial s} \right] dA = \oint_{\partial R} \langle Nz_s, Nz_t\rangle \cdot \mathbf{T}\, d\ell.$$

Thus equation (g.39) becomes

$$\iint_{\mathcal{S}} \text{curl}(\mathbf{F}) \cdot d\mathbf{S} = \oint_{\partial R} \left(\langle Lx_s, Lx_t \rangle \cdot \mathbf{T} + \langle My_s, My_t \rangle \cdot \mathbf{T} + \langle Nz_s, Nz_t \rangle \cdot \mathbf{T} \right) d\ell$$

$$= \oint_{\partial R} \langle Lx_s + My_s + Nz_s, Lx_t + My_t + Nz_t \rangle \cdot \mathbf{T} \, d\ell \qquad \text{(g.41)}$$

> Reminder: the line integral over ∂R is happening in the parameter domain.

We finish the proof by showing that this is the same as the circulation of $\mathbf{F}$ around $\mathcal{C}$. Suppose $\mathbf{p}(\tau)$ is a smooth parameterization of ∂R when $a \leq \tau \leq b$. That is, the point at $\mathbf{p}(\tau) = \langle s(\tau), t(\tau) \rangle$ moves smoothly around ∂R in the st-plane as τ increases from $\tau = a$ to $\tau = b$, and $\|\mathbf{p}'(\tau)\| \neq 0$. Then

$$\mathbf{T} \, d\ell = \frac{\mathbf{p}'(\tau)}{\|\mathbf{p}'(\tau)\|} \|\mathbf{p}'(\tau)\| d\tau = \mathbf{p}'(\tau) \, d\tau = \left\langle \frac{ds}{d\tau}, \frac{dt}{d\tau} \right\rangle d\tau,$$

and equation (g.41) is, after performing the dot product and collecting like terms,

$$\iint_{\mathcal{S}} \text{curl}(\mathbf{F}) \cdot \mathbf{n} \, dS = \int_a^b \left[L \left(\frac{\partial x}{\partial s} \frac{ds}{d\tau} + \frac{\partial x}{\partial t} \frac{dt}{d\tau} \right) + M \left(\frac{\partial y}{\partial s} \frac{ds}{d\tau} + \frac{\partial y}{\partial t} \frac{dt}{d\tau} \right) + N \left(\frac{\partial z}{\partial s} \frac{ds}{d\tau} + \frac{\partial z}{\partial t} \frac{dt}{d\tau} \right) \right] d\tau$$

Since x depends on s and t, each of which depend on τ, the Chain Rule tells us that

$$\frac{dx}{d\tau} = \frac{\partial x}{\partial s} \frac{ds}{d\tau} + \frac{\partial x}{\partial t} \frac{dt}{d\tau}.$$

Similarly,

$$\frac{dy}{d\tau} = \frac{\partial y}{\partial s} \frac{ds}{d\tau} + \frac{\partial y}{\partial t} \frac{dt}{d\tau} \quad \text{and} \quad \frac{dz}{d\tau} = \frac{\partial z}{\partial s} \frac{ds}{d\tau} + \frac{\partial z}{\partial t} \frac{dt}{d\tau},$$

so equation (g.41) says that

$$\iint_{\mathcal{S}} \text{curl}(\mathbf{F}) \cdot d\mathbf{S} = \int_a^b \left[L \frac{dx}{d\tau} + M \frac{dy}{d\tau} + N \frac{dz}{d\tau} \right] d\tau = \int_a^b \langle L, M, N \rangle \cdot \langle x_\tau, y_\tau, z_\tau \rangle \, d\tau$$

$$= \int_a^b \mathbf{F} \cdot \frac{\langle x_\tau, y_\tau, z_\tau \rangle}{\|\langle x_\tau, y_\tau, z_\tau \rangle\|} \|\langle x_\tau, y_\tau, z_\tau \rangle\| \, d\tau = \int_{\mathcal{C}} \mathbf{F} \cdot \mathbf{T} \, d\ell. \qquad \blacksquare$$

Selected Answers

Section 11.1:

1 (a) **C**, **H** and **K**; (b) The pairs **A**, **I** and **D**, **G**. **5**

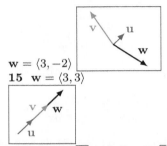

7

9

11

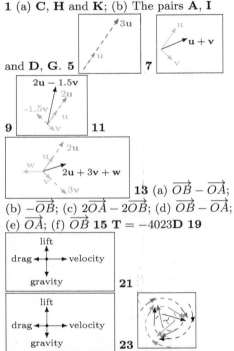

13 (a) $\overrightarrow{OB} - \overrightarrow{OA}$; (b) $-\overrightarrow{OB}$; (c) $2\overrightarrow{OA} - 2\overrightarrow{OB}$; (d) $\overrightarrow{OB} - \overrightarrow{OA}$; (e) $\overrightarrow{OA}$; (f) $\overrightarrow{OB}$ **15** $\mathbf{T} = -4023\mathbf{D}$ **19**

21

23

25 north pole **27** The planet Venus has a retrograde ("backwards") spin, so $\boldsymbol{\omega}_2$ points in the direction opposite of Earth's. The planet Uranus is "on its side," so $\boldsymbol{\omega}_7$ lies almost in the plane of the planets' orbits.

Section 11.2:

1 (a) $\mathbf{u} = 9\mathbf{i} + \mathbf{j}$; (b) $\mathbf{u} = \langle 9, 1 \rangle$ **3**

$\mathbf{u} = \langle 5, 3 \rangle$ **5**

$\mathbf{u} = \langle 2, -3 \rangle$ **7** $2\mathbf{i} + 4\mathbf{j}$

9 $-7\mathbf{i} + 4\mathbf{j}$ **11** $-2\mathbf{i} + 7\mathbf{j} + 8\mathbf{k}$ **13**

$\mathbf{w} = \langle 3, -2 \rangle$
15 $\mathbf{w} = \langle 3, 3 \rangle$

17 $\|\mathbf{u}\| = 2\sqrt{17}$ **19** $\|\mathbf{u}\| = 5\sqrt{2}$
21 $\|\mathbf{u}\| = 2\sqrt{7}$ **23** $\|\mathbf{u}\| = \sqrt{6}$ **25** $\sqrt{34}$ units
27 $\sqrt{3}$ units **29** $\langle -3/5, 4/5 \rangle$ **31**
$\langle 1/\sqrt{26}, 4/\sqrt{26}, 3/\sqrt{26} \rangle$ **33** (a)
$\mathbf{v} = \frac{30}{\sqrt{58}}\mathbf{i} + \frac{70}{\sqrt{58}}\mathbf{j}$; (b) $\mathbf{v} = \left\langle \frac{30}{\sqrt{58}}, \frac{70}{\sqrt{58}} \right\rangle$
35 $\mathbf{v} = \frac{1}{\sqrt{2}}\mathbf{i} + \frac{2}{\sqrt{2}}\mathbf{j} + \frac{3}{\sqrt{2}}\mathbf{k}$; (b)
$\mathbf{v} = \left\langle \frac{1}{\sqrt{2}}, \frac{2}{\sqrt{2}}, \frac{3}{\sqrt{2}} \right\rangle$ **37** (a)
$\mathbf{v} = -\frac{\sqrt{3}}{\sqrt{5}}\mathbf{i} - \frac{2\sqrt{3}}{\sqrt{5}}\mathbf{j}$; (b) $\mathbf{v} = \left\langle -\frac{\sqrt{3}}{\sqrt{5}}, -\frac{2\sqrt{3}}{\sqrt{5}} \right\rangle$
39 (a) $\mathbf{v} = -\frac{9\sqrt{62}}{31}\mathbf{i} + \frac{6\sqrt{62}}{31}\mathbf{j} + \frac{7\sqrt{62}}{62}\mathbf{k}$; (b)
$\mathbf{v} = \left\langle -\frac{9\sqrt{62}}{31}, \frac{6\sqrt{62}}{31}, \frac{7\sqrt{62}}{62} \right\rangle$ **41** $\langle -3, 1 \rangle$

$\langle -1, -1 \rangle$

43 $\langle -8, 1, -5 \rangle$ **45** $k = \frac{1}{2\sqrt{5}}$ **47** $(-2, -1, 6)$

49

Speed is $2\sqrt{26} \approx 10.2$ m/s. **51** 3N of force in the positive x-direction, and 18N of force in the positive y-direction.

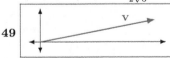

53

55

57 (b)

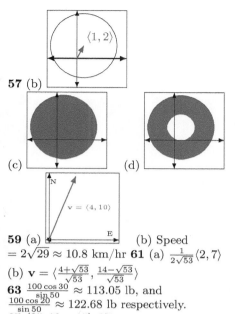

(c)   (d)

59 (a)   (b) Speed
$= 2\sqrt{29} \approx 10.8$ km/hr **61** (a) $\frac{1}{2\sqrt{53}}\langle 2, 7\rangle$

(b) $\mathbf{v} = \langle \frac{4+\sqrt{53}}{\sqrt{53}}, \frac{14-\sqrt{53}}{\sqrt{53}} \rangle$

63 $\frac{100\cos 30}{\sin 50} \approx 113.05$ lb, and
$\frac{100\cos 20}{\sin 50} \approx 122.68$ lb respectively.
65 $\langle 25, 10, -15\rangle$ **67**

$$\frac{80}{\sqrt{15625+\sin^2 15^\circ}} \begin{bmatrix} 75 \\ 100 \\ \sin 15^\circ \end{bmatrix} \approx 0.64 \begin{bmatrix} 75 \\ 100 \\ 0.26 \end{bmatrix}$$

69 (a) $\mathbf{F}_g = \langle 0, -9.8m\rangle$ (b)
$\mathbf{F}_c = \langle \frac{|q_1 q_2|}{4\pi\varepsilon r^2}, 0 \rangle$ (c)
$\mathbf{F}_g + \mathbf{F}_c = \langle \frac{|q_1 q_2|}{4\pi\varepsilon r^2}, -9.8m \rangle$ (d)
$\theta = \sin^{-1}\left(\frac{|q_1 q_2|}{\sqrt{(q_1 q_2)^2 + (39.2m\pi\varepsilon r^2)^2}} \right)$ (e)
The tension force; $\langle -\frac{|q_1 q_2|}{4\pi\varepsilon r^2}, 9.8m\rangle$ (e) The
tension force; $\langle -\frac{|q_1 q_2|}{4\pi\varepsilon r^2}, 9.8m \rangle$

Section 11.3:
1 $16\sqrt{3}$ **3** 0.25 **5** -11 **7** 68 **9** 3 **11** 22 **13**
$\frac{\pi}{2}$ radians **15** $\theta = \arccos\left(\frac{11}{\sqrt{146}} \right) \approx 0.4275$
radians **17** $\theta = \frac{2\pi}{3}$ **19** $\frac{\pi}{2}$ radians **21** $\sqrt{53}$
23 $\sqrt{26}$ **25** $\sqrt{145}$ **27** $\mathbf{v}, \mathbf{w}$ **29** $\mathbf{u}, \mathbf{v}$ and
$\mathbf{u}, \mathbf{w}$. **31** None **33** (a) $\text{comp}_{\mathbf{v}}\mathbf{u} = 3$, (b)
$\text{proj}_{\mathbf{v}}\mathbf{u} = 3\mathbf{i}$ **35** (a) $\text{comp}_{\mathbf{v}}\mathbf{u} = \frac{12}{\sqrt{26}}$, (b)
$\text{proj}_{\mathbf{v}}\mathbf{u} = \frac{6}{13}\langle 5, 1\rangle$ **37** (a) $\text{comp}_{\mathbf{v}}\mathbf{u} = -\frac{25}{290}$,
(b) $\text{proj}_{\mathbf{v}}\mathbf{u} = \frac{5}{58}\langle 1, 17\rangle$ **39** (a)
$\text{comp}_{\mathbf{v}}\mathbf{u} = -4$, (b) $\text{proj}_{\mathbf{v}}\mathbf{u} = -4\mathbf{k}$ **41** (a)
$\text{comp}_{\mathbf{v}}\mathbf{u} = \frac{41}{\sqrt{14}}$, (b) $\text{proj}_{\mathbf{v}}\mathbf{u} = \frac{41}{14}\langle 1, 2, 3\rangle$
43 (a) $\text{comp}_{\mathbf{v}}\mathbf{u} = \frac{73\sqrt{54}}{54}$, (b)
$\text{proj}_{\mathbf{v}}\mathbf{u} = \frac{73}{54}\langle 1, 7, 2\rangle$ **45** $\langle 4, -3\rangle$ or $\langle -4, 3\rangle$
47 $\langle b, -a\rangle$ or $\langle -b, a\rangle$ **49** $\langle 1, 2, 0\rangle$ and
$\langle 0, 3, 1\rangle$ and many others. **51** (a) any
non-zero multiple of $\langle 1, -1\rangle$, (b) $a = 5/2$,
$b = -1/2$ **53** (a) any non-zero multiple of
$\langle 1, 4\rangle$, (b) $a = -5/68$, $b = -7/34$ **55**
$\hat{\mathbf{u}} \cdot \hat{\mathbf{v}} = \frac{\sqrt{3}}{2}$ **57** The angle between the
vectors is obtuse. **59** (a) They lie on the
vertical line $x = 3$. (b) They all line on
the vertical line $x = 6$. (c) The vectors
have the form $\mathbf{r} = c\mathbf{i} + k\mathbf{j}$ for $k \in \mathbb{R}$. **61**

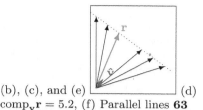

(b), (c), and (e)   (d)
$\text{comp}_{\mathbf{v}}\mathbf{r} = 5.2$, (f) Parallel lines **63**

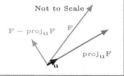
θ must be obtuse. **65**

$k = 2 \pm 2\sqrt{3}$ **69** (a) $m = \frac{y_1}{x_1}$, (b)
$\mathbf{r} = \langle x_1, y_1\rangle$, (c) $\langle y_1, -x_1\rangle$ or $\langle -y_1, x_1\rangle$,
(d) $m = -\frac{x_1}{y_1}$, (e) Reversed and one is
negated, (f) negative reciprocals **71** (a)
$\|\mathbf{r}_1\|$ is the distance from the center of the
circle to (x_1, y_1) which lies on the circle.
So, $\|\mathbf{r}_1\| = r$, (b) $\langle -y_1, -x_1\rangle$ **73** (a)
$\text{comp}_{\mathbf{i}}\mathbf{v} = 2$, $\text{comp}_{\mathbf{j}}\mathbf{v} = 3$ **77** (a)

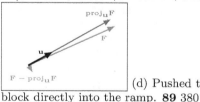

79 (a) 494, total number
of items sold during the month; (b) 2050,
revenue from the sale of one of each type
of item; (c) 164200, total revenue from
the month at that particular store from
the sales of those three items. **81**
$\frac{4}{5\sqrt{17}} \approx 0.194$ hours or $\frac{48}{\sqrt{17}} \approx 11.64$
minutes **83** 0.0435 hours or approximately
2.61 minutes. **85** (a) $\frac{365\sqrt{34}}{17} \approx 125.19$
newtons, (b) $\frac{1095\sqrt{34}}{34} \approx 187.791$ joules, (c)
$\mathbf{F} - \text{proj}_{\mathbf{u}}\mathbf{F} = \langle -\frac{465}{17}, \frac{775}{17} \rangle$

(d) $\text{proj}_{\mathbf{u}}\mathbf{F}$ lifts
the block directly away from the ramp.
87 (a) $\text{comp}_{\mathbf{u}}\mathbf{F} = 100(1)(\cos 5^\circ) \approx 99.6$
newtons, (b) $150\cos 5^\circ \approx 149.4$ joules, (c)
$\mathbf{F} - \text{proj}_{\mathbf{u}}\mathbf{F} =$
$25\langle \cos 25 - \sqrt{3}\sin 25, 3\sin 25 - \sqrt{3}\cos 25\rangle$

(d) Pushed the
block directly into the ramp. **89** 380
joules **91** $\frac{610,000}{\sqrt{5017}} \approx 8612$ joules **93** (a)
$\hat{\mathbf{v}} = \langle \sin\theta, -\cos\theta\rangle$, (b)
$\text{comp}_{\hat{\mathbf{v}}}\mathbf{F}_g = mg\cos\theta$, (c) Recall that
$\cos 0 = 1$ so all of $\mathbf{F}_g$ points in the $\hat{\mathbf{v}}$
direction. As θ increases, what happens
to $\cos\theta$? (d) Up the plane, (e)
$\text{comp}_{-\hat{\mathbf{u}}}\mathbf{F}_g = mg\sin\theta$ is the amount of
force due to gravity that pushes the block

down the plane, (f) If the component of force due to gravity that is pulling the block down the plane is greater than the friction force that opposes the motion, the block will slide. **95** $2\sqrt{10} \approx 6.3$ yards per second.

Section 11.4:

1 $\|\mathbf{u} \times \mathbf{v}\| = 16$, points into the page **3** $\|\mathbf{u} \times \mathbf{v}\| = \frac{\sqrt{3}}{4}$, points into the page **5** $\langle -2, -8, 3\rangle$ **7** $\langle 0, 0, 0\rangle$ **9** $\langle 6, -5, 23\rangle$ **11** 1 **13** -20 **15** (a) correct, (b) $\mathbf{i} \times \mathbf{k} = -\mathbf{j}$, (c) $\mathbf{j} \times \mathbf{i} = -\mathbf{k}$ **17** $\langle x, 1, 0\rangle$ **19** $\mathbf{u} \times \mathbf{v} = 0$ **21** The scalar triple product must be positive to be a volume. **23** Always true. Consider the signs of $|\mathbf{u} \cdot \mathbf{v}|$ and $\|\mathbf{u} \times \mathbf{v}\|$. **25** $\|\mathbf{u}\| = \sqrt{29}$ **27** 10 units^2 **29** 0 units^2 **31** $3\sqrt{66} \approx 24.37$ units^2 **33** 7 units^3 **35** 19 units^3 **37** 0 units^3 **39** $2\left(\sqrt{30} + \sqrt{29} + \sqrt{74}\right) \approx 38.9$ units^2 **41** $2\left(3\sqrt{2} + 2\sqrt{3}\right) \approx 15.4$ units^2 **43** Coplanar **45** Not Coplanar **47** No. **49** (b) Directed out of the page, (c) Directed into the page **51** $\mathbf{F} = 9.6 \times 10^{-20}\langle 24, -18, -5\rangle$ **53** (a) east (b) west **55** (a) 0.403113 (b) 0.58 meters **57** $\ell = \langle 148, 4, 100\rangle$ **59** $\mathbf{u} \times \mathbf{v} = \langle u_2 v_3 - u_3 v_2, u_3 v_1 - u_1 v_3, u_1 v_2 - u_2 v_1\rangle$

Section 11.5:

1 $\frac{x-14}{3} = \frac{y}{3} = -\frac{z+9}{8}$ **3** $\frac{x-1}{4} = \frac{y-1}{7} = -\frac{z+2}{5}$ **5** $y = -11$, and $\frac{1-x}{4} = \frac{z-3}{5}$ **7** $x = 14$ and $\frac{y+3}{3} = \frac{z+11}{2}$ OR $x = 14$ and $\frac{y}{3} = \frac{z+9}{2}$ **9** $\frac{x-4}{1} = \frac{13-y}{4} = \frac{z+1}{2}$ OR $\frac{x-5}{1} = \frac{9-y}{4} = \frac{z-1}{2}$ **11** Parallel **13** Skew **15** $\mathbf{r} = \begin{bmatrix} 1 - 4t/\sqrt{29} \\ 6 + 10t/\sqrt{29} \end{bmatrix}$ **17**

$\mathbf{r} = \begin{bmatrix} 3 + 28t/\sqrt{278} \\ -1 - 8t/\sqrt{278} \\ 10 + 60t/\sqrt{278} \end{bmatrix}$ **19**

$\mathbf{r} = \begin{bmatrix} t \\ 8 + 4t \\ 13 - 17t \end{bmatrix}$ **21** $\mathbf{r} = \begin{bmatrix} 2 + t \\ -3 + \frac{1}{2}t \\ 1 - \frac{5}{2}t \end{bmatrix}$

23 $\mathbf{r} = \begin{bmatrix} 1 + 4t \\ -2 - 3t \end{bmatrix}$ **25**

$\mathbf{r} = \begin{bmatrix} 4 + 6t/\sqrt{291} \\ -2 + 78t/\sqrt{291} \\ 9 + 66t/\sqrt{291} \end{bmatrix}$ **27**

$12x + 22y + 70z = 0$ **29** $2x + 2y + 7z = 17$ **31** $-2x + y + 8z = 136$ **33** $-10x + 17y - 2z = -94$ **35** $37x - 6y + 10z = 130$ **37** $-71x - 14y + 4z = -140$ **39** $x - 3y + 5z = 6$ **41** $\frac{21}{\sqrt{26}}$ **43** $\frac{6}{\sqrt{14}}$ **45** $\sqrt{\frac{249}{5}}$ **47** $15x + 10y - 12z = 79$ **49** $10x - 5y - 3z = 8$ **51** $2x - 5y + 6z = 14$ **53** $x + y + z = 10.5$ **55** (a) initial position at $t = 0$, (b) velocity in the $\mathbf{i}$ and $\mathbf{j}$ directions. **57** $\mathbf{r} = \langle 4 - \sqrt{5}t, 5 + \sqrt{5}t\rangle$ **59** b indicates the rate of change in the $\mathbf{k}$

direction. **61** (a) Plane passes through the origin. (b) increasing d moves the plane in the direction of $\mathbf{n}$, but the orientation does not change. **63** Rotates the plane about the vertical line through $\left(\frac{\sqrt{2}}{2}, \frac{\sqrt{2}}{2}\right)$. **65** $\theta = \arccos\left(\frac{19\sqrt{2}}{\sqrt{1113}}\right)$ **67** $\theta = \frac{\sqrt{3}}{2}$ **69** Looking at the planes "edge

on" **71** (a) $\frac{x-3}{2} = \frac{y-2}{2} = \frac{z-4}{7}$ (b) $y = x - 1$, $z = 7x - 17$ (c) $x = -\frac{203}{57}$ (d) $y = \frac{82}{57}$, $z = \frac{116}{57}$, (e) $\frac{16}{\sqrt{57}}$ **73** (a) $\mathbf{r}(t) = \langle 2t - 3, 2t + 2, 7t + 4\rangle$, (b) $t = -\frac{16}{57}$, (c) $\left(-\frac{203}{57}, \frac{82}{57}, \frac{116}{57}\right)$ **75** (c) the line is parallel to the xy-plane, (d) $(8, -5, 0)$, (e) $\langle 55, -38, -8\rangle$, (f) $\frac{x-8}{55} = -\frac{x+5}{38} = -\frac{x}{8}$, (g) $\frac{x-29/38}{55} = -\frac{y}{38} = -\frac{z-20/19}{8}$; no; no. **77** $-\frac{x}{28} = \frac{y+9/14}{98}$, $z = -\frac{6}{7}$ **79** (a) $\mathbf{n} = \langle 1, 3\rangle$, (b) any nonzero multiple of $\langle 3, -1\rangle$, (c) 1, 1, 0 (d) $a = -2\sqrt{10}$, $b = \sqrt{10}$, (e) and (f) (below), (g) $\tilde{\mathbf{v}} = \langle 5, 5\rangle$

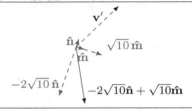

81 $\langle 109, -44, 202\rangle$ **83** $\mathbf{r}(t) = \left\langle \left(\frac{19}{45}t + 45\right)\cos(39°), \left(\frac{19}{45}t + 45\right)\sin(39°)\right\rangle$ **85** $103x + 98y + 500z \geq 3000$, $89x + 8.4y + 174z \geq 90$, $0.78x + 0.33y + 0.65z \geq 15$ **87** (a) $x + y + z = 10{,}000$, (b) plane, (c) shifts along the vector $\langle 1, 1, 1\rangle$ **89** $x + 3y - 2z = 0$

Chapter 11 Review:

1 F **3** T **5** T **7** T **9** F **11** F **13** F **15** T **17** F **19** T **21** T **23** (c) and (d) **25** (d) **27** (d) **29** (e) **31** (a) and (d) **33** (d) **35** (a) $\mathbf{u} \cdot \mathbf{v}$ is a scalar, not a vector; (b) $\mathbf{u}$ is a vector, not a scalar **37** $\mathbf{u} = 2\mathbf{v}$ **39** (a) The angle between $\hat{\mathbf{u}}$ and $\mathbf{v}$ is $\theta = \pi/3$, (b) Similarly, $\pi/3 \leq \theta \leq \pi/2$ **41** $\left\langle -\frac{65}{\sqrt{170}}, \frac{5}{\sqrt{170}}\right\rangle$ **43** (a) $\mathbf{v} \cdot \mathbf{w} = 0$; (b) $a = {}^{14}/_{17}$ and $b = -{}^{5}/_{17}$ **45** any scaled versions of $\langle 8, -3\rangle$ or $\langle -8, 3\rangle$ **47** 19 square units **51** $29x - 22y - 12z = -15$ **53** $-\frac{8}{5}\langle 1, -2\rangle$ **55** (a) and (d) Definition of an altitude, (g) vectors coincide with the altitudes, (i) $\overrightarrow{OD} - \overrightarrow{OB}$ lies on the altitude. **57** (b) We need to work with the *direction* of the point's position vector, but not it's

magnitude. **63** $\frac{x-3}{-7} = \frac{x-4}{-3} = \frac{x+10}{12}$ **65**
$-3x + 5y + z = -16$ **67** $2x + y - 2z = 0$

Section 12.1:

1 $\mathbf{r}(t) = \frac{1}{9}t^3 \langle 2, 2, 1 \rangle$ **3**
$\mathbf{r}(t) = \langle 3 + \frac{\sqrt{24}}{256}e^{5t}, 1, 4 + \frac{1}{25}e^{5t} \rangle$ **5**
$\mathbf{r}(t) = \langle -1, 10, 3 \rangle + \frac{\arctan t}{\sqrt{29}} \langle 0, 5, -2 \rangle$ **7**
$\mathbf{r}(t) = \langle 8\cos(2\pi t), 8\sin(2\pi t), 12t \rangle$ **9**
$\mathbf{r}(t) = \langle 16\cos(6\pi t), t, 16\sin(6\pi t) \rangle$ **11**
$\mathbf{r}(z) = \left(1 + \frac{7}{3}z\right)\cos\left(\frac{4\pi}{7}z\right)\mathbf{i} +$
$\left(1 + \frac{7}{3}z\right)\sin\left(\frac{4\pi}{7}z\right)\mathbf{j} + z\mathbf{k}$ **13** $\mathbf{r}(t) =$
$-6t\mathbf{i} + 3e^{-6t}\cos(10\pi t)\mathbf{j} + 3e^{-6t}\sin(10\pi t)\mathbf{k}$
15 $\mathbf{r}(t) = 45\cos(39°)$
$\cos(1.5t)\mathbf{i} + 45\cos(39°)\sin(1.5t)\mathbf{j} +$
$45\cos(39°)\sin(1.5t)\mathbf{k}$ (all trigonometric
arguments in degrees) **17** (a) start
slowing at $T = 50$ seconds; (b)
$\mathbf{r}(t) = f(t)\langle\cos(39°), 0, \sin(39°)\rangle$ where f
is the function defined piecewise as
follows:
$f(t) = \frac{3}{20}t^2 + \frac{15}{8\pi^2}\cos(0.4\pi t) + 45 - \frac{15}{8\pi^2}$
when $t \in [0,5]$, $f(t) = 48.75 + 1.5(t-5)$
when $t \in [5,50]$, and $f(t) = 120 - \frac{3}{20}(55 - t)^2 - \frac{15}{8\pi^2}\cos\left(0.4\pi(55-t)\right) + \frac{15}{8\pi^2}$ when
$t \in [50,55]$. **19**
$\mathbf{r}(t) = (500t - 18\sin\pi t)\mathbf{i} + (30 - 18\cos\pi t)\mathbf{j}$
cm **21** $\mathbf{r}(t) =$
$\mathbf{u}(t) - 1.1\sin\left(\frac{15\pi}{7}t\right)\mathbf{i} - 1.1\cos\left(\frac{15\pi}{7}t\right)\mathbf{j}$
(assuming that the distance from the
bottom of his foot to his ankle is 10 cm)
23 (a)
$\mathbf{r}(\theta) = \left(\frac{R+R\theta}{\sqrt{2}} + R\cos\left(\frac{5\pi}{4} - \theta\right)\right)\mathbf{i} +$
$\left(\frac{R-R\theta}{\sqrt{2}} + R\sin\left(\frac{5\pi}{4} - \theta\right)\right)\mathbf{j}$; (b)
$\mathbf{r}(t) = \left(\frac{R+10\pi Rt}{\sqrt{2}} + R\cos\left(\frac{5\pi}{4} - 10\pi t\right)\right)\mathbf{i} +$
$\left(\frac{R-10\pi Rt}{\sqrt{2}} + R\sin\left(\frac{5\pi}{4} - 10\pi t\right)\right)\mathbf{j}$ **25** (a)
$\mathbf{r}_1(t) = \cos(8\pi t)\mathbf{i} + \sin(8\pi t)\mathbf{j}$; (b)
$\mathbf{r}_2(t) = 1.2t$; (c)
$\mathbf{r}(t) = \cos(8\pi t)\mathbf{i} + \sin(8\pi t)\mathbf{j} + 1.25t$
parameterizes a helix **27** Linear decrease
in y, sinusoidal increase/decrease in x as
seen below

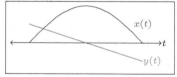

Section 12.2:

1 $\langle 2/5, 4/39 \rangle$ **3** $\langle -1/21, 0, -2/\pi \rangle$ **5** does not
exist because the cosine does not
converge to a particular value as $t \to \infty$ **7**
$\mathbf{k}$ **9** $\mathbf{r}(0) = \mathbf{i}$, $\mathbf{r}'(0) = 3\mathbf{j}$, $\mathbf{r}''(0) = 2\mathbf{i} + 6\mathbf{j}$
are drawn below

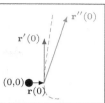

11 $\mathbf{r}(c) = \mathbf{i}$, $\mathbf{r}'(c) = -2\mathbf{j}$, $\mathbf{r}''(c) = -4\mathbf{i}$ are
drawn below

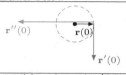

13 $\mathbf{r}(c) = \langle 1, -1 \rangle$, $\mathbf{r}'(c) = \mathbf{0}$, $\mathbf{r}''(c) = \langle 1, 4 \rangle$
are drawn below

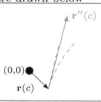

15 $18\mathbf{i} + (7 + e^2)\mathbf{j} + 11\mathbf{k}$ **17**
$324\mathbf{i} + 15e^3\mathbf{j} + 27\mathbf{k}$ **19** $124.5 + 17e^{1.5}$ **21**
846 **23** 0 **25** $\langle 6, 20, 32 \rangle$ **27** $\langle 3\sqrt{3}, -4/\pi \rangle$ **29**
$(\ln(4) - 1)\mathbf{i} + (1/\pi)\mathbf{j} + \mathbf{k}$ **31**
$\mathbf{r}(t) = \left(\frac{1}{6}\exp(3t^2) + \frac{11}{6}\right)\mathbf{i} + \left(1 + \frac{1}{7}t^7 - \frac{1}{2}t^2\right)\mathbf{j} - \left(\frac{55+\cos 8t}{8}\right)\mathbf{k}$ **33**
$\mathbf{r}(t) = (t\arctan(t) - 0.5\ln(t^2 + 1) + 3)\mathbf{i} + (0.5t^2 + t + 1)\mathbf{j} + \left(\frac{1}{9}\sin(9t) - 1\right)\mathbf{k}$ **35**
$(4t^2 + t)\mathbf{i} + \frac{1}{13}e^{2t}\left(2\sin 3t - 3\cos 3t\right)\mathbf{j} + (t^3 - 4t^2)\mathbf{k} + \mathbf{c}$ **37**
$\mathbf{v}(t) = -\ln|1 + t|\mathbf{i} + \arctan(t)\mathbf{j} + \frac{1}{2}\left(\sec t\tan t - \ln|\sec t + \tan t|\right)\mathbf{k} + \mathbf{c}$ **39**

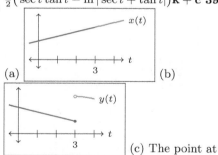

(a) (b)

(c) The point at
$\mathbf{r}(t)$ moves smoothly from left-to-right,
but teleports in the y-direction at time
$t = 3$, as shown below.

41 (b) As time evolves forward, the point
at $\mathbf{r}(t)$ descends toward the horizontal
line $y = e^{-4}$, and moves arbitrarily far to
the right. The line $y = 4$ is a kind of
"horizontal asymptote" for the path
followed by $\mathbf{r}(t)$. **43** (a) The point at $\mathbf{r}(t)$

teleports among the points shown on the square below. It stays at each red point for an interval of time, but is at each blue point for only an instant (e.g., $\mathbf{r}(t)$ is at the point $(0,1)$ when $t = \frac{1}{2}$ but is at $(1,1)$ before that [while $0 < t < \frac{1}{2}$] and is at $(-1,1)$ after that [while $\frac{1}{2} < t^2/3$)]; (b) at odd multiples of $\frac{1}{2}$ and even multiples of $\frac{1}{3}$

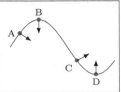

45 $\langle 60, 80 \rangle$ **47** $\left(\frac{e^4 - 1}{4} \right) \mathbf{i} + \left(\frac{e^5 - 1}{5} \right) \mathbf{j} + \left(\frac{e^6 - 1}{6} \right) \mathbf{k}$ **49** (a) $\mathbf{v} = (\sqrt{2}/2)\mathbf{i} - (\sqrt{2}/2)\mathbf{j}$ and $\mathbf{a} = -(\sqrt{2}/2)\mathbf{i} - (\sqrt{2}/2)\mathbf{j}$; (b) right **51** (a) $\mathbf{v} = \langle -1, 1 \rangle$ and $\mathbf{a} = \langle 6, 2 \rangle$; (b) right **53** (b) The object is at the same location at those times. **55** $\langle 29.5, 13.5 \rangle$ **57**

$\mathbf{r}(t) = e^{6t}\mathbf{i} + e^{6t}\mathbf{j}$ **59** (b) the should be orthogonal; (c) $\mathbf{r}(t) \cdot \mathbf{r}'(t) = 0$ at all t **61** (a) $\|\mathbf{r}(t)\|$ is an underestimate of the value of the portfolio (the actual value is $x + y + z$); (b) it's increasing; (c) Sure. $\frac{d}{dt}\|\mathbf{r}(t)\| = \frac{1}{\|\mathbf{r}(t)\|}\mathbf{r}(t) \cdot \mathbf{r}'(t)$ can be positive even if $z'(t) < 0$, provided that $x'(t)$ and $y'(t)$ are large enough that the angle between $\mathbf{r}$ and $\mathbf{r}'$ is acute.

Section 12.3:

1 $\mathbf{T}(t) = \langle 3\sqrt{73}/73, 8\sqrt{73}/73 \rangle$ **3** $\mathbf{T}(t) = \langle \sin 5t, \cos 5t \rangle$ **5** $\mathbf{T}(t) = |\cos t| \tan(t)\mathbf{j} + |\cos t|\mathbf{k}$ **7** no ($r'(t)$ is continuous but $\mathbf{r}'(0) = \mathbf{0}$) **9** yes **11** no ($r'(t)$ is continuous but $\mathbf{r}'(0) = \mathbf{0}$) **13** $4\sqrt{5}$ **15** $2\sqrt{89}$ **17** e **19** 0 **21** $240(233)^{-3/2}$ **23** $9(74)^{-3/2}$ **25** 0 **27** 1 **29** $e(1 + e^2)^{-3/2}$ **31** $\mathbf{r}(s) = \left(4 + \frac{3s}{\sqrt{73}}\right)\mathbf{i} + \left(-1 + \frac{8s}{\sqrt{73}}\right)\mathbf{j}$ **33** $\mathbf{r}(s) = \left[\frac{s + \sqrt{s^2 + 4}}{2} + \frac{2}{s + \sqrt{s^2 + 4}}\right]\mathbf{i} + \left[2\ln\left(\frac{s + \sqrt{s^2 + 4}}{2}\right) - 3 \right]\mathbf{j}$

35 $\mathbf{r}(s) = 4\left[\frac{1}{6}\sqrt{\frac{1}{4} + 12s} - \frac{1}{12}\right]^{3/2}\mathbf{i} + \left[5 + 3\left(\frac{1}{6}\sqrt{\frac{1}{4} + 12s} - \frac{1}{12}\right)^2\right]\mathbf{j} + \left[\frac{1}{2}\sqrt{\frac{1}{4} + 12s} - \frac{33}{4}\right]\mathbf{k}$

37 (a) it's a line; (b) it should be 0; (c) 0 **39** your friend made the mistake (curvature cannot be negative) **41** (b) max $\|\mathbf{r}(t)\| = a$ and min $\|\mathbf{r}(t)\| = b$; (d) $ab/\sqrt{a^2 \sin^2 t + b^2 \cos^2 t}$ **43** (a) increasing α results in more coils per unit along the z-axis, but increasing β results in fewer **45** (a) $\mathbf{r}'(t) = \langle 2t, -3t^2 \rangle$ has continuous component functions; (b) not smooth because $\mathbf{r}'(0) = \mathbf{0}$; (c) see plot below, **47** $\frac{1}{37500}\left(2501^{3/2} - 1\right) \approx 3.34$ miles **49** (b) $R = \frac{m\|\mathbf{v}_\perp\|^2}{\omega c}$; (c) $\mathbf{r}_\perp(t) = \frac{mv_2^2}{\omega c}\cos\left(\frac{\omega c}{mv_2}t\right)\mathbf{i} + \frac{mv_2^2}{\omega c}\sin\left(\frac{\omega c}{mv_2}t\right)\mathbf{j}$; (d) $\mathbf{r}(t) = \frac{mv_2^2}{\omega c}\cos\left(\frac{\omega c}{mv_2}t\right)\mathbf{i} + \frac{mv_2^2}{\omega c}\sin\left(\frac{\omega c}{mv_2}t\right)\mathbf{j} + (v_3 t - 4.9t^2)\mathbf{k}$ until $t = v_3/4.9$

Section 12.4:

1 $a_\mathrm{T} = 430(145)^{-1/2}$ and $a_\mathrm{N} = 60(145)^{-1/2}$ **3** $a_\mathrm{T} = -\pi^3(2 + \pi^2)^{-1/2}$ and $a_\mathrm{N} = \sqrt{2\left(1 + \frac{\pi^4}{2 + \pi^2}\right)}$

5 $\mathbf{T} = \mathbf{j}, \mathbf{N} = \frac{\sqrt{2}}{2}\mathbf{i} + \frac{\sqrt{2}}{2}\mathbf{k}, \mathbf{B} = \frac{\sqrt{2}}{2}\mathbf{i} - \frac{\sqrt{2}}{2}\mathbf{k}$ **7** $\mathbf{T} = \frac{2}{\sqrt{13}}\mathbf{i} - \frac{3}{\sqrt{13}}\mathbf{k}$, $\mathbf{B} = \frac{3}{\sqrt{2317}}\mathbf{i} - \frac{48}{\sqrt{2317}}\mathbf{j} + \frac{2}{\sqrt{2317}}\mathbf{k}$, $\mathbf{N} = \frac{144}{\sqrt{30121}}\mathbf{i} + \frac{13}{\sqrt{30121}}\mathbf{j} + \frac{96}{\sqrt{30121}}\mathbf{k}$ **9** $\mathbf{T}(t) = \frac{3t^2}{\sqrt{1 + 9t^4}}\mathbf{i} + \frac{1}{\sqrt{1 + 9t^4}}\mathbf{j}$, $\mathbf{N}(t) = \frac{1}{\sqrt{1 + 9t^4}}\mathbf{i} - \frac{3t^2}{\sqrt{1 + 9t^4}}\mathbf{j}, \mathbf{B}(t) = -\mathbf{k}$

11 $\mathbf{T}(t) = \frac{t}{f(t)}\mathbf{i} + \frac{12t^3}{f(t)}\mathbf{j} + \frac{1}{f(t)}\mathbf{k}$ where $f(t) = \sqrt{1 + t^2 + 144t^6}$, $\mathbf{B}(t) = -\frac{36t^2}{q(t)}\mathbf{i} + \frac{1}{q(t)}\mathbf{j} + \frac{24t^3}{q(t)}\mathbf{k}$ where $q(t) = \sqrt{1 + 1296t^4 + 576t^6}$, $\mathbf{N}(t) = \frac{1 - 288t^3}{p(t)}\mathbf{i} + \frac{t^2(36 + 24t^2)}{p(t)}\mathbf{j} - \frac{t(432t^4 + 1)}{p(t)}\mathbf{k}$ where $p(t) = \sqrt{(1 - 288t^3)^2 + (36t^2 + 24t^4)^2 + (432t^5 + t)^2}$ **13** $\mathbf{T}(t) = \frac{2\cos(2t)}{3}\mathbf{i} - \frac{2\sin(2t)}{3}\mathbf{j} + \frac{1}{3}\mathbf{k}$, $\mathbf{B}(t) = \frac{\cos(2t)}{\sqrt{6}}\mathbf{i} - \frac{\sin(2t)}{\sqrt{6}}\mathbf{j} - \frac{2}{\sqrt{6}}\mathbf{k}$, $\mathbf{N}(t) = -\sin(2t)\mathbf{i} - \cos(2t)\mathbf{j}$ **15** $\mathbf{N} = \mathbf{i}$ and $\mathbf{B} = \mathbf{k}$ **17** $x + 24y + z = 55$ **19** $z = 0$ **21** (a) $r = 1 + \frac{16}{\pi^2}$; (b) $(-16/\pi^2, 0, 8)$ **23** (a) $r = 14\sqrt{7/48}$; (b) $(27/38, 15/19, 47/38)$ **25** $\mathbf{r}(\theta) = \langle -1/2, -1/2, 2 \rangle + \frac{\cos\theta}{\sqrt{2}}\langle 111 \rangle + \frac{\sin\theta}{2}\langle -1, -1, 2 \rangle$ **27** $\mathbf{r}(\theta) = \langle -84/5, 178/5, 22 \rangle + \frac{21\cos\theta}{\sqrt{5}}\langle 1, -2, 4 \rangle + \frac{21\sin\theta}{5}\langle -4, 8, 5 \rangle$ **29** $\mathbf{T} = \mathbf{j}$ and $\mathbf{N} = \mathbf{i}$ **31** (a) shown in the diagram below; (b) out of the page at points A and B, into the page at points C and D

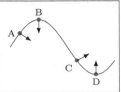

33 $\langle 1, 1, -2 \rangle \cdot \mathbf{N} < 0$ tells us that the the angle between them is obtuse **35** 1 **37** (b)

the switch happens at $t = {}^4/_3$ which locates an inflection point on the curve

39 $x = 0$ and $y = \frac{279}{112} - \sqrt{\frac{7113}{12544}}$

Chapter 12 Review:
1 T **3** T **5** F **7** F **9** T **11** F **13** F (need to include $+\mathbf{c}$) **15** T **17** F (denominator should be $\|\mathbf{v}\|^3$) **19** c **21** a **23** b **25** $\mathbf{r}(t) = \langle 3, -1, -2 \rangle + \frac{1000t}{\sqrt{62}} \langle 6, 5, -1 \rangle$ **27** (a) This happens when the center is moving slower than it "should," as if the wheel were on ice, and unable to gain traction; (b) Again, imagine a car on ice. This time, the car is trying to slow down. The brakes slow the wheels, but the wheels slip on the ice, so the car continues to move faster than it "should." Hopefully, it slows down before it hits something! (c) Here, the car is moving backwards even though the wheels are spinning forwards. **29** $\mathbf{r}(t) = \langle 1.1 - 0.8t, t, 6t - 7 \rangle$ **31** $({}^8/_{13})\mathbf{j}$ **33** 0 **35** $\mathbf{v} = \langle 3, \pi, 8e^4 \rangle$, speed$= \sqrt{9 + \pi^2 + 64e^8}$ **37** $(384t^5 - 12t^2 - 16)\mathbf{i} - (120t^4 + 32t^3 + 64t)\mathbf{j} + (192t^2 + 12)\mathbf{k}$ **39** $\frac{3t^2}{2}\mathbf{i} + \frac{8t}{3}\mathbf{j} + (2t + \frac{1}{4}t^4)\mathbf{k}$ **41** $\langle 18, {}^{448}/_3, 84 \rangle$ **43** $\mathbf{T} = \langle {}^3/\sqrt{74}, {}^8/\sqrt{74}, {}^1/\sqrt{74} \rangle$, $\mathbf{B} = \langle -{}^8/\sqrt{2449}, {}^9/\sqrt{2449}, -{}^{48}/\sqrt{2449} \rangle$, $\kappa = \sqrt{2449}/74$ **45** (a) z must decrease; (b) $\frac{\Delta z}{\Delta x} = -{}^2/_5$ is a rise-to-run ratio; (c) $\mathbf{r}(t) = \langle 1, 1, 4 \rangle + t\langle 1, 0, -\frac{2}{5}t \rangle$ **47** The last component of the direction vector is the ratio of the x-coefficient (or the y-coefficient) to the z-coefficient in the defining equation. **49** $t = 2$ **51** $(x + 4)^2 + (y + {}^8/_3)^2 = {}^{250}/_9$ **53** $\mathbf{r}(\theta) = \langle -{}^{485}/_{41}, -{}^{1738}/_{41}, {}^{976}/_{41} \rangle + R\cos(\theta)\mathbf{T} + R\sin(\theta)\mathbf{N}$ where $\mathbf{T} = \langle \sqrt{2}/6, \sqrt{2}/6, 2\sqrt{2}/3 \rangle$, $\mathbf{N} = \langle -7\sqrt{738}/738, -25\sqrt{738}/738, 8\sqrt{738}/738 \rangle$ and $R = {}^{243\sqrt{82}}/_{41}$

Section 13.1:
1 hyperboloid of 2 sheets **3** hyperboloid of 1 sheet **5** hyperboloid of 1 sheet rotated by pi/4 **7** ellipsoid **9** nothing (no points satisfy this equation) **11** (a) hyperboloid; (b) centered about $(0, {}^1/_8, 0)$; (c) 1 **13** (a) paraboloid; (b) vertex at $(-3, 0, 0)$; (c) the x-axis **15** (a) hyperboloid; (b) centered at the point $(-1, 0, 0)$; (c) 1 **17** (a) paraboloid; (b) vertex at $(\frac{1}{16}, -\frac{45}{224}, -\frac{2}{7})$; (c) the line through the vertex that's parallel to the y-axis **19** (a)

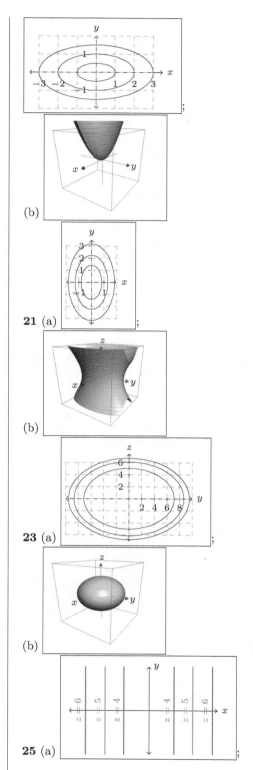

21 (a)
 (b) ;

23 (a)
 (b) ;

25 (a) ;

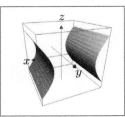

(b)

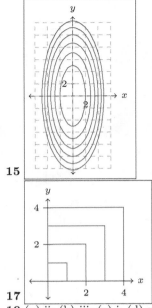

27 $x + y - z = 7$ **29** $x - 2y + z = 13$ **31** $\frac{x^2}{16} + \frac{y^2}{9} + \frac{z^2}{49} = 1$ **33** $y = a(x-2)^2 + b(z+1)^2 - 7$ where a and b are any nonzero numbers with the same sign **35** $x^2 - y^2 - z^2 = 9$ **37** $-x^2 - y^2 + (z-7)^2 = 0.059$ **39** (a) circle centered at the origin; (b) this is a sphere; (c) when $k < 0$ there is no surface at all, $k = 0$ allows for a single point (the origin), and $k > 0$ corresponds to a sphere of radius $\sqrt{1/k}$ **41** The point (a, b) has to lie in the bounded region between the parabolas $b = a^2 - a$ and $a = b^2 - b$. **43** (b) $\mathcal{S}$ is a cone that intersects the xy-plane along the lines $y = m_1 x$ and $y = m_2 x$; (c) The two lines divide the xy-plane into four sections. The surfaces $\mathcal{S}$ sits over two of them, and the surface $\tilde{\mathcal{S}}$ sits over the other two. **47** the axis is the line that passes through the origin in the direction of $\langle 1, -1, -1 \rangle$ **49** $\sqrt{2} : 1$ **51** (a) kg^2/m^2; (b) an elliptic paraboloid with vertex at $(u, v, P) = (0, 0, \rho k)$ **53** (a) $0.5mu^2 + 0.5mv^2 + 0.5I\omega^2 = c$; (b) ellipsoid; (c) this ellipsoid has a circular cross section at each constant ω, and m determines its radius, and the number I affects the aspect ratio of the ellipse at each constant-u or constant-v cross section.

Section 13.2:

1 $x \geq 0$ (but y is unconstrained) **3** $f(x-1)(y-4) \geq 1$ (a disconnected region with a hyperbolic boundary, symmetric about the line $y = x + 3$) **5** $y \geq x^3$ (the set of points that lie above the curve $y = x^3$) **7** $[0, \infty)$ **9** $[-1, 1]$ **11**

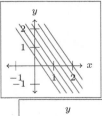

13

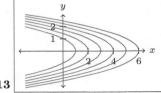

15

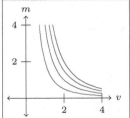

17

19 (a) ii; (b) iii; (c) i; (d) none **21** The curve $f(x, y) = c$ lies in the xy-plane, whereas the trace is on the surface (directly above the curve). **23** This surface is the plane $z - 19x + 20y = 0$. **25** The surfaces are parallel planes in 3-space. The graph of g sits two units above the graph of f. **27** Lines parallel to the z-axis intersect the ellipsoid twice, so there are points (x, y) in the "domain" that correspond to two outputs. That's not a function. The same thing happens if you try to make y a function of x and z, or x a function of y and z. **29** Steeper at point A because the level curves are closer together **31** (a) a parabola; (b) also a parabola, but 1 unit higher up **33** (a) a sinusoid with an amplitude of 9 and an average value of 1; (b) a sinusoid with an amplitude of 10 and an average value of 1 **35** (a) a line with positive slope (z increases as x does) and an intercept of $z = 169$; (b) a parallel line, but higher up ($z = 196$ when $x = 0$) **37** (a) the curve $z = 3e^x$; (b) the curve $z = 4e^x$ is a stretched version of the curve in part (a) **39** (a) m and v must be nonnegative; (b)

(c) All the points on a given level curve correspond to systems that have the same kinetic

energy.
41 (a) x and y must be positive in order for p to be physically meaningful, because length and width cannot be negative; (b) lines in the xy-plane with slope -1 and positive y-intercept; (c) All points on the same segment correspond to rectangles with the same perimeter. **43** Each level surface of T is a hyperbolic paraboloid in PVN-space. The points on a given level surface all correspond to gases with the same temperature, but under different pressure P, occupying different volumes V, and with different numbers of molecules N. **45** All points on a level curve of T are at the same temperature.
47 (c) $w = 10\sin(\theta)\left(\frac{4}{r-4\cos(\theta)}\right) + 10\sin(\theta)\left(\frac{q}{r+q\cos(\theta)}\right)$ when either $r\sin(\theta) > 18$ or $|r\cos(\theta)| > 22$ (the constraints place the foul outside the penalty box); (d) assuming an 18-inch shoulder-to-shoulder player width, the number of players is $p(r, \theta) = \lceil w/18 \rceil$, where $\lceil x \rceil$ is the least integer (i.e., "ceiling") function—you cannot use $1/2$ of a player in the wall. Either the player is there, or not! **49** (a) $C(x, y, z) = 200x + 321y + 250z$; (b) The level surfaces of C are planes in 3-space. Only the portion of a plane in the first octant is physically relevant (since it's impossible to ship negative quantities). Any of x or y or z could be 0. **51** (a) the average rate of return you should expect from the portfolio; (b) $c(x, y) = r_3 + (r_1 - r_3)x + (r_2 - r_3)y - a\sqrt{\sigma_1^2 x^2 + \sigma_2^2 y^2 + \sigma_3^2(1 - x - -y)^2}$, where (x, y) must lie in the triangle with vertices $(0,0), (1,0), (0,1)$; (c) see below; (d) the level curves seem to be centered near the point $(0.3, 0.3)$

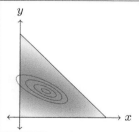

53 (a) because S_2 becomes less volatile, but maintains the same average rate of return, which is higher than the other stocks, we should move to a point favoring y over x and z; (b) see level curves below (which agree with our part (a))

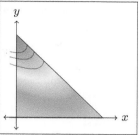

55 (a) This curve tells us, for a given amount of available labor, how our ability to make a product changes with capital investment. (b) All points on a given level curve of Q correspond to levels of labor and capital investment that result in the same production levels. The prefix "iso" means "same" and the term "quant" is an abbreviation of the work "quantity." So "isoquant" means "same quantity" of product.

Section 13.3:
7 0 **9** $1/4$ **11** -1 **13** 1 **15** $1/2$ **17** 2 **19**

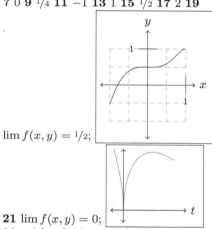

$\lim f(x, y) = 1/2$;

21 $\lim f(x, y) = 0$;
23 neither limit exists because you can find different limiting values by approaching each point along different paths **25** 0 **27** -1 **29** (a)

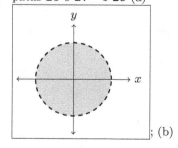

; (b)

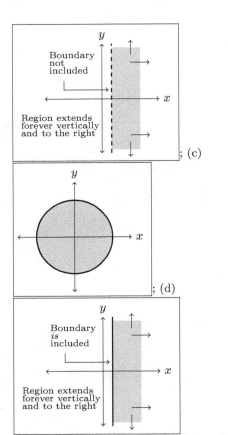

; (c)

; (d)

31 closed, unbounded **33** The region R is not closed. **35** 1 **37** $-1/35$ **39** 0 **41** (b) $f \to \beta/(1+\beta^2)$ when $(x, y) \to (0, 0)$ along the path $y = \beta x$. Since the limiting value is not the same along *every* path, the limit does not exist. **43** (c) The limit does not exist. **45** $f(x, y) = \frac{15x^6 y}{22x^{12}+22y^2}$ (other answers possible) **49** 0

Section 13.4:

1 $f_x = 4x^3$; $f_{xx} = 12x^2$; $f_y = -6y^5$; $f_{yy} = -30y^4$ **3** $f_x = 6xe^y$; $f_{xx} = 6e^y$; $f_y = 3x^2 e^y$; $f_{yy} = 3x^2 e^y$ **5** $f_x = 15x^2 y$; $f_{xx}30xy$; $f_y = 5x^3$; $f_{yy} = 0$ **7** $f_x = 3x^2 y e^{x^3 y + y^2}$; $f_{xx} = (6xy + 9x^4 y^2)e^{x^3 y + y^2}$; $f_y = 2ye^{x^3 y + y^2}$; $f_{yy} = (2 + 4y^2)e^{x^3 y + y^2}$ **9** $f_x = 2x \cos(x^2) \cos(y)$; $f_{xx} = (2\cos(x^2) - 4x^2 \sin(x^2)) \cos(y)$; $f_y = -\sin(x^2) \sin(y)$; $f_{yy} = -\sin(x^2) \cos(y)$ **11** $f_{xy} = 0 = f_{yx}$ **13** $f_{xy} = -xy \cos(xy) = f_{yx}$ **15** $f_{xy} = -4x^3 y^3 (x^4 + y^4 + 2)^{-3/2} = f_{yx}$ **17** $f_{xy} = 6xe^{x^2+3y} = f_{yx}$ **19** $-36e^{3x} \cos 2y$ **21** $\frac{4(50x+20y)^2}{(1+(5x+2y)^2)^3} - \frac{100}{(1+(5x+2y)^2)^2}$ **23** 0 **25** $f_{xx}(x, y) = 0 = f_{yy}(x, y)$; f satisfies Laplace's equation everywhere **27** $f_{xx}(x, y) = \frac{2}{x^2+y^2} - \frac{4x^2}{(x^2+y^2)^2}$, $f_{yy}(x, y) = \frac{2}{x^2+y^2} - \frac{4y^2}{(x^2+y^2)^2}$, (b) f

satisfies Laplace's equation away from the origin **29** $f_x(2.01, 5.1) \approx 15$ and $f_y(2.01, 5.1) \approx 4.5$ (from averaging the one-sided difference quotients) **31** (a) $f_x \approx 8/3$ (the average of the left-hand and right-hand difference quotients between level curves), and $f_y \approx 5/3$ (the average of the upward and downward difference quotients between level curves); (b) $f_y \approx 58/21$; (c) $f_y \approx 0$ **33** $r(t) = \langle \frac{\pi}{2} + 1t, 3, \frac{\pi^3}{8} - 9 + \frac{3\pi^2}{4}t \rangle$ **35** $r(t) = \langle -2 + t, -5, -1738 - 887t \rangle$ **37** $r(t) = \langle 1, 4 + t, 75e^4 + 105e^4 t \rangle$ **39** down **41** down **43** up **45** (a) $r(t) = \langle 1, 4, -1 \rangle + t\langle 1, 0, 15 \rangle$; (b) $r(t) = \langle 1, 4, -1 \rangle + t\langle 0, 1, -4 \rangle$; (c) $-15x + 4y + z = 0$ **47** (a) $r(t) = \langle 9, 4, 1 \rangle + t\langle 6, 0, 1 \rangle$; (b) $r(t) = \langle 9, 4, 1 \rangle + t\langle 0, 4, -1 \rangle$; (c) $-4x + 6y + 24z = 12$ **49** (a) $r(t) = \langle 2, 30 \rangle + t\langle 1, 0, 135 \rangle$; (b) $r(t) = \langle 2, 3, 0 \rangle + t\langle 0, 1, -81 \rangle$; (c) $-135x + 81y + z = -27$ **51** (a)

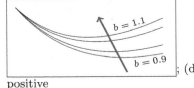

; (b) positive;

(c)

; negative

53 (a)

; (b) positive; (c)

; (d)

positive

55 (a) hyperbolic paraboloid; (b) $f_{xx} > 0$; (c) $f_{yy} < 0$ **57** (a) $\frac{\partial x}{\partial t} = \frac{4r^2(4*r^2 - t^2)}{(4r^2+t^2)^2}$ tells us whether the x-coordinate of the projection increases or decreases with t, and at what rate; (b) $\frac{\partial x}{\partial r} = \frac{8rt^3}{(4*r^2+t^2)^2}$ tells us whether the x-coordinate of the projection increases or decreases with r, and at what rate; (c) $\frac{\partial^2 x}{\partial r \partial t} = \frac{8rt^2(12*r^2-t^2)}{(4*r^2+t^2)^3}$, which is $39/250$ when $t = 2$ and $r = 3$; (d) $x_t(2,3) = 18/25$ and $x_t(2, 3 + \Delta r) \approx \frac{18}{25} + \frac{39}{250}\Delta r$; (d) $x_{tt}(t,r) = \frac{32r^2t^3}{(4r^2+t^2)^3} - \frac{24r^2t}{(4r^2+t^2)^2}$, which is $-117/500$ at $(t,r) = (2,3)$; (e) $x_t(2 + \Delta t, 3) \approx \frac{18}{25} - \frac{117}{500}\Delta t$ **59** (a) $y(,t,b) = 1 + b - \frac{2(1+b)^2}{t^2+(1+b)^2}$; (b) $y_t(2,3) = 8/25$ tells us that increasing t increases the y-coordinate of the stereographic projection; (c) y_{tb} tells us the rate at which y_t changes when b increases; (d) $y_{tb}(2,3) = -\frac{12}{125}$; (e) $y_t(2, 3 + db) \approx \frac{8}{25} - \frac{12}{125}db$ **61** (b) ν/ω has units of m/sec, and is the speed of the wave through space **63** (a)

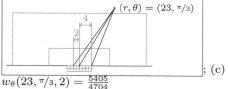

$(r, \theta) = (23, \pi/3)$

; (c) $w_\theta(23, \pi/3, 2) = \frac{5405}{4704}$

65 (a) $\partial Q/\partial L$ tells us the slope of this curve; (b) The derivative tells us the rate at which production capacity changes with additional hours of labor. Since more labor typically results in more product, we expect this derivative to be positive. **67** (b) increasing the wind speed will make you feel colder, but increasing the temperature will make you feel warmer **69** (a) $c_x(x,y) =$

$$r_1 - r_3 - \frac{a(x\sigma_1^2-(1-x-y)\sigma_3^2)}{\sqrt{(\sigma_1 x)^2+(\sigma_2 y)^2+(\sigma_3(1-x-y))^2}} \text{ and}$$

$c_y(x,y) =$

$$r_2 - r_3 - \frac{a(y\sigma_2^2-(1-x-y)\sigma_3^2)}{\sqrt{(\sigma_1 x)^2+(\sigma_2 y)^2+(\sigma_3(1-x-y))^2}};\text{ (b)}$$

graph shown below; (c) the function has its maximum value where the line crosses curve $c_x = 0$; (d) how to choose x in order to maximize confidence, given y; (e) graph shown below; (f) For the graph, see answers to exercise #51; each level curve is a collection of points—a group of portfolios—in which you have equal confidence

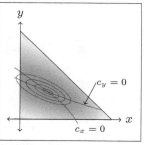

Section 13.5:

1 $z = 2(x - 1) + 4(y + 1)$ **3** $z = 14 + 6(x - 5) - 16(y - 2)$ **5** $z = 6\sqrt{21} - \sqrt{21}(x + 3) - \frac{9\sqrt{21}}{21}(y + 7)$ **7** $z = e^2 + e^2(x - 2) - 4e^2(y + 1)$ **9** $x_1 = \frac{2573}{1572} \approx 1.636768448$ and $y_1 = \frac{6913}{2096} \approx 3.298187023$; $x_2 \approx 1.624914144$ and $y_2 \approx 3.293917095$ **11** $x_1 \approx 0.554246924$ and $y_1 \approx 1.080019395$; $x_2 \approx 0.551256585$ and $y_2 \approx 1.074431537$ **13** $df = -5565dx - 8988dy$ **15** $df = \left(12ln(7) + \frac{12}{7}\right)dx + \frac{24}{7}dy$ **17** $df = 6dx + 27dy + 4dz$ **19** $df = 0dx - \frac{3\sqrt{2}}{2}dy + 0dz$ **21** $f(4.1, 1.01) \approx 8.24$ **23** $f(5.99, 2.98) \approx 0.92$ **25** $f(5.02, 2.97) \approx -5.74$ **27** (a) 0; (b) 0.2 **29** (a) 4; (b) 2.9 **31** (a) 1; (b) 1.21 **33** (a) 3; (b) 2.74 **35** $\frac{31\sqrt{137}}{137}$ **37** $\frac{27\sqrt{53}}{53}$ **39** $\frac{5\sqrt{82}}{82}$ **43** (a) $\frac{140}{9}$; (b) $I_m = \frac{4}{9}$ and $I_h = -\frac{560}{27}$; (c) $I = \frac{140}{9} + \frac{4}{9}(m - 35) - \frac{560}{27}(h - 1.4)$; (d) $\frac{2087}{135}$ **45** (a) 20π cm^3; (b) 2.04π cm^3 **47** (a) $83\sqrt{9530}$ m; (b) $\frac{3981}{9530}\sqrt{9530} \approx 40.78$ m **49** (a) 0.8899; (b) error of $\approx 0.01101 \Rightarrow$ best grade is 0.9009 and worst is 0.8789; (c) the change in percentage **51** (a) labor; (b) the total differential indicates that changing labor and capital expenses by $dL = 8$ and $dK = -8 \times 18 = 144$ increases production by about 36 units, so bringing in an additional worker makes sense. This results in $L = 1736$ and $K = 50481$. Checking the total differential in the same manner at these values of L and K indicates that we can increase production by bringing in a second worker. Continuing like this, it seems that we can bring in 108 workers. The 109th worker causes $dQ < 0$, so we ask her to stay home. **53** it is **55** (e) there is not a well-defined tangent plane at the origin

(see the figure)
57 The tangent plane to the graph of f is parallel to $z = 0$, so it never intersects that plane.

Section 13.6:

1 $\langle 7, 8 \rangle$ **3** $\left\langle -\frac{x^2 - y}{(x^2 + y)^2}, -\frac{x}{(x^2 + y)^2} \right\rangle$ **5** $\langle 6, -7, 10 \rangle$ **7** $\langle yz, xz, xy \rangle$ **9** $\langle 52, 48 \rangle$ **11** $\langle \frac{1}{2}(1 - \pi)e^{-2}, \frac{\pi}{4}e^{-2} \rangle$ **13** $\langle 3, -2, 8 \rangle$ **15** $\langle 0, -2, 0 \rangle$ **17** $-\frac{1}{2}\sqrt{26}$ **19** $-\frac{2 + 5\pi}{\sqrt{29}}$ **21** $\frac{7}{3}\sqrt{30}$ **23** $\frac{\sqrt{6}}{6}$ **25** $\frac{x-3}{-2} = \frac{y-5}{4} = \frac{z-45}{-12}$ **27** $\frac{x-2}{4} = \frac{y-1}{1} = \frac{z-5}{18}$ **29** $\frac{x-y}{13} = \frac{2y-\pi}{4} = -\frac{z}{2}$ **31** 49 **33** $\frac{228}{13}$ **35** 6 **37** $\frac{2}{5}e^{90}$ **39** 26 **41** 26 **43** -60 **45** (a) both $\mathbf{r}_1$ and $\mathbf{r}_2$ parameterize the circle $x^2 + y^2 = 1$, and $\mathbf{r}_1(\pi/4)$ and $\mathbf{r}_2(\pi/8)$ both point to the point $(\frac{\sqrt{2}}{2}, \frac{\sqrt{2}}{2})$; (b) $\sqrt{2}/2$; (c) $\sqrt{2}$; (d) the two parameterizations proceed around the circle at different speeds ($\mathbf{r}_2$ moves twice as fast as $\mathbf{r}_1$). **47** $\left\langle \frac{11\sqrt{5}}{25}, -\frac{2\sqrt{5}}{25} \right\rangle$ **49** in the direction of the vector $\langle 8 + 2\pi, \pi \rangle$ **51** in the direction of the vector $\langle 1, 96, 16 \rangle$ **53** in the direction of the vector $\langle 0, 3, -1 \rangle$ **55**

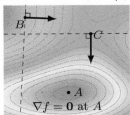

$\langle 1, 3 \rangle$ **59**

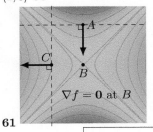

61

63 (a) and (c) (d) it should be (and is) 0 **65** $\frac{160}{31}$ **67** (a) $f = 3(14 + 2t)^2 + (8t - 1)^2$; (b) $t^* = -1$; (c) $\mathbf{r}'(-1) = \langle 12, -9 \rangle$ and

$\nabla f(12, -9) = \langle 78, -18 \rangle$; (d) $\mathbf{r}'(-1) \cdot \nabla f(12, -9) = 0$ **69** (a) $\mathbf{r}'(t) = \langle 7, 8 \rangle$; (b) $\frac{df}{dt} = \nabla f \cdot \mathbf{r}'$ **73** $\nabla f = \left\langle \frac{43}{29}, -\frac{4}{29} \right\rangle$ **75** $\mathbf{r}(t) = \langle 3 + 2t, 2, 7 + 63t \rangle$ **57** $D_{\mathbf{u}}f > 0$, $D_{\mathbf{v}}f < 0$ and $D_{\mathbf{w}}f = 0$ **77** move away from the point $(T, V) = (300, 0.3)$ in the direction of $\langle 1, -1000 \rangle$ **79** (a) $x_1(r, b) = \frac{2r(b+r)}{1 + (b+r)^2}$; (b) $\nabla x(0.5, 0.5) = \langle 1, 0 \rangle \Rightarrow$ we should increase r but leave b fixed **81** Using $T_x \approx \frac{125}{9} \frac{^\circ\text{F}}{\text{cm}}$ (the average of one-sided difference quotients between level curves) and $T_y \approx -2 \frac{^\circ\text{F}}{\text{cm}}$ (from a single one-sided difference quotient between the curves $T = 90$ and $T = 85$), we get $\frac{dT}{dt} = \frac{179\sqrt{10}}{180} \frac{^\circ\text{F}}{\text{sec}}$. **83** $\nabla c(12, 156000) = \langle -\frac{103850}{3}, \frac{8}{3} \rangle$, so we should move away from the point $(n, N) = (12, 156000)$ in the direction of $\langle \frac{103850}{3}, -\frac{8}{3} \rangle$. That is, we should reduce our inventory by a little bit, and order many more times from the supplier each year (thereby raising the handling fee but reducing the warehousing cost). **85** (a) $\frac{120}{30}$; (b) $\langle \frac{13}{169}, \frac{16}{169}, \frac{9}{169} \rangle$; (c) $9/1600$ ohms per second

Section 13.7:

1 (a) $\nabla f = \langle 3, 6 \rangle$; (b) $f_r = \frac{3\sqrt{3} + 6}{2}$ and $f_\theta = -3 + 6\sqrt{3}$ **3** (a) $\nabla f = \langle 2^{1.75}, 2^{-2.25} \rangle$; (b) $f_r = 2^{-2.75} + 2^{1.25}$ and $f_\theta = 2^{-2.75} - 2^{1.25}$ **5** (a) $\nabla f = \langle 13, 9 \rangle$; (b) $f_s = 84$ and $f_t = -46$ **7** (a) $\nabla f = \left\langle \frac{1989\sqrt{25}}{50}, \frac{289\sqrt{25}}{50} \right\rangle$; (b) $f_s = \frac{20757\sqrt{25}}{50}$ and $f_t = -\frac{5389\sqrt{25}}{50}$ **9** (a) $\nabla f = \langle \pi, \pi/2 \rangle$; (b) $f_s = 17\pi$ and $f_t = 16.25\pi$ **11** (a) $(x, y, z) = (17, 510)$; (b) $\langle f_x, f_y, f_z \rangle = \langle 5, -4, 11 \rangle$; (c) $f_s = 87$ and $f_t = -89$ **13** (a) $(x, y, z) = (1/2, 2, 84)$; (b) $\langle f_x, f_y, f_z \rangle = \langle 1, -4, 21168 \rangle$; (c) $f_s = \frac{846737}{8}$ and $f_t = \frac{2709489}{16}$ **15** (a) $(x, y, z) = (0, 3, 0)$; (b) $\langle f_x, f_y, f_z \rangle = \langle -3, 0, -3 \rangle$; (c) $f_s = -12$ and $f_t = 0$ **17** (a) $f_y(1, 2) = 1 \neq 0$; (b) -12 **19** (a) $f_y(1, \pi) = -\pi \neq 0$; (b) $2/\pi$ **21** (a) $f_z(-1, 0, 1) = 1 \neq 0$; (b) $z_x = 2$ and $z_y = 1$ **23** $f_z(1, 1, -2) = -3 \neq 0$; (b) $z_x = -1$ and $z_y = -\frac{5}{3}$ **25** -4 **27** 10 **29** (a) $f_z(1, 2, 0) = 27 \neq 0$ when $f(x, y, z) = \sin(z) + 4(x + z)^6 + yz$; (b) $z = -\frac{24}{27}(x - 1)$ **31** (a) $f_z(3, 2, 0) = -\pi \neq 0$ when $f(x, y, z) = z \arctan(yz) + \sin(xz)$; (b) $z = 1 - \frac{1}{\pi}(x - \pi) + \frac{1}{\pi}y$ **35** (a)

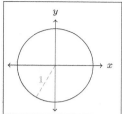

; (b) both are 3; (c) when only t is allowed to change, the velocity vector of the trajectory $\langle x(0,t), y(0,t) \rangle$ is $\mathbf{j}$, so the directional derivative of f is really $\nabla f \cdot \mathbf{j} = f_y$.

Section 13.8:

1 None **3** $(0,0)$ **5** $(6 \pm \sqrt{33}, 0)$ **7** points where x is an odd multiple of $\pi/2$ and y is an even multiple of $\pi/2$, or vise versa **9**
$$H = \begin{bmatrix} 0 & 0 \\ 0 & -4 \end{bmatrix}$$ **11**
$$H = \begin{bmatrix} 0 & \pi\cos(\pi y) \\ \pi\cos(\pi y) & -\pi^2 x \sin(\pi y) \end{bmatrix}$$ **13** down **15** down **17** 34 **19** 6.25 **21** local minimum **23** saddle **25** (a) $(0,0)$; (b) inconclusive **27** (a) $(1/4, -1/2)$; (b) saddle **29** (a) $(1,2)$; (b) local min **31** $f(x,y) \approx -44 - 9(x-7) + 2(y-3)$ Note: this is actually equality since all higher-order derivatives vanish **33** $f(x,y) \approx 1 - 3x + 2x^2 + 8y^2$ Note: this is actually equality since all higher-order derivatives vanish **35** $f(x,y) \approx 21 + e^2 + (3-e^2)(x+2) + 25(y-3) + \frac{1}{2}e^2(x+2)^2 + (x+2)(y-3) + 9(y-3)^2$ **37** $f(x,y) \approx \frac{\pi}{4} + 4(x-1) - \frac{15}{2}(y-1) - 14(x-1)^2 + 60(x-1)(y-1) + \frac{285}{4}(y-1)^2$ **39** $f(x,y) \approx$ $\frac{12}{25} + \frac{28}{625}(x-3) - \frac{21}{625}(y-4) - \frac{468}{15625}(x-3)^2 + \frac{527}{31250}(x-3)(y-4) - \frac{132}{15625}(y-4)^2$ **41** $(x_0,y_0) = (0.1, -0.2)$, $(x_1,y_1) = (0,0)$, $(x_2,y_2) = (0,0)$, $(x_3,y_3) = (0,0)$ **43** $(x_0,y_0) = (1.5, -0.5)$, $(x_1,y_1) = (1.474184864, -0.163275394)$, $(x_2,y_2) = (1.474184864, -0.163275394)$, $(x_3,y_3) = (1.499989598, -0.001506207)$ **45** $f(2,1) = 12$ **47** $f(\pi/2, 0) = 1$ **49** $f(2.028757838, 1) \approx 1.819705741$ **51** $f(0.957420731, -0.288696283) \approx 5.453249974$ **53** $f(x,y) = (x-2)^2 - (y-3)^2$ (other answers possible) **55** The points A and c are critical points (the others are not); A is a saddle point and C is an extremum **57** $(2, -0.5, 0.5)$ **59** $a = 2, b = 4/3, c = 12$ **63** $4\sqrt[3]{30} \times 4\sqrt[3]{30} \times 6\sqrt[3]{30}$ **65** $x \approx 0.300643465$ and $y \approx 0.311424048$ (from NRM) **69** (a) $g(x,y) \approx -1 - \frac{3}{2}\ln(2) - \frac{19}{4}(x - 0.25) + \left(\ln(2) - \frac{13}{8}\right)(y - 0.5) + 5(x - 0.25)^2 - \frac{13}{2}(x - 0.25)(y - 0.5) + 4(y - 0.5)^2$; (c) fluctuations are least likely in the

direction along the minor axis of the elliptical level curves; (d) fluctuations are most likely in the direction along the major axis of the elliptical level curves;

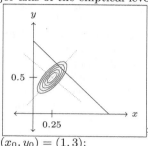

(b)

73 $(x_0, y_0) = (1,3)$;
$(x_1, y_1) = (-9/17, 12/17)$;
$(x_2, y_2) = \left(\frac{36}{221}, \frac{54}{221}\right)$;
$(x_3, y_3) = \left(-\frac{162}{3179}, \frac{216}{3179}\right)$ **75**
$(x_0, y_0) = (0, 3)$;
$(x_1, y_1) = (-1.559727293, 3.220108728)$;
$(x_2, y_2) := (-1.570807264, 3.141594197)$;
$(x_3, y_3) = (-1.570796327, 3.141592654)$

Section 13.9:

1 (a)

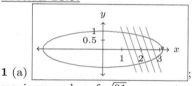

; (b) maximum value of $\sqrt{91}$ occurs at $(x,y) = \left(\frac{30\sqrt{91}}{91}, \frac{\sqrt{91}}{91}\right)$

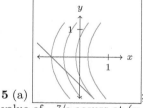

3 (a) ; (b) maximum value of $-\sqrt{8}$ occurs at $(x,y) = \left(\frac{3\sqrt{8}}{8}, \frac{\sqrt{8}}{8}\right)$

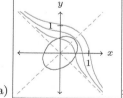

5 (a) ; (b) maximum value of $-7/8$ occurs at $(x,y) = (3/4, -7/4)$

7 (a) ; (b) maximum value of $1/4$ occurs at $(x,y) = (0.5, 0.5)$ **9** maximum $f \approx 1.321161232$ occurs when $x \approx 0.7390851332$ and $y \approx 0.6736120292$ **11** maximum $f \approx 6.346841866$ occurs when $x \approx 2.450696332$ and $y = 0.372594782$ **13** $-\sqrt{6}$ **15** -1 **17** -1 **19** $\frac{57}{49}$ **21** $\frac{\sqrt{3}}{3}$ **23** 2 **25** $\frac{-1+\sqrt{37}}{3} - \left(\frac{-1+\sqrt{37}}{3}\right)^2 \approx -1.1762430387$ **27** The components of ∇f are not both positive, so it cannot be a scaled version

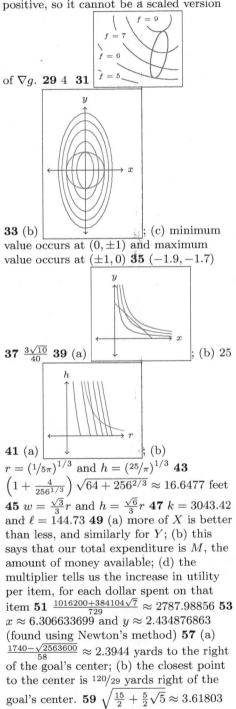

of ∇g. **29** 4 **31**

33 (b) ; (c) minimum value occurs at $(0, \pm 1)$ and maximum value occurs at $(\pm 1, 0)$ **35** $(-1.9, -1.7)$

37 $\frac{3\sqrt{10}}{40}$ **39** (a) ; (b) 25

41 (a) ; (b) $r = (1/5\pi)^{1/3}$ and $h = (25/\pi)^{1/3}$ **43** $\left(1 + \frac{4}{256^{1/3}}\right)\sqrt{64 + 256^{2/3}} \approx 16.6477$ feet **45** $w = \frac{\sqrt{3}}{3}r$ and $h = \frac{\sqrt{6}}{3}r$ **47** $k = 3043.42$ and $\ell = 144.73$ **49** (a) more of X is better than less, and similarly for Y; (b) this says that our total expenditure is M, the amount of money available; (d) the multiplier tells us the increase in utility per item, for each dollar spent on that item **51** $\frac{1016200 + 384104\sqrt{7}}{729} \approx 2787.98856$ **53** $x \approx 6.306633699$ and $y \approx 2.434876863$ (found using Newton's method) **57** (a) $\frac{1740 - \sqrt{2563600}}{58} \approx 2.3944$ yards to the right of the goal's center; (b) the closest point to the center is $120/29$ yards right of the goal's center. **59** $\sqrt{\frac{15}{2} + \frac{5}{2}\sqrt{5}} \approx 3.61803$

61 $\sqrt{19 + 5\sqrt{13}} \approx 6.08504$ **63** $\sqrt{\frac{25}{2} + \frac{1}{2}\sqrt{337}} \approx 4.65605$

Chapter 13 Review:
1 F (the equation doesn't describe any points at all when all coefficients are negative) **3** T **5** T **7** F **9** T **11** F **13** T **15** F (not necessarily) **17** F (technical detail: the partial derivatives must be continuous in order for Clairaut's Theorem to apply) **19** T **21** d (hyperboloid of two sheets) **23** b **25** c **27** c **29** $a = b$ and (a, b, c) lies inside the cone $c^2 = ab$

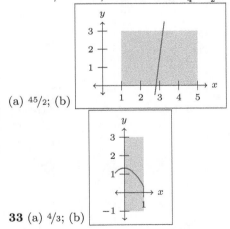

31
33 Each level surface is an elliptic paraboloid that opens in the direction of $-\mathbf{k}$ **35** $f_x(1, 2) = 12$ **37** (a) $f_{xx}(x, y) = 24x + 2y^3$; (b) $f_{yx}(x, y) = 6xy^2$ **39** $1 \neq 7$ **41** $z = 12 + 4(x - 1) + 2(y - 10)$ **43** 4.01 **45** $78 - 24\pi$ **47** $\mathbf{u} = \langle 1, 24 \rangle$ **49** local minimum **51** (a) $\partial_x f_{xy} = \frac{\partial^2 f_x}{\partial x \partial y}$ and $\partial_y f_{xx} = \frac{\partial^2 f_x}{\partial y \partial x}$ are the mixed second partial derivatives of f_x. When they're continuous, Clairaut's Theorem applies. (b) $\partial_x f_{xy} = 3$ and $\partial_y f_{xx} = 2xy$ are not the same. **53** max $f \approx 601.8344936$ (max on the boundary located with Newton's method) **55** $\sqrt{19}$ **57** $\sqrt{\frac{31 + 5\sqrt{37}}{2}}$ **59** 8

Section 14.1:
1 30 **3** 2.3125 cubic units **5** 1275 **7** 432 **9** $62/3$ **11** 1026 **13** 42 **15** 144 **17** 0 **19** 15 **21** 4.5 **23** $48/\pi$ **25** $355/12$ **27** 2898 **29** $\frac{\pi}{4} - \frac{1}{2}$ **31**

(a) $45/2$; (b)

33 (a) $4/3$; (b)

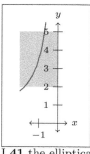

35 (a) 4.5; (b)
37 64 g **39** 56 J **41** the elliptical disk
$x^2 + 7y^2 \le 1$ **43** the square connecting
the points $(-4, 0), (0, 4), (4, 0), (0, -4)$ **45**
$\iint_R f(x, y)\, dA < 0$ **47** overestimated,
because f_x and f_y are both negative in
that region **49** $f(x, y) = (5 - x)(y - 6.5)$
for example (other answers possible) **51**
(a) $^{415}/_{16} \approx 25.94$ meters; (b) no change
53 $7^1/_2$ J/mm^2 **55** $^3/_4$ mm^3 **57** 12 mm^2
59 (a) 1; (b) above **61** (a) -4; (b) below
65 ≈ 119.8817 cm^2 **67** ≈ 67.74788687 **69**
$18\sqrt{3}$ **71** $9\sqrt{21}$ **73**
$36\left(\arcsin(^1/_3) + \arcsin(^2/_3) \right)$ **75**
$2\sqrt{258} - \frac{1}{4}\ln(\sqrt{129} - 8\sqrt{2})$ **77**
$\ln\left| \frac{1+\sqrt{681}}{1+\sqrt{1531}} \right| + \ln(1.5) + \sqrt{1531} - \sqrt{681}$ **79**
(a) bacteria (i.e., number of); (b) 125,000;
(c) 5,000

Section 14.2:

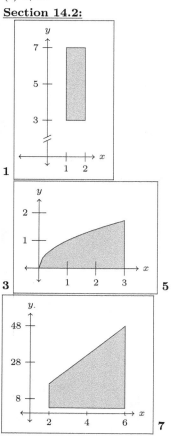

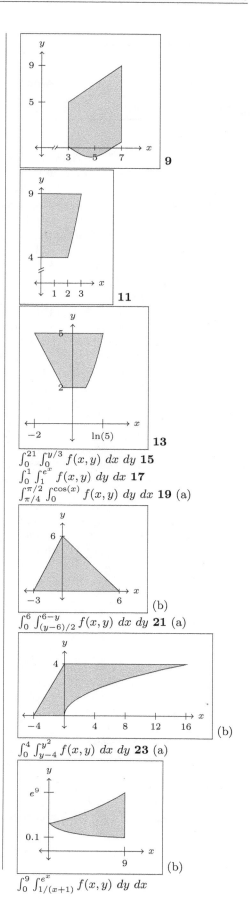

9

11

13

$\int_0^{21} \int_0^{y/3} f(x, y)\, dx\, dy$ **15**
$\int_0^1 \int_1^{e^x} f(x, y)\, dy\, dx$ **17**
$\int_{\pi/4}^{\pi/2} \int_0^{\cos(x)} f(x, y)\, dy\, dx$ **19** (a)

(b)
$\int_0^6 \int_{(y-6)/2}^{6-y} f(x, y)\, dx\, dy$ **21** (a)

(b)
$\int_0^4 \int_{y-4}^{y^2} f(x, y)\, dx\, dy$ **23** (a)

(b)
$\int_0^9 \int_{1/(x+1)}^{e^x} f(x, y)\, dy\, dx$

25 $\int_0^1 \int_{y(y^2-1)(y+2)}^0 f(x,y)\,dx\,dy + \int_0^2 \int_0^{1+0.5(x^2-2x)} f(x,y)\,dy\,dx +$
$\int_{-2}^0 \int_{y(y^2-1)(y+2)}^2 f(x,y)\,dx\,dy$

27 $\int_0^1 \int_{(1+x)/2}^{\sqrt{1-x^2}} f(x,y)\,dy\,dx + \int_{1/2}^1 \int_0^{2x-1} f(x,y)\,dy\,dx + \int_1^2 \int_0^{\sqrt{1-x^2}} f(x,y)\,dy\,dx$

29 $\int_{-\pi}^{-1} \int_{p(y)}^{\sin(y)} f(x,y)\,dx\,dy + \int_{-1}^0 \int_{\arcsin(y)}^{\sin(y)} f(x,y)\,dx\,dy$ where $p(y) = -\frac{\pi}{2}\sqrt{\frac{y+\pi}{\pi-1}}$

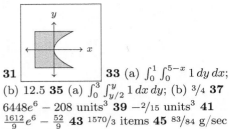

31 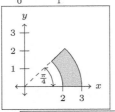 **33** (a) $\int_0^1 \int_0^{5-x} 1\,dy\,dx$;
(b) 12.5 **35** (a) $\int_0^3 \int_{y/2}^y 1\,dx\,dy$; (b) $3/4$ **37**
$6448e^6 - 208$ units^3 **39** $-2/15$ units^3 **41**
$\frac{1612}{9}e^6 - \frac{52}{9}$ **43** $1570/3$ items **45** $83/84$ g/sec
47 $1/6$

Section 14.3:
1 $\int_0^{2\pi} \int_1^2 f(r,\theta)\,r\,dr\,d\theta$

3 $\int_{\pi/2}^{2\pi} \int_1^2 f(r,\theta)\,r\,dr\,d\theta$

5 $\int_{\pi/4}^{3\pi/4} \int_1^2 f(r,\theta)\,r\,dr\,d\theta$

7 $\int_0^{\pi/2} \int_1^{2/(\cos\theta+\sin\theta)} f(r,\theta)\,r\,dr\,d\theta$ **9**

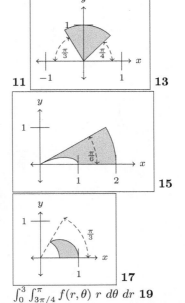

11 **13**

15

17
$\int_0^3 \int_{3\pi/4}^{\pi} f(r,\theta)\,r\,d\theta\,dr$ **19**
$\int_{\arctan(0.4)}^{\pi/2} \int_2^{5\csc(\theta)} f(r,\theta)\,r\,dr\,d\theta$ **21**

$\int_0^{\pi/2} \int_0^{8/(\cos(\theta)+\sin(\theta))} f(r,\theta)\,r\,dr\,d\theta$ **23**
$\frac{202}{9} + \frac{113\pi}{2}$ **25** $\frac{867\pi}{16}$ **27** 0 **29** (a)
$\int_0^{\pi/3} \int_{0.5}^{2.5} f(r,\theta)\,r\,dr\,d\theta$ (b) $29\pi/48$ **31** (b)
$8/3$ **33** $1 + \frac{2}{a}$ g **35** because the improper
integral $\int_0^1 r^{-0.5}\,dr$ converges, but the
improper integral $\int_0^1 r^{-1.1}\,dr$ does not **37**
$\frac{1}{4}e^{2\pi} - \frac{1}{4} - \frac{4}{3}\pi^3$ **39** $\frac{\pi}{4}(B^2 - A^2)$ **41**
$\pi + 56/3$ **43** $7\pi/2$ **45** $\frac{\pi}{6}(17^{3/2} - 1)$ **47** $\frac{7\sqrt{30}}{4}\pi$
49 3 km^3 **51** 31.25

Section 14.4:
1 $\iint_R \rho(x,y)\,dA = 23.7$ **3** The lamina's
center of mass has an x-coordinate of 13.
5 125 g **7** $\ln(2) + 1/6$ g **9** $\frac{\pi}{4}(1 - 1/e)$ **11**
$\overline{x} = \frac{43}{65}, \overline{y} = \frac{63}{45}$ **13** $\overline{x} = \frac{173}{51}, \overline{y} = \frac{43}{17}$ **15**
$\overline{x} = \frac{18}{\ln(7)+3}, \overline{y} = \frac{9+7\ln(7)}{63+21\ln(7)}$ **17**
$\overline{x} = \frac{9}{1280}(8 + 11\pi + 2\pi^2), \overline{y} = \frac{9\pi}{20} - \frac{1}{3}$ **19**
No, because $\overline{x} = \frac{1}{2}\left(\frac{k+2}{k+3}\right)$, and the second
factor cannot be 1. **21** $\overline{x} = 2$ and $\overline{y} = 0$
23 $I_y = 6475$ kg-m^2 **25** $I_y = \frac{2}{9} + \frac{3\pi}{64}$ **27**
$I_x = \frac{31}{504}$ **29** $\frac{775678}{25515} \approx 30.4009$ **31** (b) $4/3$;
(c) $2/3$; (d) an object has more rotational
inertia when its mass is farther away from
the axis of revolution (so it takes more
energy to change the rotation) **33** (a)
$\iint_R \rho(x,y)\,dA = 1$; (b) $28/87$ **35** (a)
$F(t) = 0.125t^2$ when $t \in [0,2]$ and
$F(t) = 1 - 0.125(4-t)^2$ when $t > 2$; (b)

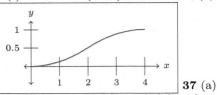

37 (a)
The first integral is the probability that a
shot on goal comes from inside the
penalty box. This is larger than the
probability that a shot on goal comes
from the right wing, so the first integral is
larger. (b) 0 (shots don't come from off
the field) **39** ≈ 0.6516 **41**
$2 + \frac{8}{5}\sqrt{6} - \frac{5}{4}\sqrt{15} + 20\left[\arcsin(0.2) - \arcsin(0.25)\right] \approx 0.0515$ **43** $8/3$ **45** $1/4$

Section 14.5:
1 $0.5\ln(5/4)\ln(3/2)$ **3** -8 **5** $\frac{25375}{4}$ **7** (a)
$\int_0^{7/3} \int_0^{7-3y} \int_0^{(7-3y-z)/2} f(x,y,z)\,dx\,dz\,dy$;
(b)
$\int_0^{7/2} \int_0^{7-2x} \int_0^{(7-2x-z)/3} f(x,y,z)\,dy\,dz\,dx$;
(c)

$\int_0^{7/2} \int_0^{(7-2x)/3} \int_0^{(7-2x-3y)} f(x,y,z)\,dz\,dy\,dx$
9 (a) $\int_0^{3.5} \int_{1.5}^{5-y} \int_0^{4-z} f(x,y,z)\,dx\,dz\,dy$ (b)
$\int_0^{0.25(5+\sqrt{45})} \int_{1/(x+1)+0.5}^{4-x} \int_0^{5-z} f(x,y,z)\,dy\,dz\,dx$;
(c)
$\int_0^4 \int_0^{1+x} \int_{1/(x+1)+0.5}^{4-x} f(x,y,z)\,dz\,dy\,dx +$
$\int_1^5 \int_0^{y-1} \int_{1/(x+1)+0.5}^{5-y} f(x,y,z)\,dz\,dx\,dy$ **11**
$-\frac{8599}{20}$ **13** $\frac{131887}{960} + \frac{145}{4}e^{-4} + \frac{39}{64}e^{-8} - 12e^{-2}$
15 $6667/8$ **17** $625/8$ **19** $\frac{371581}{3840} - 12\ln(2)$ **21**
$\frac{6869}{3640}$ **23** $8/3$ **25** $1747/420$ **27** $3040\sqrt{10}/21$ **29**
(a) $\int_0^1 \int_0^1 \int_{4x(x-1)}^{-z} f(x,y,z)\,dy\,dz\,dx$; (b)
$\int_0^1 \int_{4x(x-1)}^0 \int_0^{-y} f(x,y,z)\,dz\,dy\,dx$; (c)
$\int_0^1 \int_{-1}^{-z} \int_{(1-\sqrt{1-y})/2}^{(1+\sqrt{1-y})/2} f(x,y,z)\,dx\,dy\,dz$ **31**
z-simple (only) **33** None **35** $\frac{61}{9}$ **37** $\frac{81\pi}{8}$ **39**
$\int_{-\frac{3}{\sqrt{2}}}^{\frac{3}{\sqrt{2}}} \int_{1.5-\sqrt{2.25-0.5x^2}}^{1.5+\sqrt{2.25-0.5x^2}} \int_{3-y}^{\sqrt{9-x^2-y^2}} 1\,dz\,dy\,dx$
41 $\frac{\text{kg}}{\text{m}^3}$ **43** $(1/12, 1/2, 1)$ **45** $(-\frac{243}{1780}, 0, -\frac{1}{89})$
47 160 g-mm^2 **49** 12800 g-mm^2 **51** $\frac{209312}{15}$
g-mm^2

Section 14.6:

1 (a) $(r,\theta,z) = (2, \pi/3, 7)$; (b)
$(r,\theta,z) = (2, 2\pi/3, -4)$; (c)
$(r,\theta,z) = (5, \arctan(4/3), -5)$; (d)
$(r,\theta,z) = (\sqrt{5}, \arctan(2)+\pi, 3)$ **3** (a)
$(\rho,\theta,\phi) = (4\sqrt{2}, \pi/6, \pi/4)$; (b)
$(\rho,\theta,\phi) = (1, 5\pi/3, \pi/6)$; (c)
$(\rho,\theta,\phi) = (3, 0, \pi/2)$; (d)
$(\rho,\theta,\phi) = (1, 0, 0)$, but any angle θ will do
because $\phi = 0$ **5** ellipsoid **7** paraboloid **9**
cone **11** cylinder **13** plane **15** plane **17**
cylinder **19** plane **21** $r^2 + z^2 = 16$ **23** (a)
$\int_0^{2\pi} \int_0^2 \int_r^5 f(r,\theta,z)\,r\,dz\,dr\,d\theta$; (b)
$\int\limits_0^{2\pi} \int\limits_0^{\tan^{-1}0.4} \int\limits_0^{5\sec\phi} f(\rho,\theta,\phi)\,\rho^2 \sin(\phi)\,d\rho\,d\phi\,d\theta$
25 $\frac{2000\pi}{9}$ **27** $3/8$ **29**
$\frac{19488}{5}\pi^5 + 1482\pi^7 + 3577\pi^3 - \frac{21}{2}\pi$ **31** 0 **33**
$1/6$ **35** $\frac{5173}{30}\pi$ **37** $37\pi/3$ **39** $9\sqrt{3}/15$ **41**
$7\pi^2/64 + 7\pi/12$ **43** $\frac{8\pi}{3} \times 10^{10}$ particulates
45 $2\pi\phi_0^2 \sin(\phi_0)$ where $\phi_0 \approx 1.5608$ solves
the equation $\tan(x) = -2x$ **47** $9\pi(2 + \sqrt{2})$
49 $\frac{\pi}{6} - \frac{4\pi}{3}\left(\left(\frac{1}{4}\right)^{3/2} - \left(\frac{99}{400}\right)^{3/2}\right)$
cm$^3 \approx 0.1642\pi$ cm^3 **51** $16\pi\left(\frac{10\sqrt{2}}{3} - 1\right)$
53 $128\pi/15$ **55** (b) $dA = \frac{1}{2}\,du\,dy$; (c) $891\pi/4$
grams **57** $(x,y,z) = \left(0, 0, \frac{150-24\sqrt{2}}{50\sqrt{2}-15}\right)$ **59**
$(x,y,z) = \left(0, 0, \frac{77}{18}\right)$ **61**
$(x,y,z) = \left(\frac{280}{389}, -\frac{117}{778}, \frac{755}{389}\right)$ **63**
$128\pi\left(\frac{3\sqrt{2}-1}{3}\right)$ g-cm^2 **65** $\frac{8\pi}{9}$ kg-m^2

Section 14.7:

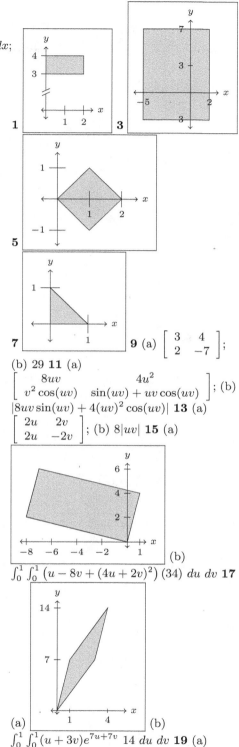

1 **3** **5** **7** **9** (a) $\begin{bmatrix} 3 & 4 \\ 2 & -7 \end{bmatrix}$;
(b) 29 **11** (a)
$\begin{bmatrix} 8uv & 4u^2 \\ v^2\cos(uv) & \sin(uv) + uv\cos(uv) \end{bmatrix}$; (b)
$|8uv\sin(uv) + 4(uv)^2\cos(uv)|$ **13** (a)
$\begin{bmatrix} 2u & 2v \\ 2u & -2v \end{bmatrix}$; (b) $8|uv|$ **15** (a)
(b)
$\int_0^1 \int_0^1 \left(u - 8v + (4u + 2v)^2\right) (34)\,du\,dv$ **17**
(a) (b)
$\int_0^1 \int_0^1 (u + 3v)e^{7u+7v}\,14\,du\,dv$ **19** (a)

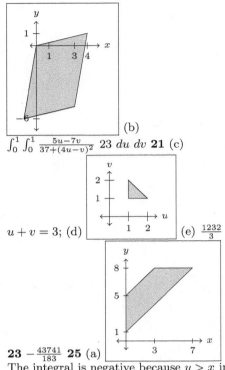

(b)

$\int_0^1 \int_0^1 \frac{5u-7v}{37+(4u-v)^2} \ 23 \ du \ dv$ **21** (c)

$u+v=3$; (d)

(e) $\frac{1232}{3}$

23 $-\frac{43741}{183}$ **25** (a)

The integral is negative because $y > x$ in the region, so the integrand is always negative in R; (b) $x = \frac{1}{2}u + \frac{1}{2}v$ and $y = \frac{1}{2}u - \frac{1}{2}v$; (c)

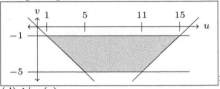

(d) $^1/_2$; (e)

$\int -5^{-1} \int_{-v}^{v+16} \frac{u}{2v} \ du \ dv = 32 - 64\ln(5)$ **27** $\frac{15}{2}\ln(2) - \frac{5}{2}\ln(3) - \frac{205}{4}$ **29** $|r|$ **31** 16 **33** 60 **35** $\frac{115}{2}$ **37** 8720 **39** $^1/_8$ **41** (a) $AD - BC$; (b) **v** must be a multiple of **u 43** (a) $u^2 + v^2 = 1$; (b) ab; (c) πab **45** $45\pi - 54$ **47** $m = \iint_R 1 + x^2 + y \ dA$, $\overline{x} = \frac{1}{m} \iint_R x(1 + x^2 + y) \ dA$, $\overline{y} = \frac{1}{m} \iint_R y(1 + x^2 + y) \ dA$; (b) $\overline{x} = \frac{2442}{299}$ and $\overline{y} = \frac{2016}{299}$ **49** $m = \iint_R 12 + x^2 - xy \ dA$, $\overline{x} = \frac{1}{m} \iint_R x(12 + x^2 - xy) \ dA$, $\overline{y} = \frac{1}{m} \iint_R y(12 + x^2 - xy) \ dA$; (b) $\overline{x} = -\frac{701}{187}$ and $\overline{y} = \frac{509}{187}$ **51** 260 **53** $\frac{5}{12}(3^{4/5} - 2^{4/5})(2^{6/5} - 1)$ **55** $107800(11 - 5\sin(6.75°) - 1.75\cos(6.75°))$ **57** (a) $u^2 + v^2 + w^2 = 1$; (b) abc; (c) $\frac{4}{3}\pi abc$

Chapter 14 Review:

1 F **3** T **5** F **7** F **9** T **11** T **13** T **15** F **17** F **19** b **21** c **23** a **25** 3240 **27** $\frac{2}{3} + \frac{1}{3}e^3 - e$ **29** $^2/\pi$ **31** (a) $^3/_{20}$; (b) $^3/_{20}$ **33** $\frac{10449}{640}$ **35** $\overline{x} = \frac{5\pi(44+505\pi+150\pi^2)}{84+1000\pi+225\pi^2}$ **37** $\frac{28,963\rho}{1,024,000} \approx 0.28284\rho$ kg-m^2 **39** 2 **41**

$\frac{32\pi}{3}(\sqrt{2} - 1)$ **43** $\frac{13}{32}$ **45** $e^\pi(\pi - 2) + \frac{1}{2}e^{\pi/2}(4 - \pi)$ **47** $^1/_2$ **49** $\rho\sin(\phi) = 3$ **51** $\frac{4\pi}{3}(4 - \sqrt{2})$ **53**

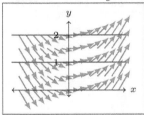

55

$\frac{1}{6}\left(\frac{1}{3}u - \frac{1}{3}v\right)^{-1/2}$

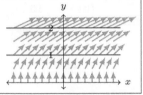

57 (a) ; (b) $u = y - x$ and $v = y - 3x$; (c) $^1/_2$; (d) $4(e^5 - e^3)$

Section 15.1:

1 $y = 3.5x + C$ **3** $y = 0.5x^2 + C$ **5** $y = \ln|x| + C$ **7** $\mathbf{F} = \langle 6x + y\cos(x), \sin(x)\rangle$ **9** $\mathbf{F} = \langle yz, xz, xy\rangle$ **11** (a) no **13** (b) $f(x,y) = x^3 + 8x + C$ **15** (b) $f(x,y) = \sin(xy) - 3x + 8y^2 + C$ **17** (a)

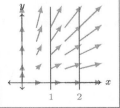

(b) The vector $\mathbf{F}(x,y)$ has a magnitude of $\sqrt{1 + y^2}$ and is parallel to a line with slope $1/y$, so the vectors on $y = 1$ are steeper, but the vectors on the line $y = 2$ are longer **19** (a)

(b) Because $\mathbf{F}$ does not depend on y, the vectors at $(x, 1)$ and $(x, 2)$ are equal **21** (a)

(b) $\mathbf{F}$ is steeper at $(1, y)$ than it is at $(2, y)$, but the vectors on the line $x = 2$ are larger than their respective counterparts on the line $x = 1$ **23** None (graph A is closest, but shows the wrong slope) **25** graph C **27** graph D **29** If $\mathbf{F}$ were ∇f, we could increase f by following $\mathbf{F}$ around a circle, but then $f(1,0) > f(1,0)$, which is impossible. **31**

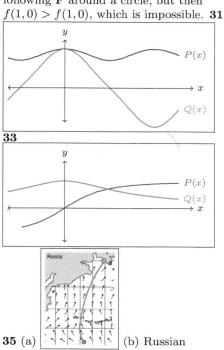

33

35 (a) 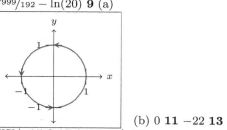 (b) Russian

Section 15.2:
1 $65\pi/48$ **3** $14\sqrt{5} + 7(1 + \sqrt{2})$ **5** (a)

(b) 117 **7** (a)

(b)
$^{7999}/_{192} - \ln(20)$ **9** (a)

(b) 0 **11** -22 **13**
$^{7879}/_6$ **15** 2 **17** 0 **19** $-^1/_3$ **21**
$24 + 2(4 - \pi)^2$ **23** $22\sqrt{37}$ **25** 85.5 **27** $^{325}/_2$

29 $^{59}/_6$ **31** $-^{4000}/_3$ **33** -350 **35**
$0.25\sqrt{16 + \pi^2}\left(3 - \frac{8\sqrt{2}}{\pi^2} + \frac{4}{\pi}\right)$ **37**
$\sqrt{77}\left(\frac{7}{4} + \frac{5}{32}\ln(9)\right)$ **39** $\frac{4}{9}\sqrt{270}$ **43** (A)
negative (B) positive (C) zero **45** (A)
negative (B) zero (C) positive **47** (a)

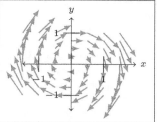

(b) positive
(c) the field will tend to increase an object's kinetic energy (and so speed) **49**
(a) $\frac{20}{3}$ (b) the field tends to increase kinetic energy **51** (b) 2π **53** (a)
$f(2,0) < 0$ and $f(0,2) > 0$ (b) $4 - \pi$ more units of area above than below **55** (a) grams (b)
$\frac{59}{2}\sqrt{13} - \frac{27}{2} + \frac{207}{2}\ln\left|\frac{2+\sqrt{13}}{3}\right| \approx 157.566$
grams **57** $\frac{\sqrt{2}}{2} - \frac{2}{e} + 2e + \frac{e^2}{\sqrt{2}} \approx 10.633$
coulombs **59** $\frac{23}{20c}\sqrt{2}$ seconds **61** $\frac{13}{10c}\sqrt{2}$
seconds

Section 15.3:
1 $e - 1$ **3** (a) $f(x,y) = 3x - 5y$ (b) 13 **5**
(a) $f(x,y) = xy + y$ (b) 7 **7** (a)
$f(x,y) = 2y^2 + \cos(\pi xy)$ (b) 8 **9** (a)
$f(x,y,z) = 10z + 7y - 5x$ (b) 125 **11** (a)
$f(x,y,z) = x^2 + 2y^2 + 4^2$ (b) 65 **13** (a)
$f(x,y,z) = x^2z + y$ (b) $64\pi^3$ **15**
$\int \mathbf{F} \cdot d\mathbf{r} = 0.5$ **17** 0 **19** (a) 17 (b) 18 (c) 0
21 $x = \sqrt{2\sqrt{41} - 1.75} + 0.5\sqrt{41}$ and
$y = 6 + \sqrt{2\sqrt{41} - 1.75} - 0.5\sqrt{41}$ **23** yes
(it's the gradient field of a function whose graph is mound that extends along the line $y = x$) **25** yes (it's the gradient field of a linear function) **27** 2 **29** -23 **31** (a)
$f(x,y) = 3x + 4y$ (b) the field increases the object's kinetic energy by 6 joules

Section 15.4:
1 $8 + 18y$ **3** $2xy$ **5** 0 **7** both are 9π **9** both are $-\pi$ **11** both are 0 **13** both are 63 **15**
flux≈ 19607.45221 **17** 0 **19** $20\pi \approx 62.8319$
21 simple but not closed **23** simple and closed **25** neither simple nor closed **29** (a) the material is expanding due to the traction (b) the divergence of the deformation field will be small where the material is less elastic **31** (c) $-\pi^2$ **33** π
grams per second **39** (a) this minimizes the variation in pixel intensities so that shading varies smoothly; (b) because f agrees with I on $\mathcal{C}$, any other function must agree with f on $\mathcal{C}$, which allows us to characterize it as a perturbation of f;

(c) because f minimizes the energy integral; (d) write
$$\|\nabla(f+tg)\|^2 = \nabla(f+tg) \cdot \nabla(f+tg),$$
which expands into a quadratic polynomial in t; (e) because f minimizes the energy integral; (f) $\iint_R 2\nabla f \cdot \nabla g \, dA$; (h) if Δf were positive at (x,y), it would have to be positive in a small region about that point (because it's continuous), so we'd be able to put a small bump function inside that region and get a positive integral (but we can't because the integral is always 0)

Section 15.5:
1 0 **3** 2 **5** $7x^6 \cos(y) - 2xy$ **7** (a) 0 (b) 0 **9** (a) 0 (b) 0 **11** (a) 187 (b) 187 **13** (a) $-\frac{2471}{3}$ (b) $-\frac{2471}{3}$ **15** (a) 85 (b) 85 **17** (a) $2 - 3\pi$ (b) $2 - 3\pi$ **19** ≈ -235.2088 **21** ≈ -2.7649 **23** ≈ 13.3518 **25** none of these expressions make sense (they're all the curl of a number instead of the curl of a vector field) **27** 12π **29** (a) 6 joules (c) $-3\pi/4$ (d) $-6 - 3\pi/4$ joules **31** $-\arctan(0.5)$ **37** center of mass at $(2/\pi, 2/\pi)$ **39** both are $3\pi/16$ **41** ≈ 23.0123 m^2 (using a left-sampled Riemann sum)

Section 15.6:
1 -12 **3** 224 **5** $-\frac{165}{4}$ **7** -60 **9** 76 **11** $-\frac{544}{3}$

13 $-\frac{\pi+180}{3\pi}$ **15** 4π **17** -8 **19** $-\frac{2673}{8}$ **21** $-\frac{494}{15}$ **23** $24 + 18\pi$ **25** 0 **27** $\pi^2 - 8$ **29** $2\pi(2 - \sqrt{2})$ **31** $\frac{995\pi}{72}$ **33** ≈ -1.0364098 (use Newton's method to determine that the curves intersect at $x \approx 0.756387$ and $x \approx 2.229637$) **35** $48\pi - 8\pi^3$ **37** $\frac{91701\pi}{64000}$ **39** (a) the flux of $\mathbf{F}_1$ is -12 and the flux of $\mathbf{F}_2$ is 12, which happens because the normal vector to the surface opposes $\mathbf{F}_1$ but makes an acute angle with $\mathbf{F}_2$; (b) the flux of $\mathbf{F}_1$ is -8 and the flux of $\mathbf{F}_2$ is -2, which happens because $\mathbf{F}_1$ is opposed to $\mathbf{n}$ to a greater extent than $\mathbf{F}_2$ **41** (a) The plane in which $\mathcal{S}$ is embedded pivots parallel to the xy-plane as t increases, but the shadow of $\mathcal{S}$ on the xy-plane remains the $[1,4] \times [2,6]$ rectangle, so the area of $\mathcal{S}$ decreases as t increases. (b) The function $f(t)$ has a constant value of 12 at all $t \neq 0$, so its graph is a horizontal line. **43** (a) $f(s,t) = \frac{9}{t}(s-2)$; (b) $f_s = \frac{9}{t} > 0 > -\frac{9}{t^2}(s-2) = f_t$; (c) increasing t tends to tip $\mathcal{S}$ parallel to the xy-plane, thereby reducing the area of $\mathcal{S}$ and bringing it parallel to $\mathbf{F}$, so doesn't pass through; but increasing s makes the surface larger, regardless of its orientation **45** $k > 3$ **47** $\pi - \frac{8}{3} \frac{\text{g}}{\text{sec}}$ **51** $\frac{\mu_0 I}{4\pi} \ln\left(\frac{2}{5}\right)$

53
$$\frac{\mu_0 I}{2\pi}\left(\frac{27}{13}\ln 2 - \frac{21}{4}\ln 37 + \frac{105}{2}\tan^{-1}\frac{5}{7} - \frac{10}{13}\tan^{-1}5 + \frac{165}{26}\ln 5 - \frac{105}{2}\tan^{-1}\frac{1}{7} + \frac{10}{13}\tan^{-1}18 + 2\pi - 8\tan^{-1}6\right) \approx \frac{6.47835\mu_0 I}{\pi}$$

55 $\mathcal{E} = \frac{\mu_0 \ln(10)}{8}\sin(\pi t)$ **57** $\mathcal{E} = 0$

Section 15.7:
1
$\mathbf{r}(s,t) = \langle -1+8s+t, 4+s+14t, -7-3s+9t\rangle$ (other answers possible) **3**
$\mathbf{r}(s,t) = \langle 2+3s+t, 1-2s-t, s+2t\rangle$ (other answers possible) **5**
$\mathbf{r}(\theta,t) = \langle \sqrt{1/3}\cos(\theta), \sin(\theta)/4, t\rangle$, where $\theta \in [0, 2\pi]$ and $t \in [-7, 7]$ (other answers possible) **7**
$\mathbf{r}(s,t) = \langle \sqrt{3}\, t\cos(s), \sqrt{3}\, t\sin(s), t\rangle$ where $s \in [0, 2\pi]$ and $t \geq 0$ (other answers possible) **9**
$\mathbf{r}(s,t) = \langle t\cos(s), t\sin(s), \frac{11}{5}t^2\rangle$ (other answers possible) **11** $s \in [0, \pi/2]$ and $t \in [\pi/2, 2\pi]$ (other answers possible) **13** $s \in [0, \pi]$ and $t \in [3\pi/4, 7\pi/4]$ (other answers possible) **15**
$\mathbf{r}(s,t) = \langle \cos(t), s, \sin(t)\rangle$ where $t \in [0, 2\pi]$ and $s \in [0, 2]$ (other answers possible) (other answers possible) **17**
$\mathbf{r}(s,t) = \langle s\cos(4t), s\sin(4t), t\rangle$ where $s \in [1, 2]$ and $t \in [0, \pi]$ (other answers

possible) **19** $8x + 5y - 2z = 22$ **21** $16x + 24y - z = 48$ **23** $20x + 126y = 103$ **25** $76\sqrt{46}$ **27** $\frac{1}{48}(12^3 - 1)$ **29** ≈ 104.9963 **31** ≈ 1.8857 **33** (a)
$x(s,t) = 3 + \frac{20\sqrt{26}}{26}s\cos(t),$
$y(s,t) = 7 + \frac{40\sqrt{101}}{101}s\sin(t),$
$z(s,t) = -1 - \frac{4\sqrt{26}}{26}s\cos(t) - \frac{3\sqrt{101}}{101}s\sin(t)$
where $s \in [0,1]$ and $t \in [0, 2\pi]$ (other answers possible); (b) $r(s,t) = \langle -5, k^{-1}, 1\rangle + 4s\cos(t)\hat{\mathbf{u}} + 4s\sin(t)\hat{\mathbf{v}}$ where $\hat{\mathbf{u}} = \frac{\sqrt{26}}{26}\langle 5, 0, -1\rangle$,
$\hat{\mathbf{v}} = \frac{\sqrt{100+k^2}}{100+k^2}\langle 0, 10, -k\rangle$, $s \in [0,1]$ and $t \in [0, 2\pi]$; increasing k pivots the disk toward being parallel with the xz-plane and pulls it toward the origin **35** (a) $t = 0 \Rightarrow$ a circle centered at $(1,0,0)$ that's in the xz-plane, $t = \pi/2 \Rightarrow$ a circle centered at $(0,1,0)$ that's in the yz-plane, and a circle centered at $(-1,0,0)$ that's in the xz-plane; (b) these are circles in planes of the form $z =$ constant, centered on the z-axis; (c)

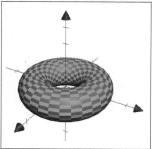

37 This is a cylinder of radius 1 whose axis of symmetry is the y-axis. It extends from $y = -3$ to $y = 3$. Constant values of t correspond to circles perpendicular to the y-axis, and constant values of s to line segments that are parallel to the y-axis. **39** (a) When $t = 1$, $\mathbf{r}(s, 1) = \langle s, 1, 1 - s \rangle$ parameterizes a line segment in the $y = 1$ plane, say ℓ_1, and $\mathbf{r}(s, 0) = \langle s, 3s - 10, s \rangle$ parameterizes another line segment, say ℓ_2. (b) For fixed values of s, we start on ℓ_2 and move along a line to ℓ_1 as t ranges from 0 to 1 (in short $\mathbf{r}(s, t)$ gives us a "weighted average" of the two line segments when $t \in [0, 1]$); (d)

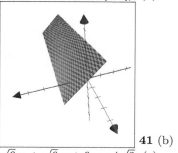

41 (b) $\sqrt{6}\, x + \sqrt{6}\, y + 6z = 4\sqrt{3}$; (c) $\sqrt{6}\, x + \sqrt{6}\, y + 6z = 4\sqrt{3}$; (d) Both $\mathbf{r}_1(0.25\sqrt{2}, 0.25\sqrt{2})$ and $\mathbf{r}_2(\pi/4, \pi/6)$ are the same point on the same surface. Fundamentally, the tangent plane is determined by the surface, not our way of describing the surface (i.e., our parameterization of it). **43** ≈ 1.74336 **45**

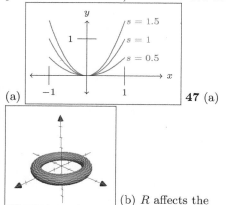

(a)　　　　　　　　　　　　　　　　　　**47** (a)

(b) R affects the

radius of the circle that runs along the "center" of the torus, and r affects how "thick" the torus is. The image shown for part (a) uses $R = 2.5$ and $r = 0.5$; (c) It's always true that $A_r > A_R$ (because $R > r$), so increasing the "thickness" of the torus raises its surface area more quickly than increasing the diameter of the torus.

Section 15.8:

1 13 **3** $\frac{289\pi}{60}\sqrt{17} - \frac{41\pi}{60}$ **5** $\frac{14}{9}$ **7** $\frac{48}{5}e^{-2.5} - 8e^{-3} - \frac{8}{5}$ **9** ≈ 76.9803 **11** ≈ -18167.3653 **13** $-\frac{25331}{53130}$ **15** ≈ 4.130572326 **17** (a)

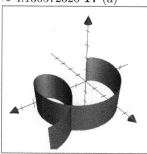

(b) there are two directions that could be "up" at points of self intersection **19** 43 **21** $\frac{1}{7500}\left(434^{5/2} - 426^{5/2} + 126^{5/2} - 134^{5/2}\right)$ **23** $1.5\sqrt{12}(e - 1)$ **25** $352\sqrt{101}$ J **27** $\frac{14}{15}$ g/sec **29** $\frac{24\ln(2) - 7}{\left(\ln(2)\right)^2} - \frac{9}{2}$ N-cm^2/coulomb

Section 15.9:

1 $z + e^x + 1$ **3** $6z - 3z\cos(y)$ **5** $8z + 2e^x + 2 - 3z\cos(y)$ **7** $z^2(z + e^x + 3) - y(3z + 2e^x + 1)$ **9** $z^2(z + e^x + 3) - y(3z + 2e^x + 1) - 2z(x^2 + y - 2z^2) - y(y^2 - z)\cos(y) + z\sin(y)$ **11** $2yz(1 + e^x) + yz^2 - y^2$ **13** 12 **15** 840 **17** $\frac{17}{12}$ **19** $\frac{160}{3}$ **21** $\frac{143}{2}\pi$ **23** $\frac{283}{20}\pi$ **25** $\iint_{S_3} \mathbf{F} \cdot d\mathbf{S} < \iint_{S_1} \mathbf{F} \cdot d\mathbf{S} < \iint_{S_2} \mathbf{F} \cdot d\mathbf{S}$ **27**

$y = 2s^3$ when $0 \leq s$ is small **31** div($\mathbf{F}$) < 0 because the material is being compressed

Section 15.10:

1 $\langle 4, 8, 3 \rangle$ **3** $\langle -7x, 2z + 4y, 3z \rangle$ **5** $\langle 0 - 2x - \sin(z), 0 \rangle$ **7** $\langle 7x - 12y - 60z, 4y - 24x - 40z, -11z - 6x - 16y \rangle$ **9** $\langle xe^x - 10yze^x, -y(x + 1)e^x, (5z^2 - 12)ye^x \rangle$ **11** 0 **13** $-\pi/2$ **15** 0 **17** $\frac{3\pi}{163}\sqrt{326}$ **19** $k = -17$ **21** $k = \frac{-7 \pm \sqrt{73}}{2}$ **23** yes **25** no **27** (a) meaningless (the curl of a scalar-valued function; (b) and (c) and

(d) make sense **33** (a) spheres; (b) they're parallel **35** $\nabla \times \mathbf{E} = -\partial_t \mathbf{B}$

Chapter 15 Review:

1 F **3** T **5** F **7** F **9** T **11** F **13** T **15** T **17** F **19** d **21** d **23** b **25** e **27** d **29** No **31** $^{37}/_6$ **33** (a) $-^{110}/_3$ joules (b) the force field acts to decrease the object's kinetic energy (and so its speed) **35** (b) $15\pi^2$ **37** $^{2500}/_3$ **39** $^{13}/_8$ **41** $-4z^3 + x\cos(y)z^2 + (2x^2+2y)z - x\sin(y) - xy\cos(y)$ **43** $\langle -1, x-y-1, e^x(1+x-y)+z\rangle$ **45** $^{135}/_2$ g/sec, opposed to the positively oriented normal vector **47** $25\left(1-\frac{\sqrt{2}}{2}\right)\left(\frac{\sqrt{3}}{4}+\frac{\pi}{6}\right)$ **51** $\pm\langle -8,-41,6\rangle/\sqrt{1781}$ **53** (a) $4\pi GM$; (c) $4\pi GM$; (d) $4\pi GM$; (e) the flux is the same **57** (a) 0; (b) 0

Appendix A:

1 5 **3** $\sqrt{53}$ **5** $\sqrt{15}$ **7** $\sqrt{55}$ **9** $4\pi/3$ **11** $15\pi/9$ **13** $240°$ **15** $270°$ **17** $\left(-\frac{1}{2}, \frac{\sqrt{3}}{2}\right)$ **19** $(0,1)$ **21** $\left(-\frac{\sqrt{2}}{2}, \frac{\sqrt{2}}{2}\right)$ **23** $\left(\frac{\sqrt{3}}{2}, \frac{1}{2}\right)$ **25** it continues to grow, and eventually surpasses each finite value

Appendix B:

1 $(t+6)^2 + 44$ **3** $(t+9)^2 - 11$ **5** $(t-4)^2 + 6$ **7** $\left(t-\frac{7}{2}\right)^2 - \frac{9}{4}$ **9** $2(t+3)^2 + 82$ **11** $5(t+9)^2 + \frac{269}{5}$ **13** $2(t-2)^2 + 14$ **15** $3\left(t-\frac{7}{6}\right)^2 + \frac{71}{12}$ **17** $3x - 2 + \frac{11}{x+2}$ **19** $8x - \frac{1}{2} + \frac{19/2}{2x+1}$ **21** $7x + 5 + \frac{14-8x}{x^2+1}$ **23** $\frac{4}{7}x^3 - \frac{40}{49}x + \left(1 + \frac{792}{49}x\right)/(7x^2+10)$ **27** yes **29** no **33** $\frac{x+1}{x^2+x+5} + \frac{6x-2}{(x^2+x+5)^2} + \frac{4x-1}{(x^2+x+5)^3}$

Appendix C:

1 1 **5** 8881600973913295056 **7** $32 + 80x + 80x^2 + 40x^3 + 10x^4 + x^5$ **9** $32 + 240x + 720x^2 + 1080x^3 + 810x^4 + 243x^5$ **11** 214200 **13** (a) $\Omega_T = 15905368710$; (b) see below

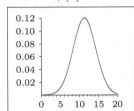

Appendix D: 1 (a) 6; (b) $(\pm 3, 0)$; (c) $(\pm\sqrt{5}, 0)$ **3** (a) 8; (b) $(0, \pm 4)$; (c) $(0, \pm\sqrt{7})$ **5** (a) $(-2,0)$; (b) $(-2\pm\sqrt{5}, 0)$; (c) $\left(-2\pm\frac{\sqrt{70}}{4}, 0\right)$ **7** (a) $\left(\frac{4}{3}, -1\right)$; (b) $\left(\frac{4}{3}, -1\pm\frac{\sqrt{33}}{3}\right)$; (c) $\left(\frac{4}{3}, -1\pm\frac{\sqrt{11}}{3}\right)$ **9** (a) $\varepsilon = \frac{4\sqrt{5}}{5}$; (b) see below

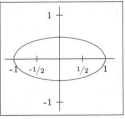

11 (a) $\varepsilon = 0$ (b) see below

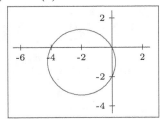

13 $\frac{x^2}{4} + \frac{y^2}{3} = 1$ **15** $\frac{x^2}{64} + \frac{y^2}{16} = 1$ **17** (a) $(\pm 3, 0)$; (b) $(\pm\sqrt{13}, 0)$; (c) $y = \pm\frac{2}{3}x$ **19** (a) $(0, \pm 3)$; (b) $(0, \pm\sqrt{14})$; (c) $y = \pm\frac{3\sqrt{5}}{5}x$ **21** (a) $(0, 3\pm 3)$; (b) $(0, 3\pm 3\sqrt{2})$; (c) $y = 3\pm x$ **23** (a) $\left(-\frac{1}{6}, -4\pm\frac{\sqrt{95}}{6}\right)$; (b) $\left(-\frac{1}{6}, -4\pm\frac{\sqrt{665}}{6}\right)$; (c) $y = -4\pm 6\left(x+\frac{1}{6}\right)$ **25** (a) $27\sqrt{6}/12$; (b) see below

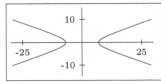

27 (a) $\sqrt{30}/5$; (b) see below

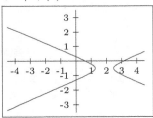

29 $\frac{x^2}{16} - \frac{y^2}{84} = 1$ **31** $\frac{x^2}{4} - \frac{y^2}{2} = 1$ **33** $\frac{x^2}{1} - \frac{4y^2}{5} = 1$ **35** (a) vertex: origin, focus: $(0, 7/4)$, directrix: $y = -7/4$; (b) see below

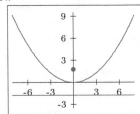

37 (a) vertex: origin, focus: $(-2/5, 0)$, directrix: $x = 2/5$; (b) see below

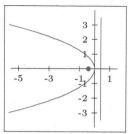

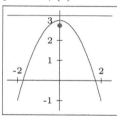

39 (a) vertex: $(0,3)$, focus: $(0,2.75)$,
directrix: $y = 3.25$; (b) see below

41 (a) vertex: $(-1/3,-1)$, focus: $(5/12,-1)$,
directrix: $x = -13/12$; (b) see below

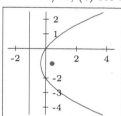

43 $x = \frac{5}{2} + \frac{1}{6}y^2$ **45** $y = \frac{7}{2} + \frac{1}{10}x^2$ **47**
$x = 1 + \frac{1}{8}y^2$ **49** $y = 10 + \frac{1}{36}x^2$ **51**
$x = 7 + \frac{1}{4}y^2$ **53** $y = -5 - \frac{3}{4}x^2$ **55**
$\frac{(x+21122.6652)^2}{(384748)^2} + \frac{y^2}{0.99698599(384748)^2} = 1$ **59**
$\frac{(y-0.6)^2}{0.16} - \frac{x^2}{0.2496} = 1$ **61** (a) $y = \frac{1}{52}x^2$ (b)
$\frac{152}{44}$ m   **63** the parabola

Index